DIRECT MEASUREMENT

U.S. CUSTOMARY

Length or Distance
12 inches (in.) = 1 foot (ft)

3 feet (ft) = 1 yard (yd)

36 inches (in.) = 1 yard (yd)

5280 feet (ft) = 1 mile (mi)

To Change From	To	Multiply By
feet	inches	12
inches	feet	0.0833333
yards	feet	3
feet	yards	0.333333
yards	inches	36
inches	yards	0.027778
miles	feet	5280
feet	miles	0.000189

Weight or Mass
16 ounces (oz) = 1 pound (lb)

2000 pounds (lb) = 1 ton (T)

From	To	Multiply By
pounds	ounces	16
ounces	pounds	0.0625
pounds	tons	2000
tons	pounds	0.0005

Liquid Capacity or Volume
8 ounces (oz) = 1 cup (c)

2 cups (c) = 1 pint (pt)

2 pints (pt) = 1 quart (qt)

4 quarts (qt) = 1 gallon (gal)

From	To	Multiply By
cups	ounces	8
ounces	cups	0.125
cups	pints	2
pints	cups	0.5
quarts	pints	2
pints	quarts	0.5
gallons	quarts	4
quarts	gallons	0.25

METRIC SYSTEM

Length or Distance
1 kilometer (km) = 1,000 meters (m)

1 hectometer (hm) = 100 meters

1 dekameter (dkm) = 10 meters

1 decimeter (dm) = 0.1 meters

1 centimeter (cm) = 0.01 meters

1 millimeter (mm) = 0.001 meters

From	To	Multiply By
kilometers	meters	1,000
meters	kilometers	0.001
hectometers	meters	100
meters	hectometers	0.01
dekameters	meters	10
meters	dekameters	0.1
decimeters	meters	0.1
meters	decimeters	10
centimeters	meters	0.01
meters	centimeters	100
millimeters	meters	0.001
meters	millimeters	1,000

Weight
1 kilogram (kg) = 1,000 grams (g)

1 hectogram (hg) = 100 grams

1 dekagram (dkg) = 10 grams

1 decigram (dg) = 0.1 grams

1 centigram (dg) = 0.01 grams

1 milligram (mg) = 0.001 grams

From	To	Multiply By
kilograms	grams	1,000
grams	kilograms	0.001
hectograms	grams	100
grams	hectograms	0.01
dekagrams	grams	10
grams	dekagrams	0.1
decigrams	grams	0.1
grams	decigrams	10
centigrams	grams	0.01
grams	centigrams	100
milligrams	grams	0.001
grams	milligrams	1,000

Capacity
1 kiloliter (kl) = 1,000 liters (l)

1 hectoliter (hl) = 100 liters

1 dekaliter (dkl) = 10 liters

1 deciliter (dl) = 0.1 liters

1 centiliter (cl) = 0.01 liters

1 milliliter (ml) = 0.001 liters

From	To	Multiply By
kiloliters	liters	1.000
liters	kiloliters	0.001
hectoliters	liters	100
liters	hectoliters	0.01
dekaliters	liters	10
liters	dekaliters	0.1
deciliters	liters	0.1
liters	deciliters	10
centiliters	liters	0.01
liters	centiliters	100
milliliters	liters	0.001
liters	milliliters	1,000

U.S. CUSTOMARY AND METRIC COMPARISONS

Length
1 meter = 39.37 inches

1 meter = 3.28 feet

1 meter = 1.09 yards

1 centimeter = 0.39 inch

1 millimeter = 0.04 inch

1 kilometer = 0.62 miles

From	To	Multiply By
meters	inches	39.37
inches	meters	0.0254
meters	feet	3.2808
feet	meters	0.3048
meters	yards	1.0936
yards	meters	0.9144
centimeters	inches	0.3936
inches	centimeters	2.54
millimeters	inches	0.03937
inches	millimeters	25.4
kilometers	miles	0.6214
miles	kilometers	1.6093

Weight
1 gram = 0.04 ounce

1 kilogram = 2.2 pounds

From	To	Multiply By
grams	ounces	0.0353
ounces	grams	28.3495
kilograms	pounds	2.2046
pounds	kilograms	0.4536

Liquid Capacity
1 liter = 1.06 quarts

From	To	Multiply By
liters	quarts	1.0567
quarts	liters	0.9463

Fraction and Decimal Equivalents

1/8	0.125	1/12	0.0833
2/8 = 1/4	0.25	2/12 = 1/6	0.1667
3/8	0.375	3/12 = 1/4	0.25
4/8 = 1/2	0.5	4/12 = 1/3	0.3333
5/8	0.625	5/12	0.4167
6/8 = 3/4	0.75	6/12 = 1/2	0.5
7/8	0.875	7/12	0.5833
		8/12 = 2/3	0.6667
1/3	0.3333	9/12 = 3/4	0.75
2/3	0.6667	10/12 = 5/6	0.8333
		11/12	0.9167

1/10	0.1
2/10 = 1/5	0.2
3/10	0.3
4/10 = 2/5	0.4
5/10 = 1/2	0.5
6/10 = 3/5	0.6
7/10	0.7
8/10 = 4/5	0.8
9/10	0.9

Perimeter, Area, Surface Area, and Volume

	Perimeter (Circumference)	Area	
Square	$P = 4s$	$A = s^2$	
Rectangle	$P = 2l + 2w$ or $P = 2(l + w)$	$A = lw$	
Parallelogram	$P = 2b + 2s$ or $P = 2(b + s)$	$A = bh$	
Triangle	$P = a + b + c$	$A = \frac{1}{2}bh$	
Circle	$C = \pi d$ or $C = 2\pi r$	$A = \pi r^2$	

	Lateral Surface Area	Total Surface Area	Volume
Right Rectangular Prism	$LSA = (2l + 2w)h$	$TSA = (2l + 2w)(h) + 2lw$	$V = lwh$
Right Circular Cylinder	$LSA = (\pi d)h$	$TSA = (\pi d)(h) + 2\pi r^2$	$V = \pi r^2 h$

Business Math

Sixth Edition

Cheryl Cleaves
Southwest Tennessee Community College

Margie Hobbs
The University of Mississippi

Prentice
Hall

Upper Saddle River, New Jersey 07458

Library of Congress Cataloging-in-Publication Data

Cleaves, Cheryl S., 1944–
    Business math / Cheryl Cleaves, Margie Hobbs.—6th ed.
      p. cm.
Includes index.
ISBN 0-13-089719-1
  1. Business mathematics.   I. Hobbs, Margie J., 1943–II. Title.
HF5691 .C53 2002
650'.01'513—dc21

                        2001033938

Publisher: Stephen Helba
Executive Acquisitions Editor: Frank Mortimer, Jr.
Editorial Assistant: Barbara Rosenberg
Managing Editor: Mary Carnis
Production Management: WordCrafters Editorial Services, Inc.
Production Editor: Linda Zuk
Production Liaison: Adele M. Kupchik
Director of Manufacturing and Production: Bruce Johnson
Manufacturing Buyer: Ilene Sanford
Creative Director: Cheryl Asherman
Senior Design Coordinator: Miguel Ortiz
Formatting: Clarinda Co.
Electronic Art Creation: Clarinda Co.
Marketing Manager: Tim Peyton
Marketing Assistants: Melissa Orsborn and Adam Kloza
Composition: Clarinda Co.
Printer/Binder: R.R. Donnelley & Sons, Willard
Copy Editor: Patsy Fortney
Proofreader: Shirley Ratliff
Interior Design: Amy Rosen
Cover Design: Wanda España
Cover Illustration: Jeff Brice
Cover Printer: Coral Graphics

Screenshots on pages 124, 125, 127, 128, 146, 147, 148, 153, 157, 158, 200, 250, 292, 330, 368, 410, 442, 474, 523, 564, 604, 616, 650, 677, 711, and 743 reprinted by permission from Microsoft Corporation. Excel is a registered trademark of Microsoft.

Pearson Education LTD.
Pearson Education Australia PTY, Limited
Pearson Education Singapore, Pte. Ltd.
Pearson Education North Asia Ltd.
Pearson Education Canada, Ltd.
Pearson Educacion de Mexico, S.A. de C.V.
Pearson Education–Japan
Pearson Education Malaysia, Pte. Ltd.

10 9 8 7 6 5
ISBN 0-13-089719-1
(High School Edition) ISBN 0-13-094690-7

Contents

Preface

To the Student

In almost any career you pursue, the business math you learn in this book will be useful. We have given much thought to the best way to present business math topics and have done extensive research on how students learn. We suggest that you use the special features included in the text to get the most out of this book and out of this course. The following features are designed to help you learn business math procedures.

Learning Outcomes   The chapter opening pages for each chapter include the learning outcomes for that chapter. Also, each section begins with its particular learning outcomes to show you what you should learn in that section. If you read and think about the outcomes before you begin the section, you will know what to look for as you work through the section.

Good Decisions Through Teamwork   Each chapter opens with a class project designed to promote teamwork. The projects incorporate a wide variety of team-building strategies. Each project involves students in a unique way. The various projects emphasize computational skills, interpersonal skills, oral or written communication skills, organizational skills, research skills, critical thinking, and/or decision-making skills. Project reports may be presented to a variety of audiences including instructors, peers, employers, and immediate supervisors.

Your instructor may use some or all of the projects, or may organize teams within the class and have each team select a project from a different chapter. Even if a particular project is not used in your class, reading the project will broaden your perception of the usefulness of mathematics.

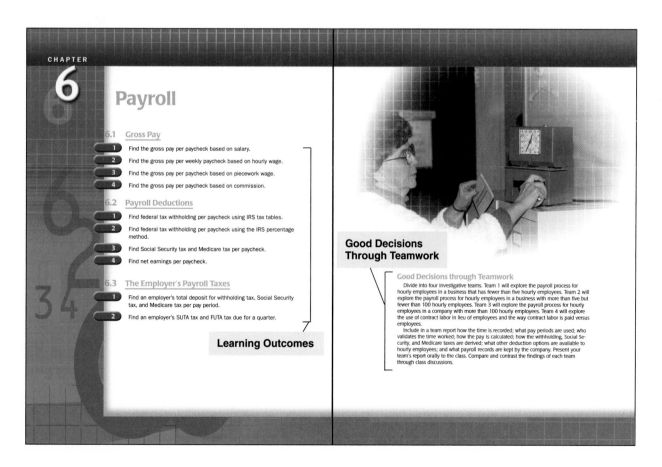

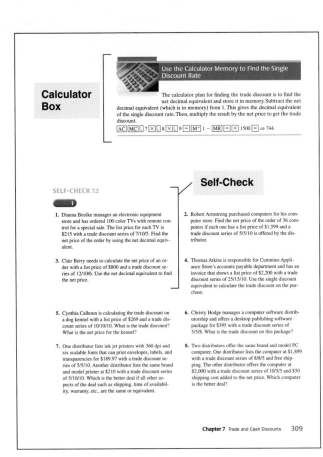

Calculator Box

Use the Calculator Memory to Find the Single Discount Rate

The calculator plan for finding the trade discount is to find the net decimal equivalent and store it in memory. Subtract the net decimal equivalent (which is in memory) from 1. This gives the decimal equivalent of the single discount rate. Then, multiply the result by the net price to get the trade discount.

AC MC . 7 × . 8 × . 9 = M⁺ 1 − MR = × 1500 = ⇒ 744.

Self-Check

SELF-CHECK 7.2

1

1. Dianna Beulke manages an electronic equipment store and has ordered 100 color TVs with remote control for a special sale. The list price for each TV is $215 with a trade discount series of 7/10/5. Find the net price of the order by using the net decimal equivalent.

2. Robert Armstrong purchased computers for his computer store. Find the net price of the order of 36 computers if each one has a list price of $1,599 and a trade discount series of 5/5/10 is offered by the distributor.

3. Clair Berry needs to calculate the net price of an order with a list price of $800 and a trade discount series of 12/10/6. Use the net decimal equivalent to find the net price.

4. Thomas Atkins is responsible for Cummins Appliance Store's accounts payable department and has an invoice that shows a list price of $2,200 with a trade discount series of 25/15/10. Use the single discount equivalent to calculate the trade discount on the purchase.

5. Cynthia Calhoun is calculating the trade discount on a dog kennel with a list price of $269 and a trade discount series of 10/10/10. What is the trade discount? What is the net price for the kennel?

6. Christy Hodge manages a computer software distributorship and offers a desktop publishing software package for $395 with a trade discount series of 5/5/8. What is the trade discount on this package?

7. One distributor lists ink jet printers with 360 dpi and six scalable fonts that can print envelopes, labels, and transparencies for $189.97 with a trade discount series of 5/5/10. Another distributor lists the same brand and model printer at $210 with a trade discount series of 5/10/10. Which is the better deal if all other aspects of the deal such as shipping, time of availability, warranty, etc., are the same or equivalent.

8. Two distributors offer the same brand and model PC computer. One distributor lists the computer at $1,899 with a trade discount series of 8/8/5 and free shipping. The other distributor offers the computer at $2,000 with a trade discount series of 10/5/5 and $50 shipping cost added to the net price. Which computer is the better deal?

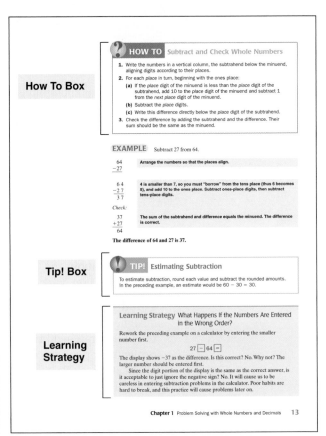

How To Box

? HOW TO Subtract and Check Whole Numbers

1. Write the numbers in a vertical column, the subtrahend below the minuend, aligning digits according to their places.
2. For each *place* in turn, beginning with the ones place:
   (a) If the *place* digit of the minuend is less than the *place* digit of the subtrahend, add 10 to the *place* digit of the minuend and subtract 1 from the *next* place digit of the minuend.
   (b) Subtract the *place* digits.
   (c) Write this difference directly below the *place* digit of the subtrahend.
3. Check the difference by adding the subtrahend and the difference. Their sum should be the same as the minuend.

EXAMPLE   Subtract 27 from 64.

$$\begin{array}{r} 64 \\ -27 \end{array}$$ Arrange the numbers so that the places align.

$$\begin{array}{r} 6\,4 \\ -2\,7 \\ \hline 3\,7 \end{array}$$ 4 is smaller than 7, so you must "borrow" from the tens place (thus 6 becomes 5), and add 10 to the ones place. Subtract ones-place digits, then subtract tens-place digits.

Check:

$$\begin{array}{r} 37 \\ +27 \\ \hline 64 \end{array}$$ The sum of the subtrahend and difference equals the minuend. The difference is correct.

The difference of 64 and 27 is 37.

Tip! Box

! TIP! Estimating Subtraction

To estimate subtraction, round each value and subtract the rounded amounts. In the preceding example, an estimate would be 60 − 30 = 30.

Learning Strategy

Learning Strategy What Happens If the Numbers Are Entered in the Wrong Order?

Rework the preceding example on a calculator by entering the smaller number first.

27 − 64 =

The display shows −37 as the difference. Is this correct? No. Why not? The larger number should be entered first.

Since the digit portion of the display is the same as the correct answer, is it acceptable to just ignore the negative sign? No. It will cause us to be careless in entering subtraction problems in the calculator. Poor habits are hard to break, and this practice will cause problems later on.

Self-Checks   These short practice sets are keyed to learning outcomes and appear at the end of each section. Use these exercises to check your understanding of the section. The self-check solutions are at the end of each chapter, so you can get immediate feedback on your level of understanding of the material.

How To Boxes   These boxes appear throughout the text to introduce a new procedure. To make these procedures as clear as possible, we break them down for you into step-by-step instructions. Each box contains or is followed by an example. The chapter Overview repeats these procedures with additional examples.

Tip! Boxes and Calculator Boxes   These boxes point out helpful hints and calculator strategies involved in business math procedures. The hints draw your attention to generalizations or restrictions you might otherwise overlook. Many of our own students tell us that just as they have a question, a Tip! box appears that has anticipated their question.

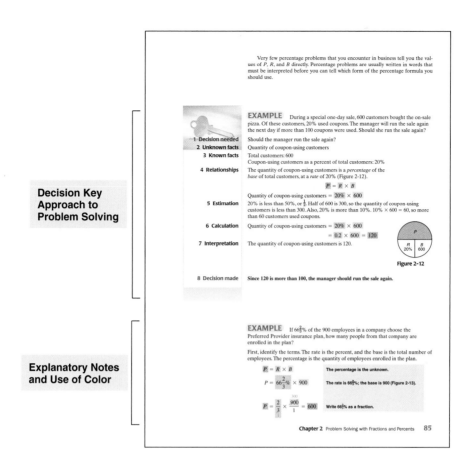

Decision Key Approach to Problem Solving

Explanatory Notes and Use of Color

Learning Strategies   In each chapter you will find a number of learning strategies. These strategies can help you build a framework for successful learning. The strategies show ways to manage your learning of mathematics that you may not have thought of before. Use them to improve your "mathematical sense" and to give you a greater appreciation for the power of mathematics in your workplace and everyday life. You may also find them useful in other areas of study.

Decision Key Approach to Problem Solving   This format enables you to take a systematic approach to solving problems in the business world. In this feature you are asked to analyze and compare, and then to make a business decision based on the data.

Explanatory Notes and Use of Color   To assist you in understanding the solution of an example, explanatory notes are included in shaded boxes. Different colors of shading are used within the solution of an example to help you follow the path of key values.

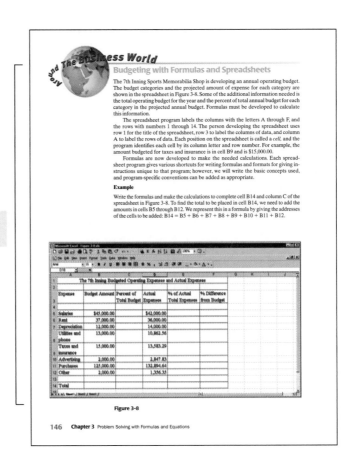

Around the Business World A stand-alone business or consumer application is presented, complete with explanations, examples, exercises, and answers. You will simulate real-life experiences in the business world. These units are included to capture your interest in a variety of business topics. This feature appears in each chapter and may also serve as a catalyst for initiating class discussion on complex business issues or may motivate you to further investigate the topic.

Words to Know Terminology is important for communication and for locating topics and additional information. The Words to Know that follow the Overview can be used as a checklist for reviewing new terminology. The page number reference will direct you to the first occurence and the definition of the term.

Words to Know

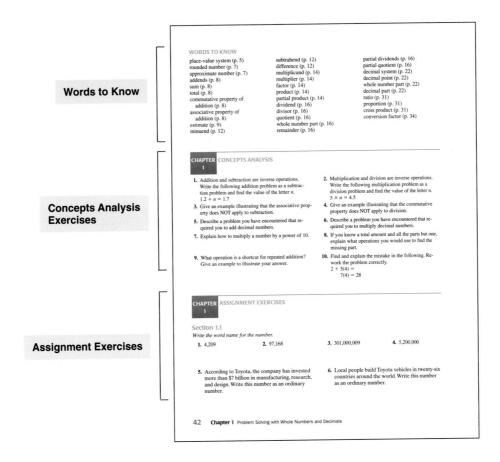

CHAPTER 1 CONCEPTS ANALYSIS

1. Addition and subtraction are inverse operations. Write the following addition problem as a subtraction problem and find the value of the letter n.
   $1.2 + n = 1.7$

2. Multiplication and division are inverse operations. Write the following multiplication problem as a division problem and find the value of the letter n.
   $5 \times n = 4.5$

3. Give an example illustrating that the associative property does NOT apply to subtraction.

4. Give an example illustrating that the commutative property does NOT apply to division.

5. Describe a problem you have encountered that required you to add decimal numbers.

6. Describe a problem you have encountered that required you to multiply decimal numbers.

7. Explain how to multiply a number by a power of 10.

8. If you know a total amount and all the parts but one, explain what operations you would use to find the missing part.

9. What operation is a shortcut for repeated addition? Give an example to illustrate your answer.

10. Find and explain the mistake in the following. Rework the problem correctly.
    $2 + 5(4) =$
    $7(4) = 28$

CHAPTER 1 ASSIGNMENT EXERCISES

Section 1.1

Write the word name for the number.

1. 4,209

2. 97,168

3. 301,000,009

4. 5,200,000

5. According to Toyota, the company has invested more than $7 billion in manufacturing, research, and design. Write this number as an ordinary number.

6. Local people build Toyota vehicles in twenty-six countries around the world. Write this number as an ordinary number.

42   **Chapter 1** Problem Solving with Whole Numbers and Decimals

Concepts Analysis Exercises   An important feature of the text is the Concepts Analysis exercises. Often we focus on the "how to" and overlook the "why" and "where" associated with the mathematical concept. These questions allow you to formalize your understanding of a concept and to connect to other concepts and uses. Error analysis is another way that the understanding of concepts is encouraged.

Assignment Exercises   An extensive set of exercises appears at the end of each chapter to review all the procedures and outcomes presented in the chapter. These exercises may be assigned by your instructor as homework, or you may want to work them on your own for extra practice. The answers to odd-numbered exercises are at the end of the book. Solutions to odd-numbered exercises appear in a separate Student Solutions Manual. Your instructor has the worked-out solutions to the even-numbered exercises.

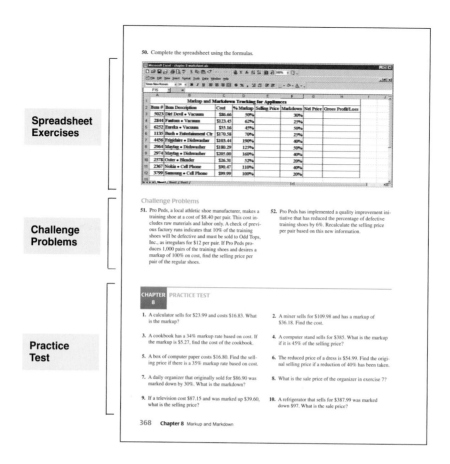

50. Complete the spreadsheet using the formulas.

Item #	Item Description	Cost	% Markup	Selling Price	Markdown	Net Price	Gross Profit/Loss
5023	Dirt Devil • Vacuum	$86.66	50%		30%		
2844	Fantom • Vacuum	$123.45	62%		25%		
6252	Eureka • Vacuum	$55.16	45%		50%		
1135	Bush • Entertainment Ctr	$170.58	70%		25%		
4456	Frigidaire • Dishwasher	$103.44	190%		40%		
2964	Maytag • Dishwasher	$180.29	125%		50%		
2974	Maytag • Dishwasher	$205.00	160%		40%		
2578	Oster • Blender	$26.31	52%		20%		
2367	Nokia • Cell Phone	$90.47	110%		40%		
3799	Samsung • Cell Phone	$99.99	100%		20%		

Challenge Problems

51. Pro Peds, a local athletic shoe manufacturer, makes a training shoe at a cost of $8.40 per pair. This cost includes raw materials and labor only. A check of previous factory runs indicates that 10% of the training shoes will be defective and must be sold to Odd Tops, Inc., as irregulars for $12 per pair. If Pro Peds produces 1,000 pairs of the training shoes and desires a markup of 100% on cost, find the selling price per pair of the regular shoes.

52. Pro Peds has implemented a quality improvement initiative that has reduced the percentage of defective training shoes by 6%. Recalculate the selling price per pair based on this new information.

CHAPTER 8 PRACTICE TEST

1. A calculator sells for $23.99 and costs $16.83. What is the markup?

2. A mixer sells for $109.98 and has a markup of $36.18. Find the cost.

3. A cookbook has a 34% markup rate based on cost. If the markup is $5.27, find the cost of the cookbook.

4. A computer stand sells for $385. What is the markup if it is 45% of the selling price?

5. A box of computer paper costs $16.80. Find the selling price if there is a 35% markup rate based on cost.

6. The reduced price of a dress is $54.99. Find the original selling price if a reduction of 40% has been taken.

7. A daily organizer that originally sold for $86.90 was marked down by 30%. What is the markdown?

8. What is the sale price of the organizer in exercise 7?

9. If a television cost $87.15 and was marked up $39.60, what is the selling price?

10. A refrigerator that sells for $387.99 was marked down $97. What is the sale price?

368　　**Chapter 8** Markup and Markdown

Spreadsheet Exercises　The most common use of technology in the business world is with the electronic spreadsheet. Spreadsheets are introduced in Chapter 3 and spreadsheet exercises are included in every subsequent chapter. You will see that technology plays a major role in the mathematics needed in the workplace but it doesn't take the place of understanding the concepts that will be used.

Challenge Problems　Each set of Assignment Exercises ends with a few challenge problems. These problems may extend slightly beyond the scope of the text; but you have been introduced to all the necessary skills for completing these problems. They may be used for individual, group, or team exercises.

Practice Test　Do this before you take the class test to check your understanding of the material. You should be able to work each problem without referring to any examples in your text or your notes. Answers to odd-numbered exercises appear at the end of the book. Solutions to odd-numbered exercises appear in a separate Student Solutions Manual. Your instructor has the worked-out solutions to the even-numbered exercises.

Supplementary Student Materials

Student Solutions Manual   This manual can be purchased at your bookstore. The manual contains worked-out solutions to the odd-numbered exercises of the assignment exercises and the practice test from each chapter of the text. Answers to these exercises appear in the back of your text, but using this manual to study the full worked-out solutions can enhance your problem-solving skills and your understanding of the concepts.

StudyWizard CD-ROM   This software, packaged with the text, provides additional practice with the business math concepts presented in the text. Each question contains a reference to the section and learning outcome number in the text where the concept first appears, making it easier to find the sections you want to review. Immediate feedback is provided to all questions, enabling you to strengthen your skills and test your knowledge of the concepts before a class test. The glossary included with the software enables you to review the terms and concepts presented in the text.

How to Study Business Math   Your instructor can obtain free copies of this booklet, which describes various learning techniques you can use in class and in preparation for class that can make learning business math much more efficient and effective.

Business Math Quick Reference Tables   Annual percentage rate, simple interest, compound interest, present value tables, future value tables, payroll tax tables, income tax tables, and more are all bound into a free-standing manual to facilitate your homework preparation and in-class testing.

Companion Website   This free website, available at *www.prenhall.com/cleaves*, provides even more practice with the math concepts presented in the form of short quizzes for each section of the text. These quizzes are graded immediately, and you have the opportunity to send the results to your instructor via email.

Reading Your Math Textbook

In developing an effective study plan it is important to use all your available resources to their maximum advantage. The most accessible of these resources is your textbook. Incorporate an effective strategy for reading your textbook into your study plan.

Beginning a Chapter

1. Examine the chapter opening pages. Read the Chapter Title, Section Titles, and Learning Outcomes to determine what will be covered in the chapter.

2. Read the Chapter Overview that is near the end of the chapter. The Chapter Overview lists each learning outcome of the chapter with some tips on what to remember and at least one example. Use the summary as a checklist to rate your initial knowledge of the chapter's learning outcomes.

   This rating can be a numerical one. For example, 0 means that you know nothing about this topic; 1 means that you know a little about this topic; 2 means that you know quite a bit, but there may be a few gaps in your understanding; and 3 means that you know this topic very well.

Another possible rating strategy can be a minus/check/plus system. Minus means you need to work on this topic, check means you know the topic moderately well, and plus means you know the topic very well.

Beginning a Section

1. Read the section title and the learning outcomes for the section.
2. Read the introductory paragraph.
3. Locate the Self-Check Exercises at the end of the section. Read the directions for each "clump" of exercises. This will give you an idea of the type of problems you will be working and what to look for as you read the section.
4. Begin reading the section. Make notes on concepts that you do not understand or examples for which you are not able to follow the explanation. This will be the basis for questions to ask in class.

Continuing Through the Chapter

1. Work on one learning outcome at a time. After reading and studying one learning outcome, try some of the exercises for that outcome. Always check your answers with the text or Study Wizard and ask questions as appropriate. Assess your understanding of each outcome and practice or get help as you think necessary. Be realistic in your self-assessment!
2. Continue outcome by outcome, section by section, checking your understanding as you go.

Reviewing the Chapter

1. After finishing a chapter, thumb through the entire chapter, reading the Tip! boxes and Learning Strategies.
2. Read the Chapter Overview again and rate your understanding of each outcome again. Review or get assistance as necessary.
3. Use the Words to Know list at the end of the Chapter Outcomes as a checklist for your understanding of the new terminology used in the chapter.
4. Work the Practice Test at the end of the chapter and check your answers. Review or get assistance as necessary.

Finishing the Chapter

1. Prepare for the test on the chapter. Ask your instructor which outcomes require mastery for testing purposes. Some outcomes may not require mastery, and others may even be optional.
2. Read the special feature *Good Decisions through Teamwork* to gain some insight about where these concepts are used in real life.

General Tips

1. Practice an outcome until you feel comfortable that you understand the concept. Abundant practice material is available to you that is specifically geared to your text (Self-Study Exercises, Assignment Exercises, Study Wizard, and Companion Web site). Other practice is available through

generic mathematics software and other texts. Only you know when you have practiced enough. Be realistic in the self-assessment of your understanding. Practice helps you retain the information for a longer period of time, but don't wear yourself out! Finding that approprite balance is your goal.

2. The Concepts Analysis exercises help you check your conceptual understanding.

3. Don't forget the Glossary/Index! As you move through the text you will forget definitions and concepts. Perhaps you are not starting your study at the beginning of the text and need to review a few concepts that were in the chapters not covered. Examining the Glossary/Index should be your first step in accomplishing your review.

We wish you much success in your study of mathematics. Many of the features in this book were suggestions made by students such as yourself. If you have suggestions for improving the presentation, please give them to your instructor or email the authors at *ccleaves@bellsouth.net* or *mhobbs@watervalley.net*.

Good luck on your study of business mathematics.

To the Instructor

In the development of the text we have tried to address a wide variety of teaching and learning styles and modes of instruction, including online course delivery. A holistic approach to student learning is our goal.

We suggest that you encourage your students to read the "To the Student" portion of the preface, having them pay particular attention to the suggestions provided in the section "Reading your Math Textbook."

Most of the learning in mathematics originates in the classroom, and you are responsible for that. To help you, we have first tried to provide a solid, reliable textbook that will prepare students for class, serve them (and you) in class, help them review outside of class, and give them a reference document for later.

Our second area of concern is to help you in your classroom presentation—as much as any outside source can help someone else in the classroom. For this we have prepared an Annotated Instructor's Edition and an extensive supplements package that accompanies it.

A good text needs sound pedagogy and an appealing presentation.

Writing Style   The text communicates clearly and simply. Math terms and business vocabulary are introduced when needed. All terms are explained in everyday language as much as possible. Our language speaks directly to students in a friendly tone.

Four-Color Presentation   We have tried to create a text that a student would want to read. There are four-color graphs showing business applications, and color is used in artwork so that business forms look the way that they do in real life (an example is the bank checks in Chapter 5, Bank Records). Color is also used to highlight specific features such as How To or Tip! boxes so they can be easily located. Finally, and perhaps most importantly, color is used as a teaching tool to emphasize and trace certain amounts in examples. This will help students follow the logic of working through the examples.

The Annotated Instructor's Edition

The Annotated Instructor's Edition was devised to make your teaching life easier. It is the same as the student text with the answer inserted after each exercise and with teaching aids in the margins. These teaching aids include points to stress in the chapter, suggestions for collaborative classroom activities, common student errors and how to correct them, additional examples and applications, helpful hints for students, math tips, and calculator tips. Other more extensive activities and suggestions are in a separate *Instructor's Resource Manual*.

Instructor's Supplements Package

The teaching supplements package extends the support from the Annotated Instructor's Edition. The following is a list of supplements and a brief description of each.

Instructor's Resource Manual   This manual includes notes and suggested activities for each chapter along with class presentation outlines. A variety of reproducible activities is included for both in-class and out-of-class use. These activities can be used in both individual and collaborative formats. Worked-out solutions to even numbered text exercises are included as well as suggested answers for Concepts Analysis questions.

Transparency masters are provided to facilitate your classroom presentation. Included are selected pieces of art, blank business forms from the text, and selected How-To boxes. Other reproducible teaching aids are included.

Test Item File (print version)   The test item file consists of approximately 200 items per chapter (over 3,600 items in all), identified by section and learning outcome to match the text. In addition to exercises, it contains fill-in, short-answer, multiple-choice, true-false, and essay questions. It has been class-tested along with the text to provide an accurate, reliable testing tool.

Prentice Hall Test Manager   The test item file and accompanying software are available for the Windows platform. The program gives the instructor maximum flexibility in preparing tests and worksheets. It can create custom tests; print math symbols, equations, and graphs; create custom graphic images; assemble tests of up to 200 questions and print up to 99 different versions of a test; and build tests randomly by chapter, level of difficulty, or question type. The software also allows online testing and record keeping and the ability to add your own problems to the database.

Achievement Tests   One of the things we have found in preparing this text and talking to people who teach the course is that everyone uses somewhat different types of testing materials! In response to this, we have tried to provide as wide a variety of test questions as you would need in your classroom: a pretest, mid-term, and final exam; quizzes or assignment problems for each text section; problem-solving tests for each chapter—both drill type and application problems; and chapter achievement tests. These are provided in a format that is ready for reproduction.

PowerPoint Transparencies for Windows   This supplement provides some of the transparency masters in an electronic format and is available from Prentice Hall.

Acknowledgments

The following reviewers provided advice and insights we have valued through several editions. We are grateful for their interest and help.

Fay Armstrong, Houston Community College
Carol Baker, Napa Valley College
Corine Baker, South Seattle Community College
Jerome Baness, Illinois Valley Community College
Walter R. Bayless, Brown-Mackie College
Rex Bishop, Charles County Community College
Elizabeth Bliss, Trident Technical College
Marg Y. Blyth, Detroit College of Business
Don Boyer, Jefferson College
Lee Brainerd, Altadena, California
James Carey, Onondaga Community College
Janet Caruso, Briarcliffe College
Charles Cheetham, County College of Morris
George Chiv, Technical Career Institutes
Janet Ciccarelli, Herkimer County Community College
Dick Clark, Portland Community College
J. Cluver, Rockford Business School
Kim Collier, State Technical Institute at Memphis
Rita Cross, Northland Community College
John Cuniffe, Northland Pioneer College
William H. Dorrity, III, Eastern Maine Technical College
James F. Dowis, Des Moines Area Community College
Norm Dreisen, Essex Community College
William L. Drezdzon, Oakton Community College
Elise Earl, Tulsa Junior College
Glenda Echert, Rogers State College
Nell Edmundson, Miami Dade Community College
Chuck Ellison, Bessemer State Technical School
Susan Ellison, Bessemer, Alabama
Marsha Faircloth, Thomas Technical Institute
Cheryl H. Fante, Central Florida Community College
Margaret Ferguson, Houston Community College
Carol Flakus, Lower Columbia College
Robert Forbes, McIntosh College
Clark Ford, Middle Tennessee State University
Paul S. Franklin, DeVry Institute of Technology
Jim Fuhr, Milwaukee Area Technical College
John F. Galio, Cuyahoga Community College District
Frank Goulard, Portland Community College
Cecil Green, Riverside Community College
Stephen Griffin, Tarrant County Junior College
Vi Harrington, The Culinary Arts Institute of Louisiana
Suzanne Hawk, Chaparral College
Jackie Hedgpeth, Antelope Valley College
Joseph Hinsburg, Pima County Community College
Patricia Hirschy, Asnutuck Community Technical College

Mary Hjelter-Squire, Blackhawk Technical College
S. Hunt, San Diego Mesa College
Ilhan A. Izmirli, Strayer College
John Johnson, Seattle Central Community College
Carolyn Karnes, Macomb Community College
Kenneth Ketelhohn, Milwaukee Area Technical College
Ed Laughbaum, Columbus State Community College
S. Lee, Heald Business College
Kenneth Leibham, Columbia Gorge Community College
Barb Leonard, Skagit Valley College
Nolan Lickey, Westark Community College
Sean Liston, Heald Business College
Rena Lombardi, The Huntington Institute
Jane Loprest, Bucks County Community College
D. Maas, Lansing Community College
Lynn Mack, Piedmont Technical College
Robert Malena, Community College of Allegheny County, South Campus
Gary Martin, DeVry Institute of Technology, Atlanta
Paul Martin, Aims Community College
Harold R. Miller, Washington State Community College
Roberta Miller, Indian River Community College
Linda Morgren, DeKalb Technical Institute
Barbara Nasewicz, Blake Business School
Nancy Nelson, Salish Kootenai College
Howard L. Newhouse, Berkeley College
James Page, Mountain View College
Frank A. Paliotta, Berkeley College
Mary Pretti, State Technical Institute at Memphis
Nancy J. Priselac, Garrett Community College
Dave Randall, Oakland Community College
Louise Rickman, Redlands Community College
Sam Robinson, NHTC-Manchester
Joan Ryan, Lane Community College
Janice C. Salles, Merced College
Lona P. Scala, Roberts-Walsh Business School
Janet Schilling, Washington State Community College
Lynn Schuster, Central Penn Business School
Gerald W. Shields, Austin Community College
Georgia N. Simpson, Robeson Community College
Beverly Sisk, Gwinnett Technical Institute
Jim and Renee Smith, West Memphis
Debiruth Stanford, DeVry Institute of Technology
Herbert Stein, Merritt College
Alice Steljes, Illinois Valley Community College
Louise Stevens, Golden West College
Jack Stowers, Johnston Community College
Scott Swearingen, Tulsa, Oklahoma

Kitty Tabers, Oakton Community College
Ron Trontuet, Northwest Technical College—Thief
    River Falls
Joan Van Glaebeck, Edison Community College

Rich Vitto, Abbie Business Institute
Keith Wilson, Oklahoma City Community College
Chuck Wiseman, Oakland Community College
Toby Wraye, Santa Rosa, California

Accuracy is always a concern in mathematics, and we were fortunate to have the help of several colleagues who worked with us to produce the level of accuracy needed in a college textbook. The reviewers mentioned were of course our first source of corrections and queries. We also had the help of Jim and Renee Smith.

The production of a book would not come together without the help and input of many individuals. Although the list of persons who made contributions to the text is extensive, we would like to single out experts in the business world who provided technical information. We especially thank the following:

Teamwork Chapter Openers and Other Suggested Team Projects Ken Johnson, 1st Tennessee Bank, Collierville, TN (Chapter 5); Bill Butler, Piggly Wiggly Inc. Corporate Office, Memphis, TN (Chapter 7); Michael Bobilio, Piggly Wiggly Store Owner, Memphis, TN (Chapter 8).

Around the Business World Features Ken Johnson, 1st Tennessee Bank, Collierville, TN (Chapter 5); George Gibson, Farmcraft, Inc., West Memphis, AR (Chapter 6 and Chapter 15); Mark Speciale, Beall Manufacturing, East Alton, IL (Chapter 7); Joyce Gibson, CPA, McDonald & Doherty Co., Chicago, IL (Chapter 11 and Chapter 15); Ron Gant, Collierville Insurance Agency, Collierville, TN (Chapter 16).

We especially acknowledge our editor Frank Mortimer, who guided this edition through the months of its preparations. We thank Linda Zuk, the production editor, for her contributions and attention to detail. In fact, the Prentice Hall staff that we have worked with has been a well-organized, efficient team.

Dr. Warner Dickerson and Dr. Howard Lawrence are responsible for initially suggesting that we write a business math text. Warner Dickerson, a perennial optimist, had faith in our abilities and gave us the confidence we needed. Howard Lawrence, an innovative administrator, provided guidance and encouragement. We take this opportunity to thank each of these colleagues who were so influential in starting us on a long and satisfying career of serving students and colleagues.

Finally, we express our deepest gratitude to our families: Charles Cleaves and Allen and Holly Hobbs. Their love, support and encouragement are sources of our strength.

Cheryl Cleaves

Margie Hobbs

Business Math

1

Problem Solving with Whole Numbers and Decimals

1.1 Problem Solving with Whole Numbers

1 Read and write whole numbers.

2 Round whole numbers.

3 Add whole numbers.

4 Subtract whole numbers.

5 Multiply whole numbers.

6 Divide whole numbers.

1.2 Problem Solving with Decimals

1 Read, write, and round decimals.

2 Add and subtract decimals.

3 Multiply and divide decimals.

1.3 Problem Solving Using Proportions

1 Verify that two fractions form a proportion.

2 Find a missing term in a proportion.

3 Use proportions in changing units of measure.

Good Decisions through Teamwork

Choose a specific job in your team's target career field and investigate the job's net monthly pay. Based on this figure, create a monthly budget for a single person living in rented housing.

Begin by listing all categories of expenses, reflecting on everything a person might spend money on in a year's time. Obvious categories are rent, utilities, and food. Often overlooked categories are clothing, entertainment, and miscellaneous expenses such as dry cleaning.

Once your team has agreed on the categories, research various sources to determine monthly amounts for each category. Search the newspaper, for example, to determine local rental costs. Check with car dealers to determine monthly car payments. Try to use actual figures for each category. The Internet is another good source for actual data.

Now balance the monthly expenses with the monthly pay, adjusting expenses as necessary. While some categories are essential to every good budget, other categories, or the amounts assigned to them, depend on the team's priorities. Setting priorities, then, is an important part of balancing expenses to fit an income.

Much of our world—especially the business part of our world—runs on numbers and calculations. We go to the store that advertises the sale, take out a CD at the bank with the highest rates, apply for mortgages at the bank with the best terms, and grumble about lower take-home pay when Social Security withholding goes up.

This course will prepare you to enter the business world with mathematical tools for a variety of career paths. The chapters on business topics build on your knowledge of mathematics, so it is important to begin the course with a review of the mathematics and problem-solving skills you will need in the chapters to come.

In most businesses, arithmetic computations are done on a calculator or computer. Even so, every businessperson needs a thorough understanding of mathematical concepts and a basic number sense in order to make the best use of a calculator. A machine will do only what you tell it to do. Pressing a wrong key or performing the wrong operations on a calculator will result in a rapid but incorrect answer. If you understand the mathematics and know how to make reasonable estimates, you can catch and correct many errors.

1.1 Problem Solving with Whole Numbers

1 Read and write whole numbers.

2 Round whole numbers.

3 Add whole numbers.

4 Subtract whole numbers.

5 Multiply whole numbers.

6 Divide whole numbers.

We begin our review with *whole numbers,* that is, numbers like 0, 1, 2, 3, 4 . . . . Most business calculations involving whole numbers involve one or more of four basic *mathematical operations:* addition, subtraction, multiplication, and division.

1 Read and write whole numbers.

What business situations require that we read and write whole numbers? Communication is one of the most important skills of successful businesspersons. Both the giver and receiver of communications must have the same interpretation for the communication to be effective. That is why understanding terminology and the meanings of symbolic representations are important skills. How is the amount of a bill communicated at a fast-food drive-through window? It is often given

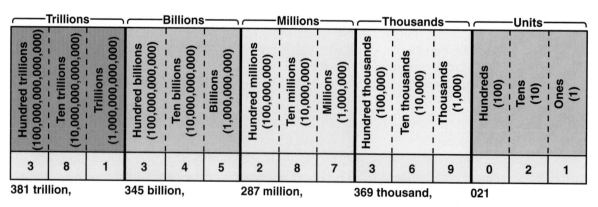

Figure 1-1   Place-Value Chart for Whole Numbers

verbally. At the supermarket the amount is often given verbally and then symbolically on a receipt. We will start communicating with numbers by reading and writing whole numbers.

Reading numbers is based on an understanding of the **place-value system** that is part of our decimal number system. The chart in Figure 1-1 shows that system applied to the number 381,345,287,369,021.

To apply the place-value chart to any number, follow the steps in the How-To box. You'll find these boxes, and examples illustrating their use, throughout this text.

? HOW TO   Read a Whole Number

1. Commas separate the number into groups of three digits each.	**Read the number 4,693,107**
2. Identify the group name of the leftmost group.	4 million
3. For each group, beginning with the leftmost group:	
(a) Read the three-digit number from left to right.	4,693,107 four *million*, six hundred ninety-three *thousand*, one hundred seven
(b) Name the group.	
4. Note these exceptions:	
(a) Do not read or name a group that is all zeros.	
(b) Do not name the units group.	

Another feature you will find throughout the text is the Learning Strategy box. This feature will help you develop your own successful study plan.

Learning Strategy   Reading and Illustrating Rules

Sometimes the language of mathematics and the details in procedures and rules seem overwhelming. Here are some suggestions that may help.

- Illustrate the rule with an example.
- Make your example with reasonable numbers.
- Reword the rule in your own words.
- Discuss your rule and illustration with a classmate or study partner.
- Be sure you understand the concept of the rule or procedure rather than memorizing meaningless words and steps.

EXAMPLE   Read the number 3,007,047,203.

3 007 047 203	Identify each group name.
3	three billion
007	seven million
047	forty-seven thousand
203	two hundred three

The number is read: three billion, seven million, forty-seven thousand, two hundred three.

TIP! Points to Remember in Reading Whole Numbers

1. Commas separating groups are inserted from right to left between groups of three numbers. The leftmost group may have fewer than three digits.

2. The group name will be read at each comma.

3. Group names are read in the singular: *million* instead of *millions,* for example.

4. Since no comma follows the units group, that will serve as your reminder that the group name *units* is not read.

In the preceding example a group name is read at each comma: 3 billion, 7 million, 47 thousand, 203.

5. *Hundreds* is NOT a group name.

6. Every group has a ones, tens, and hundreds *place*.

7. The word *and* is NOT used when reading whole numbers.

8. Commas ordinarily do not appear in calculator displays.

9. If a number has more than four digits, but no commas, such as you see on a calculator display, insert commas when you write the number.

Suppose you are in a sales meeting and the marketing manager presents a report of the sales for the previous quarter, the projected sales for the current quarter, and the projected sales for the entire year. How would you record these figures in the notes you are taking for the meeting? You will need to have a mental picture of the place-value structure of our numbering system. You begin recording digits, and when you hear the first group name, insert a comma. From this point, you can anticipate how many digits will follow. If a group name is skipped, three zeros are placed in that group followed by a comma. Look at the next example to see how this thinking process is used.

EXAMPLE   Write the number given its word name.

(a) Fifteen million, three hundred sixty-two thousand, five hundred thirty-eight

(b) Five hundred forty-two billion, five hundred thousand, twenty-nine

(a) 15, __ __ __ , __ __ __

> Record the first digits followed by a comma when the group name *millions* is heard (or read). Then anticipate the groups to follow (thousands and units).
>
> Fill in each remaining group as the digits and group names are heard (or read).

15,362,538

The number is 15,362,538.

(b) 542,___ ___ ,___ ___ ,___ ___ ,

| Record the first group and anticipate the groups to follow (millions, thousands, and units). |

542, ___ ___ ___ ,500, ___ ___ ___ ,

| The next group name you hear (or read) is *thousands,* so you place the 500 in the thousands group, saving space to place 3 zeros in the millions group. |

542,000,500,029

| Place three zeros in the *millions* group and listen for (read) the last three digits. You hear (read) twenty-nine, which is a two-digit number. Thus, a 0 is placed in the hundreds place. |

The number is 542,000,500,029.

Learning Strategy Practicing with a Study Partner

When writing the digits for a number that you hear or read, the group name always indicates that a comma should be used. One difficulty in writing the digits for a number that is spoken is that you delay writing the digits for a group until you hear a group name. Then while you are writing, the next digits are already being spoken. You can build skill through practice. Pair with a classmate and take turns reading and writing numbers.

---

2 Round whole numbers.

Exact numbers are not always necessary or desirable. For example, the board of directors does not want to know to the penny how much was spent on office supplies (though the accounting staff should know). Approximate or rounded numbers are often used. A **rounded number** does not represent an exact amount. It is instead an **approximate number.** In general, you round a number either to a specified place or to the first digit from the left in a number.

? HOW TO Round a Whole Number to a Specified Place

	Round 2,748 to the nearest hundred.
1. Find the digit in the specified place.	2, 7 48
2. Look at the next digit to the right.	2,7 4 8
(a) If this digit is less than 5, replace it and all digits to its right with zeros.	
(b) If this digit is 5 or more, add 1 to the digit in the specified place, and replace all digits to the right of the specified place with zeros.	2,700

EXAMPLE Round 2,748 to the first digit.

The specified place is the place of the first digit.

2,748	The first digit is 2.
2,748	The digit to the right of 2 is 7.
3,000	7 is 5 or more, so step 2b applies: add 1 to 2 to get 3, and replace all digits to its right with zeros.

2,748 rounded to the first digit is 3,000.

3 Add whole numbers.

If you purchase more than one item, you do not ordinarily pay for each item separately. Instead, the prices of all items are added together and you pay the total amount.

Numbers being added are called **addends.** The answer, or result, of addition is called the **sum** or **total.**

$$2 + 3 = 5$$
$$5 + 4 = 9$$

addends: 2, 3, +4

sum or total: 9

Only two numbers are added at a time. These two numbers can be added in either order without changing the sum. This property is called the **commutative property of addition.** It is casually referred to as the *order property of addition.*

When more than two numbers are added, two are grouped and added first. Then, the sum of these two numbers is added to another number. When three or more numbers are added, the addends can be grouped in any way. This property is called the **associative property of addition** and is casually referred to as the *grouping property of addition.*

? HOW TO Add Whole Numbers

1. Write the numbers in a vertical column, aligining digits according to their places.
2. For each *place* in turn, beginning with the ones place:
   (a) Add the *place* digits
   (b) Write the units digit of this sum directly below the *place* digit of the last addend.
   (c) Write the remaining digits of the sum sirectly above the *next place* digit of the first addend.

Calculator Suggestions

General instructions for performing operations using a calculator are provided on the inside back cover. Look for the calculator icon throughout the text for additional tips for using a calculator.

EXAMPLE Add 472 + 83 + 3,255.

Write the numbers in a vertical column, aligning digits by place value.

$$\begin{array}{r} 472 \\ 83 \\ \underline{3,255} \\ 3,810 \end{array}$$

Add the ones place digits, carrying 1 to the tens place. Add the tens place digits, carrying 2 to the hundreds place. Add the hundreds place digits. Finally, add the thousands place digits.

The sum is 3,810.

 TIP! Does Everyone Add the Same Way?

Sometimes it is preferable to add two numbers at a time and then add other numbers instead of adding in columns. The preceding example could also be worked the following way:

$$\begin{array}{r} 472 \\ + 83 \\ \hline 555 \end{array} \qquad \begin{array}{r} 555 \\ + 3,255 \\ \hline 3,810 \end{array}$$

There are several ways to improve your accuracy for calculations. One is to re-calculate. A second way is to recalculate using a calculator. A third way is to **estimate** the result before or after you calculate.

A quick and often-used way to estimate a sum is to round each addend to its first digit and add the rounded addends. In the previous example, if we round 472 to 500, 83 to 80, 3,255 to 3,000, the estimated sum is 3,580.

HOW TO Estimate and Check Addition

Estimate 472 + 83 + 3,255.

1. Estimate the sum by rounding each addend.
2. Add the rounded amounts.

$$\begin{array}{r} 472 \\ 83 \\ +3,255 \\ \hline 3,810 \end{array} \qquad \begin{array}{r} 500 \\ 80 \\ 3,000 \\ \hline 3,580 \end{array}$$

3. Check addition by adding the numbers again. The second time the numbers can be added in a different order or using a different method.

$$\text{check} \qquad \begin{array}{r} 3,255 \\ 472 \\ + 83 \\ \hline 3,810 \end{array}$$

EXAMPLE Estimate the sum by rounding each addend to its first digit. Compare the estimate to the exact sum.

$$\begin{array}{rll} 885 & \text{rounds to} & 900 \\ 569 & \text{rounds to} & 600 \\ 343 & \text{rounds to} & 300 \\ 231 & \text{rounds to} & 200 \\ + 562 & \text{rounds to} & + 600 \\ \hline 2,590 & & 2,600 \end{array}$$

The estimate is 2,600; the exact sum is 2,590.

When we perform our calculations with a calculator or computer software, it is always important to estimate and to check the reasonableness of our answer. There are many different types of calculators, and each type of model may operate slightly differently. You can teach yourself how to use your calculator using some helpful learning strategies.

Learning Strategy Testing Your Calculator by Entering a Problem that You Can Do Mentally

Add 3 + 5 on your calculator. Some options are

$$3 \boxed{+} 5 \boxed{=}$$

$$3 \boxed{+} 5 \boxed{+} \boxed{T} \qquad \boxed{T} \text{ represents Total.}$$

$$3 \boxed{+} 5 \boxed{ENTER}$$

$$3 \boxed{+} 5 \boxed{EXE} \qquad \boxed{EXE} \text{ represents Execute or complete the instructions}$$

To add more than two numbers, does your calculator accumulate the total in the display as you enter numbers? Or, does your calculator wait and give the total after the $\boxed{ENTER}$, $\boxed{EXE}$, $\boxed{T}$, or $\boxed{=}$ key is pressed? We use the symbol $\Rightarrow$ to indicate that the digits showing in the calculator display will follow.

Another important use of a calculator is to verify concepts. We sometimes remember part of a concept, but may not be sure of the exact details of the concept. Let's look at the commutative property of addition (two numbers can be added in any order). This concept is illustrated symbolically $a + b = b + a$.

Learning Strategy Using Your Calculator to Verify Concepts

The process of verifying a concept with a calculator does not constitute a formal proof, but it can be used to investigate speculations. Verify several examples to be sure you aren't making an imporper generalization.

EXAMPLE Use your calculator to verify that $a + b = b + a$.

Try several examples. It helps to organize the results of your investigation in a table.

a	b	$a + b$	$b + a$
5	8	13	13
27	39	66	66
207	417	624	624

Are there any situations that might not work? Investigate them. What is your conclusion?

$$a + b = b + a \quad \text{for all whole numbers}$$

A Decision Key for Problem Solving   Decision making or problem solving is an important skill for the successful businessperson. The decision-making process can be applied by either individuals or action teams. Many strategies have been developed to enable individuals and teams to *organize* the information given and to *develop* a plan for finding the information needed to make effective business decisions or to solve business-related problems.

The plan we have developed is an eight-step process. This feature of the text will be indicated throughout the text by the decision key located in the margin as shown here. The key words to identify each of the eight steps are:

1 Decision needed

2 Unknown facts

3 Known facts
4 Relationships

5 Estimation

6 Calculation
7 Interpretation

8 Decision made

1. **Decision needed** means "What decision do I need to make?" Sometimes the problem to be solved is to find an unknown fact. In problems of this type, the *decision needed* step is not required.
2. **Unknown fact(s)** means "What facts do I need to find to make a decision?" or in the case that no decision is required, "What facts am I trying to find?"
3. **Known fact(s)** means "What relevant facts are known or given?"
4. **Relationships** means "How are the known and unknown facts related?" and "What formulas or definitions are used to establish a model?"
5. **Estimation** means "Approximately, what should be the result of my calculation?"
6. **Calculation** means to perform the operations identified in the relationships.
7. **Interpretation** means "What does the result of the calculation represent within the context of the problem?"
8. **Decision made** means "Based on the result of the calculation to find unknown facts, what is my decision?" When the situation calls for determining unknown facts only, this step is not necessary.

EXAMPLE   Holly Hobbs supervises the shipping department at AH Transportation and must schedule her employees to handle all shipping requests within a specified time frame while keeping the payroll amount within the amount budgeted. Complete the payroll report (Table 1-1) for the first quarter and decide if Holly has kept the payroll within the quarterly department payroll budget of $25,000.

Table 1-1   Quarterly Payroll Report
for the Shipping Department

Employee	Quarterly Payroll
Oluwatoyin, Adesipe	$5,389
Campbell, Karen	5,781
Linebarger, Lydia	6,463
Ores, Vincent	5,389
Department Total	

1 Decision needed   Is the quarterly payroll within budget?

2 Unknown facts   Quarterly total for the department

3 Known facts   Quarterly total for each employee (in chart)
Quarterly department budget: $25,000

4 Relationships   Quarterly department total = sum of quarterly total for each employee
Quarterly department total = 5,389 + 5,781 + 6,463 + 5,389

5 Estimation

Round each employee's quarterly total to its first digit, then add to estimate the sum:

$$
\begin{array}{ccc}
5{,}389 & \longrightarrow & 5{,}000 \\
5{,}781 & \longrightarrow & 6{,}000 \\
6{,}463 & \longrightarrow & 6{,}000 \\
5{,}389 & \longrightarrow & \underline{5{,}000} \\
& & 22{,}000
\end{array}
$$

The estimated quarterly department total is $22,000.

6 Calculation

Calculate by hand or using a calculator the actual sum of employee quarterly totals.

$$
\begin{array}{r}
5{,}389 \\
5{,}781 \\
6{,}463 \\
\underline{5{,}389} \\
23{,}022
\end{array}
$$

Add the digits for each place.

7 Interpretation

The quarterly department total is $23,022.

8 Decision made

Is the quarterly department total less than or equal to $25,000? The total $23,022 is less than the budgeted amount of $25,000. **Holly's department expenditure for payroll *is* within the amount budgeted for the department.**

 TIP! **Alternative Method for Estimating**

A reasonable estimate may be a range of values that you expect the exact value to fall within. In the preceding example, all values are at least $5,000. This amount added four times will be $20,000. All values except 1 are also less than $6,000. This amount added four times would be $24,000. Therefore, we expect the exact amount to probably be between $20,000 and $24,000. The one value over $6,000 could make the total be a small amount over $24,000.

---

4 Subtract whole numbers.

Many situations require the operation of subtraction. We may need to know the amount of change when a price has increased to a higher price. If we do not have enough materials to complete a job, we may need to know how much more material is needed.

When subtracting one number from another, the number subtracted from is called the **minuend.** The number being subtracted is called the **subtrahend.** The result of subtraction is called the **difference.**

$$
\begin{array}{rcl}
135 & \longrightarrow & \text{minuend} \\
\underline{-\ 72} & \longrightarrow & \text{subtrahend} \\
63 & \longrightarrow & \text{difference}
\end{array}
$$

Using a common phrase from the technology era, subtraction is not as "user friendly" as addition. The order of the numbers in a subtraction problem *is* important. That is, subtraction is not commutative. For example, $5 - 3 = 2$, but $3 - 5$ does not equal 2.

Grouping in subtraction *is* important. That is, subtraction is not associative. For example,

$$(8 - 3) - 1 = 5 - 1 = 4 \qquad \text{but,} \qquad 8 - (3 - 1) = 8 - 2 = 6.$$

1. Write the numbers in a vertical column, the subtrahend below the minuend, aligning digits according to their places.
2. For each *place* in turn, beginning with the ones place:
   (a) If the *place* digit of the minuend is less than the *place* digit of the subtrahend, add 10 to the *place* digit of the minuend and subtract 1 from the *next place* digit of the minuend.
   (b) Subtract the *place* digits.
   (c) Write this difference directly below the *place* digit of the subtrahend.
3. Check the difference by adding the subtrahend and the difference. Their sum should be the same as the minuend.

EXAMPLE   Subtract 27 from 64.

$$\begin{array}{r} 64 \\ -27 \\ \hline \end{array}$$

Arrange the numbers so that the places align.

$$\begin{array}{r} 6\ 4 \\ -2\ 7 \\ \hline 3\ 7 \end{array}$$

4 is smaller than 7, so you must "borrow" from the tens place (thus 6 becomes 5), and add 10 to the ones place. Subtract ones-place digits, then subtract tens-place digits.

Check:

$$\begin{array}{r} 37 \\ +27 \\ \hline 64 \end{array}$$

The sum of the subtrahend and difference equals the minuend. The difference is correct.

The difference of 64 and 27 is 37.

 TIP! Estimating Subtraction

To estimate subtraction, round each value and subtract the rounded amounts. In the preceding example, an estimate would be $60 - 30 = 30$.

Learning Strategy What Happens If the Numbers Are Entered in the Wrong Order?

Rework the preceding example on a calculator by entering the smaller number first.

$$27 \boxed{-} 64 \boxed{=}$$

The display shows -37 as the difference. Is this correct? No. Why not? The larger number should be entered first.

Since the digit portion of the display is the same as the correct answer, is it acceptable to just ignore the negative sign? No. It will cause us to be careless in entering subtraction problems in the calculator. Poor habits are hard to break, and this practice will cause problems later on.

5 Multiply whole numbers.

One purpose for multiplication is a shortcut for repeated addition. If five items are purchased and each item costs the same amount, we can add the cost of five identical items or we can multiply the cost of one item by five.

When multiplying one number by another, the number being multiplied is called the **multiplicand.** The number we multiply by is called the **multiplier.** Each number can also be called a **factor.** The result of multiplication is called the **product.** Numbers can be multiplied in any order without changing the product. When the multiplier has more than one digit, the product of each digit and the multiplicand is called a **partial product.**

```
  75  ◄——— multiplicand  ⎫
  32  ◄——— multiplier     ⎬ ◄——— factors
 150  ⎫                   ⎭
 225  ⎬ ◄——— partial products
2400  ◄——— product
```

HOW TO | Multiply Whole Numbers

1. Write the numbers in a vertical column, aligning digits according to their place.
2. For each place of the multiplier in turn, beginning with the ones place:
   (a) Multiply the multiplicand by the *place* digit of the multiplier.
   (b) Write the partial product directly below the multiplier (or the last partial product), aligning the ones digit of the partial product with the *place* digit of the multiplier (and aligning all other digits, to the left accordingly).
3. Add the partial products.

EXAMPLE Multiply 127 by 53.

```
    127     ◄——— multiplicand
 ×   53     ◄——— multiplier
    381     ◄——— first partial product: 3 × 127 = 381; 1 in 381 aligns with 3 in 53.
   6 35     ◄——— second partial product: 5 × 127 = 635; 5 in 635 aligns with 5 in 53.
  6,731     ◄——— product: add the partial products
```

The product of 127 and 53 is 6,731.

TIP! | Placing Partial Products Properly

When you multiply numbers that contain two or more digits, it is crucial to *place the partial products* properly. A common mistake in multiplying is to forget to "indent" the partial products that follow the first partial product.

```
    265                                              265
 ×   23                                           ×   23
    795     We get the second partial product, 530, by     795
   5 30     multiplying 265 × 2. Therefore, the 0 in       530
  6,095     530 should be directly below the 2 in 23.    1,325
```

CORRECT   **INCORRECT**

As in addition, you can improve your multiplication accuracy by recalculating manually, by recalculating using a calculator, and by estimating the product.

Zeros are used in many helpful shortcuts to multiplying. You must pay careful attention to the position of zeros in partial products. When one of the numbers being multiplied is 10, 100, 1,000, and so on, or has ending zeros, you can use a shortcut to find the product.

? HOW TO Multiply When Numbers End in Zero

1. Mentally eliminate zeros from the end of each number.
2. Multiply the new numbers.
3. Attach to the end of the product the total number of zeros mentally eliminated in step 1.

EXAMPLE Multiply 20,700 by 860.

$$
\begin{array}{r}
20700 \\
\times \quad 860 \\
\hline
1\ 242 \\
16\ 56 \\
\hline
17,802,000
\end{array}
$$

Mentally eliminate three zeros from the ends of 20,700 and 860. Multiply 207 by 86, aligning digits and finding partial products.

Attach the three zeros that were mentally eliminated in step 1.

The product of 20,700 and 860 is 17,802,000.

If the multiplier has a zero in the middle, such as 102, 507, or 1,306, for example, you can use another shortcut to multiplication. Instead of writing a partial product consisting only of zeros, write a partial product of zero directly below the zero in the multiplier and then write the next partial product on the same line.

EXAMPLE Max Wertheimer works at the Wendy's warehouse and is processing store orders totaling 45,000 eight-ounce cups. He found 303 packages of eight-ounce cups. Each package contains a gross of cups. Does Max need to order more cups from the manufacturer to fill the store orders if one gross is 144 items?

1 Decision needed   Should more cups be ordered?

2 Unknown facts   Total quantity of cups on hand

3 Known facts   Store orders: 45,000 cups

Packages of cups on hand: 303

Cups per package: 1 gross, or 144

4 Relationships   Total quantity of cups on hand = quantity of packages × cups per package

Total quantity of cups on hand = 303 × 144

5 Estimation   If each package contained 100 cups and there were 300 packages on hand, the total would be 100 × 300. This is easier to multiply mentally and gives us an estimate. 100 × 300 = 30,000. It appears there are not enough cups on hand. However, since both numbers were rounded down, we know that this estimate is less than the actual number of cups on hand.

$$\begin{array}{r} 303 \\ \times \quad 144 \\ \hline \end{array}$$

1 212	Partial product of 303 × 4
12 12	Partial product of 303 × 4
30 3	Partial product of 303 × 1
43,632	Add the partial products.

7 Interpretation

The total quantity of cups on hand is 43,632.

8 Decision made

There are 43,632 cups in the warehouse, but store orders totaled 45,000. Therefore, **Max needs to order more cups from the manufacturer to fill all the store orders.**

Learning Strategy The Mind is Often Quicker than the Fingers

Don't use your calculator as a crutch. It is a tool! When multiplying 2,500 times 30, you can multiply 25 times 3 mentally: 25 × 3 = 75. Then, attach three zeros to that product.

$$2,500 \times 30 = 75,000$$

This skill does not come automatically. You have to practice it! Like playing a musical instrument or mastering a sport, you don't develop skill by watching. You have to practice, practice, practice.

---

6 Divide whole numbers.

Christine Shott received a price quote by fax for a limited quantity of discontinued telephone answering machines. The fax copy was not completely readable, but Christine could read that the total bill, including shipping, was $880 and each answering machine costs $35. How many answering machines were available and how much was the shipping cost? This type of situation involves division.

When dividing one number by another, the number being divided is called the **dividend.** The number divided by is called the **divisor.** The result of division is called the **quotient.** When the quotient is not a whole number, the quotient has a **whole number part** and a **remainder.** When a dividend has more digits than a divisor, parts of the dividend are called **partial dividends,** and the quotient of a partial dividend and the divisor is called a **partial quotient.**

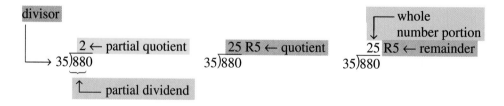

Christine now knows that 25 answering machines are available. What does the remainder represent? The dividend, $880, is in dollars, so the remainder also represents dollars. The remainder of $5 is the shipping cost.

HOW TO Divide Whole Numbers

1. Beginning with its leftmost digit, identify the first group of digits of the dividend that is larger than or equal to the divisor. This group of digits is the first *partial dividend*.

2. For each partial dividend in turn, beginning with the first:

   (a) Divide the partial dividend by the divisor. Write this partial quotient above the rightmost digit of the partial dividend.

   (b) Multiply the partial quotient by the divisor. Write the product below the partial dividend, aligning places.

   (c) Subtract the product from the partial dividend. Write the difference below the product, aligning places. The difference must be less than the divisor.

   (d) Next to the ones place of the difference, write the next digit of the dividend. This is the new partial dividend.

3. When all the digits of the dividend have been used, write the final difference in step 2c as the remainder (unless the remainder is 0). The whole number part of the quotient is the number written above the dividend.

4. To check, multiply the quotient by the divisor and add the remainder to the product. This sum equals the dividend.

$$880 \div 35$$

$$35\overline{)880}$$

$$\begin{array}{r} 25 \\ 35\overline{)880} \\ 70 \\ \hline 180 \\ 175 \\ \hline 5 \end{array}$$

$$\begin{array}{r} 25 \\ \times\ 35 \\ \hline 125 \\ 75 \\ \hline 875 \end{array} \qquad \begin{array}{r} 875 \\ +\ \ 5 \\ \hline 880 \end{array}$$

! TIP! What Types of Situations Require Division?

Two types of common business situations require division. Both types involve distributing items equally into groups.

1. Distribute a specified total quantity of items so that each group gets a specific equal share. Division determines the number of groups.

   For example, you need to ship 78 crystal vases. With appropriate packaging to avoid breakage, only five vases fit in each box. How many boxes are required? You divide the total quantity of vases by the quantity of vases that will fit into one box to determine how many boxes are required.

2. Distribute a specified total quantity so that we have a specific number of groups. Division determines each group's equal share.

   For example, how many ounces will each of four cups contain if a carafe of coffee containing 32 ounces is poured equally into the cups? The capacity of the carafe is divided by the number of coffee cups: $32 \div 4 = 8$. Eight ounces of coffee are contained in each of the four cups.

1 Decision needed

2 Unknown facts

3 Known facts

EXAMPLE Leroy needs to ship 78 crystal vases. With standard packing to avoid damage, five vases fit in each available box. Does Leroy need to arrange for extra packing or will each box contain exactly five vases?

Is extra packing required?

The quantity of boxes required to ship the vases

Total quantity of vases to be shipped: 78
Quantity of vases per box without the extra packing: 5

4 Relationships

Quantity of boxes needed = total vases ÷ quantity of vases per box

Quantity of boxes needed = 78 ÷ 5

5 Estimation

$$70 \div 5 = 14 \qquad \textbf{Round down the dividend.}$$

$$80 \div 5 = 16 \qquad \textbf{Round up the dividend.}$$

6 Calculation

Since 78 is between 70 and 80, the number of boxes needed is between 14 and 16.

$$\begin{array}{r} 1 \\ 5\overline{)78} \end{array}$$

7 is the first partial dividend since it is at least as large as 5. Divide 7 by 5 and write the partial quotient 1 above 7.

$$\begin{array}{r} 1 \\ 5\overline{)78} \\ 5 \\ \hline 2 \end{array}$$

The product of 1 and 5 is 5, so write 5 below 7, and subtract.

The difference, 2, is less than the divisor, 5.

$$\begin{array}{r} 1 \\ 5\overline{)78} \\ 5 \\ \hline 28 \end{array}$$

The next digit of the dividend is 8, so write 8 next to 2.

$$\begin{array}{r} 15 \\ 5\overline{)78} \\ 5 \\ \hline 28 \\ 25 \\ \hline 3 \end{array}$$

Divide 28 by 5, and write the partial quotient 5 above 8. Multiply 5 by 5, and subtract the product 25 from 28.

$$\begin{array}{r} 15 \text{ R3} \\ 5\overline{)78} \\ 5 \\ \hline 28 \\ 25 \\ \hline 3 \end{array}$$

The whole number part of the quotient is 15; the remainder is 3.

Check:

Check the quotient by multiplying the whole number part 15 by the divisor 5. Then add the remainder. The sum should equal the dividend 78.

$$\begin{array}{r} 15 \\ \times\ 5 \\ \hline 75 \end{array} \qquad \begin{array}{r} 75 \\ +\ 3 \\ \hline 78 \end{array} \qquad \textbf{The result checks.}$$

7 Interpretation

The quantity of boxes needed is 15 boxes containing five vases, and one box containing three vases.

8 Decision made

Fifteen boxes will have five vases each, needing no extra packing. One additional box is required to ship the remaining three vases. **Extra packing is needed to fill the additional box.**

Learning Strategy Using Guess and Check to Solve Problems

An effective strategy for solving problems involves guessing. Make a guess that you think might be reasonable and check to see if the answer is correct. If your guess is not correct, decide if it is too high or too low. Make another guess based on what you learned from your first guess. Continue until you find the correct answer.

Let's try guessing in the previous example. In the estimation we found that we could pack 70 vases in 14 boxes and 80 vases in 16 boxes. Since we need to pack 78 vases, how many vases can we pack with 15 boxes? 15 × 5 = 75. Still not enough. Therefore, we will need 16 boxes, but the last box will not be full.

TIP! Carefully Align Partial Dividends and Partial Quotients

Be very careful in lining up the numbers in a division problem and in entering zeros in the quotient.

$$
\begin{array}{r}
507 \\
5\overline{)2{,}535} \\
25 \\
\hline
3 \\
0 \\
\hline
35 \\
35 \\
\hline
0
\end{array}
$$

CORRECT

$$
\begin{array}{r}
570 \\
5\overline{)2{,}535} \\
25 \\
\hline
35 \\
35 \\
\hline
0
\end{array}
$$

INCORRECT

Estimating unit cost is an everyday application in the business world. Estimate the following unit costs and then find the exact unit cost.

(a) The cost for an order of 6 printers is $1,020. Find the unit cost.
(b) The cost of manufacturing 24 toy trains is $2,352. Find the unit cost.

(a) Estimate:	$1,000 ÷ 10 = $100
Exact:	$1,020 ÷ 6 = $170
(b) Estimate:	$2,000 ÷ 20 = $100
Exact:	$2,352 ÷ 24 = $98

You will find Self-Check exercises throughout each chapter. These exercises give you a chance to review the material you have just read and see how well you understand the chapter so far. After you have done the exercises, check your answers against the solutions provided at the end of the chapter.

SELF-CHECK 1.1

 Write the word name for the number.

1. 5,702,005   **2.** 317,000,171   **3.** 4,204,049,201

 Round 3,645 to the specified place.

4. hundreds   **5.** first digit   **6.** tens

3 *Add and check the sum.*

7.
```
  328
  583
+ 726
```

8.
```
  671
  982
+  57
```

9. 791 + 1,000 + 52

 4 *Subtract and check the difference.*

10.
```
  55
 -36
```

11.
```
  308
 -275
```

12. 5,409 − 2,176

5 *Multiply and check the product.*

13.
```
  730
× 60
```

14.
```
  904
× 24
```

15. 1,005 by 89

6 *Divide and check the quotient.*

16. 96 ÷ 6

17. 13,838 ÷ 34

18. 3,808 ÷ 15

19. The menswear department of the Gap has a sales goal of $1,384,000 for its Spring Sale. Complete the worksheet (Table 1-2) for the sales totals by region and by days. Decide if the goal was reached. What is the difference between the goal and the actual total sales amount?

Table 1-2

Region	W	Th	F	S	Su	Region Totals
Eastern	$72,492	$81,948	$32,307	$24,301	$32,589	$
Southern	81,897	59,421	48,598	61,025	21,897	
Central	71,708	22,096	23,222	21,507	42,801	
Western	61,723	71,687	52,196	41,737	22,186	
Daily Sales Total	$	$	$	$	$	$

20. Atkinson's Candy Company manufactures seven types of hard candy for its Family Favorites mixed candy which is packaged in three-pound bags. Brenda Jinkins, the floor supervisor, must supervise the repackaging of bulk candy from 84 containers that each contain 25 pounds of candy. The bulk candy will be bagged in three-pound bags, then packed in boxes for shipping. Each box will contain 12 of the bags of mixed candy. Wilma Jackson-Randle is responsible for inventory of containers for the company and reports that she currently has 1,000 three-pound bags on hand and 100 boxes of the size that will be used to ship this candy. Decide if enough materials are in inventory to complete the mixing and packaging process.

21. University Trailer Sales Company sold 352 utility trailers during a recent year. If the gross annual sales for the company was $324,800, what was the average selling price for each trailer?

22. An acre of ground is a square piece of land that is 210 feet on each of the four equal sides. Fencing can be purchased in 50-foot rolls for $49 per roll. You are giving a bid to install the fencing at a cost of $1 per foot of fencing plus the cost of materials. If the customer has bids of $1,700, $2,500, and $2,340 in addition to your bid, decide if your bid is the low bid for the job to determine if you will likely get the business.

23. If you are paying three employees $7 per hour and the fence installation in exercise 22 requires 21 hours when all three employees are working, determine how much you will be required to pay in wages. What will be your gross profit on the job?

24. The 7th Inning Baseball Card Shop buys cards from eight vendors. In the month of November the company purchased 8,832 boxes of cards. If an equal number of boxes were purchased from each vendor, how many boxes of cards were supplied by each vendor?

25. If you have 348 packages of Halloween candy to re-box for shipment to a discount store and you can pack 12 packages in each box, how many boxes will you need?

26. Bio Fach, Germany's biggest ecologically sound consumer goods trade fair, had 21,960 visitors. This figure was up from the 18,090 the previous year and the 16,300 two years earlier. What is the increase in visitors to Bio Fach from two years earlier to the present?

27. The "communication revolution" has given us pre-paid phone calling cards. These cards are used to make long-distance phone calls from certain public phones. In a recent year the industry posted sales of $500,000. Three years later, the sales figure had risen to $200,000,000. What is the increase in sales over the three-year period?

28. Strategic Telecomm Systems, Inc. (STS) in Knoxville, Tennessee, made one of the largest single purchases of long-distance telephone time in history. STS purchased 42 million minutes. If STS paid 12 cents per minute, how much did they pay for the purchase? To convert cents to dollars, divide by 100.

29. If STS resells the phone time at an average of 36 cents per minute, how much profit will they make on the purchase?

30. Sales of prepaid phone cards one year exceeded $1.5 billion. Write this number as an ordinary number.

31. American Communications Network (ACN) of Troy, Michigan, also markets prepaid phone cards, which they refer to as "equity calling cards." If ACN employs 214,302 persons in 32 locations, on the average, how many employees work at each location?

32. If ACN has an annual payroll of $5,602,497,186 for its 214,302 employees, what is the average salary of an employee at ACN?

1 Read, write, and round decimals.

2 Add and subtract decimals.

3 Multiply and divide decimals.

Decimal numbers allow us to write quantities smaller than one whole. We use decimals in some form or another every day—even our money system is based on decimals. Calculators use decimals, and decimals are the basis of percent, interest, markups, and markdowns.

1 Read, write, and round decimals.

Our money system, which is based on the dollar, uses the **decimal system.** In the decimal system, as you move right to left from one digit to the next, the place value of the digit increases by 10 times (multiply by 10). As you move left to right from one digit to the next, the place value of the digit gets 10 times smaller (divide by 10). The place value of the digit to the right of the ones place is 1 divided by 10.

There are several ways for indicating 1 divided by 10. In the decimal system, we write 1 divided by 10 as 0.1. Other ways to write 1 divided by 10 are:

$$10\overline{)1} \qquad 1 \div 10$$

Figure 1-2 1 whole divided into 10 parts. The shaded part is 0.1.

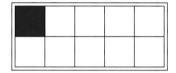

How much is 0.1? How much is 1 divided by 10? It is one part of a 10-part whole. We read 0.1 as one-tenth. Using decimal notation, we can extend our place-value chart to the right of the ones place and express quantities that are not whole numbers. When extending to the right of the ones place, a period called a **decimal point** separates the **whole number part** from the **decimal part.**

The names of the places to the right of the decimal are tenths, hundredths, thousandths, and so on. These place names are similar to the place names for whole numbers, but they all end in *ths*. In Figure 1-3, we show the place names for the digits in the number 2,315.627432.

	Millions			Thousands			Units		Decimal point	Tenths 0.1	Hundredths 0.01	Thousandths 0.001	Ten-thousandths 0.0001	Hundred-thousandths 0.00001	Millionths 0.000001	Ten-millionths 0.0000001	Hundred-millionths 0.00000001
Hundred millions (100,000,000)	Ten millions (10,000,000)	Millions (1,000,000)	Hundred thousands (100,000)	Ten thousands (10,000)	Thousands (1,000)	Hundreds (100)	Tens (10)	Ones (1)									
					2	3	1	5	.	6	2	7	4	3	2		

Figure 1-3 Place Value Chart for Decimals

HOW TO   Read or Write a Decimal

1. Read or write the whole number part (to the left of the decimal point) as you would read or write a whole number.
2. Use the word *and* for the decimal point.
3. Read or write the decimal part (to the right of the decimal point) as you would read or write a whole number.
4. Read or write the place name of the rightmost digit.

Read 3.12
Three

and

twelve

hundredths

Learning Strategy Breaking a Process into Steps

Sometimes processes that involve several steps can be overwhelming. Some strategies for handling multistepped processes are:

- Examine each step of the process to identify processes that are already familiar.

Look at step 1 of reading a decimal. Step 1 refers to a skill that has already been learned. Step 2 gives specific instructions for connecting the steps. Step 3 applies the same skill as step 1 to a different part of the number. Step 4 gives specific instructions for finishing the problem.

- Be sure that you can perform each step independently.

Since both steps 1 and 3 involve reading whole numbers, review reading whole numbers if necessary.

- Examine how the steps are connected.

Step 1 focuses on the whole number part of the number, and steps 3 and 4 focus on the decimal part of the number. Step 2 connects the two parts.

 TIP! Reading Decimals as Money Amounts

When reading decimal numbers that represent money amounts:
  Read whole numbers as *dollars*. $45 is read *forty-five dollars*.
  Decimal amounts are read as *cents*. $0.72 is read *seventy-two cents* rather than *seventy-two hundredths of a dollar*. Since one cent is one hundredth of a dollar, the words *cent* and *hundredth* have the same meaning. $38.21 is read *thirty-eight dollars and twenty-one cents*.

 TIP! Informal Use of the Word *Point*

Informally, the decimal point is sometimes read as *point*. Thus, 3.6 is read *three point six*. The decimal 0.0162 can be read as *point zero one six two*. This informal process is often used in communication to ensure that numbers are not miscommunicated.

EXAMPLE Write the word name for the decimal: (a) 0.209 (b) $234.93

(a) two hundred nine thousandths | The whole number part, 0, is not written.

(b) two hundred thirty-four dollars and ninety-three cents | The whole number part is dollars, the decimal part is cents.

You round decimals for the same reasons that you round whole numbers, and in a similar way.

? HOW TO | **Round to a Specified Decimal Place**

Round to hundredths:

1. Find the digit in the specified place.

2. Look at the next digit to the right.

    (a) If this digit is less than 5, eliminate it and all digits to its right.

    (b) If this digit is 5 or more, add 1 to the digit in the specified place, and eliminate all digits to its right.

17.3754
17.3754
17.3754

17.38

EXAMPLE Round the number to the specified place: (a) $193.48 to the nearest dollar (b) $28.465 to the nearest cent

(a) $193.48 | Rounding to the nearest dollar means rounding to the ones place. The digit in the ones place is 3.

    $193.48 | The digit to the right of 3 is 4. Since 4 is less than 5, step 2a applies; eliminate 4 and all digits to its right.

    $193

$193.48 rounded to the nearest dollar is $193.

(b) $28.465 | Rounding to the nearest cent means rounding to the nearest hundredth. The digit in the hundredths place is 6.

    $28.465 | The digit to the right of 6 is 5. Since 5 is 5 or more, step 2b applies.

    $28.47

$28.465 rounded to the nearest cent is $28.47.

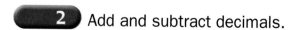 **2** Add and subtract decimals.

Some math skills are used more often than others. Adding and subtracting decimal numbers are regularly used in transactions involving money. To increase your awareness of the use of decimals, refer to your paycheck stub, grocery store receipt, fast-food ticket, odometer on your car, the bills you receive each month, and your checking account statement balance.

 **HOW TO** Add or Subtract Decimals

1. Write the numbers in a vertical column, aligning digits according to their places.
2. Attach extra zeros to the right end of each number so that each number has the same quantity of digits to the right of the decimal point. It is also acceptable to assume blank places to be zero.
3. Add or subtract as though the numbers are whole numbers.
4. Place the decimal point in the sum or difference to align with the decimal point in the addends or subtrahend and minuend.

Add 32 + 2.55 + 8.85 + 0.625

```
  32
   2.55
   8.85
   0.625
 ------
  44.025
```

 TIP! Unwritten Decimals

When we write whole numbers using numerals, we usually omit the decimal point; the decimal point is understood to be at the end of the whole number. Therefore, any whole number, such as 32, can be written without a decimal (32) or with a decimal (32.).

 TIP! Aligning Decimals in Addition or Subtraction

A common mistake in adding decimals is to misalign the digits or decimal points.

```
  15
   4.28
   3.04
   0.735
 ------
  23.055
```
All digits and decimal points are aligned correctly.

```
      15        ← not aligned correctly
    4.28
    3.04
  0.7 35        ← not aligned correctly
 ------
  1.4 82
```

CORRECT   **INCORRECT**

EXAMPLE   Subtract 26.3 − 15.84.

```
   5 12 10
  2 6 .3 0
 −1 5 .8 4
 ---------
  1 0 .4 6
```

Write the numbers so that the digits align according to their places.
Subtract the numbers, borrowing as you would in whole number subtraction.

The difference of 26.3 and 15.84 is 10.46.

3 Multiply and divide decimals.

You are frequently called on to calculate the amount of tip to add to a restaurant bill. A typical tip in the United States is 20 cents per dollar, which is 0.20 or 0.2 per dollar. To calculate the tip on a bill of $28.73 we multiply 28.73×0.2.

We multiply decimals as though they are whole numbers. Then we place the decimal point according to the quantity of digits in the decimal parts of the factors.

HOW TO Multiply Decimals

1. Multiply the decimal numbers as though they are whole numbers.

2. Count the digits in the decimal parts of both decimal numbers.

3. Place the decimal point in the product so that there are as many digits in its decimal part as there are digits you counted in step 2. If necessary, attach zeros on the left end of the product so that you can place the decimal point accurately.

Multiply 3.5×3.

$$\begin{array}{r} 3.5 \\ \times \ \ 3 \\ \hline 10.5 \end{array}$$

EXAMPLE Multiply 2.35×0.015.

$$\begin{array}{r} 2.35 \\ \times \ \ 0.015 \\ \hline 1175 \\ 235 \ \ \\ \hline 0.03525 \end{array}$$

There are two digits to the right of the decimal point in 2.35, and there are three digits to the right of the decimal point in 0.015. So the product must have five digits to the right of the decimal point. One 0 is attached on the left to accurately place the decimal point.

The product of 2.35 and 0.015 is 0.03525.

Note that the zero to the left of the decimal point in the preceding example is not necessary, but it helps to make the decimal point visible.

TIP! Don't Drop Zeros Too Soon!

A common mistake is to drop unnecessary zeros *before* placing the decimal point in the product.

$$\begin{array}{r} 2.5 \\ \times \ \ 0.14 \\ \hline 100 \\ 25 \ \ \\ \hline 0.350 \end{array}$$

There is one digit to the right of the decimal point in 2.5, and there are two digits to the right of the decimal point in 0.14. There must be three digits to the right of the decimal point in the product.

$$\begin{array}{r} 2.5 \\ \times \ \ 0.14 \\ \hline 100 \\ 25 \ \ \\ \hline 0.035\cancel{0} \end{array}$$

CORRECT   **INCORRECT**

1	Decision needed
2	Unknown facts
3	Known facts
4	Relationships
5	Estimation
6	Calculation
7	Interpretation
8	Decision made

EXAMPLE   Find the amount of tip you would pay on a restaurant bill of $28.73 if you tip 20 cents on the dollar (0.2) for the bill.

Amount of tip

Restaurant bill: $28.73
Rate of tip: 0.2 (20 cents on the dollar) of the bill

Amount of tip = restaurant bill × rate of tip
Amount of tip = 28.73 × 0.2

Round the restaurant bill to $30 and multiply by 0.2:   30 × 0.2 = 6

$$\begin{array}{r} 28.73 \\ \times\ \ 0.2 \\ \hline 5.746 \end{array}$$

The tip is $5.75 when rounded to the nearest cent.

Division of decimals has many uses in the business world. A common use is to determine how much an item costs if the cost of several items is known. Also, to compare the best buy of similar products that are packaged differently, we find the cost per common unit. A 12-ounce package and a 1-pound package of bacon can be compared by finding the cost per ounce of each package.

? HOW TO Divide a Decimal by a Whole Number

Divide 95.2 by 14.

1. Place a decimal point for the quotient directly above the decimal point in the dividend.

$$14\overline{)95.2}$$

2. Divide as though the decimal numbers are whole numbers.

$$\begin{array}{r} 6.8 \\ 14\overline{)95.2} \\ \underline{84} \\ 112 \\ \underline{112} \end{array}$$

EXAMPLE   Divide 5.95 by 17.

$$\begin{array}{r} 0.35 \\ 17\overline{)5.95} \\ \underline{5\ 1} \\ 85 \\ \underline{85} \end{array}$$

Place a decimal point for the quotient directly above the decimal point in the dividend.

The quotient of 5.95 and 17 is 0.35.

If the division does not come out even, you can continue it as far as you want by attaching zeros to the dividend. If you are planning to round a quotient to a specified place, carry the division to one place to the right of the specified place, and then round the quotient.

EXAMPLE   Find the quotient of 37.4 ÷ 24 to the nearest hundredth.

```
       1.558  rounds to 1.56
   24)37.400
       24
       ───
       13 4
       12 0
       ────
        1 40
        1 20
        ────
          200
          192
          ───
            8
```

To be able to round the quotient to the nearest hundredth, carry the division out to the thousandths place, and then round.

The quotient is 1.56 to the nearest hundredth.

! **TIP!** **Place Decimal for Quotient First**

A common mistake is to attach zeros to the dividend without placing a decimal for the quotient first. Divide: 12 ÷ 8.

```
     1.5
  8)12.0          ←──── The zero and decimal point
     8                  are placed correctly in the
     ───                dividend, and the decimal
     4 0                point in the quotient is in
     4 0                the correct place.
     ───
```

CORRECT

```
     1 5
  8)12 0          ←──── The zero was
     8                  attached, but the
     ───                decimal point was
     4 0                left out.
     4 0
     ───
```

INCORRECT

If the divisor is a decimal rather than a whole number, we make use of an important fact: Increasing both the divisor and the dividend by the same factor does not change their quotient. For instance, for each of the quotients

$$5.\overline{)10.}^{\;2.} \qquad 50.\overline{)100.}^{\;2.} \qquad 500.\overline{)1000.}^{\;2.}$$

we've increased the divisor and the dividend both by a factor of 10, and then by a factor of 10 again. The quotient is always 2. Notice that increasing by a factor of 10 makes the decimal point move one place to the right.

? **HOW TO** **Divide by a Decimal**

Divide 3.4776 by 0.72.

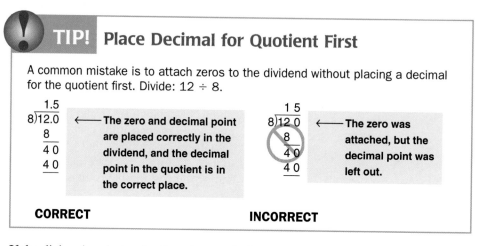

1. Change the divisor to a whole number by moving the decimal point to the right, counting the places as you go.

2. Move the decimal point in the dividend to the right as many places as you moved it in the divisor.

3. Place the decimal point for the quotient directly above the *new* decimal point in the dividend.

4. Divide as you would divide by a whole number.

You may find it helpful to mark the new location of the decimal point in both the divisor and dividend with a caret (∧).

EXAMPLE Find the quotient of 59.9 ÷ 0.39 to the nearest hundredth.

0.39)59.90 ⟶ 39∧)5,990∧

Move the decimal point two places to the right in both the divisor and the dividend.

Place the decimal point for the quotient directly above the decimal point in the dividend.

Divide, carrying out the division to the thousandths place.

$$
\begin{array}{r}
39\overline{)5,990.000}
\end{array}
$$

$$
\begin{array}{r}
153.589 \\
39\overline{)5,990.000} \\
3\ 9 \\
\hline
2\ 09 \\
1\ 95 \\
\hline
140 \\
117 \\
\hline
23\ 0 \\
19\ 5 \\
\hline
3\ 50 \\
3\ 12 \\
\hline
380 \\
351 \\
\hline
\end{array}
$$

The quotient is 153.59 to the nearest hundredth.

1 Decision needed

2 Unknown facts

3 Known facts

4 Relationships

5 Estimation

6 Calculation

7 Interpretation

8 Decision made

EXAMPLE Irene Maciol paid a tip of $8 on a restaurant bill of $43.17. How many cents per dollar (rounded to the nearest cent) of the bill did Irene pay as a tip?

The number of cents per dollar of the bill as a tip

Total bill: $43.17
Amount of tip: $8

Cents per dollar of the bill as a tip = amount of tip ÷ total bill
Cents per dollar of the bill as a tip = $8 ÷ $43.17

Round the bill to $40.

$$
\begin{array}{r}
0.20 \\
40\overline{)8.00}
\end{array}
$$

The estimate is 20 cents per dollar.

$$
\begin{array}{r}
0.185 \\
43.17∧\overline{)8.00∧000} \\
4\ 31\ 7 \\
\hline
3\ 68\ 30 \\
3\ 45\ 36 \\
\hline
22\ 940 \\
21\ 585 \\
\hline
1\ 355 \\
\end{array}
$$

This decimal is 0.19 rounded to the nearest hundredth.

Irene paid 19 cents per dollar as a tip.

Write the word name for the decimal.

1. 0.582

2. 1.0009

3. 782.07

Round to the nearest dollar.

4. $493.91

5. $785.03

6. $19.80

 Add.

7. 6.005 + 0.03 + 924 + 3.9

8. 82 + 5000.1 + 101.703

Subtract.

9. 407.96 − 298.39

10. 500.70 from 8097.125

 Multiply.

11. 19.7
    × 4

12. 0.0321 × 10

13. 73.7 by 0.02

Divide and round to the nearest hundredth.

14. 123.72 ÷ 12

15. 35)589.06

16. 0.35)0.0084

17. Laura Voight earns $8.43 per hour as a telemarketing employee. One week she worked 28 hours. What was her gross pay before any deductions?

18. Daniel Dawson is plant manager for a company that produces abrasive wheels as sharpening tools. Rubber and abrasive compounds are mixed and heated in molds to produce the abrasive wheels. One mold can produce 32 wheels from a sheet of material. If it takes nine hours to process 18 sheets of material, how many wheels are processed in nine hours?

19. Cassie James works a 26-hour week at a part-time job while attending classes at Shelby State Community College. Her weekly gross pay is $213.46. What is her hourly rate of pay?

20. Calculate the cost of 1,000 gallons of gasoline if it costs $1.47 per gallon.

21. All the employees in your department are splitting the cost of a celebratory lunch, catered at a cost of $142.15. If your department has 23 employees, will each employee be able to pay an equal share? How should the catering cost be divided?

22. Prepaid phone cards are offered by many companies. AT&T's rates range from 33 cents to 22 cents. MCI's rates range from 32 cents down to 13.9 cents, and Sprint offers a rate of 28 cents per minute for a 50-minute card. Find the cost of the 50-minute card offered by Sprint.

23. If MCI offers a 120-minute card for $12, what is the cost per minute?

24. BP Oil offers a prepaid phone card for $5. The card provides 20 minutes of long-distance phone service. Find the cost per minute.

25. A prepaid phone card purchased at Phone Ahead, an airport franchise, costs $7.50 for 60 minutes. Find the cost per minute.

26. Examine the cost per minute of the prepaid phone cards given in exercise 22, and determine which company offered the "best buy" in phone cards. Which company charged the most per minute? Explain why you might expect the rates you found to be the lowest and the highest.

27. Tel-Sales, Inc., a prepaid phone card company in Oklahoma City, has 398,253 independent representatives. Show the number of independent representatives as a number rounded to the nearest hundred thousand.

28. Destiny Telecom of Oakland, California introduced a Braille prepaid phone card. Destiny has sales exceeding two hundred fifty million dollars. Write the digits to show Destiny's sales figure.

1.3 Problem Solving Using Proportions

1 Verify that two fractions form a proportion.

2 Find a missing term in a proportion.

3 Use proportions in changing units of measure.

Many business problems involve making two calculations, one multiplication and one division. If two CDs cost $25, how much would five CDs cost? To find the cost of one CD, divide $25 by 2. Then, if each CD costs $12.50, five CDs will cost five times as much. $12.50 \times 5 = $62.50.

1 Verify that two fractions form a proportion.

A proportion is based on two pairs of related quantities. The most common way to write proportions is to use fraction notation. A number written in fraction notation is also called a **ratio**. When two fractions or ratios are equal, they form a **proportion.** In Chapter 2 we will investigate operations with fractions, but for now we make some observations about equivalent or equal fractions. Look at several fractions that we can intuitively recognize as equivalent.

$$\frac{1}{2} \quad \frac{2}{4} \quad \frac{3}{6} \quad \frac{4}{8} \quad \frac{5}{10} \quad \frac{6}{12}$$

In each case the number in the *numerator* (top) is one-half as large as the number in the *denominator* (bottom). We can pair any two of the equivalent fractions and form a proportion.

$$\frac{1}{2} = \frac{2}{4} \quad \frac{1}{2} = \frac{3}{6} \quad \frac{1}{2} = \frac{4}{8} \quad \frac{3}{6} = \frac{5}{10} \quad \frac{2}{4} = \frac{5}{10} \quad \frac{4}{8} = \frac{6}{12}$$

An important property of proportions is that the cross products are equal. A **cross product** is the product of the numerator of one fraction times the denominator of another fraction. In the proportion $\frac{1}{2} = \frac{2}{4}$, one cross product is 1×4 and the other cross product is 2×2. Notice that the two cross products have the same product, 4. Let's look at other proportions.

$$\frac{3}{6} = \frac{5}{10} \qquad \frac{2}{4} = \frac{5}{10} \qquad \frac{4}{8} = \frac{6}{12}$$

$$3 \times 10 = 5 \times 6 \qquad 2 \times 10 = 5 \times 4 \qquad 4 \times 12 = 6 \times 8$$

$$30 = 30 \qquad\qquad 20 = 20 \qquad\qquad 48 = 48$$

HOW TO Verify That Two Fractions Form a Proportion

1. Find the two cross products.
2. Compare the two cross products.
3. If the cross products are equal, the two fractions form a proportion.

Do $\frac{4}{12}$ and $\frac{6}{18}$ form a proportion?
$4 \times 18 = 72$ $6 \times 12 = 72$

Cross products are equal.

Fractions form a proportion.

Now, let's look again at the situation about the CDs. The facts of the problem form two pairs of information.

Pair 1: 2 CDs cost $25
Pair 2: 5 CDs cost $62.50

We can write these pairs of information as fractions in two different ways.

$$\frac{2 \text{ CDs}}{\$25} = \frac{5 \text{ CDs}}{\$62.50}$$
Pair 1   Pair 2

$$\frac{2 \text{ CDs}}{5 \text{ CDs}} = \frac{\$25}{\$62.50}$$ Pair 1 / Pair 2

EXAMPLE Verify that both representations for the CD proportions are truly proportions.

$$\frac{2 \text{ CDs}}{\$25} = \frac{5 \text{ CDs}}{\$62.50}$$
Pair 1   Pair 2

$$\frac{2 \text{ CDs}}{5 \text{ CDs}} = \frac{\$25}{\$62.50}$$ Pair 1 / Pair 2

$2 \times \$62.50 = 5 \times \$25$
$\$125 = \$125$

$2 \times \$62.50 = \$25 \times 5$
$\$125 = \$125$

2 Find a missing term in a proportion.

In most business situations we have one established pair, but we don't have two complete pairs of information. Instead we have one complete pair and one number of the other pair. We use the property that the cross products of proportions are equal to find the missing number of the second pair.

HOW TO Find a Missing Term in a Proportion

1. Let some symbol, normally a letter of the alphabet, represent the missing amount.
2. Multiply the cross product with two numbers.
3. Divide by the number in the other cross product.
4. Place the quotient from step 3 into the original proportion and verify the proportion.

$$\frac{5}{7} = \frac{N}{21}$$

$5 \times 21 = 105$

$105 \div 7 = 15$

$$\frac{5}{7} = \frac{15}{21}$$

$5 \times 21 = 15 \times 7$
$105 = 105$

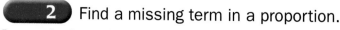

EXAMPLE Find the missing number in the proportion, $\dfrac{6}{N} = \dfrac{10}{15}$.

$$\frac{6}{N} = \frac{10}{15}$$

$6 \times 15 = 90$ **Find the cross product with two numbers.**

$90 \div 10 = 9$ **Divide by the number in the other cross product.**

Thus, the missing number in the proportion is 9.
Verify: $6 \times 15 = 90$ and $10 \times 9 = 90$

3   Use proportions in changing units of measure.

There are many common uses of proportions in the business world and in everyday life. For example, proportions are used to change units of measure, to exchange international currency, to prorate prices or taxes, to enlarge or reduce recipes or photographic images, and so on. The illustrations that we use in changing units of measure can be used as a pattern for a variety of other uses of proportions.

Units of measure are grouped in categories such as measures of length or distance, measures of weight or mass, measures of capacity or volume, measures of time, measures of light intensity, and many more. To change units of measure, examine a standard relationship between the two measures. For example, to relate inches and feet, we use the relationship that 12 inches equals one foot. Then, we can change any number of inches to an equivalent measure in feet, or vice versa, using a proportion.

 HOW TO **Change from One Unit of Measure to Another**

	How many feet are in 45 inches?
1. Investigate or research the measures to determine a relationship between two measures.	12 inches = 1 foot
2. Form a second pair of values from the original measure and the unknown measure.	45 inches = N feet
3. Make a proportion of the two pairs of values.	$\dfrac{12 \text{ in.}}{45 \text{ in.}} = \dfrac{1 \text{ ft}}{N \text{ ft}}$
4. Solve for the missing value.	$45 \times 1 = 45$ $45 \div 12 = 3.75$

1 Decision needed

2 Unknown facts

3 Known facts

4 Relationships

5 Estimation

EXAMPLE If there are 16 ounces (oz) in one pound (lb), how many ounces are in 3.5 pounds?

Number of ounces in 3.5 pounds

16 ounces = 1 pound

16 oz = 1 lb   **Pair 1**
N oz = 3.5 lb   **Pair 2**
$\dfrac{16 \text{ oz}}{N \text{ oz}} = \dfrac{1 \text{ lb}}{3.5 \text{ lb}}$ **proportion**

If one pound has 16 ounces, 3.5 pounds will have *more* than 16 ounces. $16 \times 3 = 48$; $16 \times 4 = 64$. 3.5 pounds will have between 48 and 64 ounces.

6 Calculation

$$\frac{16 \text{ oz}}{N \text{ oz}} = \frac{1 \text{ lb}}{3.5 \text{ lb}}$$

$16 \times 3.5 = 56$

$56 \div 1 = 56$

> Proportions using two pairs of values.
>
> Cross product with two values.
> Divide by number in other cross product.

7 Interpretation
8 Decision made

There are 56 ounces in 3.5 pounds.

Many reference materials give conversion factors for quickly changing from one unit of measure to another. A **conversion factor** is a value to *multiply* by to change from one unit of measure to another. The inside cover of this text lists several conversion factors for the most common units of measure for both the U.S. Customary and the metric systems of measure. Conversion factors can also be developed for changing currency, modifying recipes, prorating taxes, and many other applications.

Two conversion factors can be established from each relationship of two measures. For example, in the relationship 12 inches equal 1 foot, we can make a conversion factor to change inches to feet and a second conversion factor to change feet to inches.

 HOW TO Determine the Conversion Factors for Two Related Measures

	Determine the conversion factor for changing inches to feet and for changing feet to inches.
1. To find the conversion factor for changing from the first measure to the second measure, divide the second number by the first.	1 foot = 12 inches 12 ÷ 1 = 12 To change from feet to inches: 　　Multiply by 12.
2. To find the conversion factor for changing from the second measure to the first measure, divide the first number by the second.	1 foot = 12 inches 1 ÷ 12 = 0.083333333 To change from inches to feet: 　　Multiply by 0.083333333.

EXAMPLE   If 1 meter equals 1.0936 yards (rounded to ten-thousandths), determine conversion factors for changing from meters to yards and for changing from yards to meters.

Relationship:　　　1 meter = 1.0936 yards

Meters to yards:　　1.0936 ÷ 1 = 1.0936　　> Second number divided by first

Yards to meters:　　1 ÷ 1.0936 = 0.9144　　> First number divided by second
> (rounded to ten-thousandths)

EXAMPLE   Change the following measures using the conversion factors found in the preceding example. Round measures to the nearest tenth.

(a) 5 meters = _____ yards　　　(b) 15 yards = _____ meters

(a) 5 meters = 5 × 1.0936 yards = 5.468 yards = 5.5 yards (rounded)

(b) 15 yards = 15 × 0.9144 meters = 13.716 meters = 13.7 meters (rounded)

1 *Verify that the given fractions form a proportion.*

1. $\dfrac{7}{8} = \dfrac{21}{24}$

2. $\dfrac{3}{5} = \dfrac{12}{20}$

3. $\dfrac{7}{9} = \dfrac{49}{63}$

Show which of the fractions form a proportion. Change one number in the pair that does not form a proportion so that a proportion is formed.

4. $\dfrac{4}{5} = \dfrac{8}{10}$

5. $\dfrac{3}{8} = \dfrac{6}{24}$

6. $\dfrac{10}{6} = \dfrac{5}{8}$

7. $\dfrac{7}{11} = \dfrac{5}{22}$

8. $\dfrac{9}{10} = \dfrac{6}{8}$

Write a fraction that completes the proportion.

9. $\dfrac{5}{8} = \text{—}$

10. $\dfrac{3}{7} = \text{—}$

11. $\dfrac{15}{4} = \text{—}$

 2 *Find the missing term for the proportions.*

12. $\dfrac{3}{5} = \dfrac{N}{30}$

13. $\dfrac{16}{30} = \dfrac{8}{N}$

14. $\dfrac{N}{3} = \dfrac{10}{12}$

15. $\dfrac{N}{3.2} = \dfrac{4}{10}$

16. $\dfrac{6}{N} = \dfrac{9}{6}$

17. $\dfrac{48}{64} = \dfrac{N}{8}$

3 *Use proportions and conversion factors to change the measures. Round to tenths if necessary.*

18. 20 meters = _____ yards
(1 meter = 1.0936 yards.)

19. 150 yards = _____ meters
(1 meter = 1.0936 yards)

20. 42 ounces = _____ pounds

21. 190 pounds = _____ ounces

22. 420 kilograms = _____ pounds
(1 kilogram = 2.2 pounds)

23. 380 ounces = _____ grams
(1 gram = 0.04 ounce)

24. 1,000 US dollars = _____ pesetas
(1 US dollar = 152.649994 pesetas)

25. 500,000 lira = _____ US dollars
(1 US dollar = 1762 lira)

International Monetary Exchange

Different countries have different money systems. When traveling to another country, dollars must be exchanged for the money of that country. Currency of other countries can be purchased at most banks and at money exchanges in the United States and in other countries. Banks usually charge a transaction fee for the money exchange and also sell the money for more than the Opening Market Rate, which is the rate listed each day by the International Monetary Fund. The fee is a flat fee and the amount of money exchanged does not affect the fee. However, a fee may be charged for each different currency that is exchanged.

Most international airports have a money exchange booth where travelers can purchase money for the countries they plan to visit. These businesses usually list a "sell" rate and a "buy" rate. The sell rate is the rate at which the business will sell foreign money to the consumer. The buy rate is the rate at which the business will buy foreign money. While some exchange booths do not charge an exchange service fee, they charge a higher rate of exchange.

The rate of exchange of dollars for other currencies changes hourly. Rates of exchange can be found on the World Wide Web, and rate changes are updated regularly, though not hourly. The following exchange rates were listed recently on the Web.

Sell Rate	Buy Rate
1 Australian dollar = 0.540500 U.S. dollars	1 U.S. dollar = 1.850139 Australian dollars
1 Austrian schilling = 0.063676 U.S. dollars	1 U.S. dollar = 15.70450405 schillings
1 British pound = 1.456301 U.S. dollars	1 U.S. dollar = 0.686671 pounds
1 Canadian dollar = 0.648000	1 U.S. dollar = 1.543210 Canadian dollars
1 European euro = 0.876201 U.S. dollars	1 U.S. dollar = 1.141291 European euros
1 Italian lira = 0.000453 U.S. dollars	1 U.S. dollar = 2207.50552 lira
1 Japanese yen = 0.008933 U.S. dollars	1 U.S. dollar = 111.944476 yen
1 Mexican peso = 0.05823 U.S. dollars	1 U.S. dollar = 9.4497416 pesos
1 Spanish peseta = 0.005266 U.S. dollars	1 U.S. dollar = 189.897455 pesetas

To calculate the number of Australian dollars that can be purchased for $1,000, we can use a proportion and use either of the exchange rates for Australian dollars.

$$\frac{n}{\$1,000} = \frac{1 \text{ Australian dollar}}{0.540500 \text{ U.S. dollar}}$$

$1,000 × 1 = $1,000   **Multiply**

$1,000 ÷ 0.5405 = $1,850.14   **Divide and round**

$$n = 1,850.14 \text{ Australian dollars}$$

Exercises. Use the above information to answer exercises 1–8.

1. You are going on a business trip to Italy. While in Italy you plan to purchase some leather goods. To have enough cash in lira to pay for incidentals, you determine that you will need $1,000 U.S. dollars exchanged for an equivalent amount of lira. If you use your bank, which charges a $7.50 service fee for any exchange, how much Italian money can you expect in the exchange?

2. When you arrive in the Rome airport, you call a taxi for the trip to the hotel. The taxi informs you the trip will cost you 45,000 lira. How much is this in U.S. dollars?

3. If you normally leave $1.00 tip for the hotel cleaning staff, approximately how many lira should you leave?

4. A leather bag you select has a price tag of 345,500 lira. How much is this in US dollars?

5. Devise a quick method for converting lira to U.S. dollars so that you will be able to get a reasonable estimate of the cost of Italian goods and services while in the country.

6. Examine the list of exchange rates given earlier and determine which currency is valued most closely with U.S. currency.

7. Search the Web for currency exchange rates and compare the current rates with those given in the text. Would you say the U.S. dollar, in general, is getting stronger (worth more against foreign currency) since the printing of this text or getting weaker?

8. Which country has the greatest change in exchange rate since the text was printed? How much change has taken place?

9. On a recent day the bank offered to sell 0.6320 British pounds for 1 U.S. dollar and the Airport Foreign Exchange offered to sell 0.6000 British pounds for 1 U.S. dollar. The bank charges a $5 transaction fee and $5 to deliver the exchanged money to a bank branch where you would pick it up. Which place would give you more British pounds for $1,000 if the transaction fee is to come out of the $1,000.

10. Estimate the maximum amount of money you would need to exchange to get a better deal at the Airport Foreign Exchange.

Answers

1. 2,190,949.27 lira   2. $20.39   3. 2,208 lira   4. $156.51

5. Divide the number of lira by 100,000, then take half of the result. For example, 345,352 lira divided by 1,000 is 345. One-half of 345 is 172.50, which is fairly close to the exact exchange of $156.51.

6. 1 U.S. dollar = 1.850139 Australian dollars; a difference of 0.850139. 1 U.S. dollar = 0.876201 European euros with a difference of 0.123799. Of the currencies given, the European euro has the least difference with the dollar.

7. Answers will vary.

8. Answers will vary.

9. Bank exchange: $1,000 = 622 pounds
Airport exchange: $1,000 = 600 pounds
Bank exchange is better.

10. At approximately $200 the exchanges are equivalent. (Exact value at which the exchanges are equal is $197.50.)

CHAPTER OVERVIEW
1

| Section Outcome | Important Points with Examples |

Section 1.1

Read and write whole numbers. (page 4)

1. Notice that commas separate the number into groups of three digits each.
2. For each group, beginning with the leftmost group:
   (a) Read the three-digit number from left to right.
   (b) Name the group.

Chapter 1 Problem Solving with Whole Numbers and Decimals   **37**

3. Note these exceptions:

    (a) Do not read or name a group that is all zeros.

    (b) Do not name the units group.

The word *and* is never part of the word name for a whole number.

> **574 is read** *five hundred seventy-four.*
>
> **3,804,321 is read** *three million, eight hundred four thousand, three hundred twenty-one.*

---

2   Round whole numbers. (page 7)

1. Find the digit in the specified place.

2. Look at the next digit to the right.

    (a) If this digit is less than 5, replace it and all digits to its right with zeros.

    (b) If this digit is 5 or more, add 1 to the digit in the specified place, and replace all digits to the right of the specified place with zeros.

> **4,860 rounded to the nearest hundred is 4,900.**
>
> **7,439 rounded to the nearest thousand is 7,000.**
>
> **4,095 rounded to the first digit is 4,000.**

---

3   Add whole numbers. (page 8)

1. Write the numbers in a vertical column, aligning digits according to their places.

2. For each *place* in turn, beginning with the ones place:

    (a) Add the *place* digits.

    (b) Write the units digit of this sum directly below the *place* digit of the last addend.

    (c) Write the remaining digits of the sum directly above the *next place* digit of the first addend.

$$
\begin{array}{r}
^{1} \\
364 \\
+473 \\
\hline
837
\end{array}
\qquad
\text{Add: } 2{,}074 + 485 + 12{,}592
\qquad
\begin{array}{r}
^{1\ 2\ 1} \\
2{,}074 \\
485 \\
12{,}592 \\
\hline
15{,}151
\end{array}
$$

---

4   Subtract whole numbers. (page 12)

1. Write the numbers in a vertical column, the subtrahend below the minuend, aligning digits according to their places.

2. For each *place* in turn, beginning with the ones place:

    (a) If the *place* digit of the minuend is less than the *place* digit of the subtrahend, add 10 to the *place* digit of the minuend and subtract 1 from the *next place* digit of the minuend.

    (b) Subtract the *place* digits.

    (c) Write this difference directly below the *place* digit of the subtrahend.

3. Check the difference by adding the subtrahend and the difference. Their sum should be the same as the minuend.

$$
\begin{array}{r}
^{4\ 14} \\
75\,4 \\
-32\,9 \\
\hline
42\,5
\end{array}
\quad
\begin{array}{r}
^{7\ 10} \\
8\,0\,7 \\
-3\,2\,1 \\
\hline
4\,8\,6
\end{array}
\quad
\begin{array}{r}
^{8\ \ 99\ 10} \\
9{,}00\,0 \\
-3{,}52\,1 \\
\hline
5{,}47\,9
\end{array}
\quad
\begin{array}{r}
^{0\ 9\ 17} \\
1\,0\,7\,9 \\
-2\,9\,8 \\
\hline
7\,8\,1
\end{array}
\quad
\begin{array}{r}
^{0\ 9\ 99\ 10} \\
10{,}00\,0 \\
-99\,9 \\
\hline
9{,}00\,1
\end{array}
$$

---

5   Multiply whole numbers. (page 14)

1. Write the numbers in a vertical column, aligning digits according to their places.

2. For each *place* of the multiplier in turn, beginning with the ones place:

    (a) Multiply the multiplicand by the *place* digit of the multiplier.

    (b) Write this partial product directly below the multiplier (or the last partial product), aligning the ones digit of the partial product with the *place* digit of the multiplier (and aligning all other digits to the left accordingly).

3. Add the partial products.

543	509	8,1|00	$18 \times 10 = 180$
$\times \quad 32$	$\times \quad 87$	$\times \quad 3\|00$	$18 \times 100 = 1,800$
1 086	3 563	2,43|0,000	$18 \times 1,000 = 18,000$
16 29	40 72		
17,376	44,283		

6 Divide whole numbers. (page 16)

1. Beginning with its leftmost digit, identify the first group of digits of the dividend that is larger than or equal to the divisor. This group of digits is the first *partial dividend*.
2. For each partial dividend in turn, beginning with the first,
   (a) *Divide* the partial dividend by the divisor. Write this partial quotient above the rightmost digit of the partial dividend.
   (b) *Multiply* the partial quotient by the divisor. Write the product below the partial dividend, aligning places.
   (c) *Subtract* the product from the partial dividend. Write the difference below the product, aligning places. The difference must be less than the divisor.
   (d) Next to the ones place of the difference, *write* the next digit of the dividend. This is the new partial dividend.
3. When all the digits of the dividend have been used, *write* the final difference in step 2c as the remainder (unless the remainder is 0). The whole number part of the quotient is the number written above the dividend.
4. To check, multiply the quotient by the divisor and add the remainder to the product. This sum will equal the dividend.

Be sure the difference in step 2c is less than the divisor. If it isn't, the partial quotient in step 2b must be corrected.

```
   287 R1              804
3)862            56)45,024          21,000 ÷ 10 = 2,100
   6                 44 8            21,000 ÷ 100 = 210
  26                   22            21,000 ÷ 1,000 = 21
  24                    0
   22                 224
   21                 224
    1
```

Section 1.2

1 Read, write, and round decimals. (page 22)

Read or write a decimal.
1. Read or write the whole number part (to the left of the decimal point) as you would read or write a whole number.
2. Use the word *and* for the decimal point.
3. Read or write the decimal part (to the right of the decimal point) as you would read or write a whole number.
4. Name the place of the rightmost digit.

0.3869 is read *three thousand, eight-hundred sixty-nine ten-thousandths.*

Round to a specified decimal place.
1. Find the digit in the specified place.
2. Look at the next digit to the right.
   (a) If this digit is less than 5, eliminate it and all digits to its right.
   (b) If this digit is 5 or more, add 1 to the digit in the specified place, and eliminate all digits to its right.

37.357 rounded to the nearest tenth is 37.4.

3.4819 rounded to the first digit is 3.

2 | Add and subtract decimals. (page 24)

1. Write the numbers in a vertical column, aligning digits according to their places.
2. Attach extra zeros to the right end of each decimal number so that each number has the same quantity of digits to the right of the decimal point (optional).
3. Add or subtract as though the numbers are whole numbers.
4. Place the decimal point in the sum or difference to align with the decimal point in the addends or subtrahend and minuend.

Add: 32.68 + 3.31 + 49   **Subtract: 24.7 − 18.25**

```
                              1 14 6 10
  32.68                        2 4.7 0
   3.31                      − 1 8.2 5
  49.                           6.4 5
  84.99
```

3 | Multiply and divide decimals. (page 26)

Multiply decimals.

1. Multiply the decimal numbers as though they are whole numbers.
2. Count the digits in the decimal parts of both decimal numbers.
3. Place the decimal point in the product so that there are as many digits in its decimal part as there are digits you counted in step 2. If necessary, attach zeros on the left end of the product so that you can place the decimal point accurately.

Multiply: 36.48 × 2.52   **Multiply: 2.03 × 0.036**

```
      36.48                            2.03      3.492 × 10 = 34.92
   ×   2.52                        ×  0.0 36     3.492 × 100 = 349.2
      72 96                           1 2 18     3.492 × 1,000 = 3,492
   18 24 0                             6 0 9
   72 96                           0.07 3 08
   91.92 96
```

Divide a decimal by a whole number.

1. Place a decimal point for the quotient directly above the decimal point in the dividend.
2. Divide as though the decimal numbers are whole numbers.

Divide: 58.5 ÷ 45

```
        1.3
   45)58.5              43.7 ÷ 10 = 4.37
      45                43.7 ÷ 100 = 0.437
      13 5            43.7 ÷ 1,000 = 0.0437
      13 5
```

Divide by a decimal.

1. Change the divisor to a whole number by moving the decimal point to the right, counting the places as you go.
2. Move the decimal point in the dividend as many places as you moved it in the divisor.
3. Place the decimal point for the quotient directly above the *new* decimal point in the dividend.
4. Divide as you would divide by a whole number.

Divide: 0.770 ÷ 3.5

$$\begin{array}{r} 0.22 \\ 3.5\overline{)0.7{,}70} \\ \underline{70} \\ 70 \\ \underline{70} \end{array}$$

Divide: 0.485 ÷ 0.24
Round to the nearest tenth.

$$2.02 = 2.0 \text{ rounded}$$
$$\begin{array}{r} 0.24\overline{)0.48{,}50} \\ \underline{48} \\ 50 \\ \underline{48} \\ 2 \end{array}$$

Section 1.3

1 Verify that two fractions form a proportion. (page 31)

1. Find the two cross products.
2. Compare the two cross products.
3. If the cross products are equal, the two fractions form a proportion.

Verify that $\dfrac{3}{4} = \dfrac{21}{28}$ is a proportion.

$$3 \times 28 = 4 \times 21$$
$$84 = 84$$

Since the cross products are equal, $\dfrac{3}{4} = \dfrac{21}{28}$ forms a proportion.

2 Find a missing term in a proportion. (page 32)

1. Let some symbol represent the missing term.
2. Multiply the cross product with two numbers.
3. Divide by the number in the other cross product.
4. Place the quotient from step 3 into the original proportion and verify the proportion.

Find the missing number in the proportion, $\dfrac{5}{10} = \dfrac{15}{N}$.

$$10 \times 15 = 150$$
$$150 \div 5 = 30$$
$$N = 30$$

Check: $\quad \dfrac{5}{10} = \dfrac{15}{30}$

$$5 \times 30 = 10 \times 15$$
$$150 = 150$$

3 Use proportions in changing units of measure. (page 33)

1. Investigate or research the measures to determine a relationship between the two measures.
2. Form a second pair of values from the original measure and the unknown measure.
3. Make a proportion of the two pairs of values.
4. Solve for the missing value.

If there are 12 inches in a foot, how many inches are there in 18.5 feet?

12 inches = 1 foot   Pair 1
N inches = 18.5 feet   Pair 2

$$\dfrac{12 \text{ inches}}{1 \text{ foot}} = \dfrac{N \text{ inches}}{18.5 \text{ feet}}$$

$$12 \times 18.5 = 222$$
$$222 \div 1 = 222$$
$$N = 222 \text{ inches}$$

WORDS TO KNOW

place-value system (p. 5)
rounded number (p. 7)
approximate number (p. 7)
addends (p. 8)
sum (p. 8)
total (p. 8)
commutative property of
    addition (p. 8)
associative property of
    addition (p. 8)
estimate (p. 9)
minuend (p. 12)

subtrahend (p. 12)
difference (p. 12)
multiplicand (p. 14)
multiplier (p. 14)
factor (p. 14)
product (p. 14)
partial product (p. 14)
dividend (p. 16)
divisor (p. 16)
quotient (p. 16)
whole number part (p. 16)
remainder (p. 16)

partial dividends (p. 16)
partial quotient (p. 16)
decimal system (p. 22)
decimal point (p. 22)
whole number part (p. 22)
decimal part (p. 22)
ratio (p. 31)
proportion (p. 31)
cross product (p. 31)
conversion factor (p. 34)

CHAPTER 1 CONCEPTS ANALYSIS

1. Addition and subtraction are inverse operations. Write the following addition problem as a subtraction problem and find the value of the letter n.
$1.2 + n = 1.7$

2. Multiplication and division are inverse operations. Write the following multiplication problem as a division problem and find the value of the letter n.
$5 \times n = 4.5$

3. Give an example illustrating that the associative property does NOT apply to subtraction.

4. Give an example illustrating that the commutative property does NOT apply to division.

5. Describe a problem you have encountered that required you to add decimal numbers.

6. Describe a problem you have encountered that required you to multiply decimal numbers.

7. Explain how to multiply a number by a power of 10.

8. If you know a total amount and all the parts but one, explain what operations you would use to find the missing part.

9. What operation is a shortcut for repeated addition? Give an example to illustrate your answer.

10. Find and explain the mistake in the following. Rework the problem correctly.
$2 + 5(4) =$
$\quad 7(4) = 28$

CHAPTER 1 ASSIGNMENT EXERCISES

Section 1.1

Write the word name for the number.

1. 4,209

2. 97,168

3. 301,000,009

4. 5,200,000

5. According to Toyota, the company has invested more than $7 billion in manufacturing, research, and design. Write this number as an ordinary number.

6. Local people build Toyota vehicles in twenty-six countries around the world. Write this number as an ordinary number.

7. Toyota claims to be the fourth-largest vehicle manufacturer in America. It also claims to create more than twenty thousand direct jobs. Write this number as an ordinary number.

8. By its own claim, HFS, Inc., is the world's largest hotel franchising organization. It claims to have five thousand, four hundred hotels with four hundred ninety-five thousand rooms in over seventy countries and more than twenty percent of the franchises are minority-owned. Write each of the numbers as ordinary numbers.

Round to the specified place.

9. 378 (nearest hundred)

10. 8,248 (nearest hundred)

11. 9,374 (nearest thousand)

12. 348,218 (nearest ten thousand)

13. 834 (nearest ten)

14. 29,712 (nearest thousand)

15. 29,712 (nearest ten thousand)

16. 275,398,484 (nearest million)

17. 27,500,000,078 (nearest billion)

18. 897,284,017 (nearest ten million)

19. A color video surveillance system with eight cameras is priced at $3,899. Round this price to the nearest thousand dollars.

20. A black and white video surveillance system with eight cameras is priced at $2,499. What is the price to the nearest hundred dollars?

21. Fiber-optic cable capacity for communications such as telephones grew from 265,472 miles in 1986 to 6,316,436 miles in 1992. Round each of these numbers of miles to the nearest hundred thousand.

22. The industrialized nations of the world have six times the number of radios per capita as the underdeveloped nations. The industrialized nations have 2,017 radios per thousand people. Round the number of radios to the nearest hundred.

Round to the first digit.

23. 3,784,809

24. 2,063,948

25. 5,178

26. 17,295,183,109

27. 10,097,437

28. 5,475

29. 396

30. 18,924

31. 685,294

32. 7,098,764

Add and check the sum.

33.
```
  6
  3
  4
+7
```

34.
```
  1
  9
  5
  8
+2
```

35.
```
  6
  9
  4
  9
  6
+1
```

36.
```
  7
  2
  7
  7
  7
+8
```

37.
```
  4
  5
  6
  1
  3
+9
```

38.
```
  8
  8
  1
  2
  4
+9
```

39.
```
  8,152
  3,363
  4,529
  8,327
+6,416
```

40.
```
  9,892
  7,433
  4,090
  5,282
+1,987
```

Add.

41. 47 + 385 + 87 + 439 + 874

42. 32,948 + 6,804 + 15,695 + 415 + 7,739

43.	**44.**	**45.**	**46.**
734	683	1,661	44,349
643	252	9,342	71,486
688	867	2,994	67,565
656	867	5,778	57,971
928	325	1,770	+48,699
197	274	5,445	
785	835	1,770	
527	713	2,656	
337	118	3,874	
+278	+627	+8,724	

Estimate the sum by rounding each number to the first digit. Then find the exact sum.

47.	**48.**	**49.**	**50.**
74,374	374	3,748	3,470
82,849	847	9,409	843
72,494	521	3,577	3,872
+89,219	873	+4,601	574
	+482		

Estimate the sum by rounding each number to the nearest hundred. Then find the exact sum.

51.	**52.**
747	4,274
854	643
324	1,274
+687	+ 97

53. Mary Luciana bought 48 pencils, 96 pens, 36 diskettes, and 50 bottles of correction fluid. How many items did she buy?

54. Jorge Englade has 57 baseball cards from 1978, 43 cards from 1979, 104 cards from 1980, 210 cards from 1983, and 309 cards from 1987. How many cards does he have in all?

55. Linda Cagle collects dolls. She has 12 antique dolls, 135 Barbie dolls, 35 Shirley Temple dolls, and 287 other dolls. How many dolls are there in all?

56. A furniture manufacturing plant had the following labor-hours in one week: Monday, 483; Tuesday, 472; Wednesday, 497; Thursday, 486; Friday, 464; Saturday, 146; Sunday, 87. Find the total labor-hours worked during the week.

57. Lillie Lewis had the following test scores: 92, 87, 96, 85, 72, 84, 57, 98. What is the student's total number of points?

58. June Knox is planning to build a fence around her backyard. The sides of the yard measure 42 feet, 117 feet, 58 feet, and 119 feet. How many feet of fencing does June need to surround her yard?

Subtract and check the difference.

59.	**60.**	**61.**	**62.**
75,184	937,452	2,090,684	3,000,000
−65,428	−395,773	−224,943	−291,438

63.	**64.**	**65.**	**66.**
19,000,000	7,007,000	9,010,000	29,007,400
−14,284,394	−3,018,094	−3,687,429	−18,457,396

Estimate the difference by rounding each number to the first digit. Then find the exact difference.

67.
9,748
−5,676

68.
370,408
−187,506

69.
83,748,194
−27,209,104

70.
12,748
−5,438

71.
84,378
−28,746

72.
109,849
−35,464

73. Sam Andrews has 42 packages of hamburger buns on hand but expects to use 130 packages. How many must he order?

74. Frieda Salla had 148 tickets to sell for a baseball show. If she has sold 75 tickets, how many does she still have to sell?

75. An inventory shows 596 fan belts on hand. If the normal in-stock count is 840, how many should be ordered?

76. Veronica McCulley weighed 132 pounds before she began a weight-loss program. After eight weeks, she weighed 119 pounds. How many pounds did she lose?

77. A 1998 Ford Taurus LX is advertised for $18,795 with a $740 down payment. What is the amount that must be financed?

78. A 1998 Nissan Altima GXE is advertised for $17,990 with a down payment of $1,500. How much must be financed?

Multiply and check the product.

79.
5,931
× 835

80.
5,565
× 839

81.
1,987
× 394

82.
78,626
× 87

83.
708
× 59

84.
2,105
× 64

85.
70,803
× 98

86.
2,174
× 308

87.
1,700
× 507

88.
3,987
× 1,033

Multiply.

89. 33 × 500

90. 283 × 3,000

91. 160 × 300

92. 405 × 400

93. 50 × 600

94. 25 × 10,000

95. 7,870 × 6,000

96. 974 × 7,000

97. 270 × 600

98. 560 × 9,000

Estimate the product by rounding each number to the first digit. Then find the exact product.

99.
7,489
× 34

100.
378
× 72

Estimate the product by rounding each number to the nearest hundred. Then find the exact product.

101.
3,128
× 478

102.
378
× 546

103. An office has 15 printers. The supply coordinator is expected to keep eight cartridges for each printer. How many cartridges should be kept on hand?

104. Collierville Florist has 152 orders for 12 red roses. How many roses are required to fill the orders?

105. A day-care center has 28 children. If each child eats one piece of fruit each day, how many pieces of fruit are required for a week (five days)?

106. Auto Zone has a special on fuel filters. Normally, the price of one filter is $15, but with this sale, you can purchase two filters for only $27. How much can you save by purchasing two filters at the sale price?

107. Industrialized nations have 2,017 radios per thousand people. This is six times the number of radios per capita as the underdeveloped nations. What is the number of radios per thousand for underdeveloped nations?

108. The industrialized nations have 793 TV sets per thousand people. If this is nine times as many TVs per thousand people as there are in the underdeveloped nations, what is the number of TVs per thousand people in the underdeveloped nations?

Divide and check the quotient.

109. $7\overline{)315}$

110. $5\overline{)213}$

111. $9\overline{)216}$

112. $6\overline{)314}$

113. $1{,}232 \div 16$

114. $4{,}020 \div 12$

115. $1{,}247 \div 23$

116. $3{,}362 \div 32$

Estimate the quotient by rounding each number. Then find the exact quotient.

117. $85\overline{)748{,}431}$

118. $346\overline{)174{,}891}$

119. A parts dealer has 2,988 washers. The washers are packaged with 12 in each package. How many packages can be made?

120. A stack of countertops measures 238 inches. If each countertop is two inches thick, how many are in the stack?

121. If 127 employees earn $1,524 in one hour, what is the average hourly wage per employee?

122. Sequoia Brown has 15 New Zealand coins, 32 Canadian coins, 18 British coins, and 12 Australian coins in her British Commonwealth collection. How many coins does she have in this collection?

123. Jessica Lisker mailed 62 birthday cards, 6 get-well cards, 2 sympathy cards, and 5 graduation cards to the customers on her sales routes. How many cards did she mail?

124. John Chang ordered 48 paperback novels for his bookstore. When he received the shipment, he learned that 11 were on back order. How many novels did he receive?

125. Baker's Department Store sold 23 pairs of ladies' patent leather pumps. If the store's original inventory was 43 pairs of the shoes, how many pairs remain in inventory?

126. An oral communication textbook contains 3 pages of review at the end of each of its 16 chapters. What is the total number of pages devoted to review?

127. A sales clerk earns $8 an hour. If she works 32 hours a week, how much does she earn in a week?

128. Juan Mendez must fill a school order for 77 dozen pencils. Since a dozen is 12, how many pencils are needed for the order?

129. Galina makes $320 a week. If she works 40 hours a week, what is her hourly pay rate?

130. A garage has five cars to tune. If each car has eight cylinders, and each cylinder requires one spark plug, how many spark plugs are needed to tune the cars?

131. Holding-tank deodorant for travel trailer and marine use is sold in packages containing six 8-ounce bottles. How many ounces are in each package of six bottles?

132. Jeff Mills has 15 boxes and needs to pack 118 wood carvings. Is he able to pack an equal quantity in each box? If so, how many? If not, give Jeff instructions for packing the boxes.

Section 1.2

Write the word name for the decimal.

133. 0.5   **134.** 0.27   **135.** 0.108   **136.** 0.013

137. 0.00275   **138.** 0.120704   **139.** 17.8   **140.** 3.04

141. 128.23   **142.** 3,000.003   **143.** 500.0007   **144.** 184.271

Round to the specified place.

145. 0.1345 (nearest thousandth)   **146.** 384.72 (nearest tenth)   **147.** 384.73 (nearest ten)

148. 1,745.376 (nearest hundredth)   **149.** 1,745.376 (nearest hundred)   **150.** 32.57 (nearest whole number)

151. $175.24 (nearest dollar)   **152.** $5.333 (nearest cent)

Add.

153. 0.3 + 0.05 + 0.266 + 0.63   **154.** 31.005 + 5.36 + 0.708 + 4.16

155. 78.87 + 54 + 32.9569 + 0.0043   **156.** 9.004 + 0.07 + 723 + 8.7

157. A shopper purchased a cake pan for $8.95, a bath mat for $9.59, and a bottle of shampoo for $2.39. Find the total cost of the purchases.

158. Robert McNab ordered 18.3 square meters of carpet for his halls, 123.5 square meters of carpet for bedrooms, 28.7 square meters of carpet for the family room, and 12.9 square meters of carpet for the play room. Find the total number of square meters of carpet he ordered.

Subtract.

159. 500.05 − 123.31   **160.** 815.01 − 335.6   **161.** 125.35 − 67.8975   **162.** 404.04 − 135.8716

163. 423 − 287.4   **164.** 807.38 − 529.79   **165.** 482.073 − 62.97   **166.** 5,003.02 − 689.23

167.   486.57
         −160.83

168. 1,423.97
         −802.89

169.   21.0357
         −18.7289

170.   5.8376
         −2.9608

171.
$$\begin{array}{r} 0.02135 \\ -0.019876 \\ \hline \end{array}$$

172.
$$\begin{array}{r} 6.213502 \\ -3.098107 \\ \hline \end{array}$$

173. Four tires that retailed for $486.95 are on sale for $397.99. By how much are the tires reduced?

174. If two lengths of metal sheeting measuring 12.5 inches and 15.36 inches are cut from a roll of metal measuring 96 inches, how much remains on the roll?

175. Leon Treadwell's checkbook had a balance of $196.82 before he wrote checks for $21.75 and $82.46. What was his balance after he wrote the checks?

176. Janet Morris weighed 149.3 pounds before she began a weight-loss program. After eight weeks she weighed 129.7 pounds. How much did she lose?

Multiply.

177.
$$\begin{array}{r} 27.63 \\ \times \quad 7 \\ \hline \end{array}$$

178.
$$\begin{array}{r} 384 \\ \times \quad 3.51 \\ \hline \end{array}$$

179.
$$\begin{array}{r} 6.42 \\ \times \quad 7.8 \\ \hline \end{array}$$

180.
$$\begin{array}{r} 0.0015 \\ \times \quad 6.003 \\ \hline \end{array}$$

181.
$$\begin{array}{r} 75.84 \\ \times \quad 0.28 \\ \hline \end{array}$$

182.
$$\begin{array}{r} 73.41 \\ \times \quad 15 \\ \hline \end{array}$$

183. 27.58×10

184. 1.394×100

185. $0.19874 \times 1,000$

186. 54×100

187. $27.3 \times 1,000$

188. $38.17 \times 10,000$

189. $1,745.4 \times 10$

190. $0.1754 \times 1,000,000$

191. $37 \times 10,000$

192. 0.004×10

193. Find the cost of 1,000 gallons of paint if one gallon costs $12.85.

194. Ernie Jones worked 37.5 hours at the rate of $5.97 per hour. Calculate his earnings.

Divide. Round to the nearest hundredth if division does not terminate.

195. $1.65 \div 11$

196. $0.105 \div 15$

197. $25\overline{)54.68}$

198. $27\overline{)365.04}$

199. $34\overline{)291.48}$

200. $74\overline{)85.486}$

201. $2.8\overline{)94.546}$

202. $0.041\overline{)8.897}$

203. $296.36 \div 0.19$

204. $0.0056\overline{)0.4576}$

205. $0.68\overline{)41,285}$

206. $923.19 \div 0.541$

207. $85.72 \div 10$

208. $4.139 \div 100$

209. $19.874 \div 1,000$

210. $39 \div 10$

211. $0.18 \div 100$

212. $274.85 \div 10,000$

213. $3,749,298 \div 100,000$

214. $574 \div 10,000$

215. $0.178 \div 10$

216. $3,741.29 \div 100$

217. If 100 gallons of gasoline cost $98.90, what is the cost per gallon?

218. If sugar costs $2.87 for 80 ounces, what is the cost per ounce, rounded to the nearest cent?

Find the missing value.

219. $\dfrac{7}{10} = \dfrac{14}{N}$

220. $\dfrac{8}{N} = \dfrac{12}{24}$

Challenge Problems

221. Comparative Budgeting. Terry Kelly has recorded the following financial information for 2001. She now wants to prepare a budget for 2002 to use as a guide.

Terry is scheduled to receive a salary increase of $1,636 in 2002. She expects the dividend income to increase by 0.25 and the interest income to double. She hopes her living expenses will increase by no more than $1,000. She hopes to decrease maintenance on her home and auto by 0.4. Her accountant estimates her taxes will increase by approximately $500. Her insurance premiums will increase by $200. No change in uncovered medical expenses is expected. Terry will increase her planned investment by $500. Make the needed adjustments to prepare Terry's budget for 2002. Adjust the unspent income category so that the total expenses equal total income.

INCOME	2001	2002
Gross income	32,720	
Interest income	141	
Dividend income	364	
Total	33,225	____

EXPENSES		
Living	15,898	
Home maintenance	825	
Auto maintenance & repair	195	
Insurance premiums (medical, auto, home, life)	1,578	
Taxes (sales, income, FICA, real property, personal property)	10,630	
Medical (not covered by insurance)	450	
Planned investment	2,000	
Unspent income	1,649	____
Total	33,225	

222. Sales Quotas. A sales quota establishes a minimum amount of sales expected during a given period for a salesperson in some businesses, such as selling cars or houses. In setting sales quotas, sales managers take certain factors into consideration, such as the nature of the sales representative's territory, the experience of the salesperson, and the expectations expressed by the sales force. Such sales quotas enable a company to forecast the sales and future growth of the company for budget and profit purposes.

Try the following quota problem:

A sales representative for a time-sharing company has a monthly sales quota of 500 units.

The representative sold 120 units during the first week, 135 units during the second week, and 165 units during the third week of the month. How many units must be sold before the end of the month if the salesperson is to meet the quota?

CHAPTER 1 PRACTICE TEST

Write the word name for the number.

1. 503

2. 12,056,039

Round to the specified place.

3. 84,321 (nearest hundred)

4. 58,967 (nearest thousand)

5. 80,235 (first digit)

6. 587,213 (first digit)

Estimate by rounding to hundreds. Then find the exact result.

7. $863 + 983 + 271 =$

8. $987 - 346 =$

Estimate by rounding to the first digit. Then find the exact result.

9. $892 \times 46 =$

10. $53\overline{)4,021}$

11. An inventory clerk counted the following items: 438 rings, 72 watches, and 643 pen and pencil sets. How many items were counted?

12. A warehouse is 31 feet high. Boxes that are each two feet high are to be stacked in the warehouse. How many boxes can be stacked one on top of the other?

13. Round 30.5375 to the first digit.

14. Write the word name for 24.1007.

Perform the indicated operation.

15. $39.17 - 15.078$

16. 27.418×100

17. $0.387 + 3.17 + 17 + 204.3$

18. $28.34 \div 50$ (nearest hundredth)

19.
$$\begin{array}{r} 324 \\ \times 1.38 \\ \hline \end{array}$$

20. $0.138 \div 10$

21. $128 - 38.18$

22.
$$\begin{array}{r} 17.75 \\ \times 0.325 \\ \hline \end{array}$$

23. $2,347 + 0.178 + 3.5 + 28.341$

24. $91.25 \div 12.5$

25. $317.24 - 138$

26. $374.17 \div 100$

27. What is the cost of 5.5 pounds of chicken breasts if they cost $3.49 per pound?

28. A patient's chart showed a temperature reading of 101.2 degrees Fahrenheit at 3 P.M. and 99.5 degrees Fahrenheit at 10 P.M. What was the drop in temperature?

Solve for n.

29. $\dfrac{3}{8} = \dfrac{6}{n}$

30. $\dfrac{n}{10} = \dfrac{2}{5}$

CHAPTER 1 SELF-CHECK SOLUTIONS

SELF-CHECK 1.1

1. Five million, seven hundred two thousand, five

2. Three hundred seventeen million, one hundred seventy-one

3. Four billion, two hundred four million, forty-nine thousand, two hundred one

4. 3,6<u>4</u>5   Since 4 is less than 5 we round to 3,600.

5. <u>3</u>,645   Since 6 is 5 or more, we round to 4,000.

6. 3,6<u>4</u>5   Since 5 is 5 or more, we round to 3,650.

7.
$$\begin{array}{r} {\scriptstyle 1\,1} \\ 328 \\ 583 \\ + 726 \\ \hline 1,637 \end{array}$$

8.
$$\begin{array}{r} {\scriptstyle 2\,1} \\ 671 \\ 982 \\ + 57 \\ \hline 1,710 \end{array}$$

9.
$$\begin{array}{r} {\scriptstyle 1} \\ 791 \\ 1,000 \\ + 52 \\ \hline 1,843 \end{array}$$

10.
$$\begin{array}{r} {\scriptstyle 4\,15} \\ \cancel{5}\,\cancel{5} \\ - 3\,6 \\ \hline 1\,9 \end{array}$$

11.
$$\begin{array}{r} {\scriptstyle 2\,10} \\ \cancel{3}\,\cancel{0}\,8 \\ - 2\,7\,5 \\ \hline 3\,3 \end{array}$$

12.
$$\begin{array}{r} {\scriptstyle 3\,10} \\ 5,\cancel{4}\,\cancel{0}\,9 \\ - 2,1\,7\,6 \\ \hline 3,2\,3\,3 \end{array}$$

13.
$$\begin{array}{r} 730 \\ \times\ \ 60 \\ \hline 43{,}800 \end{array}$$

14.
$$\begin{array}{r} 904 \\ \times\ \ 24 \\ \hline 3\ 616 \\ 18\ 08 \\ \hline 21{,}696 \end{array}$$

15.
$$\begin{array}{r} 1{,}005 \\ \times\ \ \ \ 89 \\ \hline 9\ 045 \\ 80\ 40 \\ \hline 89{,}445 \end{array}$$

16.
$$\begin{array}{r} 16 \\ 6\overline{)96} \\ 6 \\ \hline 36 \\ 36 \\ \hline \end{array}$$

17.
$$\begin{array}{r} 407 \\ 34\overline{)13{,}838} \\ 13\ 6 \\ \hline 23 \\ 0 \\ \hline 238 \\ 238 \\ \hline \end{array}$$

18.
$$\begin{array}{r} 253\ \text{R}13 \\ 15\overline{)3{,}808} \\ 3\ 0 \\ \hline 80 \\ 75 \\ \hline 58 \\ 45 \\ \hline 13 \end{array}$$

19. Region Totals

Eastern	Southern	Central	Western
72,492	81,897	71,708	61,723
81,948	59,421	22,096	71,687
32,307	48,598	23,222	52,196
24,301	61,025	21,507	41,737
32,589	21,897	42,801	22,186
243,637	272,838	181,334	249,529

Total = 243,637 + 272,838 + 181,334 + 249,529 = 947,338

Daily Sales Totals

W	Th	F	S	Su
72,492	81,948	32,307	24,301	32,589
81,897	59,421	48,598	61,025	21,897
71,708	22,096	23,222	21,507	42,801
61,723	71,687	52,196	41,737	22,186
287,820	235,152	156,323	148,570	119,473

Total = 287,820 + 235,152 + 156,323 + 148,570 + 119,473 = 947,338

Difference = $1,384,000 − $947,338 = $436,662

20.

1 Decision needed	Are enough materials available to mix and package the candy?
2 Unknown facts	Number of three-pound bags needed for packaging
	Number of boxes needed for shipping
3 Known facts	84 containers each contain 25 pounds of candy. Bulk candy will be repackaged into three-pound bags. Twelve bags of candy will be packed into each box.
	There are 5,000 three-pound bags on hand.
	There are 400 boxes on hand.
4 Relationships	Total pounds of candy = number of containers × pounds per container.
	Number of bags of candy on hand = total pounds ÷ pounds per bag (3)
	Number of boxes of candy = number of bags of candy ÷ bags per box (12)
5 Estimation	Round to the first digit, then multiply 80 × 30 = 2,400. The estimated number of pounds of candy is 2,400 pounds. Then, divide by 3. Approximately 800 bags will be needed. Divide by 10 and approximately 80 boxes will be needed.
6 Calculations	Total pounds of candy equals 84 × 25 = 2,100
	Number of bags of candy = 2,100 ÷ 3 = 700
	Number of boxes of candy = 700 ÷ 12 = 58 R4
7 Interpretation	There are 58 boxes of candy and 4 bags left so 59 boxes will be needed to ship all the candy.
	Enough bags and boxes are on hand to package.
8 Decision made	

21.

$$\begin{array}{r} 922 \text{ R}256 \\ 352\overline{)324{,}800} \\ \underline{316\,8} \\ 8\,00 \\ \underline{7\,04} \\ 960 \\ \underline{704} \\ 256 \end{array}$$

The average selling price of each trailer was nearly \$923.

22. Total length of fencing needed $= 210 \times 4 = 840$ feet
Number of rolls of fencing needed $= 840 \div 50 = 16.8$
Since a partial role of fencing cannot be purchased, 17 rolls are needed. Cost of 17 rolls of fencing $= \$49 \times 17 = \$833$. Cost of installing fence $= \$1 \times 840 = \$840$. Total cost $= \$833 + \$840 = \$1{,}673$. Your bid is the lowest bid and you are likely to get the business.

23. Wages $= 3 \times 7 \times 21 = \$441$
Gross profit $=$ total $-$ cost of materials $-$ cost of labor
Gross profit $= \$1{,}673 - \$833 - \$441 = \$399$

24.

$$\begin{array}{r} 1{,}104 \\ 8\overline{)8{,}832} \end{array}$$

Each vendor supplied 1,104 boxes of cards.

25.

$$\begin{array}{r} 29 \\ 12\overline{)348} \\ \underline{24} \\ 108 \\ \underline{108} \end{array}$$

You will need 29 boxes.

26.

$$\begin{array}{r} 21{,}960 \\ -16{,}300 \\ \hline 5{,}660 \end{array}$$ increase

27.

$$\begin{array}{r} \$200{,}000{,}000 \\ -500{,}000 \\ \hline \$199{,}500{,}000 \end{array}$$ increase

28. 12 cents $\div$ 100 $= 0.12$ dollars

$$\begin{array}{r} 42{,}000{,}000 \\ \times 0.12 \\ \hline 84000000 \\ 42000000 \\ \hline \$5{,}040{,}000.00 \end{array}$$ total paid for purchase

29.

$$\begin{array}{r} 42{,}000{,}000 \\ \times 0.36 \\ \hline 2\,520\,000\,00 \\ 12\,600\,000\,0 \\ \hline \$15{,}120{,}000.00 \end{array}$$ resell price

$$\begin{array}{r} \$15{,}120{,}000 \\ -5{,}040{,}000 \\ \hline \$10{,}080{,}000 \end{array}$$ profit from resale

30. \$1,500,000,000

31.

$$\begin{array}{r} 6{,}696 \text{ R}30 = 6{,}697 \text{ employees} \\ 32\overline{)214{,}302} \\ \underline{192} \\ 22\,3 \\ \underline{19\,2} \\ 3\,10 \\ \underline{2\,88} \\ 222 \\ \underline{192} \\ 30 \end{array}$$

32.

$$\begin{array}{r} \$26{,}143 \\ 214{,}302\overline{)5{,}602{,}497{,}186} \\ \underline{4\,286\,04} \\ 1{,}316{,}457 \\ \underline{1\,285\,812} \\ 30\,645\,1 \\ \underline{21\,430\,2} \\ 9\,214\,98 \\ \underline{8\,572\,08} \\ 642\,906 \\ \underline{642\,906} \end{array}$$

Self-Check 1.2

1. Five hundred eighty-two thousandths

2. One and nine ten-thousandths

3. Seven hundred eighty-two and seven hundredths

4. $493.91
$494

5. $785.03
$785

6. $19.80
$20

7.
$$\begin{array}{r} 6.005 \\ 0.03 \\ 924 \\ 3.9 \\ \hline 933.935 \end{array}$$

8.
$$\begin{array}{r} 82 \\ 5{,}000.1 \\ 101.703 \\ \hline 5{,}183.803 \end{array}$$

9.
$$\begin{array}{r} 3\,9\,17\,8\,1\,6 \\ 4\,0\,7.9\,6 \\ -2\,9\,8.3\,9 \\ \hline 1\,0\,9.5\,7 \end{array}$$

10.
```
  7 10 6 11
  8,097.125
    500.70
  ─────────
  7,596.425
```

11.
```
   19.7
 ×    4
 ──────
   78.8
```

12.
```
   0.0321
 ×     10
 ────────
   0.3210
```

13.
```
    73.7
 ×  0.02
 ───────
   1.474
```

14.
```
         10.31
     12)123.72
         12
         ──
          3
          0
         ──
          3 7
          3 6
          ───
            12
            12
```

15.
```
        16.830 or 16.83
     35)589.060
        35
        ───
        239
        210
        ───
         29 0
         28 0
         ────
          1 06
          1 05
          ────
            10
             0
            ──
            10
```

16.
```
            0.024 or 0.02
     0.35 )0.00 840
       ∧     ∧
             70
            140
            140
```

17.
```
       $8.43
 ×        28
 ──────────
       67 44
      168 6
 ──────────
    $236.04
```

18. 32 wheels per sheet × 18 sheets = 576 576 wheels can be produced in nine hours.

19.
```
        $8.21
     26)$213.46
        208
        ───
         5 4
         5 2
         ───
           26
           26
```

20. $1.47 × 1,000 = $1,470 Shift the decimal three places to the right.

21.
```
         6.18
     23)142.15
        138
        ───
          4 1
          2 3
          ───
          1 85
          1 84
          ────
             1
```
Twenty-two employees pay $6.18 and one employee pays $6.19.

22.
```
        50  minutes
     ×0.28  cents per minute
     ─────
      4 00
     10 0
     ─────
    $14.00  cost of the card
```

23.
```
          $0.10  per minute
     120)12.00
         12 0
         ────
            0
            0
```

24.
```
         $0.25  per minute
     20)5.00
        4 0
        ───
        1 00
        1 00
```

25.
```
         $0.125  per minute
     60)$7.500
        6 0
        ───
        1 50
        1 20
        ────
         300
         300
```

26. The "best buy" is the card with the lowest cost per minute. MCI charged $0.139 or $0.14 per minute.

MCI can expect to have a large volume so they can keep the price low. AT&T charged 33 cents per minute, which was the highest.

27. 398,253 rounds to 400,000. Since the 9 is more than 5, the one is added to three.

28. $250,000,000

SELF-CHECK 1.3

1. $\frac{7}{8} = \frac{21}{24}$

7 × 24 = 168
8 × 21 = 168

2. $\frac{3}{5} = \frac{12}{20}$

3 × 20 = 60
5 × 12 = 60

3. $\frac{7}{9} = \frac{49}{63}$

7 × 63 = 441
9 × 49 = 441

4. $\dfrac{4}{5} = \dfrac{8}{10}$

$4 \times 10 = 5 \times 8$

$40 = 40$

Proportion

5. $\dfrac{3}{8} = \dfrac{6}{24}$

$3 \times 24 \neq 8 \times 6$

$72 \neq 48$

not a proportion

$\dfrac{3}{8} = \dfrac{9}{24}$ is a true proportion

(Answers will vary.)

6. $\dfrac{10}{6} = \dfrac{5}{8}$

$10 \times 8 \neq 6 \times 5$

$80 \neq 30$

not a proportion

$\dfrac{10}{16} = \dfrac{5}{8}$

(Proportions will vary.)

7. $\dfrac{7}{11} = \dfrac{5}{22}$

$7 \times 22 \neq 11 \times 5$

$154 \neq 55$

not a proportion
(Proportions will vary.)

8. $\dfrac{9}{10} = \dfrac{6}{8}$

$9 \times 8 \neq 10 \times 6$

$72 \neq 60$

not a proportion
(Proportions will vary.)

9. $\dfrac{5}{8} = \text{---}$

$\dfrac{5}{8} = \dfrac{10}{16}$ or $\dfrac{15}{24}$ etc.

10. $\dfrac{3}{7} = \text{---}$

$\dfrac{3}{7} = \dfrac{6}{14}$ or $\dfrac{9}{21}$ etc.

11. $\dfrac{15}{4} = \text{---}$

$\dfrac{15}{4} = \dfrac{30}{8}$ or $\dfrac{45}{12}$ etc.

12. $\dfrac{3}{5} = \dfrac{N}{30}$

$30 \times 3 = 90$

$90 \div 5 = 18$

$N = 18$

13. $\dfrac{16}{30} = \dfrac{8}{N}$

$30 \times 8 = 240$

$240 \div 16 = 15$

$N = 15$

14. $\dfrac{N}{3} = \dfrac{10}{12}$

$3 \times 10 = 30$

$30 \div 12 = 2.5$

$N = 2.5$

15. $\dfrac{N}{3.2} = \dfrac{4}{10}$

$3.2 \times 4 = 12.8$

$12.8 \div 10 = 1.28$

$N = 1.28$

16. $\dfrac{6}{N} = \dfrac{9}{6}$

$6 \times 6 = 36$

$36 \div 9 = 4$

$N = 4$

17. $\dfrac{48}{64} = \dfrac{N}{8}$

$48 \times 8 = 384$

$384 \div 64 = 6$

$N = 6$

18. $\dfrac{20 \text{ meters}}{N \text{ yards}} = \dfrac{1 \text{ meter}}{1.0936 \text{ yards}}$

$20 \times 1.0936 = 21.872$

$21.872 \div 1 = 21.872$

$N = 21.872$ yards

19. $\dfrac{150 \text{ yards}}{N \text{ meters}} = \dfrac{1.0936 \text{ yards}}{1 \text{ meter}}$

$150 \times 1 = 150$

$150 \div 1.0936 = 137.2$

$N = 137.2$ meters

20. $\dfrac{42 \text{ ounces}}{N \text{ pounds}} = \dfrac{16 \text{ ounces}}{1 \text{ pound}}$

$42 \times 1 = 42$

$42 \div 16 = 2.625$

$N = 2.6$ pounds

21. $\dfrac{190 \text{ pounds}}{N \text{ ounces}} = \dfrac{1 \text{ pound}}{16 \text{ ounces}}$

$190 \times 16 = 3,040$

$3,040 \div 1 = 3,040$

$N = 3,040$ ounces

22. $\dfrac{420 \text{ kilograms}}{N \text{ pounds}} = \dfrac{1 \text{ kilogram}}{2.2 \text{ pounds}}$

$420 \times 2.2 = 924$

$924 \div 1 = 924$

$N = 924$ pounds

23. $\dfrac{380 \text{ ounces}}{N \text{ grams}} = \dfrac{0.04 \text{ ounce}}{1 \text{ gram}}$

$380 \times 1 = 380$

$380 \div 0.04 = 9,500$

$N = 9,500$ grams

24. $\dfrac{1000 \text{ dollars}}{N \text{ pesetas}} = \dfrac{1 \text{ dollar}}{152.649994 \text{ pesetas}}$

$1,000 \times 152.649994 = 152,649.994$

$152,649.994 \div 1 = 152,649.994$

$N = 152,649.99$ pesetas
or
152,650 pesetas

25. $\dfrac{500,000 \text{ lira}}{N \text{ dollars}} = \dfrac{1762 \text{ lira}}{1 \text{ dollar}}$

$500,000 \times 1 = 500,000$

$500,000 \div 1,762 = 283.77$

$N = 283.77$ dollars

2

Problem Solving with Fractions and Percents

2.1 Problem Solving with Fractions

1 Identify types of fractions.

2 Change a fraction to an equivalent fraction.

3 Add and subtract fractions and mixed numbers.

4 Multiply and divide fractions and mixed numbers.

5 Write a decimal as a fraction and write a fraction as a decimal.

2.2 Problem Solving with Percents

1 Write a whole number, fraction, or decimal as a percent.

2 Write a percent as a whole number, fraction, or decimal.

3 Use the percentage formula to find the percentage.

4 Use the percentage formula to find the base.

5 Use the percentage formula to find the rate.

6 Use the percentage proportion to solve problems.

Good Decisions through Teamwork

Over the course of one week, each time you see a fraction or percent being used out-side of the classroom, take note of it, describing the situation and the use being made of the percent or fraction. For instance, you notice a grocery store advertises a half-off sale; or you see that your bank charges $9\frac{1}{2}\%$ interest on car loans; or you prepare a recipe calling for $4\frac{1}{2}$ tablespoons of sugar.

With your team, make a master list of situations, eliminating duplications. For each situation on your master list, discuss why a fraction or percent is used rather than a whole number. Discuss too why a fraction is used rather than a percent, or a percent rather than a fraction.

On the basis of your discussion, identify major categories of the use of fractions and percents. How many of these categories could apply to a business setting? Give a busi-ness-related example for each category your team judges to be business-related. Choose a team member to share the results of your discussion with the class.

2.1 Problem Solving with Fractions

1 Identify types of fractions.

2 Change a fraction to an equivalent fraction.

3 Add and subtract fractions and mixed numbers.

4 Multiply and divide fractions and mixed numbers.

5 Write a decimal as a fraction and write a fraction as a decimal.

In Chapter 1 we represented parts of whole items by using decimal notation. While decimal notation is the most common way to represent fractional parts in the business world, fraction notation is also used for some applications. Often fractions are implied in the narrative portion of reports and news articles. For example, a news article may claim that three out of four voters are in favor of a proposed change in a city ordinance.

1 Identify types of fractions.

We use fractions as another way to represent numbers. The fraction format is also used to represent two relationships between numbers. The first relationship is the relationship between a part and a whole. If one whole quantity has four equal parts, then one of the four parts is represented by the fraction $\frac{1}{4}$ (Figure 2-1).

Figure 2-1 One part out of 4 parts is $\frac{1}{4}$ of the whole.

Another relationship represented by fractions is the relationship of division. The fraction $\frac{1}{4}$ can be interpreted as one divided by four or $1 \div 4$, which is 0.25.

In the fraction $\frac{1}{4}$, 4 represents the number of parts contained in one whole quantity and is called the **denominator.** When the fraction is interpreted as division, the denominator is the divisor. The 1 in the fraction $\frac{1}{4}$ represents the number of parts under consideration and is called the **numerator.** When the fraction is interpreted as division, the numerator is the dividend.

The line separating the numerator and denominator may be written as a horizontal line ($-$) or as a slash ($/$) and is called the **fraction line.** When the fraction is interpreted as division, the fraction line is interpreted as the division symbol.

When a fraction has a value less than one it is called a **proper fraction.**

EXAMPLE Visualize the fraction to identify whether it is a proper fraction. Describe the relationship between the numerator and denominator of proper fractions.

(a) $\frac{2}{5}$ (b) $\frac{3}{2}$ (c) $\frac{4}{4}$

(a) Figure 2-2 represents $\frac{2}{5}$ or two parts out of five parts.

Figure 2-2

The fraction $\frac{2}{5}$ is a proper fraction since it is less than one whole quantity.

(b) Figure 2-3 represents $\frac{3}{2}$ or three parts when the one whole quantity contains two parts.

Figure 2-3

The fraction $\frac{3}{2}$ is more than one whole quantity. It is not a proper fraction.

(c) Figure 2-4 represents $\frac{4}{4}$ or four parts when the whole contains four parts.

Figure 2-4

The fraction $\frac{4}{4}$ represents one whole quantity. It is not a proper fraction.

The fraction $\frac{2}{5}$ is a proper fraction. In a proper fraction, the numerator is *less than* the denominator and the fraction value is less than 1.

Proper fractions are used in various business situations. For example, Dobbs Ford dealership has 125 cars on their lot. Of these, 12 are Crown Victoria cars. The number 125 is the number of items (cars) contained in one whole quantity (dealership). The number 12 is the number of items (Crown Victoria cars) being considered or used. The fraction showing the relationship between the number of Crown Victoria cars and the total number of cars on the lot is $\frac{12}{125}$ and is a proper fraction.

A fraction that has a value equal to or greater than 1 is called an **improper fraction.**

EXAMPLE Which fractions in the previous example are improper fractions? Describe the relationship between the numerator and denominator of improper fractions.

The fractions $\frac{3}{2}$ and $\frac{4}{4}$ are improper fractions. In an improper fraction, the numerator is equal to or more than the denominator.

Earlier, the fraction $\frac{3}{2}$ was shown as one whole quantity and $\frac{1}{2}$ of a second whole quantity. This amount, $\frac{3}{2}$, can also be written as $1\frac{1}{2}$. An amount written as a combination of a whole number and a fraction is called a **mixed number.** Thus, numbers such as $1\frac{1}{2}$ are called mixed numbers. Every mixed number can also be written as an improper fraction.

Learning Strategy Learning Definitions

Learning new definitions can sometimes be overwhelming. A key strategy for learning definitions is really about understanding the basic concepts, connecting the new words to other words or concepts we already know, and using memory devices.

Learning terminology is important in developing your math survival skills. When you forget the details of a procedure (and you probably will if you don't use the procedure often), the term will help you use the index or table of contents to find the text that will refresh you skills.

Improper fractions are used as a convenience in making some calculations. To interpret the meaning of an improper fraction, we use its whole number, mixed-number, or decimal equivalent. Thus, it is important to be able to convert between improper fractions and equivalent forms.

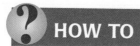

HOW TO Write an Improper Fraction as a Whole or Mixed Number

Write $\frac{12}{3}$ and $\frac{13}{3}$ as whole or mixed numbers.

$$3\overline{)12} \;\; \overset{4}{} \qquad 3\overline{)13} \;\; \overset{4R\,1}{}$$

1. Divide the numerator of the improper fraction by the denominator.

2. Examine the remainder.

   (a) If the remainder is 0, the quotient is a whole number: the improper fraction is equivalent to this whole number.

   (b) If the remainder is not 0, the quotient is not a whole number: the improper fraction is equivalent to a mixed number. The whole number part of this mixed number is the whole number part of the quotient. The fraction part of the mixed number has a numerator and a denominator. The numerator is the remainder; the denominator is the divisor (the denominator of the improper fraction).

$$\frac{12}{3} = 4 \qquad \frac{13}{3} = 4\frac{1}{3}$$

EXAMPLE   Write $\frac{139}{8}$ as a whole or mixed number.

$$
\begin{array}{r}
17 \text{ R}3, \text{ or } 17\frac{3}{8} \\
8\overline{)139} \\
\underline{8} \\
59 \\
\underline{56} \\
3
\end{array}
$$

Divide 139 by 8. The quotient is 17 R3, which equals $17\frac{3}{8}$.

$$\frac{139}{8} = 17\frac{3}{8}$$

A mixed number can be written as an improper fraction by "reversing" the steps you use to write an improper fraction as a mixed number. For example, to write $3\frac{1}{5}$ as an improper fraction, imagine starting with the improper fraction and dividing to get $3\frac{1}{5}$:

$$\frac{?}{5} = 5\overline{)?}\;\overset{3\text{ R}1}{} = 3\frac{1}{5}$$

The ? is the numerator of the improper fraction. In checking division we multiply the whole number part of the quotient by the divisor and add the remainder. The numerator must be 16, since $3 \times 5 + 1 = 16$:

$$
\begin{array}{r}
3 \text{ R}1 \\
5\overline{)16} \\
\underline{15} \\
1
\end{array}
$$

The improper fraction is $\frac{16}{5}$. But how do we get 16? We multiply 3, the whole number part of the quotient by the denominator 5 and add the remainder, 1. Visualize these operations as forming a circle (Figure 2-5).

Figure 2-5 Write $3\frac{1}{5}$ as an improper fraction.

In words, five times three plus one written over five.

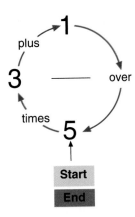

In symbols,

$$3\frac{1}{5} = \frac{5 \times 3 + 1}{5} = \frac{16}{5}$$

Learning Strategy Draw a Picture!

Representing a process visually is a good memory strategy. The old adage "A picture is worth a thousand words" works in math too.

As you work through this text, think of ways to represent the information with a picture or sketch. It will help you remember.

HOW TO Write a Mixed Number as an Improper Fraction

Write $1\frac{2}{5}$ as an improper fraction.

$$\frac{(5 \times 1) + 2}{?}$$

1. Find the numerator of the improper fraction.
   (a) Multiply the denominator of the mixed number by the whole number part.
   (b) Add the product from step 1a to the numerator of the mixed number.
2. For the denominator of the improper fraction use the denominator of the mixed number.

$$\frac{7}{5}$$

EXAMPLE Write $2\frac{3}{4}$ as an improper fraction.

$$2\frac{3}{4} = \frac{(4 \times 2) + 3}{4} = \frac{11}{4}$$

For the numerator, multiply 4 times 2 and add 3.

Thus, $2\frac{3}{4} = \frac{11}{4}$.

A whole number can be written as an improper fraction by writing the whole number as the numerator and 1 as the denominator. Visualize eight as eight whole quantities with each quantity containing only one part (Figure 2-6).

$$8 = \frac{8}{1}$$

Figure 2-6

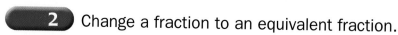

2 Change a fraction to an equivalent fraction.

Many fractions represent the same portion of a whole. Such fractions are called **equivalent fractions.** For example, $\frac{1}{2}$, $\frac{2}{4}$, and $\frac{4}{8}$ are equivalent fractions (Figure 2-7).

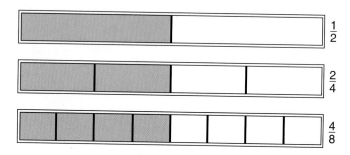

Figure 2-7 Equivalent Fractions

Equivalent Fractions in Lowest Terms To be able to recognize equivalent fractions, we often reduce fractions to lowest terms. A fraction in **lowest terms** has a numerator and denominator that cannot be evenly divided by the same number except 1.

HOW TO Reduce a Fraction to Lowest Terms

1. Inspect the numerator and denominator to find any whole number that both can be evenly divided by.

2. Divide both the numerator and denominator by that number and inspect the new fraction to find any other number that the numerator and denominator can be evenly divided by.

3. Repeat steps 1 and 2 until 1 is the only number that the numerator and denominator can be evenly divided by.

Reduce $\frac{8}{10}$ to lowest terms.
8 and 10 are divisible by 2.

$$\frac{8 \div 2}{10 \div 2} = \frac{4}{5}$$

EXAMPLE   Reduce $\frac{30}{36}$ to lowest terms.

$$\frac{30}{36} = \frac{30 \div 2}{36 \div 2} = \frac{15}{18}$$

Both the numerator and denominator can be divided evenly by 2.

$$\frac{15}{18} = \frac{15 \div 3}{18 \div 3} = \frac{5}{6}$$

Both the numerator and denominator of the new fraction can be divided evenly by 3.

Thus, $\frac{30}{36}$ is reduced to $\frac{5}{6}$.

1 is the only number that both the numerator and denominator can be evenly divided by. The fraction is now in lowest terms.

The most direct way to reduce a fraction to lowest terms is to divide the numerator and denominator by the **greatest common divisor (GCD).** The GCD is the greatest number by which both parts of a fraction can be evenly divided. Let's look at a helpful shortcut to finding the GCD.

HOW TO Find the Greatest Common Divisor of Two Numbers

1. Divide the larger number by the smaller number.
2. Divide the divisor from step 1 by the remainder from step 1.
3. Divide the divisor from step 2 by the remainder from step 2.
4. Continue this division process until the remainder is 0. The last divisor is the greatest common divisor.

EXAMPLE Find the GCD for $\frac{30}{36}$, then write it in lowest terms.

$$30\overline{)36}^{\ 1\,R\,6}$$

Divide the numerator into the denominator.

$$6\overline{)30}^{\ 5\,R\,0}$$

Divide the original divisor by the original remainder.

$$GCD = 6$$

When the remainder is 0, the divisor is the greatest common divisor.

Now reduce using the GCD.

$$\frac{30}{36} = \frac{30 \div 6}{36 \div 6} = \frac{5}{6}$$

Divide the numerator and denominator by the GCD.

Thus, $\frac{30}{36}$ reduced to lowest terms is $\frac{5}{6}$.

Equivalent Fractions in Higher Terms Just as you can reduce a fraction to lowest terms by dividing the numerator and denominator by the same number, you can write a fraction in *higher* terms by *multiplying* the numerator and denominator by the same number. This process is used in addition and subtraction of fractions.

HOW TO Write a Fraction in Higher Terms Given the New Denominator

Change $\frac{1}{2}$ to eighths or $\frac{1}{2}$ or $\frac{?}{8}$.

$$2\overline{)8}^{\ 4}$$

1. Divide the *new* denominator by the *old* denominator.
2. Multiply *both* the old numerator and denominator by the quotient from step 1.

$$\frac{1}{2} = \frac{1 \times 4}{2 \times 4} = \frac{4}{8}$$

EXAMPLE   Rewrite $\frac{5}{8}$ as a fraction with a denominator of 72.

$$\frac{5}{8} = \frac{?}{72}$$

State the problem clearly.

$$8\overline{)72}^{\,9}$$

Divide the new denominator (72) by the old denominator (8) to find the number by which the old numerator and denominator must be multiplied. That number is 9.

$$\frac{5}{8} = \frac{5 \times 9}{8 \times 9} = \frac{45}{72}$$

Multiply the numerator and denominator by 9 to get the new fraction with a denominator of 72.

Thus, $\frac{5}{8} = \frac{45}{72}$.

---

3 Add and subtract fractions and mixed numbers.

Adding Fractions and Mixed Numbers   The statement that three calculators plus four fax machines is the same as seven calculators is not true. The reason this is not true is that calculators and fax machines are *unlike* terms, and we can only add *like* terms. It is true that three calculators plus four fax machines are the same as seven office machines. What we have done is to *rename* calculators and fax machines using a like term. Calculators and fax machines are both office machines. In the same way, to add fractions that have different denominators, we must rename the fractions using a like, or common, denominator. When fractions have like denominators, we can write their sum as a single fraction.

? HOW TO **Add Fractions with Like (Common) Denominators**

Add $\frac{2}{9} + \frac{1}{9}$.

$2 + 1 = 3$

1. Find the numerator of the sum: add the numerators of the addends.

2. Find the denominator of the sum: use the like denominator of the addends.

$$\frac{2}{9} + \frac{1}{9} = \frac{3}{9}$$

3. Reduce the sum to lowest terms and/or write as a whole or mixed number.

$$\frac{3}{9} = \frac{3 \div 3}{9 \div 3} = \frac{1}{3}$$

EXAMPLE   Find the sum: $\frac{1}{4} + \frac{3}{4} + \frac{3}{4}$.

$$\frac{1}{4} + \frac{3}{4} + \frac{3}{4} = \frac{1 + 3 + 3}{4} = \frac{7}{4}$$

The sum of the numerators is the numerator of the sum. The original like (common) denominator is the denominator of the sum.

$$\frac{7}{4} = 1\frac{3}{4}$$

Convert the improper fraction to a whole or mixed number.

The sum is $1\frac{3}{4}$.

To add fractions with different denominators, find their **least common denominator (LCD)**—the smallest number that can be divided evenly by each original denominator.

To find a common denominator, you can use *prime numbers*. A **prime number** is a number greater than 1 that can be divided evenly only by itself and 1. The first ten prime numbers are 2, 3, 5, 7, 11, 13, 17, 19, 23, and 29.

 HOW TO Find the Least Common Denominator of Two or More Fractions

1. Write the denominators in a row and divide each one by the smallest prime number that any of the numbers can be evenly divided by.
2. Write a new row of numbers using the quotients from step 1 and any numbers in the first row that cannot be evenly divided by the first prime number.
3. Continue this process until you have a row of 1s.
4. Multiply all the prime numbers you used to divide the denominators. The product is the least common denominator.

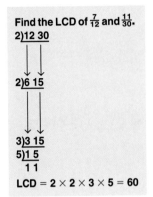

Find the LCD of $\frac{7}{12}$ and $\frac{11}{30}$.

2)12 30

2)6 15

3)3 15
5)1 5
1 1

LCD = 2 × 2 × 3 × 5 = 60

EXAMPLE   Find the least common denominator (LCD) of $\frac{5}{6}$, $\frac{5}{8}$, and $\frac{1}{12}$.

2)6 8 12
2)3 4 6
2)3 2 3
3)3 1 3
  1 1 1

$2 \times 2 \times 2 \times 3 = 24$

Find the LCD: write the denominators in a row and divide by 2, which is the smallest prime number.

Repeat the division with 2 until none of the numbers can be evenly divided by 2. Three is not evenly divisible by 2, so we bring 3 down to the next row, and use the next prime number, 3.

The LCD is the product of all the prime numbers used.

The LCD is 24.

We can use the procedure for finding a least common denominator to add fractions with different denominators.

 HOW TO Add Fractions with Different Denominators

1. Find the least common denominator.
2. Change each fraction to an equivalent fraction using the least common denominator.

3. Add the new fractions with like (common) denominators.
4. Reduce or write as a whole or mixed number.

Add $\frac{2}{3} + \frac{3}{4}$.

LCD = 12

$\frac{2}{3} = \frac{2 \times 4}{3 \times 4} = \frac{8}{12}$

$\frac{3}{4} = \frac{3 \times 3}{4 \times 3} = \frac{9}{12}$

$\frac{8}{12} + \frac{9}{12} = \frac{17}{12}$

$\frac{17}{12} = 1\frac{5}{12}$

EXAMPLE Find the sum of $\frac{5}{6}$, $\frac{5}{8}$, and $\frac{1}{12}$.

We saw in the preceding example that the least common denominator for these fractions is 24. Change each fraction to an equivalent fraction that has a denominator of 24.

$$\frac{5}{6} = \frac{5 \times 4}{6 \times 4} = \frac{20}{24} \qquad \frac{5}{8} = \frac{5 \times 3}{8 \times 3} = \frac{15}{24} \qquad \frac{1}{12} = \frac{1 \times 2}{12 \times 2} = \frac{2}{24}$$

$$\frac{20}{24} + \frac{15}{24} + \frac{2}{24} = \frac{20 + 15 + 2}{24} = \frac{37}{24}$$

Add the fractions with like denominators: add numerators and use the common denominator.

$$\frac{37}{24} = 1\frac{13}{24}$$

Write the improper fraction as a mixed number.

The sum is $1\frac{13}{24}$.

EXAMPLE Add $3\frac{2}{5} + 10\frac{3}{10} + 4\frac{7}{15}$.

Add the fraction parts first.

Step 1
Find the LCD.

Step 2
Change the fractions to equivalent fractions using the LCD.

Step 3
Add the fractions with like denominators.

$$\begin{array}{r} 2)\overline{5 \quad 10 \quad 15} \\ 3)\overline{5 \quad 5 \quad 15} \\ 5)\overline{5 \quad 5 \quad 5} \\ 1 \quad 1 \quad 1 \end{array}$$

$$\frac{2}{5} = \frac{?}{30} \quad 5\overline{)30}^{\,6} \qquad \frac{2}{5} = \frac{2 \times 6}{5 \times 6} = \frac{12}{30} \qquad \frac{12}{30} + \frac{9}{30} + \frac{14}{30} = \frac{35}{30}$$

$2 \times 3 \times 5 = 30 \quad \frac{3}{10} = \frac{?}{30} \quad 10\overline{)30}^{\,3} \qquad \frac{3}{10} = \frac{3 \times 3}{10 \times 3} = \frac{9}{30} \qquad \frac{35}{30} = \frac{7}{6} = 1\frac{1}{6}$

The LCD is 30. $\quad \frac{7}{15} = \frac{?}{30} \quad 15\overline{)30}^{\,2} \qquad \frac{7}{15} = \frac{7 \times 2}{15 \times 2} = \frac{14}{30}$

Now add the whole number parts.

$$3 + 10 + 4 = 17$$

Finally, add the whole number sum and the fraction sum:

$$\begin{array}{r} 17 \\ +1\frac{1}{6} \\ \hline 18\frac{1}{6} \end{array}$$

The sum is $18\frac{1}{6}$.

Application problems involving fractional quantities arise daily in the business world.

EXAMPLE If an employee works the following overtime hours each day, find his total overtime for the week.

$\frac{3}{4}$ hour on Monday
$\frac{1}{2}$ hour on Tuesday
$\frac{2}{3}$ hour on Wednesday
$\frac{1}{4}$ hour on Thursday
$\frac{3}{4}$ hour on Friday

$$\frac{3}{4} + \frac{1}{2} + \frac{2}{3} + \frac{1}{4} + \frac{3}{4} =$$

$$\frac{9}{12} + \frac{6}{12} + \frac{8}{12} + \frac{3}{12} + \frac{9}{12} =$$

$$\frac{35}{12} = 2\frac{11}{12}$$

The total overtime is $2\frac{11}{12}$ hours.

The construction and interior decorating industries offer numerous situations that involve adding fractions and mixed numbers since the U.S. customary rule is used to make lumber and other material measurements. The rule is divided into halfs, fourths, eights, sixteenths, and so on.

EXAMPLE A decorator determines that $25\frac{3}{8}$ yards of fabric are needed as window covering and decides to order an additional $6\frac{3}{4}$ yards of the same fabric for a tablecloth. How many yards of fabric are needed for windows and table?

$$25\frac{3}{8} = 25\frac{3}{8}$$

$$+\ 6\frac{3}{4} =\ 6\frac{6}{8}$$

$$= 31\frac{9}{8}$$

$$= 32\frac{1}{8}$$

$32\frac{1}{8}$ yards of fabric are needed.

Subtracting Fractions and Mixed Numbers In subtracting fractions, just as in adding fractions, you need to find a common denominator.

HOW TO Subtract Fractions

With like denominators

1. Find the numerator of the difference: subtract the numerators of the fraction.

2. Find the denominator of the difference: use the like denominator.

3. Reduce to lowest terms and/or write as a whole or mixed number.

With different denominators

1. Find the least common denominator.

2. Change each fraction to an equivalent fraction using the least common denominator.

3. Subtract the new fractions with like (common) denominators.

4. Reduce to lowest terms.

Subtract $\frac{5}{12} - \frac{1}{12}$.

$5 - 1 = 4$

$\frac{5}{12} - \frac{1}{12} = \frac{4}{12}$

$\frac{4}{12} = \frac{1}{3}$

Subtract $\frac{5}{12} - \frac{1}{3}$.

LCD = 12

$\frac{1}{3} = \frac{1 \times 4}{3 \times 4} = \frac{4}{12}$

$\frac{5}{12} - \frac{4}{12} = \frac{1}{12}$

EXAMPLE Subtract: $\frac{5}{12} - \frac{4}{15}$.

The denominators are different.

Step 1

Find the LCD.

$$
\begin{array}{c|c}
2)12 & 15 \\
2)\ 6 & 15 \\
3)\ 3 & 15 \\
5)\ 1 & \ 5 \\
\ 1 & \ 1
\end{array}
$$

$2 \times 2 \times 3 \times 5 = 60$

The LCD is 60.

Step 2

Change the fractions to equivalent fractions using the LCD.

$$\frac{5}{12} = \frac{5 \times 5}{12 \times 5} = \boxed{\frac{25}{60}}$$

$$\frac{4}{15} = \frac{4 \times 4}{15 \times 4} = \boxed{\frac{16}{60}}$$

Step 3

Subtract numerators, and use the like denominator. Reduce to lowest terms.

$$\boxed{\frac{25}{60}} - \boxed{\frac{16}{60}} = \frac{9}{60}$$

$$\frac{9}{60} = \frac{3}{20}$$

The difference is $\frac{3}{20}$.

Subtracting mixed numbers is like subtracting fractions. First, be sure the fraction parts of the mixed numbers have like denominators.

? HOW TO Subtract Mixed Numbers

1. If the fractions have different denominators, find the LCD and change the fractions to equivalent fractions using the LCD.
2. If necessary, borrow (subtract) 1 from the whole number in the minuend and add 1 (in the form of LCD/LCD) to the fraction in the minuend.
3. Subtract the fractions and the whole numbers.
4. Reduce to lowest terms.

Subtract $2\frac{1}{3} - 1\frac{1}{2}$.

$$2\frac{2}{6} - 1\frac{3}{6}$$

$$1\frac{8}{6} - 1\frac{3}{6}; \left(\frac{2}{6} + \frac{6}{6} = \frac{8}{6}\right)$$

$$= \frac{5}{6}$$

EXAMPLE Subtract $10\frac{1}{3} - 7\frac{3}{5}$.

Convert both fractions to equivalent fractions with denominators of 15, the LCD.

$$10\frac{1}{3} = 10\frac{5}{15} = 9\frac{20}{15}$$

$$-\ 7\frac{3}{5} = 7\frac{9}{15} = 7\frac{9}{15}$$

$$\rule{3cm}{0.4pt}$$

$$2\frac{11}{15}$$

We cannot subtract $\frac{9}{15}$ from $\frac{5}{15}$, so we borrow 1 from 10, leaving 9. Write the borrowed 1 as $\frac{15}{15}$, and add it to $\frac{5}{15}$. Rewrite the problem to show the borrowing and then subtract the whole numbers and the fractions.

The fraction is already in lowest terms, so you do not have to reduce it.

The difference is $2\frac{11}{15}$.

EXAMPLE An interior decorator had 65 yards of fabric wall covering on hand and used $35\frac{3}{8}$ yards for a client's sunroom. How many yards of fabric remain?

$$65 - 35\frac{3}{8} =$$

$$64\frac{8}{8} - 35\frac{3}{8} = \quad \boxed{\textbf{Borrow}}$$

$$29\frac{5}{8}$$

$29\frac{5}{8}$ yards of fabric remain.

Often in application problems both addition and subtraction processes must be recognized and used in order to solve the problem.

EXAMPLE Marcus Johnson, a real estate broker, owns 100 acres of land. During the year he purchased additional tracts of $12\frac{3}{4}$ acres, $23\frac{2}{3}$ acres, and $5\frac{1}{8}$ acres. If he sold a total of $65\frac{2}{3}$ acres during the year, how many acres does he still own?

$$100 \quad = 100 \qquad \boxed{\textbf{LCD = 24}}$$

$$12\frac{3}{4} = 12\frac{18}{24}$$

$$23\frac{2}{3} = 23\frac{16}{24}$$

$$5\frac{1}{8} = 5\frac{3}{24}$$

$$\overline{\qquad\qquad 140\frac{37}{24}} =$$

$$141\frac{13}{24} \qquad \boxed{\textbf{Acres owned before sale.}}$$

$$141\frac{13}{24} = 141\frac{13}{24} = 140\frac{37}{24}$$

$$-65\frac{2}{3} \; = \; 65\frac{16}{24} = \; 65\frac{16}{24}$$

$$\overline{\qquad\qquad = \; 75\frac{21}{24}}$$

$$= \; 75\frac{7}{8} \qquad \boxed{\textbf{Acres owned after sale.}}$$

There are $75\frac{7}{8}$ acres remaining after the sale.

4 Multiply and divide fractions and mixed numbers.

Multiplying Fractions and Mixed Numbers Alexa May has three Domino's Pizza stores. Her distributor shipped only $\frac{3}{4}$ of a cheese order that Alexa had expected to distribute equally among her three stores. What fractional part of the original order will each store receive?

Each store will receive $\frac{1}{3}$ of the *shipment,* but the shipment is only $\frac{3}{4}$ of the *original order.* Each store, then, will receive only $\frac{1}{3}$ of $\frac{3}{4}$ of the original order. Finding $\frac{1}{3}$ of $\frac{3}{4}$ illustrates the use of multiplying fractions, because—just as "2 boxes **of** 3 cans each" amounts to 2 × 3, or 6 cans, so too $\frac{1}{3}$ **of** $\frac{3}{4}$ amounts to $\frac{1}{3}$ × $\frac{3}{4}$.

We can visualize $\frac{1}{3}$ × $\frac{3}{4}$ or $\frac{1}{3}$ **of** $\frac{3}{4}$, by first visualizing $\frac{3}{4}$ of a whole (Figure. 2-8).

Figure 2-8   3 parts out of 4 parts $= \frac{3}{4}$ of a whole

Now visualize $\frac{1}{3}$ of $\frac{3}{4}$ of a whole (Figure. 2-9).

Figure 2-9   1 part out of 3 parts in $\frac{3}{4}$ of a whole $=$ 1 part out of 4 parts or $\frac{1}{4}$ of a whole.

$$\frac{1}{3} \quad \text{of} \quad \frac{3}{4} \quad \text{is} \quad \frac{1}{4}$$

$$\frac{1}{3} \quad \times \quad \frac{3}{4} \quad = \quad \frac{1}{4}$$

? HOW TO Multiply Fractions

1. Find the numerator of the product: multiply the numerators of the fractions.

2. Find the denominator of the product: multiply the denominators of the fractions.

3. Reduce to lowest terms.

Multiply $\frac{1}{2} \times \frac{7}{8}$.
1 × 7 = 7

2 × 8 = 16

$\frac{1}{2} \times \frac{7}{8} = \frac{7}{16}$

EXAMPLE   What fraction of the original cheese order will each of Alexa's three stores receive equally if $\frac{9}{10}$ of the original order is shipped?

1 Decision needed

2 Unknown facts   Fraction of original shipment that each store will receive equally

3 Known facts   Fraction of shipment each store can receive: $\frac{1}{3}$
Fraction of original order received for all the stores $= \frac{9}{10}$

4 Relationships   Fraction of original order each store can receive = fraction of shipment each store can receive × fraction of original order received. Fraction of original order each store can receive $= \frac{1}{3} \times \frac{9}{10}$.

5 Estimation   Since the shipment is slightly less than the original order, each store receives slightly less than $\frac{1}{3}$ of the original order. Thus, the fraction of the original order that each store will receive is slightly less than $\frac{1}{3}$.

6 Calculation

$$\frac{1}{3} \times \frac{9}{10} = \frac{1 \times 9}{3 \times 10} = \frac{9}{30}$$

Multiply numerators; multiply denominators.

$$\frac{9}{30} = \frac{3}{10}$$

Reduce to lowest terms.

Each store will receive $\frac{3}{10}$ of the original order.

TIP! Reduce before Multiplying

When you multiply fractions, you save time by reducing fractions *before* you multiply. If *any* numerator and *any* denominator can be divided evenly by the same number, divide both the numerator and the denominator by that number. You can then multiply the reduced numbers with greater accuracy than you could multiply the larger numbers.

$$\frac{1}{\overset{1}{\cancel{3}}} \times \frac{\overset{1}{\cancel{3}}}{4} = \frac{1}{4} \qquad \frac{1}{\overset{1}{\cancel{3}}} \times \frac{\overset{3}{\cancel{9}}}{10} = \frac{3}{10}$$

A numerator and a denominator can be divided evenly by 3 in both examples.

To multiply mixed numbers and whole numbers, change the mixed numbers and whole numbers to fractions.

HOW TO Multiply Mixed Numbers and Whole Numbers

1. Write the mixed numbers and whole numbers as improper fractions.
2. Reduce numerators and denominators as appropriate.
3. Multiply the fractions.
4. Reduce to lowest terms and/or write as a whole or mixed number.

EXAMPLE Multiply $2\frac{1}{3} \times 3\frac{3}{4}$.

$$2\frac{1}{3} \times 3\frac{3}{4} = \frac{(3 \times 2) + 1}{3} \times \frac{(4 \times 3) + 3}{4} =$$

Write the mixed numbers as improper fractions.

$$\frac{7}{\overset{}{\cancel{3}}_{1}} \times \frac{\overset{5}{\cancel{15}}}{4} = \frac{35}{4}$$

Divide both 3 and 15 by 3, reducing to 1 and 5. Multiply the numerators and denominators.

$$\frac{35}{4} = 8\frac{3}{4}$$

Write as a mixed number.

The product is $8\frac{3}{4}$.

EXAMPLE The outside width of a boxed cook top is $2\frac{3}{8}$ feet, and a shipment of stoves is placed in a 45-foot trailer. How many feet will 16 stove boxes require?

$$2\frac{3}{8} \times \frac{16}{1} =$$

$$\frac{19}{1} \times \frac{2}{1} = 38$$

$$= 38 \qquad \text{Feet required}$$

16 stoves require 38 feet of space.

Are Products Always Larger than Their Factors?

A product is not always greater than the factors being multiplied.

When the multiplier is a proper fraction, the product is *less than* the original number. This is true when the multiplicand is a whole number, fraction, or mixed number.

$$5 \times \frac{3}{5} = 3$$

Product 3 is less than factor 5.

$$\frac{3}{4} \times \frac{4}{9} = \frac{1}{3}$$

Product $\frac{1}{3}$ is less than factor $\frac{3}{4}$.

$$2\frac{1}{2} \times \frac{1}{2} = \frac{5}{2} \times \frac{1}{2} = \frac{5}{4} = 1\frac{1}{4}$$

Product $1\frac{1}{4}$ is less than factor $2\frac{1}{2}$.

Dividing Fractions and Mixed Numbers Division of fractions is related to multiplication. *Total amount = number of units of a specified size times (×) the specified size.* If you know the total amount and the number of equal units, you can find the size of each unit by dividing the total amount by the number of equal units. If you know the total amount and the specified size, you can find the number of equal units by dividing the total amount by the specified size.

Home Depot has a stack of plywood that is 32 inches high. If each sheet of plywood is $\frac{1}{2}$ inch, how many sheets of plywood are in the stack? We are trying to determine how many equal units of plywood are contained in the total stack, so we divide the height of the stack (total amount) by the thickness of each sheet (specified size).

$$32 \div \frac{1}{2}$$ **Total thickness divided by thickness of one sheet of plywood**

Another way of approaching the problem is to think of the number of sheets of plywood in one inch of height. If each sheet of plywood is $\frac{1}{2}$ inch, then two sheets of plywood are one inch thick. If there are two sheets of plywood for each inch, there will be 64 pieces of plywood in the 32-inch stack.

$$32 \div \frac{1}{2} = 32 \times \frac{2}{1} = 64$$

The relationship between multiplying and dividing fractions involves a concept called **reciprocals.** Two numbers are reciprocals if their product is 1. Thus, $\frac{2}{3}$ and $\frac{3}{2}$ are reciprocals $\left(\frac{2}{3} \times \frac{3}{2} = 1\right)$ and $\frac{7}{8}$ and $\frac{8}{7}$ are reciprocals $\left(\frac{7}{8} \times \frac{8}{7} = 1\right)$.

HOW TO Find the Reciprocal of a Number

Write the reciprocal of 3.

1. Write the number as a fraction.

$$\frac{3}{1}$$

2. Interchange the numerator and denominator.

$$\frac{1}{3}$$

EXAMPLE Find the reciprocal of (a) $\frac{7}{9}$ (b) 5 (c) $4\frac{1}{2}$

(a) **The reciprocal of $\frac{7}{9}$ is $\frac{9}{7}$.**

(b) Write 5 as the fraction $\frac{5}{1}$. **The reciprocal of $\frac{5}{1}$ is $\frac{1}{5}$.**

(c) Write $4\frac{1}{2}$ as the fraction $\frac{9}{2}$. **The reciprocal of $\frac{9}{2}$ is $\frac{2}{9}$.**

In the Home Depot discussion, we reasoned that $32 \div \frac{1}{2}$ is the same as 32×2. So, to divide by a fraction, we *multiply* by the *reciprocal* of the divisor.

❓ HOW TO Divide Fractions or Mixed Numbers

Divide $\frac{3}{4}$ by 5.

1. Write numbers as fractions.

$$\frac{3}{4} \div \frac{5}{1}$$

2. Find the reciprocal of the divisor.

3. Multiply the dividend by the reciprocal of the divisor.

$$\frac{3}{4} \times \frac{1}{5} = \frac{3}{20}$$

4. Reduce to lowest terms and/or write as a whole or mixed number.

$$\frac{3}{20} \quad \text{(lowest terms)}$$

EXAMPLE Madison Duke makes appliqués from brocade fabric. A customer has ordered five appliqués. Can Madison fill the order without buying more fabric? She has $\frac{3}{4}$ yard of fabric and each appliqué requires $\frac{1}{6}$ of a yard.

1 Decision needed Can Madison fill the order?

2 Unknown facts The number of appliqués that can be made from the fabric

3 Known facts Total length of fabric: $\frac{3}{4}$ yard
Length of fabric needed for each appliqué: $\frac{1}{6}$ yard

4 Relationships Number of appliqués = total length of fabric ÷ length of fabric needed for each appliqué

$$\text{Number of appliqués} = \frac{3}{4} \div \frac{1}{6}$$

5 Estimation It takes $\frac{1}{6}$ yard to make one appliqué, so one yard makes six appliqués. Since she has less than one yard, she can make fewer than six appliqués.

6 Calculation $\text{Number of appliqués} = \frac{3}{4} \div \frac{1}{6}$

$$= \frac{3}{4} \times \frac{6}{1}$$

$$= \frac{18}{4} = \frac{9}{2} = 4\frac{1}{2}$$

7 Interpretation Madison can make four complete appliqués from the $\frac{3}{4}$ yard of fabric.

8 Decision made Since the order is five appliqués, **Madison cannot fill the order without buying more fabric.**

EXAMPLE Find the quotient: $5\frac{1}{2} \div 7\frac{1}{3}$

$$5\frac{1}{2} = \frac{(2 \times 5) + 1}{2} = \frac{11}{2}$$

Write the numbers as fractions.

$$7\frac{1}{3} = \frac{(3 \times 7) + 1}{3} = \frac{22}{3}$$

The divisor is $\frac{22}{3}$. Its reciprocal is $\frac{3}{22}$.

$$\frac{11}{2} \div \frac{22}{3} =$$

$$\frac{\overset{1}{\cancel{11}}}{2} \times \frac{3}{\underset{2}{\cancel{22}}} = \frac{1 \times 3}{2 \times 2} = \frac{3}{4}$$

Multiply $\frac{11}{2}$ by the reciprocal of the divisor, $\frac{3}{22}$.

The quotient is $\frac{3}{4}$.

5 Write a decimal as a fraction and write a fraction as a decimal.

As we discussed in Chapter 1, decimals can represent parts of a whole, just as fractions can. We can write a decimal as a fraction, or a fraction as a decimal.

? HOW TO Write a Decimal as a Fraction

Write 0.8 as a fraction.
Denominator = 10

1. Find the denominator: write 1 followed by as many zeros as there are places to the right of the decimal point.

2. Find the numerator: use the digits without the decimal point.

$$\frac{8}{10}$$

3. Reduce to lowest terms and/or write as a whole or mixed number.

$$\frac{4}{5}$$

EXAMPLE Change 0.38 to a fraction.

$$\frac{38}{100}$$

The digits without the decimal point form the numerator.
There are two places to the right of the decimal point, so the denominator is 1 followed by two zeros.

$$\frac{38}{100} = \frac{19}{50}$$

Reduce the fraction to lowest terms.

Thus, 0.38 written as a fraction is $\frac{19}{50}$.

Fractions indicate division. Therefore, to write a fraction as a decimal, divide the numerator by the denominator, as you would divide decimals.

TIP! Relating the Number of Decimal Places and the Zeros in the Denominator to the Place Value

The number of places after the decimal point indicates the number of zeros in the denominator of the power of 10.

$$0.015 = \frac{15}{1,000} \qquad 2.43 = 2\frac{43}{100}$$

Note that the number after the decimal point indicates the numerator of the fraction.

HOW TO Write a Fraction as a Decimal

1. Write the numerator as the dividend and the denominator as the divisor.
2. Divide the numerator by the denominator, taking the division out as many decimal places as necessary or desirable.

EXAMPLE Change $\frac{1}{4}$ to a decimal number.

$$\begin{array}{r} 0.25 \\ 4\overline{)1.00} \\ \underline{8} \\ 20 \\ \underline{20} \end{array}$$

Divide the numerator by the denominator, adding zeros to the right of the decimal point as needed.

The decimal equivalent of $\frac{1}{4}$ is 0.25.

TIP! Divide by Which Number?

An aid to help students remember which number in the fraction is the divisor: Divide by the bottom number. Both *by* and *bottom* start with the letter *b*.

When the division comes out even (there is no remainder), we say the division terminates, and the quotient is called a **terminating decimal.** If, however, the division *never* comes out even (there is always a remainder), we call the number a **nonterminating** or **repeating decimal.** If the quotient is a repeating decimal, either write the quotient as a mixed decimal or rounded decimal.

EXAMPLE Write $\frac{2}{3}$ as a decimal number expressed to the nearest hundredth.

$$\begin{array}{r} 0.66\frac{2}{3} \text{ or } 0.67 \text{ (rounded)} \\ 3\overline{)2.00} \\ \underline{1\ 8} \\ 20 \\ \underline{18} \\ 2 \end{array}$$

Thus, $\frac{2}{3} = 0.67$.

1 *Classify the fractions as proper or improper.*

1. $\dfrac{5}{9}$
2. $\dfrac{12}{7}$
3. $\dfrac{7}{7}$
4. $\dfrac{1}{12}$
5. $\dfrac{12}{15}$
6. $\dfrac{21}{20}$

Write the fraction as a whole or mixed number.

7. $\dfrac{12}{7}$
8. $\dfrac{21}{20}$
9. $\dfrac{18}{18}$
10. $\dfrac{7}{7}$
11. $\dfrac{16}{8}$
12. $\dfrac{388}{16}$

Write the whole or mixed number as an improper fraction.

13. 6
14. 27
15. $2\dfrac{1}{3}$
16. $3\dfrac{4}{5}$
17. $1\dfrac{5}{8}$
18. $6\dfrac{2}{3}$

2 *Reduce to lowest terms.*

19. $\dfrac{12}{15}$
20. $\dfrac{12}{20}$
21. $\dfrac{18}{24}$
22. $\dfrac{18}{36}$
23. $\dfrac{24}{36}$
24. $\dfrac{13}{39}$

Change the fraction to an equivalent fraction with the given denominator.

25. $\dfrac{3}{8}, \dfrac{}{16}$
26. $\dfrac{4}{5}, \dfrac{}{20}$
27. $\dfrac{3}{8}, \dfrac{}{32}$
28. $\dfrac{5}{9}, \dfrac{}{27}$
29. $\dfrac{1}{3}, \dfrac{}{15}$
30. $\dfrac{3}{5}, \dfrac{}{15}$

3 *Perform the indicated operation. Write the sum as a fraction, whole number, or mixed number in lowest terms.*

31. $\dfrac{1}{9} + \dfrac{2}{9} + \dfrac{5}{9}$
32. $\dfrac{7}{8} + \dfrac{5}{8}$
33. $\dfrac{5}{6} + \dfrac{7}{15}$
34. $\dfrac{5}{8} + \dfrac{7}{12}$
35. $4\dfrac{5}{6} + 7\dfrac{1}{2}$

36. Loretta McBride is decorating a house and determining the amount of fabric required for window treatments. She finds that a single window requires $11\dfrac{3}{4}$ yards and a double window requires $18\dfrac{5}{8}$ yards of fabric. If she has two single windows and one double window, how much fabric will be required?

37. Marveen McCready, a commercial space designer and decorator, has taken these measurements for an office in which she plans to install a decorative wall paper border around the ceiling: $42\dfrac{3}{8}$ feet, $37\dfrac{5}{8}$ feet, $12\dfrac{3}{8}$ feet, and $23\dfrac{3}{4}$ feet. How much paper will she need for the job.

38. Rob Farinelli is building a gazebo and plans to use for the floor two boards that are $10\dfrac{3}{4}$ feet, four boards that are $12\dfrac{5}{8}$ feet, and two boards that are $8\dfrac{1}{2}$ feet. Find the total number of feet in all the boards.

39. Tenisha Gist cuts brass plates for an engraving job. From a sheet of brass, three pieces $4\dfrac{4}{5}$ inches wide and two pieces $7\dfrac{3}{8}$ inches wide are cut. What is the smallest piece of brass required to cut all five plates?

Find the difference.

40. $\dfrac{7}{8} - \dfrac{3}{8}$
41. $\dfrac{8}{9} - \dfrac{2}{9}$
42. $\dfrac{3}{4} - \dfrac{5}{7}$
43. $9\dfrac{1}{2} - 6\dfrac{2}{3}$

44. The fabric Loretta McBride has selected for the window treatment in exercise 36 has only 45 yards on the only roll available. Will she be able to use the fabric or must she make an alternate selection? If she can use the fabric, will she have enough left for throw pillows?

45. Rob Farinelli purchased two boards that are 12 feet and will cut them to make $10\frac{3}{4}$-foot boards for the gazebo he is building. How much of the board must be removed?

46. Rob purchased four boards that are expected to be 14 feet so that he can cut them to make each one $12\frac{5}{8}$ feet for the gazebo he is building. However, upon measuring, he finds they are $13\frac{15}{16}$ feet, $14\frac{1}{8}$ feet, 14 feet, and $13\frac{13}{16}$ feet. Calculate the amount that must be removed from each board to get $12\frac{5}{8}$-foot boards.

47. Charlie Carr has a sheet of brass that is 36 inches wide and cuts two pieces that are each $8\frac{3}{4}$ inches wide. What is the width of the left over brass?

 4   *Find the product.*

48. $\dfrac{3}{8} \times \dfrac{4}{5}$

49. $\dfrac{5}{7} \times \dfrac{1}{6}$

50. $5\dfrac{3}{4} \times 3\dfrac{8}{9}$

51. $\dfrac{3}{8} \times 24$

52. Carl Heinrich has six lateral filing cabinets that need to be placed on one wall of a storage closet. The filing cabinets are each $3\frac{1}{2}$ feet wide and the wall is 21 feet long. Decide if all the cabinets can be placed on the wall.

53. Each of the four walls of a room measures $18\frac{5}{8}$ feet. How much chair rail must be purchased to install the chair rail on all four walls? Disregard any openings.

54. Four office desks that are $4\frac{1}{8}$ feet long are to be placed together on a wall that is $16\frac{5}{8}$ feet long. Will they fit on the wall?

55. Ariana Pope is making 28 trophies and each requires a brass plate that is $3\frac{1}{4}$ inches long and 1 inch wide. What size sheet of brass is required to make the plates if the plates are aligned with two plates per horizontal line?

Find the reciprocal.

56. $\dfrac{7}{12}$

57. $\dfrac{3}{5}$

58. 9

59. 12

60. $5\dfrac{4}{7}$

61. $3\dfrac{3}{8}$

Find the quotient.

62. $\dfrac{5}{8} \div \dfrac{3}{4}$

63. $\dfrac{3}{5} \div \dfrac{9}{10}$

64. $2\dfrac{2}{5} \div 1\dfrac{1}{7}$

65. $5\dfrac{1}{4} \div 2\dfrac{2}{3}$

66. Pierre Hugo is handling the estate of a prominent businesswoman. The will states that the surviving spouse is to receive $\frac{1}{4}$ of the estate and the remaining $\frac{3}{4}$ of the estate will be divided equally among five surviving children. What fraction of the estate does each child receive?

67. Marvin Jones needs to estimate the number of sheets of plywood in a stack that is 75 inches tall. If each sheet of plywood is $1\frac{1}{8}$ inch thick, how many sheets should he expect?

68. A roll of carpet that contains 20 yards of carpet will carpet how many rooms if each room requires $5\frac{3}{4}$ yards of carpet?

69. A box of kitty litter is $8\frac{3}{4}$ inches tall. How many boxes of kitty litter can be stored on a warehouse shelf that can accommodate boxes up to a height of 40 inches?

 5 *Write as a fraction in lowest terms.*

70. 0.8

71. 0.68

Write as a mixed number in lowest terms.

72. 1.4

73. 3.2

Write the number as a decimal. Round to hundredths if necessary.

74. $\dfrac{3}{10}$

75. $\dfrac{3}{4}$

76. $\dfrac{7}{8}$

77. $1\dfrac{3}{5}$

78. $\dfrac{3}{7}$

79. Forest Oil stock was recently listed at $19\frac{3}{8}$. Express the stock price using decimals.

80. Microsoft stock recently listed for $141\frac{1}{2}$, up $3\frac{5}{8}$ for the week. Express the stock price and weekly change using decimals.

2.2 Problem Solving with Percents

1 Write a whole number, fraction, or decimal as a percent.

2 Write a percent as a whole number, fraction, or decimal.

3 Use the percentage formula to find the percentage.

4 Use the percentage formula to find the base.

5 Use the percentage formula to find the rate.

6 Use the percentage proportion to solve problems.

With fractions and decimals, we compare only like quantities, that is, fractions with common denominators and decimals with the same number of decimal places. We can standardize our representation of quantities so that they can be more easily compared. We standardize by expressing quantities in relation to a standard unit of 100. This relationship, called a **percent,** is used to solve many different types of business problems.

The word *percent* means *hundredths* or *out of 100* or *per 100* or *over 100* (in a fraction). That is, 44 percent means 44 hundredths, or 44 out of 100, or 44 per 100, or 44 over 100. We can write 44 hundredths as 0.44 or $\frac{44}{100}$.

The symbol for *percent* is %. You can write 44 percent using the percent symbol: 44%; using fractional notation: $\frac{44}{100}$; or using decimal notation: 0.44. 44% = 44 percent = 44 hundredths = $\frac{44}{100}$ = 0.44.

Percents can contain whole numbers, decimals, fractions, mixed numbers, or mixed decimals. Percents with mixed numbers and mixed decimals are often referred to as **mixed percents.** Examples are $33\frac{1}{3}\%$, $0.05\frac{3}{4}\%$, and $0.23\frac{1}{3}\%$.

 Write a whole number, fraction, or decimal as a percent.

The businessperson must be able to write whole numbers, decimals, or fractions as percents, and to write percents as whole numbers, decimals, or fractions. First we examine writing whole numbers, decimals, and fractions as percents.

Hundredths and percent have the same meaning: per hundred. Just as 100 cents is the same as 1 dollar, 100 percent is the same as 1 whole quantity.

$$100\% = 1$$

This fact is used to write percent equivalents of numbers, and to write numerical equivalents of percents. It is also used to calculate markups, markdowns, discounts, and numerous other business applications.

When we multiply a number by 1, the product has the same value as the original number. $N \times 1 = N$. We have used this concept to change a fraction to an equivalent fraction with a higher denominator. For example,

$$1 = \frac{2}{2} \text{ and } \frac{1}{2} \times \frac{2}{2} = \frac{2}{4}$$

$$1 = \frac{3}{3} \text{ and } \frac{1}{2} \times \frac{3}{3} = \frac{3}{6}$$

We can also use the fact, $N \times 1 = N$, to change numbers to equivalent percents.

$$1 = 100\%; \frac{1}{2} \times 100\% = \frac{1}{\cancel{2}} \times \frac{\overset{50}{\cancel{100\%}}}{1} = 50\%$$

$$1 = 100\%; 0.5 \times 100\% = 050.\% = 50\%$$

In each case when we multiply by 1 in some form, the value of the product is equivalent to the value of the original number even though the product *looks different.*

 HOW TO Write a Number as Its Percent Equivalent

Multiply the number by 1 in the form of 100%.

Write 0.3 as a percent.
0.3 = 0.3 × 100% = 030.% = 30%

 TIP! Multiplying by 1 in the form of 100%

To write a number as its percent equivalent, identify the number as a fraction, whole number, or decimal. If the number is a fraction, multiply it by 1 in the form of $\frac{100\%}{1}$. If the number is a whole number or decimal, multiply by 100% by using the shortcut rule for multiplying by 100. In each case, the percent equivalent will be expressed with a percent symbol.

EXAMPLE Write the decimal or whole number as a percent.

(a) 0.27   (b) 0.875   (c) 1.73   (d) 0.004   (e) 2

(a) $0.27 = 0.27 \times 100\% = 0\,27.\% = 27\%$
0.27 as a percent is 27%.

> Multiply 0.27 by 100% (move the decimal point two places to the right).

(b) $0.875 = 0.875 \times 100\% = 087.5\% = 87.5\%$
0.875 as a percent is 87.5%.

> Multiply 0.875 by 100% (move the decimal point two places to the right).

(c) $1.73 = 1.73 \times 100\% = 173.\% = 173\%$
1.73 as a percent is 173%.

> Multiply 1.73 by 100% (move the decimal point two places to the right).

(d) $0.004 = 0.004 \times 100\% = 000.4\% = 0.4\%$
0.004 as a percent is 0.4%

> Multiply 0.004 by 100% (move the decimal point two places to the right).

(e) $2 = 2 \times 100\% = 200.\% = 200\%$
2 as a percent is 200%.

> Multiply 2 by 100% (move the decimal point two places to the right).

As you can see, the procedure is the same regardless of the number of decimal places in the number and regardless of whether the number is greater than, equal to, or less than 1.

EXAMPLE Write the fraction as a percent.

(a) $\dfrac{67}{100}$ (b) $\dfrac{1}{4}$ (c) $3\dfrac{1}{2}$ (d) $\dfrac{7}{4}$ (e) $\dfrac{2}{3}$

(a) $\dfrac{67}{100} = \dfrac{67}{\overset{}{\underset{1}{100}}} \times \dfrac{\overset{1}{100\%}}{1} = \mathbf{67\%}$

(b) $\dfrac{1}{4} = \dfrac{1}{\overset{}{\underset{1}{4}}} \times \dfrac{\overset{25}{100\%}}{1} = \mathbf{25\%}$

(c) $3\dfrac{1}{2} = 3\dfrac{1}{2} \times \dfrac{100\%}{1} = \dfrac{7}{\overset{}{\underset{1}{2}}} \times \dfrac{\overset{50}{100\%}}{1} = \mathbf{350\%}$

(d) $\dfrac{7}{4} = \dfrac{7}{\overset{}{\underset{1}{4}}} \times \dfrac{\overset{25}{100\%}}{1} = \mathbf{175\%}$

(e) $\dfrac{2}{3} = \dfrac{2}{3} \times \dfrac{100\%}{1} = \dfrac{200\%}{3} = \mathbf{66\dfrac{2}{3}\%}$

2 Write a Percent as a Whole Number, Fraction, or Decimal.

When a number is divided by 1, the quotient has the same value as the original number. $N \div 1 = N$ or $\frac{N}{1} = N$. We have used this concept to reduce fractions. For example,

$$1 = \frac{2}{2}; \frac{2}{4} \div \frac{2}{2} = \frac{1}{2}$$

$$1 = \frac{3}{3}; \frac{3}{6} \div \frac{3}{3} = \frac{1}{2}$$

We can also use the fact $N \div 1 = N$ or $\frac{N}{1} = N$ to change percents to numerical equivalents.

$$50\% \div 100\% = \frac{50\%}{100\%} = \frac{50}{100} = \frac{1}{2}$$
$$50\% \div 100\% = 50 \div 100 = 0.50 = 0.5$$

HOW TO | Write a Percent as a Number

Divide by 1 in the form of 100%.

TIP! | Whole Number, Decimal, or Fraction Equivalents

To write a percent as its numerical equivalent, first determine what form (decimal or fraction) you want.

To get a decimal equivalent, write the number in front of the percent symbol in decimal form. Then divide by 1 in the form of 100% by using the shortcut rule for dividing by 100.

To get a fraction equivalent, write the number in front of the percent symbol in fraction form. Then divide by 1 in the form of $\frac{100\%}{1}$. This means we will multiply by $\frac{1}{100\%}$.

TIP! | Doing Part of the Calculation on the Calculator and the Other Part Mentally

When you need to find the percent equivalent of a fraction, why not change the fraction to a decimal equivalent by dividing? Then, change the decimal to a percent mentally by multiplying by 100%.

$$\frac{4}{7} = 4 \div 7 = 0.571428571$$

> **Mentally move the decimal two places to the right**

Then, $\frac{4}{7} \approx 57.14\%$

EXAMPLE   Write the percent as a decimal.

(a) 37%   (b) 26.5%   (c) 127%   (d) 7%   (e) 0.9%   (f) $2\frac{19}{20}\%$ (g) $167\frac{1}{3}\%$

(a) $37\% = 37\% \div 100\% = .37 = \mathbf{0.37}$

(b) $26.5\% = 26.5\% \div 100\% = .265 = \mathbf{0.265}$

(c) $127\% = 127\% \div 100\% = 1.27 = \mathbf{1.27}$

(d) $7\% = 7\% \div 100\% = .07 = \mathbf{0.07}$

(e) $0.9\% = 0.9\% \div 100\% = .009 = \mathbf{0.009}$

(f) $2\frac{19}{20}\% = 2.95\% \div 100\% = .0295 = \mathbf{0.0295}$

Write the mixed number in front of the percent symbol as a mixed decimal before dividing by 100%.
Write the mixed number in front of the percent symbol as a repeating mixed decimal before dividing by 100.

(g) $167\frac{1}{3}\% = 167.3\overline{3}\% \div 100\% =$

$1.673\overline{3} = \mathbf{1.673\overline{3}} \text{ or } \mathbf{1.673} \text{ (rounded)}$

 TIP! **What Happens to the % (Percent) Sign?**

Remember from multiplying fractions that we can reduce or cancel common factors from a numerator to a denominator. Percent signs and other types of labels can also cancel.

$$\frac{\%}{1} \times \frac{1}{\%} = 1$$

EXAMPLE Write the percent as a fraction or mixed number.

(a) 65%   (b) $\frac{1}{4}\%$ (c) 250%   (d) $83\frac{1}{3}\%$ (e) 12.5%

(a) $65\% = 65\% \div 100\% = \dfrac{\overset{13}{\cancel{65\%}}}{1} \times \dfrac{1}{\underset{20}{\cancel{100\%}}} = \dfrac{\mathbf{13}}{\mathbf{20}}$

(b) $\dfrac{1}{4}\% = \dfrac{1}{4}\% \div 100\% = \dfrac{1\%}{4} \times \dfrac{1}{100\%} = \dfrac{\mathbf{1}}{\mathbf{400}}$

(c) $250\% = 250\% \div 100\% = \dfrac{\overset{5}{\cancel{250\%}}}{1} \times \dfrac{1}{\underset{2}{\cancel{100\%}}} = \dfrac{5}{2} = \mathbf{2\dfrac{1}{2}}$

(d) $83\dfrac{1}{3}\% = 83\dfrac{1}{3}\% \div 100\% = \dfrac{\overset{5}{\cancel{250\%}}}{3} \times \dfrac{1}{\underset{2}{\cancel{100\%}}} = \dfrac{\mathbf{5}}{\mathbf{6}}$

(e) $12.5\% = 12\dfrac{1}{2}\% = 12\dfrac{1}{2}\% \div 100\% = \dfrac{\overset{1}{\cancel{25\%}}}{2} \times \dfrac{1}{\underset{4}{\cancel{100\%}}} = \dfrac{\mathbf{1}}{\mathbf{8}}$

 TIP! **Percent or Number?**

A number times a measure equals a measure. $2 \times 5 \text{ inches} = 10 \text{ inches}$

Similarly, a number times a percent is a percent. $0.5 \times 100\% = 50\%$

Also, a measure ÷ a measure is a number that tells how many.

$$10 \text{ inches} \div 2 \text{ inches} = 5 \text{ items each 2 inches long}$$

And, a percent divided by a percent equals a number.

$$300\% \div 100\% = \frac{300\%}{100\%} = 3$$

---

3 Use the percentage formula to find the percentage.

A formula expresses a relationship among quantities. When you use the decision key in this book, step 4, Relationships, is a formula written in words and letters.

The percentage formula, *Percentage = Rate × Base*, can be written as $P = R \times B$. The letters or words represent numbers. When the numbers are put in place of the letters, the formula guides you through the calculations.

In the formula $P = R \times B$, the **base** (B) represents the original number or entire quantity. The **percentage** (P) represents a **portion** of the base. The **rate** (R) is a percent that tells us how the base and percentage are related. In the statement "50 is 20% of 250," 250 is the base (the entire quantity), 50 is the percentage (part), and 20% is the rate (percent).

When a formula shows that two numbers are multiplied to get a product, if you know the product and one of the numbers being multiplied, you can find the missing number (factor) by division. So

$$\text{Missing factor} = \text{product} \div \text{known factor}$$

For example, if $24 = 3 \times N$, then $N = 24 \div 3$. In other words, the missing number (N) is $24 \div 3$, or 8.

We can use the percentage formula to determine alternate formulas by a similar strategy.

$$\text{Since } P = R \times B, \text{ then } B = P \div R \text{ or } \boldsymbol{B = \frac{P}{R}}$$

$$\text{Since } P = R \times B, \text{ then } R = P \div B \text{ or } \boldsymbol{R = \frac{P}{B}}$$

Normally, we put the letter that represents the missing number on the left and the letters and other symbols that represent known numbers on the right. Then, the right side of the formula guides you to make the appropriate calculations.

The three percentage formulas are

Percentage = Rate × Base	$P = R \times B$	for finding the percentage
Base = $\dfrac{\text{Percentage}}{\text{Rate}}$	$B = \dfrac{P}{R}$	for finding the base
Rate = $\dfrac{\text{Percentage}}{\text{Base}}$	$R = \dfrac{P}{B}$	for finding the rate

Figure 2-10 shows circles that help us visualize these formulas. The shaded part of the circle represents the missing amount. The unshaded parts represent the known amounts. If the unshaded parts are side by side, multiply their corresponding numbers to find the missing number.

If the unshaded parts are one on top of the other, divide the corresponding numbers to find the missing number.

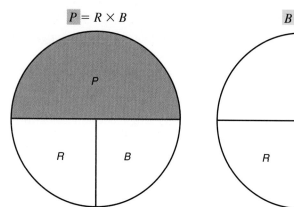

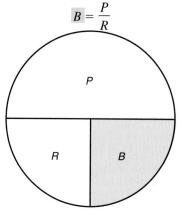

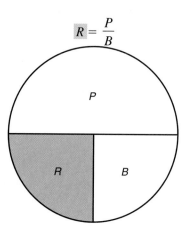

Figure 2-10 Percentage Formulas

? HOW TO Use the Percentage Formula to Find the Percentage

1. Write the formula $P = R \times B$.

2. Replace R and B by the known numbers for rate (R) and base (B).

3. Write R as a decimal or fraction.

4. Multiply R times B.

50% of 20
$P = R \times B$

$P = 50\% \times 20$

$P = \frac{50}{100} \times 20$

$P = 10$

EXAMPLE Find the percentage if the rate is 6% and the base is $20.

$P = R \times B$ The percentage is unknown (Figure 2-11).

$P = 6\% \times \$20$ The rate (R) is 6%; the base (B) is $20. Write 6% as a decimal.

$P = 0.06 \times \$20$ Multiply 0.06 by $20.

$P = \$1.20$

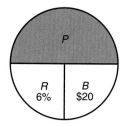

Figure 2-11

The percentage is $1.20.

! TIP! Use Decimal or Fraction Equivalent of Rate

It is important to change the rate (percent) to a decimal or a fraction *before* you make any calculations. Look at what might happen in the preceding example if you do not change the rate to a decimal number.

$P = 0.06 \times \$20 = \$1.20$ $P = 6\% \times \$20 = \$120$

CORRECT   INCORRECT

Very few percentage problems that you encounter in business tell you the values of P, R, and B directly. Percentage problems are usually written in words that must be interpreted before you can tell which form of the percentage formula you should use.

EXAMPLE   During a special one-day sale, 600 customers bought the on-sale pizza. Of these customers, 20% used coupons. The manager will run the sale again the next day if more than 100 coupons were used. Should she run the sale again?

1 Decision needed   Should the manager run the sale again?

2 Unknown facts   Quantity of coupon-using customers

3 Known facts   Total customers: 600
Coupon-using customers as a percent of total customers: 20%

4 Relationships   The quantity of coupon-using customers is a *percentage* of the *base* of total customers, at a *rate* of 20% (Figure 2-12).

$$P = R \times B$$

Quantity of coupon-using customers $= 20\% \times 600$

5 Estimation   20% is less than 50%, or $\frac{1}{2}$. Half of 600 is 300, so the quantity of coupon-using customers is less than 300. Also, 20% is more than 10%. $10\% \times 600 = 60$, so more than 60 customers used coupons.

6 Calculation   Quantity of coupon-using customers $= 20\% \times 600$

$$= 0.2 \times 600 = 120$$

7 Interpretation   The quantity of coupon-using customers is 120.

Figure 2-12

8 Decision made   **Since 120 is more than 100, the manager should run the sale again.**

EXAMPLE   If $66\frac{2}{3}\%$ of the 900 employees in a company choose the Preferred Provider insurance plan, how many people from that company are enrolled in the plan?

First, identify the terms. The rate is the percent, and the base is the total number of employees. The percentage is the quantity of employees enrolled in the plan.

$$P = R \times B$$

The percentage is the unknown.

$$P = 66\frac{2}{3}\% \times 900$$

The rate is $66\frac{2}{3}\%$; the base is 900 (Figure 2-13).

$$P = \frac{2}{\overset{1}{\cancel{3}}} \times \frac{\overset{300}{\cancel{900}}}{1} = 600$$

Write $66\frac{2}{3}\%$ as a fraction.

Figure 2-13

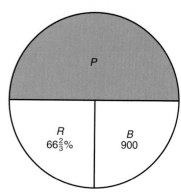

The quantity of employees enrolled in the plan is 600.

4 Use the percentage formula to find the base.

Using the percentage formula form $B = \dfrac{P}{R}$, you can find the base if the percentage and rate are known.

? HOW TO Use the Percentage Formula to Find the Base

1. Write the formula $B = \dfrac{P}{R}$.

2. Replace *P* and *R* by the known numbers for percentage (*P*) and rate (*R*).

3. Write *R* as a decimal or fraction.

4. Divide *P* by *R*.

EXAMPLE Find the base if the percentage is 42 and the rate is $33\frac{1}{3}\%$.

$$B = \frac{P}{R}$$
The base, or entire quantity, is unknown.

$$B = \frac{42}{33\frac{1}{3}\%}$$
The percentage (*P*) is 42; the rate is $33\frac{1}{3}\%$ (Figure 2-14). Write $33\frac{1}{3}\%$ as a fraction.

$$B = \frac{42}{\frac{1}{3}}$$
Divide 42 by $\frac{1}{3}$.

$$B = 42 \div \frac{1}{3} = \frac{42}{1} \times \frac{3}{1} = 126$$

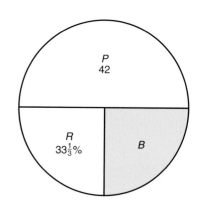

Figure 2-14

The base is 126.

Continuous Sequence Versus Noncontinuous Sequence

We can write the percent as a rounded decimal and divide using a calculator.

| AC | 1 | ÷ | 3 | = | ⟹ | 0.33333333 |

| AC | 42 | ÷ | .33333333 | = | ⟹ | 126.0000013 |

As one continuous sequence using the memory keys, enter

| AC | 1 | ÷ | 3 | = | M+ | CE/C | 42 | ÷ | MRC | = | ⟹ | 126.001 |

Note slight discrepancies due to rounding. However, the answer obtained by using a continuous sequence of steps is more accurate.

EXAMPLE Stan sets aside 25% of his weekly income for rent. If he sets aside $50 each week, what is his weekly income?

Identify the terms: The rate is the number written as a percent. The percentage is given, $50; it is a portion of his weekly income, the unknown base.

$$B = \frac{P}{R}$$ **The base is the weekly income and the unknown to be found.**

$$B = \frac{\$50}{25\%}$$ **The percentage is $50; the rate is 25% (Figure 2-15).**

$$B = \frac{\$50}{0.25} = \$200$$ **Write 25% as a decimal.**

Figure 2-15

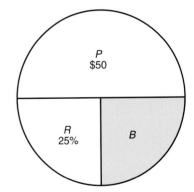

Stan's weekly income is $200.

EXAMPLE Thirty percent of Hill Community College graduates continued their education at four-year colleges. If 60 people continued their education, how many Hill Community College graduates were there?

Identify the terms: You might not recognize the rate immediately because it is written in words, thirty percent. The base is the total number of graduates, so 60 is the percentage of the graduates who continued their education.

$$B = \frac{P}{R}$$ The base is the total number of graduates and the unknown to be found.

$$B = \frac{60}{30\%}$$ The percentage is 60; the rate is 30% (Figure 2-16).

$$B = \frac{60}{0.3} = 200$$ Write 30% as a decimal.

Figure 2-16

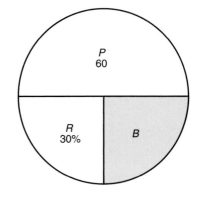

There were 200 Hill Community College graduates.

5 Use the percentage formula to find the rate.

Like solving for the base, to solve for the rate we use an alternate form of the percentage formula:

$$R = \frac{P}{B}$$

HOW TO Use the Percentage Formula to Find the Rate

1. Write the formula $R = \frac{P}{B}$.

2. Replace P and B by the known values for percentage (P) and base (B).

3. Write the fraction $\frac{P}{B}$ as a percent: multiply by 100%.

EXAMPLE Find the rate if the percentage is 20 and the base is 200.

$$R = \frac{P}{B}$$ The rate, or percent, is the unknown to find.

$$R = \frac{20}{200}$$ The percentage is 20 and the base is 200 (Figure 2-17).

$$R = \frac{\overset{10}{\cancel{20}}}{\underset{\cancel{2}}{\cancel{200}}} \times \frac{\overset{1}{\cancel{100\%}}}{1} = 10\%$$ Write $\frac{20}{200}$ as a percent.

Figure 2-17

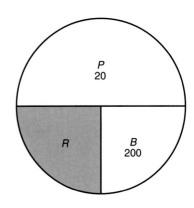

The rate is 10%.

EXAMPLE If 20 cars were sold from a lot that had 50 cars, what percent of the cars were sold?

When you identify the terms in a percent problem, look for the rate, or the number written as a percent, first. In this problem, you can see that the rate is unknown. The base is the entire lot of cars, 50; the percentage, 20, is a portion of the base.

$R = \dfrac{P}{B}$ **The rate is the unknown to find.**

$R = \dfrac{20}{50}$ **The percentage is 20; the base is 50 (Figure 2-18).**

$R = \dfrac{20}{\underset{1}{50}} \times \dfrac{\overset{2}{100\%}}{1} = \boxed{40\%}$ **Write $\frac{20}{50}$ as a percent.**

Figure 2-18

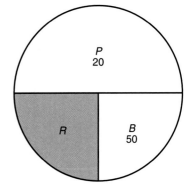

Of the cars on the lot, 40% were sold.

Many students mistakenly think that the part can never be larger than the base. The part (percentage) is smaller than the base only when the rate is less than 100%. The part is larger than the base when the percent is larger than 100%.

EXAMPLE 48 is what percent of 24?

$R = \dfrac{P}{B}$ **The rate is known.**

$R = \dfrac{48}{24}$ **The percentage is 48. The base is 24.**

$$R = 2$$ Rate written as a whole number.

$$R = 200\%$$ Rate written as a percent.

 TIP! Identify the Rate, Base, and Percentage

The following descriptions may help you recognize the rate, base, or percentage more quickly:

Rate is usually written as a percent, but it may be a decimal or fraction.

Base is the total amount, original amount, entire amount, and so on; it is the amount that the *percentage* is a portion of.

Percentage is called part, partial amount, portion, amount of increase or decrease, amount of change, and so on; it is a portion of the *base*.

6 Use the percentage proportion to solve problems.

If you would like to use one formula for solving problems involving percents, no matter which element (rate, base, or percentage) is missing, you may prefer using the percentage proportion. The **percentage proportion** is a variation of the percentage formula that is written in the form of a proportion. Besides being versatile, the percentage proportion automatically deals with the conversion of the rate to a decimal or fraction equivalent when the rate is given, or the conversion of a fraction or decimal to a percent when the rate is found.

Percentage proportion:

$$\frac{R}{100} = \frac{P}{B}$$ where R = rate or percent, P = percentage or part, and B = base or total.

Another advantage of the percentage proportion is that one of the two calculations will involve either multiplying or dividing by 100. This step can be done mentally.

 HOW TO Solve Percentage Problems with the Percentage Proportion

1. Identify the rate, base, and percentage.
2. Place known values into the percentage proportion.
3. Place a letter in the proportion for the unknown value.
4. Multiply the cross product with two numbers.
5. Divide by the number in the other cross product.

If the rate is being found, write the rate found in step 4 with a percent symbol.

EXAMPLE 20% of what number is 45?

Rate = 20%   Base is missing.   Percentage = 45

$$\frac{20}{100} = \frac{45}{B}$$ **Place known values into the proportion.**

$$100 \times 45 = 4{,}500$$ **Multiply the cross product with two numbers mentally.**

$$4{,}500 \div 20 = 225$$ **Divide by the number in the other cross product.**

The base or missing number is 225.

EXAMPLE 325% of 86 is what number?

| Rate = 325% | Base = 86 | Percentage is missing . |

$$\frac{325}{100} = \frac{P}{86}$$

Place known values into the proportion.

$$325 \times 86 = 27{,}950$$

Multiply the cross product with two numbers.

$$27{,}950 \div 100 = \boxed{279.5}$$

Divide by the number in other the cross product mentally.

The percentage or missing number is 279.5.

EXAMPLE What percent is 5 out of 45?

| Rate is missing. | Base = 45 | Percentage = 5 |

$$\frac{R}{100} = \frac{5}{45}$$

Place known values into the proportion.

$$100 \times 5 = 500$$

Multiply the cross product with two numbers mentally.

$$500 \div 45 = \boxed{11.111111}$$

Divide by the number in the other cross product.

The rate is 11.11% (rounded).

To solve for percents that are less than 1% or greater than 100%, we follow the same procedures and cautions as with other percents. However, we can use some time-savers to make our work easier and faster.

It is always advisable to anticipate the approximate size of an answer before you make any calculations. This approximation helps you discover many careless mistakes, especially when you are using your calculator. For example, 1% of any number can be found by making mental calculations.

$$1\% \text{ of } 175 \text{ is} \qquad \frac{1}{100} = \frac{P}{175}$$

$$175 = 100 \times P$$

$$\frac{175}{100} = P$$

$$1.75 = P$$

 TIP! Mentally Finding 1% of a Number

To find 1% of a number, divide the number by 100 or move the decimal two places to the left.

Because 1% of a number can be found mentally, when we work with a percent that is less than 1%, we first find 1% of the number. The answer we seek must be less than 1% of the number. This estimating procedure is very useful in checking the decimal placement. For instance, let's find $\frac{1}{4}$% of 875:

$\frac{1}{4}$% means $\frac{1}{4}$ of 1%

1% of 875 is 8.75

$\frac{1}{4}$% of 875 is $\frac{1}{4}$ of 8.75 or about 2

Let's use this estimate to check our work in the following example.

EXAMPLE $\frac{1}{4}$% of 875 is what number?

$\frac{1}{4}$% and 0.25% are equivalent. Either can be used to solve this problem. We are given the rate and the base, so we need to find the percentage.

Option 1

$$\frac{\frac{1}{4}}{100} = \frac{\boxed{P}}{875}$$

$$\frac{1}{4} \times 875 = 100 \times P$$

$$\frac{875}{4} = 100 \times P$$

$$\frac{\frac{875}{4}}{100} = P$$

$$\frac{875}{4} \div 100 = P$$

$$\frac{\cancel{875}}{4} \times \frac{1}{\cancel{100}} = P$$

$$\frac{35}{16} = P$$

$$\boxed{2\frac{3}{16}} = P$$

Option 2

$$\frac{0.25}{100} = \frac{\boxed{P}}{875}$$

$$0.25 \times 875 = 100 \times P$$

$$218.75 = 100 \times P$$

$$\frac{218.75}{100} = P$$

$$\boxed{2.1875} = P$$

$\frac{1}{4}$**% of 875 is** $2\frac{3}{16}$**, or 2.1875.** Use your calculator to verify that $\frac{3}{16} = 0.1875$ ($3 \div 16 = 0.1875$).

Recall that 100% of a number is 1 times the number, or the number itself. When working with percents that are larger than 100%, we can also roughly estimate the answer.

For instance, 325% of 86 is more than three times 86. 100% of 86 = 86. Thus, 325% of 86 must be more than three times 86, or more than 258. Thus, our estimate is more than 258.

SELF-CHECK 2.2

 Write the decimal as a percent.

1. 0.39　　　**2.** 0.693　　　**3.** 0.75　　　　**4.** 0.2　　　　**5.** 2.92　　　**6.** 0.0007

Write the fraction as a percent

7. $\frac{39}{100}$　　**8.** $\frac{3}{4}$　　**9.** $3\frac{2}{5}$　　**10.** $5\frac{1}{4}$　　**11.** $\frac{9}{4}$　　**12.** $\frac{7}{5}$　　**13.** $\frac{2}{300}$

2 *Write the percent as a decimal.*

14. $15\frac{1}{2}$%　　**15.** $\frac{1}{8}$%　　**16.** 45%　　　**17.** 150%　　　**18.** $125\frac{1}{3}$%　　**19.** $\frac{3}{7}$%

Write the percent as a fraction.

20. 45%　　　**21.** 60%　　　**22.** 250%　　　**23.** 180%　　　**24.** $\frac{3}{4}$%　　　**25.** $33\frac{1}{3}$%

3 *Use the percentage formula or one of its forms.*

26. Find P if $R = 25\%$ and $B = 300$.   **27.** Find 40% of 160.   **28.** What number is $33\frac{1}{3}\%$ of 150?

29. What number is 154% of 30?

30. At the Evans Formal Wear department store, all suits are reduced 20% from the retail price. If Charles Stewart purchased a suit that originally retailed for $258.30, how much did he save?

31. Joe Passarelli earns $8.67 per hour working for Dracken International. If Joe earns a merit raise of 12%, how much will he earn per hour?

32. An ice cream truck began its daily route with 95 gallons of ice cream. The truck driver sold 78% of the ice cream. How many gallons of ice cream were sold?

 4

33. Find B if $P = 36$ and $R = 66\frac{2}{3}\%$

34. Jenny sold 80% of the tie-dyed T-shirts she took to the Green Valley Music Festival. If she sold 42 shirts, how many shirts did she take?

35. A stockholder sold her shares and made a profit of $1,466. If this is a profit of 23%, how much were the shares worth when she originally purchased them?

36. The Drammelonnie Department Store sold 30% of its shirts in stock. If the department store sold 267 shirts, how many shirts did the store have in stock?

 5

37. Find R if $P = 70$ and $B = 280$.

38. Ali gave correct answers to 23 of the 25 questions on the driving test. What percent of the questions did he get correct?

39. A soccer stadium in Manchester, England, has a capacity of 78,753 seats. If 67,388 seats were filled, what percent of the stadium seats were vacant? Round to the nearest hundredth of a percent.

40. Holly Hobbs purchased a magazine at the Atlanta airport for $2.99. The tax on the purchase was $0.18. What is the tax rate at the Atlanta airport?

 6 *Use the percentage proportion to find the missing value. Round to hundredths if necessary.*

41. 40% of 30 is what number?

42. 52% of 17.8 is what number?

43. 30% of what number is 21?

44. 17.5% of what number is 18?

45. What percent of 16 is 4?

46. What percent of 50 is 30?

47. 172% of 50 is what number?

48. 0.8% of 50 is what number?

49. What percent of 15.2 is 12.7?

50. What percent of 73 is 120?

51. 0.28% of what number is 12?

52. 1.5% of what number is 20?

53. Debbie Beckham purchased miscellaneous items at Walmart in Atlanta. The items subtotaled $52.13. The receipt showed $1.51 for tax. What is the tax rate? Round to the nearest tenth percent.

54. A receipt from WalMart in Memphis showed $1.57 tax on a subtotal of $53.64. What is the tax rate? Round to the nearest tenth percent.

Around The Business World

2000 Census Bureau Earnings Report

Each September the US Census Bureau issues a report on U.S. personal income during the previous calendar year. The report issued in September 2000 indicated that the 1999 median income was the highest ever recorded for African American, Hispanic, and Caucasian households. The 1999 median income level for all households increased, in real terms, by 2.7 percent to $40,816. That means half of households had incomes above $40,816 and half had incomes below $40,816. The real median household income did not decline for any state in the United States and increased significantly for 14 states when based on comparisons of two-year average medians. Median earnings for men who worked fulltime, year-round increased for the third straight year in a row. An increase of 1.0 percent over 1998 was realized in 1999. The annual median earnings for women who worked full-time, year-round, in 1999 was $26,300, or 72% of comparable earnings for men. The female-to-male earnings ratio dropped from 0.73 in 1998 and from a record high of 0.74 in 1996.

A decrease in both the number of poor and the percent on poverty was reported for every racial and ethnic group, for children, and for the elderly. The number of poor people declined by 2.2 million people over 1998. There were 34.5 million living in poverty in 1998. Additionally, the proportion of the nation's children living in poverty was the lowest since 1979. The poverty rates for the nation's major racial and ethnic groups reached or equaled all-time lows.

Exercises

Use the above information to answer the following.

1. Find the annual earnings for men in 1999.
2. Calculate the average hourly rate of pay for a woman working a 40-hour week, all 52 weeks of 1999. Round to the nearest cent. How does this compare to a comparable man's hourly rate of pay?
3. Rounded to the nearest dollar how much was the household income of an average family in 1998?
4. Explain why the median income for all households in 1999 is greater than the median income for either women or men.
5. What percent of states had a significant increase in real median household income based on two-year medians?
6. By what percent did the number of poor people decline in 1999? How many were living in poverty in 1999?
7. Examine your 2000 and 2001 IRS tax returns for your gross salary. Calculate your household's percent of increase or decrease from 2000 to 2001. Now calculate what your 2001 household income would have been using the census statistics for your category. Did your household do better or worse than others in your category?
8. Use your 2001 gross income to find the average amount each member of your household spent per day.

Answers

1. Annual earnings for men are $36,527.78.
2. The average U.S. woman made $12.64 per hour, while the average man made $17.56 per hour in 1999.
3. $39,743.
4. "Household" may include more than one income, but the income listed for women or men represents a single income.
5. $14 \div 50 = 0.28; 0.28 = 28\%$
6. $2.2 \div 34.5 = 0.064; 0.064 = 6.4\%; 34.5 - 2.2 = 32.3$ million

7. Answers will vary.

8. Answers will vary.

Source: U.S. Census Bureau Press Release, September 26, 2000. http://www.census.gov/Press-Release/www/2000/cb00-158.html

---

Section Outcome   Important Points with Examples

Section 2.1

Identify types of fractions. (page 58)

Write an improper fraction as a whole or mixed number.
1. Divide the numerator of the improper fraction by the denominator.
2. Examine the remainder.
   (a) If the remainder is 0, the quotient is a whole number: the improper fraction is equivalent to this whole number.
   (b) If the remainder is not 0, the quotient is not a whole number: the improper fraction is equivalent to a mixed number. The whole number part of this mixed number is the whole number part of the quotient. The fraction part of the mixed number has a numerator and a denominator: the numerator is the remainder; the denominator is the divisor (the denominator of the improper fraction).

$$\frac{150}{3} \rightarrow 3)\overline{150}^{\,50\ R0} \rightarrow 50 \qquad \frac{152}{3} \rightarrow 3)\overline{152}^{\,50\ R2} \rightarrow 50\frac{2}{3}$$

Write a mixed number as an improper fraction.
1. Find the numerator of the improper fraction.
   (a) Multiply the denominator of the mixed number by the whole-number part.
   (b) Add the product from step 1a to the numerator of the mixed number.
2. For the denominator of the improper fraction use the denominator of the mixed number.

$$5\frac{5}{8} = \frac{(8 \times 5) + 5}{8} = \frac{40 + 5}{8} = \frac{45}{8} \qquad \text{Whole number as improper fraction: } 7 = \frac{7}{1}$$

Change a fraction to an equivalent fraction. (page 62)

Reduce a fraction to lowest terms.
1. Inspect the numerator and denominator to find any whole number that they both can be evenly divided by.
2. Divide both the numerator and denominator by that number and inspect the new fraction to find any other number that the numerator and denominator can be divided by.
3. Repeat steps 1 and 2 until 1 is the only number that the numerator and denominator can be evenly divided by.

$$\frac{12}{36} = \frac{12}{36} \div \frac{2}{2} = \frac{6}{18} \quad \text{or} \quad \frac{12}{36} \div \frac{12}{12} = \frac{1}{3} \qquad \frac{100}{250} = \frac{100}{250} \div \frac{50}{50} = \frac{2}{5}$$

$$= \frac{6}{18} \div \frac{2}{2} = \frac{3}{9}$$

$$= \frac{3}{9} \div \frac{3}{3} = \frac{1}{3}$$

Find the greatest common divisor of two numbers.
1. Divide the larger number by the smaller.
2. Divide the divisor from step 1 by the remainder from step 1.
3. Divide the divisor from step 2 by the remainder from step 2.
4. Continue this division process until the remainder is 0. The current divisor is the greatest common divisor.

Find the GCD of 27 and 36.

$$
\begin{array}{cc}
1\text{ R}9 & 3 \\
27\overline{)36} & 9\overline{)27} \\
27 & 27 \\
\,9 &
\end{array}
$$

The GCD is 9.

Find the GCD of 28 and 15.

$$
\begin{array}{cccc}
1\text{ R}13 & 1\text{ R}2 & 6\text{ R}1 & 2 \\
15\overline{)28} & 13\overline{)15} & 2\overline{)13} & 1\overline{)2} \\
15 & 13 & 12 & 2 \\
13 & \,2 & \,1 &
\end{array}
$$

The GCD is 1.

Build a fraction to higher terms, given the new denominator.
1. Divide the *new* denominator by the *old* denominator.
2. Multiply both the old numerator and denominator by the quotient from step 1.

$$\frac{3}{4} = \frac{?}{20} \qquad\qquad \frac{2}{3} = \frac{?}{60}$$

$$
\begin{array}{cc}
5 & 20 \\
4\overline{)20} & 3\overline{)60}
\end{array}
$$

$$\frac{3}{4} = \frac{3}{4} \times \frac{5}{5} = \frac{15}{20} \qquad \frac{2}{3} \times \frac{20}{20} = \frac{40}{60}$$

3 Add and subtract fractions and mixed numbers. (page 64)

Add fractions with like (common) denominators.
1. Find the numerator of the sum: add the numerators of the addends.
2. Find the denominator of the sum: use the like denominator of the addends.
3. Reduce to lowest terms and/or write as a whole or mixed number.

$$\frac{3}{5} + \frac{7}{5} + \frac{5}{5} = \frac{15}{5} = 3 \qquad \frac{82}{109} + \frac{13}{109} = \frac{95}{109}$$

Find the least common denominator of two or more fractions.
1. Write the denominators in a row and divide each one by the smallest prime number that any of the numbers can be evenly divided by.
2. Write a new row of numbers using the quotients from step 1 and any numbers in the first row that cannot be evenly divided by the first prime number.
3. Continue this process until you have a row of 1s.
4. Multiply all the prime numbers you used to divide by. The product is the least common denominator.

Find the least common denominator of $\frac{5}{6}$, $\frac{6}{15}$, and $\frac{7}{20}$.

$$2)\overline{6 \quad 15 \quad 20}$$
$$2)\overline{3 \quad 15 \quad 10}$$
$$3)\overline{3 \quad 15 \quad 5}$$
$$5)\overline{1 \quad 5 \quad 5}$$
$$1 \quad 1 \quad 1$$

$$LCD = 2 \times 2 \times 3 \times 5 = 60$$

Find the least common denominator of $\frac{4}{5}$, $\frac{3}{10}$, and $\frac{1}{6}$.

$$2)\overline{5 \quad 10 \quad 6}$$
$$3)\overline{5 \quad 5 \quad 3}$$
$$5)\overline{5 \quad 5 \quad 1}$$
$$1 \quad 1 \quad 1$$

$$LCD = 2 \times 3 \times 5 = 30$$

Add fractions with different denominators.
1. Find the least common denominator.
2. Change each fraction to an equivalent fraction using the least common denominator.
3. Add the new fractions with like (common) denominators.
4. Reduce or write as a whole or mixed number.

Add $\frac{5}{6} + \frac{6}{15} + \frac{7}{20}$.

The LCD is 60.

$$\frac{5}{6} = \frac{5}{6} \times \frac{10}{10} = \frac{50}{60}$$

$$\frac{6}{15} = \frac{6}{15} \times \frac{4}{4} = \frac{24}{60}$$

$$\frac{7}{20} = \frac{7}{20} \times \frac{3}{3} = \frac{21}{60}$$

$$\frac{5}{6} + \frac{6}{15} + \frac{7}{20} = \frac{50}{60} + \frac{24}{60} + \frac{21}{60}$$

$$\frac{95}{60} = \frac{19}{12} = 1\frac{7}{12}$$

Add $\frac{4}{5} + \frac{3}{10} + \frac{1}{6}$.

The LCD is 30.

$$\frac{4}{5} \times \frac{6}{6} = \frac{24}{30}$$

$$\frac{3}{10} \times \frac{3}{3} = \frac{9}{30}$$

$$\frac{1}{6} \times \frac{5}{5} = \frac{5}{30}$$

$$\frac{4}{5} + \frac{3}{10} + \frac{1}{6} = \frac{24}{30} + \frac{9}{30} + \frac{5}{30} = \frac{38}{30}$$

$$= \frac{19}{15} = 1\frac{4}{15}$$

Subtract fractions with like denominators.
1. Find the numerator of the difference: subtract the numerators of the fractions.
2. Find the denominator of the difference: use the like denominator.
3. Reduce to lowest terms and/or write as a whole or mixed number.

Subtract fractions with different denominators.
1. Find the least common denominator.
2. Change each fraction to an equivalent fraction using the least common denominator.

3. Subtract the new fractions with like denominators.
4. Reduce to lowest terms.

$$\frac{10}{81} - \frac{7}{81} = \frac{3}{81} = \frac{1}{27} \qquad \frac{7}{8} - \frac{1}{3} = \frac{21}{24} - \frac{8}{24} = \frac{13}{24}$$

Subtract mixed numbers.
1. If the fractions have different denominators, find the LCD and change the fractions to equivalent fractions using the LCD.
2. If necessary, borrow (subtract) 1 from the whole number in the minuend and add 1 (in the form of LCD/LCD) to the fraction in the minuend.
3. Subtract the fractions and the whole numbers.
4. Reduce to lowest terms.

$$
\begin{array}{cccc}
24\frac{1}{2} = & 24\frac{2}{4} = & 23\frac{6}{4} & \qquad 53 = 53\frac{0}{5} = 52\frac{5}{5} \\
-11\frac{3}{4} = & -11\frac{3}{4} = & -11\frac{3}{4} & \qquad -37\frac{4}{5} = 37\frac{4}{5} = 37\frac{4}{5} \\
& & 12\frac{3}{4} & \qquad\qquad\qquad 15\frac{1}{5}
\end{array}
$$

4   Multiply and divide fractions and mixed numbers. (page 69)

Multiply fractions.
1. Find the numerator of the product: multiply the numerators of the fractions.
2. Find the denominator of the product: multiply the denominators of the fractions.
3. Reduce to lowest terms.

$$\frac{3}{2} \times \frac{12}{17} = \frac{36}{34} = 1\frac{2}{34} = 1\frac{1}{17} \qquad \frac{\overset{1}{7}}{\underset{3}{9}} \times \frac{\overset{5}{15}}{\underset{4}{28}} = \frac{5}{12}$$

or

$$\frac{3}{\underset{1}{2}} \times \frac{\overset{6}{12}}{17} = \frac{18}{17} = 1\frac{1}{17}$$

Multiply mixed numbers and whole numbers.
1. Write the mixed numbers and whole numbers as improper fractions.
2. Reduce numerators and denominators as appropriate.
3. Multiply the fractions.
4. Reduce to lowest terms and/or write as a whole or mixed number.

$$3\frac{3}{4} \times 3\frac{2}{3} = \frac{15}{4} \times \frac{11}{3} = \frac{165}{12} = \frac{55}{4} = 13\frac{3}{4} \qquad 5\frac{7}{8} \times 3 = \frac{47}{8} \times \frac{3}{1} = \frac{141}{8} = 17\frac{5}{8}$$

or

$$\frac{\overset{5}{15}}{4} \times \frac{11}{\underset{1}{3}} = \frac{55}{4} = 13\frac{3}{4}$$

Find the reciprocal of a number.
1. Write the number as a fraction.
2. Interchange the numerator and denominator.

$$6 = \frac{6}{1} \quad \text{The reciprocal of 6 is } \frac{1}{6}. \qquad 0.25 = \frac{1}{4} \quad \text{The reciprocal of 0.25 is 4.}$$

$$\text{The reciprocal of } \frac{2}{3} \text{ is } \frac{3}{2}. \quad 3.2 = 3\frac{2}{10} = 3\frac{1}{5} = \frac{16}{5} \quad \text{The reciprocal of 3.2 is } \frac{5}{16}.$$

$$1\frac{1}{2} = \frac{3}{2} \quad \text{The reciprocal of } 1\frac{1}{2} \text{ is } \frac{2}{3}.$$

Divide fractions or mixed numbers.
1. Write the numbers as fractions.
2. Find the reciprocal of the divisor.
3. Multiply the dividend by the reciprocal of the divisor.
4. Reduce to lowest terms and/or write as a whole or mixed number.

$$\frac{55}{68} \div \frac{11}{17} = \frac{\overset{5}{\cancel{55}}}{\underset{4}{\cancel{68}}} \times \frac{\overset{1}{\cancel{17}}}{\underset{1}{\cancel{11}}} = \frac{5}{4} = 1\frac{1}{4} \qquad 3\frac{1}{4} \div 1\frac{1}{2} = \frac{13}{4} \div \frac{3}{2}$$

$$= \frac{13}{\underset{2}{\cancel{4}}} \times \frac{\overset{1}{\cancel{2}}}{3} = \frac{13}{6} = 2\frac{1}{6}$$

5

Write a decimal as a fraction and write a fraction as a decimal. (page 74)

Write a decimal as a fraction.
1. Find the denominator: write 1 followed by as many zeros as there are places to the right of the decimal point.
2. Find the numerator: use the decimal without the decimal point.
3. Reduce to lowest terms and/or write as a whole or mixed number.

$$0.05 = \frac{5}{100} = \frac{1}{20} \qquad 0.584 = \frac{584}{1,000} = \frac{73}{125}$$

Write a fraction as a decimal.
1. Write the numerator as the dividend and the denominator as the divisor.
2. Divide the numerator by the denominator, taking the division out as many decimal places as necessary or desirable.

$$\frac{5}{8} = 8\overline{)5.000} = 0.625 \qquad \frac{57}{76} = 76\overline{)57.00} = 0.75$$

$$
\begin{array}{r}
0.625 \\
8\overline{)5.000} \\
\underline{4\,8} \\
20 \\
\underline{16} \\
40 \\
\underline{40}
\end{array}
\qquad
\begin{array}{r}
0.75 \\
76\overline{)57.00} \\
\underline{53\,2} \\
3\,80 \\
\underline{3\,80}
\end{array}
$$

Section 2.2

Write a number as its percent equivalent.
Multiply the number by 1 in the form of 100%.

1 Write a whole number, fraction, or decimal as a percent. (page 79)

$$6 = 6 \times 100\% = 600\% \qquad \frac{3}{5} = \frac{3}{5} \times \frac{\overset{20}{\cancel{100}}}{\underset{1}{1}}\% = 60\%$$

$$0.075 = 0.075 \times 100\% = 7.5\%$$

2 Write a percent as a whole number, fraction, or decimal. (page 80)

Write a percent as a number.
Divide by 1 in the form of 100%.

$$48\% = 48\% \div 100\% = 0.48 \qquad 20\% = 20\% \div 100\% = \frac{\overset{1}{\cancel{20}}}{\underset{5}{\cancel{100}}} = \frac{1}{5}$$

$$157\% = 157\% \div 100\% = 1.57 \qquad 33\frac{1}{3}\% = 33\frac{1}{3}\% \div 100\% = 0.33\frac{1}{3}$$

$$\text{or } 0.3\overline{3}$$

3 Use the percentage formula to find the percentage. (page 83)

Find the percentage.
1. Write the formula $P = R \times B$.
2. Replace R and B by the known numbers for rate (R) and base (B).
3. Write R as a decimal or fraction.
4. Multiply R by B.

Find P if $B = 20$ and $R = 15\%$.

$P = R \times B$

$P = 15\% \times 20 = 0.15 \times 20$

$P = 3$

Find P if $B = 81$ and $R = 33\frac{1}{3}\%$.

$P = R \times B$

$P = 33\frac{1}{3}\% \times 81 = \frac{1}{3} \times 81$

$P = \frac{81}{3} = 27$

4 Use the percentage formula to find the base. (page 86)

Find the base.
1. Write the formula $B = \frac{P}{R}$.
2. Replace P and R by the known numbers for percentage (P) and rate (R).
3. Write R as a decimal or fraction.
4. Divide P by R.

Find B if $P = 36$ and $R = 9\%$

$B = \frac{P}{R}$

$B = \frac{36}{9\%} = \frac{36}{0.09}$

$B = 400$

Find B if $P = 22$ and $R = 66\frac{2}{3}\%$

$B = \frac{P}{R}$

$B = \frac{22}{66\frac{2}{3}\%} = \frac{22}{\frac{2}{3}}$

$B = \frac{\overset{11}{\cancel{22}}}{1} \times \frac{3}{\underset{1}{\cancel{2}}} = 33$

Use the percentage formula to find the rate.
(page 88)

Find the rate.

1. Write the formula $R = \frac{P}{B}$.
2. Replace P and B by the known numbers for percentage (P) and base (B).
3. Write the fraction $\frac{P}{B}$ as a percent: multiply by 1 in the form of 100%.

Find R if $P = 4$ and $B = 5$

$$R = \frac{P}{B}$$

$$R = \frac{4}{5} = \frac{4}{\underset{1}{5}} \times \frac{\overset{20}{100}}{1}\%$$

$$R = 80\%$$

Find R if $P = 75$ and $B = 50$

$$R = \frac{P}{B}$$

$$R = \frac{75}{50} = \frac{75}{\underset{1}{50}} \times \frac{\overset{2}{100}}{1}\%$$

$$R = 150\%$$

Use the percentage proportion to solve problems.
(page 90)

Solve a percentage proportion.

1. Identify the rate, base, and percentage.
2. Place known values into the percentage proportion.
3. Place a letter in the proportion for the unknown value.
4. Multiply the cross product with two numbers.
5. Divide by the number in the other cross product. If the rate is being found, write the rate found in step 4 with a percent symbol.

Use the percentage proportion to solve: **48% of 57 is what number?**

$$\frac{48}{100} = \frac{N}{57}$$

$$48 \times 57 = 2736$$

$$2736 \div 100 = 27.36$$

$$N = 27.36$$

WORDS TO KNOW

denominator (p.58)
numerator (p. 58)
fraction line (p. 58)
proper fraction (p. 58)
improper fraction (p. 58)
mixed number (p. 59)
equivalent fractions (p. 62)
lowest terms (p. 62)

greatest common divisor
  (GCD)(p. 63)
least common denominator
  (LCD) (p. 64)
prime number (p. 65)
reciprocals (p. 72)
terminating decimal (p. 75)
nonterminating decimal (p.75)

repeating decimal (p. 75)
percent (p. 78)
mixed percents (p. 79)
base (p. 83)
percentage (p. 83)
portion (p. 83)
rate (p. 83)
percentage proportion (p. 90)

CHAPTER 2 CONCEPTS ANALYSIS

1. What two operations require a common denominator?

2. What steps must be followed to find the reciprocal of a mixed number? Give an example of a mixed number and its reciprocal.

3. What is the product of any number and its reciprocal? Give an example to illustrate your answer.

4. What operation requires the use of the reciprocal of a fraction? Write an example of this operation and perform the operation.

5. What operations must be used to solve an applied problem if all of the parts but one are given and the total of all the parts is given? Write an example.

6. What number can be written as any fraction that has the same numerator and denominator? Give an example of a fraction that equals the number.

7. Under what conditions are two fractions proportional? Give an example to illustrate your answer.

8. Explain the process for finding a missing part of a proportion problem by using one of the variations of the percentage formula.

9. Explain the process for using the proportion formula to find a missing part of a percentage problem.

10. Explain one instance when you have recently used percents to solve a problem (outside this classwork or homework).

CHAPTER 2 ASSIGNMENT EXERCISES

Section 2.1

1. Give five examples of fractions whose value is less than 1. What are these fractions called?

2. Give five examples of fractions whose value is greater than or equal to 1. What are these fractions called?

Write the improper fraction as a whole or mixed number.

3. $\dfrac{124}{6}$
4. $\dfrac{52}{15}$
5. $\dfrac{84}{12}$
6. $\dfrac{83}{4}$
7. $\dfrac{17}{2}$

8. $\dfrac{77}{11}$
9. $\dfrac{62}{5}$
10. $\dfrac{19}{10}$
11. $\dfrac{372}{25}$
12. $\dfrac{904}{9}$

Write the mixed number as an improper fraction.

13. $5\dfrac{5}{6}$
14. $7\dfrac{3}{8}$
15. $4\dfrac{1}{3}$
16. $10\dfrac{1}{5}$
17. $33\dfrac{1}{3}$

Reduce to lowest terms. Try to use the greatest common divisor.

18. $\dfrac{18}{20}$
19. $\dfrac{15}{18}$
20. $\dfrac{20}{30}$
21. $\dfrac{21}{24}$
22. $\dfrac{30}{48}$

23. $\dfrac{21}{56}$
24. $\dfrac{27}{36}$
25. $\dfrac{48}{64}$
26. $\dfrac{16}{48}$
27. $\dfrac{24}{60}$

28. $\dfrac{18}{63}$
29. $\dfrac{56}{72}$
30. $\dfrac{54}{84}$
31. $\dfrac{120}{144}$
32. $\dfrac{78}{104}$

33. $\dfrac{75}{125}$
34. $\dfrac{78}{96}$
35. $\dfrac{32}{48}$
36. $\dfrac{220}{242}$
37. $\dfrac{65}{120}$
38. $\dfrac{30}{140}$

Rewrite as a fraction with the indicated denominator.

39. $\dfrac{3}{4} = \dfrac{}{72}$ **40.** $\dfrac{7}{9} = \dfrac{}{81}$ **41.** $\dfrac{5}{6} = \dfrac{}{12}$ **42.** $\dfrac{5}{8} = \dfrac{}{32}$ **43.** $\dfrac{2}{3} = \dfrac{}{15}$

44. $\dfrac{4}{7} = \dfrac{}{49}$ **45.** $\dfrac{9}{11} = \dfrac{}{77}$ **46.** $\dfrac{3}{14} = \dfrac{}{56}$ **47.** $\dfrac{9}{11} = \dfrac{}{143}$ **48.** $\dfrac{4}{15} = \dfrac{}{105}$

49. A company employed 105 people. If 15 of the employees left the company in a three-month period, what fractional part of the employees left?

50. If 8 students in a class of 30 earned grades of A, what fractional part of the class earned As?

Find the least common denominator for these fractions.

51. $\dfrac{1}{4}, \dfrac{1}{12}, \dfrac{11}{16}$ **52.** $\dfrac{7}{8}, \dfrac{1}{20}, \dfrac{13}{16}$ **53.** $\dfrac{2}{1}, \dfrac{1}{5}, \dfrac{1}{10}, \dfrac{5}{6}$

54. $\dfrac{1}{8}, \dfrac{5}{9}, \dfrac{7}{12}, \dfrac{9}{24}$ **55.** $\dfrac{5}{56}, \dfrac{7}{24}, \dfrac{7}{12}, \dfrac{5}{42}$ **56.** $\dfrac{5}{12}, \dfrac{3}{15}$

Add.

57. $\dfrac{3}{5} + \dfrac{4}{5}$ **58.** $\dfrac{7}{8} + \dfrac{1}{8}$ **59.** $\dfrac{2}{5} + \dfrac{2}{3}$ **60.** $\dfrac{3}{4} + \dfrac{7}{8}$ **61.** $\dfrac{5}{6} + \dfrac{17}{18}$

62. $\dfrac{1}{4} + \dfrac{11}{12} + \dfrac{7}{16}$ **63.** $\dfrac{1}{6} + \dfrac{7}{8} + \dfrac{5}{12}$ **64.** $\dfrac{7}{9} + \dfrac{13}{16} + \dfrac{2}{3}$ **65.** $\dfrac{5}{6} + \dfrac{1}{12} + \dfrac{4}{9}$

66. $\dfrac{3}{4} + \dfrac{7}{15} + \dfrac{5}{6} + \dfrac{3}{5} + \dfrac{3}{20}$ **67.** $7\dfrac{1}{2} + 4\dfrac{3}{8}$ **68.** $11\dfrac{5}{6} + 8\dfrac{2}{3}$

69. $15\dfrac{1}{2} + 9\dfrac{3}{4}$ **70.** $7\dfrac{2}{3} + 3\dfrac{5}{6} + 4\dfrac{1}{2}$ **71.** $8\dfrac{7}{10} + 9\dfrac{1}{5} + 5\dfrac{1}{2}$ **72.** $3\dfrac{1}{4} + 2\dfrac{1}{3} + 3\dfrac{5}{6}$

73 $\begin{array}{r} 73\dfrac{1}{2} \\ +18\dfrac{1}{3} \\ \hline \end{array}$ **74.** $\begin{array}{r} 36\dfrac{2}{3} \\ +28\dfrac{1}{2} \\ \hline \end{array}$ **75.** $\begin{array}{r} 96\dfrac{5}{6} \\ +57\dfrac{4}{7} \\ \hline \end{array}$

76. $20\frac{7}{12}$

$27\frac{5}{8}$

$+ 7\frac{5}{6}$

---

77. $54\frac{1}{2}$

$37\frac{2}{3}$

$+15\frac{5}{6}$

---

78 $11\frac{2}{3}$

$68\frac{1}{5}$

$+57\frac{5}{8}$

---

79. Two types of fabric are needed for curtains. The lining requires $12\frac{3}{8}$ yards and the curtain fabric needed is $16\frac{5}{8}$ yards. How many yards of fabric are needed?

80. Three pieces of lumber measure $5\frac{3}{8}$ feet, $7\frac{1}{2}$ feet, and $9\frac{3}{4}$ feet. What is the total length of the lumber?

Subtract. Borrow when necessary. Reduce the difference to lowest terms.

81. $\frac{5}{12} - \frac{1}{4}$

82. $\frac{2}{3} - \frac{1}{6}$

83. $\frac{1}{2} - \frac{1}{3}$

84. $\frac{6}{7} - \frac{5}{14}$

85. $\frac{13}{16} - \frac{2}{3}$

86. $\frac{11}{15} - \frac{1}{6}$

87. $7\frac{4}{5} - 4\frac{1}{2}$

88. $4\frac{1}{2} - 3\frac{6}{7}$

89. $5 - 3\frac{2}{5}$

90. $12 - 4\frac{1}{8}$

91. $4\frac{5}{6} - 3\frac{1}{3}$

92. $8\frac{2}{3} - 2\frac{1}{2}$

93. $4\frac{5}{12} - 1\frac{1}{3}$

94. $3\frac{1}{2} - 1\frac{1}{4}$

95. $7\frac{5}{9}$

$-5\frac{1}{2}$

---

96. $564\frac{5}{9}$

$-317\frac{5}{6}$

---

97. $232\frac{2}{15}$

$-189\frac{2}{5}$

---

98. $83\frac{1}{9}$

$-46\frac{1}{3}$

---

99. $9\frac{3}{7}$

$-7\frac{3}{5}$

---

100. $106\frac{1}{4}$

$- 37\frac{9}{24}$

---

101. $38\frac{1}{2}$

$-26\frac{1}{3}$

---

102. $182\frac{9}{12}$

$- 90\frac{5}{6}$

---

103. A board $3\frac{5}{8}$ feet long must be sawed from a 6-foot board. How long is the remaining piece?

104. George Mackie worked the following hours during a week: $7\frac{3}{4}$, $5\frac{1}{2}$, $6\frac{1}{4}$, $9\frac{1}{4}$, and $8\frac{3}{4}$. Maxine Ford worked 40 hours. Who worked the most hours? How many more?

Multiply and reduce to lowest terms, or write as whole or mixed numbers.

105. $\frac{1}{4} \times \frac{7}{8}$

106. $\frac{9}{10} \times \frac{3}{4}$

107. $\frac{5}{6} \times \frac{1}{3}$

108. $\frac{1}{8} \times \frac{7}{8}$

109. $\dfrac{3}{5} \times \dfrac{3}{4}$ **110.** $\dfrac{1}{2} \times \dfrac{1}{2}$ **111.** $5 \times \dfrac{2}{3}$ **112.** $\dfrac{3}{7} \times 8$

113. $\dfrac{7}{8} \times 3$ **114.** $6 \times \dfrac{4}{5}$ **115.** $\dfrac{5}{6} \times \dfrac{2}{3}$ **116.** $\dfrac{3}{4} \times \dfrac{4}{5}$

117. $\dfrac{3}{4} \times \dfrac{8}{9} \times \dfrac{7}{12}$ **118.** $\dfrac{2}{5} \times \dfrac{5}{6} \times \dfrac{7}{8}$ **119.** $\dfrac{9}{10} \times \dfrac{8}{5} \times \dfrac{7}{15}$

120. $\dfrac{9}{10} \times \dfrac{2}{5} \times \dfrac{5}{9} \times \dfrac{3}{7}$ **121.** $\dfrac{5}{9} \times \dfrac{8}{21} \times \dfrac{9}{10} \times \dfrac{6}{7}$ **122.** $\dfrac{15}{25} \times \dfrac{13}{20} \times \dfrac{14}{30}$

123. $\dfrac{1}{8} \times \dfrac{3}{5} \times \dfrac{40}{41}$ **124.** $3\dfrac{1}{3} \times 4\dfrac{1}{4}$ **125.** $4\dfrac{1}{5} \times 8\dfrac{5}{6}$

126. $6\dfrac{2}{9} \times 4\dfrac{1}{2}$ **127.** $7\dfrac{5}{8} \times 9\dfrac{5}{6}$ **128.** $8\dfrac{2}{5} \times 9\dfrac{4}{9}$

129. $9\dfrac{1}{6} \times 10\dfrac{2}{7}$ **130.** $10\dfrac{1}{2} \times 1\dfrac{5}{7}$

131. Katrina Kimble received $\dfrac{3}{4}$ of a regular day's pay as a tribute to her birthday. If she regularly earns $64 a day, how much birthday pay did she receive?

132. A recipe for pecan pralines calls for the following:

$\dfrac{3}{4}$ cup brown sugar $\dfrac{1}{4}$ teaspoon vanilla

$\dfrac{3}{4}$ cup white sugar   2 tablespoons margarine

$\dfrac{1}{2}$ cup evaporated milk   1 cup pecans

Brenda Lewis is making treats for her second-grade class, so she must make $2\dfrac{1}{2}$ times as many pralines as this recipe yields. How much of each ingredient is needed?

133. The price of computers has fallen by $\dfrac{2}{5}$. If the original price of a computer was $10,275, by how much has the price fallen?

134. After a family reunion, $10\dfrac{2}{3}$ cakes were left. If Shirley McCool took $\dfrac{3}{8}$ of these cakes, how many did she take?

Find the reciprocal of the numbers.

135. $\dfrac{5}{8}$

136. $\dfrac{2}{3}$

137. $\dfrac{1}{4}$

138. 8

139. $3\dfrac{1}{4}$

140. $2\dfrac{3}{8}$

141. $1\dfrac{3}{5}$

142. $2\dfrac{5}{9}$

Divide and reduce to lowest terms.

143. $\dfrac{3}{4} \div \dfrac{1}{4}$

144. $\dfrac{5}{6} \div \dfrac{1}{8}$

145. $\dfrac{15}{36} \div \dfrac{7}{8}$

146. $\dfrac{3}{8} \div 3$

147. $\dfrac{3}{10} \div 6$

148. $15 \div \dfrac{3}{4}$

149. $7\dfrac{1}{2} \div 2$

150. $7\dfrac{1}{2} \div 1\dfrac{2}{3}$

151. $3\dfrac{1}{7} \div 5\dfrac{1}{2}$

152. $6\dfrac{4}{5} \div 8\dfrac{5}{6}$

153. A board 244 inches long is cut into pieces that are each $7\dfrac{5}{8}$ inches long. How many pieces can be cut?

154. A stack of $1\dfrac{5}{8}$-inch plywood measures 91 inches. How many pieces of plywood are in the stack?

155. If city sales tax is $5\dfrac{1}{2}\%$ and state sales tax is $2\dfrac{1}{4}\%$, what is the total sales tax rate on purchases made in the city?

156. Sue Parsons has three lengths of $\dfrac{3}{4}$-inch PVC pipe: $1\dfrac{1}{5}$ feet, $2\dfrac{3}{4}$ feet, and $1\dfrac{1}{2}$ feet. What is the total length of pipe?

157. Bill New placed a piece of $\dfrac{5}{8}$-inch plywood and a piece of $\dfrac{3}{4}$-inch plywood on top of one another to create a spacer between two two-by-fours, but the spacer was $\dfrac{1}{8}$ inch too thick. How thick should the spacer be?

158. Brienne Smith must trim $2\dfrac{3}{16}$ feet from a board eight feet long. How long will the board be after it is cut?

159. Certain financial aid students must pass $\dfrac{2}{3}$ of their courses each term in order to continue their aid. If a student is taking 18 hours, how many hours must be passed?

160. Wallboard measuring $\dfrac{5}{8}$ inch thick is in a stack $62\dfrac{1}{2}$ inches high. How many sheets of wallboard are in the stack?

161. Sol's Hardware and Appliance Store is selling electric clothes dryers for $\dfrac{1}{3}$ off the regular price of $288. What is the sales price of the dryer?

162. A recipe for French toast that serves six calls for $\dfrac{3}{4}$ cup granulated sugar, 1 cup evaporated milk, $\dfrac{1}{3}$ teaspoon vanilla, and 12 thick slices of French bread. How much of each ingredient is needed to serve only three?

163. Chair-rail molding 144 inches long must be cut into pieces of $35\frac{1}{2}$ inches each. How many pieces can be cut from the molding?

164. A farmer wants to stock several ponds with 500 catfish fingerlings. If the farmer expects to lose $\frac{1}{6}$ of the fingerlings, would ordering 560 be enough to expect 500 to survive?

Section 2.2

Write the decimal as a percent.

165. 0.23	**166.** 0.675	**167.** 0.82	**168.** 2.63	**169.** 0.03
170. 0.007	**171.** 0.34	**172.** 3.741	**173.** 0.601	**174.** 0.0004
175. 1	**176.** 0.6	**177.** 3	**178.** 0.242	**179.** 0.37
180. 0.811	**181.** 0.2	**182.** 2.54	**183.** 4	**184.** 0.03

Write the fraction or mixed number as a percent. Round to the nearest hundredth percent if necessary.

185. $\dfrac{17}{100}$ **186.** $\dfrac{99}{100}$ **187.** $\dfrac{6}{100}$ **188.** $\dfrac{20}{100}$ **189.** $\dfrac{52}{100}$

190. $\dfrac{13}{20}$ **191.** $\dfrac{1}{10}$ **192.** $3\dfrac{2}{5}$ **193.** $\dfrac{5}{4}$ **194.** $7\dfrac{1}{2}$

195. $\dfrac{39}{100}$ **196.** $\dfrac{2}{5}$ **197.** $\dfrac{1}{3}$ **198.** $1\dfrac{5}{8}$ **199.** $\dfrac{3}{100}$

200. $\dfrac{1}{12}$

Write the percent as a decimal.

201. 98%	**202.** 84.6%	**203.** 256%	**204.** 52%	**205.** 91.7%
206. 3%	**207.** 0.5%	**208.** 0.02%	**209.** 6%	**210.** 9%
211. 36%	**212.** 274%	**213.** 6%	**214.** 30%	

Write the percent as a whole number, mixed number, or fraction, reduced to lowest terms.

215. 10%	**216.** 20%	**217.** 6%	**218.** 170%	**219.** 89%
220. 361%	**221.** 45%	**222.** 25%	**223.** 225%	**224.** $12\frac{1}{2}\%$

	Percent	Fraction	Decimal		Percent	Fraction	Decimal
225.	$33\frac{1}{3}$	_____	_____	**226.**	_____	$\frac{2}{5}$	_____
227.	_____	_____	0.125	**228.**	50%	_____	_____
229.	_____	_____	0.8	**230.**	$87\frac{1}{2}\%$	_____	_____

Find P, R, or B using the percentage formula or one of its forms.

231. $B = 300, R = 27\%$ **232.** $B = \$1,900, R = 106\%$ **233.** $B = 1,000, R = 2\frac{1}{2}\%$

234. $B = \$500, R = 7.25\%$ **235.** $P = 25, B = 100$ **236.** $P = 170, B = 85$

237. $P = 2, B = 6$ **238.** $P = \$600, R = 5\%$ **239.** $P = 26, R = 6\frac{1}{2}\%$

240. $P = \$15.50, R = 7.75\%$

Round decimals to the nearest hundredth and percents to the nearest whole number percent.

241. $B = 36, R = 42\%$ **242.** $P = 68, B = 85$ **243.** $P = \$835, R = 3.2\%$

244. $R = 72\%, B = 16$ **245.** $R = 136\%, B = 834$ **246.** $P = 397, B = 200$

247. $P = 52, R = 17\%$ **248.** $P = 512, B = 128$ **249.** $P = 125, B = 50$

250. $B = 892, R = 63\%$ **251.** $B = 643, R = 8\%$ **252.** $P = 803, B = 4,015$

Use the percentage formula or one of its forms.

253. Find 30% of 80.   **254.** Find 150% of 20.

255. 30% of 27 equals what number?   **256.** What number is 70% of 300?

257. 90% of what number is 27?   **258.** 82% of what number is 94.3?

259. $33\frac{1}{3}\%$ of what number is 60?   **260.** 112 is 14% of what number?

261. 97 is what percent of 100?   **262.** What percent of 54 is 36?

263. 51.52 is what percent of 2,576?   **264.** What percent of 180 is 60?

265. 42 is what percent of 21?   **266.** 27 is what percent of 9?

Use the percentage proportion to solve. Round to hundredths.

267. 58% of 76 is what number?   **268.** 130% of 51 is what number?

269. $\frac{1}{4}\%$ of 164 is what number?   **270.** What percent of 13 is 409?

271. 37% of what number is 86?   **272.** 0.5% of what number is 76?

273. What percent of 196 is 12?   **274.** What percent of 91 is 91?

275. Jaime McMahan received a 7% pay increase. If he was earning $2,418 per month, what was the amount of the pay increase?

276. Ernestine Monahan draws $1,800 monthly retirement. On January 1, she received a 3% cost of living increase. How much was the increase?

277. Eighty percent of one store's customers paid with credit cards. Forty customers came in that day. How many customers paid for their purchases with credit cards?

278. If a picture frame costs $30 and the tax on the frame is 6% of the cost, how much is the tax on the picture frame?

279. Seventy percent of a town's population voted in an election. If 1,589 people voted, what is the population of the town?

280. Five percent of a batch of fuses were found to be faulty during an inspection. If 27 fuses were faulty, how many fuses were inspected?

281. Thirty-seven of 50 shareholders attended a meeting. What percent of the shareholders attended the meeting?

282. In Memphis the sales tax is $8\frac{1}{4}$%. How much tax is paid on a purchase of $20.60? (Round to the nearest cent.)

283. A business math student answered 60 questions correctly on a 75-question test. What percent of the questions were answered correctly?

284. A football stadium has a capacity of 53,983. If 47,892 fans attended a game, what percent of the seats were filled?

285. A large university campus has 197 restrooms. If 38 of these are designed to accommodate persons with disabilities, what percent can accommodate persons with disabilities?

286. The United Way expects to raise $63 million in its current drive. The chairperson projects that 60% of the funds will be raised in the first 12 weeks. How many dollars are expected to be raised in the first 12 weeks?

287. The financial officer for an accounting firm allows $3,400 for supplies in the annual budget. After three months, $898.32 has been spent on supplies. Is this figure within 25% of the annual budget?

288. An accountant who is currently earning $42,380 annually expects a 6.5% raise. What is the amount of the expected raise?

Challenge Problems

289. A room is $25\frac{1}{2}$ feet by $32\frac{3}{4}$ feet. How much will it cost to cover the floor with carpet costing $12.50 a square yard (nine square feet), if four extra square yards are needed for matching? If a portion of a square yard is needed, an entire square yard must be purchased.

290. Brian Sangean has been offered a job in which he will be paid strictly on a commission basis. He expects to receive a 2% commission on all sales of computer hardware he closes. Brian's goal for a gross yearly salary is $30,000. How much computer hardware must Brian sell in order to meet his target salary?

Example: You are interested in renting an apartment for $325 a month. Your monthly gross pay is $1,050. Should you be able to afford this payment, based on this rule of thumb?

$$\frac{\$325}{\$1,050} = 0.3095 = 31\%$$

Since $325 is about 31% of your monthly salary, you may find this apartment too expensive.

In looking for an apartment, you see an advertisement for an apartment that rents for $405 a month. If your monthly salary is $1,625, is this apartment affordable for you?

291. If you have considered renting or buying a home, you may want to think about the following rule of thumb used in many real estate offices: Your rent or house payment should not be more than 25% of your monthly gross pay. If your gross pay is $1,000 a month, then your rent payment should not be more than $250 a month.

$$\$1,000 \times 25\% = \$1,000 \times 0.25 = \$250$$

If your gross pay is $1,250 a month, what is the approximate rent you should be able to pay?

If your house payment is $375 a month and your monthly gross pay is $1,115, what percent of your pay is your house payment?

292. If you own a business that occupies space in a shopping center or mall, your lease may require you to pay a percent of the common area maintenance (CAM). This fee pays for parking lot maintenance, grounds contracts, garbage collection, taxes, sign maintenance, and other expenses that are part of the operating expenses of such a project. The amount each business pays depends on the size of the building. Each percent is based on the square footage per building or space and the total square footage of the mall or shopping center.

If your building is 8,640 square feet and the shopping center has a total of 69,590 square feet, then you occupy 12.42% of the space and must pay 12.42% of the CAM.

$$\frac{8,640}{69,590} = 0.1242 = 12.42\%$$

The total common area maintenance is $9,519.34; your share of the CAM is 12.42% of this total, or $1,182.30.

$$12.42\% \times \$9,519.34 = 0.1242 \times \$9,519.34$$
$$= \$1,182.30$$

If your business occupies 1,400 square feet in a mall containing 88,260 square feet, what percent of the mall do you occupy? If the total common area maintenance is $15,621.88, what is your share of the expense?

A lease requires the owner of a business occupying 2,000 square feet of a 78,900-square-foot shopping center to pay a percent of the yearly taxes based on space occupied. If the taxes for the year are $18,789, how much must the business owner pay?

CHAPTER 2 PRACTICE TEST

Perform the indicated operation. Reduce results to lowest terms.

1. $\dfrac{5}{6} - \dfrac{4}{6}$

2. $\dfrac{5}{8} + \dfrac{9}{10}$

3. $\dfrac{5}{8} \times \dfrac{7}{10}$

4. $\dfrac{5}{6} \div \dfrac{3}{4}$

5. $10\dfrac{1}{2} \div 5\dfrac{3}{4}$

6. $56 \times 32\dfrac{6}{7}$

7. $2\dfrac{1}{2} + 3\dfrac{1}{3}$

8. $137 - 89\dfrac{4}{5}$

9. Dale Burton ordered $\frac{3}{4}$ truckload of merchandise. If approximately $\frac{1}{3}$ of the $\frac{3}{4}$ truckload of merchandise has been unloaded, how much remains to be unloaded?

10. A company that employs 580 people expects to lay off 87 workers. What fractional part of the workers are expected to be laid off?

Write the decimal as a percent.

11. 0.24

12. 0.925

13. 0.6

Write the fraction or mixed number as a percent.

14. $\dfrac{21}{100}$

15. $\dfrac{3}{8}$

16. Write $\frac{1}{4}\%$ as a fraction.

Use the percentage formula or one of its forms or the percentage proportion.

17. Find 30% of $240.

18. 50 is what percent of 20?

19. What percent of 8 is 7?

20. What is the sales tax on an item that costs $42 if the tax rate is 6%?

21. If 100% of 22 rooms are full, how many rooms are full?

22. Twelve employees at a meat packing plant were sick on Monday. If the plant employs 360 people, what percent of the employees were sick on Monday?

23. A department store had 15% turnover in personnel last year. If the store employs 600 people, how many employees were replaced last year?

24. The Dawson family left a 15% tip for a restaurant check. If the check totaled $19.47, find the amount of the tip. What was the total cost of the meal, including the tip?

25. A certain make and model of automobile was projected to have a 3% rate of defective autos. If the number of defective automobiles was projected to be 1,698, how many automobiles were to be produced?

26. Of the 26 questions on this practice test, 12 are word problems. What percent of the problems are word problems? (Round to the nearest whole number percent.)

CHAPTER 2 — SELF-CHECK SOLUTIONS

Self-Check 2.1

1. proper

2. improper

3. improper

4. proper

5. proper

6. improper

7. $7\overline{)12}$ gives $1\frac{5}{7}$, remainder $\frac{7}{5}$

8. $20\overline{)21}$ gives $1\frac{1}{20}$, $\frac{20}{1}$

9. $18\overline{)18}$ gives 1

10. $7\overline{)7}$ gives 1

11. $8\overline{)16}$ gives 2

12. $16\overline{)388}$ gives $24\frac{4}{16} = 24\frac{1}{4}$
$$\begin{array}{r} 32 \\ \hline 68 \\ 64 \\ \hline 4 \end{array}$$

13. $\dfrac{6}{1}$

14. $\dfrac{27}{1}$

15. $\dfrac{(3 \times 2) + 1}{3} = \dfrac{7}{3}$

16. $\dfrac{(5 \times 3) + 4}{5} = \dfrac{19}{5}$

17. $\dfrac{(8 \times 1) + 5}{8} = \dfrac{13}{8}$

18. $\dfrac{(3 \times 6) + 2}{3} = \dfrac{20}{3}$

19. $\dfrac{12}{15} \div \dfrac{3}{3} = \dfrac{4}{5}$

20. $\dfrac{12}{20} \div \dfrac{4}{4} = \dfrac{3}{5}$

21. $\dfrac{18}{24} \div \dfrac{6}{6} = \dfrac{3}{4}$

22. $\dfrac{18}{36} \div \dfrac{18}{18} = \dfrac{1}{2}$

23. $\dfrac{24}{36} \div \dfrac{12}{12} = \dfrac{2}{3}$

24. $\dfrac{13}{39} \div \dfrac{13}{13} = \dfrac{1}{3}$

25. $\dfrac{3}{8} \times \dfrac{2}{2} = \dfrac{6}{16}$

26. $\dfrac{4}{5} \times \dfrac{4}{4} = \dfrac{16}{20}$

27. $\dfrac{3}{8} \times \dfrac{4}{4} = \dfrac{12}{32}$

28. $\dfrac{5}{9} \times \dfrac{3}{3} = \dfrac{15}{27}$

29. $\dfrac{1}{3} \times \dfrac{5}{5} = \dfrac{5}{15}$

30. $\dfrac{3}{5} \times \dfrac{3}{3} = \dfrac{9}{15}$

31.
$$\begin{array}{r} \dfrac{1}{9} \\ \dfrac{2}{9} \\ +\dfrac{5}{9} \\ \hline \dfrac{8}{9} \end{array}$$

32.
$$\begin{array}{r} \dfrac{7}{8} \\ +\dfrac{5}{8} \\ \hline \dfrac{12}{8} = 1\dfrac{4}{8} = 1\dfrac{1}{2} \end{array}$$

33.
$$\begin{array}{r} \dfrac{5}{6} \times \dfrac{5}{5} = \dfrac{25}{30} \\ +\dfrac{7}{15} \times \dfrac{2}{2} = \dfrac{14}{30} \\ \hline \dfrac{39}{30} = 1\dfrac{9}{30} = 1\dfrac{3}{10} \end{array}$$

34.
$$\begin{array}{r} \dfrac{5}{8} \times \dfrac{3}{3} = \dfrac{15}{24} \\ +\dfrac{7}{12} \times \dfrac{2}{2} = \dfrac{14}{24} \\ \hline \dfrac{29}{24} = 1\dfrac{5}{24} \end{array}$$

35.
$$\begin{array}{r} 4\dfrac{5}{6} = 4\dfrac{5}{6} \\ +7\dfrac{1}{2} = 7\dfrac{3}{6} \\ \hline 11\dfrac{8}{6} = 12\dfrac{2}{6} = 12\dfrac{1}{3} \end{array}$$

36.
$$\begin{array}{r} 11\dfrac{3}{4} = 11\dfrac{6}{8} \\ 11\dfrac{3}{4} = 11\dfrac{6}{8} \\ +18\dfrac{5}{8} = 18\dfrac{5}{8} \\ \hline 40\dfrac{17}{8} = 42\dfrac{1}{8} \text{ yards} \end{array}$$

37.
$$\begin{array}{r} 42\dfrac{3}{8} = 42\dfrac{3}{8} \\ 37\dfrac{5}{8} = 37\dfrac{5}{8} \\ 12\dfrac{3}{8} = 12\dfrac{3}{8} \\ + 23\dfrac{3}{4} = 23\dfrac{6}{8} \\ \hline 114\dfrac{17}{8} = 116\dfrac{1}{8} \text{ feet} \end{array}$$

38.
$$10\dfrac{3}{4} + 10\dfrac{3}{4} + 12\dfrac{5}{8} + 12\dfrac{5}{8} + 12\dfrac{5}{8} + 12\dfrac{5}{8} + 8\dfrac{1}{2} + 8\dfrac{1}{2} =$$
$$10\dfrac{6}{8} + 10\dfrac{6}{8} + 12\dfrac{5}{8} + 12\dfrac{5}{8} + 12\dfrac{5}{8} + 12\dfrac{5}{8} + 8\dfrac{4}{8} + 8\dfrac{4}{8} =$$
$$84\dfrac{40}{8} = 84 + 5 = 89 \text{ feet}$$

39.
$$4\dfrac{4}{5} + 4\dfrac{4}{5} + 4\dfrac{4}{5} + 7\dfrac{3}{8} + 7\dfrac{3}{8} =$$
$$4\dfrac{32}{40} + 4\dfrac{32}{40} + 4\dfrac{32}{40} + 7\dfrac{15}{40} + 7\dfrac{15}{40} =$$
$$26\dfrac{126}{40} = 29\dfrac{6}{40} = 29\dfrac{3}{20} \text{ inches}$$

40.
$$\begin{array}{r} \dfrac{7}{8} \\ -\dfrac{3}{8} \\ \hline \dfrac{4}{8} = \dfrac{1}{2} \end{array}$$

41.
$$\begin{array}{r} \dfrac{8}{9} \\ -\dfrac{2}{9} \\ \hline \dfrac{6}{9} = \dfrac{2}{3} \end{array}$$

42.
$$\begin{array}{r} \dfrac{3}{4} \times \dfrac{7}{7} = \dfrac{21}{28} \\ -\dfrac{5}{7} \times \dfrac{4}{4} = \dfrac{20}{28} \\ \hline \dfrac{1}{28} \end{array}$$

43.
$$\begin{array}{r} 9\dfrac{1}{2} = 9\dfrac{3}{6} = 8\dfrac{9}{6} \\ -6\dfrac{2}{3} = 6\dfrac{4}{6} = 6\dfrac{4}{6} \\ \hline 2\dfrac{5}{6} \end{array}$$

44. She only needs $42\dfrac{1}{8}$ yards so she can use the fabric.
$$\begin{array}{r} 45 = 44\dfrac{8}{8} \\ -42\dfrac{1}{8} = 42\dfrac{1}{8} \\ \hline 2\dfrac{7}{8} \end{array}$$

$2\dfrac{7}{8}$ yards will make at least one very large pillow and may be enough fabric to make two or three pillows.

45.
$$\begin{array}{r} 12 = 11\dfrac{4}{4} \\ -10\dfrac{3}{4} = 10\dfrac{3}{4} \\ \hline 1\dfrac{1}{4} \text{ feet must be removed} \end{array}$$

46.

$$13\frac{15}{16} = 13\frac{15}{16}$$
$$-12\frac{5}{8} = 12\frac{10}{16}$$
$$\overline{\qquad\quad 1\frac{5}{16} \text{ feet}}$$

$$14 = 13\frac{8}{8}$$
$$-12\frac{5}{8} = 12\frac{5}{8}$$
$$\overline{\qquad\quad 1\frac{3}{8} \text{ feet}}$$

$$14\frac{1}{8} = 13\frac{9}{8}$$
$$-12\frac{5}{8} = 12\frac{5}{8}$$
$$\overline{\qquad\quad 1\frac{4}{8} = 1\frac{1}{2} \text{ feet}}$$

$$13\frac{13}{16} = 13\frac{13}{16}$$
$$-12\frac{5}{8} = 12\frac{10}{16}$$
$$\overline{\qquad\quad 1\frac{3}{16} \text{ feet}}$$

47.

$$8\frac{3}{4} + 8\frac{3}{4} = 16\frac{6}{4} = 17\frac{2}{4} = 17\frac{1}{2}$$

$$36 = 35\frac{2}{2}$$
$$-17\frac{1}{2} = 17\frac{1}{2}$$
$$\overline{\qquad\quad 18\frac{1}{2} \text{ inches}}$$

48. $\dfrac{3}{\cancel{8}_{2}} \times \dfrac{\cancel{4}^{1}}{5} = \dfrac{3}{10}$

49. $\dfrac{5}{7} \times \dfrac{1}{6} = \dfrac{5}{42}$

50. $5\dfrac{3}{4} \times 3\dfrac{8}{9} = \dfrac{23}{4} \times \dfrac{35}{9} = \dfrac{805}{36} = 22\dfrac{13}{36}$

51. $\dfrac{3}{\cancel{8}_{1}} \times \dfrac{\cancel{24}^{3}}{1} = 9$

52. $3\dfrac{1}{2} \times 6 = \dfrac{7}{\cancel{2}_{1}} \times \dfrac{\cancel{6}^{3}}{1} = 21$

53. $18\dfrac{5}{8} \times 4 = \dfrac{149}{\cancel{8}_{2}} \times \dfrac{\cancel{4}^{1}}{1} = \dfrac{149}{2} = 74\dfrac{1}{2} \text{ feet}$

Theoretically, the cabinets will fit exactly. However, practically, they may not fit.

54. $4\dfrac{1}{8} \times 4 = \dfrac{33}{\cancel{8}_{2}} \times \dfrac{\cancel{4}^{1}}{1} = \dfrac{33}{2} = 16\dfrac{1}{2} \text{ feet}$

Compare $16\frac{1}{2}$ with $16\frac{5}{8}$.
$16\frac{1}{2} = 16\frac{4}{8}$ and $16\frac{4}{8}$ is less than $16\frac{5}{8}$, so the desks together will fit on the wall if no more than $\frac{1}{8}$ inch is needed for placing, the desks.

55. $2 \times 3\dfrac{1}{4} = \dfrac{\cancel{2}^{1}}{1} \times \dfrac{13}{\cancel{4}_{2}} = 6\dfrac{1}{2}$

14 plates per column ÷ 2

Plate is $6\frac{1}{2}$ inches by 14 inches

56. $\dfrac{12}{7}$

57. $\dfrac{5}{3}$

58. $9 = \dfrac{9}{1}$, so reciprocal is $\dfrac{1}{9}$

59. $12 = \dfrac{12}{1}$, so reciprocal is $\dfrac{1}{12}$

60. $5\dfrac{4}{7} = \dfrac{39}{7}$, so reciprocal is $\dfrac{7}{39}$

61. $3\dfrac{3}{8} = \dfrac{27}{8}$, so reciprocal is $\dfrac{8}{27}$

62. $\dfrac{5}{8} \div \dfrac{3}{4} = \dfrac{5}{\cancel{8}_{2}} \times \dfrac{\cancel{4}^{1}}{3} = \dfrac{5}{6}$

63. $\dfrac{3}{5} \div \dfrac{9}{10} = \dfrac{\cancel{3}^{1}}{\cancel{5}_{1}} \times \dfrac{\cancel{10}^{2}}{\cancel{9}_{3}} = \dfrac{2}{3}$

64. $2\dfrac{2}{5} \div 1\dfrac{1}{7} = \dfrac{12}{5} \div \dfrac{8}{7} = \dfrac{\cancel{12}^{3}}{5} \times \dfrac{7}{\cancel{8}_{2}} = \dfrac{21}{10} = 2\dfrac{1}{10}$

65. $5\dfrac{1}{4} \div 2\dfrac{2}{3} = \dfrac{21}{4} \div \dfrac{8}{3} = \dfrac{21}{4} \times \dfrac{3}{8} = \dfrac{63}{32} = 1\dfrac{31}{32}$

66. $\dfrac{3}{4} \div \dfrac{5}{1} = \dfrac{3}{4} \times \dfrac{1}{5} = \dfrac{3}{20}$

67. $75 \div 1\dfrac{1}{8} = 75 \div \dfrac{9}{8} = \dfrac{75}{1} \times \dfrac{8}{9} = \dfrac{600}{9} = 66\dfrac{2}{3} \text{ sheets}$

So, the stack contains about 66 sheets.

68. $20 \div 5\dfrac{3}{4} = 20 \div \dfrac{23}{4} = \dfrac{20}{1} \times \dfrac{4}{23} = \dfrac{80}{23} = 3\dfrac{11}{23}$

The carpet will cover three rooms with enough left to carpet about half of another room.

69. $40 \div 8\dfrac{3}{4} = \dfrac{40}{1} \div \dfrac{35}{4} = \dfrac{\cancel{40}^{8}}{1} \times \dfrac{4}{\cancel{35}_{7}} = \dfrac{32}{7} = 4\dfrac{4}{7};$
only four boxes will fit.

70. $0.8 = \dfrac{8}{10} = \dfrac{4}{5}$

71. $0.68 = \dfrac{68}{100} = \dfrac{17}{25}$

72. $1.4 = 1\dfrac{4}{10} = 1\dfrac{2}{5}$

73. $3.2 = 3\dfrac{2}{10} = 3\dfrac{1}{5}$

74. $\dfrac{3}{10} = 0.3$

75.
$$
\begin{array}{r}
0.75 \\
4\overline{)3.00} \\
\underline{2\ 8} \\
20 \\
\underline{20}
\end{array}
$$

76.
$$
\begin{array}{r}
0.875 \text{ or } 0.88 \\
8\overline{)7.000} \\
\underline{6\ 4} \\
60 \\
\underline{56} \\
40 \\
\underline{40}
\end{array}
$$

77. $1\dfrac{3}{5} = \dfrac{8}{5}$
$$
\begin{array}{r}
1.6 \\
5\overline{)8.0} \\
\underline{5} \\
30 \\
\underline{30}
\end{array}
$$

78.
$$
\begin{array}{r}
0.428 \approx 0.43 \\
7\overline{)3.000} \\
\underline{2\ 8} \\
2\ 0 \\
\underline{14} \\
60 \\
\underline{56} \\
4
\end{array}
$$

79. $19\dfrac{3}{8} = \dfrac{155}{8} = \$19.375$
or $\$19.38$

80. $141\dfrac{1}{2} = \$141.50$

$3\dfrac{5}{8} = \dfrac{29}{8} = 29 \div 8 = \$3.625$
or $\$3.63$

Self-Check 2.2

1. $0.39 = 0.39 \times 100\% = 39\%$

2. $0.693 = 0.693 \times 100\% = 69.3\%$

3. $0.75 = 0.75 \times 100\% = 75\%$

4. $0.2 = 0.2 \times 100\% = 20\%$

5. $2.92 = 2.92 \times 100\% = 292\%$

6. $0.0007 = 0.0007 \times 100\% = 0.07\%$

7. $\dfrac{39}{100} = \dfrac{39}{\overset{}{\underset{1}{100}}} \times \dfrac{\overset{1}{100\%}}{1} = 39\%$

8. $\dfrac{3}{\underset{1}{4}} \times \dfrac{\overset{25}{100\%}}{1} = 75\%$

9. $3\dfrac{2}{5} = \dfrac{17}{\underset{1}{5}} \times \dfrac{\overset{20}{100\%}}{1} = 340\%$

10. $5\dfrac{1}{4} = 5\dfrac{1}{4} \times \dfrac{100\%}{1} = \dfrac{21}{\underset{1}{4}} \times \dfrac{\overset{25}{100\%}}{1} = 525\%$

11. $\dfrac{9}{4} = \dfrac{9}{\underset{1}{4}} \times \dfrac{\overset{25}{100\%}}{1} = 225\%$

12. $\dfrac{7}{\underset{1}{5}} \times \dfrac{\overset{20}{100\%}}{1} = 140\%$

13. $\dfrac{2}{\underset{3}{300}} \times \dfrac{\overset{1}{100\%}}{1} = \dfrac{2}{3}\%$

14. $15\dfrac{1}{2}\% = 15.5\%$

$= 15.5\% \div 100\% = 0.155$

15.
$$
\begin{array}{r}
0.125 \\
8\overline{)1.000} \\
\underline{80} \\
20 \\
\underline{16} \\
40 \\
\underline{40}
\end{array}
$$
$\dfrac{1}{8}\% = 0.125\% = 0.125\% \div 100\%$
$= 0.00125$

16. $45\% \div 100\% = 0.45$

17. $150\% \div 100\% = 1.5$

18. $125\dfrac{1}{3}\% = 125.\overline{3}\%$

$= 125.\overline{3}\% \div 100\%$
$= 1.253 \text{ (rounded)}$

19.

$$\begin{array}{r} 0.4285714 \\ 7\overline{)3.0000000} \\ \underline{2\,8} \\ 20 \\ \underline{14} \\ 60 \\ \underline{56} \\ 40 \\ \underline{35} \\ 50 \\ \underline{49} \\ 10 \\ \underline{7} \\ 30 \\ \underline{28} \\ 2 \end{array}$$

$\dfrac{3}{7}\% = 0.429\% \div 100\% = 0.004$

(rounded)

20. $45\% = \dfrac{45\%}{100\%} = \dfrac{9}{20}$

21. $\dfrac{60\%}{100\%} = \dfrac{3}{5}$

22. $\dfrac{250\%}{100\%} = \dfrac{5}{2} = 2\dfrac{1}{2}$

23. $180\% = \dfrac{180\%}{100\%} = \dfrac{18}{10} = \dfrac{9}{5} = 1\dfrac{4}{5}$

24. $\dfrac{3}{4}\% = \dfrac{3}{4}\% \div 100\% = \dfrac{3}{4}\% \times \dfrac{1}{100\%} = \dfrac{3}{400}$

25. $33\dfrac{1}{3}\% = 33\dfrac{1}{3}\% \div 100\% = 33\dfrac{1}{3}\% \times \dfrac{1}{100\%}$

$$= \dfrac{\overset{1}{\cancel{100}}}{3} \times \dfrac{1}{\cancel{100}} = \dfrac{1}{3}$$

26. $P = R \times B$
$P = 25\% \times 300$
$P = 0.25 \times 300$
$P = 75$

27. $P = R \times B$
$P = 40\% \times 160$
$P = 0.40 \times 160$
$P = 64$

28. $P = R \times B = 33\dfrac{1}{3}\% \times 150 = \dfrac{1}{\cancel{3}} \times \dfrac{\overset{50}{\cancel{150}}}{1} = 50$

29. $P = R \times B = 154\% \times 30 = 1.54 \times 30 = 46.2$

30. $P = R \times B = 20\% \times \$258.30 = 0.20 \times \$258.30 = \$51.66$ saved

31. $P = R \times B = 12\% \times \$8.67 = 0.12 \times \$8.67 = \$1.04$ increase
$\$8.67 + \$1.04 = \$9.71$ new pay per hour

32. $P = R \times B = 78\% \times 95 = 0.78 \times 95 = 74.1$ gallons or 74 gallons (rounded)

33. $B = \dfrac{P}{R} = \dfrac{36}{66\dfrac{2}{3}\%} = \dfrac{36}{\dfrac{2}{3}} = \dfrac{\overset{18}{\cancel{36}}}{1} \times \dfrac{3}{\cancel{2}} = 54$

34. $B = \dfrac{P}{R} = \dfrac{42}{80\%} = \dfrac{42}{0.8} = 52.5$, or 53 shirts

35. $B = \dfrac{P}{R} = \dfrac{\$1,466}{23\%} = \dfrac{\$1,466}{0.23} = \$6,373.91$ original cost

36. $B = \dfrac{P}{R} = \dfrac{267}{30\%} = \dfrac{267}{0.3} = 890$ shirts

37. $R = \dfrac{P}{B} = \dfrac{70}{280} = \dfrac{\overset{1}{\cancel{70}}}{\underset{\underset{1}{\cancel{4}}}{\cancel{280}}} \times \dfrac{\overset{25}{\cancel{100\%}}}{1} = 25\%$

38. $R = \dfrac{P}{B} = \dfrac{23}{25} = \dfrac{23}{\underset{1}{\cancel{25}}} \times \dfrac{\overset{4}{\cancel{100\%}}}{1} = 92\%$

39. $78{,}753 - 67{,}388 = 11{,}365$

$R = \dfrac{P}{B} = \dfrac{11{,}365}{78{,}753} = \dfrac{11{,}365}{78{,}753} \times \dfrac{100\%}{1}$

$= \dfrac{1{,}136{,}500}{78{,}753}\% = 14.43\%$ vacant seats

40. $P = BR$

$0.18 = 2.99\,R$

$R = \dfrac{0.18}{2.99}$

$R = 0.06$

$R = 6\%$

41. $\dfrac{40}{100} = \dfrac{N}{30}$

$40 \times 30 = 1200$

$1200 \div 100 = 12$

$N = 12$

42. $\dfrac{52}{100} = \dfrac{N}{17.8}$

$52 \times 17.8 = 925.6$

$925.6 \div 100 = 9.256$

$N = 9.26$ (rounded)

43. $\dfrac{30}{100} = \dfrac{21}{N}$

$100 \times 21 = 2100$

$2100 \div 30 = 70$

$N = 70$

44. $\dfrac{17.5}{100} = \dfrac{18}{N}$

$100 \times 18 = 1800$

$1800 \div 17.5 = 102.857$

$N = 102.86$

45. $\dfrac{N}{100} = \dfrac{4}{16}$

$100 \times 4 = 400$

$400 \div 16 = 25$

$N = 25; 25\%$

46. $\dfrac{N}{100} = \dfrac{30}{50}$

$100 \times 30 = 3000$

$3000 \div 50 = 60$

$N = 60; 60\%$

47. $\dfrac{172}{100} = \dfrac{N}{50}$

$172 \times 50 = 8600$

$8600 \div 100 = 86$

$N = 86$

48. $\dfrac{0.8}{100} = \dfrac{N}{50}$

$0.8 \times 50 = 40$

$40 \div 100 = 0.4$

$N = 0.4$

49. $\dfrac{N}{100} = \dfrac{12.7}{15.2}$

$100 \times 12.7 = 1270$

$1270 \div 15.2 = 83.5526$

$N = 83.55; 83.55\%$

50. $\dfrac{N}{100} = \dfrac{120}{73}$

$100 \times 120 = 12000$

$12000 \div 73 = 164.3835$

$N = 164.38; 164.38\%$

51. $\dfrac{0.28}{100} = \dfrac{12}{N}$

$100 \times 12 = 1200$

$1200 \div 0.28 = 4285.7142$

$N = 4{,}285.71$

52. $\dfrac{1.5}{100} = \dfrac{20}{N}$

$100 \times 20 = 2000$

$2000 \div 1.5 = 1333.3333$

$N = 1{,}333.33$

53. $\dfrac{N}{100} = \dfrac{1.51}{52.13}$

$100 \times 1.51 = 151$

$151 \div 52.13 = 2.8966$

$N = 2.9; 2.9\%$

54.

52.13
$+1.51$
$\overline{53.64}$

$\dfrac{N}{100} = \dfrac{1.57}{53.64}$

$100 \times 1.57 = 157$

$157 \div 53.64 = 2.9269$

$N = 2.9; 2.9\%$

3

Problem Solving with Formulas and Equations

3.1 Formulas

1 Evaluate formulas.

2 Write a formula to find an unknown value.

3 Write electronic spreadsheet instructions as formulas.

3.2 Equations

1 Solve equations using multiplication or division.

2 Solve equations using addition or subtraction.

3 Solve equations using more than one operation.

4 Solve equations containing multiple unknown terms.

5 Solve equations containing parentheses.

6 Solve equations that are proportions.

3.3 Using Equations to Solve Problems

1 Use the decision key approach to analyze and solve word problems.

Good Decisions through Teamwork

Form teams in which team members have an interest in a similar type of business. With your team, find samples of spreadsheets used to perform a specific function in the selected business. Examples of types of businesses to investigate are retail sales, insurance, accounting, transportation, manufacturing, hospitality, catering, tourism, and health-related services.

Gather examples of the spreadsheets used in the selected business from library research, interviews with professionals or business educators, or other appropriate sources. Select one of the spreadsheets to analyze further. This analysis should include the purpose of the spreadsheet, how the information is collected, what additional information is derived through calculations, and what formulas are used to make these calculations.

Present your team's findings to the class and be prepared to answer questions from class members.

Many business problems—determining an employee's wages, for example, or determining inventory levels or profits—involve answering the question "How much?" One way to answer the question is to write relationships as *formulas* or *equations*. Equations and formulas are similar in that they both use letters, numbers, and mathematical symbols to express a relationship. In this chapter you will see how to use both formulas and equations to solve various business problems.

3.1 Formulas

 **1** Evaluate formulas.

2 Write a formula to find an unknown value.

3 Write electronic spreadsheet instructions as formulas.

In the problem-solving techniques we have used so far, we have written the relationships among the known and unknown facts of a problem. These relationships could also be called *formulas*. A **formula** is a mathematical shorthand for expressing the process of finding an unknown value. For example, when the rate R and base B are known and the percentage P is unknown, the formula $P = R \times B$ tells us we must multiply R and B to find P. Similarly, when the percentage P and base B are known and the rate R is unknown, the formula $R = \frac{P}{B}$ tells us we must divide P by B to find R.

For a formula to be meaningful, we must know what each letter in the formula represents. For example, in the percent formulas, we must know that P represents the percentage or part, R represents the fractional or decimal equivalent of the rate or percent, and B represents the total or original amount.

 **1** Evaluate formulas.

Solving for an unknown value in a formula when all the other values are known is called **evaluating** the formula. Remember from our work with the percentage formula that, to find an unknown value in the formula—that is, to *evaluate* the formula—we chose one of three variations of the formula, depending on which value, P, B, or R, was unknown. We chose the variation in which the unknown was "isolated" on the left side of the formula.

? HOW TO Evaluate a Formula

	Find the weekly pay for 25 hours worked at a rate of $7 per hour.
1. Replace letters or words in the formula with their known values.	Pay = hours × rate per hour
2. Perform the operations indicated by the formula.	Pay = 25 × $7 Pay = $175
3. Interpret the result.	The weekly pay is $175.

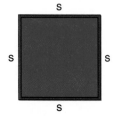

Figure 3-1

EXAMPLE Evaluate the formula $P = 4s$ to find the perimeter (P) of a square when we know the length of one side (s) is 8 feet.

To understand this formula, we first must know the meaning of the words *square* and *perimeter*. A **square** is a four-sided shape with all four sides equal and all four corner angles equal (Figure 3-1). The **perimeter** of a square is the distance around the edges of the square.

We must also know the meaning of the *expression* "4s." In the mathematical shorthand of formulas, a letter written next to a number means *multiply*. So 4s means 4 times *s*, or 4 times the value of *s*. The formula $P = 4s$, then, means "The perimeter of a square is equal to 4 times the length of one side."

Now we are ready to evaluate the formula.

$P = 4s$

$P = 4(8)$ **Replace letters in the formula with their known values: The known value of *s* is 8.**

$P = 32$ **Perform the indicated operations: Multiply 4 × 8.**

The perimeter of the square is 32 feet.

> **TIP!** **Notation Used in Formulas**
>
> | MULTIPLICATION | DIVISION |
> |---|---|
> | $2A = 2 \times A$ | $\dfrac{A}{B} = A \div B$ |
> | $2 \cdot A = 2 \times A$ | $A/B = A \div B$ |
> | $2 * A = 2 \times A$ | |
> | $AB = A \times B$ | |
> | $A = 1 \times A$ | |
> | $3(7) = 3 \times 7$ | |

When a formula indicates more than one operation to be performed, we must proceed according to a particular **standard order of operations.** This order of operations is agreed on by all those who write and use formulas. It requires us to work from *left to right*, performing *first* all multiplications and divisions as they occur in the formula and *second* all additions and subtractions as they occur in the formula. To show exceptions to this standard order, you need to use parentheses. Operations within parentheses are performed first. In the following example, we illustrate the use of the standard order of operations, and parentheses.

EXAMPLE   Find the perimeter of a rectangle that is 7 inches long and 5 inches wide using two versions of the rectangle perimeter formula: $P = 2(l + w)$ and $P = 2l + 2w$.

A **rectangle,** like a square, is a four-sided shape with equal corner angles. Unlike the square, all sides of a rectangle may not be equal. But opposite sides *are* equal (Figure 3-2). Each of the two longest sides is called the **length** of the rectangle. Length is represented by *l*. Each of the two shortest sides is called the **width** of the rectangle. Width is represented by *w*. Again, *P* represents the perimeter or distance around the shape.

$P = 2(l + w)$	$P = 2l + 2w$	**Two versions of the rectangle perimeter formula.**
$P = 2(7 + 5)$	$P = 2(7) + 2(5)$	**Substitute known values.**
$P = 2(12)$	$P = 14 + 10$	**Perform operations according to the order of operations: Operations within parentheses are done first. Then multiply. Then add.**
$P = 24$	$P = 24$	

The perimeter of the rectangle is 24 inches.

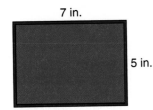

7 in.

5 in.

Figure 3-2

2 Write a formula to find an unknown value.

Any relationship involving numbers and operations can be expressed as a formula. Some formulas are common formulas, frequently used in the business world. For example, Selling Price = cost + markup is a common business formula. However, common or not, any relationship involving calculations may be expressed as a formula. We have already expressed many relationships using our decision key to solve problems.

Quarterly department totals = sum of quarterly totals for each employee	Section 1.1, Example, p. 11.
Total quantity of cups on hand = quantity of packages × cups per package	Section 1.1, second Example, p.15
Quantity of boxes needed = total number of vases ÷ vases per box	Section 1.1, Example, p. 18
Amount of tip = restaurant bill × rate of tip	Section 1.2, second Example, p. 29
Percentage = rate × base	Section 2.2, shaded box, p. 83

While formulas written in words may be easy to understand, it is cumbersome to continually write them in words. So we often use single letters in place of words. Using single letters and operation symbols, we translate relationships into mathematical shorthand.

 **HOW TO** Write a Formula to Find an Unknown Value

1. Represent the unknown value with a letter.

2. Represent each known value with a letter.

3. Write the unknown-value letter on the left side of an equal sign and the known-value letters with appropriate operation symbols on the right side of the equal sign.

Write a formula for finding the amount of tip for a restaurant bill. Let *T* represent the amount of tip

Let *B* represent the bill and *R* the rate of tip.

$T = B \times R$ or $T = BR$.

EXAMPLE Write a formula to find the perimeter of a five-sided figure if each of the five sides is equal.

We let *P* represent perimeter, the unknown value. Let *s* represent the length of a side.

One version of the formula could be $P = s + s + s + s + s$. Another version could be $P = 5s$, since, $s + s + s + s + s$ is the same as 5 times *s*.

---

3 Write electronic spreadsheet instructions as formulas.

A programmable calculator or a computer software program can make series of calculations. The person using the calculator or computer gives the instructions through a formula. The known facts are then entered and the calculator or computer performs the calculations. Examples of computer software packages that can evaluate formulas are DERIVE, Converge, Mathematica, and MathCad. Spreadsheet programs such as Excel, also can evaluate formulas. While each software package or programmable calculator has unique requirements for entering formulas, the basic concept for evaluating formulas with an electronic tool is the same.

Using an appropriate electronic tool, a formula for finding the perimeter of a rectangle, such as $P = 2l + 2w$, can be entered. Most of these applications require that the formula be written with the unknown value on the left of the equal sign and all known values on the right. When values for l and w are known, say, l is 12 inches and w is 7 inches, these values are assigned to the respective letters. Then, the program can be instructed to evaluate the formula and display the results. The specific format of the instructions depends on the particular electronic tool. One possible sequence of instructions and results is:

1. $P = 2l + 2w$ The formula is entered.
2. $l = 12$ The known value of l is entered.
3. $w = 7$ The known value of w is entered.
4. $P = 38$.   The resulting value of P is displayed.

Once the formula $P = 2l + 2w$ is entered, the formula can be evaluated for different values of l and w by reassigning l and w. For instance, let $l = 15$ and $w = 9$. The sequence of instructions that follows illustrates how different values can be used in the same formula.

1. $P = 2l + 2w$
2. $l = 12$ ⎤
3. $w = 7$ ⎦   First pair of values
4. $P = 38$
5. $l = 15$ ⎤
6. $w = 9$ ⎦   Second pair of values
7. $P = 48$

The perimeter of the rectangle with a length of 15 inches and a width of 9 inches is 48 inches.

An **electronic spreadsheet** is a computer program that displays information in the rows and columns of a table called a **spreadsheet.** In building a spreadsheet, data are entered into some of the cells, and formulas are entered into other cells. The spreadsheet program evaluates the formulas and displays the results in the same cells in which the formulas were entered.

The feature that makes spreadsheets so attractive in the business world is that key information can be changed while retaining the basic formulas of the spreadsheet. As new key data are entered, the program automatically updates the results in the spreadsheet. This process allows the businessperson to see quickly how various changes in the key data impact the results.

To illustrate the power of an electronic spreadsheet, we use data that represent budgeted amounts for each expense category of Silver's Spa. The spreadsheet program calculates the total budgeted amount using a formula to add the amounts in expense categories.

As shown in Figure 3-3, the spreadsheet program labels columns with the letters A, B, C, D, and rows with numbers 1–13. The user enters the spreadsheet title, which is displayed as row 1; data set labels, which are displayed as row 3; and the known data, which are displayed in rows 5–11, column B. The program identifies each cell by its column letter and row number.

For example, cell B5 is the cell in column B and row 5 ($25,000). The Total amount cell (B13) is calculated by adding the entries for cells B5, B6, B7, B8, B9, B10, and B11. The formula is written as B13 = B5 + B6 + B7 + B8 + B9 + B10 + B11. Each cell in the Decimal column is calculated as a decimal rate of the total expense. For instance, cell C5 is calculated by dividing B5 by B13. The formula is written as C5 = B5/B13. Each cell in the Percent column is calculated by multiplying by 100%. For instance, cell D5 is calculated by multiplying C5 by 100%. The formula is written as D5 = C5 * 100.

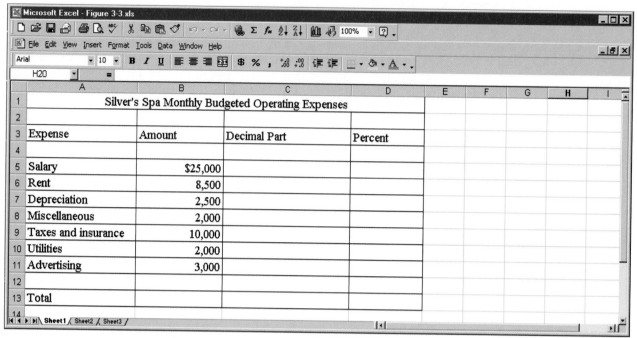

Figure 3-3 Silver's Spa Spreadsheet, Data Entered

TIP! Spreadsheet Addresses

A spreadsheet address is an individual cell that is the intersection or overlap of a column and a row. This address is generally given in two parts: column and row.

Address	Interpretation
C 8	Column C and Row 8
J 30	Column J and Row 30
AA 5	Column AA (follows Column Z) and Row 5

In a spreadsheet program it is very important to have all formulas written correctly. Since the results of one calculation may be used in another calculation, one incorrect formula can result in many mistakes on the spreadsheet.

EXAMPLE Develop spreadsheet formulas for cells B13, C5–C11, C13, D5–D11, and D13 of the spreadsheet in Figure 3-3.

$$B13 = B5 + B6 + B7 + B8 + B9 + B10 + B11$$

$$C5 = B5/B13$$
$$C6 = B6/B13$$
$$C7 = B7/B13$$
$$C8 = B8/B13$$
$$C9 = B9/B13$$
$$C10 = B10/B13$$
$$C11 = B11/B13$$
$$C13 = C5 + C6 + C7 + C8 + C9 + C10 + C11$$

$$D5 = C5 * 100$$
$$D6 = C6 * 100$$
$$D7 = C7 * 100$$
$$D8 = C8 * 100$$
$$D9 = C9 * 100$$
$$D10 = C10 * 100$$
$$D11 = C11 * 100$$
$$D13 = D5 + D6 + D7 + D8 + D9 + D10 + D11$$

Silver's Spa Monthly Budgeted Operating Expenses

Expense	Amount	Decimal Part	Percent
Salary	$25,000	0.4716981	47.2
Rent	8,500	0.1603774	16.0
Depreciation	2,500	0.0471698	4.7
Miscellaneous	2,000	0.0377358	3.8
Taxes and insurance	10,000	0.1886792	18.9
Utilities	2,000	0.0377358	3.8
Advertising	3,000	0.0566038	5.7
Total	$53,000	1.0000000*	100*

*Total is sum before rounding

Figure 3-4 Silver's Spa Spreadsheet, Results Calculated

When using some spreadsheet programs, formulas can be examined by highlighting the cell location and entering the appropriate instruction code. Figure 3-4 shows the completed spreadsheet for the budgeted expenses.

Because his spreadsheet uses formulas, as Mr. Silver's expense amounts change, he can use the same spreadsheet to determine total expenses, decimal cell values, and degree cell values.

Figure 3-5 illustrates the same spreadsheet and formulas but with actual amounts for April rather than budgeted amounts. This spreadsheet was generated by entering only new amount data. The spreadsheet program calculated all the other

Silver's Spa Monthly Operating Expenses for April

Expense	Amount	Decimal Part	Percent
Salary	$33,823	0.5487807	54.9
Rent	8,500	0.1379131	13.8
Depreciation	2,500	0.0405627	4.1
Miscellaneous	3,542	0.0574692	5.7
Taxes and insurance	8,532	0.1384323	13.8
Utilities	2,157	0.0349975	3.5
Advertising	2,579	0.0418445	4.2
Total	$61,633	1.0000000*	100*

*Total is sum before rounding

Figure 3-5 Silver's Spa Spreadsheet, New Data and New Results

entries. This enables Mr. Silver to compare his actual expenses with his budgeted or anticipated expenses. Also, this spreadsheet can be used for subsequent months; comparisons can be made and trends observed. It is common to use tables, graphs, and statistics (Chapter 4) in examining these trends.

SELF-CHECK 3.1

 The formula S = C + M is used to find the selling price S when the cost C and markup M are given.

1. Evaluate the formula $S = C + M$ if the cost of a blouse is $13.98 and the markup is $12.50.

2. Evaluate the formula $S = C + M$ if the cost of a refrigerator is $700 and the markup is $859.

The formula I = Prt is used to find the Interest I earned on money called the Principal P invested at an annual interest rate r for some number t of years.

3. Find the interest if $8,000 is invested at an annual interest rate of 7% for 2 years.

4. Find the interest on $12,000 invested at $5\frac{1}{2}$% for three years.

5. Use the formula $P = 2l + 2w$ to find the perimeter of a rectangle if the length is 12 inches and the width is 8 inches.

6. Write a formula to find the perimeter of a regular hexagon. A regular hexagon is a figure that has six equal sides.

The gross pay of an hourly worker is calculated by multiplying the number of hours worked by the pay earned per hour.

7. Write a formula to find the gross pay of an hourly worker.

8. Find the gross pay for Lou Ferrante if he worked 40 hours and earned $6.25 per hour.

9. A markdown on merchandise is a percentage of the selling price. Write a formula to find the markdown when the selling price and markdown rate are given.

10. Find the markdown on a suit that has a selling price of $259 if the markdown rate is 25%.

12. Find the reduced price of the item in exercise 10.

11. The reduced price of an item is found by subtracting the markdown from the selling price. Write a formula to find the reduced price of an item.

Sales tax on an item is found by multiplying the price of the item by the sales tax rate.

13. Write a formula to find the sales tax.

14. Find the sales tax for a calculator if its price is $12.95 and the sales tax rate is 6 percent.

To find the total cost of an item, we add the price and the sales tax.

15. Write a formula to find the total price.

16. Find the total cost of the calculator in exercise 14.

17. Use the formulas in the Silver's Spa Spreadsheet to complete the table for operating expenses for May (Figure 3-6).

	A	B	C	D	E	F	G	H	I
				Silver's Spa Monthly Operating Expenses for May					
1									
2									
3	Expense	Amount	Decimal Part	Percent					
4									
5	Salary	$33,917							
6	Rent	8,500							
7	Depreciation	2,500							
8	Miscellaneous	2,341							
9	Taxes and insurance	8,290							
10	Utilities	1,846							
11	Advertising	1,000							
12									
13	Total								
14									

Figure 3-6 Silver's Spa Spreadsheet, Exercise 17

18. Develop forumlas to complete the spreadsheet in Figure 3-7 to show data for the actual expenses for the 7th Inning Sports Memorabilia Shop.

19. Use the formulas to complete the spreadsheet for the 7th Inning Sports Memorabilia Shop.

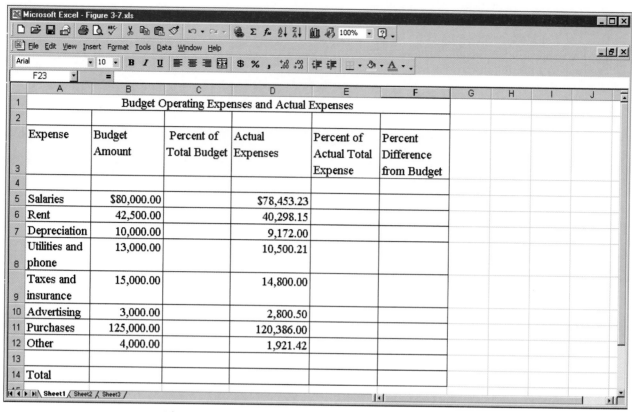

Expense	Budget Amount	Percent of Total Budget	Actual Expenses	Percent of Actual Total Expense	Percent Difference from Budget
			Budget Operating Expenses and Actual Expenses		
Salaries	$80,000.00		$78,453.23		
Rent	42,500.00		40,298.15		
Depreciation	10,000.00		9,172.00		
Utilities and phone	13,000.00		10,500.21		
Taxes and insurance	15,000.00		14,800.00		
Advertising	3,000.00		2,800.50		
Purchases	125,000.00		120,386.00		
Other	4,000.00		1,921.42		
Total					

Figure 3-7   7th Inning Spreadsheet, Exercises 18–19

3.2 Equations

1 Solve equations using multiplication or division.

2 Solve equations using addition or subtraction.

3 Solve equations using more than one operation.

4 Solve equations containing multiple unknown terms.

5 Solve equations containing parentheses.

6 Solve equations that are proportions.

In the previous section we saw how formulas are used in many business applications. However, in each formula we used, the unknown value was on the left side of the equal sign and the known values were on the right side. Variations of formulas were used to ensure that the unknown value would be on the left. In this section we look at methods for evaluating a formula no matter where the unknown value occurs in the formula. Why are these methods important? The simplest answer is: efficiency! With the methods you learn in this section, you need remember only one variation of the percentage formula, not three. Remembering, or finding a reference for, just one variation is enough to allow you to evaluate the formula for P, R, or B.

To be able to evaluate a formula no matter where the unknown value occurs, we must know how to *solve equations*. Proportions are one type of equation that we have already worked with.

1 Solve equations using multiplication or division.

An **equation** is a mathematical statement in which two quantities are equal. Like formulas, equations are represented by mathematical shorthand that uses numbers, letters, and operational symbols. In fact, *formula* is the special name we use for an equation that has at least two letters. $P = R \times B$, then, is an equation. If we replace R with 0.5, for instance, and P with, say, 10, we get an equation with just one letter: $10 = 0.5 \times B$. *Solving an equation* like $10 = 0.5 \times B$ means finding the value of B so that 0.5 times this value is the same as 10. B is called the *unknown* or variable.

To begin our examination of equations, we look at equations that involve multiplication or division, and one unknown value.

? HOW TO Solve an Equation with Multiplication or Division

Solve the equation
$5N = 20$

$$\frac{5N}{5} = \frac{20}{5}$$

1. Isolate the unknown value:

  (a) If the equation contains the *product* of the unknown factor and a known factor, then *divide* both sides of the equation by the known factor.

  (b) If the equation contains the *quotient* of the unknown value and a known factor, then *multiply* both sides of the equation by the known factor.

$N = 4$

2. Identify the solution: the solution is the number on the side opposite the isolated unknown-value letter.

$5(4) = 20$
$20 = 20$

3. Check the solution: in the original equation, replace the unknown-value letter with the solution, perform the indicated operations, and verify that both sides of the equation are the same number.

EXAMPLE Solve the equation $2A = 18$. (A number multiplied by 2 is 18.)

$2A = 18$ — The product and one factor are known.

$\dfrac{2A}{2} = \dfrac{18}{2}$ — Divide by the known factor.

$A = \boxed{9}$ — The solution is 9.

Check:

$2A = 18$ — Replace A with the solution 9 and see if both sides are equal.

$2(9) \stackrel{?}{=} 18$

$18 = 18$

The solution of the equation is 9.

 TIP! Why Divide Both Sides?

In the preceding example, both sides of the equation were divided by the known factor, 2. This applies an important property of equality. If you perform an operation on one side, you must do the same on the other side.

EXAMPLE Find the value of A if $\dfrac{A}{4} = 5$. (A number divided by 4 is 5.)

$\dfrac{A}{4} = 5$

The quotient and divisor are known. The dividend is unknown.

$\cancel{4}\left(\dfrac{A}{\cancel{4}}\right) = 5(4)$

Multiply both sides of the equation by the divisor, 4.

$A = \boxed{20}$

The solution is 20.

Check:

$\dfrac{A}{4} = 5$

Replace *A* with the solution 20 and see if both sides are equal.

$\dfrac{20}{4} \overset{?}{=} 5$

$5 = 5$

The solution of the equation is 20.

2 Solve equations using addition or subtraction.

Suppose 15 of the 25 people who work at Carton Manufacturers work on the da
shift. How many people work there in the evening? You know that 15 people wor
there during the day, that 25 people work there in all, and that some unknown quan
tity work there in the evening. Assign the letter N to the unknown number of night
shift workers. The information from the problem can then be written in words a
"the night-shift workers plus the day-shift workers equal 25" and in symbols: $N + 1.$
$= 25$. This equation is one that can be solved with subtraction.

HOW TO Solve an Equation with Addition or Subtraction

Solve the equation
$B + 2 = 8$

1. Isolate the unknown value:

   (a) If the equation contains the *sum* of an unknown value and a known value, then *subtract* the known value from both sides of the equation.

   $\begin{array}{r} B + 2 = 8 \\ -2 \quad -2 \end{array}$

   (b) If the equation contains the *difference* of an unknown value and a known value, then *add* the known value to both sides of the equation.

2. Identify the solution: the solution is the number on the side opposite the isolated unknown-value letter.

   $B = 6$

3. Check the solution: in the original equation, replace the unknown-value letter with the solution, perform the indicated operations, and verify that both sides of the equation are the same number.

   $6 + 2 \overset{?}{=} 8$

   $8 = 8$

EXAMPLE Solve the equation $N + 15 = 25$. (A number increased by 15 is
25.)

$\begin{array}{r} N + 15 = -25 \\ -15 \quad -15 \\ \hline N \quad = \quad 10 \end{array}$

The sum and one value are known.

Subtract the known value, 15, from both sides.

$N = \boxed{10}$

The solution is 10.

Check:

$$N + 15 = 25$$

Replace *N* with the solution 10 and see if both sides are equal.

$$\boxed{10} + 15 \overset{?}{=} 25$$

$$25 = 25$$

The solution is 10.

EXAMPLE Find the value of *A* if $A - 5 = 8$. (A number decreased by 5 is 8.)

$$
\begin{array}{rr}
A - 5 = & 8 \\
\underline{+\,5} & \underline{+\,5} \\
A \;\;\;\; = & \boxed{13}
\end{array}
$$

The difference and the number being subtracted, 5, are known.

Add 5 to both sides.

The solution is 13.

Check:

$$A - 5 = 8$$

Replace *A* with the solution 13 and see if both sides are equal.

$$\boxed{13} - 5 \overset{?}{=} 8$$

$$8 = 8$$

The solution is 13.

TIP! Solve by Undoing

In general, unknowns are isolated in an equation by "undoing" all operations associated with the unknown. Use addition to undo subtraction. Use subtraction to undo addition. Use multiplication to undo division. Use division to undo multiplication. To keep the equation in balance, we perform the same operation on both sides of the equation.

3 Solve equations using more than one operation.

Many business equations contain more than one operation. To solve such equations, we undo each operation in turn. Just as we follow the standard order of operations to *perform operations*, to *undo* operations we must follow the standard order *in reverse:* Working from left to right, we first undo all additions or subtractions, and then undo all multiplications or divisions. Our goal is still to isolate the unknown.

HOW TO Solve an Equation with More than One Operation

Solve the equation
$$3N - 1 = 14$$

1. Isolate the unknown value.

   (a) Working from left to right, add or subtract as necessary *first*.

   (b) Working from left to right, multiply or divide as necessary *second*.

$$
\begin{array}{rr}
3N - 1 = & 14 \\
\underline{+\,1} & \underline{+\,1} \\
3N \;\;\;\; = & 15
\end{array}
$$

$$\frac{3N}{3} = \frac{15}{3}$$

$$N = 5$$

2. Identify the solution: the solution is the number on the side opposite the isolated unknown-value letter.

3. Check the solution: in the original equation, replace the unknown-value letter with the solution, perform the indicated operations according to the standard order of operations, and verify that both sides of the equation are the same number.

$$3(5) - 1 \overset{?}{=} 14$$
$$15 - 1 \overset{?}{=} 14$$
$$14 = 14$$

EXAMPLE Find A if $2A + 1 = 15$. (Two times a number increased by 1 is 15.)

The equation contains both addition and multiplication. Subtract first, and then divide.

$$\begin{array}{rcl} 2A + 1 &=& 15 \\ -1 & & -\ 1 \\ \hline 2A &=& 14 \end{array}$$

The equation shows addition of 1, so subtract 1 from both sides.

$$2A = 14$$

$$\frac{\cancel{2}A}{\cancel{2}} = \frac{14}{2}$$

The equation shows multiplication by 2, so divide both sides by 2.

$$A = \boxed{7}$$

The solution is 7.

Check:

$$2A + 1 = 15$$

Replace A with 7 in the original equation and see if both sides are equal.

$$2\,(7) + 1 \stackrel{?}{=} 15$$

$$14 + 1 \stackrel{?}{=} 15$$

$$15 = 15$$

The solution is 7.

EXAMPLE Solve the equation $\dfrac{A}{5} - 3 = 1$. (A number divided by 5 and decreased by 3 is 1.)

The equation contains both subtraction and division: Add first and then multiply.

$$\begin{array}{rcl} \dfrac{A}{5} - 3 &=& 1 \\[2mm] +\ 3 & & +\ 3 \\ \hline \dfrac{A}{5} &=& 4 \end{array}$$

The equation shows subtraction of 3, so add 3 to both sides.

$$\frac{A}{5} = 4$$

$$\cancel{5}\left(\frac{A}{\cancel{5}}\right) = 4(5)$$

The equation shows division by 5, so multiply both sides by 5.

$$A = \boxed{20}$$

The solution is 20.

Check:

$$\frac{A}{5} - 3 = 1$$

Replace A with 20 in the original equation and see if both sides are equal.

$$\frac{20}{5} - 3 \stackrel{?}{=} 1$$

$$4 - 3 \stackrel{?}{=} 1$$

$$1 = 1$$

The solution is 20.

> **4** Solve equations containing multiple unknown terms.

In some equations, the unknown value may occur more than once. The simplest instance is when the unknown value occurs in two addends. We solve such equations by first combining these addends. Remember that $5A$, for instance, means 5 times A, or $A + A + A + A + A$. To combine $2A + 3A$, we add 2 and 3, to get 5, and then multiply 5 by A, to get $5A$. Thus, $2A + 3A$ is the same as $5A$.

 HOW TO Solve an Equation When the Unknown Value Occurs in Two Addends

1. Combine the unknown-value addends that are on the same side of the equation:

   (a) Add the numbers in each addend.

   (b) Multiply their sum by the unknown value.

2. Solve the resulting equation.

Find A if $2A + 3A = 10$

$(2 + 3)\,A = 10$
$5A = 10$

$$\frac{5A}{5} = \frac{10}{5}$$

$A = 2$

EXAMPLE   Find A if $A + 3A - 2 = 14$.

$A + 3A - 2 = 14$ **First, combine the unknown-value addends. Note, A is the same as $1A$, so $A + 3A = (1 + 3)\,A = 4A$.**

$$\begin{array}{rcr} 4A - 2 = & & 14 \\ +\ 2 & & +\ 2 \\ \hline 4A & = & 16 \end{array}$$

The equation shows subtraction of 2, so add 2 to both sides.

$$\frac{\cancel{4}A}{\cancel{4}} = \frac{16}{4}$$

The equation shows multiplication by 4, so divide both sides by 4. The solution is 4.

$A = \boxed{4}$

Check:

$A + 3A - 2 = 14$ **Replace A with 4 and see if both sides are the same.**

$\boxed{4} + 3(\,\boxed{4}\,) - 2 \overset{?}{=} 14$

$4 + 12 - 2 \overset{?}{=} 14$

$16 - 2 \overset{?}{=} 14$

$14 = 14$

The solution is 4.

 TIP! Adding Unknown Values

Remember that A is the same as $1A$. When combining unknown-value addends, and one of the addends is A, it may help you to write A as $1A$ first.

$$A + 3A = 1A + 3A = 4A$$

5   Solve equations containing parentheses.

To solve an equation containing parentheses, we first write the equation in a form that contains no parentheses. Remember the perimeter formula $P = 2(l + w)$? The formula written without parentheses is $P = 2l + 2w$. In this instance, writing the formula without parentheses means writing $2(l + w)$ as $2l + 2w$: We multiply 2 by each addend inside the parentheses, and then add the resulting products $2l$ and $2w$.

Chapter 3 Problem Solving with Formulas and Equations   **133**

HOW TO Solve an Equation Containing Parentheses

1. Eliminate the parentheses:

    (a) Multiply the number just outside the parentheses by each addend inside the parentheses.

    (b) Show the resulting products as addition or subtraction as indicated.

2. Solve the resulting equation.

Find A if $2(3A + 1) = 14$

$$6A + 2 = 14$$

$$\begin{array}{rr} 6A + 2 = & 14 \\ -2 & -2 \end{array}$$

$$\begin{array}{rl} 6A & = 12 \\ \dfrac{6A}{6} & = \dfrac{12}{6} \\ A & = 2 \end{array}$$

EXAMPLE   Solve the equation $5(A + 3) = 25$.

$$5(A + 3) = 25$$
$$5A + 15 = 25$$

First eliminate the parentheses. Multiply 5 by A, multiply 5 by 3, then show the products as addition.

$$\begin{array}{rr} 5A + 15 = & 25 \\ -15 & -15 \\ \hline 5A \quad = & 10 \end{array}$$

The equation shows addition of 15, so subtract 15 from both sides.

$$\dfrac{5A}{5} = \dfrac{10}{5}$$

The equation shows multiplication by 5, so divide both sides by 5.

$$A = 2$$

The solution is 2.

Check:

$$5(A + 3) = 25$$
$$5(\boxed{2} + 3) \stackrel{?}{=} 25$$
$$10 + 15 \stackrel{?}{=} 25$$
$$25 = 25$$

Replace A with 2 and see if both sides are equal.

The solution is 2.

TIP! Remove Parentheses First

Parentheses in an equation should grab your attention because they say ELIMINATE ME FIRST. You need to eliminate the parentheses before you do anything else in the equation. Trying to solve an equation *without* eliminating parentheses can lead to an incorrect solution, as shown here.

Find X if $5(X - 2) = 45$.

$$5(X - 2) = 45$$

$$\begin{array}{rr} 5X - 10 = & 45 \\ +10 & +10 \\ \hline 5X \quad = & 55 \end{array}$$

$$\dfrac{5X}{5} = \dfrac{55}{5}$$

$$X = 11$$

CORRECT

$$\begin{array}{rr} 5(X - 2) = & 45 \\ +2 & +2 \\ \hline 5X \quad = & 47 \end{array}$$

$$\dfrac{5X}{5} = \dfrac{47}{5}$$

$$X = 9\dfrac{2}{5}$$

INCORRECT

---

6 Solve equations that are proportions.

In Chapters 1 and 2 we solved problems using proportions. Proportions are equations that can be applied to many career and everyday applications. Again, we use proportions to solve problems. This time we will let our knowledge of equations guide us to make the appropriate calculations.

> **? HOW TO** Solve an Equation That Is a Proportion
>
> **1.** Organize the known terms and unknown terms into two pairs of information.
> **2.** Write the two pairs as a proportion.
> **3.** Solve the proportion.

EXAMPLE Real estate tax is often paid only once a year. If the annual tax on a house is $1,287 and the house is sold after seven months of the tax year, how much of the annual tax will both the buyer and seller pay?

1 Decision needed

2 Unknown facts
Amount of tax the seller pays
Amount of tax the buyer pays

3 Known facts
Annual real estate tax = $1,287
Number of months the seller pays = 7
Total months in the tax year = 12

4 Relationships
Number of months buyer pays = 12 − 7 = 5
Proportion for finding amount of tax seller pays

$$\frac{7}{12} = \frac{s}{\$1,287}$$

Part of year owned by seller
full year

Proportion for finding amount that tax buyer pays

$$\frac{5}{12} = \frac{b}{\$1,287}$$

Part of year owned by buyer
full year

5 Estimation
Half of the annual tax would be $643.50. The seller had the property more than half the year. Therefore, the seller will owe more than $643.50 and the buyer will owe less than $643.50.

6 Calculation

$$\frac{7}{12} = \frac{s}{\$1,287}$$ **Proportion for seller**

$$7(1,287) = 12s$$
$$9,009 = 12s$$ **Cross multiply.**

$$\frac{9009}{12} = \frac{12s}{12}$$ **Divide both sides by 12.**

$$\$750.75 = s$$ **Amount seller pays.**

$$\frac{5}{12} = \frac{b}{\$1,287}$$ **Proportion for buyer**

$$5(\$1,287) = 12b$$
$$\$6,435 = 12b$$ **Cross multiply.**

$$\frac{\$6,435}{12} = \frac{12b}{12}$$ **Divide both sides by 12.**

$$\$536.25 = b$$ **Amount buyer pays.**

SELF-CHECK 3.2

1. Solve the equation $5A = 20$.

2. Find the value of B if $\dfrac{B}{7} = 4$.

3. Solve the equation $7C = 56$.

4. Solve the equation $4M = 48$.

5. Find the value of R if $\dfrac{R}{12} = 3$.

6. Solve the equation $\dfrac{P}{5} = 8$.

2

7. Solve the equation for B if $B + 7 = 12$.

8. Find the value of A if $A - 9 = 15$.

9. Find the value of R if $R + 7 = 28$.

10. Solve the equation for A if $A - 16 = 3$.

11. Find the value of X if $X - 48 = 36$.

12. Solve the equation for C if $C + 5 = 21$.

3

13. Solve the equation $4A + 3 = 27$.

14. Solve the equation $\dfrac{B}{3} + 2 = 7$.

15. Solve the equation $3B - 1 = 11$.

16. Find K if $\dfrac{K}{4} - 5 = 3$.

17. Find K if $\dfrac{K}{2} + 3 = 5$.

18. Solve the equation $7B - 1 = 6$.

19. Find C if $\dfrac{C}{2} - 1 = 9$.

20. Solve the equation $8A - 1 = 19$.

4

21. Find A if $2A + 5A = 35$.

22. Find B if $B + 2B = 27$.

23. Find K if $5K - 3K = 40$.

24. Find K if $8K - 2K = 42$.

25. Find J if $3J + J = 28$.

26. Find J if $2J - J = 21$.

27. Find B if $3B + 2B - 6 = 9$.

28. Find C if $8C - C + 6 = 48$.

5

29. Solve the equation $2(X - 3) = 6$.

30. Solve the equation $4(A + 3) = 16$.

31. Solve the equation $3(B - 1) = 21$.

32. Solve the equation $6(B + 2) = 30$.

6 *Use proportions to solve each problem.*

33. The annual real estate tax on a duplex house is $2,321 and the owner sells the house after nine months of the tax year. How much of the annual tax will the seller pay? How much will the buyer pay?

34. A wholesale price list shows that 18 dozen headlights cost $702. If 16 dozen can be bought at the same rate, how much will they cost?

35. Two part-time employees share one full-time job. Charris works Monday, Wednesdays, and Fridays and Chloe works Tuesdays and Thursdays. The job pays an annual salary of $28,592. What annual salary does each employee earn?

36. A car that leases for $5,400 annually is leased for eight months of the year. How much will it cost to lease the car for the eight months?

3.3 Using Equations to Solve Problems

 Use the decision key approach to analyze and solve word problems.

Equations are powerful business tools because equations use mathematical short-hand for expressing relationships. As we know from using the decision key to solve problems, identifying relationships is a critical step. In this section, we practice how to identify relationships and how to write these relationships as equations.

 Use the decision key approach to analyze and solve word problems.

Certain key words in a problem give you clues as to whether a certain quantity is added to, subtracted from, or multiplied or divided by another quantity. For example, if a word problem tells you that Carol's salary in 2003 *exceeds* her 2002 salary by $2,500, you know that you should *add* $2,500 to her 2002 salary to find her 2003 salary. Many times, when you see the word *of* in a problem, the problem involves multiplication. Table 3-1 summarizes important key words and what they generally imply when they are used in a word problem. This list should help you analyze the information in word problems and write the information in symbols.

Table 3-1 Key Words and What They Generally Imply in Word Problems

Addition	Subtraction	Multiplication	Division	Equality
The sum of	Less than	Times	Divide(s)	Equals
Plus/total	Decreased by	Multiplied by	Divided by	Is/was/are
Increased by	Subtracted from	Of	Divided into	Is equal to
More/more than	Difference between	The product of	Half of (divided by two)	The result is
Added to	Diminished by	Twice (two times)	Third of ($\frac{1}{3}$ times)	What is left
Exceeds	Take away	Double (two times)	Per	What remains
Expands	Reduced by	Triple (three times)		The same as
Greater than	Less/minus	Half ($\frac{1}{2}$ times)		Gives/giving
Gain/profit	Loss			Makes
Longer	Lower			Leaves
Older	Shrinks			
Heavier	Smaller than			
Wider	Younger			
Taller	Slower			

Writing Equations.   If you are able to express a relationship among quantities, say,

$$\text{Tax} = \text{tax rate} \times \text{price}$$

then you are able to write an equation, because an equation uses letters rather than words:

$$t = r \times p$$

You practiced writing equations in section 3.2 when you wrote formulas that used letters rather than words. You can apply the same skill using the **decision key approach** to solve problems. Identify the **unknown fact** (value) in words, and assign a letter to it. Identify the **known facts.** Write the **relationship** using the known facts and the unknown-value *letter.* This is the equation. Solve the equation with the appropriate calculations and check your solution.

1 Decision needed

2 Unknown facts

3 Known facts

4 Relationships

5 Estimation

6 Calculation

7 Interpretation

8 Decision made

EXAMPLE   Full-time employees at Charlie's Steakhouse work more hours per day than part-time employees. If the difference of working hours is four per day, and if part-timers work six hours per day, how many hours per day do full-timers work?

Hours per day that full-timers work: n

Hours per day that part-timers work: 6

Difference between hours worked by full-timers and hours worked by part-timers: 4

The word *difference* implies subtraction. Full-time hours − part-time hours = difference of hours

$$n - 6 = 4$$

Full-time workers work *more* hours than part-time workers, so we anticipate that n is more than 6.

$$
\begin{array}{rcl}
n - 6 &=& 4 \\
+\,6 & & +\,6 \\
\hline
n &=& 10
\end{array}
$$

Add 6 to both sides.
The solution is 10.

Check:

$$10 - 6 \overset{?}{=} 4$$

Replace *n* with 4.

$$4 = 4$$

The sides are equal.

The hours per day that full-timers work is 10.

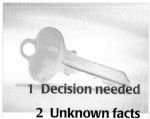

1 Decision needed

2 Unknown facts

3 Known facts

4 Relationships

EXAMPLE   Wanda plans to save $\frac{1}{10}$ of her salary each week. If her weekly salary is $350, how much will she save each week?

Amount to be saved: S

Salary = $350

Rate of saving: $\dfrac{1}{10}$

The word *of* implies multiplication. (Also, the relationship is the percentage formula.)

Amount to be saved = rate of saving × salary

$$S = \frac{1}{10}(\$350)$$

5 Estimation

1 of 10 parts is a small amount. Therefore, the solution should be significantly less than $350.

6 Calculation

$$S = \frac{1}{\cancel{10}_{1}}(\cancel{\$350}^{35}) \qquad \textbf{Multiply.}$$

$$S = \$35 \qquad \textbf{The solution is 35.}$$

Check:

$$\$35 \stackrel{?}{=} \frac{1}{\cancel{10}_{1}}(\cancel{\$350}^{35}) \qquad \textbf{Replace } \textit{S} \textbf{ with \$35 and see if the sides are equal.}$$

$$\$35 = \$35$$

7 Interpretation
8 Decision made

Wanda will save \$35 per week.

  TIP! Reading Problems Several Times

It's a good idea to read a word problem several times. With each reading a different aspect of the problem is analyzed.

1. Read for a general understanding of the problem.
2. Read to determine what you want to find: the unknown fact.
3. Read to locate the given and implied facts: the known facts.
4. Read to relate the known and unknown facts: the relationship, the equation.
5. After solving the equation, read to see if the solution satisfies the conditions of the problem. Does it make sense?

Many times a problem requires finding more than one unknown value. Our strategy will be to choose one unknown value to represent with a letter. Using known facts, we should then be able to express all other unknown values *in terms of* the one letter. For instance, if we know that twice as many men as women attended a conference, then we might represent the number of women as *W*, and the number of men as 2*W*, twice as many as *W*.

EXAMPLE At Alexander's Cafe last Wednesday, there were twice as many requests for seats in the nonsmoking section as there were requests for seats in the smoking section. If 342 customers came to the cafe that day, how many requested the smoking section? How many requested the nonsmoking section?

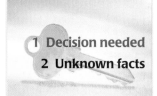

1 Decision needed
2 Unknown facts

Both the number of smokers and the number of nonsmokers are unknown, but we choose one—smokers—to be represented by a letter, *S*.

Number of smokers: *S*

3 Known facts

Since the number of nonsmokers is *twice* the number of smokers, we represent the number of nonsmokers as 2*S*, or 2 times *S*.

Number of nonsmokers: 2*S*
Total customers: 342

4 Relationships

Smokers + nonsmokers = total customers

$$S + 2S = 342$$

5 Estimation

The numbers of smokers and nonsmokers are not equal. There are more nonsmokers. If half the customers is 171, then the smokers will be less than 171 and the nonsmokers will be more than 171.

6 Calculation

$$S + 2S = 342$$

$$3S = 342 \qquad \text{Combine addends.}$$

$$\frac{3S}{3} = \frac{\overset{114}{342}}{3} \qquad \text{Divide both sides by 3.}$$

$$S = 114 \qquad \text{The solution is 114, which represents the number of smokers.}$$

$$2S = 2(114)$$

$$2S = 228 \qquad \text{Twice } S \text{ is twice 114, or 228 nonsmokers.}$$

Check:

$$114 + 228 \overset{?}{=} 342 \qquad \text{Substitute } S = 114 \text{ and } 2S = 228.$$

$$342 = 342$$

7 Interpretation
8 Decision made

There were 114 smokers and 228 nonsmokers.

Learning Strategy Understanding the Concepts

When calculators and computers can so easily be used to find solutions to all types of equations, why do we spend so much time with paper-and-pencil techniques? For our knowledge of mathematics to be useful in real-world situations, we must understand the concepts and know when to use them, and we must understand what the solutions represent.

In developing this understanding of the concepts, we must examine a wide range of situations that might be encountered with the concept. In practice, technological tools can be used to solve equations once you have established appropriate equations through a critical examination of the situation.

EXAMPLE   Juana supervises six times as many data entry clerks as Millie. There are 10 fewer clerks working for Millie than for Juana. How many clerks are working for Millie? How many clerks are working for Juana?

1 Decision needed

2 Unknown facts

Number of Millie's clerks: *M*

3 Known facts

Since the number of Juana's clerks is *six times* the number of Millie's clerks, we represent the number of Juana's clerks as 6*M*, or 6 times *M*. Also we know that the difference of Juana's clerks and Millie's clerks is 10, since *10 fewer* work for Millie than for Juana.

Number of Juana's clerks: $6M$

Difference of Juana's clerks and Millie's clerks: 10

4 Relationships

Juana's clerks − Millie's clerks = difference

$$6M - M = 10$$

5 Estimation

The clerks supervised by Juana and Millie are not equal and Juana supervises the larger number of clerks.

6 Calculation

$6M - M = 10$ — Since $6M$ represents the larger amount, it should come first in the subtraction.

$5M = 10$ — Combine.

$$\frac{\cancel{5}M}{\cancel{5}} = \frac{\overset{2}{\cancel{10}}}{\cancel{5}}$$ — Divide both sides by 5.

$M = 2$ — The solution is 2, which represents Millie's clerks.

$6M = 6(2)$

$6M = 12$ — 6 times M is 6(2), or 12, Juana's clerks.

Check:

$12 - 2 \overset{?}{=} 10$ — Substitute $6M$ with 12 and M with 2.

$10 = 10$

7 Interpretation

8 Decision made

Millie supervises 2 clerks; Juana supervises 12 clerks.

Many problems give a *total* number of two types of items. You want to know the number of each of the two types of items. The next example illustrates this type of problem.

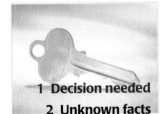

EXAMPLE The Cheerful Card Shop spent a total of $950 ordering 600 cards from Wit's End Co., whose humorous cards cost $1.75 each and whose nature cards cost $1.50 each. How many of each style card did the card shop order?

1 Decision needed

2 Unknown facts

There are two unknown facts, but we choose one—the number of humorous cards—to be represented by a letter, H.

Number of humorous cards: H

3 Known facts

Knowing that the total number of cards is 600, we represent the number of nature cards as 600 minus the humorous cards, or $600 - H$.

Total cost of cards: $950
Number of nature cards: $600 - H$
Cost per humorous card: $1.75
Cost per nature card: $1.50

4 Relationships

Total cost = (cost per humorous card)(number of humorous cards) + (cost per nature card)(number of nature cards)

$$950 = (1.75)(H) + (1.50)(600 - H)$$

$$950 = 1.75H + 1.50(600 - H)$$

5 Estimation

Half of 600 is 300. More than 300 cards of one type were purchased and less than 300 of the other were purchased.

6 Calculation

$$950 = 1.75H + (1.50)(600) - 1.50H$$

$$950 = 1.75H + 900 - 1.50H$$

Eliminate parentheses showing grouping.

$$950 = 0.25H + 900$$
$$\underline{-900 \qquad\qquad -900}$$
$$50 = 0.25H$$

Combine letter terms.
Subtract 900 from both sides.

$$\frac{50}{0.25} = \frac{0.25H}{0.25}$$

Divide both sides by 0.25.

$$200 = H$$

The solution is 200, which represents the number of humorous cards.

$$600 - H = 600 - 200$$

$$600 - H = 400$$

Subtract *H*, or 200, from 600 to find 600 − *H*, or 400, the number of nature cards.

Check:

$$950 \overset{?}{=} (1.75)(200) + (1.50)(600 - 200)$$

$$950 \overset{?}{=} 350 + (1.50)(400)$$

$$950 \overset{?}{=} 350 + 600$$

$$950 = 950$$

Substitute 200 in place of *H*. Then perform calculations using the order of operations.

7 Interpretation

8 Decision made

The card shop ordered 200 humorous cards and 400 nature cards.

Equations That Are Proportions. Many problems encountered daily involve two pairs of values that are proportional.

A proportion is an equation in which each side is a ratio. For example, using two ounces out of a four-gallon bottle of cleaning fluid is proportional to using four ounces out of an eight-gallon bottle. Expressed as a proportion, this example would be

$$\frac{2 \text{ oz}}{4 \text{ gal}} = \frac{4 \text{ oz}}{8 \text{ gal}} \quad \text{or} \quad \frac{2 \text{ oz}}{4 \text{ oz}} = \frac{4 \text{ gal}}{8 \text{ gal}}$$

EXAMPLE Your car gets 23 miles to a gallon of gas. How far can you go on 16 gallons of gas?

1 Decision needed

2 Unknown facts Distance traveled using 16 gallons: *x* miles **(Pair 1)**

3 Known facts Distance traveled using 1 gallon: 23 miles **(Pair 2)**

4 Relationships Miles traveled per 16 gallons is proportional to miles traveled per 1 gallon.

$$\underset{\textbf{Pair 1}}{\frac{x \text{ miles}}{16 \text{ gallons}}} = \underset{\textbf{Pair 2}}{\frac{23 \text{ miles}}{1 \text{ gallon}}} \quad \text{or} \quad \frac{x \text{ miles}}{23 \text{ miles}} = \frac{16 \text{ gallons}}{1 \text{ gallon}} \quad \begin{array}{l} \textbf{Pair 1} \\ \textbf{Pair 2} \end{array}$$

5 Estimation If the car travels at 20 miles per gallon, 320 miles could be traveled on 16 gallons. More miles could be traveled if the car traveled 23 miles per gallon.

6 Calculation

$$\frac{x}{16} = \frac{23}{1}$$

$$1x = (16)(23) \qquad \textbf{Cross multiply.}$$

$$x = 368$$

Check:

$$\frac{368}{16} \overset{?}{=} \frac{23}{1}$$

Substitute 368 for *x*.

$$(1)(368) \overset{?}{=} (16)(23)$$

$$368 = 368$$

7 Interpretation

You can travel 368 miles using 16 gallons of gas.

8 Decision made

EXAMPLE The label on a container of concentrated weed killer gives directions to mix three ounces of weed killer with every two gallons of water. For five gallons of water, how many ounces of weed killer should you use?

1 Decision needed

2 Unknown facts   Amount of weed killer for five gallons of water: *x* ounces   **Pair 1**

3 Known facts   Amount of weed killer for two gallons of water: three ounces   **Pair 2**

4 Relationships   Amount of weed killer per five gallons is proportional to an amount of weed killer per two gallons.

$$\frac{x \text{ ounces}}{5 \text{ gallons}} = \frac{3 \text{ ounces}}{2 \text{ gallons}}$$

Pair 1   **Pair 2**

5 Estimation   If three ounces of weed killer are needed for two gallons of water, more weed killer will be needed for more water.

6 Calculation

$$\frac{x}{5} = \frac{3}{2}$$

$$2x = (5)(3)$$ Cross multiply.

$$2x = 15$$

$$\frac{2x}{2} = \frac{15}{2}$$ Divide both sides by 2.

$$x = 7\frac{1}{2}$$ The solution is $7\frac{1}{2}$.

Check:

$$\frac{7\frac{1}{2}}{5} \overset{?}{=} \frac{3}{2}$$ Substitute $7\frac{1}{2}$ for *x*.

$$(2)(7\tfrac{1}{2}) \overset{?}{=} (5)(3)$$

$$\left(\frac{2}{1}\right)\left(\frac{15}{2}\right) \overset{?}{=} 15$$

$$15 = 15$$

7 Interpretation   **You should use $7\frac{1}{2}$ ounces of weed killer.**

8 Decision made

Another format that is handy for using the decision key approach to solving word problems is a table format. Examine the solution to the preceding example using this format.

Unknown	Knowns	Relationship	Estimation	Calculation
Weed killer for 5 gallons of water: x	Weed killer for 2 gallons of water: 3 ounces	x ounces weed killer per 5 gallons water is proportional to 3 ounces weed killer per 2 gallons water $$\frac{x \text{ ounces}}{5 \text{ gallons}} = \frac{3 \text{ ounces}}{2 \text{ gallons}}$$	If three ounces of weed killer are needed for two gallons of water, more weed killer will be needed for more water.	$$\frac{x}{5} = \frac{3}{2}$$ $$2x = (5)(3)$$ $$2x = 15$$ $$\frac{2x}{2} = \frac{15}{2}$$ $$x = 7\frac{1}{2}$$

Interpretation		Check
You should use $7\frac{1}{2}$ ounces of weed killer.		$$7\frac{1}{2} \stackrel{?}{=} \frac{3}{2}$$ $$2\left(7\frac{1}{2}\right) = (5)(3)$$ $$\frac{2}{1}\left(\frac{15}{2}\right) = 15$$ $$15 = 15$$

Learning Strategy Additional Problem-Solving Strategies

- Read the problem carefully. Read it several times and phrase by phrase.
- Understand all the words in the problem.
- Analyze the problem:
  What are you asked to find?
  What facts are given?
  What facts are implied?
- Visualize the problem.
- State the conditions or relationships of the problem "symbolically."
- Examine the options.
- Develop a *plan* for solving the problem.
- Write your *plan* symbolically; that is, write an equation.
- Anticipate the characteristics of a reasonable solution.
- Solve the equation.
- Verify your answer with the conditions of the problem.

There are many different problem-solving plans. Additional strategies can be considered.

1. The difference in hours between full-timers and the part-timers who work five hours a day is four hours. How long do full-timers work?

2. Manny plans to save $\frac{1}{12}$ of his salary each week. If his weekly salary is $372, find the amount he will save each week.

3. Last week at the Sunshine Valley Rock Festival, Joel sold three times as many tie-dyed T-shirts as silk-screened shirts. He sold 176 shirts altogether. How many tie-dyed shirts did he sell?

4. Elaine sold three times as many magazine subscriptions as Ron did. Ron sold 16 fewer subscriptions than Elaine did. How many subscriptions did each sell?

5. Will ordered two times as many boxes of ballpoint pens as boxes of felt-tip pens. Ballpoint pens cost $3.50 per box, and felt-tip pens cost $4.50. If Will's order of pens totaled $46, how many boxes of each type of pen did he buy?

6. A real estate salesperson bought promotional calendars and date books to give to her customers at the end of the year. The calendars cost $0.75 each and the date books cost $0.50 each. She ordered a total of 500 promotional items and spent $300. How many of each item did she order?

7. A scale drawing of an office building is not labeled, but indicates $\frac{1}{4}$ inches = 5 feet. On the drawing, one wall measures two inches. How long is the wall?

8. A recipe uses three cups of flour to $1\frac{1}{4}$ cups of milk. If you have two cups of flour, how much milk should you use?

9. For 32 hours of work, you are paid $241.60. How much would you receive for 37 hours?

Budgeting with Formulas and Spreadsheets

The 7th Inning Sports Memorabilia Shop is developing an annual operating budget. The budget categories and the projected amount of expense for each category are shown in the spreadsheet in Figure 3-8. Some of the additional information needed is the total operating budget for the year and the percent of total annual budget for each category in the projected annual budget. Formulas must be developed to calculate this information.

The spreadsheet program labels the columns with the letters A through F, and the rows with numbers 1 through 14. The person developing the spreadsheet uses row 1 for the title of the spreadsheet, row 3 to label the columns of data, and column A to label the rows of data. Each position on the spreadsheet is called a *cell*, and the program identifies each cell by its column letter and row number. For example, the amount budgeted for taxes and insurance is in cell B9 and is $15,000.00.

Formulas are now developed to make the needed calculations. Each spreadsheet program gives various shortcuts for writing formulas and formats for giving instructions unique to that program; however, we will write the basic concepts used, and program-specific conventions can be added as appropriate.

Example

Write the formulas and make the calculations to complete cell B14 and column C of the spreadsheet in Figure 3-8. To find the total to be placed in cell B14, we need to add the amounts in cells B5 through B12. We represent this in a formula by giving the addresses of the cells to be added: B14 = B5 + B6 + B7 + B8 + B9 + B10 + B11 + B12.

Microsoft Excel - Figure 3-8.xls

	A	B	C	D	E	F
1	The 7th Inning Budgeted Operating Expenses and Actual Expenses					
2						
3	Expense	Budget Amount	Percent of Total Budget	Actual Expenses	% of Actual Total Expenses	% Difference from Budget
4						
5	Salaries	$45,000.00		$42,000.00		
6	Rent	37,000.00		36,000.00		
7	Depreciation	12,000.00		14,000.00		
8	Utilities and phone	13,000.00		10,862.56		
9	Taxes and insurance	15,000.00		13,583.29		
10	Advertising	2,000.00		2,847.83		
11	Purchases	125,000.00		132,894.64		
12	Other	2,000.00		1,356.35		
13						
14	Total					

Figure 3-8

Figure 3-9

To calculate the percent of the total budget, the specific amount is divided by the total budget and then multiplied by 100. We will write a formula for each line of data. Most programs use an asterisk (*) to show multiplication and a forward slash (/) to show division.

C5 = B5/B14*100	C6 = B6/B14*100	C7 = B7/B14*100
C8 = B8/B14*100	C9 = B9/B14*100	C10 = B10/B14*100
C11 = B11/B14*100	C12 = B12/B14*100	

There are two ways to determine the value for cell C14. If we use the percent method, the percentage and the base would be the same amount, so the total percent would be 100%. To build in a check against the spreadsheet formulas, however, it is advisable to find the total percent by adding the calculated percents. It is easy to make a typing error in the formulas or to place the formula in the wrong cell. The total should be 100% or extremely close. There may be a small discrepancy due to the effects of rounding. C14 = C5 + C6 + C7 + C8 + C9 + C10 + C11 + C12. The spreadsheet with the completed calculations is shown in Figure 3-9.

Exercises

1. Develop formulas to complete cell D14 and columns E and F of the spreadsheet in Figure 3-9 to show data for the actual expenses for the 7th Inning Sports Memorabilia Shop.

2. Use the formulas to complete the spreadsheet for the 7th Inning Sports Memorabilia Shop (Figure 3-10).

Microsoft Excel - Figure 3-10.xls

File Edit View Insert Format Tools Data Window Help

Arial · 10 · B I U $ % ,

G22 =

	A	B	C	D	E	F	G	H	I	J
1	The 7th Inning Budgeted Operating Expenses and Actual Expenses									
2										
3	Expense	Budget Amount	Percent of Total Budget	Actual Expenses	% of Actual Total Expenses	% Difference from Budget				
4										
5	Salaries	$45,000.00		$42,000.00						
6	Rent	37,000.00		36,000.00						
7	Depreciation	12,000.00		14,000.00						
8	Utilities and phone	13,000.00		10,862.56						
9	Taxes and insurance	15,000.00		13,583.29						
10	Advertising	2,000.00		2,847.83						
11	Purchases	125,000.00		132,894.64						
12	Other	2,000.00		1,356.35						
13										
14	Total									
15										

Sheet1 / Sheet2 / Sheet3 /

Figure 3-10

CHAPTER 3   OVERVIEW

Section
Outcome   **Important Points with Examples**

Section 3.1

1

Evaluate
formulas.
(page 120)

1. Replace letters or words in the formula with their known values.
2. Perform the operations indicated by the formula.
3. Interpret the result.

Evaluate the formula $I = Prt$ when P is $2,000, r is 5%, and t is 2 years.

$I = Prt$
$I = 2,000(0.05)(2)$ Change 5% to its decimal equivalent.
$I = 200$

The interest is $200.

2

Write a
formula to
find an
unknown
value.
(page 122)

1. Represent the unknown value with a letter.
2. Represent each known value with a letter.
3. Write the unknown-value letter on the left side of an equal sign and the known-value letters with appropriate operation symbols on the right side of the equal sign.

> **Write a formula to find the net pay (take-home pay) if net pay is equal to the total deductions subtracted from the gross pay.**
>
> $N = G - D$, where N is net pay, G is gross pay, and D is deductions.

3 Write electronic spreadsheet instructions as formulas. (page 122)

Write the formula in words. Develop the formula by substituting specific cell addresses for appropriate words in the formula.

> **Write a formula to sum employees' salaries if the salaries are to be placed in the cells indicated. Place the sum in cell B7.**
>
> \$42,843 → B3
> \$39,273 → B4
> \$45,200 → B5
> B7 = B3 + B4 + B5

Section 3.2

Solve equations using multiplication or division. (page 129)

1. Isolate the unknown value:
   (a) If the equation contains the *product* of the unknown value and a number, then *divide* both sides of the equation by the number.
   (b) If the equation contains the *quotient* of the unknown value and a number, then *multiply* both sides of the equation by the number.
2. Identify the solution: The solution is the number on the side opposite the isolated unknown-value letter.
3. Check the solution: In the original equation, replace the unknown-value letter with the solution, perform the indicated operations, and verify that both sides of the equation are the same number.

> **Find the value of A.**
>
> $$4A = 36$$
>
> $$\frac{4A}{4} = \frac{36}{4} \qquad \textbf{Divide both sides by 4.}$$
>
> $$A = 9$$
>
> $$\frac{A}{7} = 6$$
>
> $$\frac{A}{7} \times 7 = 6 \times 7 \qquad \textbf{Multiply both sides by 7.}$$
>
> $$A = 42$$

2 Solve equations using addition or subtraction. (page 130)

1. Isolate the unknown value:
   (a) If the equation contains the *sum* of the unknown value and another number, then *subtract* the number from both sides of the equation.
   (b) If the equation contains the *difference* of the unknown value and another number, then *add* the number to both sides of the equation.
2. Identify the solution: The solution is the number on the side opposite the isolated unknown-value letter.
3. Check the solution: In the original equation, replace the unknown-value letter with the solution, perform the indicated operations, and verify that both sides of the equation are the same number.

Find the value of A.

$$A - 7 = 12$$
$$\underline{+7 \quad +\ 7} \quad \text{Add 7 to both sides.}$$
$$A \quad = \quad 19$$

$$A + 5 = 32$$
$$\underline{-5 \quad -\ 5} \quad \text{Subtract 5 from}$$
$$A \quad = \quad 27 \quad \text{both sides.}$$

3

Solve equations using more than one operation. (page 131)

1. Isolate the unknown value:
   (a) Working from left to right, add or subtract as necessary *first*.
   (b) Working from left to right, multiply or divide as necessary *second*.
2. Identify the solution: The solution is the number on the side opposite the isolated unknown-value letter.
3. Check the solution: In the original equation, replace the unknown-value letter with the solution, perform the indicated operations according to the standard order, and verify that both sides of the equation are the same number.

Find the value of A.

$$4A + 4 = 20$$
$$\underline{-4 \quad -\ 4} \quad \text{Undo addition first.}$$
$$4A \quad = \quad 16$$

$$\frac{4A}{4} = \frac{16}{4} \quad \text{Then undo multiplication.}$$

$$A = 4$$

$$\frac{A}{3} - 5 = 12$$
$$\underline{+5 \quad +\ 5} \quad \text{Undo sub-}$$
$$\frac{A}{3} \quad = \quad 17 \quad \text{traction first.}$$

$$\frac{A}{3} \times 3 = 17 \times 3 \quad \text{Then undo}$$
$$\text{division.}$$

$$A = 51$$

4

Solve equations containing multiple unknown terms. (page 132)

Solve an equation when the unknown value occurs in two or more addends.
1. Combine the unknown value addends:
   (a) Add the numbers in each addend.
   (b) Multiply their sum by the unknown value.
2. Solve the resulting equation.

Find the value of A.

$$A - 5 + 5A = 25$$

$$6A - 5 = 25 \quad \text{Combine addends that have unknown factors.}$$
$$\underline{+5 \quad +\ 5} \quad \text{Add 5 to both sides.}$$
$$6A \quad = \quad 30$$

$$\frac{6A}{6} = \frac{30}{6} \quad \text{Divide both sides by 6.}$$

$$A = 5$$

5

Solve equations containing parentheses. (page 133)

1. Eliminate the parentheses:
   (a) Multiply the number just outside the parentheses by each addend inside the parentheses.
   (b) Show the resulting products as addition.
2. Solve the resulting equation.

Find the value of A.

$3(A + 4) = 27$

$3A + 12 = 27$ **Eliminate parentheses first.**
$\underline{ -12 \quad -12}$ **Subtract 12 from both sides.**
$3A = 15$

$\dfrac{3A}{3} = \dfrac{15}{3}$ **Divide both sides by 3.**

$A = 5$

 Solve equations that are proportions. (page 135)

1. Organize the knowns and unknowns into two pairs of information.
2. Write the two pairs as a proportion.
3. Solve the proportion.

If four printer cartridges cost \$28.80, how much would seven cartridges cost?

4 cartridges cost \$28.80.   **Pair 1**
7 cartridges cost \$N.   **Pair 2**

$\dfrac{4}{7} = \dfrac{\$28.80}{\$N}$ **Pair 1**
            Pair 2

$4N = 7(28.80)$

$4N = 201.60$

$\dfrac{4N}{4} = \dfrac{201.60}{4}$

$N = \$50.40$

Seven cartridges cost \$50.40.

Section 3.3

Use the decision key approach to analyze and solve word problems. (page 137)

Key words and what they imply in word problems.

Addition	Subtraction	Multiplication	Division	Equality
The sum of	Less than	Times	Divide(s)	Equals
Plus/total	Decreased by	Multiplied by	Divided by	Is/was/are
Increased by	Subtracted from	Of	Divided into	Is equal to
More/more than	Difference between	The product of	Half of (divided by two)	The result is
Added to	Diminished by	Twice (two times)		What is left
Exceeds	Take away	Double	Third of ($\frac{1}{3}$ times)	What remains
Expands	Reduced by	(two times)		The same as
Greater than	Less/minus	Triple	Per	Gives/giving
Gain/profit	Loss	(three times)		Makes
Longer	Lower	Half ($\frac{1}{2}$ times)		Leaves
Older	Shrinks			
Heavier	Smaller than			
Wider	Younger			
Taller	Slower			

formula (p. 120)
evaluating formulas (p. 120)
square (p. 120)
perimeter (p. 120)
standard order of operations
  (p. 121)

rectangle (p. 121)
length (p. 121)
width (p. 121)
electronic spreadsheet (p. 123)
spreadsheet (p. 123)
equation (p. 129)

decision key approach (p. 138)
unknown fact (p. 138)
known fact (p.138)
relationship (p. 138)
proportion (p. 142)

CHAPTER 3 CONCEPTS ANALYSIS

1. Briefly describe the procedure for evaluating a formula when numerical values are given for every variable in the formula except one.

2. Describe the similarities and differences in the formulas for the perimeter of a square and the perimeter of a rectangle.

3. Give some instances when it would be desirable to have more than one version of a relationship. For example, $P = R \times B$, $R = \dfrac{P}{B}$, $B = \dfrac{P}{R}$

4. Explain why $1.2 + n = 1.7$ and $1.7 - 1.2 = n$ will give the same result for n.

5. Explain why $5 \times n = 4.5$ and $n = \dfrac{4.5}{5}$ give the same result for n.

6. Either of the two formulas $P = 2l + 2w$ and $P = 2(l + w)$ can be used to find the perimeter of a rectangle. Explain why.

7. Test both of the formulas $P = s + s + s + s$ and $P = 4s$ to see if each formula gives the same perimeter for a square of your choosing. If each formula gives the same result, explain why.

8. Find the mistake in the following problem. Explain the mistake and rework the problem correctly.

$$10 + 7(8 + 4) =$$
$$17(8 + 4) =$$
$$17(12) = 204$$

9. If the wholesale cost of 36 printer cartridges is $188, explain how a proportion can be used to find the cost of one cartridge.

10. If the cartridges in exercise 9 are to be priced for resale at 50% over cost, how do you determine the resale price of each?

CHAPTER 3 ASSIGNMENT EXERCISES

Section 3.1

Evaluate the formulas.

1. Use the formula $P = RB$ to find P when $R = 12\%$ and $B = \$1,000$.

2. Use the formula $P = RB$ to find P when $R = 8\%$ and $B = \$2,500$.

3. Use the formula $P = 2l + 2w$ to find the perimeter P, when $l = 42$ feet and $w = 29$ feet.

4. Use the formula $P = 2l + 2w$ to find the perimeter P when $l = 96$ inches and $w = 82$ inches.

5. Use the formula $I = Prt$ to find I when $P = \$4,500$, $r = 9\%$, and $t = 5$ years.

6. Use the formula $I = Prt$ to find I when $P = \$8,250$, $r = 8\%$, and $t = 2$ years.

7. Write the formula to find the perimeter (P) of a regular octagon. A regular octagon is a figure that has eight equal sides(s).

8. Write a formula to find the amount of Social Security (S) that is withheld from a paycheck if the gross pay (G) is multiplied by the withholding rate (R).

9. Use the formula in exercise 7 to find the perimeter of an octagon if the length of a side is 17 inches.

10. Use the formula in exercise 8 to find the amount of Social Security withheld from a gross pay of $\$4,322.00$ if the rate is 5.85%.

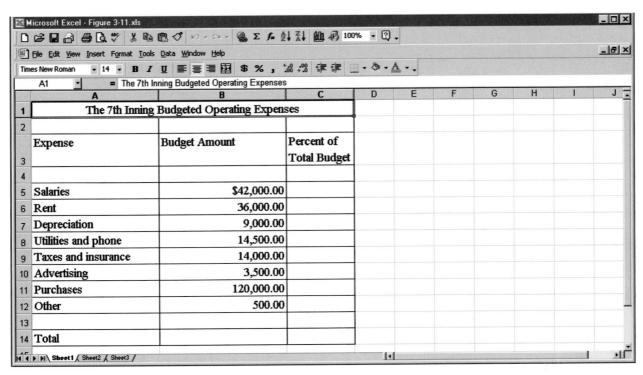

Figure 3-11

11. The 7th Inning Sports Memorabilia Shop is developing an annual operating budget. The budget categories and the projected amount of expense for each category are shown in the spreadsheet in Figure 3-11. Additional information needed is the total operating budget for the year and the percent of total annual budget for each category in the projected annual budget. Develop formulas to calculate this information.

12. Perform the calculations to complete the spreadsheet in exercise 11.

Section 3.2

Find the value of the variable.

13. $5N = 35$

14. $3N = 27$

15. $\dfrac{A}{6} = 2$

16. $\dfrac{A}{2} = 3$

17. $N - 5 = 12$

18. $N + 8 = 20$

19. $2N + 4 = 12$

20. $3N - 5 = 10$

21. $\dfrac{A}{3} + 4 = 12$

22. $\dfrac{A}{2} - 5 = 1$

23. $2(x - 3) = 8$

24. $5(A - 9) = 10$

25. $3(x - 1) = 30$

26. $7(B - 2) = 21$

27. $8A - 3A = 40$

28. $4A - A = 3$

29. $4X - X = 21$

30. $3X - 4 + 2X = 11$

Section 3.3

31. Ace Motors sold a total of 15 cars and trucks during one promotion sale. Six of the vehicles sold were trucks. What is the number of cars that were sold?

32. Edna's Book Carousel ordered several cookbooks and received 12. The shipping invoice indicated that six books would be shipped later. What is the number of books that was ordered?

33. The Queen of Diamonds Card Shop ordered an equal number of 12 different cards. If a total of 60 cards were ordered, how many of each type of card were ordered?

34. The Stork Club is a chain of baby clothing stores. The owner of the chain divided a number of Easter bonnets by the seven stores in the chain. If each store got nine bonnets, what was the number of bonnets distributed by the owner of the chain?

35. An electrician pays $\frac{2}{5}$ of the amount he charges for a job for supplies. If he was paid $240 for a certain job, how much did he spend on supplies?

36. Liz Bliss spends 18 hours on a project and estimates that she has completed $\frac{1}{3}$ of the project. How many hours does she expect the project to take?

37. An inventory clerk is expected to have 2,000 fan belts in stock. If the current count is 1,584 fan belts, how many more should be ordered?

38. A personal computer costs $4,000, and a postscript printer costs $1,500. What is the total cost of the equipment?

39. Carrie McConnel spends $\frac{1}{6}$ of her weekly earnings on groceries. How much does she spend on groceries if her weekly earnings are $345?

40. A purse that sells for $68.99 is reduced by $25.50. What is the price of the purse after the reduction?

41. Shaquita Davis earns $350 for working 40 hours. How much does she make for each hour of work?

42. Wilson's Auto, Inc., has 37 employees and a weekly payroll of $10,878. If each employee makes the same amount, how much does each make?

43. Molly McWherter earns $7.36 per hour. How much would she make for 37 hours of work?

44. An imprint machine makes 1,897 imprints per hour. How many imprints can be made in 12 hours?

45. Wallpaper costs $12.97 per roll and a kitchen requires nine rolls. What is the cost of the wallpaper needed to paper the kitchen?

46. Mack Construction Co. was billed for plasterboard installation. If the job required 3,582 square feet of plasterboard and cost $2,435.76, what was the cost per square foot?

47. Allen Brent purchased 250 pounds of tomatoes, 400 pounds of potatoes, 50 pounds of broccoli, and 130 pounds of birdseed for his chain stores. If all items are placed on the same shipment, what is the total weight of the shipment?

48. Harks Manufacturer is negotiating a waste-removal contract. A study indicates that, in general, 304 pounds of waste are produced on Monday, 450 pounds are produced on Tuesday, 483 pounds are produced on Wednesday, 387 pounds are produced on Thursday, and 293 pounds are produced on Friday. The plant is closed on Saturday and Sunday. How many pounds of waste are produced per week?

49. Cecil Hastings was overstocked with men's shirts and reduced the price from $18.99 to $15.97. By how much was each shirt reduced?

50. Cecil (exercise 49) counted 216 shirts to be reduced. What was the total amount of reduction for 216 shirts?

51. The wholesale cost of an executive desk is $375, and the wholesale cost of a secretarial desk is $300. Allen Furniture Company filled an order for 40 desks, costing a total of $12,825. How many desks of each type were ordered?

52. A computer store sold 144 cases of two grades of computer paper. Microperforated paper cost $15.97 per case, and standard perforated paper cost $9.75 per case. If the store had paper sales totaling $1,715, how many cases of each type were sold? What was the dollar value of each type sold?

53. Bright Ideas purchased 1,000 light bulbs. Headlight bulbs cost $13.95 each, and taillight bulbs cost $7.55 each. If Bright Ideas spent $9,342 on light bulb stock, how many headlights and how many taillights did it get? What was the dollar value of the headlights ordered? What was the dollar value of the taillights ordered?

54. If a delivery van travels 252 miles on 12 gallons of gas, how many gallons are needed to travel 378 miles?

55. If five dozen roses can be purchased for $62.50, how much will eight dozen cost?

Challenge Problem

56. Find a variation of the formula $P = 2L + 2W$ so that W is alone on the left. When would you use this formula? Explain some of the advantages that are gained from using formulas and equations to solve problems.

1. Evaluate the formula $S = C + M$ for S if $C = \$296$ and $M = \$150$.

2. Evaluate the formula $G = hr$ if $h = 40$ hours and $r = \$9.83$.

3. Write a formula for the relationship. The markup (M) on an item is the difference between the selling price (S) and the cost (C).

4. Write a formula to find the sales-tax rate (r) if it is the amount of tax (t) divided by the price of an item (p).

Solve.

5. $N + 7 = 18$

6. $5N = 45$

7. $\dfrac{A}{3} = 6$

8. $B - 8 = 7$

9. $3A - 5 = 10$

10. $5A + 8 = 33$

11. $2(N + 1) = 14$

12. $5A + A = 30$

13. An employee who was earning $249 weekly received a raise of $36. How much is the new salary?

14. An inventory clerk is expected to keep 600 filters on hand. A physical count shows there are 298 filters in stock. How many filters should be ordered?

15. A container of oil holds 585 gallons. How many containers each holding 4.5 gallons will be needed if all the oil is to be transferred to the smaller containers?

16. The buyer for a specialty gift store purchased an equal number of two types of designer telephones for a total cost of $7,200. The top-quality phones cost $120 each, and the plastic phones cost $80 each. How many of each type of phone were purchased and what was the total dollar value of each type?

17. A discount store sold plastic cups for $3.50 each and ceramic cups for $4 each. If 400 cups were sold for a total of $1,458, how many cups of each type were sold? What was the dollar value of each type of cup sold?

18. An appliance dealer sold nine more washing machines than dryers. Washing machines sell for $480 and dryers sell for $350. If total dollar sales were $21,750, how many of each appliance were sold? What was the dollar value of washing machines sold and the dollar value of dryers sold?

19. Find the cost of 200 suits if 75 suits cost $10,200.

20. Lashonna Harris is a buyer for Plough. She can purchase 100 pounds of chemicals for $97. At this same rate, how much would 2,000 pounds of the chemical cost?

Self-Check 3.1

1. $S = C + M$
   $S = 13.98 + 12.50$
   $S = 26.48$
   The blouse sells for $26.48.

2. $S = C + M$
   $S = 700 + 859$
   $S = 1,559$
   The refrigerator sells for $1,559.

3. $I = Prt$
   $I = 8,000(0.07)(2)$
   $I = 1,120$
   The interest is $1,120.

4. $I = Prt$
$I = 12{,}000(0.055)(3)$
$I = 1{,}980$
The interest is \$1,980.

5. $P = 2l + 2w$
$P = 2(12) + 2(8)$
$P = 24 + 16$
$P = 40$
The perimeter is 40 inches.

6. $P = s + s + s + s + s + s$ or
$P = 6s$

7. $P = hr$, where P is gross pay, h is hours worked, and r is pay per hour

8. $P = 40(6.25)$
$P = \$250$
The gross pay is \$250.

9. $M = rs$, where M is markdown, r is markdown rate, and s is selling price.

10. $M = (0.25)(259)$
$M = \$64.75$
The markdown is \$64.75.

11. $p = s - m$, where p is reduced price, s is selling price, and m is markdown.

12. $p = 259 - 64.75$
$p = \$194.25$
The reduced price is \$194.25.

13. $t = rp$, where t is sales tax, p is price, and r is sales tax rate.

14. $t = (0.06)12.95$
$t = 0.777$ or 0.78 (rounded)
The sales tax is \$0.78.

15. $c = p + t$, where c is total cost, p is price, and t is sales tax.

16. $c = 12.95 + 0.78$
$c = \$13.73$
The total cost of the calculator is \$13.73.

17.

Expense	Amount	Decimal Part	Percent
Silver's Spa Operating Expenses for May			
Salary	\$33,917	0.5808302	58.1
Rent	8,500	0.1455629	14.6
Depreciation	2,500	0.0428126	4.3
Miscellaneous	2,341	0.0400897	4.0
Taxes and insurance	8,290	0.1419666	14.2
Utilities	1,846	0.0316128	3.2
Advertising	1,000	0.0171250	1.7
Total	\$58,394	0.9999998	100.1

Total $= 33{,}917 + 8{,}500 + 2{,}500 + 2{,}341 + 8{,}290 + 1{,}846 + 1{,}000 = 58{,}394$

Salary decimal $= \dfrac{33{,}917}{58{,}394} = 0.5808302$

Percent $= 0.5808302 \times 100\% = 58.1\%$

Rent decimal $= \dfrac{8{,}500}{58{,}394} = 0.1455629$

Percent $= 0.1455629 \times 100\% = 14.6\%$

Depreciation decimal $= \dfrac{2{,}500}{58{,}394} = 0.0428126$

Percent $= 0.0428126 \times 100\% = 4.3\%$

Miscellaneous decimal $= \dfrac{2{,}341}{58{,}394} = 0.0400897$

Percent $= 0.0400897 \times 100\% = 4.0\%$

Taxes and insurance decimal $= \dfrac{8{,}290}{58{,}394} = 0.1419666$

Percent $= 0.1419666 \times 100\% = 14.2\%$

Utilities decimal $= \dfrac{1{,}846}{58{,}394} = 0.0316128$

Percent $= 0.0316128 \times 100\% = 3.2\%$

Advertising decimal $= \dfrac{1{,}000}{58{,}394} = 0.0171250$

Percent $= 0.0171250 \times 100\% = 1.7\%$

Total percent $= 58.1 + 14.6 + 4.3 + 4.0 + 14.2 + 3.2 + 1.7 = 100.1$

18. B14 = B5 + B6 + B7 + B8 + B9 + B10 + B11 + B12

   D14 = D5 + D6 + D7 + D8 + D9 + D10 + D11 + D12

   C5 = B5 ÷ B14 × 100

   C6 = B6 ÷ B14 × 100

   C7 = B7 ÷ B14 × 100

   ⋮

   C12 = B12 ÷ B14 × 100

   E5 = D5 ÷ D14 × 100

   E6 = D6 ÷ D14 × 100

   E7 = D7 ÷ D14 × 100

   ⋮

   E12 = D12 ÷ D14 × 100

   F5 = (B5 − D5) ÷ B5 × 100

   F6 = (B6 − D6) ÷ B6 × 100

   ⋮

   F12 = (B12 − D12) ÷ B12 × 100

   F14 = (B14 − D14) ÷ B14 × 100

19. See the figure.

19.

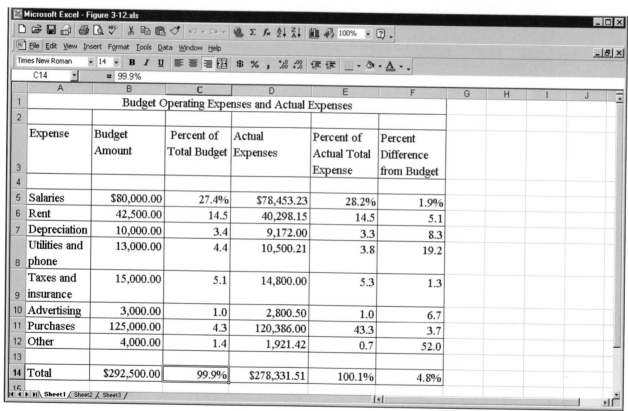

Self-Check 3.2

1. $\dfrac{5A}{5} = \dfrac{20}{5}$

$A = 4$

2. $(7)\dfrac{B}{7} = 4(7)$

$B = 28$

3. $\dfrac{7C}{7} = \dfrac{56}{7}$

$C = 8$

4. $\dfrac{4M}{4} = \dfrac{48}{4}$

$M = 12$

5. $(12)\dfrac{R}{12} = 3(12)$

$R = 36$

6. $(5)\dfrac{P}{5} = 8(5)$

$P = 40$

7. $B + 7 = 12$

$\dfrac{-7 \quad -7}{B = 5}$

8. $A - 9 = 15$

$\dfrac{+9 \quad +9}{A = 24}$

9. $R + 7 = 28$

$\dfrac{-7 \quad -7}{R = 21}$

10. $A - 16 = \quad 3$

$\dfrac{+16 \quad +16}{A = 19}$

11. $X - 48 = 36$
$+48 \quad +48$
$X = 84$

12. $C + 5 = 21$
$-5 \quad -5$
$C = 16$

13. $4A + 3 = 27$
$-3 \quad -3$
$4A = 24$
$\dfrac{4A}{4} = \dfrac{24}{4}$
$A = 6$

14. $\dfrac{B}{3} + 2 = 7$
$-2 \quad -2$
$\dfrac{B}{3} = 5$
$(3)\dfrac{B}{3} = 5(3)$
$B = 15$

15. $3B - 1 = 11$
$+1 \quad +1$
$3B = 12$
$\dfrac{3B}{3} = \dfrac{12}{3}$
$B = 4$

16. $\dfrac{K}{4} - 5 = 3$
$+5 \quad +5$
$\dfrac{K}{4} = 8$
$(4)\dfrac{K}{4} = 8(4)$
$K = 32$

17. $\dfrac{K}{2} + 3 = 5$
$-3 \quad -3$
$\dfrac{K}{2} = 2$
$(2)\dfrac{K}{2} = 2(2)$
$K = 4$

18. $7B - 1 = 6$
$+1 \quad +1$
$7B = 7$
$\dfrac{7B}{7} = \dfrac{7}{7}$
$B = 1$

19. $\dfrac{C}{2} - 1 = 9$
$+1 \quad +1$
$\dfrac{C}{2} = 10$
$(2)\dfrac{C}{2} = 10(2)$
$C = 20$

20. $8A - 1 = 19$
$+1 \quad +1$
$8A = 20$
$\dfrac{8A}{8} = \dfrac{20}{8}$
$A = \dfrac{20}{8}$
$A = 2\dfrac{4}{8}$
$A = 2\dfrac{1}{2}$

21. $2A + 5A = 35$
$7A = 35$
$\dfrac{7A}{7} = \dfrac{35}{7}$
$A = 5$

22. $B + 2B = 27$
$3B = 27$
$\dfrac{3B}{3} = \dfrac{27}{3}$
$B = 9$

23. $5K - 3K = 40$
$2K = 40$
$\dfrac{2K}{2} = \dfrac{40}{2}$
$K = 20$

24. $8K - 2K = 42$
$6K = 42$
$\dfrac{6K}{6} = \dfrac{42}{6}$
$K = 7$

25. $3J + J = 28$
$4J = 28$
$\dfrac{4J}{4} = \dfrac{28}{4}$
$J = 7$

26. $2J - J = 21$
$J = 21$

27. $3B + 2B - 6 = 9$
$5B - 6 = 9$
$+6 \quad +6$
$5B = 15$
$\dfrac{5B}{5} = \dfrac{15}{5}$
$B = 3$

28. $8C - C + 6 = 48$
$7C + 6 = 48$
$-6 \quad -6$
$7C = 42$
$\dfrac{7C}{7} = \dfrac{42}{7}$
$C = 6$

29. $2(X - 3) = 6$
$2X - 6 = 6$
$+6 \quad +6$
$2X = 12$
$\dfrac{2X}{2} = \dfrac{12}{2}$
$X = 6$

30. $4(A + 3) = 16$
$4A + 12 = 16$
$-12 \quad -12$
$4A = 4$
$\dfrac{4A}{4} = \dfrac{4}{4}$
$A = 1$

31. $3(B - 1) = 21$
$3B - 3 = 21$
$+3 \quad +3$
$3B = 24$
$\dfrac{3B}{3} = \dfrac{24}{3}$
$B = 8$

32. $6(B + 2) = 30$
$6B + 12 = 30$
$-12 \quad -12$
$6B = 18$
$\dfrac{6B}{6} = \dfrac{18}{6}$
$B = 3$

33.

1 Decision needed

2 Unknown facts

Amount of tax the seller pays
Amount of tax the buyer pays

3 Known facts

Annual real estate tax = $2,321
Number of months seller pays = 9
Total months in tax year = 12

4 Relationships

Number of months buyer pays = 12 − 9 = 3
Proportion for finding amount of tax that seller pays:

$$\frac{9}{12} = \frac{s}{\$2,321}$$

Proportion for finding amount of tax that buyer pays:

$$\frac{3}{12} = \frac{b}{\$2,321}$$

or equation for finding amount of tax that buyer pays:

$$b = \$2,321 - s.$$

5 Estimation

Half the annual tax would be about $1,150. The seller owned the property for more than half the year. Therefore the seller should pay more than $1,150 and the buyer should pay less than $1,150.

6 Calculation

$$\frac{9}{12} = \frac{s}{\$2,321}$$ **Proportion for seller**

$$9(2,321) = 12s$$ **Cross multiply.**

$$20,889 = 12s$$

$$\frac{20,889}{12} = \frac{12s}{12}$$ **Divide both sides by 12.**

$$s = \frac{20,889}{12} = 1,740.75$$

$$s = \$1,740.75$$ **Amount seller pays**

$$\frac{3}{12} = \frac{b}{\$2,321}$$ **Amount buyer pays**

$$3(2,321) = 12b$$ **Cross multiply.**

$$6,963 = 12b$$

$$\frac{6,963}{12} = \frac{12b}{12}$$ **Divide both sides by 12.**

$$\$580.25 = b$$ **Amount buyer pays**

or

$$b = \$2{,}321 - s$$

$$b = \$2{,}321 - \$1{,}740.75$$

$$b = \$580.25$$

7 Interpretation   The seller pays **$1,740.75** and the buyer pays **$580.25.**

8 Decision made

34.

1 Decision needed

2 Unknown facts   Cost for a lesser quantity of headlights

3 Known facts   Cost for a given quantity of headlights
The 16 dozen can be purchased at the same cost per dozen as the 18 dozen.

4 Relationships   Cost of 18 dozen headlights = $702
Proportion for finding cost of 16 dozen headlights (N)

$$\frac{18}{702} = \frac{16}{N}$$

5 Estimation   16 dozen headlights should cost less than 18 dozen. So the cost should be less than $702.

6 Calculation

$$\frac{18}{702} = \frac{16}{N}$$ Proportion for 16 dozen headlights

$$702(16) = 18N$$ Cross multiply.

$$11{,}232 = 18N$$

$$\frac{11{,}232}{18} = \frac{18N}{18}$$ Divide both sides by 18.

$$\$624 = N$$ Cost of 16 dozen headlights

7 Interpretation   16 dozen headlights cost **$624,** which is less than **$702,** the cost of **18 dozen headlights.**

8 Decision made

35. Let N represent the salary earned by Charris, who works on Mondays, Wednesdays, and Fridays. Since Charris works three of the five days, the fraction should be $\frac{3}{5}$.

$$\frac{3}{5} = \frac{N}{28{,}592}$$

$$5N = 3(28{,}592)$$

$$5N = 85{,}776$$

$$\frac{5N}{5} = \frac{85{,}776}{5}$$

$$N = \$17{,}155.20$$

Since Chloe works two of the five days, the fraction should be $\frac{2}{5}$. Let M represent Chloe's salary for a year.

$$\frac{2}{5} = \frac{M}{28{,}592}$$

$$5M = 2(28{,}592)$$

$$5M = 57{,}184$$

$$\frac{5M}{5} = \frac{57{,}184}{5}$$

$$M = \$11{,}436.80$$

36. Let N represent the cost to lease the car for eight months.

$$\frac{8}{12} = \frac{N}{\$5{,}400}$$

$$12N = 8(5{,}400)$$

$$12N = 43{,}200$$

$$\frac{12N}{12} = \frac{43{,}200}{12}$$

$$12N = \$3{,}600$$

The cost of an eight-month lease for the car is \$3,600.

Self-Check 3.3

1.

Unknown	Knowns	Relationship	Estimation	Calculation
Number of full-time hours: N	Number of part-time hours worked: 5 Difference of full-time hours and part-time hours: 4	Full-time hours − part-time hours = difference $N - 5 = 4$	Full-timers work more than part-timers so result should be more than 5.	$\begin{aligned} N - 5 &= 4 \\ +5 & +5 \\ \hline N &= 9 \end{aligned}$

Interpretation		Check
The number of full-time hours is 9.		$9 - 5 \stackrel{?}{=} 4$ $4 = 4$

2.

Unknown	Knowns	Relationship	Estimation	Calculations
Amount saved: S	Salary = \$372 Rate of saving: $\frac{1}{12}$	Amount saved = Rate × Salary $S = \frac{1}{12} \times 372$	$\frac{1}{12}$ is less than $\frac{1}{10}$, so Manny will save less than $\frac{1}{10}$ or \$37.20 of his salary.	$S = \frac{1}{12}(372)$ $S = \frac{1}{\cancel{12}} \cdot \frac{\overset{31}{\cancel{372}}}{1}$ $S = 31$

Interpretation		Check
Manny will save \$31 each week.		$\frac{1}{\cancel{12}}\left(\frac{\overset{31}{\cancel{372}}}{1}\right) \stackrel{?}{=} 31$ $31 = 31$

3.

Unknown	Knowns	Relationship	Estimation	Calculations
Number of silk-screened shirts sold: N	Number of tie-dyed shirts sold: $3N$ (three times as many) Total number of shirts sold: 176	Number of silk-screened shirts sold + number of tie-dyed shirts sold = total number sold $N + 3N = 176$	If equal numbers of shirts were sold, there would be 88 shirts sold of each type. There should be more than 88 tie-dyed shirts sold and fewer than 88 silk-screened shirts sold.	$N + 3N = 176$ $4N = 176$ $\dfrac{4N}{4} = \dfrac{176}{4}$ $N = 44$ $3N = 132$

Interpretation		Check
There were 44 silk-screened and 132 tie-dyed shirts sold.		$44 + 3(44) \overset{?}{=} 176$ $44 + 132 \overset{?}{=} 176$ $176 = 176$

4.

Unknown	Knowns	Relationship	Estimation	Calculations
Number of subscriptions Ron sold: M	Number of subscriptions Elaine sold: $3M$ (three times as many) Difference of Elaine's subscriptions and Ron's subscriptions: 16	Elaine's subscriptions − Ron's subscriptions = difference $3M - M = 16$	Elaine sold more than 16 magazines since the difference in their sales was 16.	$3M - M = 16$ $2M = 16$ $\dfrac{2M}{2} = \dfrac{16}{2}$ $M = 8$ $3M = 24$

Interpretation		Check
Ron sold 8 magazine subscriptions and Elaine sold 24.		$3(8) - 8 \overset{?}{=} 16$ $24 - 8 \overset{?}{=} 16$ $16 = 16$

5.

Unknown	Knowns	Relationship	Estimation	Calculations
Number of boxes of felt-tip pens: N	Number of boxes of ballpoint pens: $2N$ Total value of felt-tip pens: $\$4.50N$ Total value of ballpoint pens: $\$3.50\,(2N)$ Total order: $\$46$	Total value of felt-tip pens + total value of ballpoint pens = total order $4.50N + 3.50(2N) = 46$	Will ordered more boxes of ballpoint pens than felt-tip pens.	$4.50N + (3.50 \times 2N) = 46$ $4.50N + 7.00N = 46$ $11.50N = 46$ $\dfrac{11.50N}{11.50} = \dfrac{46}{11.50}$ $N = 4$ $2N = 8$

Interpretation		Check
Will ordered four boxes of felt-tip pens and eight boxes of ballpoint pens.		$4.50(4) + (3.50 \times 8) \overset{?}{=} 46$ $18 + 28 \overset{?}{=} 46$ $46 = 46$

6.

Unknown	Knowns	Relationship	Estimation	Calculations
Number of calendars: C	Number of date books: $500 - C$ Total cost of calendars: $\$0.75C$ Total cost of date books: $\$0.50(500 - C)$ Total order: $\$300$	Cost of calendars + cost of the date books = total order $0.75C$ $+ 0.50(500 - C)$ $= 300$	The number of calendars or date books is each less than 500. Date books outnumber calendars.	$0.75C + 0.50(500 - C) = 300$ $0.75C + 250 - 0.50C = 300$ $0.25C + 250 = 300$ $ -250 \quad -250$ $\overline{0.25C } = 50$ $\dfrac{0.25C}{0.25} = \dfrac{50}{0.25}$ $C = 200$ $500 - C = 300$

Interpretation		Check
200 calendars and 300 date books were ordered.		$0.75(200) + 0.50(500 - 200) \overset{?}{=} 300$ $150 + 0.50(300) \overset{?}{=} 300$ $300 = 300$

7.

Unknown	Known	Relationship	Estimation	Calculations
Number of feet represented by 2 inches: x	Number of feet represented by $\frac{1}{4}$ inch: 5	2 inches per x feet is proportional to $\frac{1}{4}$ inch per 5 feet $\dfrac{2 \text{ in.}}{x \text{ ft}} = \dfrac{\frac{1}{4} \text{ in.}}{5 \text{ ft}}$	If $\frac{1}{4}$ inch represents 5 feet, 1 inch represents 4×5 or 20 feet. So 2 inches represent twice 20 feet or 40 feet.	$\dfrac{2 \text{ in.}}{x \text{ ft}} = \dfrac{\frac{1}{4} \text{ in.}}{5 \text{ ft}}$ $\dfrac{1}{4}x = 2(5)$ $\dfrac{1}{4}x = 10$ $4\left(\dfrac{1}{4}x\right) = 10 \cdot 4$ $x = 40$

Interpretation		Check
2 inches represents 40 feet.		$\dfrac{2}{40} \overset{?}{=} \dfrac{\frac{1}{4}}{5}$ $\dfrac{1}{\cancel{4}}\left(\dfrac{\cancel{40}^{10}}{1}\right) \overset{?}{=} 2(5)$ $10 = 10$

8.

Unknown	Known	Relationship	Estimation	Calculations
Number of cups of milk for two cups of flour: x	Number of cups of milk for three cups of flour: $1\frac{1}{4}$	Two cups flour per x cups milk is proportional to three cups flour per $1\frac{1}{4}$ cups milk. $$\frac{2 \text{ c flour}}{x \text{ c milk}} = \frac{3 \text{ c flour}}{1\frac{1}{4}\text{ c milk}}$$	Since two cups of flour is less than three cups of flour, the amount of milk should be less than $1\frac{1}{4}$ cups.	$$\frac{2 \text{ c flour}}{x \text{ c milk}} = \frac{3 \text{ c flour}}{1\frac{1}{4}\text{ c milk}}$$ $$3x = 2\left(1\frac{1}{4}\right)$$ $$3x = \frac{\overset{1}{2}}{1} \cdot \frac{5}{\underset{2}{4}}$$ $$\frac{\cancel{3}x}{\cancel{3}} = \frac{\frac{5}{2}}{3}$$ $$x = \frac{5}{2} \div 3$$ $$x = \frac{5}{2}\left(\frac{1}{3}\right)$$ $$x = \frac{5}{6}$$

Interpretation			Check
$\frac{5}{6}$ cup of milk is used for two cups of flour.			$$\frac{2}{\frac{5}{6}} \overset{?}{=} \frac{3}{1\frac{1}{4}}$$ $$3\left(\frac{5}{6}\right) \overset{?}{=} 2\left(1\frac{1}{4}\right)$$ $$\frac{\overset{1}{\cancel{3}}}{1}\left(\frac{5}{\underset{2}{\cancel{6}}}\right) \overset{?}{=} \frac{\overset{1}{\cancel{2}}}{1}\left(\frac{5}{\underset{2}{\cancel{4}}}\right)$$ $$\frac{5}{2} = \frac{5}{2}$$

9.

Unknown	Known	Relationship	Estimation	Calculations
Pay for 37 hours of work: x	Pay for 32 hours of work: $241.60	Pay per 37 hours of work is proportional to pay per 32 hours of work. $$\frac{x \text{ dollars}}{37 \text{ hours}} = \frac{\$241.60}{32 \text{ hours}}$$	Since 37 is more than 32, your pay should be more than $241.60.	$$\frac{x \text{ dollars}}{37 \text{ hours}} = \frac{\$241.60}{32 \text{ hours}}$$ $$32x = 37(241.60)$$ $$\frac{32x}{32} = \frac{8,939.20}{32}$$ $$x = \$279.35$$

Interpretation			Check
$279.35 would be received for 37 hours of work.			$$\frac{37}{279.35} \overset{?}{=} \frac{32}{241.60}$$ $$32(279.35) \overset{?}{=} 37(241.60)$$ $$8,939.20 = 8,939.20$$

4

Statistics, Tables, and Graphs

4.1 Statistics

1 Find the range.

2 Find the mean.

3 Find the median.

4 Find the mode.

5 Put statistics to work.

4.2 Tables and Graphs

1 Read and construct a table.

2 Read and construct a bar graph.

3 Read and construct a line graph.

4 Read and construct a circle graph.

5 Put tables and graphs to work.

Good Decisions through Teamwork

Your team has been hired to conduct market research for a major consumer magazine. Your assignment is to choose an area of interest, conduct a survey, and prepare a report of your findings.

Begin by determining a suitable multiple-choice survey question. For example, *Which soft drink do you prefer?* Then identify four or five possible responses, including *None of the above.*

Next, determine your team's survey methods: How many survey responses will you try to get? Twenty responses per team member may be realistic, but keep in mind that the more responses you get, the more reliable your results will be. Where and when will you get the responses? On campus? At a mall? Discuss how location and time of day can affect survey results.

Conduct the survey, recording your responses. Then tabulate, calculating the number of respondents choosing each possible response. Construct a circle, bar, and line graph illustrating the results.

Write a report documenting your methods, results, and conclusions, including the tabulation of responses and the summary graphs. Keep in mind: A high-quality report could mean another high-paying market research assignment for your team!

Galileo once said that mathematics is the language of science. In the 21st century, he might have said that mathematics is also the language of business. Through numbers, businesspeople communicate their business history, status, and goals. And statistics, tables, and graphs are three important tools with which to do so.

4.1 Statistics

1 Find the range.

2 Find the mean.

3 Find the median.

4 Find the mode.

5 Put statistics to work.

All through the year, a business records its daily sales. At the end of the year, 365 values—one for each day—are on record. These values are a **data set.** With this data set, and using the right *statistical* methods, we may calculate manageable and meaningful information; this information is called **statistics.** Recording the statistics, we should be able to reconstruct—well enough—the original data set, or make predictions about a future data set. Statistical methods and statistical results are the domain of the science called statistics.

1 Find the range.

One of the first statistics we can calculate for a data set is its **range,** also called its **spread.** The range of a data set is the difference of the largest value and the smallest value. A small range indicates that the values in the data set are very similar to each other, whereas a large range indicates at least some variety.

HOW TO Find the Range of a Data Set

1. Identify the largest value and the smallest value of the set.

2. Subtract the smallest value from the largest.

   Range = largest value − smallest value

Find the range for 22, 25, 28, 21
largest value = 28
smallest value = 21

Range = 28 − 21 = 7

Table 4-1 Prices of Used Automobiles Sold in Tyreville over the Weekend of May 1−2

$1,850	$ 5,600
2,300	6,100
4,600	5,800
2,750	9,400
4,800	11,500
5,200	5,450

EXAMPLE Find the range in the used automobile prices in Table 4-1.

Inspection shows that the lowest price is $1,850 and the highest price is $11,500.

Range = largest value − smallest value
= $11,500 − $1,850
= $9,650

Subtract the smallest from the largest to find the range.

The range is **$9,650,** which is quite large. That is, the smallest price and the largest price are very different.

2 Find the mean.

Another statistic we may calculate for a data set is its mean. The **mean** is the statistical term for the ordinary arithmetic average. To find the mean, or arithmetic average, we divide the sum of the values by the total number of values.

HOW TO Find the Mean of a Data Set

1. Find the sum of the values.

2. Divide the sum by the total number of values.

$$\text{Mean} = \frac{\text{sum of values}}{\text{number of values}}$$

Find the mean for the scores: 96, 86, 95, 89, 92
96 + 86 + 95 + 89 + 92 = 458

$$\text{Mean} = \frac{458}{5} = 91.6$$

EXAMPLE Find the mean used car price for the prices in Table 4-1.

First find the sum of the values.

$1,850   **Add all the prices.**
2,300
4,600
2,750
4,800
5,200
5,600
6,100
5,800
9,400
11,500
+ 5,450
─────────
$65,350

$65,350 ÷ 12 = $5,445.8\overline{3}   **There are 12 prices listed, so find the mean by dividing the sum of values by 12.**

The mean price is $5,450, rounded to the nearest ten dollars.

3 Find the median.

A second kind of average is a statistic called the **median.** To find the median of a data set, we arrange the values in order from the smallest to the largest or from largest to smallest and select the value in the middle. If the data set has an even number of values, then there are two values "in the middle." In this case, the median of the data set is the mean of the middle two values.

? **HOW TO** Find the Median of a Data Set

	Find the median for 22, 25, 28, 21
1. Arrange the values in order from smallest to largest or largest to smallest.	21, 22, 25, 28
2. Count the number of values.	**four values**
(a) If the number of values is odd, identify the value in the middle.	
(b) If the number of values is even, find the mean of the middle two values.	$\dfrac{22 + 25}{2} = 23.5$

Median = middle value or mean of middle two values

EXAMPLE   Find the median price of used cars in Table 4-1.

$11,500 9,400 6,100 5,800 5,600 5,450 ← 5,200 ← 4,800 4,600 2,750 2,300 1,850	**Arrange the values from largest to smallest. There are 12 prices, an even number; so there are two "middle" prices.** ⎰ **There are two "middle" values: 5 values above and** ⎱ **5 values below the pair.**

$$\frac{5{,}450 + 5{,}200}{2} = 5{,}325$$ **Find the mean of the middle two values by dividing their sum by 2.**

The median price is $5,325.

4 Find the mode.

A third kind of average is the **mode.** The mode is the value or values that occur most frequently in a data set. If no value occurs most frequently, then there is no mode for that data set. Since no used car price in Table 4-1 occurs more than once, there is no mode for that set of prices.

? **HOW TO** Find the Mode(s) of a Data Set

	Find the mode(s) for 95, 96, 98, 72, 96, 95, 96
	95 occurs twice 96 occurs three times
1. For each value, count the number of times the value occurs.	
2. Identify the value or values that occur most frequently.	96 occurs most frequently
Mode = most frequent value(s)	96 is the mode

EXAMPLE   Find the mode(s) for this set of test grades in a mathematics class:

$$76, 83, 94, 76, 53, 83, 74, 76, 97, 83, 65, 77, 76, 83$$

The grade of 76 occurs four times. The grade of 83 also occurs four times. All other grades occur once each. Therefore, both 76 and 83 occur the same number of times and are modes.

Both 76 and 83 are modes for this set of test grades.

 5 Put statistics to work.

The range of a data set describes the spread of values. The mean, median, and mode may each be called an *average*. Taken together, the mean, median, and mode describe the tendencies of a data set to cluster between the smallest and largest values. Sometimes it is useful to know all three of these statistical averages, since each represents a different way of describing the data set. It is like looking at the same thing from three different points of view.

To look at just one statistic for a set of numbers often distorts the total picture. It is advisable to find the range, mean, median, and mode and then analyze the results.

 TIP!   **What Does the Range Show?**

When the range for a set of data is small, the mean, median, and mode usually have values that are very similar. When the range is very large, it is especially important to examine each of the three averages—mean, median, and mode—to determine which is most representative of the data. The mean can be greatly affected by extreme values in a set of data. In this case the mean is less descriptive of the set.

EXAMPLE   A real estate agent told a prospective buyer that the average cost of a home in Tyreville was $71,000 during the past three months. The agent based this statement on this list of selling prices: $170,000, $150,000, $50,000, $50,000, $50,000, $50,000, $49,000, $45,000, $25,000.

Which statistic—the mean, the median, or the mode—gives the most realistic picture of how much a home in Tyreville is likely to cost?

1 Decision needed

Which statistic gives the most realistic picture of how much a home in Tyreville is likely to cost?

2 Unknown facts

The range, mean, median, and mode

3 Known facts

Houses sold during the period: 9
Prices of these houses: $170,000, $150,000, $50,000, $50,000, $50,000, $50,000, $49,000, $45,000, and $25,000.

4 Relationships

Range = largest value − smallest value
Mean = sum of values ÷ number of values
Median = middle value when values are arranged in order
Mode = most frequent value

5 Estimation

The mean, median, and mode are between $25,000 (smallest value) and $170,000 (largest value). To estimate the mean, group values that total approximately 100,000 or 200,000, then add the estimates and divide by 9. 170,000 + 25,000 is approximately

200,000. 150,000 + 50,000 is 200,000; 50,000 + 50,000 + 50,000 + 49,000 is approximately 200,000. 200,000 + 200,000 + 200,000 + 45,000 = 645,000; 645,000 ÷ 9 is approximately 70,000. Thus, the estimated mean is $70,000. Estimation of the range, median, and mode is not appropriate.

6 Calculation

Range = largest value − smallest value
  = $170,000 − $25,000
  = $145,000

Mean = sum of values ÷ number of values
  = $639,000 ÷ 9
  = $71,000

The values are listed in order from largest to smallest, and the middle value is $50,000.
Median = middle value = $50,000
Mode = most frequent amount = $50,000

The range is $145,000. The mean is $71,000. The median is $50,000. The mode is $50,000.

7 Interpretation

The large range indicates extremes in prices, so the mean is probably not the most useful statistic.

8 Decision made

The median and mode give a more realistic picture of how much a home is likely to cost: about $50,000.

SELF-CHECK 4.1

1. Find the range of the numbers: 3,850; 5,300; 8,550; 4,200; 5,350.

2. Salaries for the research and development department of Richman Chemical were given as: $48,397, $27,982, $42,591, $19,522, $32,400, and $37,582. Find the range.

3. Sales in thousand dollars for men's suits for a major department store chain for a 12-month period were: 127, 215, 135, 427, 842, 687, 321, 512, 351, 742, 482, 305. Find the range.

4. Find the range for the following prices of cars sold by Autoland Cars on the given Friday: $17,485; $14,978; $13,592; $14,500; and $18,540.

2

5. Find the mean of the numbers: 3,850; 5,300; 8,550; 4,200; 5,350.

6. Find the mean for the salaries given in exercise 2.

7. Find the mean for the men's suit sales in exercise 3.

8. Find the mean price of cars sold in exercise 4.

3

9. Find the median of the numbers: 3,850; 5,300; 8,550; 4,200; 5,350.

10. Find the median for the salaries in exercise 2.

11. Find the median for the men's suit sales in exercise 3.

12. Find the median for the price of cars sold in exercise 4.

13. Find the mode for the numbers: 86, 94, 73, 94, 84, 86, 94.

14. Find the mode for the test scores of students who took the test on Chapter 3: 85, 92, 72, 80, 43, 97, 86, 99, 86, 93, 75, 86, 92, 100, 49, 85.

15. The recorded temperatures for a seven-day period were: 83, 78, 85, 79, 82, 82, 80. What is the mode?

16. The following scores are recorded by a researcher: 109, 83, 89, 89, 83, 89, 95, 93, 83, 79, 106. What is the mode?

5

17. Last Saturday, Autoland sold cars for the prices: $15,300, $17,500, $11,400, $14,500, and $13,500. Find the range, the mean, the median, and the mode for these car prices. What do these prices tell us about the cost of cars sold last Saturday? Which statistic(s) would give the most realistic description of Autoland's prices on Saturday?

18. Accountants often use the median when studying salaries for various businesses. What is the median of the following salary list? $32,084, $21,983, $27,596, $43,702, $38,840, $25,997

19. What is the range of the salaries given in exercise 18?

20. Weather forecasters sometimes give the average (mean) temperature for a particular city. The following temperatures were recorded as highs on June 30 of the last 10 years in a certain city: 89°, 88°, 90°, 92°, 95°, 89°, 93°, 98°, 93°, 97°. What is the mean high temperature for June 30 for the last 10 years?

21. What is the range of temperatures in exercise 20?

22. What is the median temperature on June 30 for the city in exercise 20?

23. What is the mode(s) of the temperature(s) in exercise 20?

24. Analyze the results of exercises 20–23.

4.2 Tables and Graphs

1 Read and construct a table.

2 Read and construct a bar graph.

3 Read and construct a line graph.

4 Read and construct a circle graph.

5 Put tables and graphs to work.

Scan a newspaper, a magazine, or a business report, and you are likely to see tables and graphs. Tables and graphs do more than present sets of data. They make visual the relationship between the sets. The relationship between data sets might be visualized by a table, a bar graph, a line graph, or a circle graph. Depending on "what you want to see," one of these forms helps you to see the relationship more meaningfully.

1 Read and construct a table.

A **table** displays data in rows and columns. Each place that a row and column intersect is called an **entry** or a **cell** of the table. It is important to give a meaningful title to a table and to label the columns and rows according to what each measures. In this way, data can be read and interpreted accurately.

A table may be a simple correspondence or a complex one. Table 4-2 displays membership data for the Monroe Fitness Club. This simple table relates the months of 2001 to the numbers of men registered as members of the club at the end of each month.

Table 4–2 2001 Monthly Male Membership for the Monroe Fitness Club

Month	Jan.	Feb.	Mar.	Apr.	May	June	July	Aug.	Sept.	Oct.	Nov.	Dec.
Members Joining	169	176	151	153	154	152	150	148	151	157	159	166

A table with just two rows, or two columns, is easy to read, but only a little more useful than a simple list. The more data you pack into a table, the more useful it may be. Naturally, reading the table becomes more difficult. Table 4-3 adds to the data in Table 4-2 and displays not only male membership, but also female membership.

Table 4-3 2001 Monthly Membership for the Monroe Fitness Club, Male and Female

Month	Jan.	Feb.	Mar.	Apr.	May	June	July	Aug.	Sept.	Oct.	Nov.	Dec.
Male	169	176	151	153	154	152	150	148	151	157	159	166
Female	173	179	154	155	156	158	156	155	159	163	165	172

Reading Table 4-3, we can compare male and female membership for the same month. Reading the July column, for instance, we see that the male July entry is 150 and the female July entry is 156: At the end of July there were 150 men and 156 women in the club.

Table 4-4 is a more complicated table still: Not only does the table display male/female membership for 2001; it does so for 1997, 1998, 1999, and 2000 as well. Reading Table 4-4 requires more attention: in looking for a particular cell, we must find the year, month, and male or female data.

EXAMPLE How many men belonged to the Monroe Fitness Club by the end of November 1998?

We find the 1998 rows, then the male row, then the November column. The column and row intersect at the cell whose entry is 95.

1998   Nov
Male 101 108 87 88 89 89 86 88 88 91 95 98

By the end of November 1998, 95 men belonged to the club.

When constructing a table, we must decide on the most convenient and revealing arrangement. The data in Table 4-4, for instance, can be constructed in a new table by reversing the rows and columns.

Table 4-4 Monthly Membership for the Monroe Fitness Club, 1997–2001

Month	Jan.	Feb.	Mar.	Apr.	May	June	July	Aug.	Sept.	Oct.	Nov.	Dec.
1997 Male	82	84	21	29	35	38	49	53	59	65	71	79
Female	29	32	8	12	14	15	15	17	20	23	25	28
1998 Male	101	108	87	88	89	89	86	88	88	91	95	98
Female	66	70	33	39	43	44	44	45	47	51	58	61
1999 Male	129	135	108	110	111	109	107	107	109	113	118	127
Female	105	115	74	76	78	79	78	77	79	86	92	101
2000 Male	148	148	138	141	140	135	132	133	135	138	140	143
Female	147	151	117	125	126	125	125	127	132	137	142	144
2001 Male	169	176	151	153	154	152	150	148	151	157	159	166
Female	173	179	154	155	156	158	156	155	159	163	165	172

EXAMPLE Construct a table of membership data for the Monroe Fitness Club using months as the first column.

Since months are to be the first column, we reverse the data in Table 4-4. The labels for the rows and columns are interchanged and the data are rearranged accordingly. Notice that Table 4-5 has a significantly different visual appearance. If the focus is to compare monthly data from year to year, Table 4-4 may be preferred. If the focus is to examine the membership patterns of female members or male members, either table may be preferred.

Table 4-5 Monthly* Membership for the Monroe Fitness Club, 1997–2001

Month	1997		1998		1999		2000		2001	
	Male	Female	Male	Female	Male	Female	Male	Female	Male	Female
January	82	29	101	66	129	105	148	147	169	173
February	84	32	108	70	135	115	148	151	176	179
March	21	8	87	33	108	74	138	117	151	154
April	29	12	88	39	110	76	141	125	153	155
May	35	14	89	43	111	78	140	126	154	156
June	38	15	89	44	109	79	135	125	152	158
July	49	15	86	44	107	78	132	125	150	156
August	53	17	88	45	107	77	133	127	148	155
September	59	20	88	47	109	79	135	132	151	159
October	65	23	91	51	113	86	138	137	157	163
November	71	25	95	58	118	92	140	142	159	165
December	79	28	98	61	127	101	143	144	166	172

*Number of members at the end of each month.

Like tables, **bar graphs** are used to make visual the relationship between data. As its name implies, a bar graph uses horizontal or vertical bars to show relative quantities. Figure 4-1 is a bar graph of the 2001 membership data for the Monroe Fitness Club, as originally given in Table 4-3.

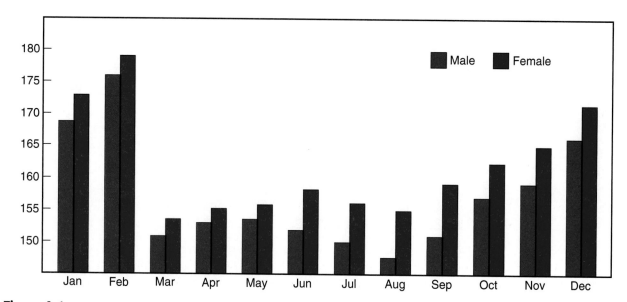

Figure 4-1   2001 Monthly Membership for the Monroe Fitness Club, Male and Female

Along the bottom of the bar graph are the months, which correspond to the first row of Table 4-3. Along the left side of the bar graph is a scale from 150 to 180. In relation to the scale, each bar corresponds to the cells of Table 4-3. The colors of the bars distinguish data for males and females. The height of each bar corresponds to the numbers of female or male members in the club at the end of the month.

Figure 4-1 demonstrates why bar graphs are so useful: we can easily grasp the rise and fall of membership throughout the year and see at a glance how male and female membership compare. Figure 4-1 also demonstrates a disadvantage of bar graphs, compared to tables: we lose precision. For instance, the height of the bar for female members in October looks to be between 160 and 165, but Table 4-3 tells us the precise value is 163.

To construct a bar graph, first establish appropriate scales and labels.

? HOW TO Draw a Bar Graph

1. Write an appropriate title.
2. Make appropriate labels for bars and scale. The intervals on the scale should be equally spaced and include the smallest and largest values.
3. Draw bars to represent the data. Bars should be of uniform width.
4. Make additional notes as appropriate. For example, "Amounts in Thousand Dollars" allows values such as $30,000 to be represented as 30.

TIP! **Constructing Graphs Electronically**

Electronic spreadsheets have a function that translates the data from a spreadsheet to various types of graphs. The type of graph (bar, line, circle), title scales, and labels are still determined by the user. The software then produces the graph electronically.

EXAMPLE The data show Corky's Barbecue Restaurant sales during January through June.

Draw a bar graph that represents the data.

January	$37,734	April	$52,175
February	$43,284	May	$56,394
March	$58,107	June	$63,784

The title of the graph is "Corky's Barbecue Restaurant Sales, January–June."

The smallest value is $37,734 and the largest value is $63,784. Therefore, the graph should show values from $30,000 to $70,000. To avoid using very large numbers, indicate on the graph that the numbers represent dollars in thousands. Therefore, 65 on the graph would represent $65,000. The bars can be either horizontal or vertical. In Figure 4-2 we make the bars horizontal. Months are labeled along the vertical line, and the dollar scale is labeled along the horizontal line. For each month, the length of the bar corresponds to the sales for the month.

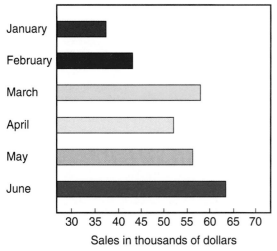

Figure 4-2 Horizontal Bar Graph Showing Corky's Barbecue Restaurant Sales, January–June

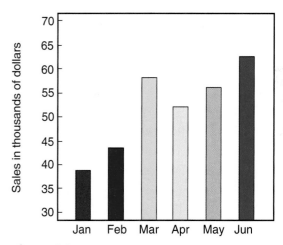

Figure 4-3 Vertical Bar Graph Showing Corky's Barbecue Restaurant Sales, January–June

Figure 4-3 interchanges the labeling of the scales and the bars are drawn vertically.

3 Read and construct a line graph.

Line graphs are very similar to vertical bar graphs. The difference is that a line graph uses a single dot to represent height, rather than a whole bar. When the dots are in place, they are connected by a line. Line graphs make even more apparent the rising and falling trends of the data. Figure 4-4 is a line graph of the vertical bar graph in Figure 4-3.

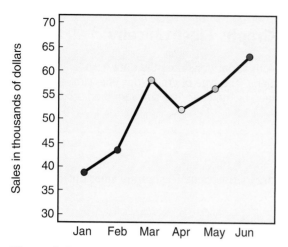

Figure 4-4 Line Graph Showing Corky's Barbecue Restaurant Sales, January–June

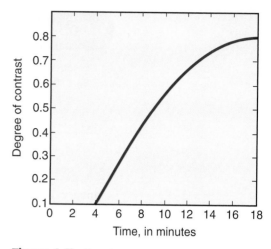

Figure 4-5 Developing Time Required for Degrees of Contrast

Line graphs may have enough points that connecting them yields a curve rather than angles. Figure 4-5 shows such a line graph, relating how long film must be developed to the degree of contrast achieved in the developed film. To read the graph, we locate a specific degree of contrast on the vertical scale, then move horizontally until we intersect the curve. From that point, we move down to locate the corresponding number of minutes on the horizontal scale.

EXAMPLE   Use Figure 4-5 to answer the following questions:

Figure 4-6   Reading a Line Graph

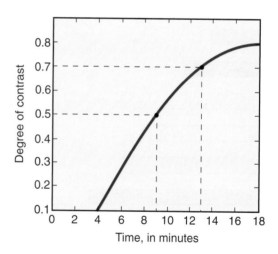

(a) If the film is to be developed to a contrast of 0.5, how long must it be developed?

(b) If the film is developed for 13 minutes, what is its degree of contrast?

(a) Find 0.5 on the vertical scale, then move horizontally until you intersect the curve. From the point of intersection, move down to locate the corresponding number of minutes on the horizontal scale. **Figure 4-6 shows the minutes are 9.**

(b) Find 13 minutes on the horizontal scale and move up until you intersect the curve. From the point of intersection, move across to locate the corresponding degree of contrast. **Figure 4-6 shows the degree of contrast is 0.7.**

As in drawing bar graphs, drawing line graphs often means using approximations of the given data.

HOW TO Draw a Line Graph

1. Write an appropriate title.
2. Make and label appropriate horizontal and vertical scales, each with equally spaced intervals. Often, the horizontal scale represents time.
3. Use points to locate data on the graph.
4. Connect data points with line segments or a smooth curve.

Table 4-6 Neighborhood Grocery Daily Sales for Week Beginning Monday, June 21

Monday	$1,567
Tuesday	1,323
Wednesday	1,237
Thursday	1,435
Friday	1,848
Saturday	1,984

EXAMPLE Draw a line graph to represent the data in Table 4-6.

The smallest and greatest values in the table are $1,237 and $1,984, respectively, so the graph may go from $1,000 to $2,000 in $100 intervals. Do not label every interval. This would crowd the side of the graph and make it hard to read. The purpose of any graph is to give information that is quick and easy to understand and interpret.

The horizontal side of the graph will show the days of the week, and the vertical side will show the daily sales. Plot each day's sales by placing a dot directly above the appropriate day of the week across from the approximate value. For example, the sales for Monday totaled $1,567. Place the dot above Monday in the interval between $1,500 and $1,600. After each amount has been plotted, connect the dots with straight lines.

Figure 4-7 shows the resulting graph.

Figure 4-7 Neighborhood Grocery Daily Sales for Week Beginning Monday, June 21

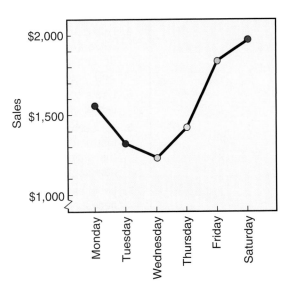

4 Read and construct a circle graph.

A **circle graph** is a circle divided into sections to give a visual picture of *how some whole quantity* (represented by the whole circle) *is being divided.* Each section represents a portion of the total amount. Figure 4-8 shows a circle graph illustrating how different portions of a family's total income are spent on nine categories of expenses: food, housing, contributions, savings, clothing, insurance, education, personal items, and miscellaneous items.

Circle graphs are relatively easy to read, and they make it easy to visually compare categories. Constructing a circle graph requires that you make several calculations and use a measuring device called a **protractor** that measures angles. Each

Chapter 4 Statistics, Tables, and Graphs **179**

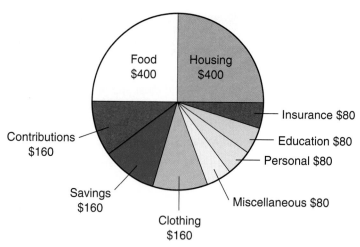

Figure 4-8 Distribution of Family Monthly Take-Home Pay

value in the data set must be represented as a fraction of the sum of all the values. We must calculate these fractions and then draw the graph.

? HOW TO Draw a Circle Graph

1. Write an appropriate title.
2. Find the sum of the values in the data set.
3. Represent each value as a fractional or decimal part of the sum of values.
4. For each fraction or decimal, find the number of degrees in the sector of the circle to be represented by the fraction or decimal: multiply the fraction or decimal by 360 degrees. The sum of the degrees for all sectors should be 360 degrees.
5. Use a compass (a tool for drawing circles) to draw a circle. Indicate the center of the circle and a starting point on the circle.
6. For each degree value, draw a sector: use a protractor (a measuring instrument for angles) to measure the number of degrees for the sector of the circle to be represented by the value. Where the first sector ends, the next sector begins. The last sector should end at the starting point.
7. Label each sector of the circle and make additional explanatory notes as necessary.

EXAMPLE   Construct a circle graph showing the budgeted operating expenses for one month for Silver's Spa: salary, $25,000; rent, $8,500; depreciation, $2,500; miscellaneous, $2,000; taxes and insurance, $10,000; utilities, $2,000; advertising, $3,000. The title of the graph is "Silver's Spa Monthly Budgeted Operating Expenses." Since several calculations are required, it is helpful to organize the calculation results in a chart.

Decimal equivalents can be used instead of fractions of total expenses. The sum of the fractions or decimal equivalents is 1. To the nearest thousandth, the decimal equivalents are 0.472, 0.160, 0.047, 0.038, 0.189, 0.038, and 0.057. The sum is 1.001. Rounding causes the sum to be slightly more than 1, just as the sum of the degrees is slightly more than 360°.

Use a compass to draw a circle. Then measure the sectors of the circle with a protractor, using the calculations you just made. **The finished circle graph is shown in Figure 4-9.**

Table 4-7   Silver's Spa Monthly Budgeted Operating Expenses

Type of Expense	Amount of Expense	Expense as Fraction of Total Expenses	Degrees in Sector: Fraction × 360
Salary	$25,000	$\dfrac{25,000}{53,000}$ or $\dfrac{25}{53}$	$\dfrac{25}{53} \times 360$, or 170
Rent	8,500	$\dfrac{8,500}{53,000}$ or $\dfrac{85}{530}$	$\dfrac{85}{530} \times 360$, or 58
Depreciation	2,500	$\dfrac{2,500}{53,000}$ or $\dfrac{25}{530}$	$\dfrac{25}{530} \times 360$, or 17
Miscellaneous	2,000	$\dfrac{2,000}{53,000}$ or $\dfrac{2}{53}$	$\dfrac{2}{53} \times 360$, or 14
Taxes and insurance	10,000	$\dfrac{10,000}{53,000}$ or $\dfrac{10}{53}$	$\dfrac{10}{53} \times 360$, or 68
Utilities	2,000	$\dfrac{2,000}{53,000}$ or $\dfrac{2}{53}$	$\dfrac{2}{53} \times 360$, or 14
Advertising	3,000	$\dfrac{3,000}{53,000}$ or $\dfrac{3}{53}$	$\dfrac{3}{53} \times 360$, or 20
Total	$53,000		361*

*Extra degree due to rounding

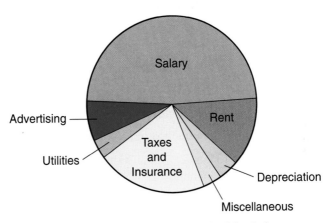

Figure 4-9   Monthly Budgeted Operating Expenses for Silver's Spa

5   Put tables and graphs to work.

Being able to read tables and graphs allows us to pull out data and make calculations to get new data. Doing so is often referred to as *analyzing* the data. For instance, let's look again at the table of membership data for the Monroe Fitness Club.

EXAMPLE   How many more males were members of the Monroe Fitness Club at the end of May 1997 than at the end of April 1997? (See Table 4-8.)

$$\begin{array}{r} 35 \\ -\ 29 \\ \hline 6 \end{array}$$ (male members at the end of May, 1997)
(male members at the end of April, 1997)

> Subtract the number of male club members in April 1997 from the number of male club members in May 1997.

Six men joined during May 1997.

Table 4-8 Monthly* Membership for the Monroe Fitness Club, 1997–2001

Month	1997 Male	1997 Female	1998 Male	1998 Female	1999 Male	1999 Female	2000 Male	2000 Female	2001 Male	2001 Female
January	82	29	101	66	129	105	148	147	169	173
February	84	32	108	70	135	115	148	151	176	179
March	21	8	87	33	108	74	138	117	151	154
April	29	12	88	39	110	76	141	125	153	155
May	35	14	89	43	111	78	140	126	154	156
June	38	15	89	44	109	79	135	125	152	158
July	49	15	86	44	107	78	132	125	150	156
August	53	17	88	45	107	77	133	127	148	155
September	59	20	88	47	109	79	135	132	151	159
October	65	23	91	51	113	86	138	137	157	163
November	71	25	95	58	118	92	140	142	159	165
December	79	28	98	61	127	101	143	144	166	172

*Number of members at the end of each month.

Comparing data in a graph or table may involve the concept of *ratio*. The **ratio** of one number to another is a fraction whose numerator is the one number and whose denominator is the other number. When we say, for instance, that the ratio of 15 to 20 is 3 to 4 or $\frac{3}{4}$, we mean that $\frac{15}{20}$ is $\frac{3}{4}$ in reduced form. The ratio 15 to 20 can also be written as 15:20, or 3:4. Finally, ratios can also be written as a decimal equivalent. The decimal equivalent of $\frac{15}{20}$ is 0.75. The ratio can be expressed as 0.75 to 1.

EXAMPLE   Find the ratio of men to women in the Monroe Fitness Club at the end of June 2000.

Make a fraction of the values.

$\dfrac{135 \text{ men}}{125 \text{ women}}$ **The numerator is the number of men; the denominator is the number of women.**

$\dfrac{135}{125} = \dfrac{27}{25}$ **Reduce. Decimal equivalent is $27 \div 25$ or 1.08.**

The ratio of men to women at the end of June 2000 is $\frac{27}{25}$ or 27 to 25, 27:25, or 1.08 to 1.

Comparing data in a table or graph may also involve the concept of *rate of change*. Change, or the difference between two amounts, is often expressed in terms of a percent. When the change is from a smaller amount to a larger amount, the difference in the two amounts is an **increase.** Likewise, when the change is from a larger amount to a smaller amount, the difference in the two amounts is a **decrease.** Whether an increase or a decrease, this amount of change is a *percentage* of the original amount, the *base*. The **rate of change** (increase or decrease) is a *percent*. We can find the rate of change, then, by using the percentage formula $R = \frac{P}{B}$.

HOW TO | Find Percent or Rate of Change (Increase or Decrease)

1. Find the amount of change: subtract the smaller of the original amount and new amount from the larger of the two.
2. Write the percentage formula $R = \frac{P}{B}$.
3. Replace P by the amount of change, and replace B by the original amount.
4. Write the fraction $\frac{P}{B}$ as a percent: multiply by 100%.
5. If the new amount is larger, the change is an increase. If the original amount is larger, the change is a decrease.

EXAMPLE   What is the rate of change from the previous year in female membership at the Monroe Fitness Club for the year 1998?

On the table, we locate female membership at the end of December 1997: 28. Then we locate female membership at the end of December 1998: 61.

$$\begin{array}{r} 61 \\ -\ 28 \\ \hline 33 \end{array}$$

Subtract the larger amount from the smaller amount to find the amount of change.

$$R = \frac{P}{B}$$

The percentage formula

$$R = \frac{33}{28}$$

Replace *P* by the amount of change and *B* by the original amount.

$$\frac{33}{28} \times 100\% = 118\%$$

Write $\frac{33}{28}$ as a percent, rounded to the nearest whole percent.

The rate of change is 118% or a 118% increase.

When the rate of change is 100%, the original amount has doubled. A rate of change that is more than 100% is more than doubled.
    Another way to find the rate of change is to write the fraction $\frac{\text{new amount}}{\text{original amount}}$ as a percent. If the percent is more than 100%, subtract 100% from it and the rate of change is an increase. Otherwise, subtract the percent from 100% and the rate of change is a decrease. In either case, the difference is the rate of change.

EXAMPLE   Find the rate of change in male membership from January to February 1999.

$$\frac{135}{129} \quad \begin{array}{l} \text{new amount} \\ \text{original amount} \end{array}$$

Write the fraction $\frac{\text{new amount}}{\text{original amount}}$.

$$\frac{135}{129} = \frac{135}{129} \times 100\%$$

Write the fraction as a percent.

$$= 105\% \text{ rounded to nearest percent}$$

105% is more than 100%, so subtract 100% from it.

$$105\% - 100\% = 5\%$$

The rate of change is 5% or a 5% increase.

We can find ratios and rates of change by analyzing data from a line or bar graph, too. Because of their visual form, bar or line graphs lend themselves to other kinds of analysis as well.

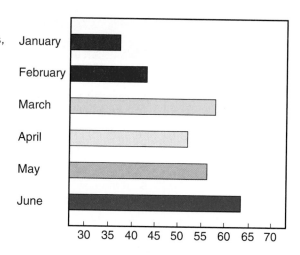

Figure 4-10 Corky's Barbecue Restaurant Sales, January–June

EXAMPLE Use Figure 4-10 to answer the following questions:

(a) Which month had the highest sales?
(b) Estimate the total sales for the three-month period from January through March.
(c) Find the ratio of January sales to June sales.

(a) The longest bar is for the month of June; therefore, **the sales were highest for June.**
(b) January sales are estimated at $38,000; February sales are estimated at $43,000; March sales are estimated at $58,000. The estimated total sales for the three-month period is the sum of the estimated monthly sales:

$$\$38,000 + \$43,000 + \$58,000 = \$139,000.$$

The estimated sales for the three-month period are $139,000.

(c) January sales are estimated at $38,000, June sales at $64,000.

$$\frac{38,000}{64,000} = \frac{38}{64} = \frac{19}{32} \qquad \boxed{19 \div 32 = 0.59375}$$

The ratio of January sales to June sales is 19 to 32 or $0.59 to $1.

Circle graphs show portions of a whole, so it is natural to interpret the data in percent form. In Figure 4–11, we see the percent (rate) of take-home pay for the

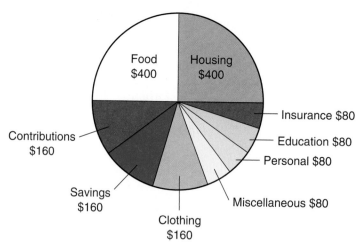

Figure 4-11 Take-Home Pay Distribution

nine categories of expenses. Again using the formula $R = \frac{P}{B}$, we identify the amount of any category as the percentage, and the sum of all the categories as the base.

EXAMPLE Use Figure 4-11 to find the percent of total take-home pay spent for food.

Use the formula $R = \frac{P}{B}$. The total take-home pay is the base B; the amount spent on food is the percentage P.

$$\$400 + \$400 + \$80 + \$80$$
$$+ \$80 + \$80 + \$160 + \$160$$
$$+ \$160 = \$1,600$$

Add the amounts for each section of the graph to find the total take-home pay. Write the formula.

$$R = \frac{\text{food}}{\text{take-home pay}} = \frac{400}{1,600} = \frac{4}{16}$$

Divide the amount spent on food by the total take-home pay.

$$= \frac{1}{4}$$

$$\frac{1}{4} = \frac{1}{4} \times 100\% = 25\%$$

Convert $\frac{1}{4}$ to a percent.

25% of the family's take-home pay is spent on food.

EXAMPLE Find the percent of take-home pay available for a vacation if the family's savings and education expenses for one month are used.

Savings	$160
Education	+ 80
	$240

Add savings and education costs for one month.

$$\text{(Part)} \rightarrow \frac{240}{1,600} = \frac{3}{20} = 0.15 \times 100\% = 15\%$$
$$\text{(Whole)} \rightarrow$$

Write a fraction with the part as the numerator and the whole as the denominator. Multiply by 100%.

Using the %̲ Key

The calculator sequence is

$$\boxed{AC} \quad 160 \quad \boxed{+} \quad 80 \quad \boxed{=} \quad \boxed{\div} \quad 1600 \quad \boxed{\times} \quad 100 \quad \boxed{=} \Rightarrow 15$$

The percent is 15%.

Many calculators have a "percent" key %̲ that functions similar to the "equal" key and *is used in place of the "equal" key.* The "percent" key automatically changes the numerical result of division to a percent when finding the rate. The "percent" key automatically changes a percent to its numerical equivalent when finding the percentage or base.

Using the "percent" key, the calculator sequence is:

$$\boxed{AC} \quad 160 \quad \boxed{+} \quad 80 \quad = \quad \boxed{\div} \quad 1600 \quad \boxed{\%} \Rightarrow 15$$

Since changing percents to decimal equivalents, and vice versa, is most often done mentally, many persons choose not to use the percent key at all when using the calculator.

1   *Use Table 4-9 for exercises 1–4.*

Table 4-9   Sales by Each Salesperson at Happy's Gift Shoppe

Salesperson	Sales						
	Mon.	Tues.	Wed.	Thurs.	Fri.	Sat.	Total
Brown	Off	$110.25	$114.52	$186.42	$126.81	$315.60	$853.60
Jackson	$121.68	Off	$118.29	Off	$125.42	Off	$365.39
Ulster	$112.26	$119.40	$122.35	$174.51	$116.78	Off	$645.30
Young	Off	$122.90	Off	$181.25	Off	$296.17	$600.32
Totals	$233.94	$352.55	$355.16	$542.18	$369.01	$611.77	$2,464.61

1. What day of the week had the highest amount in sales? What day had the lowest amount in sales?

2. Which day did Ulster have higher sales than any other salesperson?

3. Which salesperson made the most sales for the week? Which salesperson made the second highest amount in sales?

4. Construct a new table so that the days of the week are the first column and the names of the salespersons are the first row.

 2   *Use Figure 4-12 for exercises 5–7.*

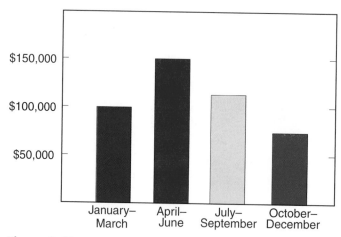

Figure 4-12   Quarterly Dollar Volume of Batesville Tire Company

5. Which quarter had the highest dollar volume?

6. What percent of the yearly sales was the sales for October–December?

7. What was the percent of increase in sales from the first to the second quarter?

8. Draw a bar graph comparing the quarterly sales of the Oxford Company: January–March, $280,000; April–June, $310,000; July–September, $250,000; October–December, $400,000.

3 *Use Figure 4-13 for exercises 9–12.*

9. What speed gave the highest gasoline mileage for both types of automobiles?

10. What speed gave the lowest gasoline mileage for both types of automobiles?

11. At what speed did the first noticeable decrease in gasoline mileage occur? Which car showed this decrease?

12. Identify factors other than gasoline mileage that should be considered when deciding which type of car to purchase, full size or compact.

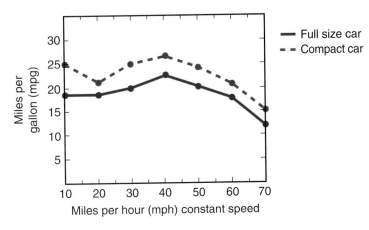

Figure 4-13 Automobile Gasoline Mileage Comparisons

4

13. The family budget does not include transportation expenses. Redistribute the budget to include expenses for a vehicle. Draw a circle graph to represet the redistributed budget in Figure 4-14.

14. Match the dollar values with the names in the circle graph of Figure 4-15: $192, $144, $96, $72, $72

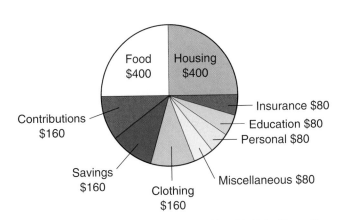

Figure 4-14 Distribution of Family Monthly Take-Home Pay

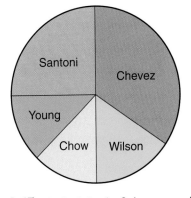

Figure 4-15 Daily Sales by Salesperson, in Hundreds of Dollars

5 *Use Table 4-5 on page 175 for exercises 15–17.*

15. How many more women members than men members were there in October of 2001?

16. Find the ratio of men to women in the club as of the end of December 2000.

17. What percent of the increase in club members between December 2000 and December 2001 was men?

Use Table 4-9 on page 186 for exercises 18 and 19.

18. What percent of the week's sales was made on Thursday? What percent was made on Monday? (Round to the nearest whole percent.)

19. What percent of the day's sales for Saturday did Young make? (Round to the nearest whole percent.)

Use Figure 4-8 on page 180 for exercises 20 and 21.

20. What percent of take-home pay is spent for contributions?

21. What percent of take-home pay is spent for education if education, savings, and miscellaneous funds are used for education?

Use Figure 4-16 for exercises 22–25.

22. What is the percent of increase in Dale's salary from 1996 to 1997?

23. Calculate the amount and percent of increase in Dale's salary from 1998 to 1999.

24. Calculate the amount and percent of increase in Dale's salary from 2000 to 2001.

25. If the cost-of-living increase was 10% from 1995 to 1999, determine if Dale's salary for this period of time kept pace with inflation.

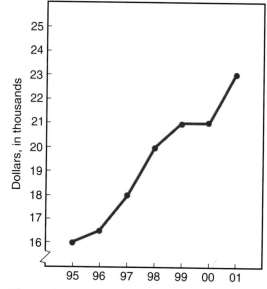

Figure 4-16   Dale Crosby's Salary History

Around The Business World

Reporting Average Salary

You've heard it said that "statistics don't lie," but a savvy businessperson carefully chooses which statistic to report to a target audience. Statistics from all aspects of business operations (inventory, sales, profit, assets, liabilities, etc.) can be presented in a variety of ways so that the company can be seen in the best possible light by the intended viewer. For example, company employees' average salary is reported to several different audiences such as prospective employees, shareholders, lending institutions, chambers of commerce, government agencies, professional publications, and the general media, each of whom has a unique self-interest. The measures of central tendency most often used to describe a company's most typical or "average" salary are *mean, median,* and *mode.*

Exercises

A farm implement manufacturing company using a robotic assembly line employs 13 people with the following annual salaries:

$120,000 President $100,000 Vice president
$75,000 Financial manager $65,000 Sales manager
$40,000 Production manager $30,000 Production supervisor
$30,000 Warehouse supervisor

and six unskilled laborers who make an average of $16,000 a year.

1. Just by inspection of the above salaries, what do you guess the average salary to be?
2. Calculate the salary mean, median, and mode for this company rounded to the nearest thousand. Which statistic is closest to your guess?
3. The statistic most often used to describe average salary is the mean. Do you think the mean gives the fairest picture of this company's wages? Explain why or why not.
4. Most financial institutions request the median salary when processing business loans. For this company, do you think the median is a more accurate description of average salary? Why do you think banks request the median statistic?
5. Which statistic would this company's labor union representative be most likely to cite during contract negotiations, and why?
6. Which statistic would the company president most likely report at the annual shareholders' meeting after a very profitable year, and why? Do you think the same statistic would be reported after a not so good year?
7. Name two additional target audiences that would probably have the highest average salary statistic reported to them, and by whom.
8. Name two additional target audiences that would probably have the lowest average salary statistic reported to them, and by whom.

Answers

1. Answers will vary.
2. The mean salary is $43,000, median salary is $30,000, and the mode salary is $16,000.
3. The mean gives an inflated salary view since nine out of thirteen employees earn less than the mean. The four extremely high salaries at the top pull up the low bottom salaries, which are in the majority. This is true for most companies since typically the relatively few employees with the most expertise, education, training, experience, seniority, responsibilities, and employee risk are paid much higher salaries than the larger number of

employees who are new to the company, are receiving on-the-job training, have less risk and responsibilities, and little or no education.

4. For businesses the median usually gives the fairest description of average salary, because while the mean is usually inflated (due to a few high salaries), the mode is usually an underestimate (since it typically reflects salaries of large numbers of new employees and employees in the least skilled jobs).

5. A labor union negotiator would use the lowest salary statistic (mode) as a bargaining tool for higher salaries in the new contract.

6. Answers will vary. If the company had a profitable year, the president would probably report a high average salary, showing that management was good enough to make a profit while paying high wages to its workers. But if the company had a bad year financially, the president might report a low average salary to indicate that despite management holding down labor costs, other factors caused low profits. Or the president might report the high wage statistic and use it as a reason for a drop in profits.

7. Answers will vary. Business management, shareholders, personnel directors, want ads, and present employees would probably cite the highest average salary statistic to friends, prospective employees, internal and external reports, professional publications, government agencies, chambers of commerce, and the general media in order to show the good this company has done for its community.

8. Answers will vary. Labor negotiators, disgruntled and former employees, and competing businesses would probably quote the lowest average salary statistic in order to present the company in the worst possible light, in hopes of furthering their cause.

CHAPTER 4 OVERVIEW

Section Outcome	Important Points with Examples

Section 4.1

Find the range. (page 168)

1. Identify the largest value and the smallest value of the set.
2. Subtract the smallest value from the largest.

$$\text{Range} = \text{largest value} - \text{smallest value}$$

> **A survey of computer stores in a large city shows that a certain printer was sold for the following prices: $435, $398, $429, $479, $435, $495, and $435. Find the range.**
>
> $$\text{Range} = \text{largest value} - \text{smallest value} = \$495 - \$398 = \$97$$

2

Find the mean. (page 169)

1. Find the sum of the values.
2. Divide the sum by the total number of values.

$$\text{Mean} = \frac{\text{sum of values}}{\text{number of values}}$$

Find the median price of the printers (see the preceding example).

$$\text{Mean} = \frac{\text{sum of values}}{\text{number of values}}$$

$$= \$435 + \$398 + \$429 + \$479 + \$435 + \$495 + \$435 = \frac{\$3,106}{7}$$

$$= \$443.71$$

3

Find the
median.
(page 169)

1. Arrange the values in order from smallest to largest or largest to smallest.
2. Count the number of values:
   (a) If the number of values is odd, identify the value in the middle.
   (b) If the number of values is even, find the mean of the middle two values.

Median = middle value or mean of middle two values

Find the median price of the printers (see the preceding example).

Median = middle value of $495, $479, $435, $435, $435, $429, $398

$$= \$435$$

4

Find the
mode.
(page 170)

1. For each value, count the number of times the value occurs.
2. Identify the value or values that occur most frequently.

Mode = most frequent value(s)

Find the mode price of the printers (see the preceding example).

Mode = most frequent value

$$= \$435$$

5

Put statistics
to work.
(page 171)

When the range for a set of data is small, the mean, median, and mode usually have values that are very similar. When the range is very large, it is especially important to examine each of the three averages—mean, median, and mode—to determine which is most representative of the data. The mean can be greatly affected by extreme values in a set of data. In this case, the mean is less descriptive of the set.

Find the range, mean, median, and mode for the scores: 95, 97, 98, 95, 92, 93, 97, 95, 98, 93

Range = 98 − 92 = 6

$$\text{Mean} = \frac{95 + 97 + 98 + 95 + 92 + 93 + 97 + 95 + 98 + 93}{10} = \frac{953}{10} = 95.3$$

Arranged from smallest to largest: 92, 93, 93, 95, 95, 95, 97, 97, 98, 98

Median = 95

Mode = 95 since 95 occurs three times

Since the range is small, the mean, median, and mode are very close.

Section 4.2

A table consists of sets of data grouped horizontally in rows and vertically in columns. In this way, values of one data set correspond to values of another data set.

Payroll Register	M	T	W	T	F	S	S	Total
Brown	8	8	8	8	8			40
James	8	6	8	8	8	4		42
Warwick	8	8	8	8	0	8		40
Zedick	8	0	8	8	8	0		32

How many hours did James work on Tuesday?   **6**
Which employee worked the least number of hours for the week?   **Zedick**

Draw a bar graph.
1. Write an appropriate title.
2. Make appropriate labels for bars and scale. The intervals on the scale should be equally spaced and include the smallest and largest values.
3. Draw bars to represent the data. Bars should be of uniform width.
4. Make additional notes as appropriate. For example, "Amounts in Thousand Dollars" allows values such as $30,000 to be represented by 30.

Draw a bar graph to represent daily sales for the week.

Monday: $18,000
Tuesday: $30,000
Wednesday: $50,000
Thursday: $29,000
Friday: $40,000
Saturday: $32,000
Sunday: $8,000

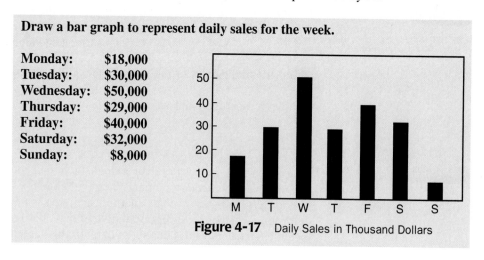

Figure 4-17   Daily Sales in Thousand Dollars

Draw a line graph.
1. Write an appropriate title.
2. Make and label appropriate horizontal and vertical scales, each with equally spaced intervals. Often, the horizontal scale represents time.
3. Use points to locate data on the graph.
4. Connect data points with line segments or a smooth curve.

Draw a line graph to show temperature changes: 12 A.M., 62°; 4 A.M., 65°; 8 A.M., 68°; 12 P.M., 73°; 4 P.M., 76°; 8 P.M., 72°; 12 A.M., 59°.

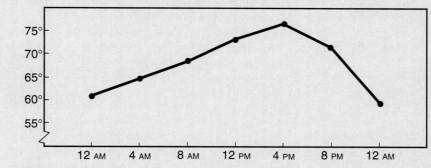

Figure 4-18   Temperature for a 24-Hour Period

4   Read and construct a circle graph. (page 179)

Draw a circle graph.

1. Write an appropriate title.
2. Find the sum of the values in the data set.
3. Represent each value as a fractional or decimal part of the sum of values.
4. For each fraction or decimal, find the number of degrees in the sector of the circle to be represented by the fraction or decimal: multiply the fraction or decimal by 360 degrees. The sum of the degrees for all sectors should be 360 degrees.
5. Use a compass (a tool for drawing circles) to draw a circle. Indicate the center of the circle and a starting point on the circle.
6. For each degree value, draw a sector: use a protractor (a measuring instrument for angles) to measure the number of degrees for the sector of the circle to be represented by the value. Where the first sector ends, the next sector begins. The last sector should end at the starting point.
7. Label each sector of the circle and make additional explanatory notes as necessary.

Draw a circle graph to represent the data.

Total salary: $28,000
Housing: $8,000
Food: $6,000
Clothing: $1,000
Transportation: $2,000
Taxes: $5,000
Insurance: $1,800
Utilities: $1,200
Savings: $3,000

Housing: $\dfrac{\$8,000}{\$28,000} \times 360° = 103°$

Food: $\dfrac{\$6,000}{\$28,000} \times 360° = 77°$

Clothing: $\dfrac{\$1,000}{\$28,000} \times 360° = 13°$

Transportation: $\dfrac{\$2,000}{\$28,000} \times 360° = 26°$

Taxes: $\dfrac{\$5,000}{\$28,000} \times 360° = 64°$

Insurance: $\dfrac{\$1,800}{\$28,000} \times 360° = 23°$

Utilities: $\dfrac{\$1,200}{\$28,000} \times 360° = 15°$

Savings: $\dfrac{\$3,000}{\$28,000} \times 360° = 39°$

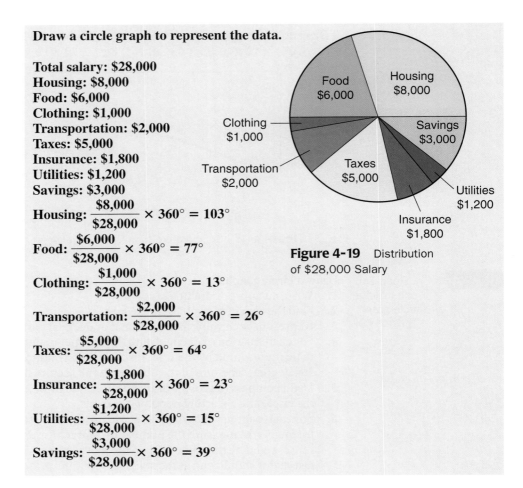

Figure 4-19   Distribution of $28,000 Salary

5	Put tables and graphs to work. (page 181)

Find Percent or Rate of Change (Increase or Decrease).
1. Find the amount of change: subtract the larger of the original amount and new amount from the smaller of the two.
2. Write the percentage formula $R = \dfrac{P}{B}$.
3. Replace P by the amount of change and replace B by the original amount.
4. Write the fraction $\dfrac{P}{B}$ as a percent: multiply by 100%.

Mario's salary increased from $53,840 to $62,500. What was the percent increase?

$62,500 - \$53,840 = \$8,660$ increase

$\dfrac{\$8,660}{\$53,840} \times 100\% = 16.1\%$ increase

WORDS TO KNOW

data set (p.168)
statistics (p. 168)
range (p. 168)
spread (p. 168)
mean (p. 169)
median (p. 169)

mode (p. 170)
table (p. 174)
entry (p. 174)
cell (p. 174)
bar graphs (p. 176)
line graphs (p. 177)

circle graph (p. 179)
protractor (p. 179)
ratio (p. 182)
increase (p. 182)
decrease (p. 182)
rate of change (p. 182)

1. What type of information does a circle graph show?

2. Give a situation in which it would be appropriate to organize the data in a circle graph.

3. What type of information does a bar graph show?

4. Give a situation in which it would be appropriate to organize the data in a bar graph.

5. What type of information does a line graph show?

6. Give a situation in which it would be appropriate to organize the data in a line graph.

7. Explain the differences among the three types of averages: the mean, the median, and the mode.

8. What can we say about the mean for a data set with a large range?

9. What can we say about the mean for a data set with a small range?

10. What components of a table enable us to analyze and interpret the data given in the table?

CHAPTER
4

ASSIGNMENT EXERCISES

Section 4.1

Find the range, mean, median, and mode for the following. Round to the nearest hundredth if necessary.

1. New car mileages
   17 mi/gal
   16 mi/gal
   25 mi/gal
   22 mi/gal
   30 mi/gal

2. Test scores
   61
   72
   63
   70
   93
   87

3. Sandwiches
   $0.95
   $1.65
   $1.27
   $1.97
   $1.65
   $1.15

4. Credit hours
   16
   12
   18
   15
   16
   12
   12

5. Find the range, mean, median, and mode of the hourly pay rates for the employees.

Thompson	$13.95	Cleveland	$ 5.25
Chang	$ 5.80	Gandolfo	$ 4.90
Jackson	$ 4.68	DuBois	$13.95
Smith	$ 4.90	Serpas	$13.95

6. Find the range, mean, median, and mode of the weights of the metal castings after being milled.

Casting A	1.08 kg	Casting D	1.1 kg
Casting B	1.15 kg	Casting E	1.25 kg
Casting C	1.19 kg	Casting F	1.1 kg

7. During the past year, Piazza's Clothiers sold a certain sweater at different prices: $42.95, $36.50, $40.75, $38.25, and $43.25. Find the range, mean, median, and mode of the selling prices.

8. Which statistic in exercise 7 best represents the price of the sweater?

Section 4.2

Use Table 4-10 for exercises 9–17.

9. How many students were enrolled in class on Wednesday during period 5?

10. How many students were enrolled in class on Monday during period 11?

11. What is the total class enrollment for period 3 Monday through Friday?

12. What is the total class enrollment for period 9 Monday through Friday?

13. How many more people are enrolled in period 3 Monday through Friday than in period 9?

Table 4-10 Class Enrollment by Period and Days of the First Week for the Second Semester

Period	Mon.	Tues.	Wed.	Thur.	Fri.	Sat.
1. 7:00– 7:50 A.M.	277	374	259	340	207	0
2. 7:55– 8:45 A.M.	653	728	593	691	453	361
3. 8:50– 9:40 A.M.	908	863	824	798	604	361
4. 9:45–10:35 A.M.	962	782	849	795	561	361
5. 10:40–11:30 A.M.	914	858	795	927	510	361
6. 11:35–12:25 P.M.	711	773	375	816	527	182
7. 12:30– 1:20 P.M.	686	734	696	733	348	161
8. 1:25– 2:15 P.M.	638	647	659	627	349	85
9. 2:20– 3:10 P.M.	341	313	325	351	136	78
10. 3:15– 4:05 P.M.	110	149	151	160	45	0
11. 4:10– 5:00 P.M..	46	72	65	67	11	0
12. 5:05– 5:55 P.M.	37	91	68	48	0	0
13. 6:00– 6:50 P.M.	809	786	796	705	373	0
14. 6:55– 7:45 P.M.	809	786	796	705	373	0
15. 7:50– 8:40 P.M.	565	586	577	531	373	0
16. 8:45– 9:35 P.M.	727	706	817	758	373	0
17. 9:40–10:30 P.M.	702	706	817	758	27	0
18. 10:35–11:25 P.M.	76	70	46	98	0	0

14. Find the total class enrollment by periods Monday through Friday.

Period	Students	Period	Students
1		10	
2		11	
3		12	
4		13	
5		14	
6		15	
7		16	
8		17	
9		18	

15. What period has the highest enrollment during the day (periods 1–12)?

16. What period has the highest enrollment at night (periods 13–18)?

17. If 1,768 day students were enrolled during the second semester, what percent of the students were enrolled in a period-4 class on Monday? Round to the nearest tenth of a percent.

18. Complete Table 4-11, calculating day enrollment (periods 1–12) and night enrollment (periods 13–18).

Table 4-11 Day and Night Class Enrollment, Second Semester

	Periods	Mon.	Tues.	Wed.	Thurs.	Fri.	Sat.
Day	1–12						
Night	13–18						

Use Table 4-12 for exercises 19–20 and 25–26.

Table 4–12 Sales for The Family Store, 2002–2003

	2002	**2003**
Girls' clothing	$74,675	$81,534
Boys' clothing	65,153	68,324
Women's clothing	125,115	137,340
Men's clothing	83,895	96,315

19. What is the least value for 2002 sales? For 2003 sales?

20. What is the greatest value for 2002 sales? For 2003 sales?

Use Figure 4-20 for exercises 21–24.

Figure 4-20 Distribution of Tax Dollars

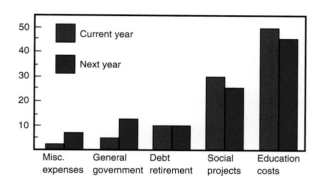

21. What expenditure is expected to be the same next year as this year?

22. What two expenditures are expected to increase next year?

23. What two expenditures are expected to decrease next year?

24. What is the percent of decrease in the education costs?

25. Using the values in Table 4-12, which of the following interval sizes would be more appropriate in making a bar graph? Why?
(a) $1,000 intervals ($60,000, $61,000, $62,000, . . .)
(b) $10,000 intervals ($60,000, $70,000, $80,000, . . .)

26. Draw a comparative bar graph to show both the 2002 and 2003 values for The Family Store (see Table 4-12). Be sure to include a title, explanation of the scales, and any additional information needed.

Sales for The Family Store, 2002–2003

Use Figure 4-21 for exercises 27–30.

27. What three-month period maintained a fairly constant sales record?

28. Calculate the approximate annual sales.

29. What are some factors that could contribute to the dramatic drop in sales for the month of September?

30. What are some factors that could contribute to the high sales in December?

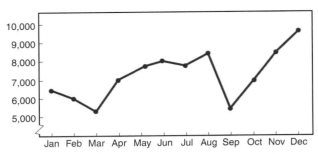

Figure 4-21 Monthly Sales for 7th Inning Sports Memorabilia

Use the following information for exercises 31–34. The temperatures were recorded at two-hour intervals on June 24.

12 A.M.	76°	8 A.M.	70°	2 P.M.	84°	8 P.M.	82°
2 A.M.	75°	10 A.M.	76°	4 P.M.	90°	10 P.M.	79°
4 A.M.	72°	12 P.M.	81°	6 P.M.	90°	12 A.M.	77°
6 A.M.	70°						

31. What is the smallest value?

32. What is the greatest value?

33. Which interval size is most appropriate when making a line graph? Why?
(a) 1°   (b) 5°   (c) 50°   (d) 100°

34. Draw a line graph representing the data. Be sure to include the title, explanation of the scales, and any additional information needed.

35. Which of the following terms would describe this line graph?
(a) Continually increasing (b) Continually decreasing (c) Fluctuating

Temperatures on June 24

Use Figure 4-22 for exercises 36–39.

36. What percent of the gross pay goes into savings? (Round to tenths.)

37. What percent of the gross pay is federal income tax? (Round to tenths.)

38. What percent of the gross pay is the take-home pay? (Round to tenths.)

39. What are the total deductions for this payroll check?

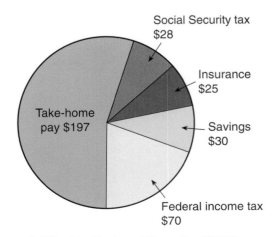

Figure 4-22 Distribution of Gross Pay ($350)

Use Figure 4-23 for exercises 40–42.

40. What percent of the overall cost does the lot represent? (Round to the nearest tenth.)

41. What is the cost of the lot with landscaping? What percent of the total cost does this represent? (Round to the nearest tenth.)

42. What is the cost of the house with furnishings? What percent of the total cost does this represent? (Round to the nearest tenth.)

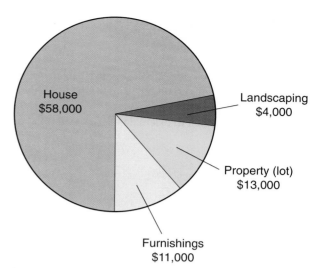

Figure 4-23   Distribution of Costs for an $86,000 Home

Use the Automobile Dealership table (Table 4-13) for exercises 43–46.

43. What was the total number of cars sold?

44. How many degrees should be used to represent the new business on a circle (to the nearest whole degree)?

45. How many degrees should be used to represent the repeat business on the circle graph (to the nearest whole degree)?

46. Construct a circle graph for these data. Label the parts of the graph as "New" and "Repeat." Be sure to include a title and any additional information needed.

47. What are some advertising strategies that could be used to increase repeat business?

Table 4–13   Automobile Dealership's New and Repeat Business

Customer	Cars Sold
New	920
Repeat	278

Automobile Dealership's New and Repeat Business

Use Table 4-14 for exercises 48 and 49.

48. Give the range and mode of grades for each semester.

49. Give the range and mode of grades for the entire two-year program.

Table 4–14

First Semester Fall			Second Semester Spring			Third Semester Fall			Fourth Semester Spring		
Course	Cr. Hr.	Gr.	Course	Cr. Hr.	Gr.	Course	Cr. Hr.	Gr.	Course	Cr. Hr.	Gr.
BUS MATH	4	90	SOC.	3	92	FUNS.	4	88	CAL I	4	89
ACC I	4	89	PSYC	3	91	ACC II	4	89	ACC IV	4	90
ENG I	3	91	ENG II	3	90	ENG 888	3	95	ENG IV	3	96
HISTORY	3	92	ACC II	4	88	PURCH	3	96	ADV	3	93
ECON	5	85	ECON II	4	86	MGMT I	5	84	MGMT II	5	83

50. Write formulas to complete the spreadsheet that provides information to make a circle graph.

  (a) Write a formula to find the sum of the monthly expenses for Jason Harrison.

  (b) Write a formula to calculate the percent of the total expenses for each category.

  (c) Write a formula to calculate the number of degrees of the circle graph allotted for each category.

51. Complete the spreadsheet using the formulas.

	A	B	C	D
1	**Jason Harrison's Monthly Expenses**			
2	**Expenses**	**Amount**	**Percent**	**Degrees**
3	Savings	$30.00		
4	Housing	$600.00		
5	Food	$500.00		
6	Utilities	$150.00		
7	Car Note	$300.00		
8	Gasoline	$140.00		
9	Insurance	$130.00		
10	Clothing	$40.00		
11	Entertainment	$50.00		
12				

Challenge Problem

52. Have the computers made a mistake? You have been attending Northeastern State College (which follows a percentage grading system) for two years. You have received good grades, but after four semesters you have not made the Dean's List, which requires an overall average of 90% for all accumulated credits or 90% for any given semester. Your grade reports are shown in Table 4-14.

To find the grade point average for a semester, multiply each grade by the credit hours. Add the products and then divide by the total number of credit hours for the semester. To calculate the overall grade point average, proceed similarly, but divide the sum of the products for all semesters by the total accumulated credit hours. Find the grade point average for each semester and the overall grade point average.

CHAPTER 4 PRACTICE TEST

Use the following data for exercises 1–4.

| 42 | 86 | 92 | 15 | 32 | 67 | 48 | 19 | 87 | 63 |
| 15 | 19 | 21 | 17 | 53 | 27 | 21 | 15 | 82 | 15 |

1. What is the range?   **2.** What is the mean?   **3.** What is the median?   **4.** What is the mode?

Use the following data for exercises 5–8.

105	215	165	172	138
198	165	170	165	146
187	170	165	146	200

5. What is the range?   **6.** What is the mean?   **7.** What is the median?   **8.** What is the mode?

The costs of producing a piece of luggage at ACME Luggage Company are: labor, $45; materials, $40; overhead, $35. Use this information for exercises 9–14.

9. What is the total cost of producing a piece of luggage?

10. What percent of the total cost is attributed to labor?

11. What percent of the total cost is attributed to materials?

12. What percent of the total cost is attributed to overhead?

13. Compute the number of degrees for labor, materials, and overhead needed for a circle graph.

14. Construct a circle graph for the cost of producing a piece of luggage.

Katz Florist recorded the sales for a six-month period for fresh and silk flowers in Table 4-15. Use the table for exercises 15–18.

Table 4–15   Sales for Katz Florist, January–June

	January	February	March	April	May	June
Fresh	$11,520	$22,873	$10,380	$12,562	$23,712	$15,816
Silk	$8,460	$14,952	$5,829	$10,621	$17,892	$7,583

15. What is the greatest value of fresh flowers? Of silk flowers?

16. What is the smallest value of fresh flowers? Of silk flowers?

17. What interval size would be most appropriate when making a bar graph? Why?
(a) $100   (b) $1,000   (c) $5,000   (d) $10,000

18. Construct a bar graph for the sales at Katz Florist.

Sales for Katz Florist, January–June

Use the following data for exercises 19–20. The totals of the number of laser printers sold in the years 1998 through 2003 by Smart Brothers Computer Store are as follows:

1998	1999	2000	2001	2002	2003
983	1,052	1,117	615	250	400

19. What is the smallest value? The greatest value?

20. Draw a line graph representing the data. Use an interval of 250. Be sure to include a title and explanation of the scales.

Sales of Laser Printers by Smart Brothers Computer Store

Use Figure 4-24 for exercises 21–24.

21. In what year(s) did women use more sick days than men?

22. In what year(s) did men use five sick days?

23. In what year(s) did men use more sick days than women?

24. What was the greatest number of sick days for men?

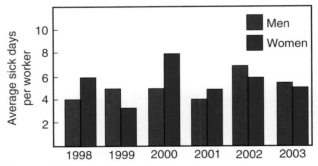

Figure 4-24   Comparison of Sick Days for Men and Women

Self-Check 4.1

1. Range = 8,550 − 3,850 = 4,700

2. Range = $48,397 − $19,522 = $28,875

3. Range = 842 − 127 = 715 thousand dollars, or $715,000

4. Range = $18,540 − $13,592 = $4,948

5. Mean = (3,850 + 5,300 + 8,550 + 4,200 + 5,350) ÷ 5 = $\dfrac{27,250}{5}$ = 5,450

6. Mean = ($48,397 + $27,982 + $42,591 + $19,522 + $32,400 + $37,582) ÷ 6 = $\dfrac{\$208,474}{6}$ = $34,745.67

7. Mean = (127 + 215 + 135 + 427 + 842 + 687 + 321 + 512 + 351 + 742 + 482 + 305) ÷ 12 = $\dfrac{5,146}{12}$ = 428.833 thousand dollars, or $428,833

8. Mean = ($17,485 + $14,978 + $13,592 + $14,500 + $18,540) ÷ 5 = $\dfrac{\$79,095}{5}$ = $15,819

9. Arrange the numbers from smallest to largest:
3,850   4,200   5,300   5,350   8,550
          ↑
     middle number
Median: 5,300

10. $19,522; $27,982; $32,400; $37,582; $42,591; $48,397
Median: $\dfrac{\$32,400 + \$37,582}{2}$ = $34,991

11. 127, 135, 215, 305, 321, 351, 427, 482, 512, 687, 742, 842
Median: $\dfrac{351 + 427}{2}$ = 389 thousand dollars, or $389,000

12. $13,592; $14,500; $14,978; $17,485; $18,540
Median: $14,978

13. Arrange the numbers from smallest to largest:
73, 84, 86, 86, 94, 94, 94
Mode: 94

14. 43, 49, 72, 75, 80, 85, 85, 86, 86, 86, 92, 92, 93, 97, 99, 100
Mode: 86

15. 78, 79, 80, 82, 82, 83, 85
Mode: 82

16. 79, 83, 83, 83, 89, 89, 89, 93, 95, 106, 109
Mode: 83 and 89

17. Arrange the prices in order from smallest to largest:
$11,400 $13,500 $14,500 $15,300 $ 17,500
Range = $17,500 − $11,400 = $6,100
Mean = ($11,400 + $13,500 + $14,500 + $15,300 + $17,500) ÷ 5 = $72,200 ÷ 5 = $14,440
Median: = $14,500
No mode.
Since the mean and median are close but the range is large, we can use the mean and median to get a realistic picture of the cost of an automobile in this area.

18. $21,983, $25,997, $27,596, $32,084, $38,840, $43,702
Median: $\dfrac{\$27,596 + \$32,084}{2}$ = $29,840

19. Range = $43,702 − $21,983 = $21,719

20. Mean = (89 + 88 + 90 + 92 + 95 + 89 + 93 + 98 + 93 + 97) ÷ 10 = 92.4°

21. Range = 98 − 88 = 10°

22. 88, 89, 89, 90, 92, 93, 93, 95, 97, 98.
Median: $\dfrac{92 + 93}{2}$ = 92.5°

23. Modes: 89° and 93°

24. The mean and median and one of the modes are very close. A value of 92 or 93 is a typical representation for the data set.

Self-Check 4.2

1. Highest: Saturday ($611.77); Lowest: Monday ($233.94)

2. Wednesday ($122.35)

3. most sales: Brown ($853.60); second highest sales: Ulster ($645.30)

4. Sales by Salesperson at Happy's Gift Shoppe

	Salesperson				
Day	Brown	Jackson	Ulster	Young	Total
Mon.	Off	$121.68	$112.26	Off	$233.94
Tues.	$110.25	Off	119.40	$122.90	352.55
Wed.	114.52	118.29	122.35	Off	355.16
Thur.	186.42	Off	174.51	181.25	542.18
Fri.	126.81	125.42	116.78	Off	369.01
Sat.	315.60	Off	Off	296.17	611.77
Total	$853.60	$365.39	$645.30	$600.32	$2,464.61

5. April–June

6. $100,000 + $150,000 + $125,000 + $80,000 = $455,000

$$\frac{\$80,000}{\$455,000} = 17.6\%$$

7. $150,000 − $100,000 = $50,000

$$\frac{\$50,000}{\$100,000} = 50\%$$

8.

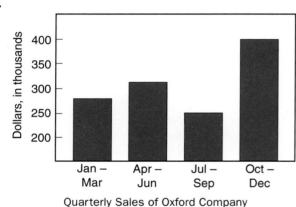

Quarterly Sales of Oxford Company

9. 40 mph

10. 70 mph

11. 20 mph, compact car

12. Answers will vary; consider price, safety, room or space, comfort.

13. Answers will vary.

14. Chevez, $192; Young, $72; Chow, $72; Santoni, $144; Wilson, $96

15. 163 − 157 = 6

16. $\dfrac{\text{Men}}{\text{Women}} = \dfrac{143}{144}$

17. Total club members at the end of December 2000 = 143 + 144 = 287
Total club members at the end of December 2001 = 166 + 172 = 338
New club members in 1998 = 338 − 287 = 51
New male club members in 1998 = 166 − 143 = 23

Male percent of new club members $= \dfrac{P}{B} = \dfrac{23}{51} =$

$\dfrac{23}{51} \times 100\% = 45\%$

18. Percent of week's sales made on Thursday $= \dfrac{P}{B} = \dfrac{\$542.18}{\$2,464.61} = 0.2199861 \times 100\% = 22\%$

Percent of week's sales made on Monday $= \dfrac{P}{B} = \dfrac{\$233.94}{\$2,464.61} = 0.0949196 \times 100\% = 9\%$

19. Percent of day's sales made by Young on Saturday $= \dfrac{P}{B} = \dfrac{\$296.17}{\$611.77} = 0.4841198 \times 100\% = 48\%$

20. Percent of total take-home pay spent for contributions $= \dfrac{P}{B} = \dfrac{\$160}{\$1,600} = \dfrac{\$160}{\$1,600} \times 100\% = 10\%$

21. Percent of total take-home pay spent for education if education, savings, and miscellaneous funds are used =

$\dfrac{P}{B} = \dfrac{\$80 + \$160 + \$80}{\$1,600} = \dfrac{\$320}{\$1,600} = \dfrac{\$320}{\$1,600} \times 100\% = 20\%$

22. $18,000 - $16,500 = $1,500

$\dfrac{\$1,500}{\$16,500} \times 100\% = 9.1\%$

23. $21,000 - $20,000 = $1,000

$\dfrac{\$1,000}{\$20,000} = 100\% = 5\%$

24. $23,000 - $21,000 = $2,000

$\dfrac{\$2,000}{\$21,000} \times 100\% = 9.5\%$

25. $21,000 - $16,000 = $5,000

$\dfrac{\$5,000}{\$16,000} \times 100\% = 31\%$

Yes, the percent of increase was 31%, and it exceeded the rate of inflation.

5

Bank Records

5.1 Checking Account Forms

1 Make account deposits.

2 Make account withdrawals.

3 Record account transactions.

4 Endorse a check.

5.2 Bank Statements

1 Read a bank statement.

2 Reconcile a bank statement with an account register.

Good Decisions through Teamwork

Investigate and report on the advantages and disadvantages of using bank debit cards, including these and other aspects:

- Convenience to account holder
- Financial privacy/safety
- Card theft liability loss
- Record of transactions
- Checkbook balancing
- "Float" time
- Vendor acceptance

As a team, brainstorm ideas for other aspects and then assign aspects to each team member. Individually, research your assigned aspects and prepare a brief report of your findings. Together, read, critique, and edit each member's findings. Then organize a final report. Be sure to include introductory and summary paragraphs, cover all aspects of using bank debit cards, and represent all viewpoints about their benefits and drawbacks.

When it's time to pay the bills, whether personal or business related, most Americans turn to a checkbook. However, as technology continues to improve methods of doing business, an increasing number of Americans are using automated bank drafts to pay creditors and debit cards for transactions made on a one-time basis. In recent years, checking account transactions have changed drastically. The specific forms, policies, and procedures for checking accounts still vary from bank to bank. Once you know the reasoning behind these banking procedures, it is easy enough to understand the minor variations among banks. For business or personal use, it is important to use banking forms correctly, to keep accurate records, and to track financial transactions carefully.

Most businesses and many individuals use a computer and computer software for writing, recording, and reconciling transactions for a bank account. All of the processes discussed in this chapter are easily adapted when using a computer.

5.1 Checking Account Forms

1 Make account deposits.

2 Make account withdrawals.

3 Record account transactions.

4 Endorse a check.

Various checking account forms are needed to maintain a checking account for your personal or business financial matters. The bank must be able to account for all funds that flow into and out of your account, and written evidence of changes in your account is necessary.

1 Make account deposits.

When money is put into a checking account, the transaction is called a **deposit.** The bank refers to this transaction as a **credit.** A deposit or credit *increases* the amount of the account. One bank record for deposits made by the account holder is called the **deposit ticket.** Figure 5-1 shows a sample deposit ticket for a personal account. Figure 5-2 shows a sample deposit ticket for a business account. Deposit tickets are available to the person opening an account along with a set of preprinted checks. The bank's account number and the customer's account number are written at the bottom of the ticket in magnetic ink using specially designed characters and symbols to facilitate machine processing.

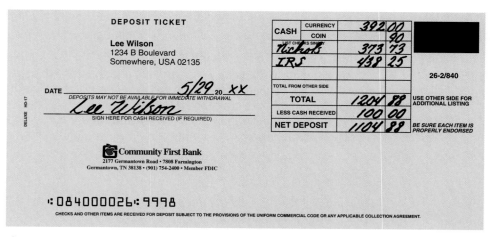

Figure 5-1 Deposit Ticket for a Personal Account

Figure 5-2 Deposit Ticket for a Business Account

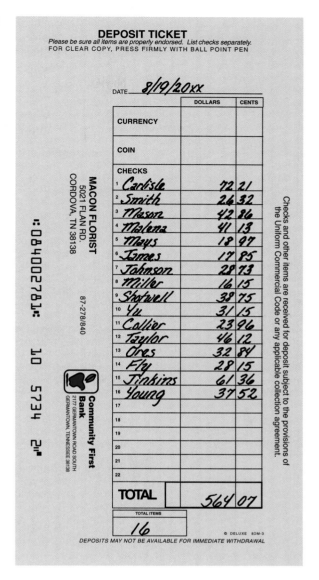

DEPOSIT TICKET
Please be sure all items are properly endorsed. List checks separately.
FOR CLEAR COPY, PRESS FIRMLY WITH BALL POINT PEN

DATE 8/19/20xx

	DOLLARS	CENTS
CURRENCY		
COIN		
CHECKS		
1 Carlisle	72	21
2 Smith	26	32
3 Mason	42	86
4 Molena	41	13
5 Mays	18	97
6 Ismes	17	85
7 Johnson	28	73
8 Miller	16	15
9 Shotwell	38	75
10 Yu	31	15
11 Collier	23	96
12 Taylor	46	12
13 Ones	32	84
14 Fly	28	15
15 Jinkins	61	36
16 Young	37	52
17		
18		
19		
20		
21		
22		
TOTAL	564	07
TOTAL ITEMS 16		

MACON FLORIST
5021 FLAN RD.
CORDOVA, TN 38138

87-278/840

Community First Bank
2177 GERMANTOWN ROAD SOUTH
GERMANTOWN, TENNESSEE 38138

⑈084002781⑈ 10 5734 2⑈

Checks and other items are received for deposit subject to the provisions of the Uniform Commercial Code or any applicable collection agreement.

© DELUXE 8DM-3
DEPOSITS MAY NOT BE AVAILABLE FOR IMMEDIATE WITHDRAWAL

A deposit ticket has places for the date and for listing the checks and cash to be deposited. Checks and cash are listed separately, and each individual check is listed. The amounts to be deposited are then added and the sum is written in the place marked "Total." If the bank discovers an error in the deposit transaction, it will notify you of the correction through a **bank memo.** If the error correction increases your balance, the bank memo is called a **credit memo.** If the error correction decreases your balance, the bank memo is called a **debit memo.**

For a personal account, if the depositor wants to get some of the total deposit back in cash, the depositor writes this amount in the place marked *"Less cash received,"* and subtracts it from the total. The difference is entered in the place marked *"Net deposit."* Other notations and reminders vary from bank to bank. In general, banks will not honor requests for "less cash received" from business account holders.

Deposits to bank accounts can be made electronically. Individuals may make deposits using a debit card or an automatic teller machine (ATM) card. Individuals may also request their employer to deposit their paychecks directly to their bank account by completing a form that gives the banking information, including the account number. The government encourages recipients of Social Security and other government funds to have these funds **electronically deposited.** Businesses that permit customers to use credit cards to charge merchandise may receive payment through electronic deposit from the credit card company. These transactions are sometimes called **point-of-sale** transactions since the money is transferred electronically when the sale is made. VISA, Master Card, and Discover are examples of major credit card companies that electronically transmit funds to business accounts. Transactions made electronically are called **electronic funds transfers** (EFTs).

EXAMPLE Complete a deposit ticket to deposit $392.48 in cash and two checks for $135.92 and $143.17 on March 31.

The completed deposit ticket is shown in Figure 5-3.

Figure 5-3 Completed Deposit Ticket

2 Make account withdrawals.

When money is taken from a checking account, this transaction is called a **withdrawal.** The bank refers to this transaction as a **debit.** A withdrawal or debit *decreases* the amount of the account. One bank record for withdrawals made by the account holder is called a **check** or **bank draft.** Figure 5-4 shows the basic features of a check.

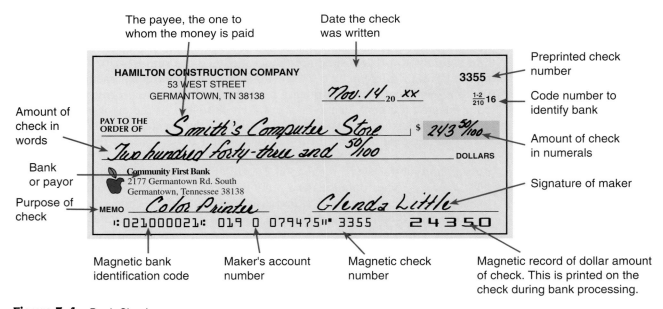

Figure 5-4 Bank Check

Notice that, when the amount of the check is written in numerals, the number of cents is written as a fraction. But cents can be written in decimal form, too. When the amount of the check is written in words, however, the number of cents is still written in numerals, and always in fraction form. The word *and* separates the dollar amount from the cent amount.

Personal checks and some business checks have a line called "Memo" or "For," which provides space for the maker to describe the purchase. Some business checks have more space for noting the purpose of a check and have a special tear-off portion for listing the information necessary for internal accounting procedures.

When a checking account is opened, those persons authorized to write checks on the account must sign a **signature card,** which is kept on file at the bank. Whenever a question arises regarding whether a person is authorized to write checks on an account, the bank refers to the signature card to resolve the question.

Withdrawals from personal and business bank accounts can also be made electronically. Many persons elect to have regular monthly bills such as house note, rent, utilities, insurance, and so forth, paid electronically through **automatic drafts** from their bank account. The amount of the debit is shown on the monthly bank statement. Individuals may also use a **debit card** to pay for services and goods. A debit card looks very similar to a credit card and often even includes a credit card name and logo such as Visa. The debit card works just like a check except the transaction is handled electronically at the time the transaction is made.

 **TIP!** Don't Toss Those ATM or Debit Card Receipts

Customers are issued receipts when they deposit or withdraw money from an automatic teller machine. Use these receipts to update your account register and to verify against your next bank statement. When you are certain the transaction has been properly posted by your bank, dispose of the receipts by shredding or by some other means to maintain the security of your banking record.

 TIP! Know Your Cards—They All Look Alike!

The ATM card, the credit card, and the debit card may all look very similar. If you have a combination of these cards, look carefully when using a card.

The ATM card is used only at ATM machines to get cash and make deposits. The credit card is used to make charges that are paid on a monthly basis, either full or partial payment. The debit card is used in the same way as an ATM card or a check and the amount is deducted from your bank account immediately.

Many people now take advantage of the Internet to do their banking online. This service is expected to increase dramatically in the future as more and more individuals become comfortable with technology.

EXAMPLE   Write a check dated April 8, 20XX, to Disk-O-Mania in the amount of $84.97, for computer diskettes.

Enter the date: 4/8/XX.

Write the name of the payee: Disk-O-Mania.

Enter the amount of the check in numerals: 84.97.

Enter the amount of the check in words. Note the fraction $\frac{97}{100}$ showing cents, or hundredths of dollars: eighty four and $\frac{97}{100}$.

Write the purpose of the check on the memo line: computer diskettes.

Sign your name.

The completed check is shown in Figure 5-5.

Figure 5-5 Completed Check

3 Record account transactions.

Businesses and individuals who have checking accounts use either a check stub or an account register to record all the checks they write and all the deposits they make. Some record the transactions in computer software designed to enable one to keep track of funds moving into and out of the account.

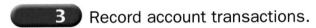

TIP! **Keep Accurate Up-to-Date Account Records!**

The key to maintaining control of your checking account balance is to record and track every transaction. In today's busy world, it is easy to use a debit card to make many charges in a short time. Recording every transaction *when it is made* will help you keep track of your balance.

Check writing supplies are available for handwritten, typed, or computer-generated checks.

A **check stub** has a place to list the check number (if it is not preprinted), the date, the amount of the check, the person to whom the check is made, and what the check is written for. There is also a place to record the balance forward (the balance after the previous check was written), the amount deposited since that time, the amount of the check, and the new balance.

When recording the check stub, add any deposits and subtract the amount of the check to get the new balance. You should complete the check stub *before* writing the check so that you won't forget to do it.

EXAMPLE Complete the stub for the check written in the preceding example. The balance forward is $8,324.09. Deposits of $325, $694.30, and $82.53 were made after the previous check was written.

The check number, 123, is preprinted in this case.

Enter the date: 4/8/XX.

Enter the amount of this check: $84.97.

Enter the payee: Disk-O-Mania.

Enter the purpose: computer diskettes.

Enter the balance forward: $8,324.09

Enter the total of the deposits: $1,101.83.

Add the balance forward and the deposits to find the total: $9,425.92.

Enter the amount of this check: $84.97.

Subtract the amount of the check from the total to find the balance: $9,340.95.

The completed stub is shown in Figure 5-6. Carry the balance to the next stub as the Balance Forward.

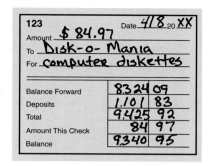

123		Date 4/8 20 XX
Amount $ 84.97		
To Disk-o- Mania		
For computer diskettes		

Balance Forward	8324	09
Deposits	1,101	83
Total	9,425	92
Amount This Check	84	97
Balance	9,340	95

Figure 5-6 Completed Stub

Like check stubs, an **account register** allows you to maintain a record of all transactions made to the account. Transactions that increase the account balance are called **credits.** Transactions that decrease the account balance are called **debits.** Account registers for individual account holders are generally supplied with an order of personalized checks. Most banks also supply an account register upon request. On the bank's preprinted account register, space is provided for entering the transaction number, the date, a description of the transaction, the amount of the transaction (be it a check, a deposit, or a fee), a check mark √ (used to balance the account register), and the account balance. Figure 5-7 shows a sample of a standard account register page.

		RECORD ALL TRANSACTIONS THAT AFFECT YOUR ACCOUNT					BALANCE	
NUMBER	DATE	DESCRIPTION OF TRANSACTION	DEBIT	√	FEE	CREDIT	6843	00
543	8/9	Golden Wheat Dist.	685 56		$		6157	44
544	8/9	Consolidated Berry Farms	89 78				6067	66
	8/9	Cash withdrawal	250 00				5817	66
	8/10	Deposit				1,525 61	7,343	27

Figure 5-7 Account Register

As banking becomes increasingly complex and more electronic and the penalty for overdrawing bank accounts escalates, it becomes more important to carefully maintain an account register of all transactions. Computer programs are becoming increasingly more popular among individuals as well as businesses for keeping bank account records. Debit cards are also rising in popularity as a substitute for checks. However, with the increased use of electronic transactions, it becomes more important to keep systematic records of all account transactions. Thus, the bank register can be used to record transactions made while away from your computer. Then the computer can be used to keep balances as new transactions are entered.

In addition to computer software for keeping bank records, access to bank accounts is available through the Internet and online services.

4 Endorse a check.

Before a check can be cashed, it must be **endorsed.** That is, the payee must sign or stamp the check on the back. There are several ways to endorse a check. The simplest way is for the payee to sign the back of the check exactly as the name is written on the front of the check. Banks generally cash checks drawn on their own bank or for payees who are account holders. Banks cashing checks drawn on their own bank may require the payee to present appropriate identification if they are not account holders at that bank. Banks will cash checks drawn on a different bank for payees who are account holders and require the payee's account number to be written below the signature. The payee's account will be debited if the check is returned unpaid.

While banking procedures are designed to prevent misuse of checks, it is a good idea to use a **restricted endorsement** for signing checks. One type of restricted endorsement changes the payee of the check. The original payee writes "pay to the order of," lists the name of the new payee, then signs the check. This choice would be used when you want to receive cash from the bank for the check or if you want to assign the check to someone else. Another type of restricted endorsement is used for depositing the check into the payee's bank account. The payee writes "for deposit only," lists the account number, then endorses the check. Most banking practices will only allow checks to be deposited if they have a business listed as the payee. For greater security most businesses endorse checks as soon as they are received. Many businesses imprint the endorsement on checks using an electronic cash register or an ink stamp.

The Federal Reserve Board regulates the way endorsements can be placed on checks. As Figure 5-8 shows, the endorsement must be placed within $1\frac{1}{2}$ inches from the left edge of the check. The rest of the back of the check is reserved for bank endorsements. Many check-printing companies now mark this space and provide lines for endorsements.

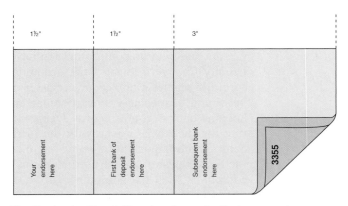

Figure 5-8 The Back of a Check Showing Areas for Endorsements

1. On April 29, 20XX, Mr. Yan Yu made a deposit to the account for Park's Oriental Shop. He deposited $850.00 in cash, $8.63 in coins, and two checks, one in the amount of $157.38, the other in the amount of $32.49. Fill out Mr. Yu's deposit ticket for April 29, 20XX.

Figure 5-9 Deposit Ticket
for Park's Oriental Shop

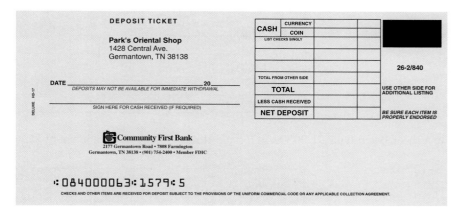

2. Complete the deposit ticket for Delectables Candies. The deposit is made on March 31, 20XX, and includes the following items: cash: 196.00; checks: Cavanaugh, $14.72; Bryan, $31.18; Wossum, $16.97; Wright, $28.46; Howell, $17.21; Coe, $32.17; Beulke, $17.84; Palinchak, $31.96; and Paszel, $19.16.

Figure 5-10 Deposit Ticket
for Delectables Candies

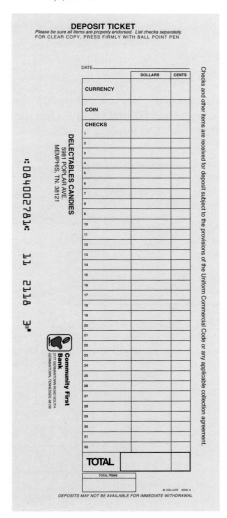

3. On April 29, 20XX, after Mr. Yu made his deposit (see exercise 1), he wrote a check to Green Harvest in the amount of $155.30 for fresh vegetables. Write a check as Mr. Yu wrote it.

Figure 5-11 Check
Number 456

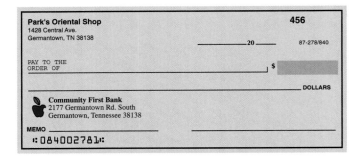

4. Write a check dated June 20, 20XX, to Ronald H. Cox Realty in the amount of $596.13 for house repairs.

Figure 5–12 Check
Number 3215

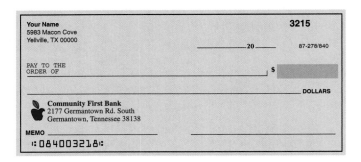

5. Before Mr. Yu made his deposit (see exercise 1), the balance in the account was $7,869.40. Complete the check stub for the check you wrote in exercise 3.

6. Complete the check stub for the check you wrote in exercise 4 if the balance brought forward is $2,213.56.

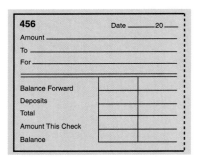

Figure 5-13 Check Stub Number 456

3215	Date ____ 20 ___
Amount	
To	
For	
Balance Forward	
Deposits	
Total	
Amount This Check	
Balance	

Figure 5-14 Check Stub Number 3215

7. Enter in the account register all the transactions described in exercises 1, 3, and 5, and find the ending balance.

Figure 5-15 Account
Register

		RECORD ALL TRANSACTIONS THAT AFFECT YOUR ACCOUNT						
NUMBER	DATE	DESCRIPTION OF TRANSACTION	DEBIT	√	FEE	CREDIT	BALANCE	
			$			$		

8. On September 30 you deposited your payroll check of $932.15. You then wrote the following checks on the same day.

Check Number	Payee	Amount
3176	Electric Coop.	$107.13
3177	Amoco	$47.15
3178	Visa	$97.00

Show these transactions in your account register and show the ending balance if your beginning balance was $435.97.

		RECORD ALL TRANSACTIONS THAT AFFECT YOUR ACCOUNT					BALANCE	
NUMBER	DATE	DESCRIPTION OF TRANSACTION	DEBIT	√	FEE	CREDIT		
			$			$		

Figure 5-16   Account Register

9. Show how the check in exercise 4 would be endorsed for deposit to account number 26-8224021. What type of endorsement is this called?

10. If you were the owner of Green Harvest (exercise 3), would you be able to exchange this check for cash? If so, show how you would endorse the check. If not, explain how you could handle the check.

5.2   Bank Statements

1 Read a bank statement.

2 Reconcile a bank statement with an account register.

Each month, banks send statements to their checking account customers to enable account holders to reconcile any differences between that statement and the customer's own account register.

1 Read a bank statement.

The primary tool for reconciling an account is the monthly **bank statement,** a listing of all transactions that took place in the customer's account during the past month. It includes checks and other debits and deposits and other credits. A sample bank statement is shown in Figure 5-17.

Most bank statements explain the various letter codes and symbols contained in the statement. One of the first steps to take when you receive a bank statement is to check this explanatory section for any terms that you do not understand in the statement.

One of the items that may appear on a bank statement is a **service charge.** This is a fee the bank charges for maintaining the checking account; it may be a standard monthly fee, a charge for each check or transaction, or some combination.

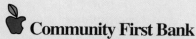

Community First Bank

2177 Germantown Rd. South • Germantown, Tennessee 38138 • (901) 555-2400 • Member FDIC

Pope Animal Clinic
5012 Winchester
Memphis, TN 38118

ACCOUNT NUMBER   43-7432156
FEDERAL ID NUMBER   46-076435176   DATE 5/30/20XX   PAGE 1

			BALANCE OF YOUR FUNDS
PREVIOUS BALANCE -----			$2,571.28
	3	DEPOSITS TOTALING	835.00
	5	WITHDRAWALS TOTALING	228.46
NEW BALANCE ----------			$3,177.82

ACCOUNT TRANSACTIONS FOR THE PERIOD FROM 5/1/20XX THROUGH 5/30/20XX

DATE	AMOUNT	DESCRIPTION
5/1	110.00	DEPOSIT
5/8	200.00	DEPOSIT
5/20	525.00	DEPOSIT
5/30	5.00	SERVICE FEE

DATE	CHECK #	AMOUNT	DATE	CHECK #	AMOUNT
5/1	235	42.95	5/7	237	72.63
5/3	236	12.15	5/15	238	95.73

CHECKING DAILY BALANCE SUMMARY

DATE	BALANCE OF YOUR FUNDS	DATE	BALANCE OF YOUR FUNDS
5/1	2,638.33	5/15	2,657.82
5/3	2,626.18	5/20	3,182.82
5/7	2,553.55	5/30	3,177.82
5/8	2,753.55		

Figure 5-17   Bank Statement

Another type of bank charge appearing on a bank statement is for checks that "bounce" (are not backed by sufficient funds). Suppose Joe writes you a check and you cash the check or deposit it. Later your bank is notified that Joe does not have enough money in his bank account to cover the check. So Joe's bank returns the check to your bank. Such a check is called a **returned check.** Your bank will deduct the amount of the returned check from your account. Your bank may also deduct a **returned check fee** from your account to cover the cost of handling this transaction. If you write a check for which you do not have sufficient funds in your account, your bank will charge you a **nonsufficient funds fee (NSF).** The bank notifies you through a **debit memo** of the decrease in your account balance.

Your statement may also include a debit for **FDIC insurance premium.** The federal government set up the Federal Deposit Insurance Corporation to guarantee bank deposits against bank failure. To pay for this insurance, banks are charged an FDIC insurance fee.

All costs of FDIC insurance were assumed by most banks prior to 1991. In 1991 this insurance increased significantly due to the failure of several banks. As a result many banks began the practice of passing on all or part of the cost of FDIC insurance to customers. The cost of insurance to the financial institution was raised from 12 cents to 23 cents per hundred dollars. This increase of 11 cents per one hundred dollars is the same as 0.11 percent or 0.0011 per one dollar. Some banks pass only the increase along to customers, while other banks pass the entire cost of the insurance to customers, and still others pass along no cost.

Your bank statement also reflects electronic funds transfers such as withdrawals and deposits made using an **automatic teller machine (ATM)** debit cards, wire transfers, online transfers, and authorized electronic withdrawals and deposits.

What does *not* appear on the bank statement is the amount of any check you wrote or deposit you made that reaches the bank *after* the statement is printed. Such transactions may be called **outstanding checks** or **deposits.** This is one reason your bank statement and your account register may not agree initially.

EXAMPLE   Refer to the bank statement in Figure 5-17.

(a) How many deposits were made during the month?
(b) What amount of service charge was paid?
(c) On what day did check 237 clear the bank?
(d) Which of the following types of transactions are not illustrated in the bank statement: service charge, returned check, returned check fee, FDIC insurance premium, automatic teller transaction?

(a) 3 (b) $5.00 (c) 5/7 (d) returned check, returned check fee, FDIC insurance premium, automatic teller transaction

2   Reconcile a bank statement with an account register.

When a bank statement and an account register do not agree initially, you need to take steps to make them agree. The process of making the bank statement agree with the account register is called reconciling a bank statement or **bank reconciliation.**

The first thing to do when you receive a bank statement is to go over it and compare its contents with your account register. You can check off all the checks and deposits listed on the statement by using the √ column in the account register (Figure 5-7) or by marking the check stub.

There are several methods for reconciling your banking records. We will use a method that uses an account reconciliation form. Figure 5-18 shows two samples of

Figure 5-18   Account Reconciliation Forms

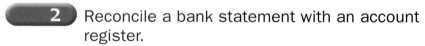

OUTSTANDING DEPOSITS AND OTHER CREDITS		OUTSTANDING CHECKS AND OTHER DEBITS					
DATE	AMOUNT	CHECK #	AMOUNT	CHECK #	AMOUNT	CHECK #	AMOUNT
TOTAL	$					TOTAL	$

STATEMENT BALANCE	$
ADD OUTSTANDING CREDITS	+
SUBTOTAL	
SUBTRACT OUTSTANDING DEBITS	−

UPDATED ACCOUNT REGISTER BALANCE	$	=	ADJUSTED STATEMENT BALANCE	$

Figure 5-18 Continued

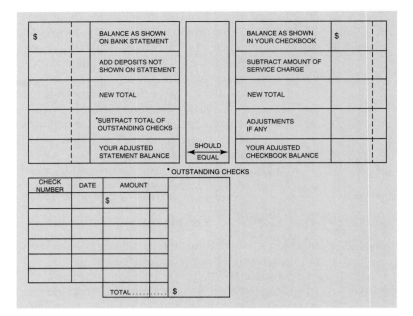

blank bank statement reconcillation forms. A reconciliation form is often printed on the back of the bank statement. The form leads you through a reconciliation process that may be different from the one given in this book, but the result is the same: a reconciled statement.

? HOW TO Reconcile a Bank Statement

1. Check off all matching transactions appearing on both the bank statement and the account register.

2. Enter into the register the transactions appearing on the bank statement that have not been checked off. Check off these transactions in the register as they are entered. Update the register balance accordingly.

3. Make a list of all the checks and other debits appearing in the register that have not been checked off. Add the amounts on the list to find the *total outstanding debits.* Use Figure 5-18 as a guide.

4. Make a list of all the deposits and other credits appearing in the register that have not been checked off in step 1. Add the amounts on the list to find the *total outstanding credits.* Use Figure 5-18 as a guide.

5. Calculate the *adjusted statement balance* by adding the statement balance and the total outstanding deposits and other credits, and then subtracting the total outstanding checks and other debits: Adjusted statement balance = statement balance + total outstanding credits − total outstanding debits.

6. Compare the adjusted statement balance with the register balance. These amounts should be equal.

7. If the adjusted statement balance does not equal the register balance, locate the cause of the discrepancy and correct the register accordingly.

8. Write *statement reconciled* on the next blank line in the account register and record the statement date.

When your adjusted statement balance does not equal your account register balance, you need to locate the cause of the discrepancy and correct the register accordingly.

To do so, first be sure you have calculated the adjusted statement balance accurately. Double check, for instance, that the list of outstanding debits is complete and their sum is accurate. Double check the list of outstanding credits, too. Double check that you correctly added the total outstanding credits and subtracted the total outstanding debits from the statement balance. If you are sure you have carried out all the reconciliation steps correctly, the discrepancy may be due to an error that you made in the account register or to an error made by the bank. Here are some common errors and strategies to locate them.

Error: You entered a transaction in the register but you did not update the account register balance.
Strategy: To locate the transaction, calculate the difference of the adjusted statement balance and the register balance (subtract one from the other). Compare this difference with each transaction amount in the register to see if this difference matches a transaction amount exactly.

Error: You transposed digits, for instance 39 was entered as 93, when entering the amount in the register or when listing outstanding items from the statement.
Strategy: Divide the difference between the adjusted statement balance and the adjusted register balance by 9. If the quotient has no remainder, check the entries to find the transposed digits.

Error: You entered the check number as the amount of the check.
Strategy: Check the amount of each check as you check off the correct amount.

Error: You entered a transaction in the register but to update the register balance you added the transaction amount when you should have subtracted, or vice versa.
Strategy: To locate the transaction, calculate the difference of the adjusted statement balance and the adjusted register balance (subtract one from the other). Now calculate half of this difference (divide the difference by 2). Compare this result with each transaction in the register to see if it matches a transaction amount exactly.

Error: You entered a transaction in the register, but to update the register balance you added (or subtracted) the transaction amount incorrectly.
Strategy: To locate the transaction, begin with the first transaction in the register following the previous reconciliation. From this point on, redo your addition (or subtraction) for each transaction to see if you originally added (or subtracted) the transaction amount correctly.

When using software programs to keep banking records, the user enters transaction amounts into the computer, and the program updates the register balance. At reconciliation time, the user enters information from the bank statement into the computer, and the program reconciles the bank statement with the account register.

These programs can also be useful for budgeting and tax purposes. Transactions can be categorized and tracked according to the user's specifications. Monthly and yearly budgets can be prepared accordingly, for both individuals and businesses. At tax time, these programs may even be used to generate and fill in tax forms.

EXAMPLE Pope Animal Clinic regularly transfers money from its checking account to a special account used for one-time expenditures such as equipment. The decision to transfer is made each month when the bank statement is reconciled. Money is transferred only if the adjusted statement balance exceeds $2500; all the excess is transferred. The bank statement is shown in Figure 5-17, and the register is shown in Figure 5-19. Should money be transferred? If so, how much?

RECORD ALL TRANSACTIONS THAT AFFECT YOUR ACCOUNT

NUMBER	DATE	DESCRIPTION OF TRANSACTION	DEBIT (−)	√ T	FEE (IF ANY) (−)	CREDIT (+)	BALANCE	
							2,571	28
235	4/20	Pet Supply Company	42 95				2,528	33
Deposit	5/1	Customer Receipts				110 00	2,638	33
236	5/1	K-mart	12 15				2,626	18
237	5/1	Telephone Company	72 63				2,553	55
Deposit	5/8	Customer Receipts				200 00	2,753	55
238	5/10	Chickasaw Electric Co.	95 73				2,657	82
239	5/15	Protein Technologies Dog Food	117 28				2,540	54
240	5/15	Rand M Drug Co.	92 69				2,447	85
Deposit	5/20	Customer Receipts				525 00	2,972	85
Deposit	5/25	Customer Receipts				200 00	3,172	85

REMEMBER TO RECORD AUTOMATIC PAYMENTS/DEPOSITS ON DATE AUTHORIZED.

Figure 5-19 Pope Animal Clinic Account Register

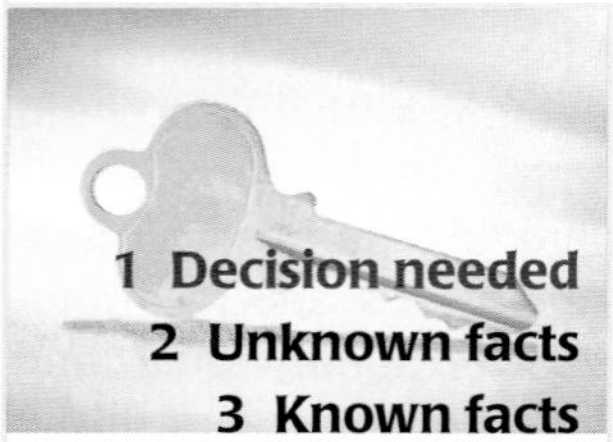

1 Decision needed	Should money be transferred? If so, how much?
2 Unknown facts	The adjusted statement balance
3 Known facts	Bank statement transactions (Figure 5-17) and register transactions (Figure 5-19)
4 Relationships	Adjusted statement balance = statement balance + total outstanding credits − total outstanding debits

Option 1

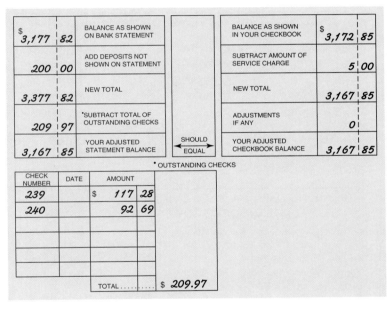

OUTSTANDING DEPOSITS AND OTHER CREDITS			OUTSTANDING CHECKS AND OTHER DEBITS					
DATE	AMOUNT		CHECK #	AMOUNT	CHECK #	AMOUNT	CHECK #	AMOUNT
5/25	200.00		239	117.28				
			240	92.69				
TOTAL	$200.00						TOTAL	$209.97

Account Register
 Balance $3,172.85
 Service Fee   — 5.00
Updated Balance $3,167.85

STATEMENT BALANCE	$3,177.82
ADD OUTSTANDING CREDITS	+ 200.00
SUBTOTAL	3,377.82
SUBTRACT OUTSTANDING DEBITS	- 209.97
ADJUSTED STATEMENT BALANCE	$3,167.85

UPDATED ACCOUNT REGISTER BALANCE	$3,167.85	=	ADJUSTED STATEMENT BALANCE	$3,167.85

Option 2

$ 3,177	82	BALANCE AS SHOWN ON BANK STATEMENT	
200	00	ADD DEPOSITS NOT SHOWN ON STATEMENT	
3,377	82	NEW TOTAL	
209	97	*SUBTRACT TOTAL OF OUTSTANDING CHECKS	
3,167	85	YOUR ADJUSTED STATEMENT BALANCE	

SHOULD ← EQUAL →

BALANCE AS SHOWN IN YOUR CHECKBOOK	$ 3,172	85
SUBTRACT AMOUNT OF SERVICE CHARGE	5	00
NEW TOTAL	3,167	85
ADJUSTMENTS IF ANY	0	
YOUR ADJUSTED CHECKBOOK BALANCE	3,167	85

* OUTSTANDING CHECKS

CHECK NUMBER	DATE	AMOUNT	
239		$ 117	28
240		92	69
	TOTAL	$ 209	97

Figure 5-20 Account Reconciliation Form

5 Estimation   Not appropriate for this situation

6 Calculation   Check off all matching transactions appearing on both the statement and the register (Figures 5-21 and 5-22).

Now enter into the register the transactions appearing on the bank statement that have not been checked off. The service fee is the only unchecked-off transaction. As you enter it into the register, check it off the bank statement and the register.

Now use the account reconciliation form (Figure 5-20) to list the outstanding credits and debits: transactions appearing on the register that have not been checked off.

7 Interpretation   The adjusted statement balance is more than $2,500.

8 Decision made   **Money should be transferred.** Since the excess over $2,500 should be transferred, **the amount transferred is** $3,167.85 − $2,500, or **$667.85.**

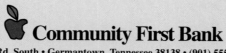

Community First Bank

2177 Germantown Rd. South • Germantown, Tennessee 38138 • (901) 555-2400 • Member FDIC

Pope Animal Clinic
5012 Winchester
Memphis, TN 38118

ACCOUNT NUMBER   43-7432156
FEDERAL ID NUMBER   46-076435176   DATE 5/30/20XX   PAGE 1

	BALANCE OF YOUR FUNDS
PREVIOUS BALANCE -----	$2,571.28
3 DEPOSITS TOTALING	835.00
5 WITHDRAWALS TOTALING	228.46
NEW BALANCE -----------	$3,177.82

ACCOUNT TRANSACTIONS FOR THE PERIOD FROM 5/1/20XX THROUGH 5/30/20XX

DATE	AMOUNT	DESCRIPTION
5/1	110.00 ✔	DEPOSIT
5/8	200.00 ✔	DEPOSIT
5/20	525.00 ✔	DEPOSIT
5/30	5.00	SERVICE FEE

DATE	CHECK #	AMOUNT	DATE	CHECK #	AMOUNT
5/1	235	42.95 ✔	5/7	237	72.63 ✔
5/3	236	12.15 ✔	5/15	238	95.73 ✔

CHECKING DAILY BALANCE SUMMARY

DATE	BALANCE OF YOUR FUNDS	DATE	BALANCE OF YOUR FUNDS
5/1	2,638.33	5/15	2,657.82
5/3	2,626.18	5/20	3,182.82
5/7	2,553.55	5/30	3,177.82
5/8	2,753.55		

Figure 5-21   Matching Transactions Checked Off the Bank Statement

 **TIP!** **Make Your Own Checklist on a Bank Statement**

While the bank statement does not have a √ column, it is helpful to verify that every transaction is recorded in the account register by checking each item on the bank statement as it is checked in the register.

The check method on both the bank statement and account register makes it easier to identify errors, omissions, and outstanding transactions.

RECORD ALL TRANSACTIONS THAT AFFECT YOUR ACCOUNT

NUMBER	DATE	DESCRIPTION OF TRANSACTION	DEBIT (−)		√ T	FEE (IF ANY) (−)	CREDIT (+)		BALANCE	
									2,571	28
235	4/20	Pet Supply Company	42	95	✓				2,528	33
Deposit	5/1	Customer Receipts			✓		110	00	2,638	33
236	5/1	K-mart	12	15	✓				2,626	18
237	5/1	Telephone Company	72	63	✓				2,553	55
Deposit	5/8	Customer Receipts			✓		200	00	2,753	55
238	5/10	Chickasaw Electric Co.	95	73	✓				2,657	82
239	5/15	Protein Technologies Dog food	117	28					2,540	54
240	5/15	Rand M Drug Co.	92	69					2,447	85
Deposit	5/20	Customer Receipts			✓		525	00	2,972	85
Deposit	5/25	Customer Receipts					200	00	3,172	85
	5/30	Service Fee	5	00	✓				3,167	85
	5/30	Statement reconciled							——	

REMEMBER TO RECORD AUTOMATIC PAYMENTS/DEPOSITS ON DATE AUTHORIZED.

Figure 5-22 Reconciled Account Register

SELF-CHECK 5.2

1 *Use Tom Deskin's bank statement (Figure 5-23) for exercises 1-3.*

1. Does Tom pay bills through electronic funds transfer? If so, which ones?

2. Did Tom use the automatic teller machine during the month? If so, what transactions were made and for what amounts?

3. What were the lowest and highest daily bank balances for the month?

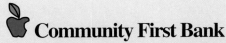

Community First Bank

2177 Germantown Rd. South • Germantown, Tennessee 38138 • (901) 555-2400 • Member FDIC

Tom Deskin
1234 South Street
Germantown, TN 38138

ACCOUNT NUMBER   13-2882139
SOCIAL SECURITY NUMBER   213-44-6688   DATE 9-29-20XX   PAGE 1

		BALANCE OF YOUR FUNDS
PREVIOUS BALANCE -----		$2,472.86
3	DEPOSITS TOTALING	4,812.76
16	WITHDRAWALS TOTALING	4,685.04
NEW BALANCE ----------		$2,600.58

ACCOUNT TRANSACTIONS FOR THE PERIOD FROM 8-28-20XX THROUGH 9-27-20XX

DATE	AMOUNT	DESCRIPTION
9/1	2,401.32	DEPOSIT - SCHERING-PLOUGH PAYROLL 213446688
9/1	942.18	WITHDRAWAL - LEADER FEDERAL MTG PMT 314123
9/4	217.17	WITHDRAWAL - LG&W PMT 21814
9/15	2,401.32	DEPOSIT - SCHERING-PLOUGH PAYROLL 213446688
9/20	60.00	WITHDRAWAL - ATM KIRBY WOODS
9/27	.64	FDIC INSURANCE PREMIUM
9/27	10.12	INTEREST EARNED

DATE	CHECK #	AMOUNT	DATE	CHECK #	AMOUNT	DATE	CHECK #	AMOUNT
8/31	1094	42.37	9/10	1099	583.21	9/25	1106*	1,238.42
9/2	1095	12.96	9/16	1100	283.21	9/25	1107	500.00
9/5	1096	36.01	9/18	1102*	48.23			
9/5	1097	178.13	9/21	1103	71.16			
9/5	1098	458.60	9/23	1104	12.75			

CHECKING DAILY BALANCE SUMMARY

DATE	BALANCE OF YOUR FUNDS	DATE	BALANCE OF YOUR FUNDS
8/28	2,472.86	9/15	4,804.87
8/31	2,430.49	9/16	4,521.66
9/1	3,889.63	9/18	4,473.43
9/2	3,876.67	9/20	4,413.43
9/4	3,659.50	9/21	4,342.27
9/5	2,986.76	9/23	4,329.52
9/10	2,403.55	9/25	2,591.10
		9/27	2,600.58

Figure 5-23   Tom Deskin's Bank Statement

4. A bank statement shows a balance of $12.32. The service charge for the month was $2.95. The account register shows deposits of $300, $100, and $250 that do not appear on the statement. Outstanding checks are in the amount of $36.52, $205.16, $18.92, $25.93, and $200. The register balance is $178.74. Find the adjusted statement balance.

5. Tom Deskin's account register is shown in Figure 5-24. Use the account reconciliation form in Figure 5-25 to reconcile the bank statement (Figure 5-23) with the account register.

RECORD ALL TRANSACTIONS THAT AFFECT YOUR ACCOUNT

NUMBER	DATE	DESCRIPTION OF TRANSACTION	DEBIT (−)		√ T	FEE (IF ANY) (−)	CREDIT (+)		BALANCE	
									2472	86
1094	8/28	K-mart	42	37					2,430	49
1095	8/28	Walgreen's	12	96					2417	53
Deposit	9/1	Payroll Schering-Plough					2401	32	4,818	85
A W	9/1	Leader Federal	942	18					3,876	67
A W	9/1	LG & W	217	17					3,659	50
1096	9/1	Kroger	36	01					3,623	49
1097	9/1	Texaco	178	13					3,445	36
1098	9/1	Univ. of Memphis	458	60					2,986	76
1099	9/5	GMAC Credit Corp	583	21					2,403	55
1100	9/8	VISA	283	21					2,120	34
1101	9/10	Radio Shack	189	37					1,930	97
1102	9/10	Auto Zone	48	23					1,882	74
Deposit	9/15	Payroll- Schering Plough					2401	32	4,284	06

REMEMBER TO RECORD AUTOMATIC PAYMENTS/DEPOSITS ON DATE AUTHORIZED.

Figure 5-24   Tom Deskin's Account Register

RECORD ALL TRANSACTIONS THAT AFFECT YOUR ACCOUNT

NUMBER	DATE	DESCRIPTION OF TRANSACTION	DEBIT (−)		√T	FEE (IF ANY) (−)	CREDIT (+)	BALANCE	
								4,284	06
1103	9/15	Geoffrey Beane	71	16				4,212	90
1104	9/14	Heaven Scent Flowers	12	75				4,200	15
1105	9/20	Kroger	87	75				4,112	40
ATM	9/20	Kirby Woods	60	00				4,052	40
1106	9/21	Traveler's Insurance	1,238	42				2,813	98
1107	9/23	Nation's Bank - Savings	500	00				2,313	98

Figure 5-24 (continued)

OUTSTANDING DEPOSITS AND OTHER CREDITS

DATE	AMOUNT
TOTAL	$

OUTSTANDING CHECKS AND OTHER DEBITS

CHECK #	AMOUNT	CHECK #	AMOUNT	CHECK #	AMOUNT
				TOTAL	$

Account Register
Balance $2,313.98
FDIC Ins.   −   .64
Interest Earned   + 10.12
Updated Balance $2,323.46

STATEMENT BALANCE	$
ADD OUTSTANDING CREDITS	+
SUBTOTAL	
SUBTRACT OUTSTANDING DEBITS	

UPDATED ACCOUNT REGISTER BALANCE	$	=	ADJUSTED STATEMENT BALANCE	$

Figure 5-25 Account Reconciliation Form

Corporate Bank Accounts

A business's banking needs are usually much more complex than those of an individual primarily because of the higher volume of checks, deposits, debits, and transfers. For this reason banks typically charge higher overall maintenance fees and also may charge a per item fee for each transaction according to type. But corporate customers have a wider range of services available to them than individual customers. For example, businesses can have a night depository key that enables them to make coin deposits after hours; they can request a statement at any point in their banking cycle; and they can have a list of outstanding checks posted on each monthly statement. They can hire the bank to reconcile their monthly checking account, partially or fully. Companies can also purchase a lockbox service in which their customers mail their payments directly to the bank (via a P.O. box address) and the bank deposits these payments into the appropriate business account. The following is a schedule of prices for corporate account services:

Account Maintenance $14.00 per month

Account Statement:

Check alignment (numerical order)   .03 per item
Paid check listing   .04 per item
Outstanding check listing   .02 per item
Deposit listing   .03 per item
Reconciliation:
   Fine sort only   25.00 per month
   Partial reconciliation   45.00 per month
   Full reconciliation   60.00 per month
Special cycles   10.00 per cycle

Cash Processing:

Cash deposit verification   .90 per $1000
Wrapped coin rolls   .06 per roll
Money orders   4.00 per order
Food stamps   1.00 per deposit

Deposits:

Local   .08 per item
Out-of-town   .12 per item

Deposited Returned Items:

Return item   3.00 per item
Redeposit   1.50 per item

Interest:

Earned on average daily balance   .75% per month
Paid on account reserve fund   1.5% per month

Insufficient Funds   20.00 per item
                                                        60.00 maximum per day

Research   10.00 per hour
                                                        1.00 per item

Stop Payments   21.00 per check

Wire Transfer:

Incoming	9.50 per transfer
Outgoing	10.00 per transfer

In a typical month a farm equipment manufacturing company with about $3 million a year in sales had 25 deposits (all out-of-town checks), paid out 100 checks (excluding payroll), paid 75 workers a weekly check, had one returned deposit (which was usually redeposited and cleared in five days), one outgoing wire transfer, and 15 outstanding checks.

Exercises

Use the above information to answer the following.

1. Find the company's monthly statement fee assuming they receive the fine sort only.
2. Find the total of the other miscellaneous bank fees for this company.
3. Now add your answers from exercises 1 and 2 to get the total monthly bank fees to be deducted from this company's account. Instead of using minus signs, accountants use "⟨ ⟩" to enclose negative items: e.g., ⟨$25.00⟩.
4. Use the simple interest formula $I = prt$ to calculate the interest earned monthly if this account maintains an average daily balance of $10,000.
5. Did this account earn enough interest to pay its total bank fees? Find the difference between the total bank fees and the interest.
6. How much in bank fees would be saved each month if this company paid its employees monthly instead of weekly? How much would be saved in a year? What other financial savings would be had by paying salaries monthly?

Answers

1. Account statement fees on 400 (100 + 300 payroll) checks per month.

Check alignment	400 @ .03 = 12.00
Paid check listing	400 @ .04 = 16.00
Outstanding check listing	15 @ .02 = .30
Deposit listing	25 @ .03 = .75
Fine sort reconciliation	25.00
Total account statement fees	**$54.05**

2. Other miscellaneous bank fees

Account maintenance	14.00
Out-of-town deposits	25 @ .12 = 3.00
Returned deposit	3.00
Redeposit	1.50
Total misc. bank fees	**$21.50**

3. The typical monthly banking fees are ⟨$75.55⟩.
4. The monthly interest earned by this account is
$I = 10{,}000 \times .0075 \times 1 = \$75.00$.
5. This account typically did not earn quite enough interest to pay its monthly bank fees. The difference between them is ⟨$0.55⟩.
6. The company would pay out 225 fewer checks per month, resulting in the following monthly statement preparation savings:

Check alignment	225 @ .03 = 6.75
Paid check listing	225 @ .04 = 9.00
Total monthly savings	**$15.75**

The yearly savings would amount to $189 plus interest. Additional financial savings include the interest that would be earned by the payroll money kept until the end of the month and the labor costs of preparing payroll once a month instead of at least four times per month.

CHAPTER	OVERVIEW	
5	**Section Outcome**	**Important Points with Examples**

Section 5.1

1 Make account deposits (page 208)

A deposit ticket is a form that tells the bank which account should receive money (cash or checks) that is being deposited. The bank provides the account holder with deposit tickets that carry the name and address of the account holder and the account number. For every deposit, a deposit ticket must be filled out to describe each check and all the cash being deposited.

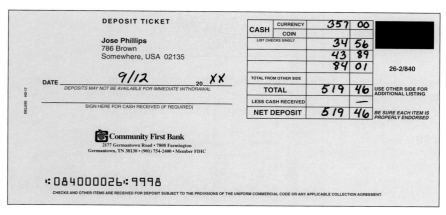

Figure 5-26 Deposit Ticket

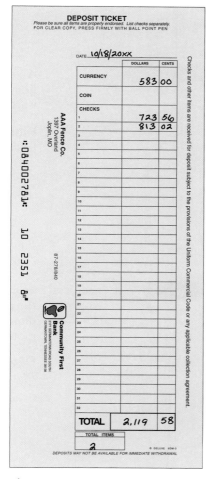

Figure 5-27 Deposit Ticket

2

Make
account
withdrawals
(page 210)

A check is a form that authorizes the bank to pay someone money from an account. The bank provides an account holder with checks that carry the name and address of the account holder and the account number. A check must be filled out with the name of the person or company to whom money should be paid, and the amount of money to pay.

Figure 5-28 Business
Check

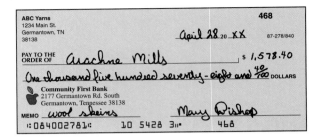

3

Record
account
transactions.
(page 212)

A check stub is a form attached to a check. When a check is written, the stub is filled out to record information about the check. A check stub also has space to write information about deposits made between checks.

Figure 5-29 Check Stub

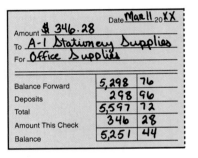

An account register is a form on which the account holder records every transaction made for an account. The register indicates the current balance brought forward and lists all checks, withdrawals, deposits, and other charges.

Figure 5-30 Account
Register

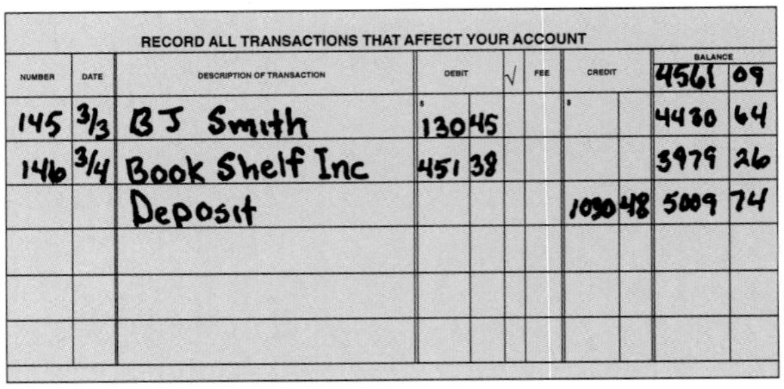

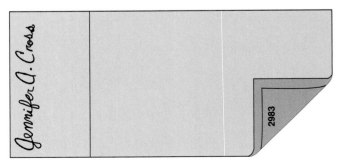

4

Endorse a
check.
(page 214)

To endorse a check means to sign or stamp the back of a check with the name of the payee, the person or company to whom the money should be paid. A bank ordinarily will not honor a check that is not endorsed. A check can be endorsed in more than one way.

Figure 5-31 Check
Endorsement

1 Read a bank statement. (page 217)

A bank statement is a monthly record that most banks send to each account holder. The statement shows all deposits, withdrawals, and service charges and summarizes all other activity for the account. The account holder must compare the bank statement with the account register to make sure that both records are complete and accurate and that the records agree with each other.

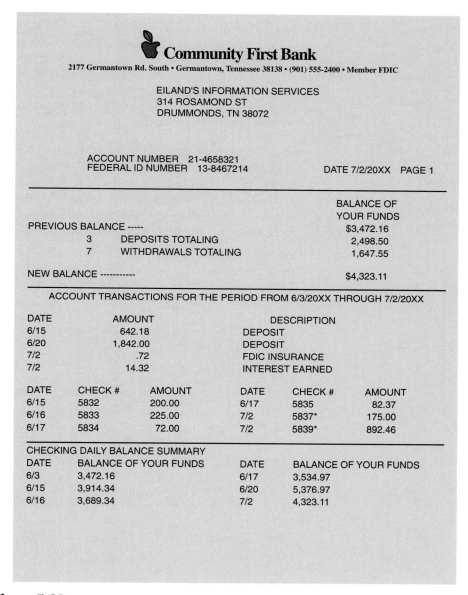

Figure 5-32 Bank Statement

2 Reconcile a bank statement with an account register. (page 219)

This is the process of comparing the account register with the bank statement to make sure that both records are complete and accurate and that the records agree with each other.

1. Check off all matching transactions appearing on both the bank statement and the account register.
2. Enter into the register the transactions appearing on the bank statement that have not been checked off. Check off these transactions in the register as they are entered. Update the register balance accordingly.

3. Make a list of all the checks and other debits appearing in the register that have not been checked off. Add the amounts on the list to find the *total outstanding debits*.
4. Make a list of all the deposits and other credits appearing in the register that have not been checked off in step 1. Add the amounts on the list to find the *total outstanding credits*.
5. Calculate the *adjusted statement balance* by adding the statement balance and the total outstanding credits, and then subtracting the total outstanding debits: Adjusted statement balance = statement balance + total outstanding credits − total outstanding debits.
6. Compare the adjusted statement balance with the register balance. These amounts should be equal.
7. If the adjusted statement balance does not equal the register balance, locate the cause of the discrepancy and correct the register accordingly.
8. Write *statement reconciled* on the next blank line in the account register and record the statement date.

Figure 5-34 shows the account register and Figure 5-35 shows the bank statement for Eiland's Information Services. Steps 1 and 2 of the reconciliation process have already been carried out: matching transactions have been checked off, and all transactions appearing on the bank statement have been entered in the register and checked off, including FDIC insurance of $0.72 and interest earned of $14.32. The updated register balance is $18,020.36.

Now we complete the account reconciliation form in Figure 5–33 by recording the total outstanding debits and the total outstanding credits, transactions in the register that do not appear on the bank statement.

OUTSTANDING DEPOSITS AND OTHER CREDITS		OUTSTANDING CHECKS AND OTHER DEBITS					
DATE	AMOUNT	CHECK #	AMOUNT	CHECK #	AMOUNT	CHECK #	AMOUNT
TOTAL	$					TOTAL	$

Updated Balance $18,020.36
Deposit Correction + 1,284.36
New Updated $19,304.72
Balance

STATEMENT BALANCE	$
ADD OUTSTANDING CREDITS	+
SUBTOTAL	
SUBTRACT OUTSTANDING DEBITS	−

UPDATED ACCOUNT REGISTER BALANCE	$	=	ADJUSTED STATEMENT BALANCE	$

Figure 5-33 Account Reconciliation Form

The adjusted statement balance does not equal the register balance. To locate the error, first find the difference of the two amounts: 19,304.72 − 18,020.36 = 1,284.36. This amount does not match any transaction exactly. So, divide the difference by 2: 1,284.36 ÷ 2 = 642.18. This amount matches a deposit made on 6/15. The deposit was subtracted from the balance when it should have been added. Make an entry in the account register to offset the error: deposit $1,284.36, which is the amount that was subtracted in error plus the amount of the 6/15 deposit. Figure 5-34 shows the reconciled register. Notice the entry "statement reconciled" dated 7/2.

NUMBER	DATE	DESCRIPTION OF TRANSACTION	DEBIT (–)		√ T	FEE (IF ANY) (–)	CREDIT (+)		BALANCE	
		RECORD ALL TRANSACTIONS THAT AFFECT YOUR ACCOUNT							3,472	16
5832	6/13	City of Chicago	200	00	√				3,272	16
5833	6/13	City of Phoenix	225	00	√				3,047	16
5834	6/14	City of Fresno	72	00	√				2,975	16
5835	6/15	Hardware house	82	37	√				2,892	79
Deposit	6/15	Can Com, Inc.	642	18	√				2,250	61
5836	6/18	Office Max copies	42	18					2,208	43
5837	6/20	City of New Orleans	175	00	√				2,033	43
Deposit	6/20	List Purchases			√		1842	00	3,875	43
Deposit	6/25	Federal Credit Union Small business loan					20,000	00	23,875	43
5838	6/30	Hardware house computer	4976	21					18,899	22
5839	6/30	Wade office Furniture Desk chair, file Cabinet	892	46	√				18,006	76
	7/2	FDIC Insurance			√	72			18,006	04
	7/2	Interest earned			√		14	32	18,020	36

REMEMBER TO RECORD AUTOMATIC PAYMENTS/DEPOSITS ON DATE AUTHORIZED.

NUMBER	DATE	DESCRIPTION OF TRANSACTION	DEBIT (–)		√ T	FEE (IF ANY) (–)	CREDIT (+)		BALANCE	
		RECORD ALL TRANSACTIONS THAT AFFECT YOUR ACCOUNT							18,020	36
	7/4	Correction to deposit on 6/15			√		1,284	36	19,304	72
	7/2	Statement Reconciled			√				—	

Figure 5-34 Account Register

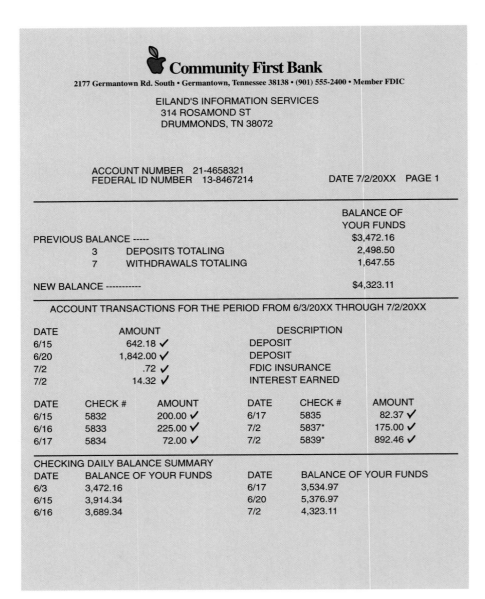

Figure 5-35 Bank Statement

WORDS TO KNOW

deposit (p. 208)
credit (pp. 208, 213)
deposit ticket (p. 208)
bank memo (p. 209)
credit memo (p. 209)
debit memo (pp. 209, 218)
electronically deposited (p. 209)
point-of-sale (p. 210)
electronic funds transfers (p. 210)
withdrawal (p. 210)
debit (pp. 210, 213)

check (p. 210)
bank draft (p. 210)
signature card (p. 211)
automatic drafts (p. 211)
debit card (p. 211)
check stub (p. 212)
account register (p. 213)
endorse (p. 214)
restricted endorsement (p.214)
bank statement (p. 217)
service charge (p. 217)

returned check (p. 218)
returned check fee (p. 218)
nonsufficient funds fee (p. 218)
FDIC insurance premium (p. 218)
automatic teller machine (ATM) (p. 219)
outstanding checks (p. 219)
outstanding deposits (p. 219)
bank reconciliation (p. 219)

1. If adjacent digits of an account register entry have been transposed, the error will produce a difference that is divisible by 9. Give an example of a two-digit number and the number formed by transposing the digits and show that the difference is divisible by 9.

2. Give an example of a three-digit number and the number formed by transposing two adjacent digits. Show that the difference is divisible by 9.

3. Give an example of a three-digit number and a number formed by transposing any two adjacent digits. Show that the difference is divisible by 9.

4. Will the difference be divisible by 9 if two digits that are *not* adjacent are interchanged to form a new number? Illustrate your answer.

5. What if more than two digits are interchanged? Will the difference still be divisible by 9? Illustrate your answer.

6. When you receive your bank statement, you should first identify any items on the statement that are not listed in your account register. Discuss some items you may find on a bank statement and explain what should be done with them.

7. Explain the various types of endorsements for checks.

8. Explain why you would not want to use a deposit ticket that had someone else's name printed on it to make a deposit for your account even if you cross out the account number and name and enter your own.

9. Describe the process for reconciling a bank statement with the account register.

10. Discuss at least three advantages for a business to have a checking account.

CHAPTER 5   ASSIGNMENT EXERCISES

Section 5.1

1. Write a check dated June 13, 20XX, to Byron Johnson in the amount of $296.83 for a washing machine.

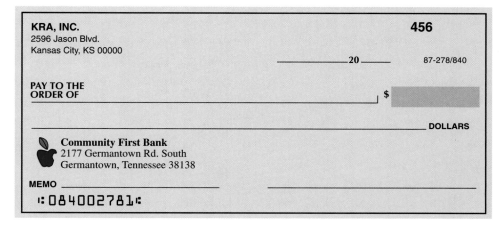

Figure 5-36   Check number 456

2. Write a check dated August 18, 20XX, to Valley Electric Co-op in the amount of $189.32 for utilities.

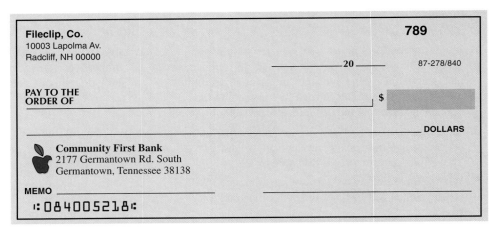

Figure 5-37   Check number 789

3. Complete a deposit slip to add checks in the amounts of $136.00 and $278.96, and $480 cash on May 8, 20XX.

Figure 5-38   Deposit ticket for S & R Consulting Co.

4. Complete a deposit slip on November 11, (Figure 5-39) 20XX, to show the deposit of $100 in cash, checks in the amounts of $87.83, $42.97, and $106.32, with a $472.13 total from the other side of the deposit slip. Your account number is 8021346.

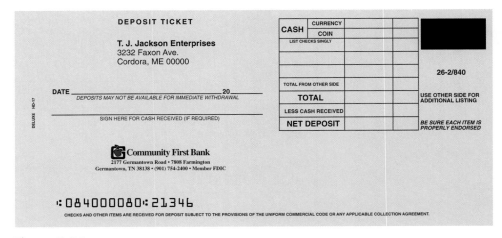

Figure 5-39   Deposit ticket T. J. Jackson Enterprises

5. Complete the stub for check 786 (Figure 5-40), written on May 10, 20XX, to Jacqueline Voss Office Supplies in the amount of $28.97 for office supplies. The amount brought forward is $4,307.21.

6. Complete the stub for check 1021 (Figure 5-41), written on September 30, 20XX, to Louis Jenkins Plumbing Service for plumbing repairs. The amount brought forward is $1,021.03 and the amount of the check is $65. Deposits of $146 and $297.83 were made before the check was written.

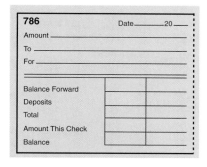

Figure 5-40 Check stub number 786

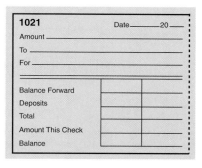

Figure 5-41 Check Stub number 1021

7. Enter the following information and transactions in the check register for Happy Center Day Care (Figure 5-42). On July 10, 20XX, with an account balance of $983.47, check 1213 was written to Linens Inc. for $220 for laundry services, and check 1214 was written to Bugs Away for $65 for extermination services. On July 11, $80 was withdrawn from an automatic teller machine, and on July 12, checks in the amount of $123.86, $123.86, and $67.52 were deposited. Show the balance after these transactions.

		RECORD ALL TRANSACTIONS THAT AFFECT YOUR ACCOUNT					BALANCE	
NUMBER	DATE	DESCRIPTION OF TRANSACTION	DEBIT (−)	√T	FEE (IF ANY) (−)	CREDIT (+)		

Figure 5-42 Check Register

8. Fill out a deposit slip (Figure 5-43) to show a check for $524.75 and $75 cash deposited on April 7, 20XX, to the May Company account.

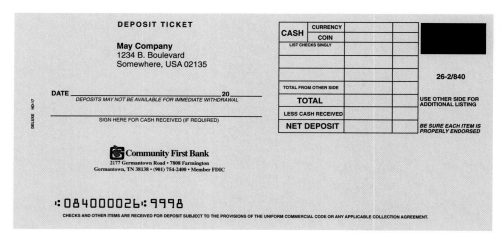

Figure 5-43 Deposit Ticket for May Company

9. Write a check (Figure 5-44) dated June 12, 20XX, to Alpine Industries in the amount of $85.50 for building supplies.

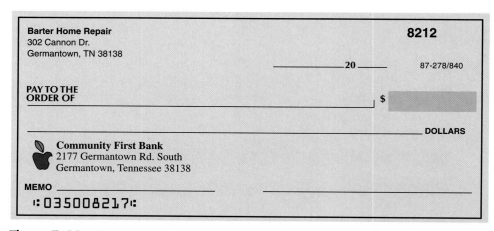

Figure 5-44 Check number 8212

10. Fill out the check stub (Figure 5-45) for a check payable to Turner Wallcoverings for wallpaper installation in the amount of $145. The amount brought forward is $37.43. A cash deposit of $200 was made May 3.

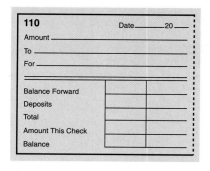

Figure 5-45 Check Stub number 110

11. Enter the following information and transactions in the check register for Sloan's Tree Service (Figure 5-46). On May 3, 20XX, with an account balance of $876.54, check 234 was written to Organic Materials for $175 for fertilizer and check 235 was written to Klean Kuts in the amount of $524.82 for a chain saw. On May 5, checks in the amount of $147.63 and $324.76 were deposited. Show the balance after these transactions.

		RECORD ALL TRANSACTIONS THAT AFFECT YOUR ACCOUNT					
NUMBER	DATE	DESCRIPTION OF TRANSACTION	DEBIT (−)	√ T	FEE (IF ANY) (−)	CREDIT (+)	BALANCE

Figure 5-46 Account Register

12. Show how Byron Johnson would endorse the check in exercise 1 if he wanted the bank to give him cash for it.

13. How would the check in exercise 2 be endorsed if it was to be deposited to account number 15-271 3140 which is held by Valley Electric Co-op? What type of endorsement is this?

14. Discuss the use of the deposit ticket in maintaining a checking account.

15. Discuss the advantages and disadvantages of having your paycheck electronically deposited to your account.

Tree Top Landscape Service's bank statement is shown in Figure 5–47.

16. How many deposits were cleared during the month?

17. What amount of service charge was paid?

18. What was the amount of the largest check written?

19. How many checks appear on the bank statement?

20. What is the balance at the beginning of the statement period?

21. What is the balance at the end of the statement period?

22. What is the amount of check 718?

23. On what date did check 717 clear the bank?

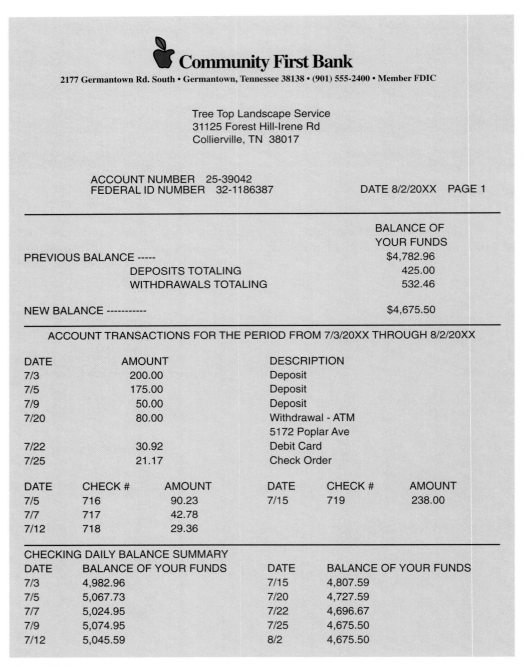

Figure 5-47 Bank Statement for Tree Top Landscape Service

Enrique Anglade's bank statement is shown in Figure 5–48.

24. How many deposits were made during the month?

25. What amount of service charge was paid?

26. What was the amount of the smallest check written?

27. How many checks appear on the bank statement?

28. What is the balance at the beginning of the statement period?

29. What is the balance at the end of the statement period?

30. What is the amount of check 5375?

31. On what date did check 5376 clear the bank?

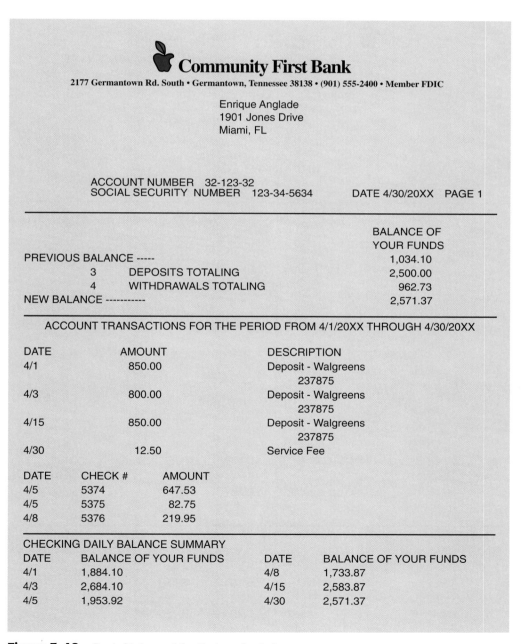

Community First Bank

2177 Germantown Rd. South • Germantown, Tennessee 38138 • (901) 555-2400 • Member FDIC

Enrique Anglade
1901 Jones Drive
Miami, FL

ACCOUNT NUMBER   32-123-32
SOCIAL SECURITY NUMBER   123-34-5634   DATE 4/30/20XX   PAGE 1

			BALANCE OF YOUR FUNDS
PREVIOUS BALANCE -----			1,034.10
	3	DEPOSITS TOTALING	2,500.00
	4	WITHDRAWALS TOTALING	962.73
NEW BALANCE -----------			2,571.37

ACCOUNT TRANSACTIONS FOR THE PERIOD FROM 4/1/20XX THROUGH 4/30/20XX

DATE	AMOUNT	DESCRIPTION
4/1	850.00	Deposit - Walgreens 237875
4/3	800.00	Deposit - Walgreens 237875
4/15	850.00	Deposit - Walgreens 237875
4/30	12.50	Service Fee

DATE	CHECK #	AMOUNT
4/5	5374	647.53
4/5	5375	82.75
4/8	5376	219.95

CHECKING DAILY BALANCE SUMMARY

DATE	BALANCE OF YOUR FUNDS	DATE	BALANCE OF YOUR FUNDS
4/1	1,884.10	4/8	1,733.87
4/3	2,684.10	4/15	2,583.87
4/5	1,953.92	4/30	2,571.37

Figure 5-48   Bank Statement for Enrique Anglade

The bank statement for Tracie Burke's Apparel Shop is shown in Figure 5–49.

32. How many deposits were made during the month?

33. What amount of interest was earned?

34. How much were the total deposits?

35. How many checks appear on the bank statement?

36. What is the balance at the beginning of the statement period?

37. What is the balance at the end of the statement period?

38. What is the amount of check 8214?

39. On what date did check 8219 clear the bank?

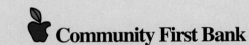

Community First Bank

2177 Germantown Rd. South • Germantown, Tennessee 38138 • (901) 555-2400 • Member FDIC

TRACIE BURKE'S APPAREL SHOP
1396 MALL OF AMERICA
MINNEAPOLIS, MN

ACCOUNT NUMBER   12-324134523
FEDERAL ID NUMBER   33-35462445   DATE 6/30/20XX   PAGE 1

		BALANCE OF YOUR FUNDS
PREVIOUS BALANCE -----		700.81
4	DEPOSITS TOTALING	8,218.83
6	WITHDRAWALS TOTALING	5,433.91
NEW BALANCE -----------		3,485.73

ACCOUNT TRANSACTIONS FOR THE PERIOD FROM 6/1/20XX THROUGH 6/30/20XX

DATE	AMOUNT	DESCRIPTION
6/1	1,830.00	DEPOSIT
6/5	2,583.00	DEPOSIT
6/15	3,800.00	DEPOSIT
6/30	.83	FDIC INSURANCE
6/30	5.83	INTEREST EARNED

DATE	CHECK #	AMOUNT	DATE	CHECK #	AMOUNT
6/2	8213	647.93	6/12	8217*	416.83
6/3	8214	490.00	6/20	8219*	3,150.00
6/5	8215	728.32			

CHECKING DAILY BALANCE SUMMARY

DATE	BALANCE OF YOUR FUNDS	DATE	BALANCE OF YOUR FUNDS
6/1	2,530.81	6/12	2,830.73
6/2	1,882.88	6/15	6,630.73
6/3	1,392.88	6/20	3,480.73
6/5	3,247.56	6/30	3,485.73

Figure 5-49   Bank Statement for Tracie Burke's Apparel Shop

40. Tree Top Landscape's account register is shown in Figure 5-50 and its bank statement is Figure 5-47. Update the account register and use the reconciliation form in Figure 5-51 to reconcile the bank statement (see exercises 16–23) with the account register.

NUMBER	DATE	DESCRIPTION OF TRANSACTION	DEBIT (-)		√ T	FEE (IF ANY) (-)	CREDIT (+)		BALANCE	
									4,782	96
716	7/1	Dabney Nursery	90	23					4,692	73
717	7/5	Office Max	42	78					4,649	95
Deposit	7/3	Louis Lechlefter					200	00	4,849	95
Deposit	7/5	Tony Trim					175	00	5,024	95
Deposit	7/9	Dale Crosby					50	00	5,074	95
718	7/10	Texaco Gas	29	36					5,045	59
719	7/10	Nation's Bank	238	00					4,807	59
Deposit	7/15	Bobby Cornelius					300	00	5,107	59
ATM	7/20	Withdrawl Branch	80	00					5,027	59
Debit card	7/20	AT&T	30	92					4,996	67
720	7/20	Visa	172	83					4,823	84

REMEMBER TO RECORD AUTOMATIC PAYMENTS/DEPOSITS ON DATE AUTHORIZED.

RECORD ALL TRANSACTIONS THAT AFFECT YOUR ACCOUNT

Figure 5-50 Account Register for Tree Top Landscape

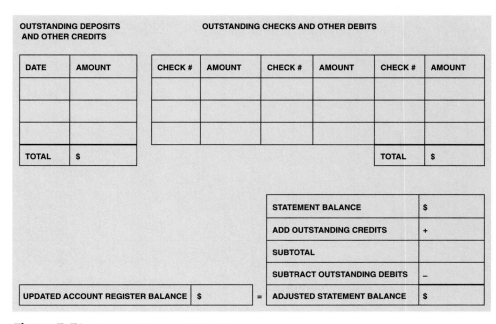

Figure 5-51 Account Reconciliation Form

41. Enrique Anglade's account register is shown in Figure 5-52. Update the account register and reconcile the bank statement (see Figure 5-48) with the account register by using the reconciliation form in Figure 5-53.

RECORD ALL TRANSACTIONS THAT AFFECT YOUR ACCOUNT

NUMBER	DATE	DESCRIPTION OF TRANSACTION	DEBIT (-)	√ T	FEE (IF ANY) (-)	CREDIT (+)	BALANCE	
							1,034	10
Deposit	4/1	Payroll				850 00	1,884	10
Deposit	4/3	Payroll - Bonus				800 00	2,684	10
5374	4/3	First Union Mortgage Co.	647 53				2,036	57
5375	4/3	South Florida Utility	82 75				1,953	82
5376	4/5	First Federal Credit Union	219 95				1,733	87
5377	4/15	Banc Boston	510 48				1,223	39
Deposit	4/15	Payroll				850 00	2,073	39
5378	4/20	Northwest Airlines	403 21				1,670	18
5379	4/26	Auto Zone	18 97				1,651	21
ATM	5/4	Cordova Branch	100 00				1,551	21

REMEMBER TO RECORD AUTOMATIC PAYMENTS/DEPOSITS ON DATE AUTHORIZED.

Figure 5-52 Account Register for Enrique Anglade

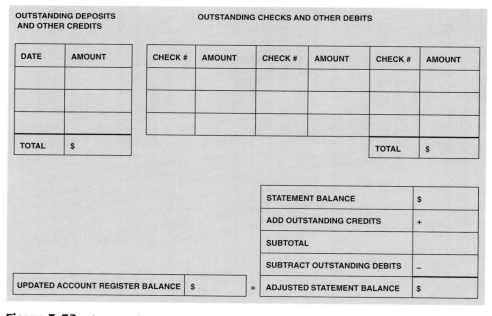

Figure 5-53 Account Reconciliation Form

42. The account register for Tracie Burke's Apparel Shop is shown in Figure 5–54. Update the register and reconcile the bank statement (see Figure 5–49) with the account register using the account reconciliation form in Figure 5–55.

RECORD ALL TRANSACTIONS THAT AFFECT YOUR ACCOUNT

NUMBER	DATE	DESCRIPTION OF TRANSACTION	DEBIT (−)	√T	FEE (IF ANY) (−)	CREDIT (+)	BALANCE 700	81
8213	5/28	Lands End	647 93				52	88
Deposit	6/1	Receipts				1,830 00	1,882	88
8214	6/11	Collier Management Co.	490 00				1,392	88
8215	6/13	Jinkins Wholesale	728 32				664	56
Deposit	6/5	Receipts				2,583 00	3,247	56
8216	6/15	Minneapolis Utility Co.	257 13				2,990	43
8217	6/10	State of MN	416 83				2,573	60
Deposit	6/15	Receipts				3,800 00	6,373	60
8218	6/15	Tracie Burke salary	2,000 00				4,373	60
8219	6/20	Brown's Wholesale	3,150 00				1,223	60
Deposit	7/2	Receipts				1,720 00	2,943	60

REMEMBER TO RECORD AUTOMATIC PAYMENTS/DEPOSITS ON DATE AUTHORIZED.

Figure 5-54 Account Register for Tracie Burke's Apparel Shop

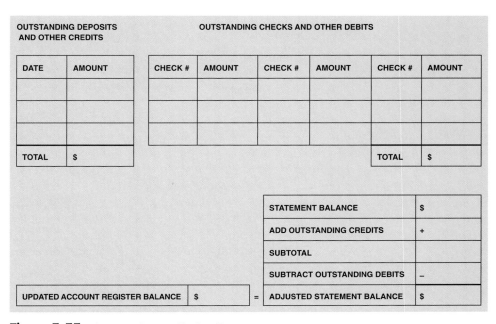

Figure 5-55 Account Reconciliation Form

43. The July bank statement for A & H Iron Works shows a balance of $37.94 and a service charge of $8.00. The account register shows deposits of $650 and $375.56 that do not appear on the statement. Checks in the amounts of $217.45, $57.82, $17.45, and $58.62 are outstanding. The register balance before reconciliation is $720.16. Reconcile the bank statement with the account register using the form in Figure 5-56.

OUTSTANDING DEPOSITS AND OTHER CREDITS			OUTSTANDING CHECKS AND OTHER DEBITS					
DATE	AMOUNT		CHECK #	AMOUNT	CHECK #	AMOUNT	CHECK #	AMOUNT
TOTAL	$						TOTAL	$

STATEMENT BALANCE	$
ADD OUTSTANDING CREDITS	+
SUBTOTAL	
SUBTRACT OUTSTANDING DEBITS	−

UPDATED ACCOUNT REGISTER BALANCE	$	=	ADJUSTED STATEMENT BALANCE	$

Figure 5-56 Account Reconciliation Form

44. The September bank statement for Dixon Fence Company shows a balance of $275.25 and a service charge of $7.50. The account register shows deposits of $120.43 and $625.56 that do not appear on the statement. Checks in the amounts of $144.24, $154.48, $24.17, and $18.22 are outstanding. A $100 ATM withdrawal does not appear on the statement. The register balance before reconciliation is $587.63. Reconcile the bank statement with the account register using the form in Figure 5-57.

OUTSTANDING DEPOSITS AND OTHER CREDITS			OUTSTANDING CHECKS AND OTHER DEBITS					
DATE	AMOUNT		CHECK #	AMOUNT	CHECK #	AMOUNT	CHECK #	AMOUNT
TOTAL	$						TOTAL	$

STATEMENT BALANCE	$
ADD OUTSTANDING CREDITS	+
SUBTOTAL	
SUBTRACT OUTSTANDING DEBITS	−

UPDATED ACCOUNT REGISTER BALANCE	$	=	ADJUSTED STATEMENT BALANCE	$

Figure 5-57 Account Reconciliation Form

45. Taylor Flowers' bank statement shows a balance of $135.42 and a service charge of $8.00. The account register shows deposits of $112.88 and $235.45 that do not appear on the statement. The register shows outstanding checks in the amounts of $17.42 and $67.90 and two cleared checks recorded in the account register as $145.69 and $18.22. The two cleared checks actually were written for and are shown on the statement as $145.96 and $18.22. The register balance before reconciliation is $406.70. Reconcile the bank statement with the account register using the form in Figure 5-58.

OUTSTANDING DEPOSITS AND OTHER CREDITS		OUTSTANDING CHECKS AND OTHER DEBITS					
DATE	AMOUNT	CHECK #	AMOUNT	CHECK #	AMOUNT	CHECK #	AMOUNT
TOTAL	$					TOTAL	$

STATEMENT BALANCE	$
ADD OUTSTANDING CREDITS	+
SUBTOTAL	
SUBTRACT OUTSTANDING DEBITS	−

UPDATED ACCOUNT REGISTER BALANCE	$	=	ADJUSTED STATEMENT BALANCE	$

Figure 5-58 Account Reconciliation Form

46. The bank statement for Randazzo's Market shows a balance of $1,102.35 and a service charge of $6.50. The account register shows a deposit of $265.49 that does not appear on the statement. The account register shows outstanding checks in the amounts of $617.23 and $456.60 and two cleared checks recorded as $45.71 and $348.70. The two cleared checks actually were written for $45.71 and $384.70. The register balance before reconciliation is $336.51. Reconcile the bank statement with the account register using the form in Figure 5-59.

OUTSTANDING DEPOSITS AND OTHER CREDITS		OUTSTANDING CHECKS AND OTHER DEBITS					
DATE	AMOUNT	CHECK #	AMOUNT	CHECK #	AMOUNT	CHECK #	AMOUNT
TOTAL	$					TOTAL	$

STATEMENT BALANCE	$
ADD OUTSTANDING CREDITS	+
SUBTOTAL	
SUBTRACT OUTSTANDING DEBITS	−

UPDATED ACCOUNT REGISTER BALANCE	$	=	ADJUSTED STATEMENT BALANCE	$

Figure 5-59 Account Reconciliation Form

47. Write formulas to complete the spreadsheet that gives the check register account balances after each transaction for Enrique Anglade.

48. Complete the spreadsheet using the formulas.

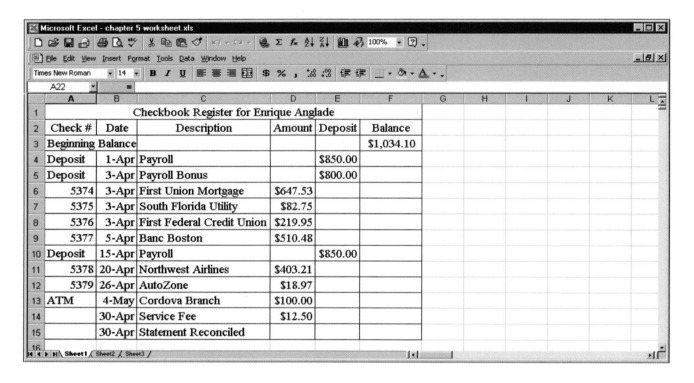

Challenge Problem

49. Terry Kelly (whom we met in Chapter 1) talked with her investment counselor. She was advised to calculate her current net worth and to project her 2002 net worth to determine if her 2003 budget would accomplish her objective of increasing her net worth. She listed the following assets and liabilities for 1999. To calculate her net worth, she found the difference between total assets and total liabilities.

ASSETS:

Checking account	2,099	
Savings account	2,821	
Auto	10,500	
Home and furnishings	65,000	
Stocks and bonds	4,017	
Other personal property	3,200	
Total assets		

LIABILITIES:

Car loan	8,752	6,652
Home mortgage	54,879	53,992
Personal loan	1,791	0
Total liabilities		

Terry's home appreciated (increased) in value by 0.04 times the 1999 value while her car depreciated (decreased) in value by 0.125 times the 2002 value. Her car loan decreased by $2,100 while her home mortgage balance decreased by $887. Kelly plans to pay her personal loan in full by the end of 2000. Of her $2,000 planned investment, she will place $1,000 in savings and $1,000 in stocks and bonds. She also plans to reinvest the interest income of $141 (in savings) and the dividend income of $364 (in stocks and bonds) earned in 2002. She projects her checking account balance will be $1,500 at year-end for 2003.

Calculate Terry's total assets and total liabilities for 2002. Then calculate her net worth for 2002. Use the information given to project Terry's assets and liabilities for 2003. Then project her 2003 net worth. How much does Terry expect her net worth to increase (or decrease) from 2002 to 2003?

CHAPTER 5 PRACTICE TEST

1. Fill out the check stub provided. The balance brought forward is $2,301.42, deposits were made for $200 on May 12 and $83.17 on May 20, and check 195 was written on May 25 to Lon Associates for $152.50 for supplies.

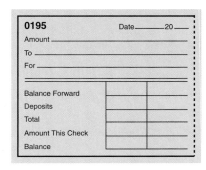

Figure 5-60 Check Stub number 0195

D. G. Hernandez Equipment's bank statement is shown in Figure 5-61.

2. What is the balance at the beginning of the statement period?

3. How many checks cleared the bank during the statement period?

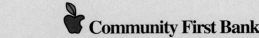

Community First Bank

2177 Germantown Rd. South • Germantown, Tennessee 38138 • (901) 555-2400 • Member FDIC

D. G. Hernandez Equipment
25 Santa Rosa Dr.
Piperton, TN 38027

ACCOUNT NUMBER 8-523145
FEDERAL ID NUMBER 46-28345135   DATE 3/31/20XX   PAGE 1

		BALANCE OF YOUR FUNDS
PREVIOUS BALANCE -----		5,283.17
2	DEPOSITS TOTALING	3,600.00
6	WITHDRAWALS TOTALING	1,900.49
NEW BALANCE ----------		6,982.68

ACCOUNT TRANSACTIONS FOR THE PERIOD FROM 3/1/20xx THROUGH 3/31/20xx

DATE	AMOUNT	DESCRIPTION
3/15	1,600.00	Deposit
3/17	19.00	Returned Check Charge
3/31	2,000.00	Deposit

DATE	CHECK #	AMOUNT	DATE	CHECK #	AMOUNT
3/2	3784	96.03	3/15	3788	973.12
3/7	3786*	142.38	3/31	3792*	182.03
3/12	3787	487.93			

CHECKING DAILY BALANCE SUMMARY

DATE	BALANCE OF YOUR FUNDS	DATE	BALANCE OF YOUR FUNDS
3/2	5,187.14	3/15	5,183.71
3/7	5,044.76	3/17	5,164.71
3/12	4,556.83	3/31	6,982.68

Figure 5–61   Bank Statement for D. G. Hernandez Equipment

4. What was the service charge for the statement period?

5. Check 3786 was written for what amount?

6. On what date did check 3788 clear the account?

7. What was the total of the deposits?

8. What was the balance at the end of the statement period?

9. What was the total amount for all checks written during the period?

10. D.G. Hernandez Equipment's account register is shown in Figure 5-62. Reconcile the bank statement in Figure 5-61 with the account register in Figure 5-62.

RECORD ALL TRANSACTIONS THAT AFFECT YOUR ACCOUNT

NUMBER	DATE	DESCRIPTION OF TRANSACTION	DEBIT (–)		√ T	FEE (IF ANY) (–)	CREDIT (+)	BALANCE	
								5,283	17
3784	2/27		96	03				5,187	14
3785	3/5		346	18				4,840	95
3786	3/5		142	38				4,698	58
3787	3/11		487	93				4,210	65
3788	3/11		973	12				3,237	53
3789	3/15		72	83				3,164	70
Dep.	3/15						1,600 00	4,764	70
3790	3/17		146	17				4,618	53
3791	3/20		152	03				4,466	50
3792	3/31		182	08				4,284	42
Deposit	3/31						2000 00	6,284	42

REMEMBER TO RECORD AUTOMATIC PAYMENTS/DEPOSITS ON DATE AUTHORIZED.

OUTSTANDING DEPOSITS AND OTHER CREDITS

DATE	AMOUNT
TOTAL	$

OUTSTANDING CHECKS AND OTHER DEBITS

CHECK #	AMOUNT	CHECK #	AMOUNT	CHECK #	AMOUNT
				TOTAL	$

STATEMENT BALANCE	$
ADD OUTSTANDING CREDITS	+
SUBTOTAL	
SUBTRACT OUTSTANDING DEBITS	–
ADJUSTED STATEMENT BALANCE	$

UPDATED ACCOUNT REGISTER BALANCE $ = ADJUSTED STATEMENT BALANCE

Figure 5–62 Account Register and Account Reconciliation Form

11. Before reconciliation, an account register balance is $1,817.93. The bank statement balance is $860.21. A service fee of $15 and one returned item of $213.83 were charged against the account. Deposits in the amounts of $800 and $412.13 are outstanding. Checks written for $243.17, $167.18, $13.97, $42.12, and $16.80 are outstanding. Complete the account reconciliation form in Figure 5-63 to reconcile the bank statement with the account register.

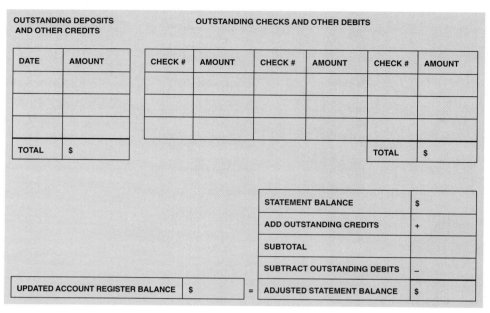

Figure 5-63   Account Reconciliation Form

Self-Check 5.1

1.

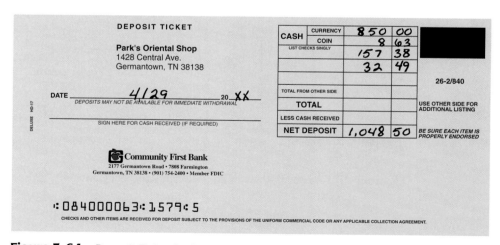

Figure 5-64   Deposit Ticket for Park's Oriental Shop

2.

DEPOSIT TICKET

Please be sure all items are properly endorsed. List checks separately.
FOR CLEAR COPY, PRESS FIRMLY WITH BALL POINT PEN

DATE *March 31, 20xx*

	DOLLARS	CENTS
CURRENCY	196	00
COIN		
CHECKS		
1 *Cavanaugh*	14	72
2 *Bryan*	31	18
3 *Wassum*	16	97
4 *Wright*	28	46
5 *Howell*	17	21
6 *Coe*	32	17
7 *Beulke*	17	84
8 *Palinchak*	31	96
9 *Orzel*	19	16
10		
11		
12		
13		
14		
15		
16		
17		
18		
19		
20		
21		
22		
23		
24		
25		
26		
27		
28		
29		
30		
31		
32		
TOTAL	**405**	**67**
TOTAL ITEMS		
9		

Checks and other items are received for deposit subject to the provisions of the Uniform Commercial Code or any applicable collection agreement.

DELECTABLES CANDIES
5981 POPLAR AVE.
MEMPHIS, TN. 38121

87-278/840

⑆084002781⑆ 11 2118 3⑈

Community First Bank
2177 GERMANTOWN ROAD SOUTH
GERMANTOWN, TENNESSEE 38138

© DELUXE 6DM-3

DEPOSITS MAY NOT BE AVAILABLE FOR IMMEDIATE WITHDRAWAL

Figure 5-65 Deposit Ticket for
Delectables Candies

3.

Park's Oriental Shop   456
1428 Central Ave.
Germantown, TN 38138

april 29, 20xx   87-278/840

PAY TO THE
ORDER OF   *Green Harvest* $ *155.30*

One hundred fifty-five and 30/100 ———— DOLLARS

Community First Bank
2177 Germantown Rd. South
Germantown, Tennessee 38138

MEMO *fresh vegetables*   *Yan Yu*

⑆084002781⑆

Figure 5-66 Check Number 456

4.

Your Name   3215
5983 Macon Cove
Yellville, TX 00000

June 20, 20 XX   87-278/840

PAY TO THE
ORDER OF   *Ronald H. Cox Realty* $ *596.13*

Five Hundred Ninety-Six and 13/100 ———— DOLLARS

Community First Bank
2177 Germantown Rd. South
Germantown, Tennessee 38138

MEMO *house repairs*   *Your Signature*

⑆084003218⑆

Figure 5-67 Check Number 3215

5.

456	Date 4/29 20 XX
Amount $155.30	
To Green Harvest	
For fresh vegetables	

Balance Forward	7,869	40
Deposits	1,048	50
Total	8,917	90
Amount This Check	155	30
Balance	8,762	60

Figure 5-68 Check Stub
Number 456

6.

3215	Date 6/20 20 XX
Amount 596.13	
To Ronald H. Cox Realty	
For house repairs	

Balance Forward	2213	56
Deposits		0
Total	2,213	56
Amount This Check	596	13
Balance	1,617	43

Figure 5-69 Check Stub Number
3215

7.

		RECORD ALL TRANSACTIONS THAT AFFECT YOUR ACCOUNT					BALANCE	
NUMBER	DATE	DESCRIPTION OF TRANSACTION	DEBIT	√	FEE	CREDIT	7,869	40
	4/29	Deposit				1,048 50	8,917	90
456	4/29	Green Harvest	155 30				8,762	60

Figure 5-70 Account Register

8.

		RECORD ALL TRANSACTIONS THAT AFFECT YOUR ACCOUNT					BALANCE	
NUMBER	DATE	DESCRIPTION OF TRANSACTION	DEBIT	√	FEE	CREDIT	435	97
Dep.	9/30	Payroll Deposit				932 15	1,368	12
3176	9/30	Electric Coop	107 13				1,260	99
3177	9/30	Amoco	47 15				1,213	84
3178	9/30	Visa	97 00				1,116	84

Figure 5-71 Account Register

9.

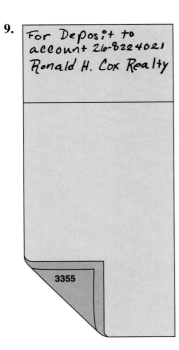

For Deposit to
account 26-8224021
Ronald H. Cox Realty

3355

Figure 5-72 Restricted Check Endorsement

This is called a restricted endorsement.

10. The check cannot be exchanged for cash because the payee is a business. It will need to be deposited into an account owned by Green Harvest.

Self-Check 5.2

1. Leader Federal: $942.18; LG & W: $217.17
3. lowest balance: $2,403.55; highest balance: $4,804.87

2. Withdrawal: $60.00
4. After entering the $2.95 service charge in the account register, the updated account balance is $175.79 (Figure 5-73).

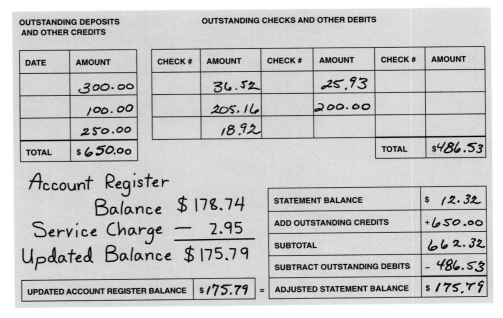

Figure 5-73 Account Reconciliation Form

5. Figure 5-74 shows Tom's account register after he has checked off transactions matching those on the bank statement, and after he has entered and checked off transactions appearing on the bank statement that had not been checked off in the bank statement. The account reconciliation form is shown in Figure 5-75. Since the updated statement balance equals the updated account balance, the statement is reconciled.

Figure 5-74 Account Register

RECORD ALL TRANSACTIONS THAT AFFECT YOUR ACCOUNT

NUMBER	DATE	DESCRIPTION OF TRANSACTION	DEBIT (−)		√ T	FEE (IF ANY) (−)	CREDIT (+)		BALANCE	
								2472	86
1094	8/28	K-mart	42	37	√				2430	49
1095	8/28	Walgreen's	12	96	√				2417	53
Deposit	9/1	Payroll Schering-Plough			√		2401	32	4,818	85
AW	9/1	Leader Federal	942	18	√				3,876	67
AW	9/1	LG & W	217	17	√				3,659	50
1096	9/1	Kroger	36	01	√				3,623	49
1097	9/1	Texaco	178	13	√				3445	36
1098	9/1	Univ. of Memphis	458	60	√				2986	76
1099	9/15	GMAC Credit Corp	583	21	√				2403	55
1100	9/18	Visa	283	21	√				2,120	34
1101	9/10	Radio Shack	189	37					1,930	97
1102	9/10	Auto Zone	48	23	√				1,882	74
Deposit	9/15	Payroll- Schering Plough			√		2401	32	4,284	06

REMEMBER TO RECORD AUTOMATIC PAYMENTS/DEPOSITS ON DATE AUTHORIZED.

RECORD ALL TRANSACTIONS THAT AFFECT YOUR ACCOUNT

NUMBER	DATE	DESCRIPTION OF TRANSACTION	DEBIT (−)		√ T	FEE (IF ANY) (−)	CREDIT (+)		BALANCE	
								4,284	06
1103	9/15	Geoffrey Beane	71	16	√				4,212	90
1104	9/14	Heaven Scent Flowers	12	75	√				4,200	15
1105	9/20	Kroger	87	75					4,112	40
ATM	9/20	Kirby Woods	60	00	√				4,052	40
1106	9/21	Traveler's Insurance	1,238	42	√				2,813	98
1107	9/23	Nation's Bank - Savings	500	00	√				2,313	98
	9/27	FDIC Insurance			√	.64			2,313	34
	9/27	Interest earned			√		10	12	2,323	46
	9/29	Statement reconciled							—	

Figure 5-75 Account Reconciliation Form

OUTSTANDING DEPOSITS AND OTHER CREDITS			OUTSTANDING CHECKS AND OTHER DEBITS					
DATE	AMOUNT		CHECK #	AMOUNT	CHECK #	AMOUNT	CHECK #	AMOUNT
			1101	189.37				
			1105	87.75				
TOTAL	$ 0						TOTAL	$277.12

Account Register
Balance $2,313.98
FDIC Insurance   − .64
                   $2,313.34
Interest Earned   10.12
Adjusted Balance $2,323.46

STATEMENT BALANCE	$2,600.58
ADD OUTSTANDING CREDITS	+ 0
SUBTOTAL	2,600.58
SUBTRACT OUTSTANDING DEBITS	− 277.12
ADJUSTED STATEMENT BALANCE	$2,323.46

UPDATED ACCOUNT REGISTER BALANCE	$ 2,323.46	=	ADJUSTED STATEMENT BALANCE	$ 2,323.46

Payroll

6.1 Gross Pay

1 Find the gross pay per paycheck based on salary.

2 Find the gross pay per weekly paycheck based on hourly wage.

3 Find the gross pay per paycheck based on piecework wage.

4 Find the gross pay per paycheck based on commission.

6.2 Payroll Deductions

1 Find federal tax withholding per paycheck using IRS tax tables.

2 Find federal tax withholding per paycheck using the IRS percentage method.

3 Find Social Security tax and Medicare tax per paycheck.

4 Find net earnings per paycheck.

6.3 The Employer's Payroll Taxes

1 Find an employer's total deposit for withholding tax, Social Security tax, and Medicare tax per pay period.

2 Find an employer's SUTA tax and FUTA tax due for a quarter.

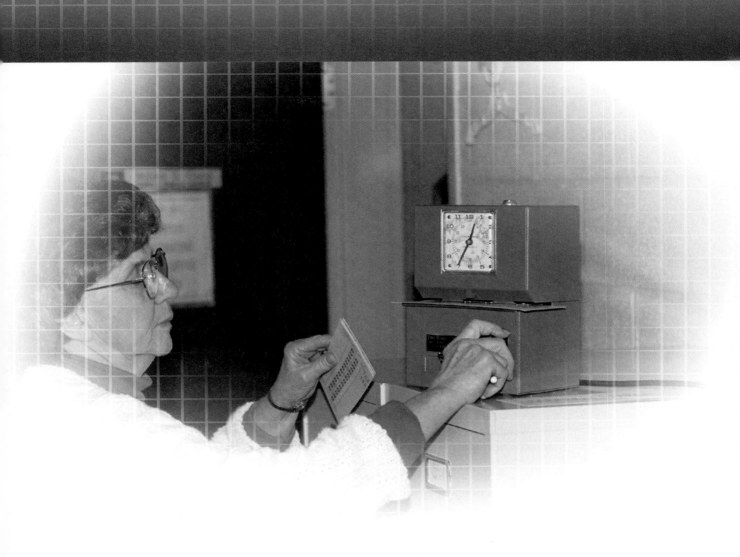

Good Decisions through Teamwork

Divide into four investigative teams. Team 1 will explore the payroll process for hourly employees in a business that has fewer than five hourly employees. Team 2 will explore the payroll process for hourly employees in a business with more than five but fewer than 100 hourly employees. Team 3 will explore the payroll process for hourly employees in a company with more than 100 hourly employees. Team 4 will explore the use of contract labor in lieu of employees and the way contract labor is paid versus employees.

Include in a team report how the time is recorded; what pay periods are used; who validates the time worked; how the pay is calculated; how the withholding, Social Security, and Medicare taxes are derived; what other deduction options are available to hourly employees; and what payroll records are kept by the company. Present your team's report orally to the class. Compare and contrast the findings of each team through class discussions.

Pay is an important concern of employees and employers alike. If you have worked and received a paycheck, you know that part of your earnings is taken out of your paycheck before you ever see it. Your employer *withholds* (deducts) taxes, union dues, medical insurance payments, and so on. Thus there is a difference between **gross earnings (gross pay),** the amount earned before deductions, and **net earnings (net pay)—take-home pay**—the amount of your paycheck.

This chapter considers payroll issues from the point of view of the employee and the employer. Employers have the option of paying their employees in salary or in wages and of distributing these earnings at various time intervals. Employers are required to withhold taxes from employee paychecks and forward them to federal, state, and local governments.

6.1 Gross Pay

1 Find the gross pay per paycheck based on salary.

2 Find the gross pay per weekly paycheck based on hourly wage.

3 Find the gross pay per paycheck based on piecework wage.

4 Find the gross pay per paycheck based on commission.

Employees may be paid according to a yearly salary, an hourly wage, a piecework rate, or a commission rate. Companies differ in how often they pay employees, which determines how many paychecks an employee receives in a year. If employees are paid **weekly,** they receive 52 paychecks a year; if they are paid **biweekly** (every other week), they receive 26 paychecks a year. **Semimonthly** (twice a month) paychecks are issued 24 times a year, and **monthly** paychecks come 12 times a year. This section shows what all of these possibilities mean to the employee earning the paycheck.

1 Find the gross pay per paycheck based on salary.

Salary is usually stated as a certain amount of money paid each year. Salaried employees are paid the agreed-upon salary whether they work fewer or more than the usual number of hours. To find the amount of a salaried employee's paycheck before deductions, divide the salary per year by the number of paychecks the employee receives in the course of a year.

? HOW TO Find the Gross Pay per Paycheck Based on Annual Salary

1. Identify the number of pay periods per year:
Monthly—12 pay periods per year
Semimonthly—24 pay periods per year
Biweekly—26 pay periods per year
Weekly—52 pay periods per year

2. Divide the annual salary by the number of pay periods per year.

EXAMPLE Charles Demetriou earns a salary of $30,000 a year.

(a) If Charles is paid biweekly, how much is his gross pay before taxes are taken out?

(b) If Charles is paid semimonthly, how much is his gross pay?

(a) $\$30{,}000 \div 26 = \$1{,}153.85$
Charles earns \$1,153.85 bi-weekly before deductions.

> Biweekly paychecks are issued 26 times a year, so divide Charles's salary by 26.

(b) $\$30{,}000 \div 24 = \$1{,}250$
Charles earns \$1,250 semi-monthly before deductions.

> Semimonthly paychecks are issued 24 times a year, so divide Charles's salary by 24.

 2 Find the gross pay per weekly paycheck based on hourly wage.

Some jobs pay according to an *hourly wage*. The **hourly rate,** or **hourly wage,** is the amount of money paid for each hour the employee works in a standard 40-hour week. The Fair Labor Standards Act of 1938 set the standard work week at 40 hours. When hourly employees work more than 40 hours in a week, they earn the hourly wage for the first 40 hours, and they earn an **overtime rate** for the remaining hours. The overtime rate is often called **time and a half.** By law it must be at least 1.5 (one and one-half) times the hourly wage. Earnings based on the hourly wage are called **regular pay.** Earnings based on the overtime rate are called **overtime pay.** An hourly employee's gross pay for a pay period is the sum of his or her regular pay and his or her overtime pay.

? HOW TO Find the Gross Pay per Week Based on Hourly Wages

1. Find the regular pay:
   (a) If the hours worked in the week are 40 or fewer, multiply the hours worked by the hourly wage.
   (b) If the hours worked are more than 40, multiply 40 hours by the hourly wage.

2. Find the overtime pay:
   (a) If the hours worked are 40 or fewer, the overtime pay is \$0.
   (b) If the hours worked are more than 40, subtract 40 from the hours worked and multiply the difference by the overtime rate.

3. Add the regular pay and the overtime pay.

 TIP! When Does the Week Start?

Even if an employee is paid biweekly, overtime pay is still based on the 40-hour standard work week. So overtime pay for each week in the pay period must be calculated separately. Also, each employer establishes the formal work week. For example, an employer's work week may begin at 12:01 A.M. Thursday and end at 12:00 midnight on Wednesday of the following week, allowing the payroll department to process payroll checks for distribution on Friday. Another employer may begin the work week at 11:01 P.M. on Sunday evening and end at 11:00 P.M. the following week so that the new week coincides with the beginning of the 11–7 shift.

EXAMPLE   Marcia Scott, whose hourly wage is $10.25, worked 46 hours last week. Find her gross pay for last week if she earns time and a half for overtime.

$$40 \times \$10.25 = \boxed{\$410}$$

Find the regular pay for 40 hours of work at the hourly wage.

$$6 \times \$10.25 \times 1.5 = \boxed{\$92.25}$$
$$\underbrace{\hspace{2cm}}_{\text{overtime rate}}$$

Find the overtime pay by multiplying the overtime hours by the overtime rate, which is the hourly wage times 1.5. Round to the nearest cent.

$$\boxed{\$410} + \boxed{\$92.25} = \$502.25$$

Add the regular pay and the overtime pay to find Marcia's total gross earnings.

Marcia's gross pay is $502.25.

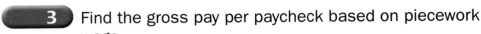 **3** Find the gross pay per paycheck based on piecework wage.

Some employers motivate employees to produce more by paying according to the quantity of acceptable work done. Such **piecework rates** are typically offered in production or manufacturing jobs. Garment makers and some other types of factory workers, agricultural workers, and employees who perform repetitive tasks such as stuffing envelopes or packaging parts may be paid by this method. In the simplest cases the gross earnings of such workers are calculated by multiplying the number of items produced by the **straight piecework rate.**

Sometimes employees earn wages at a **differential piece rate,** also called an **escalating piece rate.** As the number of items produced by the worker increases, so does the pay per item. This method of paying wages offers employees an even greater incentive to complete more pieces of work in a given period of time.

EXAMPLE   A shirt manufacturer pays a worker $0.47 for each acceptable shirt completed under the prescribed job description. If the worker had the following work record, find the gross earnings for the week: Monday, 250 shirts; Tuesday, 300 shirts; Wednesday, 178 shirts; Thursday, 326 shirts; Friday, 296 shirts.

$$250 + 300 + 178 + 326 + 296$$
$$= \boxed{1{,}350} \text{ shirts}$$

Find the total number of shirts made.

$$\boxed{1{,}350} \times \$0.47 = \$634.50$$

Multiply the number of shirts by the piecework rate.

The weekly gross earnings are $634.50.

 **HOW TO**   Find the Gross Pay per Paycheck Based on Piecework Wage

1. If a *straight piecework rate* is used, multiply the number of items completed by the straight piecework rate.

2. If a *differential piecework rate* is used:

   (a) For each rate category, multiply the number of items produced for the category by the rate for the category.

   (b) Add the pay for all rate categories.

EXAMPLE   Last week, Jorge Sanchez assembled 317 microchip boards. Find Jorge's gross earnings for the week if the manufacturer pays at the following differential piece rates.

Boards assembled per week	Pay per board
1–100	$1.32
101–300	$1.42
301 and over	$1.58

Find how many boards were completed at each pay rate, multiply the number of boards by the rate, and add the amounts.

First 100 items: $100 \times 1.32 = \$132.00$
Next 200 items: $200 \times 1.42 = \$284.00$
Last 17 items: $17 \times 1.58 = \underline{\$26.86}$
$\$442.86$

Jorge's gross earnings were $442.86.

 4 Find the Gross Pay per Paycheck Based on Commission.

Many salespeople earn a **commission,** a percentage based on sales. Those whose entire pay is commission are said to work on **straight commission.** Those who receive a salary in addition to a commission are said to work on a **salary plus commission** basis.

A **commission rate** can be a percent of total sales, or a percent of sales greater than a specified **quota** of sales.

 HOW TO Find the Gross Pay per Paycheck Based on Commission

1. Find the commission:
   (a) If the commission is *commission based on total sales*, multiply the commission rate by the total sales for the pay period.
   (b) If the commission is *commission based on quota*, subtract the quota from the total sales and multiply the difference by the commission rate.
2. Find the salary:
   (a) If the wage is *straight commission*, the salary is $0.
   (b) If the wage is *commission-plus-salary*, use the How-To steps for finding gross pay based on salary.
3. Add the commission and the salary.

EXAMPLE Shirley Garcia is a restaurant supplies salesperson and receives 5% of her total sales as commission. Her sales totaled $15,000 during a given week. Find her gross earnings.

Use the percentage formula $P = R \times B$.

$P = 0.05 \times \$15,000 = \$750$ Change the rate of 5% to a decimal and multiply it times the base of $15,000.

Shirley's gross earnings were $750.

EXAMPLE Eloise Brown is paid on a salary-plus-commission basis. She receives $150 weekly in salary and 3% of all sales over $2,000. If she sold $15,000 worth of goods, find her gross pay.

$\$15,000 - \$2,000 = \$13,000$ Subtract the quota from total sales to find the sales on which commission is paid.

$$P = R \times B$$
$$P = 0.03 \times 13{,}000$$
$$P = \boxed{\$390} \text{ (commission)}$$
$$\boxed{\$390} + \$150 = \$540$$

> Change the rate of 3% to a decimal. Multiply the rate by the base of $13,000. Eloise Brown's commission is $390.
>
> Add the commission and salary to find gross pay.

Eloise Brown's gross earnings were $540.

SELF-CHECK 6.1

1. If Timothy Oaks earns a salary of $24,804 a year and is paid weekly, how much is his weekly paycheck before taxes?

2. If Nita McMillan earns a salary of $27,988 a year and is paid biweekly, how much is her biweekly paycheck before taxes are taken out?

3. Gregory Maksi earns a salary of $52,980 annually and is paid monthly. How much is his gross monthly income?

4. Amelia Mattix is an accountant and is paid semi-monthly. Her annual salary is $38,184. How much is her gross pay per period?

5. William Melton worked 47 hours in one week. His regular pay was $7.60 per hour with time and a half for overtime. Find his gross earnings for the week.

6. Bethany Colangelo, whose regular rate of pay is $8.25 per hour, with time and a half for overtime, worked 44 hours last week. Find her gross pay for the week.

7. Carlos Espinosa earns $15.90 per hour with time and a half for overtime and worked 47 hours during a recent week. Find his gross pay for the week.

8. A belt manufacturer pays a worker $0.84 for each buckle she correctly attaches to a belt. If Yolanda Jackson had the following work record, find the gross earnings for the week: Monday, 132 buckles; Tuesday, 134 buckles; Wednesday, 138 buckles; Thursday, 134 buckles; Friday, 130 buckles.

9. Last week, Laurie Golson packaged 189 boxes of Holiday Cheese Assortment. Find her gross weekly earnings if she is paid at the following differential piece rate.

Cheese Boxes Packaged per Week	Pay per Package
1–100	$1.88
101–300	$2.08
301 and over	$2.18

10. Joe Thweatt makes icons for a major distributor. He is paid $8.13 for each icon and records the following number of completed icons: Monday, 9; Tuesday, 11; Wednesday, 10; Thursday, 12; Friday, 4. How much will he be paid for his work for the week?

4

11. Mark Moses is a paper mill sales representative who receives 6% of his total sales as commission. His sales last week totaled $8,972. Find his gross earnings for the week.

12. Mary Lee Strode is paid a straight commission on sales as a real estate salesperson. In one pay period she had a total of $452,493 in sales. What is her gross pay if the commission rate is $3\frac{1}{2}\%$?

13. Dwayne Moody is paid on a salary-plus-commission basis. He receives $275 weekly in salary and a commission based on 5% of all weekly sales over $2,000. If he sold $7,821 in merchandise in one week, find his gross earnings for the week.

14. Vincent Ores sells equipment to receive satellite signals. He earns a 3% commission on monthly sales above $2,000. One month his sales totaled $145,938. What is his commission for the month?

6.2 Payroll Deductions

1 Find federal tax withholding per paycheck using IRS tax tables.

2 Find federal tax withholding per paycheck using the IRS percentage method.

3 Find Social Security tax and Medicare tax per paycheck.

4 Find net earnings per paycheck.

As anyone who has ever drawn a paycheck knows, many deductions may be deducted from gross pay. Deductions include federal, state, and local income or payroll taxes, Social Security and Medicare taxes, union dues, medical insurance, credit union payments, and a host of others. By law, employers are responsible for withholding and paying their employee's taxes. In fact, the bookkeeping involved in payroll provides a major source of employment for many people in the business world.

One of the largest deductions from an employee's paycheck usually comes in the form of *income tax*. The tax paid to the federal government is called **federal tax withholding.** The tax withheld is based on three things: the employee's gross earnings, the employee's tax filing status, and the number of *withholding allowances* the person claims. A **withholding allowance,** called an **exemption,** is a portion of gross earnings that is not subject to tax. Each employee is permitted one withholding allowance for himself or herself, one for a spouse, and one for each dependent (such as a child or elderly parent). (A detailed discussion on eligibility for various allowances can be found in several IRS publications such as Publication 15 [Circular E, Employer's Tax Guide], Publication 505 [Tax Withholding and Estimated Tax], and Publication 17 [Your Federal Income Tax For Individuals].) Each employee fills out a *W-4 form* showing how many withholding allowances or exemptions he or she claims. The employer uses this information to figure how much tax to deduct from the employee's paycheck. Figure 6-1 shows a 2001 W-4 form.

There are several ways to figure the withholding tax for an employee. The most common methods are using tax tables and tax rates. These and other methods are referenced in IRS Publication 15 (Circular E, Employer's Tax Guide).

 TIP! **Getting Tax Information from the IRS**

The IRS provides recorded tax information on numerous topics that answer many individual and business tax topics. Touch-tone service is available 24 hours a day, seven days a week using the toll-free number 1-800-TAX-IIRS or 1-800-829-4477.

The information can be obtained by requesting an IRS publication through an order form or by placing the order by phone at 1-800-829-3676 or by fax at 703-368-9694.

The IRS also has a web page on the Internet. The addresses are: www.irs.gov and ftp.irs.gov.

Form W-4 (2001)

Purpose. Complete Form W-4 so your employer can withhold the correct Federal income tax from your pay. Because your tax situation may change, you may want to refigure your withholding each year.

Exemption from withholding. If you are exempt, complete only lines 1, 2, 3, 4, and 7, and sign the form to validate it. Your exemption for 2001 expires February 18, 2002.

Note: *You cannot claim exemption from withholding if (1) your income exceeds $750 and includes more than $250 of unearned income (e.g., interest and dividends) and (2) another person can claim you as a dependent on their tax return.*

Basic instructions. If you are not exempt, complete the **Personal Allowances Worksheet** below. The worksheets on page 2 adjust your withholding allowances based on itemized deductions, certain credits, adjustments to income, or two-earner/two-job situations. Complete all worksheets that apply. They will help you figure the number of withholding allowances you are entitled to claim. **However, you may claim fewer (or zero) allowances.**

Head of household. Generally, you may claim head of household filing status on your tax return only if you are unmarried and pay more than 50% of the costs of keeping up a home for yourself and your dependent(s) or other qualifying individuals. See line E below.

Tax credits. You can take projected tax credits into account in figuring your allowable number of withholding allowances. Credits for child or dependent care expenses and the child tax credit may be claimed using the **Personal Allowances Worksheet.** See **Pub. 919**, How Do I Adjust My Tax Withholding? for information on converting your other credits into withholding allowances.

Nonwage income. If you have a large amount of nonwage income, such as interest or dividends, consider making estimated tax payments using **Form 1040-ES**, Estimated Tax for Individuals. Otherwise, you may owe additional tax.

Two earners/two jobs. If you have a working spouse or more than one job, figure the total number of allowances you are entitled to claim on all jobs using worksheets from only one Form W-4. Your withholding usually will be most accurate when all allowances are claimed on the Form W-4 for the highest paying job and zero allowances are claimed on the others.

Check your withholding. After your Form W-4 takes effect, use Pub. 919 to see how the dollar amount you are having withheld compares to your projected total tax for 2001. Get Pub. 919 especially if you used the **Two-Earner/Two-Job Worksheet** on page 2 and your earnings exceed $150,000 (Single) or $200,000 (Married).

Recent name change? If your name on line 1 differs from that shown on your social security card, call 1-800-772-1213 for a new social security card.

Personal Allowances Worksheet (Keep for your records.)

A Enter "1" for **yourself** if no one else can claim you as a dependent . . . . **A** _____

B Enter "1" if:
- You are single and have only one job; or
- You are married, have only one job, and your spouse does not work; or
- Your wages from a second job or your spouse's wages (or the total of both) are $1,000 or less.

B _____

C Enter "1" for your **spouse**. But, you may choose to enter -0- if you are married and have either a working spouse or more than one job. (Entering -0- may help you avoid having too little tax withheld.) . . . . **C** _____

D Enter number of **dependents** (other than your spouse or yourself) you will claim on your tax return . . . . **D** _____

E Enter "1" if you will file as **head of household** on your tax return (see conditions under **Head of household** above) . **E** _____

F Enter "1" if you have at least $1,500 of **child or dependent care expenses** for which you plan to claim a credit . . **F** _____
(**Note:** *Do not include child support payments. See Pub. 503, Child and Dependent Care Expenses, for details.*)

G **Child Tax Credit** (including additional child tax credit):
- If your total income will be between $18,000 and $50,000 ($23,000 and $63,000 if married), enter "1" for each eligible child.
- If your total income will be between $50,000 and $80,000 ($63,000 and $115,000 if married), enter "1" if you have two eligible children, enter "2" if you have three or four eligible children, or enter "3" if you have five or more eligible children. **G** _____

H Add lines A through G and enter total here. (**Note:** *This may be different from the number of exemptions you claim on your tax return.*) ▶ **H** _____

For accuracy, complete all worksheets that apply.
- If you plan to **itemize or claim adjustments to income** and want to reduce your withholding, see the **Deductions and Adjustments Worksheet** on page 2.
- If you are **single**, have **more than one job** and your combined earnings from all jobs exceed $35,000, **or** if you are **married** and have a **working spouse or more than one job** and the combined earnings from all jobs exceed $60,000, see the **Two-Earner/Two-Job Worksheet** on page 2 to avoid having too little tax withheld.
- If **neither** of the above situations applies, **stop here** and enter the number from line H on line 5 of Form W-4 below.

- - - - - - - - - - - - - - Cut here and give Form W-4 to your employer. Keep the top part for your records. - - - - - - - - - - - - - -

Form **W-4** Department of the Treasury Internal Revenue Service	**Employee's Withholding Allowance Certificate** ▶ **For Privacy Act and Paperwork Reduction Act Notice, see page 2.**	OMB No. 1545-0010 **2001**

1 Type or print your first name and middle initial   Last name

2 Your social security number

3 ☐ Single ☐ Married ☐ Married, but withhold at higher Single rate.
Note: *If married, but legally separated, or spouse is a nonresident alien, check the Single box.*

Home address (number and street or rural route)

City or town, state, and ZIP code

4 If your last name differs from that on your social security card, check here. You must call 1-800-772-1213 for a new card. ▶ ☐

5 Total number of allowances you are claiming (from line **H** above **or** from the applicable worksheet on page 2) **5** _____

6 Additional amount, if any, you want withheld from each paycheck . . . . **6** $ _____

7 I claim exemption from withholding for 2001, and I certify that I meet **both** of the following conditions for exemption:
- Last year I had a right to a refund of **all** Federal income tax withheld because I had **no** tax liability **and**
- This year I expect a refund of **all** Federal income tax withheld because I expect to have **no** tax liability.
If you meet both conditions, write "Exempt" here . . . . ▶ **7** _____

Under penalties of perjury, I certify that I am entitled to the number of withholding allowances claimed on this certificate, or I am entitled to claim exempt status.

Employee's signature
(Form is not valid unless you sign it.) ▶

Date ▶

8 Employer's name and address (Employer: Complete lines 8 and 10 only if sending to the IRS.)

9 Office code (optional)

10 Employer identification number

Figure 6-1   Employee's Withholding Allowance Certificate

 Find federal tax withholding per paycheck using IRS tax tables.

To calculate federal withholding tax using IRS tax tables, an employer must know the **employee's filing status** (single, married, and so on), the number of withholding

allowances the employee claims, the type of pay period (weekly, biweekly, and so on), and the employee's *adjusted gross income.* When an employee is hired for a job, he or she is asked for payroll purposes to complete a federal W-4 form. On this form an employee must indicate tax-filing status and number of exemptions claimed. This information is necessary in order to compute the amount of federal income tax to be withheld from the employee's earnings.

In many cases, adjusted gross income is the same as gross pay. However, earnings contributed to funds such as qualifying IRAs, tax-sheltered annuities, 401Ks, or employee-sponsored child care and medical plans are called *adjustments* to income, and are subtracted from gross pay to determine the **adjusted gross income.**

Figures 6-2 and 6-3 show two IRS tax tables.

? HOW TO   Find Federal Tax Withholding per Paycheck Using the IRS Tax Tables

1. Find the adjusted gross pay by subtracting the total qualified adjustments from the gross pay per pay period. Select the appropriate table according to the employee's filing status (single, married, and so on) and according to the type of pay period (weekly, biweekly, and so on).

2. Find the income row: in the columns labeled "If the wages are—," select the "At least" and "But less than" interval that includes the employee's adjusted gross pay for the pay period.

3. Find the allowances column: in the columns labeled "And the number of withholding allowances claimed is—," select the number of allowances the employee claims.

4. Find the cell where the income row and allowance column intersect. The correct tax is given in this cell.

EXAMPLE   Jeremy Dawson has a gross semimonthly income of $840, is single, and claims three withholding allowances. Find the amount of federal tax withholding to be deducted from his gross earnings by using Figure 6-2.

The amount $840 is seen in the row "At least $840 but less than $860." Now choose the column for three withholding allowances. **The withholding tax is $57.**

EXAMPLE   Haruna Jing is married, has a gross weekly salary of $515, and claims two withholding allowances. Find the amount of withholding tax to be deducted from her gross salary.

In Figure 6-3, find the $510–$520 income row and withholding allowance column 2.

The amount of withholding tax is $42.

2   Find federal tax withholding per paycheck using the IRS percentage method

Instead of using the tax tables, many companies calculate federal tax withholding using *tax rates.* In order to use tax rates, the employer must deduct from the employee's adjusted gross income a tax-exempt amount based on the number of withholding allowances the employee claims. The resulting amount is sometimes called the **percentage method income.**

SINGLE Persons- SEMIMONTHLY Payroll Period
(For Wages Paid in 2001)

If the wages are-		And the number of withholding allowances claimed is-										
At least	But less than	0	1	2	3	4	5	6	7	8	9	10
		The amount of income tax to be withheld is-										
$840	$860	111	93	75	57	38	20	2	0	0	0	0
860	880	114	96	78	60	41	23	5	0	0	0	0
880	900	117	99	81	63	44	26	8	0	0	0	0
900	920	120	102	84	66	47	29	11	0	0	0	0
920	940	123	105	87	69	50	32	14	0	0	0	0
940	960	126	108	90	72	53	35	17	0	0	0	0
960	980	129	111	93	75	56	38	20	2	0	0	0
980	1,000	132	114	96	78	59	41	23	5	0	0	0
1,000	1,020	135	117	99	81	62	44	26	8	0	0	0
1,020	1,040	138	120	102	84	65	47	29	11	0	0	0
1,040	1,060	141	123	105	87	68	50	32	14	0	0	0
1,060	1,080	144	126	108	90	71	53	35	17	0	0	0
1,080	1,100	147	129	111	93	74	56	38	20	2	0	0
1,100	1,120	150	132	114	96	77	59	41	23	5	0	0
1,120	1,140	153	135	117	99	80	62	44	26	8	0	0
1,140	1,160	156	138	120	102	83	65	47	29	11	0	0
1,160	1,180	159	141	123	105	86	68	50	32	14	0	0
1,180	1,200	162	144	126	108	89	71	53	35	17	0	0
1,200	1,220	167	147	129	111	92	74	56	38	20	2	0
1,220	1,240	172	150	132	114	95	77	59	41	23	5	0
1,240	1,260	178	153	135	117	98	80	62	44	26	8	0
1,260	1,280	184	156	138	120	101	83	65	47	29	11	0
1,280	1,300	189	159	141	123	104	86	68	50	32	14	0
1,300	1,320	195	162	144	126	107	89	71	53	35	17	0
1,320	1,340	200	167	147	129	110	92	74	56	38	20	2
1,340	1,360	206	172	150	132	113	95	77	59	41	23	5
1,360	1,380	212	178	153	135	116	98	80	62	44	26	8
1,380	1,400	217	183	156	138	119	101	83	65	47	29	11
1,400	1,420	223	189	159	141	122	104	86	68	50	32	14
1,420	1,440	228	195	162	144	125	107	89	71	53	35	17
1,440	1,460	234	200	166	147	128	110	92	74	56	38	20
1,460	1,480	240	206	172	150	131	113	95	77	59	41	23
1,480	1,500	245	211	178	153	134	116	98	80	62	44	26
1,500	1,520	251	217	183	156	137	119	101	83	65	47	29
1,520	1,540	256	223	189	159	140	122	104	86	68	50	32
1,540	1,560	262	228	194	162	143	125	107	89	71	53	35
1,560	1,580	268	234	200	166	146	128	110	92	74	56	38
1,580	1,600	273	239	206	172	149	131	113	95	77	59	41
1,600	1,620	279	245	211	177	152	134	116	98	80	62	44
1,620	1,640	284	251	217	183	155	137	119	101	83	65	47
1,640	1,660	290	256	222	188	158	140	122	104	86	68	50
1,660	1,680	296	262	228	194	161	143	125	107	89	71	53
1,680	1,700	301	267	234	200	166	146	128	110	92	74	56
1,700	1,720	307	273	239	205	171	149	131	113	95	77	59
1,720	1,740	312	279	245	211	177	152	134	116	98	80	62
1,740	1,760	318	284	250	216	183	155	137	119	101	83	65
1,760	1,780	324	290	256	222	188	158	140	122	104	86	68
1,780	1,800	329	295	262	228	194	161	143	125	107	89	71
1,800	1,820	335	301	267	233	199	166	146	128	110	92	74
1,820	1,840	340	307	273	239	205	171	149	131	113	95	77
1,840	1,860	346	312	278	244	211	177	152	134	116	98	80
1,860	1,880	352	318	284	250	216	182	155	137	119	101	83
1,880	1,900	357	323	290	256	222	188	158	140	122	104	86
1,900	1,920	363	329	295	261	227	194	161	143	125	107	89
1,920	1,940	368	335	301	267	233	199	165	146	128	110	92
1,940	1,960	374	340	306	272	239	205	171	149	131	113	95
1,960	1,980	380	346	312	278	244	210	177	152	134	116	98
1,980	2,000	385	351	318	284	250	216	182	155	137	119	101
2,000	2,020	391	357	323	289	255	222	188	158	140	122	104
2,020	2,040	396	363	329	295	261	227	193	161	143	125	107
2,040	2,060	402	368	334	300	267	233	199	165	146	128	110
2,060	2,080	408	374	340	306	272	238	205	171	149	131	113
2,080	2,100	413	379	346	312	278	244	210	176	152	134	116
2,100	2,120	419	385	351	317	283	250	216	182	155	137	119
2,120	2,140	424	391	357	323	289	255	221	188	158	140	122

$2,140 and over   Use Table 3(a) for a **SINGLE person** on page 34. Also see the instructions on page 32.

Figure 6-2   IRS Tax Table for Single Persons Paid Semimonthly

MARRIED Persons- WEEKLY Payroll Period

(For Wages Paid in 2001)

If the wages are-		And the number of withholding allowances claimed is-										
At least	But less than	0	1	2	3	4	5	6	7	8	9	10
		The amount of income tax to be withheld is-										
$0	$125	0	0	0	0	0	0	0	0	0	0	0
125	130	1	0	0	0	0	0	0	0	0	0	0
130	135	1	0	0	0	0	0	0	0	0	0	0
135	140	2	0	0	0	0	0	0	0	0	0	0
140	145	3	0	0	0	0	0	0	0	0	0	0
145	150	4	0	0	0	0	0	0	0	0	0	0
150	155	4	0	0	0	0	0	0	0	0	0	0
155	160	5	0	0	0	0	0	0	0	0	0	0
160	165	6	0	0	0	0	0	0	0	0	0	0
165	170	7	0	0	0	0	0	0	0	0	0	0
170	175	7	0	0	0	0	0	0	0	0	0	0
175	180	8	0	0	0	0	0	0	0	0	0	0
180	185	9	0	0	0	0	0	0	0	0	0	0
185	190	10	1	0	0	0	0	0	0	0	0	0
190	195	10	2	0	0	0	0	0	0	0	0	0
195	200	11	3	0	0	0	0	0	0	0	0	0
200	210	12	4	0	0	0	0	0	0	0	0	0
210	220	14	5	0	0	0	0	0	0	0	0	0
220	230	15	7	0	0	0	0	0	0	0	0	0
230	240	17	8	0	0	0	0	0	0	0	0	0
240	250	18	10	1	0	0	0	0	0	0	0	0
250	260	20	11	3	0	0	0	0	0	0	0	0
260	270	21	13	4	0	0	0	0	0	0	0	0
270	280	23	14	6	0	0	0	0	0	0	0	0
280	290	24	16	7	0	0	0	0	0	0	0	0
290	300	26	17	9	1	0	0	0	0	0	0	0
300	310	27	19	10	2	0	0	0	0	0	0	0
310	320	29	20	12	4	0	0	0	0	0	0	0
320	330	30	22	13	5	0	0	0	0	0	0	0
330	340	32	23	15	7	0	0	0	0	0	0	0
340	350	33	25	16	8	0	0	0	0	0	0	0
350	360	35	26	18	10	1	0	0	0	0	0	0
360	370	36	28	19	11	3	0	0	0	0	0	0
370	380	38	29	21	13	4	0	0	0	0	0	0
380	390	39	31	22	14	6	0	0	0	0	0	0
390	400	41	32	24	16	7	0	0	0	0	0	0
400	410	42	34	25	17	9	0	0	0	0	0	0
410	420	44	35	27	19	10	2	0	0	0	0	0
420	430	45	37	28	20	12	3	0	0	0	0	0
430	440	47	38	30	22	13	5	0	0	0	0	0
440	450	48	40	31	23	15	6	0	0	0	0	0
450	460	50	41	33	25	16	8	0	0	0	0	0
460	470	51	43	34	26	18	9	1	0	0	0	0
470	480	53	44	36	28	19	11	2	0	0	0	0
480	490	54	46	37	29	21	12	4	0	0	0	0
490	500	56	47	39	31	22	14	5	0	0	0	0
500	510	57	49	40	32	24	15	7	0	0	0	0
510	520	59	50	42	34	25	17	8	0	0	0	0
520	530	60	52	43	35	27	18	10	2	0	0	0
530	540	62	53	45	37	28	20	11	3	0	0	0
540	550	63	55	46	38	30	21	13	5	0	0	0
550	560	65	56	48	40	31	23	14	6	0	0	0
560	570	66	58	49	41	33	24	16	8	0	0	0
570	580	68	59	51	43	34	26	17	9	1	0	0
580	590	69	61	52	44	36	27	19	11	2	0	0
590	600	71	62	54	46	37	29	20	12	4	0	0
600	610	72	64	55	47	39	30	22	14	5	0	0
610	620	74	65	57	49	40	32	23	15	7	0	0
620	630	75	67	58	50	42	33	25	17	8	0	0
630	640	77	68	60	52	43	35	26	18	10	1	0
640	650	78	70	61	53	45	36	28	20	11	3	0
650	660	80	71	63	55	46	38	29	21	13	4	0
660	670	81	73	64	56	48	39	31	23	14	6	0
670	680	83	74	66	58	49	41	32	24	16	7	0
680	690	84	76	67	59	51	42	34	26	17	9	0
690	700	86	77	69	61	52	44	35	27	19	10	2
700	710	87	79	70	62	54	45	37	29	20	12	3
710	720	89	80	72	64	55	47	38	30	22	13	5
720	730	90	82	73	65	57	48	40	32	23	15	6
730	740	92	83	75	67	58	50	41	33	25	16	8

Figure 6-3 IRS Tax Table for Married Persons Paid Weekly

Figure 6-4 shows how much of an employee's adjusted gross income is exempt for each withholding allowance claimed, according to the type of pay period—weekly, biweekly, and so on. The table in Figure 6-4 is available from the IRS and is one of the tables used for calculating employees' withholding taxes. This method is called the **percentage method of withholding.**

Figure 6-4 IRS Table for Figuring Withholding Allowance According to the Percentage Method

Table 5. Percentage Method–2001 Amount for One Withholding Allowance

Payroll Period	One Withholding Allowance
Weekly	$ 55.77
Biweekly	111.54
Semimonthly	120.83
Monthly	241.67
Quarterly	725.00
Semiannually	1,450.00
Annually	2,900.00
Daily or miscellaneous (each day of the payroll period)	11.15

HOW TO Find the Percentage Method Income per Paycheck

1. Find the exempt-per-allowance amount: from the withholding allowance table (in Figure 6-4), identify the amount exempt for one withholding allowance according to the type of pay period.
2. Find the total exempt amount: multiply the number of withholding allowances the employee claims by the exempt-per-allowance amount.
3. Subtract the total exempt amount from the employee's adjusted gross income for the pay period.

EXAMPLE Find the percentage method income on Dollie Calloway's biweekly gross earnings of $3,150. She has no adjustments to income, is single, and claims two withholding allowances on her W-4 form.

Since Dollie has no adjustments to income, her gross earnings of $3,150 is her adjusted gross income. From the table in Figure 6-4, the amount exempt for one withholding allowance in a biweekly pay period is $111.54.

$2 \times \$111.54 = \$223.08$ Multiply the number of withholding allowances by the exempt-per-allowance amount.

$\$3,150 - \$223.08 = \$2,926.92$ Subtract the total exempt amount from the adjusted gross income.

The percentage method income is $2,926.92.

Once an employee's percentage method income is found, the employer consults the percentage method tables, also available from the IRS, to know how much of this income should be taxed at which tax rate, according to the employee's marital status and the type of pay period. Figure 6-5 shows the IRS percentage method tables.

Tables for Percentage Method of Withholding
(For Wages Paid in 2001)

TABLE 1- WEEKLY Payroll Period

(a) SINGLE person (including head of household)-

If the amount of wages (after subtracting withholding allowances) is:	The amount of income tax to withhold is:
Not over $51	$0

Over-	But not over-		of excess over-
$51	- $552 . .	15%	- 51
$552	- $1,196 . .	$75.15 plus 28%	- 552
$1,196	- $2,662 . .	$255.47 plus 31%	- 1,196
$2,662	- $5,750 . .	$709.93 plus 36%	- 2,662
$5,750	. . . . .	$1,821.61 plus 39.6%	- 5,750

(b) MARRIED person-

If the amount of wages (after subtracting withholding allowances) is:	The amount of income tax to withhold is:
Not over $124	$0

Over-	But not over-		of excess over-
$124	- $960 . .	15%	- $124
$960	- $2,023 . .	$125.40 plus 28%	- $960
$2,023	- $3,292 . .	$423.04 plus 31%	- $2,023
$3,292	- $5,809 . .	$816.43 plus 36%	- $3,292
$5,809	. . . . .	$1,722.55 plus 39.6%	- $5,809

TABLE 2- BIWEEKLY Payroll Period

(a) SINGLE person (including head of household)-

If the amount of wages (after subtracting withholding allowances) is:	The amount of income tax to withhold is:
Not over $102	$0

Over-	But not over-		of excess over-
$102	- $1,104 . .	15%	- $102
$1,104	- $2,392 . .	$150.30 plus 28%	- $1,104
$2,392	- $5,323 . .	$510.94 plus 31%	- $2,392
$5,323	- $11,500 . .	$1,419.55 plus 36%	- $5,323
$11,500	. . . . .	$3,643.27 plus 39.6%	- $11,500

(b) MARRIED person-

If the amount of wages (after subtracting withholding allowances) is:	The amount of income tax to withhold is:
Not over $248	$0

Over-	But not over-		of excess over-
$248	- $1,919 . .	15%	- $248
$1,919	- $4,046 . .	$250.65 plus 28%	- $1,919
$4,046	- $6,585 . .	$846.21 plus 31%	- $4,046
$6,585	- $11,617 . .	$1,633.30 plus 36%	- $6,585
$11,617	. . . . .	$3,444.82 plus 39.6%	- $11,617

TABLE 3- SEMIMONTHLY Payroll Period

(a) SINGLE person (including head of household)-

If the amount of wages (after subtracting withholding allowances) is:	The amount of income tax to withhold is:
Not over $110	$0

Over-	But not over-		of excess over-
$110	- $1,196 . .	15%	- $110
$1,196	- $2,592 . .	$162.90 plus 28%	- $1,196
$2,592	- $5,767 . .	$553.78 plus 31%	- $2,592
$5,767	- $12,458 . .	$1,538.03 plus 36%	- $5,767
$12,458	. . . . .	$3,946.79 plus 39.6%	- $12,458

(b) MARRIED person-

If the amount of wages (after subtracting withholding allowances) is:	The amount of income tax to withhold is:
Not over $269	$0

Over-	But not over-		of excess over-
$269	- $2,079 . .	15%	- $269
$2,079	- $4,383 . .	$271.50 plus 28%	- $2,079
$4,383	- $7,133 . .	$916.62 plus 31%	- $4,383
$7,133	- $12,585 . .	$1,769.12 plus 36%	- $7,133
$12,585	. . . . .	$3,731.84 plus 39.6%	- $12,585

TABLE 4- MONTHLY Payroll Period

(a) SINGLE person (including head of household)-

If the amount of wages (after subtracting withholding allowances) is:	The amount of income tax to withhold is:
Not over $221	$0

Over-	But not over-		of excess over-
$221	- $2,392 . .	15%	- $221
$2,392	- $5,183 . .	$325.65 plus 28%	- $2,392
$5,183	- $11,533 . .	$1,107.13 plus 31%	- $5,183
$11,533	- $24,917 . .	$3,075.63 plus 36%	- $11,533
$24,917	. . . . .	$7,893.87 plus 39.6%	- $24,917

(b) MARRIED person-

If the amount of wages (after subtracting withholding allowances) is:	The amount of income tax to withhold is:
Not over $538	$0

Over-	But not over-		of excess over-
$538	- $4,158 . .	15%	- $538
$4,158	- $8,767 . .	$543.00 plus 28%	- $4,158
$8,767	- $14,267 . .	$1,833.52 plus 31%	- $8,767
$14,267	- $25,171 . .	$3,538.52 plus 36%	- $14,267
$25,171	. . . . .	$7,463.96 plus 39.6%	- $25,171

Figure 6-5 IRS Tables for Percentage Method of Withholding

HOW TO Find Federal Tax Withholding per Paycheck Using the IRS Percentage Method Tables

1. Select the appropriate table according to the employee's filing status and the type of pay period.

2. Find the income row: In the columns labeled "If the amount of wages is . . .," select the "Over—" and "But not over—" interval that includes the employee's percentage method income for the pay period.

3. Find the cell where the income row and the column labeled "of excess over—" intersect, and subtract the amount given in this cell from the employee's percentage method income for the pay period.

4. Multiply the difference from step 3 by the percent given in the income row.

5. Add the product from step 4 to the amount given with the *percent* in the income row and amount of tax column.

EXAMPLE Find the federal tax withholding to be deducted from Dollie's income in the previous example.

From Figure 6-5 select Table 3(a) for single employees paid semimonthly. We found Dollie's percentage method income to be $2,926.92 for the pay period. Table 3(a) tells us that the tax for that income is $553.78 plus 31% of the income in excess of $2,592.

$2,926.92 − $2,592 = $334.92   **Subtract $2,592.00 from the percentage method income to find the amount in excess of $2,592.**

$334.92 × 0.31 = $103.83   **Find 31% of the income in excess of $2,592.**

$553.78 + $103.83 = $657.61   **Add $553.73 to $103.83 to find the withholding tax.**

The federal tax withholding is $657.61 for the pay period.

Withholding tax calculated by the percentage method may differ slightly from the withholding tax given in the tax table. The tax table amounts are rounded to the nearest dollar.

 Find **Social Security tax and Medicare tax** per paycheck.

Two other amounts withheld from an employee's paycheck are the deduction for Social Security and Medicare tax. The **Federal Insurance Contribution Act (FICA)** was established by Congress during the depression of the 1930s. Prior to 1991, funds collected under the Social Security tax act were used for both Social Security and Medicare benefits. Beginning in 1991, funds were collected separately for these two programs.

The Social Security tax rate and the income subject to Social Security tax change periodically as Congress passes new legislation. In a recent year, the Social Security tax rate was 6.2% (0.062) of the first $80,400 gross earnings. This means that after a person has earned $80,400 in a year, no Social Security tax will be withheld on any additional money he or she earns during that year. A person who earns $100,000 in a year pays exactly the same Social Security tax as a person who earns $80,400. In this same year, the rate for Medicare was 1.45% (0.0145). Initially, there was a maximum income subject to Medicare tax; however, all wages earned are now subject to Medicare tax, unless the employee participates in a flexible benefits plan that is exempt from Medicare tax and under certain other conditions specified in Internal Revenue Code.

TIP! Can Any Income Be Exempt from Social Security and Medicare?

Under certain conditions employers may provide *flexible benefits plans* for employees. These plans are written to provide employees with a choice or "menu" of benefits such as health insurance, child care, and so on. In some instances the wages used to pay for these benefits are subtracted from gross earnings to give an adjusted gross income that is used as the basis for withholding tax, Social Security tax, and Medicare tax.

Employers also pay a share of Social Security and Medicare tax: The employer contributes the same amount as the employee contributes to an employee's Social Security account and Medicare account. Employers can figure Social Security tax for employees and themselves by multiplying 6.2% by the employee's accumulated gross pay for the period as long as the employee's gross pay for the year does not exceed $80,400. Similarly, employers figure Medicare tax, both the employee contribution and the employer contribution, by multiplying 1.45% by the employee's gross pay for the period.

EXAMPLE   Mickey Beloate has a gross weekly income of $667. How much Social Security and Medicare tax should be withheld?

$$\text{Social Security tax on } \$667 = 667 \times 0.062 = \$41.35$$

$$\text{Medicare tax on } \$667 = 667 \times 0.0145 = \$9.67$$

The Social Security tax withheld should be $41.35, and the Medicare tax withheld should be $9.67.

EXAMPLE   John Friedlander, vice president of marketing for Golden Sun Enterprises, earns $81,744 annually, or $1,572 per week. Find the amount of Social Security and Medicare taxes that should be withheld for the 51st week.

At the end of the 50th week, John will have earned a total gross salary for the year of $78,600. Since Social Security tax is withheld on the first $80,400 annually, he needs to pay Social Security tax on $1,800 of his 51st week's earnings since $80,400 − $78,600 = $1,800.

$$\$1,800 \times 0.062 = \$111.60$$ Multiply $1,800 by the 6.2% tax rate to find the Social Security tax for the 51st week.

Since Medicare tax is paid on the entire salary, John must pay the Medicare tax on the full week's salary of $1,572.

$$\$1,572 \times 0.0145 = \$22.79$$

The Social Security tax for the 51st week is $111.60, and the Medicare tax is $22.79.

A person who is self-employed must also pay Social Security tax and Medicare tax. Since there is no employer involved to make matching contributions, the self-employed person must pay the equivalent of both amounts. The self-employment rates are 12.4% Social Security and 2.9% Medicare tax for a total of 15.3%. The tax is called the **self-employment (SE) tax.** However, one-half of the self-employment tax can be deducted as an adjustment to income when finding the adjusted income for paying income tax. Self-employed persons report and pay taxes differently. This process will be discussed in Chapter 17.

4 Find net earnings per paycheck.

In addition to federal taxes, a number of other deductions may be made from an employee's paycheck. Often state and local income taxes must also be withheld by the employer. Other deductions are made at the employee's request, such as insurance or union dues. Some retirement plans and insurance are tax exempt; others are not. When all these deductions have been made, the amount left is called net earnings, net pay, or take-home pay.

? HOW TO Find Net Earnings Per Paycheck

1. Find the gross pay for the pay period.
2. Find the adjustments-to-income deductions, such as tax-exempt retirement, medical insurance, and so on.
3. Find the Social Security tax and Medicare tax based on gross pay.
4. Find the federal tax withholding based on (a) or (b).
   (a) adjusted gross income (gross pay minus adjustments to income) using IRS tax tables
   (b) percentage method income (adjusted gross income minus amount exempt for withholding allowances) using IRS percentage method tables
5. Find other withholding taxes, such as local or state taxes.
6. Find the sum of all deductions from steps 3–5 and subtract the sum from the gross pay.

EXAMPLE Jeanetta Grandberry's gross weekly earnings are $576. She is married and claims two withholding allowances. Five percent of her gross earnings is deducted for her nonexempt retirement fund and $25.83 is deducted for nonexempt insurance. Find her net earnings.

Income tax withholding:
$51.00

> In Figure 6-3, find the amount of income tax to be withheld.

Social Security tax withholding:
$576 × 0.062 = $35.71

> Find the Social Security tax by the percentage method.

Medicare tax withholding:
$576 × 0.0145 = $8.35

> Find the Medicare tax by the percentage method.

Retirement fund withholding:
0.05 × $576 = $28.80

> Use the formula $P = R \times B$. Multiply rate (5% = 0.05) by base (gross pay of $576).

Add all deductions:
Total deductions
= income tax + Social Security tax + Medicare + insurance + retirement fund
= $51.00   + $35.71   + $8.35   + $25.83   + $28.80 = $149.69

Gross earnings − total deductions = net earnings
$576   − $149.69   = $426.31

The net earnings are $426.31.

1

1. Khalid Khouri is married, has a gross weekly salary of $486 (all of which is taxable), and claims three withholding allowances. Use the tax tables to find the federal tax withholding to be deducted from his weekly salary.

2. Mae Swift is married and has a gross weekly salary of $583. She has $32 in adjustments to income for tax exempt health insurance and claims two withholding allowances. Use the tax tables to find the federal tax withholding to be deducted from her weekly salary.

3. Paul Thomas is paid semimonthly an adjusted gross income of $1,431. He is single and claims two withholding allowances. Use the tax tables to find the federal tax withholding to be deducted from his salary.

2

4. Dieter Tillman earns a semimonthly salary of $1,698. He has a $100 adjustment-to-income flexible benefits package, is single, and claims three withholding allowances. Find the federal tax withholding to be deducted from his salary using the percentage method tables.

5. Mohammad Hajibeigy has a weekly adjusted gross income of $580, is single, and claims one withholding allowance. Find the federal tax withholding to be deducted from his weekly paycheck using the percentage method tables.

6. Margie Young is an associate professor at a major research university and earns $4,598 monthly with no adjustments to income. She is married and claims one withholding allowance. Find the federal tax withholding that is deducted from her monthly paycheck using the percentage method tables.

3

7. Dr. Josef Young earns an adjusted gross weekly income of $2,583. How much Social Security tax should be withheld the first week of the year? How much Medicare tax should be withheld?

8. Dierdri Williams earns a gross biweekly income of $1,020 and has no adjustments to income. How much Social Security tax should be withheld? How much Medicare tax should be withheld?

9. Rodney Whitaker earns $80,608 annually and is paid monthly. How much Social Security tax will be deducted from his December earnings? How much Medicare tax will be deducted from his December earnings?

4

10. Pam Trim earns $5,291 monthly, is married, and claims four withholding allowances. Her company pays her retirement, but she pays $52.83 each month for nonexempt insurance premiums. Find her net pay.

11. Shirley Riddle earns $1,319 biweekly. She is single and claims no withholding allowances. She pays 2% of her salary for retirement and $22.80 in nonexempt insurance premiums each pay period. What are her net earnings for each pay period?

12. Donna Wood's gross weekly earnings are $615. Three percent of her gross earnings is deducted for her nonexempt retirement fund and $25.97 is deducted for nonexempt insurance. Find the net earnings if Donna is married and claims two withholding allowances.

6.3 The Employer's Payroll Taxes

1 Find an employer's total deposit for withholding tax, Social Security tax, and Medicare tax per pay period.

2 Find an employer's SUTA tax and FUTA tax due for a quarter.

1 Find an employer's total deposit for withholding tax, Social Security tax, and Medicare tax per pay period.

The employer must deposit income tax withheld and both the employees' and employer's Social Security and Medicare taxes by mailing or delivering a check, money order, or cash to an authorized financial institution or federal reserve bank. If the employer's accumulated tax is less than $500, this payment may be made with the tax return (generally Form 941, Employer's Quarterly Federal Tax Return). Other circumstances create a different employer's deposit schedule. This schedule varies depending on the amount of tax liability and other criteria. IRS Publication 15 (Circular E, Employer's Tax Guide) and Publication 334 (Tax Guide for Small Business) give the criteria for depositing and reporting these taxes.

 HOW TO Find an Employer's Total Deposit for Withholding Tax, Social Security Tax, and Medicare Tax per Pay Period

1. Find the withholding tax deposit: from employee payroll records, find the total withholding tax for all employees for the period.

2. Find the Social Security tax deposit: find the total Social Security tax paid by all employees and multiply this total by 2 to include the employer's matching tax.

3. Find the Medicare tax deposit: find the total Medicare tax for all employees for the pay period and mutiply the total by 2.

4. Add the withholding tax deposit, Social Security tax deposit, and Medicare tax deposit.

EXAMPLE Determine the employer's total deposit of withholding tax, Social Security tax, and Medicare tax for the payroll register.

Payroll for June 1 through June 15, 2001

Employee	Gross Earnings	Withholding	Social Security	Medicare	Net Earnings
Plumlee, C.	$1,050.00	$141.00	$65.10	$15.23	$ 828.67
Powell, M.	2,085.00	379.01	129.27	30.23	1,546.50
Randle, M.	1,995.00	318.00	123.69	28.93	1,524.38
Robinson, J.	2,089.00	413.00	129.52	30.29	1,516.19

Total withholding = $141.00 + $379.00 + $318.00 + $413.00 = $1,251.00
Total Social Security = $65.10 + $129.27 + $123.69 + $129.52 = $447.58
Total Medicare = $15.23 + $30.23 + $28.93 + $30.29 = $104.68
Total Social Security and Medicare $\times$ 2 = ($447.58 + $104.68) $\times$ 2 = $552.26 $\times$ 2 = $1,104.52
Total employer's deposit = $1,251.00 + $1,104.52 = $2,355.52

The total amount of the employer's deposit for this payroll is $2,355.52.

2 Find an employer's SUTA tax and FUTA tax due for a quarter.

The major employee-related taxes paid by employers are the employer's share of the Social Security and Medicare taxes, which we have already discussed, and federal and state unemployment taxes. Federal and state unemployment taxes do not affect the paycheck of the employee. They are paid entirely by the employer. Under the Federal Unemployment Tax Act (FUTA) most employers pay a federal unemployment tax. This tax, along with state unemployment tax provides for payment of unemployment compensation to workers who have lost their job. **Federal unemployment (FUTA) tax** is currently 6.2% of the first $7,000 earned by an employee in a year *minus* any amount that the employer has paid in **state unemployment (SUTA) tax,** up to a limit of 5.4% on the first $7,000. In most states SUTA is 5.4%. The SUTA rate may vary depending on the company's unemployment record or the state's unemployment record. Thus, in most cases FUTA calculations are made using 0.8% (6.2% − 5.4%). FUTA tax is accumulated for all employees and is deposited quarterly if the amount exceeds $100. Amounts less than $100 are paid with the annual tax return that is due January 31 of the following year.

 HOW TO Find the SUTA Tax Due for a Quarter

1. For each employee, multiply 5.4% or the appropriate rate by the employee's cumulative earnings for the quarter (up to $7,000 annually).
2. Add the SUTA tax owed on all employees.

 HOW TO Find the FUTA Tax Due for a Quarter

1. For each employee:
   (a) If no SUTA tax is paid, multiply 6.2% by the employee's cumulative earnings for the quarter (up to $7,000 annually).
   (b) If 5.4% of the employee's cumulative earnings for the quarter (up to $7,000 annually) is paid as SUTA tax, multiply 0.8% by the employee's cumulative earnings for the quarter (up to $7,000 annually).
2. Add the FUTA tax owed on all employees' wages for the quarter.
3. If the total from step 2 is less than $100, no FUTA tax is due for the quarter, but the total from step 2 must be added to the amount due for the next quarter.

EXAMPLE Melanie McFarren earned $32,500 last year and over $7,000 in the first quarter of this year. If the state unemployment (SUTA) tax is 5.4% of the first $7,000 earned in a year, how much SUTA tax must Melanie's employer pay on her behalf? Also, how much FUTA must be paid?

SUTA = tax rate × taxable wages

SUTA = 5.4% × $7,000

SUTA = 0.054 × $7,000 = $378

$7,000 is subject to SUTA tax in the first quarter.

FUTA = 0.8% × taxable wages

0.008 × $7,000 = $56

$7,000 is subject to FUTA tax in the first quarter.

SUTA tax is $378 and FUTA is $56.

EXAMPLE AAA Plumbing Company has two employees who are paid semimonthly. One employee earns $1,040 per pay period and the other earns $985 per pay period. Based on the SUTA tax rate of 5.4%, the FUTA tax rate is 0.8% of the first $7,000 of each employee's annual gross pay. At the end of which quarter should the FUTA tax first be deposited?

1 Decision needed

At the end of which quarter should the FUTA tax first be deposited?

2 Unknown facts

The first quarter in which the cumulative FUTA tax owed exceeds $100.

3 Known facts

Employee 1 pay: $1,040
Employee 2 pay: $985
Pay period: semimonthly
Cumulative FUTA tax owed per employee: 0.8% of employee's cumulative earnings, up to $7,000.

4 Relationships

FUTA tax per employee per pay period = employee salary × 0.008
FUTA tax for employee 1 per pay period = $1,040 × 0.008 (on first $7,000 of salary)
FUTA tax for employee 2 per pay period = $985 × 0.008 (on first $7,000 of salary)
Total FUTA tax per quarter = sum of quarterly FUTA tax for each employee

5 Estimation

Approximate annual FUTA tax per employee: $7,000 × 1% = 7,000 × 0.01 = $70
Approximate annual FUTA tax for two employees: $70 × 2 = $140
Thus, a deposit may need to be made before the end of the fourth quarter.

6 Calculation

Pay Period	Employee 1 Salary	Accumulated Salary Subject to FUTA Tax	FUTA Tax	Employee 2 Salary	Accumulated Salary Subject to FUTA Tax	FUTA Tax
Jan. 15	1,040	1,040	8.32	985	985	7.88
Jan. 31	1,040	2,080	8.32	985	1,970	7.88
Feb. 15	1,040	3,120	8.32	985	2,955	7.88
Feb. 28	1,040	4,160	8.32	985	3,940	7.88
Mar. 15	1,040	5,200	8.32	985	4,925	7.88
Mar. 31	1,040	6,240	8.32	985	5,910	7.88

First quarter FUTA tax totals: 49.92 + 47.28 = $97.20
$97.20 is less than $100.00, so no deposit should be made at the end of the first quarter.

Pay Period	Employee 1 Salary	Accumulated Salary Subject to FUTA Tax	FUTA Tax	Employee 2 Salary	Accumulated Salary Subject to FUTA Tax	FUTA Tax
Apr. 15	1,040	7,000	6.08*	985	6,895	7.88
Apr. 30	1,040			985	7,000	0.84**
May 15	1,040			985		
May 31	1,040			985		
Jun. 15	1,040			985		
Jun. 30	1,040			985		

*$7,000 − $6,240 = $760; $760 × 0.008 = $6.08
**$7,000 − $6,895 = $105; $105 × 0.008 = $0.84

7 Interpretation

Second quarter FUTA tax totals: $6.08 + $8.72 = $14.80
Total FUTA tax for first two quarters = $97.20 + $14.80 = $112.00

8 Decision made

FUTA tax in the amount of $112 should be deposited by the end of the month following the second quarter .

1. Carolyn Luttrell owns Just the Right Thing, a small antique shop with four employees. For one payroll period the total withholding tax for all employees was $1,633. The total Social Security tax was $482 and the total Medicare tax was $113. How much tax must Carolyn deposit as the employer's share of Social Security and Medicare? What is the total tax that must be deposited?

2. Hughes' Trailer Manufacturer makes utility trailers and has seven employees who are paid weekly. For one payroll period the withholding tax for all employees was $1,661. The total Social Security tax withheld from employees' paychecks was $608, and the total Medicare tax withheld was $142. What is the total tax that must be deposited by Hughes?

3. Determine the employer's deposit of withholding, Social Security, and Medicare for the payroll register.

Employee	Gross Earnings	Withholding	Social Security	Medicare	Net Earnings
Paszel, J.	$1,905	$376.00	$118.11	$27.62	$1,375.27
Thomas, P.	1,598	255.00	99.08	23.17	1,266.04
Tillman, D.	1,431	179.00	88.72	20.75	1,129.53

4. Heaven Sent Gifts, a small business that provides custom meals, flowers, and other specialty gifts, has three employees who are paid weekly. One employee earns $475 per week, is married, and claims one withholding allowance. Another employee earns $450 per week, is married, and claims two withholding allowances. The manager earns $740 per week, is married, and claims one withholding allowance. Calculate the amount of withholding tax, Social Security tax, and Medicare tax that will need to be deposited by Heaven Sent Gifts.

2 *Bruce Young earned $20,418 last year. His employer's SUTA tax rate is 5.4% of the first $7,000.*

5. How much SUTA tax must Bruce's employer pay for him?

6. How much FUTA tax must Bruce's company pay for him?

7. Bailey Plyler has three employees in his carpet cleaning business. The payroll is semimonthly and the employees earn $745, $780, and $1,030 per pay period. Calculate when and in what amounts FUTA tax payments are to be made.

Pretax Medical Insurance Premiums and Garnishments

Under a recent law, medical insurance premiums that are deducted from an employee's paycheck can be paid with pretax dollars. The premium is deducted from the gross salary before withholding taxes, Social Security, and Medicare deductions are calculated on the lower adjusted gross salary.

Garnishments are court-ordered payments on past or present debts that are subtracted from an employee's net income. The most common garnishments are for child support and IRS taxes.

A senior citizens' day care center pays the major portion of its employees' medical insurance—it pays $150 of the $204 monthly premium for an individual employee. If an employee wishes coverage for a spouse or family, the employer must pay $126 or $212 per month, respectively, to cover her- or himself and the additional person(s). Suppose you work in the payroll department when this center hires three new employees. Calculate their semimonthly take-home pay using the percentage method tables. This company pays time and a half for overtime hours in excess of 40 hours in any given week.

Exercises

Round all answers to the nearest cent.

1. An activities director is hired at an annual salary of $32,000. He is single with two dependent children (three withholding allowances) and wants family medical insurance coverage. Find his total deductions and his net income.

2. A dietitian is hired at a monthly salary of $3,500 paid semimonthly. She is married with one withholding allowance and wants medical insurance for herself and her spouse. Find her take-home pay if she pays an IRS garnishment of $100 per month.

3. A van driver is hired at $12 per hour. He is single and claims no withholding allowances. He needs medical coverage on himself only. Find his net pay if he worked 37 hours the first week, 48 hours the second week, and has $200 per month taken out for court-ordered child support payments.

Answers

1. With a semimonthly gross salary of $1,333.33 and deductions of $313.12, his net pay is $1,020.21. Federal withholding ($113.23), Social Security ($76.09), and Medicare ($17.80) taxes are based on an adjusted gross income of $1,227.33 (due to the $106 tax-exempt medical insurance premium).

2. With a semimonthly gross salary of $1,750.00 and deductions of $469.90, her net pay is $1,288.10. Federal withholding ($188.13), Social Security ($101.93), and Medicare ($23.84) taxes are based on an adjusted gross income of $1,644.00 (due to the $106 tax-exempt medical insurance premium). Her IRS garnishment is $50.

3. The driver earned $1,068 for this pay period (which included 8 hours of overtime). His deductions included medical insurance ($27), federal withholding ($139.65), Social Security ($64.54), Medicare ($15.09), and child support ($100.00), which totaled $346.28. So his take-home pay was $721.72.

Section
Outcome   **Important Points with Examples**

Section 6.1

Find the gross pay per paycheck based on salary. (page 262)

1. Identify the number of pay periods per year: monthly, 12; semimonthly, 24; biweekly, 26; weekly, 52

2. Divide the annual salary by the number of pay periods per year.

If Barbara earns $23,500 per year, how much is her weekly gross pay?

$$\frac{\$23,500}{52} = \$451.92$$

Clemetee earns $32,808 annually and is paid twice a month. What is her gross pay per pay period?

$$\frac{\$32,808}{24} = \$1,367$$

Find the gross pay per weekly paycheck based on hourly wage. (page 263)

1. Find the regular pay:
   (a) If the hours worked in the week are 40 or fewer, multiply the hours worked by the hourly wage.
   (b) If the hours worked are more than 40, multiply 40 hours by the hourly wage.
2. Find the overtime pay:
   (a) If the hours worked are 40 or fewer, the overtime pay is $0.
   (b) If the hours worked are more than 40, subtract 40 from the hours worked and multiply the difference by the overtime rate.
3. Add the regular pay and the overtime pay.

Aldo earns $10.25 per hour. He worked 38 hours this week. What is his gross pay?

$$38 \times \$10.25 = \$389.50$$

Belinda worked 44 hours one week. Her regular pay was $7.75 per hour and time and a half for overtime. Find her gross earnings.

$$40 \times \$7.75 = \$310$$

$$4 \times \$7.75 \times 1.5 = \$46.50$$

$$\$310 + \$46.50 = \$356.50$$

Find the gross pay per paycheck based on piecework wage. (page 264)

1. If a *straight piecework* rate is used, multiply the number of items completed by the straight piecework rate.
2. If a *differential piecework* rate is used:
   (a) For each rate category, multiply the number of items produced for the category by the rate for the category.
   (b) Add the pay for all rate categories.

Willy earns $0.53 for each widget he twists. He twisted 1,224 widgets last week. Find his gross earnings.

$$1,224 \times \$0.53 = \$648.72$$

Nadine does piecework for a jeweler and earns $0.65 per piece for finishing 1 to 25 pins, $0.70 per piece for 26 to 50 pins, and $0.75 per piece for pins over 50. Yesterday she finished 130 pins. How much did she earn?

$$(25 \times \$0.65) + (25 \times \$0.70) + (80 \times \$0.75) =$$
$$\$16.25 \quad + \quad \$17.50 \quad + \quad \$60 \quad = \$93.75$$

4 Find the gross pay per paycheck based on commission. (page 265)

1. Find the commission:
   (a) If the commission is *commission based on total sales*, multiply the commission rate by the total sales for the pay period.
   (b) If the commission is *commission based on quota*, subtract the quota from the total sales and multiply the difference by the commission rate.
2. Find the salary:
   (a) If the wage is *straight commission*, the salary is $0.
   (b) If the wage is *commission-plus-salary*, use the How-To steps for finding gross pay based on salary.
3. Add the commission and the salary.

Bart earns a 4% commission on the appliances he sells. His sales last week totaled $18,000. Find his gross earnings.

$$0.04 \times \$18,000 = \$720$$

Elaine earns $250 weekly plus 6% of all sales over $1,500. Last week she made $9,500 worth of sales. Find her gross earnings.

$$\$9,500 - \$1,500 = \$8,000$$
$$\text{Commission} = 0.06 \times \$8,000 = \$480$$
$$\$250 + \$480 = \$730$$

Section 6.2

1 Find federal tax withholding per paycheck using IRS tax tables. (page 268)

1. Find the adjusted gross pay by subtracting the total qualified adjustments from the gross pay per pay period. Select the appropriate table according to the employee's filing status (single, married, and so on) and according to the type of pay period (weekly, biweekly, and so on).
2. Find the income row: in the rows labeled "If the wages are—," select the "At least" and "But less than" interval that includes the employee's adjusted gross pay for the pay period.
3. Find the allowances column: in the columns labeled "And the number of withholding allowances claimed is—," select the number of allowances the employee claims.
4. Find the cell where the income row and allowance column intersect. The correct tax is given in this cell.

Archy is married, has a gross weekly salary of $480, and claims two withholding allowances. Find his withholding tax.

Look in the first two columns of Figure 6-3 to find the range for $480. Move across to the column for two withholding allowances. The amount of federal tax to be withheld is $37.

Lexie Lagen is married and has a gross weekly salary of $655. He claims three withholding allowances and has $20 weekly deducted from his paycheck for a flexible benefits plan, which is exempted from federal income taxes. Find the amount of his withholding tax.

Adjusted gross income = $655 − $20 = $635

Find the range for $635 and three withholding allowances in Figure 6-3. The tax is $52.

2

Find
federal tax
withholding
per paycheck
using the IRS
percentage
method.
(page 269)

Find the percentage method income per paycheck.
1. Find the exempt-per-allowance amount: from the withholding allowance table (Figure 6-4), identify the amount exempt for one withholding allowance according to the type of pay period.
2. Find the total exempt amount: multiply the number of withholding allowances the employee claims by the exempt-per-allowance amount.
3. Subtract the total exempt amount from the employee's adjusted gross income for the pay period.

Edith Sailor has weekly gross earnings of $890. Find her percentage method income if she has no adjustments to income, is married, and claims three withholding allowances.

Use Figure 6-4 to find one withholding allowance for a weekly payroll period. Multiply by 3.

$55.77 × 3 = $167.31

Percentage method income = $890.00 − $167.31 = $722.69.

Find the federal tax withholding per paycheck using the IRS percentage method tables.
1. Select the appropriate table in Figure 6-5 according to the employee's filing status and the type of pay period.
2. Find the income row: In the rows labeled "If the amount of wages is . . .," select the "Over—" and "But not over—" interval that includes the employee's percentage method income for the pay period.
3. Find the cell where the income row and the column labeled "of excess over—" intersect, and subtract the amount given in this cell from the employee's percentage method income for the pay period.
4. Multiply the difference from step 3 by the percent given in the income row.
5. Add the product from step 4 to the amount given with the *percent* in the income row and amount of tax column.

Find the federal tax on Ruth's monthly income of $1,938. She is single and claims one exemption.

1 exemption = $241.67
$1,938 − $241.67 = $1,696.33
$1,696.33 is in the $221 to $2,392 range (Figure 6-5), so the amount of withholding tax is 15% of the amount over $221.

$1,696.33 − $221 = $1,475.33
$1,475.33 × 0.15 = $221.30

3

Find
Social
Security tax
and Medicare
tax per
paycheck.
(page 274)

For Social Security tax: Multiply 6.2% by the employee's gross pay, up to $80,400 annually. For Medicare tax: Multiply 1.45% by the employee's gross pay.

Find the Social Security and Medicare tax for Abbas Laknahour, who earns $938 every two weeks.

Social Security = $938 × 0.062 = $58.16
Medicare = $938 × 0.0145 = $13.60

Donna Shroyer earns $7,123 monthly. Find the Social Security and Medicare tax that will be deducted from her December paycheck.

Pay for first 11 months = $7,123 × 11 = $78,353
December pay subject to Social Security = $80,400 − $78,353 = $2,047
Social Security tax = $2,047 × 0.062 = $126.91
Medicare tax = $7,123 × 0.0145 = $103.28

4

Find
net earnings
per paycheck.
(page 276)

1. Find the gross pay for the pay period.
2. Find the adjustments-to-income deductions, such as retirement, insurance, and so on.
3. Find the Social Security tax and Medicare tax based on gross pay.
4. Find the federal tax withholding based on (a) or (b):
   (a) adjusted gross income (gross pay minus adjustments to income) using IRS tax tables;
   (b) percentage method income (adjusted gross income minus amount exempt for withholding allowances) using IRS percentage method tables.
5. Find other withholding taxes, such as local or state taxes.
6. Find the sum of all deductions from steps 2–5, and subtract the sum from the gross pay.

Beth Cooley's gross weekly earnings are $588. Four percent of her gross earnings is deducted for her nonexempt retirement fund and $27.48 is deducted for insurance. Find her net earnings if Beth is married and claims three withholding allowances.

Retirement fund = $588 × $0.04 = $23.52
Withholding tax = $44.00 (from Figure 6-3)
Social Security = $588 × 0.062 = $36.46
Medicare = $588 × 0.0145 = $8.53
Total deductions = $23.52 + $27.48 + $44.00 + $36.46 + $8.53 = $139.99
Net earnings = $588 − $139.99 = $448.01

Section 6.3

1

Find an
employer's
total deposit
for withholding
tax, Social
Security tax,
and Medicare
tax per pay
period.
(page 278)

1. Find the withholding tax deposit: from employee payroll records, find the total withholding tax for all employees for the pay period.
2. Find the Social Security tax deposit: find the total Social Security tax for all employees for the pay period and multiply this total by 2 to include the employer's matching tax.
3. Find the Medicare tax deposit: find the total Medicare tax for all employees for the pay period and multiply this total by 2.
4. Add the withholding tax deposit, Social Security tax deposit, and Medicare tax deposit.

Determine the employer's total deposit.

Employee	Gross Earnings	Withholding	Social Security	Medicare	Net Earnings
Davis, T. (2)	$485.00	$37.00	$30.07	$7.03	$410.90
Dobbins, L. (0)	632.00	77.00	39.18	9.16	506.66
Harris, M. (2)	590.00	54.00	36.58	8.56	490.86
Totals	$1,707.00	$168.00	$105.83	$24.75	$1,408.42

Employer's tax deposit = $168 + (2 × 105.83) + (2 × 24.75) = $429.16

2 Find an employer's SUTA tax and FUTA tax due for a quarter. (page 279)

Find the SUTA tax due for a quarter.
1. For each employee, multiply 5.4% or the appropriate rate by the employee's cumulative earnings for the quarter (up to $7,000 annually).
2. Add the SUTA tax owed on all employees.

Kim Brown has three employees who each earn $8,250 in the first three months of the year. How much SUTA tax should Kim pay for the first quarter if the SUTA rate is 5.4% of the first $7,000 earnings?

$7,000 × 0.054 × 3 = $1,134

Kim should pay $1,134 in SUTA tax for the first quarter.

Find the FUTA tax due for a quarter.
1. For each employee:
   (a) If no SUTA tax is paid, multiply 6.2% by the employee's cumulative earnings for the quarter (up to $7,000 annually).
   (b) If at least 5.4% of the employee's cumulative earnings for the quarter (up to $7,000 annually) is paid as SUTA tax, multiply 0.8% by the employee's cumulative earnings for the quarter (up to $7,000 annually).
2. Add the FUTA tax owed on all employees for the quarter.
3. If the total from step 2 is less than $100, no FUTA tax is due for the quarter, but the total from step 2 must be added to the amount due for the next quarter.

How much FUTA tax should Kim pay for the three employees?

$7,000 × 0.008 × 3 = $168

WORDS TO KNOW

gross earnings (p. 262)
gross pay (p. 262)
net earnings (p. 262)
net pay (p. 262)
take-home pay (p. 262)
weekly (p. 262)
biweekly (p. 262)
semimonthly (p. 262)
monthly (p. 262)
salary (p. 262)
hourly rate (p. 263)
hourly wage (p. 263)
overtime rate (p. 263)
time and a half (p. 263)
regular pay (p. 263)

overtime pay (p. 263)
piecework rate (p. 264)
straight piecework rate (p. 264)
differential piece rate (p. 264)
escalating piece rate (p. 264)
commission (p. 265)
straight commission (p. 265)
salary plus commission (p. 265)
commission rate (p. 265)
quota (p. 265)
federal tax withholding (p. 267)
withholding allowance (p. 267)
exemption (p. 267)
employee's filing status (p. 268)
adjusted gross income (p. 269)

percentage method income (p. 269)
percentage method withholding (p. 272)
Federal Insurance Contribution Act (FICA) (p. 274)
Medicare tax (p. 274)
Social Security tax (p. 274)
Self-employment (SE) tax (p. 275)
federal unemployment (FUTA) tax (p. 279)
state unemployment (SUTA) tax (p. 279)

1. Anita Loyd works 45 hours in one week, is paid $8.98 per hour, and earns 1.5 times her hourly wage for all hours worked over 40 in a given week. Calculate Anita's gross pay using the method described in the chapter.

2. Calculate Anita Loyd's gross pay by multiplying the total number of hours worked by the hourly rate and multiplying the hours over 40 by 0.5 the hourly rate. Compare this gross pay to the gross pay found in exercise 1.

3. Explain why the methods for calculating gross pay in exercises 1 and 2 are mathematically equivalent.

4. Most businesses prefer to use the method used in exercise 1 to calculate gross pay. Discuss reasons for this preference.

5. If a person is paid weekly and is married, what annual salary range causes the person's salary to fall in the "28% bracket" for withholding purposes?

6. Compare the annual salary range found in exercise 5 with the annual salary range for a person who is paid biweekly, is married, and whose salary is in the "28% bracket."

7. Predict the annual salary range a married person who is paid semimonthly would need to earn to fall in the "28% bracket." Use Table 3 of Figure 6-5 to verify or refute your prediction.

8. Use exercises 5, 6, and 7 to make a general statement about the amount of withholding tax on an annual salary for the various types of pay periods. To what can you attribute any differences you noted?

9. Many people think that if an increase in earnings moves their salary to a higher tax bracket, their entire salary will be taxed at the higher rate. Is this true? Give an example to justify your answer.

10. Shaneka Jones earns $92,520 and is paid semimonthly. Her last pay stub for the year shows $239.01 is deducted for Social Security and $55.90 is deducted for Medicare. Should she call her payroll office for a correction? If so, what would that correction be?

Section 6.1

1. Brian Williams is a salaried employee who earns $95,256 and is paid monthly. What is his pay each payroll period?

2. Arsella Gallagher earns a salary of $63,552 and is paid semimonthly. What is her gross salary for each pay period?

3. Varonia Reed is paid a weekly salary of $1,036. What is her annual salary?

4. John Edmonds is paid a biweekly salary of $1,398. What is his annual salary?

5. Melanie Michael has a salaried job. She earns $425 a week. One week she worked 46 hours. Find her gross earnings for the week.

6. Fran Coley earns $896 biweekly on a salaried job. If she works 89 hours in one pay period, how much does she earn?

7. Glenda Chaille worked 27 hours in one week at $9.45 per hour. Find her gross earnings.

8. Robert Stout worked 40 hours at $12 per hour. Find his gross earnings for the week.

9. Susan Wood worked 52 hours in a week. She was paid at the hourly rate of $6.50 with time and a half for overtime. Find her gross earnings.

10. Leslie Jinkins worked a total of 58 hours in one week. Of these hours, he was paid for 8 hours at the overtime rate of 1.5 times his hourly wage, and for 10 hours at the holiday overtime rate of 2 times his hourly wage. Find his gross earnings for the week if his hourly wage is $14.95.

11. Ronald James is paid 1.5 times his hourly wage for all hours worked in a week exceeding 40. He worked 52 hours and earns $8.50 per hour. Calculate his gross pay.

12. Mike Kelly earns $21.30 per hour in his job as a chemical technician. One week he works 38 hours. What is his gross pay for the week?

Find the gross earnings of each employee in Table 6-1. Use a 40-hour regular week and 1.5 times regular rate for overtime.

Table 6–1

| Employee | Hours Worked | | | | | | | Hourly Wage | Regular Hours | Regular Pay | Overtime Hours | Overtime Pay | Gross Pay |
	M	T	W	T	F	S	S						
13. Allen, H.	8	9	8	7	10	4	0	$9.86					
14. Brown, J.	4	6	8	9	9	5	0	$10.43					
15. Pick, J.	8	8	8	8	8	4	0	$9.87					
16. Sayer, C.	9	10	8	9	11	9	0	$8.45					
17. Lovet, L.	8	8	8	8	0	0	0	$7.15					
18. Stacy, C.	8	8	8	8	8	0	0	$8.21					

Complete the payroll records (Table 6-2) for employees who earn time and a half for more than 40 hours on Monday through Friday, time and a half on Saturday, and double time on Sunday.

Table 6-2

| Employee | Hours Worked | | | | | | | Regular Hours | Hourly Wage | Regular Pay | Time and a Half Hours | Time and a Half Pay | Double Time Hours | Double Time Pay | Gross Earnings |
	M	T	W	T	F	S	S								
19. Mitze, A.	8	8	4	3	8	2	4		$8.00						
20. James, Q.	8	8	8	8	8	0	4		$11.38						
21. Adams, A.	5	6	8	11	10	9	5		$9.75						
22. Smith, M.	8	8	8	8	8	8	8		$12.17						

23. For sewing buttons on shirts, employees are paid $0.20 a shirt. Marty Hughes completes an average of 500 shirts a day. Find her average gross weekly earnings for a five-day week.

24. Employees are paid $3.50 per piece for a certain job. In a week's time, Maria Sanchez produced a total of 168 pieces. Find her gross earnings for the week.

Use the Widgets International differential piece rates to find the gross weekly earnings for employees who twisted the number of widgets in a week.

Widgets per Week	Pay Per Widget
1–150	$2.60
151–300	$2.82
301 and over	$2.99

25. 148 widgets

26. 158 widgets

27. 257 widgets

28. 325 widgets

29. Patsy Hilliard is paid 5% commission on sales of $18,200. Find her gross pay.

30. Ada Shotwell, a computer salesperson, is paid 4% commission for all sales. If she needs a monthly income of $1,500, find the monthly sales volume she must meet.

31. Pamela Slagg sells cars and earns 5% commission on $62,000 in car sales. Find her gross pay on this sale.

32. Find the gross pay of Minda Waller, a yarn company sales representative, who earns 5% of her total sales of $38,200.

33. Find the gross pay of Jerome Ware, a salesperson who receives a 10% commission on $8,000 in sales.

34. Jewel Warner, a salesperson, is paid $200 plus 3% of all sales. Find her gross income if her sales are $8,000.

35. William Kelly is a real estate salesperson and receives a 6% commission on the sale of a piece of property for $130,000. Find his gross pay for this sale.

36. Debra Young sells $250,000 in equipment. At a 7% straight commission, calculate the gross earnings.

37. Vincent Ores is paid a salary of $400 plus 8% of sales. Calculate the gross income if new sales are $9,890.

38. Cassie Lyons earns $350 plus 7% commission on all sales over $2,000. What are the gross earnings if sales for a week are $3,276?

39. Find the gross earnings if Juanita Wilson earns $275 plus 2% of all sales over $3,000 and the sales for a week are $5,982.

40. Dieter Tillman is paid $2,000 plus 5% of the total sales volume. If he sold $3,000 in merchandise, find the gross earnings.

Section 6.2

Use Figure 6-3 (weekly payroll period) to find the amount of federal tax withholding for the gross earnings of the following married persons with the indicated number of withholding allowances.

41. $525, four allowances

42. $724, two allowances

43. $475, zero allowances

44. $695, three allowances

45. $495, three allowances

46. $728, two allowances

Use Figures 6-4 and 6-5 and the percentage method tables to find the amount of federal income tax to be withheld from the gross earnings of married persons who are paid weekly and have the indicated number of withholding allowances.

47. $755, five allowances

48. $620, eight allowances

49. $2,215, two allowances

50. $983, four allowances

51. $875, two allowances

52. $2,020, three allowances

Use the percentage method tables to find the Social Security and Medicare taxes.

53. Weekly gross income of $842

54. Monthly gross income of $3,500

55. Yearly gross income of $24,000

56. Semimonthly gross income of $1,226

57. Yearly gross income of $28,225

58. Yearly gross income of $78,500

Complete the payroll register in Table 6-3. All employees are married and paid weekly, and the number of withholding allowances that each person claims is in parentheses. Use Figure 6-3 to find the withholding tax.

Table 6-3

Employee and Withholding Allowances	Gross Earnings	Withholding Tax	Social Security	Medicare	Other Nonexempt Deductions	Total Deductions	Net Earnings
59. Abrams (3)	$525.00				$21.94		
60. Cowgill (0)	$582.40				$15.21		
61. Mason (4)	$735.04				$0		
62. Sachs (2)	$476.28				$19.38		

63. Irene Gamble earns $585 weekly. Deductions are as follows: withholding tax, $44; Social Security tax, $36.27; Medicare, $8.48; nonexempt retirement, $24.95; nonexempt insurance, $8.45. Find the total deductions and net income.

64. Anita Loyd earns $983 semimonthly. She is single and claims no withholding allowances. She also pays $12.83 each pay period for nonexempt health insurance. What is her net pay?

Section 6.3

65. Use the payroll register for exercises 59–62 to determine the employer's total withholding, Social Security, and Medicare tax deposit.

66. How much tax should the employer deposit for Irene Gamble in exercise 63?

Vince Brimaldi earned $32,876 last year. The state unemployment tax is 5.4% of the first $7,000 earned in a year.

67. How much SUTA tax must Vince's employer pay for him if the employer pays at the 5.4% rate?

68. How much FUTA tax must Vince's employer pay?

Elisa Marus has three employees who earn $2,500, $1,980, and $3,200 monthly.

69. How much SUTA tax will she need to pay at the end of the first quarter if the SUTA tax rate is 5.4%?

70. How much FUTA tax is due with the first payment and when must it be paid?

Spreadsheet Exercises

71. In most spreadsheet software, percent and decimal equivalents of percents are interchangeable. That is, you may enter a percent and the program will automatically calculate with the decimal equivalent. The result may then be displayed as a percent or decimal equivalent by appropriate formatting functions. In the writing the formulas use the decimal equivalent notation.

(a) Write formulas to complete the spreadsheet to give the Social Security tax for the employees of Starbrite Cleaners.

(b) Write formulas to complete the spreadsheet to give the Medicare tax withheld from each person's payroll.

(c) Write formulas to complete the spreadsheet to give the Total Deductions for the employees at Starbrite Cleaners.

(d) Write formulas to complete the spreadsheet to give the Net Earnings for the employees at Starbrite Cleaners.

72. Complete the spreadsheet using the formulas.

	A	B	C	D	E	F	G	H
1			Starbrite Cleaners		Week of January 18			
2	Employee	Gross Earnings	Withholding tax	SS tax	Medicare	Nonexempt	Total Ded	Net Earnings
3	Adams, K.	$885.00	$137.00			$62.00		
4	Bethel, H.	$752.00	$133.00			$48.00		
5	Duenhaur, R.	$927.00	$180.00			$53.00		
6	Laughlin, J.	$596.00	$61.00			$20.00		
7	Markle, S.	$680.00	$84.00			$75.00		
8	Newton, Q.	$620.00	$75.00			$0.00		
9	Sewell, A.	$660.00	$31.00			$56.00		
10	Thomas, P.	$660.00	$73.00			$24.00		
11	Underwood, J	$620.00	$42.00			$36.00		

Challenge Problem

73. Complete the following time card for Janice Anderson. She earns time and a half overtime when she works more than eight hours on a weekday or on Saturday. She earns double time on Sundays and holidays. Calculate Janice's net pay if she earns $9.75 per hour, is single, and claims one allowance.

WEEKLY TIME CARD
CHD Company

Name *Janice Anderson* SS# *000-00-0000*

Pay for period ending

DATE	IN	OUT	IN	OUT	Total Regular Hours	Total Overtime Hours
M 8/4	7:00	11:00	11:30	7:30		
Tu 8/5	8:00	12:00	12:30	4:30		
W 8/6	8:00	12:00	12:30	4:30		
Th 8/7	7:00	11:00	12:30	5:30		
F 8/8	8:00	12:00	12:30	4:30		
Sa 8/9	7:00	12:00				
Su 8/10						

	HOURS	RATE	GROSS PAY
Regular			
Overtime (1.5X)			
Overtime (2X)			
Total			

Figure 6-6

---

1. Cheryl Douglas works 43 hours in a week for a salary of $498 per week. What are Cheryl's gross weekly earnings?

2. June Jackson earns $7.59 an hour. Find her gross earnings if she worked 46 hours (time and a half for overtime over 40 hours).

3. Willy Bell checks wrappers on cans in a cannery. He receives $0.07 for each case of cans. If he checks 1,400 cases on an average day, find his gross weekly salary. (A work week is five days.)

4. Stacey Ellis is paid at the following differential piece rate: 1–100, $1.58; 101–250, $1.72; 251 and up, $1.94. Find her gross earnings for completing 475 pieces.

5. Dorothy Ford, who sells restaurant supplies, works on 6% commission. If her sales for a week are $14,200, find her gross earnings.

6. Carlo Mason works on 5% commission. If he sells $7,500 in merchandise, find his gross earnings.

7. Find the gross earnings of Sallie Johnson who receives a 9% commission and whose sales totaled $5,800.

8. Find the Social Security tax (at 6.2%) and the Medicare tax (at 1.45%) for Anna Jones, whose gross earnings are $213.86. Round to the nearest cent.

9. Find the Social Security and Medicare tax for Michele Cottrell, whose gross earnings are $761.25.

10. How much income tax should be withheld for Terry McLean, a married employee who earns $486 weekly and claims two allowances? (Use Figure 6-3.)

11. Use Figure 6-3 to find the federal income tax paid by Charlotte Jordan, who is married with four exemptions, if her weekly gross earnings are $576.

12. Jo Ann Maxwell has gross earnings of $418. She has a 3% nonexempt retirement deduction and pays $21 for insurance. What is the total of these deductions?

13. If LaQuita White had net earnings of $877.58 and total deductions of $261.32, find her gross earnings.

14. Rita Rainey has a gross income of $481.53 and total deductions of $79.15. Find the net earnings.

Complete the weekly register for married employees. The number of each person's allowances is listed after each name. Round to the nearest cent. Use Figure 6-3.

Table 6-4

Employee (Exemptions)	Gross Earnings	Social Security	Medicare	Withholding Tax	Other Nonexempt Deductions	Net Earnings
15. Jackson (0)	$735.00				$25.12	
16. Love (1)	673.80				12.87	
17. Chow (2)	492.17				0	
18. Ferrante (3)	577.15				4.88	
19. Towns (4)	610.13				0	

20. How much SUTA tax must Anaston, Inc., pay to the state for a part-time employee who earns $5,290 in the first quarter? The SUTA tax rate is 5.4% of the wages.

21. How much SUTA tax must University Dry Cleaners pay to the state for an employee who earns $38,200?

22. How much FUTA tax must University Dry Cleaners pay to the state for the employee in exercise 21? The FUTA tax rate is 6.2% of the first $7,000 minus the SUTA tax.

23. How much SUTA tax does the employee in exercise 21 pay?

24. How much withholding, Social Security, and Medicare tax should the employer deposit for the payroll in exercises 15–19?

25. Describe the difference between gross earnings and net earnings.

CHAPTER 6 SELF-CHECK SOLUTIONS

Self-Check 6.1

1. $24,804 ÷ 52 = $477.00

2. $27,988 ÷ 26 = $1,076.46

3. $52,980 ÷ 12 = $4,415.00

4. $38,184 ÷ 24 = $1,591.00

5. 40 × $7.60 = $304 (regular pay)
7 × $7.60 × 1.5 =+ $ 79.80 (overtime pay)
         $383.80 (gross earnings)

6. 40 × $8.25 = $330
4 × $8.25 × 1.5 = +$ 49.50
         $379.50

7. 40 × $15.90 = $636.00
7 × $15.90 × 1.5 = + $166.95
         $802.95

8. Total buckles = 132 + 134 + 138 + 134 + 130 = 668
Gross earnings = 668 × $0.84 = $561.12

9. First 100 boxes: $1.88 × 100 = $188
Last 89 boxes: $2.08 × 89 = + $185.12
         $373.12 (gross earnings)

10. $9 + 11 + 10 + 12 + 4 = 46$
$46 \times \$8.13 = \$373.98$

11. $P = RB$
$P = 0.06 \times \$8,972$
$P = \$538.32$ (gross earnings)

12. $\$452,493 \times 0.035 = \$15,837.26$

13. $\$7,821 - \$2,000 = \$5,821$ (amount on which commission is paid)
$P = RB$
$P = 0.05 \times \$5,821$
$P = \$291.05$
$\$291.05 + \$275 = \$566.05$ (gross earnings)

14. $\$145,938 - \$2,000 = \$143,938$
$\$143,938 \times 0.03 = \$4,318.14$

Self-Check 6.2

1. Find the table for Married Persons—Weekly Payroll Period. Move down the *at least* column to the amount $480. Then move across to the column marked 3 at the top. The amount is $29.

2. $\$583 - \$32 = \$551$. Use the table for Married Persons—Weekly Payroll Period. Move down the *at least* column to $550. Move across to the column marked 2 at the top. The amount is $48.

3. Use the table for Single Persons—Semimonthly Payroll Period. Move down the *at least* column to $1,420. Move across to the column marked 2 at the top. The amount is $162.

4. $\$1,698 - \$100 = \$1,598$ (adjusted gross income)
Use Figure 6-4 to find the amount for one withholding allowance for a semimonthly payroll. The amount is $120.83.
$\$120.83 \times 3 = \$362.49$ (total withholding allowance).
Percentage method income = $\$1,598.00 - \$362.49 = \$1,235.51$
Use Table 3a in the percentage method tables. The tax is $162.90 plus 28% of excess over $1,196.
Excess over $1,196 = $\$1,235.51 - \$1,196 = \$39.51$
$\$39.51 \times 0.28 = \$11.06$
Withholding tax = $\$162.90 + \$39.51 = \$173.96$.

5. Using Figure 6-4 for a weekly salary of a single person with one withholding allowance, we see that the amount is $55.77. We subtract $55.77 from gross pay, $580, and get $524.23; this is the taxable income. Look at Table 1a in Figure 6-5. The tax is 15% of the excess amount over $51, so you subtract $51 from $524.23 and get $473.23, and multiply that times 15%: $\$473.23 \times 0.15 = \$70.98$. The tax is $70.98.

6. From Figure 6-4 we get $241.67 for each withholding allowance. She has one allowance.
Percentage method income = $\$4,598 - \$241.67 = \$4,356.33$
Use Table 4b in tables for percentage method. The tax is $543.00 plus 28% of excess over $4,158.00.
$\$4,356.33 - \$4,158.00 = \$198.33$
$\$198.33 \times 0.28 = \$55.53$
Withholding tax = $\$543.00 + \$55.53 = \$598.53$

7. Social Security tax = $\$2,583 \times 0.062 = \$160.15$
Medicare tax = $\$2,583 \times 0.0145 = \$37.45$

8. Social Security tax = $\$1,020 \times 0.062 = \$63.24$
Medicare tax = $\$1,020 \times 0.0145 = \$14.79$

9. Social Security tax during this tax year is paid on the first $80,400 earned. Rodney's monthly salary is $80,608 ÷ 12 = $6,717.33. Earnings for the first eleven months are $\$6,717.33 \times 11 = \$73,890.67$. Rodney must pay Social Security on the portion of his December check that would make his earnings equal $80,400. That is, $\$80,400 - \$73,890.67 = \$6,509.33$
Social Security tax for December = $\$6,509.33 \times 0.062 = \$403.58$
Medicare tax for December = $\$6,717.33 \times 0.0145 = \$97.40$

10. Use Figure 6-4 to find $241.67 for each withholding allowance for monthly payroll.
Total withholding allowance = $\$241.67 \times 4 = \$966.68$
Percentage method income = $\$5,291 - \$966.68 = \$4,324.32$
Use Table 4b in tables for percentage method of withholding to find withholding tax. The tax is $543 plus 28% of excess over $4,158.
Excess = $\$4,324.32 - \$4,158 = \$166.32$
$\$166.32 \times 0.28 = \$46.57$
Total withholding tax = $\$543 + \$46.57 = \$589.57$
Social Security = $\$5,291 \times 0.062 = \$328.04$
Medicare = $\$5,291 \times 0.0145 = \$76.72$
Total deductions = $\$589.57 + \$328.04 + \$76.72 + \$52.83 = \$1,047.16$
Net earnings = $\$5,291 - \$1,047.16 = \$4,243.84$

11. Since Shirley claims zero withholding allowances, we skip Figure 6-4 and use her full salary to calculate the amount of withholding. Use Table 2a of percentage method of withholding to find the withholding tax. The tax is $150.30 plus 28% of excess over $1,104.

Excess = $1,319 − $1,104 = $215

$215 × 0.28 = $60.20

Total withholding tax = $150.30 + $60.20= $210.50

Social Security = $1,319 × 0.062 = $81.78

Medicare = $1,319 × 0.0145 = $19.13

Retirement = $1,319 × 0.02 = $26.38

Total deductions = $210.50 + $81.78 + $19.13 + $26.38 + $22.80 = $360.59

Net earnings = $1,319 − $360.59 = $958.41

12. Use the withholding table for Married Persons— Weekly Payroll Period. Move down the *at least* column to $410 then move to the right to the column for 2 deductions. The amount of tax is $57.

Social Security = $615 × 0.062 = $38.13

Medicare = $615 × 0.0145 = $8.92

Nonexempt retirement = $615 × 0.03 = $18.45

Total deductions = $57 + $38.13 + $8.92 + $18.45 + $25.97 = $148.47

Net earnings = $615 − $148.47 = $466.53

Self-Check 6.3

1. Total Social Security and Medicare = $482 + $113 = $595

Employer's share of Social Security and Medicare = $595

Employer's tax deposit = $1,633 + (2 × $595) = $2,823

3. Total withholding = $376.00 + $255.00 + $179.00 = $810

Total Social Security = $118.11 + $99.08 + $88.72 = $305.91

Total Medicare = $27.62 + $23.17 + $20.75 = $71.54

Employer's deposit = $810.00 + [2 × ($305.91 + $71.54)] =

$810.00 + (2 × $377.45) = $1,564.90

2. Social Security and Medicare = $608 + $142 = $750

Employer's tax deposit = $1,661 + (2 × $750) = $3,161

4. Use the tax tables or percentage method tables to make a payroll chart for the employees.

	Filing Status/Allowances	Gross Earnings	Withholding	Social Security	Medicare
Employee 1	Single/1	$475	$55.23	$29.45	$6.89
Employee 2	Married/2	$450	$32.17	$27.90	$6.53
Manager	Married/1	$740	$84.03	$45.88	$10.73
Totals			$171.43	$103.23	$24.15

For *Employee 1,* use percentage method for withholding tax.

Figure 6-4 shows $55.77 for one withholding allowance.

Percentage method income = $475 − $55.77 = $419.23

Use Table 1a in percentage method tables. Tax is 15% of excess over $51.

$419.23 − $51.00 = $368.23

Withholding tax = $368.23 × 0.15 = $55.23

Social Security = $475 × 0.062 = $29.45

Medicare = $375 × 0.0145 = $6.89

For *Employee 2,* withholding allowances = $55.77 × 2 = $111.54.

Percentage method income = $450 − $111.54= $338.46

Use Table 1b in percentage method tables. Tax is 15% of excess over $124.

$338.46 − $124 = $214.46

Withholding tax = $214.46 × 0.15 = $32.17

Social Security = $450 × 0.062 = $27.90

Medicare = $450 × 0.0145 = $6.53

For *Manager,* withholding allowance = $55.77

Percentage method income = $740 − $55.77 = $684.23

Use Table 1b in percentage method tables. Tax is 15% of excess over $124.

$684.23 − $124 = $560.23

Withholding tax = $560.23 × 0.15 = $84.03

Social Security = $740 × 0.062 = $45.88

Medicare = $740 \times 0.0145 = $10.73

Employer's withholding tax deposit = $55.23 + $32.17 + $84.03 = $171.43

Social Security tax deposit = 2 × ($29.45 + $27.90 + $45.88) = 2 × $103.23 = $206.46

Medicare tax deposit = 2 × ($6.89 + $6.53 + $10.73) = 2 × $24.15 = $48.30

5. $7,000 × 0.054 = $378.00

6. $7,000 × 0.008 = $56.00

7.

Pay Period	Employee 1 Accumulated Salary	FUTA Tax	Employee 2 Accumulated Salary	FUTA Tax	Employee 3 Accumulated Salary	FUTA Tax
Jan 15	745	5.96	780	6.24	1,030	8.24
Jan 31	1,490	5.96	1,560	6.24	2,060	8.24
Feb 15	2,235	5.96	2,340	6.24	3,090	8.24
Feb 28	2,980	5.96	3,120	6.24	4,120	8.24
Mar 15	3,725	5.96	3,900	6.24	5,150	8.24
Mar 31	4,470	5.96	4,680	6.24	6,180	8.24

First Quarter Totals = $35.76 + $37.44 + $49.44 = $122.64

Payment of $122.64 must be deposited by April 30.

Pay Period	Employee 1 Accumulated Salary	FUTA Tax	Employee 2 Accumulated Salary	FUTA Tax	Employee 3 Accumulated Salary	FUTA Tax
April 15	5,215	5.96	5,460	6.24	7,000	6.56
April 30	5,960	5.96	6,240	6.24		
May 15	6,705	5.96	7,000	6.08		
May 31	7,000	2.36				
June 15						
June 30						

7,000 − 6,705 = 295;   7,000 − 6,240 = 760;   7,000 − 6,180 = 820

$295 × 0.008 = $2.36; $760 × 0.008 = $6.08; $820 × 0.008 = 6.56

Second Quarter Totals = $20.24 + $18.56 + $6.56 = $45.36

Payment of $45.36 must be deposited by January 31 of the next year since it does not exceed $100.

Trade and Cash Discounts

7.1 Net Price and the Trade Discount

1 Find the trade discount using a single trade discount rate; find the net price using the trade discount.

2 Find the net price using the complement of the single trade discount rate.

7.2 Net Price and the Trade Discount Series

1 Find the net price, applying a trade discount series and using the net decimal equivalent.

2 Find the trade discount, applying a trade discount series and using the single discount equivalent.

7.3 Net Amount and the Cash Discount

1 Find the cash discount and the net amount using ordinary dating terms.

2 Interpret and apply end-of-month (EOM) terms.

3 Interpret and apply receipt-of-goods (ROG) terms.

4 Find the amount credited and the outstanding balance from partial payments.

5 Interpret freight terms.

Good Decisions through Teamwork

Ebony Products offers its customers credit terms of 4/15 n/30 with a 1.5% service charge on late payments. The customer pays all shipping charges. Of the $300,000 monthly sales, typically 25% are paid within the cash discount period and 10% are assessed the late fee.

A consulting firm has suggested that a free shipping incentive for all merchandise and cash discount terms of 2/15 n/30 would improve Ebony's cash flow (amount of money they receive each month). Research shows that free shipping typically improves total sales by 10%.

With your team members, analyze the financial impact of changing the shipping and cash discount policies and decide what the company should do. Prepare a summary report and make an oral presentation to the class.

A discount is money deducted from money owed. Manufacturers and distributors give *trade discounts* as incentives for a sale and *cash discounts* as incentives for paying promptly. Discounts are usually established by *discount rates,* given in percent or decimal form, based on the money owed. The discount, then, is a percentage of the money owed. In learning about discounts, you will continually apply the percentage formula $P = RB$. You will also learn to interpret and apply various sales terms to determine the dates that cash discounts are allowed.

7.1 Net Price and the Trade Discount

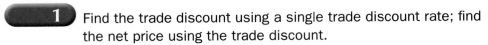

1 Find the trade discount using a single trade discount rate; find the net price using the trade discount.

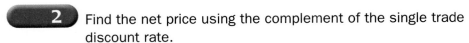

2 Find the net price using the complement of the single trade discount rate.

Most products go from the manufacturer to the consumer by way of the wholesale merchant (wholesaler or distributor) and the retail merchant (retailer).

Manufacturer
↓
Wholesaler
↓
Retailer
↓
Consumer

Manufacturers often describe each of their products in a book or catalog that is made available to wholesalers or retailers. In such catalogs, manufacturers suggest a price at which each product should be sold to the consumer. This price is called the **suggested retail price,** the **catalog price,** or, most commonly, the **list price.**

When a manufacturer sells an item to the wholesaler, the manufacturer deducts a certain amount from the list price of the item. The amount deducted is called the **trade discount.** The wholesaler pays the **net price,** which is the difference between the list price and the trade discount. Likewise, the wholesaler discounts the list price when selling to the retailer. The discount rate that the wholesaler gives the retailer is smaller than the discount rate that the manufacturer gives the wholesaler. The consumer pays the list price.

The trade discount is not usually stated in the published catalog. Instead, the wholesaler or retailer calculates it using the list price and the **discount rate.** The discount rate is a *percent* of the list price.

The manufacturer makes available lists of discount rates for all items in the catalog. The discount rates vary considerably depending on such factors as the customer class, the season, the condition of the economy, whether a product is being discontinued, and the manufacturer's efforts to encourage larger purchases. Each time the discount rate changes, the manufacturer updates the listing. Each new discount rate applies to the original list price in the catalog.

For a variety of reasons, manufacturers may establish "discounts on discounts." This situation, known as *discount series,* is covered in the next section. For now, we concentrate on the trade discount allowed by a **single discount rate.**

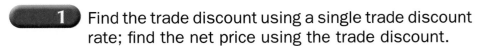

1 Find the trade discount using a single trade discount rate; find the net price using the trade discount.

To find the trade discount for an item when the list price and a single discount rate are given, we use

Percentage (part) = rate (percent) × base (whole) or $P = R \times B$

In this case, percentage is the trade discount T, rate is the single trade discount rate R, and the base is the list price L.

$$P = R \times B$$
$$T = R \times L$$

 **HOW TO** **Find the Trade Discount Using a Single Trade Discount Rate**

Multiply the list price by the single trade discount rate.

Trade discount = single trade discount rate × list price

$T = RL$

Since the trade discount is deducted from the list price to get the net price, once you know the trade discount, you can calculate the net price.

 HOW TO **Find the Net Price Using the Trade Discount**

Subtract the trade discount from the list price.

Net price = list price − trade discount

$N = L - T$

EXAMPLE The list price of a refrigerator is $1,200. Young's Appliance Store can buy the refrigerator at the list price less 20%.

(a) Find the trade discount.
(b) Find the net price of the refrigerator.

(a) Trade discount = single trade discount rate × list price

$$20\% \times \$1,200 = 0.20 \times \$1,200$$
$$= \$240$$

Discount rate is 20%; list price is $1,200.
Change the percent to a decimal.
Multiply.

The trade discount is $240.

(b) Net price = list price − trade discount

$$= \$1,200 - \$240$$

List price is $1,200; trade discount is $240.

$$= \$960$$

The net price is $960.

 Find the net price using the complement of the single trade discount rate.

Another method for calculating the net price uses the *complements* of percents. The **complement** of a percent is the difference between that percent and 100%. For example, the complement of 35% is 65%, since $100\% - 35\% = 65\%$. The complement of 20% is 80% because $100\% - 20\% = 80\%$.

The complement of the single trade discount rate can be used to find the net price. Here's why. Say the single trade discount rate is 25%. We know that

$$\text{Net price} = \text{list price} - \text{trade discount}$$

Because the trade discount is 25% of the list price, using percents we can write this formula as

$$\text{Net price} = 100\% \text{ of list price} - 25\% \text{ of list price}$$

The right side of this equation is the difference between two products, and each product includes the list price. An equivalent equation finds the difference between the two percents, then multiplies the difference by the list price.

$$\text{Net price} = (100\% - 25\%) \times \text{list price}$$

But 100% − 25% is the *complement* of the single trade discount rate. So,

$$\text{Net price} = \text{complement of single trade discount rate} \times \text{list price}$$

This is the complement formula for finding the net price given the single trade discount rate, without having first to calculate the trade discount.

Since the complement is a percent, it is a rate. You might think of the complement as the "net price rate." The single trade discount rate is used to calculate the amount the retailer *does not* pay: the trade discount; the complement of the single trade discount rate is used to calculate the amount the retailer *does* pay: the net price.

HOW TO **Find the Net Price Using the Complement of the Single Trade Discount Rate**

> **Find the net price of a computer that lists for $3,200 with a trade discount of 35%.**
> 100% − 35% = 65%

1. Find the complement: subtract the single trade discount rate from 100%.

Complement of single trade discount rate = 100% − single trade discount rate

2. Multiply the list price by the complement of the single trade discount rate.

> Net price = 0.65 ($3,200)
> = $2,080

Net price = complement of single trade discount rate × list price

OR

Net Price = (100 % − single trade discount rate) × list price

$N = CL$ or $N = (100\% - R)L$

where N = net price, C = complement of single trade discount rate, R = single discount rate, and L = list price.

 TIP! **To summarize the concept of trade discounts,**

Trade discount = amount list price is reduced
= part of list price you *do not* pay

Net price = part of list price you *do* pay

EXAMPLE   Mays' Stationery Store buys 300 pens at $0.30 each, 200 legal pads at $0.60 each, and 100 boxes of paper clips at $0.90 each. The single trade discount rate for the order is 12%. Find the net price of the order.

$$300 \times \$0.30 = \$\ 90$$ **Find the list price of the pens.**

$$200 \times \$0.60 = \$120$$ **Find the list price of the legal pads.**

$$100 \times \$0.90 = \underline{\$\ 90}$$ **Find the list price of the paper clips.**
$$\$300$$ **Add to find the total list price.**

Net price = (100% − single trade discount rate) × list price

$$= (100\% - 12\%) \times \$300$$ **The single trade discount rate is 12%; the list price is $300.**

$$= 88\% \times \$300$$ **The complement of 12% is 88%.**

$$= 0.88 \times \$300$$ **Write 88% as a decimal.**

$$= \$264$$ **Multiply.**

The net price is $264.

SELF-CHECK 7.1

1. Find the trade discount on a computer that lists for $400 if a discount rate of 30% is offered.

2. Find the net price of a printer if the list price is $400 and a single discount rate of 30% is offered.

3. Calculate the trade discount for 20 boxes of computer paper if the unit price is $14.67 and a single trade discount rate of 20% is allowed.

4. Calculate the trade discount for 30 cases of antifreeze coolant if each case contains 6 one-gallon units that cost $2.18 per gallon and a single trade discount rate of 18% is allowed.

5. Calculate the net price for the 20 boxes of computer paper in exercise 3.

6. Calculate the net price for the 30 cases of antifreeze coolant in exercise 4.

2

7. Use the complement method to calculate the net price for the 20 boxes of computer paper in exercise 3. Compare this net price with the net price found in exercise 5.

8. Use the complement method to calculate the net price for the 30 cases of antifreeze coolant in exercise 4. Compare this net price with the net price found in exercise 6.

9. Which method of calculating net price do you prefer? Why?

10. If you were writing a spreadsheet program to calculate the net price for several items and you were not interested in showing the trade discount, which method would you be likely to use? Why?

11. Complete invoice 2501 below, finding the net price using the single trade discount rate.

| Invoice No. 2501 |
| October 15, 20XX |

Qty.	Item	Unit Price	List Price
15	Notebooks	$1.50	
10	Looseleaf paper	0.89	
30	Ballpoint pens	0.79	
	Total list price		
	40% trade discount		
	Net price		

12. Verify that the net price calculated in exercise 11 is correct by recalculating the net price using the complement of the single trade discount rate.

7.2 Net Price and the Trade Discount Series

1 Find the net price, applying a trade discount series and using the net decimal equivalent.

2 Find the trade discount, applying a trade discount series and using the single discount equivalent.

Sometimes a manufacturer wants to promote a particular item or encourage additional business from a buyer. Also, buyers may be entitled to additional discounts as a result of buying large quantities. In such cases, the manufacturer may offer additional discounts that are deducted one after another from the list price. Such discounts are called a **trade discount series.** An example of a discount series is $400 (list price) with a discount series of 20/10/5 (discount rates). That is, a discount of 20% is allowed off the list price, a discount of 10% is allowed off the amount that was left after the first discount, and a discount of 5% is allowed off the amount that was left after the second discount. It *does not* mean a total discount of 35% is allowed on the original list price.

One way to calculate the net price is to make a series of calculations:

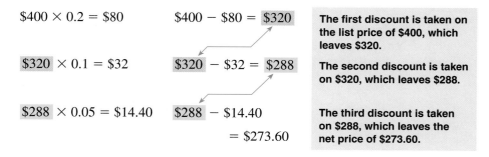

$400 \times 0.2 = \$80$ $400 - \$80 = \boxed{\$320}$ **The first discount is taken on the list price of $400, which leaves $320.**

$\boxed{\$320} \times 0.1 = \$32$ $\boxed{\$320} - \$32 = \boxed{\$288}$ **The second discount is taken on $320, which leaves $288.**

$\boxed{\$288} \times 0.05 = \$14.40$ $\boxed{\$288} - \$14.40 = \$273.60$ **The third discount is taken on $288, which leaves the net price of $273.60.**

Thus, the net price of a $400 order with a discount series of 20/10/5 is $273.60.

It is time consuming to calculate a trade discount series this way. The business world uses a faster way of calculating the net price of a purchase when a series discount is taken.

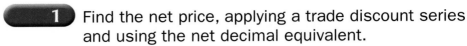

1 Find the net price, applying a trade discount series and using the net decimal equivalent.

Complements are used to find net prices directly. For the $400 purchase with discounts of 20/10/5, the net price after the first discount is 80% of $400 since 100% − 20% = 80%.

$$0.8 \times 400 = \boxed{\$320}$$

The net price after the second discount is 90% of $320.

$$0.9 \times \boxed{\$320} = \$288$$

The net price after the third discount is 95% of $\boxed{\$288}$.

$$0.95 \times \boxed{\$288} = \$273.60$$

To condense this process, the decimal equivalents of the complements of the discount rates can be multiplied to give a single decimal, the "net price rate." This single decimal is called the **net decimal equivalent.**

? HOW TO Find Net Price Using the Net Decimal Equivalent of a Trade Discount Series

Find the net price of a copy machine if the list price is $1,830 with a series discount of 10/10.
0.9 (0.9) = 0.81

1. Find the net decimal equivalent: multiply the decimal form of the complement of each trade discount rate in the series.

Net decimal equivalent = product of complements of the trade discount rates.

2. Multiply the list price by the net decimal equivalent.

Net price = 0.81 ($1,830)
Net price = $1,482.30

Net price = net decimal equivalent × list price

N = DL

EXAMPLE Find the net price of an order with a list price of $600 and a trade discount series of 15/10/5.

$$100\% - 15\% = 85\% = \boxed{0.85}$$

$$100\% - 10\% = 90\% = \boxed{0.9}$$

$$100\% - 5\% = 95\% = \boxed{0.95}$$

Find the complement of each discount rate and write it as an equivalent decimal.

$$\boxed{0.85} \times 0.9 \times \boxed{0.95} = \boxed{0.72675}$$

Multiply the complements to find the net decimal equivalent.

Net price = net decimal equivalent × list price

$$= \boxed{0.72675} \times \$600$$

The net decimal equivalent is 0.72675; the list price is $600.

$$= \$436.05$$

The net price for a $600 order with a trade discount series of 15/10/5 is $436.05.

TIP! **A Trade Discount Series Does Not Add Up!**

The trade discount series of 20/10/5 is *not* equivalent to the single discount rate of 35% (which is the *sum* of 20%, 10%, and 5%). Look at an example worked correctly and incorrectly.

Example: Find the net price of an article listed at $100 with a discount of 20/10/5.

$$\text{Net price} = \text{net decimal equivalent} \times \text{list price}$$

$$= (0.8 \times 0.9 \times 0.95) \times \$100$$

$$= 0.684 \times \$100$$

$$= \$68.40$$

CORRECT

$$20\% + 10\% + 5\% = 35\%$$

$$\text{Net price} = \text{net decimal equivalent} \times \text{list price}$$

$$= (100\% - 35\%) \times \text{list price}$$

$$= 0.65 \times \$100$$

$$= \$65$$

INCORRECT

In a series of discounts, it is difficult to estimate the single discount rate equivalent. Look at the first example. In reality, three discounts are applied in turn. A 15% discount is taken off the original price, then the 10% discount is taken off the reduced price to give a further reduced price. Finally, a 5% discount is taken off the lowest price to give the final reduced price. The final reduced price is what percent of the original price?

Examine these facts.

$600.00	original amount
−436.05	reduced price
$163.95	trade discount

$436.05 is what percent of $600?

$$\frac{R}{100} = \frac{\$436.05}{\$600} \qquad \$436.05 \times 100 \div 600 = 72.675\%$$

Compare this to the net decimal equivalent 0.72675. The net decimal equivalent is the decimal form of the rate that the customer pays or the *net price rate*.

Now, $163.95 is what percent of $600?

$$\frac{R}{100} = \frac{\$163.95}{\$600} \qquad \$163.95 \times 100 \div 600 = 27.325\%$$

This is the *single discount rate* that is equivalent to the series 15/10/5. The single discount rate is the complement of the net decimal equivalent expressed as a percent or the *trade discount rate*.

EXAMPLE   One manufacturer lists a desk at $700 with a discount series of 20/10/10. A second manufacturer lists the same desk at $650 with a discount series of 10/10/10. Which is the better deal?

1 Decision needed	Which deal on the desk is better?
2 Unknown facts	Net price for the first deal
	Net price for the second deal
3 Known facts	List price for first deal: $700
	Discount series for first deal: 20/10/10
	List price for second deal: $650
	Discount series for second deal: 10/10/10
4 Estimation	The net prices for both deals will be relatively close.
5 Relationships	Net price = net decimal equivalent × list price
6 Calculations	Decimal equivalents of complements of 20%, 10%, and 10% are 0.8, 0.9, and 0.9, respectively.

Net decimal equivalent = 0.8(0.9)(0.9)

= 0.648

Net price for first deal = (0.648) $700

= $453.60

Decimal equivalents of complements of 10%, 10%, and 10% are 0.9, 0.9, and 0.9, respectively.

Net decimal equivalent = 0.9(0.9)(0.9)

= 0.729

Net price for second deal = (0.729) $650

= $473.85

7 Interpretation

The net price for the first deal is $20.25 less than the net price for the second deal ($473.85 − $453.60).

8 Decision made

The first deal—the $700 desk with the 20/10/10 discount series—is the better deal.

---

 2 Find the trade discount applying a trade discount series and using the single discount equivalent.

If you want to know how much you have *saved* by using a discount series, you can calculate the savings—the trade discount—the long way, by finding the net price and then subtracting the net price from the list price. Or, you can apply another, quicker complement method. In percent form, the complement of the net decimal equivalent is the **single discount equivalent.** The product of the single discount equivalent and the list price is the trade discount.

 HOW TO Find the Trade Discount Using the Single Discount Equivalent

1. Find the single discount equivalent: subtract the net decimal equivalent from 1.

Single discount equivalent = 1 − net decimal equivalent

2. Multiply the list price by the single discount equivalent.

Trade discount = single discount equivalent × list price

OR

Trade discount = (1 − net decimal equivalent) × list price

Even using a calculator, it is still desirable to make some calculations mentally. This makes calculations with the calculator less cumbersome. If the complements of each discount rate can be found mentally, then the remaining calculations will all be multiplication steps that can be made using the calculator: Multiply the complements to find the net decimal equivalent, then multiply by the list price. Since the order and grouping of factors does not matter, they can be entered in various ways. Try each of the following sequences from the second example.

1. $\boxed{\text{AC}}\,\boxed{.}\,8\,\boxed{\times}\,\boxed{.}\,9\,\boxed{\times}\,\boxed{.}\,9\,\boxed{=} \Rightarrow 0.648$
   (do not clear) $\boxed{\times}\,700\,\boxed{=} \Rightarrow 453.6$
2. $\boxed{\text{AC}}\,\boxed{.}\,8\,\boxed{\times}\,\boxed{.}\,9\,\boxed{\times}\,\boxed{.}\,9\,\boxed{\times}\,700\,\boxed{=} \Rightarrow 453.6$
3. $\boxed{\text{AC}}\,700\,\boxed{\times}\,\boxed{.}\,8\,\boxed{\times}\,\boxed{.}\,9\,\boxed{\times}\,\boxed{.}\,9\,\boxed{=} \Rightarrow 453.6$

Finding the complements using a basic calculator and then performing the multiplications requires that you record intermediate steps and later reenter them. One of the calculations could be stored in memory, but the others would have to be recorded and reentered unless your calculator has multiple memories.

4. $\boxed{\text{AC}}\,1\,\boxed{-}\,\boxed{.}\,2\,\boxed{=} \Rightarrow 0.8$ (record and reenter later)
   $\boxed{\text{AC}}\,1\,\boxed{-}\,\boxed{.}\,1\,\boxed{=} \Rightarrow 0.9$ (record and reenter later)
   $\boxed{\text{AC}}\,\boxed{.}\,8\,\boxed{\times}\,\boxed{.}\,9\,\boxed{\times}\,\boxed{.}\,9$ etc (same as steps 1 or 2 from above)

With a scientific calculator and parentheses, the sequence would be

$\boxed{\text{AC}}\,\boxed{(}\,1\,\boxed{-}\,\boxed{.}\,2\,\boxed{)}\,\boxed{\times}\,\boxed{(}\,1\,\boxed{-}\,\boxed{.}\,1\,\boxed{)}\,\boxed{\times}\,\boxed{(}\,1\,\boxed{-}\,\boxed{.}\,1\,\boxed{)}\,\boxed{\times}\,700\,\boxed{=} \Rightarrow 453.6$

We strongly encourage you to develop calculator proficiency by performing mentally as many steps as possible.

To find the net price for the second deal in the second example, use mental calculations and the calculator:

$\boxed{\text{AC}}\,650\,\boxed{\times}\,\boxed{.}\,9\,\boxed{\times}\,\boxed{.}\,9\,\boxed{\times}\,\boxed{.}\,9\,\boxed{=} \Rightarrow 473.85$

EXAMPLE Use the single discount equivalent to calculate the trade discount on a $1,500 fax machine with a discount series of 30/20/10.

The single discount equivalent is the complement of the net decimal equivalent. So first find the net decimal equivalent.

$100\% - 30\% = 70\% = 0.7$
$100\% - 20\% = 80\% = 0.8$ **Find the complement of each discount rate and write it as an equivalent decimal.**
$100\% - 10\% = 90\% = 0.9$

$0.7(0.8)(0.9) = \boxed{0.504}$ **Multiply the decimals to find the net decimal equivalent.**
$1.000 - \boxed{0.504} = \boxed{0.496}$ **Subtract the net decimal equivalent from 1 to find the single discount equivalent.**

Thus, the single discount equivalent for the trade discount series 30/20/10 is 0.496 or 49.6%.

Trade discount = single discount equivalent × list price **The single discount equivalent is 0.496; the list price is $1,500.**

$\qquad = \boxed{0.496} \times \$1,500$

$\qquad = \$744$

The trade discount on the $1,500 fax machine with a trade discount series of 30/20/10 is $744.

Use the Calculator Memory to Find the Single Discount Rate

The calculator plan for finding the trade discount is to find the net decimal equivalent and store it in memory. Subtract the net decimal equivalent (which is in memory) from 1. This gives the decimal equivalent of the single discount rate. Then, multiply the result by the net price to get the trade discount.

$\boxed{AC}$ $\boxed{MC}$ $\boxed{.}$ 7 $\boxed{\times}$ $\boxed{.}$ 8 $\boxed{\times}$ $\boxed{.}$ 9 $\boxed{=}$ $\boxed{M^+}$ 1 $-$ $\boxed{MR}$ $\boxed{=}$ $\boxed{\times}$ 1500 $\boxed{=}$ $\Rightarrow$ 744.

SELF-CHECK 7.2

1. Dianna Beulke manages an electronic equipment store and has ordered 100 color TVs with remote control for a special sale. The list price for each TV is $215 with a trade discount series of 7/10/5. Find the net price of the order by using the net decimal equivalent.

2. Robert Armstrong purchased computers for his computer store. Find the net price of the order of 36 computers if each one has a list price of $1,599 and a trade discount series of 5/5/10 is offered by the distributor.

3. Clair Berry needs to calculate the net price of an order with a list price of $800 and a trade discount series of 12/10/6. Use the net decimal equivalent to find the net price.

4. Thomas Atkins is responsible for Cummins Appliance Store's accounts payable department and has an invoice that shows a list price of $2,200 with a trade discount series of 25/15/10. Use the single discount equivalent to calculate the trade discount on the purchase.

5. Cynthia Calhoun is calculating the trade discount on a dog kennel with a list price of $269 and a trade discount series of 10/10/10. What is the trade discount? What is the net price for the kennel?

6. Christy Hodge manages a computer software distributorship and offers a desktop publishing software package for $395 with a trade discount series of 5/5/8. What is the trade discount on this package?

7. One distributor lists ink jet printers with 360 dpi and six scalable fonts that can print envelopes, labels, and transparencies for $189.97 with a trade discount series of 5/5/10. Another distributor lists the same brand and model printer at $210 with a trade discount series of 5/10/10. Which is the better deal if all other aspects of the deal such as shipping, time of availability, warranty, etc., are the same or equivalent.

8. Two distributors offer the same brand and model PC computer. One distributor lists the computer at $1,899 with a trade discount series of 8/8/5 and free shipping. The other distributor offers the computer at $2,000 with a trade discount series of 10/5/5 and $50 shipping cost added to the net price. Which computer is the better deal?

9. Stephen Black orders a large volume of merchandise from a particular furniture manufacturer in North Carolina and currently receives a trade discount series of 5/10/10 on merchandise purchased from the company. However, he is negotiating with another furniture manufacturer to purchase similar furniture of the same quality. The North Carolina company lists a dining room table and six chairs for $1,899. The other company lists a similar set of furniture for $1,800 and offers a trade discount series of 5/5/10. Considering just the cost factor, which deal is better?

10. We have seen that the trade discount series 20/10/5 is *not* equal to a single trade discount rate of 35%. Does the trade discount series 20/10/5 equal the trade discount series 5/10/20? Use an item with a list price of $1,000 and calculate the trade discount for both series to justify your answer.

11. One distributor lists an ink jet printer at $460 with a trade discount series of 15/12/5. Another distributor lists the same printer at $410 with a trade discount series of 10/10/5. Which is the better deal?

7.3   Net Amount and the Cash Discount

1 Find the cash discount and the net amount using ordinary dating terms.

2 Interpret and apply end-of-month (EOM) terms.

3 Interpret and apply receipt-of-goods (ROG) terms.

4 Find the amount credited and the outstanding balance from partial payments.

5 Interpret freight terms.

To encourage prompt payment, many manufacturers and wholesalers allow buyers to take a **cash discount,** a reduction of the amount due on an invoice. The cash discount is a specified percentage of the price of the goods. Customers who pay their bills within a certain time receive a cash discount. Many companies use computerized billing systems that compute the exact amount of a cash discount and show it on the invoice, so that the customer does not need to calculate the discount and resulting net price. But the customer still determines when the bill must be paid to receive the discount.

Bills are often due within 30 days from the date of the invoice. To determine the exact day of the month the payment is due, you have to know how many days are in the month, 30, 31, or 28 in the case of February. There are two ways to help remember which months have 30 days and which have 31. The first method, shown in Figure 7-1, is called the *knuckle method.* Each knuckle represents a month with 31 days and each space between knuckles represents a month with 30 days (except February, which has 28 days except in a leap year, when it has 29.)

Another way to remember which months have 30 days and which have 31 is the following rhyme:

Thirty days has September,

April, June, and November.

All the rest have 31,

'cept February has 28 alone.

And leap year, that's the time

When February has 29.

Figure 7-1 The knuckle months (Jan., Mar., May, July, Aug., Oct., and Dec.) have 31 days. The other months have 30 or fewer days.

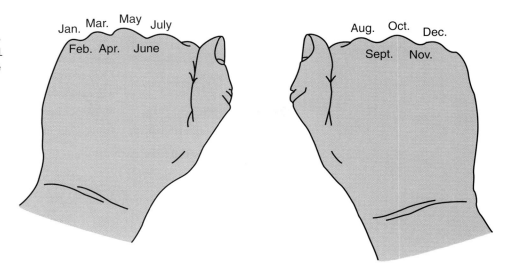

With this in mind, let's look at one of the most common credit terms and dating methods.

1 Find the cash discount and the net amount using ordinary dating terms.

Many firms offer credit terms 2/10, n/30 (read *two ten, net thirty*). The 2/10 means a 2% cash discount rate may be applied if the bill is paid within 10 days of the invoice date. The n/30 means that the full amount or net amount of the bill is due within 30 days. After the 30th day, the bill is overdue, and the buyer may have to pay interest charges or late fees.

For example, say an invoice is dated January 4 with credit terms of 2/10, n/30. If the buyer pays on or before January 14, then a 2% cash discount rate is applied. If the buyer pays on or after January 15, no cash discount is allowed. Finally, since 30 days from January 4 is February 3, if the buyer pays on or after February 4, interest charges on the bill may be required.

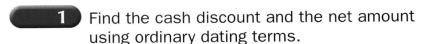

TIP! Ordinary Dating Terms across Months

To find the last day to receive a discount, add to the invoice date the number of days specified in the credit terms. If this sum is greater than the number of days in the month the invoice is dated, subtract from the sum the number of days in the month the invoice is dated. This gives the number of days that go into the next month.

HOW TO Find the Cash Discount

Multiply the cash discount rate by the net price.

Cash discount = cash discount rate × net price

EXAMPLE An invoice dated July 27 shows a net price of $450 with the terms 2/10, n/30.
(a) Find the latest date the cash discount is allowed.
(b) Find the cash discount.

(a) The cash discount is allowed up to and including 10 days from the invoice date, July 27.

27th of July	Invoice date
+ 10 days	Days allowed according to terms 2/10
"37th of July"	If July had 37 days . . .
− 31 days in July	July has 31 days.
6th of August	Latest date allowed

August 6 is the latest date the cash discount is allowed.

(b) Cash discount = Cash discount rate × net price

$$\text{Cash discount} = 2\% \times \$450$$
$$= 0.02\,(\$450)$$
$$= \$9.00$$

The cash discount is $9.00.

Once a cash discount is deducted from a net price, the amount remaining is called the **net amount.** The net amount is the amount the buyer actually pays. Like the net price, there are two ways to calculate the net amount.

Because we attempt to use terms that are commonly used in the business world, the terms *net price* and *net amount* can be confusing. The list price is the suggested retail price, the net price is the price a retailer pays to the distributor or manufacturer for the merchandise, and the net amount is the net price minus any additional discount for paying the bill promptly.

? HOW TO **Find the Net Amount**

Using the cash discount: Subtract the cash discount from the net price.

Net amount = net price − cash discount

OR

Using the complement of the cash discount rate: Multiply the net price by the complement of the cash discount rate.

Net amount = Complement of cash discount rate × net price

OR

Net amount = (100% − cash discount rate) × net price

EXAMPLE Find the net amount for the invoice in the proceding example.

$$\text{Net amount} = \text{net price} - \text{cash discount}$$
$$= \$450 - \$9$$
$$= \$441$$

or

$$\text{Net amount} = \text{complement of cash discount rate} \times \text{net price}$$
$$= (100\% - 2\%)\,(\,\$450\,)$$
$$= 0.98\,(\,\$450\,)$$
$$= \$441$$

The net amount is $441.

Another common set of discount terms is 2/10, 1/15, n/30. These terms are read *two ten, one fifteen, net thirty.* A 2% cash discount is allowed if the bill is paid within 10 days after the invoice date, a 1% cash discount is allowed if the bill is paid during the 11th through 15th days, and no discount is allowed during the 16th through the 30th days. Interest charges or past due charges may accrue if the bill is paid after the 30th day from the date of the invoice.

For example, a bill dated September 2 with sales terms 2/10, 1/15, n/30 receives a 2% discount if paid on or before September 12. A 1% discount is allowed if the bill is paid on September 13 or any day up to and including September 17. The net amount is due if the bill is paid on September 18 through October 2. If the bill is paid on October 3 or any day after October 3, it is subject to interest charges.

 TIP! **The Check Is in the Mail**

The requirement for a bill to be paid on or before a specific date means that the payment must be *received* by the supplier on or before that date. For the payment to be postmarked by the due date does not generally count.

EXAMPLE Sycamore Enterprises received a $1,248 bill for computer supplies, dated September 2, with sales terms 2/10, 1/15, n/30. A 5% penalty is charged for payment after 30 days. Find the amount due if the bill is paid (a) on or before September 12; (b) on or between September 13 and September 17; (c) on or between September 18 and October 2; and (d) on or after October 3.

(a) If the bill is paid on or before September 12 (within 10 days), the 2% discount applies:

$$\text{Cash discount} = 2\% \times \$1{,}248 = 0.02 \times \$1{,}248 = \boxed{\$24.96}$$
$$\text{Net amount} = \$1{,}248 - \boxed{\$24.96} = \$1{,}223.04$$

The net amount due on or before September 12 is $1,223.04.

(b) If the bill is paid on or between September 13 and September 17 (within 15 days), the 1% discount applies:

$$\text{Cash discount} = 1\% \times \$1{,}248 = 0.01 \times \$1{,}248 = \boxed{\$12.48}$$
$$\text{Net amount} = \$1{,}248 - \boxed{\$12.48} = 1{,}235.52$$

The net amount due on or between September 13 and September 17 is $1,235.52.

(c) If the bill is paid on or between September 18 and October 2, no cash discount applies. **The net price of $1,248 is due.**

(d) If the bill is paid on or after October 3, a 5% interest penalty is added:

$$\text{Interest} = 5\% \times \$1{,}248 = 0.05 \times \$1{,}248 = \boxed{\$62.40}$$
$$\text{Net amount} = \$1{,}248 + \boxed{\$62.40} = \$1{,}310.40$$

The net amount due on or after October 3 is $1,310.40.

2 Interpret and apply end-of-month (EOM) terms.

Included in the types of sales terms are **end-of-month (EOM) terms**. For example, the term might be 2/10 EOM, meaning that a 2% discount is allowed if the bill is paid during the first 10 days of the month *after* the month in the date of the invoice. Thus, if a bill is dated November 19, a 2% discount is allowed as long as the bill is paid on or before December 10.

EXAMPLE   Newman, Inc., received a bill for cleaning services dated September 17 for $5,000 with terms 2/10 EOM. The invoice was paid on October 9. How much did Newman, Inc., pay?

Since the bill was paid within the first 10 days of the next month, a 2% discount was allowed. The complement of 2% is 98%.

$$\text{Net amount} = 98\% \times \$5,000 = 0.98 \times \$5,000 = \$4,900$$

The net amount due on October 9 is $4,900.

An exception to this rule occurs when the invoice is dated *on or after the 26th of the month*. When this happens, the discount is allowed if the bill is paid during the first 10 days of the month after the next month. Thus, if an invoice is dated May 28 with terms 2/10 EOM, a 2% discount is allowed as long as the bill is paid on or before *July 10*. This exception allows retailers adequate time to receive and pay the invoice.

 TIP! **How EOM Terms Apply**

- To an invoice dated **before the 26th** day of the month: a cash discount is allowed when the bill is paid by the specified day of the *next month*.
- To an invoice dated **on or after the 26th day** of the month: a cash discount is allowed when the bill is paid by the specified day of the *month after the next month*.

EXAMPLE   Archie's Shoes received a $200 bill for copying services dated April 27. The terms on the invoice were 3/10 EOM. The firm paid the bill on June 2. How much did it pay?

Since the bill was paid within the first 10 days of the second month after the month on the invoice, a 3% discount was allowed. The complement of 3% is 97%.

$$\text{Net amount} = 97\% \times \$200 = 0.97 \times \$200 = \$194$$

The net amount paid was $194.

 Interpret and apply receipt-of-goods (ROG) terms.

Sometimes sales terms hinge on the day the *goods are received* instead of the invoice date. In such cases, the terms may be written 1/10 *ROG*, where ROG stands for **receipt of goods.** These terms mean that a 1% discount is allowed on the bill if it is paid within 10 days of the receipt of goods.

For instance, an invoice is dated September 6 but the goods do not arrive until the 14th. If the sales terms are 2/15 ROG, then a 2% discount is allowed if the bill is paid on any date up to and including September 29.

 TIP! **How ROG Terms Apply**

A cash discount is allowed when the bill is paid within the specified number of days from the **receipt of goods,** not from the date of the invoice.

EXAMPLE   An invoice for machine parts for $400 is dated November 9 and has sales terms 2/10 ROG. The machine parts arrive November 13.

(a) If the bill is paid on November 21, what is the net amount due?

(b) If the bill is paid on December 2, what is the net amount due?

(a) Since the bill is being paid within 10 days of the receipt of goods, a 2% discount is allowed. The complement of 2% is 98%.

$$\text{Net amount} = 98\% \times \$400 = 0.98 \times \$400 = \$392$$

The net amount due is $392.

(b) No discount is allowed since the bill is not being paid within 10 days of the receipt of goods. **Thus, $400 is due.**

TIP! Carefully Examine the Terms of a Purchase

It is important to be able to distinguish types of payment terms as they appear on an invoice. For example, an invoice for $200 is dated September 28 but the merchandise arrives on October 15. The sales terms are 2/10 ROG, but the account manager thinks this means the bill can be paid within 10 days of the second month after the month in the date of the invoice (EOM) and pays the bill with a 2% discount on November 5. Does the discount apply? No, since the bill should have been paid within 10 days of the receipt of the goods. The last date to pay the bill and receive the discount is October 25th.

4 Find the amount credited and the outstanding balance from partial payments.

A company sometimes cannot pay the full amount due in time to take advantage of cash discount terms. Most sellers allow buyers to make a **partial payment** and still get a **partial cash discount** off the net price if the partial payment is made within the time specified in the credit terms. The **amount credited** to the account, then, is the partial payment plus this partial cash discount. The **outstanding balance** is the amount still owed and is expected to be paid within the time specified by the sales terms.

HOW TO Find the Amount Credited and the Outstanding Balance from Partial Payments

1. Find the amount credited to the account: divide the partial payment by the complement of the cash discount rate.

$$\text{Amount credited} = \frac{\text{partial payment}}{\text{complement of cash discount rate}}$$

2. Find the outstanding balance: subtract the amount credited from the net price.

$$\text{Outstanding balance} = \text{net price} - \text{amount credited}$$

OR

$$\text{Outstanding balance} = \text{net price} - \frac{\text{partial payment}}{\text{complement of cash discount rate}}$$

EXAMPLE The Semmes Corporation received an $875 invoice for cardboard cartons with terms of 3/10, n/30. The firm could not pay the entire bill within 10 days but sent a check for $500. What amount was credited to Semmes' account?

$$\text{Amount credited} = \frac{\text{partial payment}}{\text{complement of rate}} = \frac{\$500}{0.97}$$

$$= \$515.46$$

Divide the amount of the partial payment by the complement of the discount rate to find the amount credited.

$$\text{Outstanding balance} = \$875 - \$515.46 = \$359.54$$

Subtract the amount credited from the net price to find the outstanding balance.

A $515.46 payment was credited to the account, and the outstanding balance was $359.54.

 TIP! **Get Proper Credit for Partial Payments**

Remember to find the *complement* of the discount rate and then divide the partial payment by this complement. Students sometimes just multiply the discount rate times the partial payment, which does not allow the proper credit.

From the preceding example,

$$\frac{\$500}{0.97} = \$515.46$$

$$\$875 - \$515.46 = \$359.54$$

CORRECT

From the preceding example,

$$\$500 \times 0.03 = \$15$$

$$\$500 + \$15 = \$515$$

$$\$875 - \$515 = \$360$$

INCORRECT

---

5 Interpret freight terms.

Manufacturers rely on a wide variety of carriers (truck, rail, ship, plane, and the like) to distribute their goods. The terms of freight shipment are indicated on a document called a **bill of lading** that is attached to each shipment. This document includes a description of the merchandise, the number of pieces, weight, name of consignee, destination, and method of payment of freight charges. Freight payment terms are usually specified on the **manufacturer's price list** so that purchasers clearly understand who is responsible for freight charges and under what circumstances before purchases are made. The cost of shipping may be paid by the buyer or seller. If the freight is paid by the buyer, the bill of lading is marked **FOB shipping point**—meaning "free on board" at the shipping point—or **freight collect.** For example, CCC Industries located in Tulsa purchased parts from Rawhide in Chicago. Rawhide ships FOB Chicago, so CCC Industries must pay the freight from Chicago to Tulsa. The freight company then collects freight charges from CCC upon delivery of the goods.

If the freight is paid by the seller, the bill of lading may be marked **FOB destination**—meaning "free on board" at the destination point—or **freight paid.** If Rawhide paid the freight in the preceding example, the term *FOB Tulsa* could also have been used. Many manufacturers pay shipping charges for shipments above some minimum dollar value. Some shipments of very small items may be marked **prepay and add.** That is, the seller pays the shipping charge and adds it to the invoice, so the buyer pays the shipping charge to the seller rather than to the freight company. Cash discounts do *not* apply to freight or shipping charges.

 TIP! **Interpreting Freight Terms**

- If the bill of lading is marked **FOB (free on board) shipping point,** or **freight collect,** the buyer is responsible for paying freight expenses directly to the freight company.
- If the bill of lading is marked **FOB destination** or **freight paid,** the seller is responsible for paying freight expenses directly to the freight company.
- If the bill of lading is marked **prepay and add,** the buyer is responsible for paying the freight expenses to the seller, who pays the freight company.
- Cash discounts do not apply to freight charges.

EXAMPLE Calculate the cash discount and the net amount paid for an $800 order of business forms with sales terms of 3/10, 1/15, n/30 if the cost of shipping was $40 (which is included in the $800). The invoice was dated June 13, marked *freight prepay and add,* and paid June 24.

Net price of merchandise	**Apply the cash discount rate *only* to the net amount of the merchandise.**
= total invoice − shipping fee	
= $800 − $40 = $760	**The net price is $760.**
Cash discount	
= $760 × 0.01 = $7.60	**The bill was paid within 15 days, so the 1% discount applies.**
Net amount	
= $800 − $7.60 = $792.40	**Discount is taken from total bill.**

The cash discount was $7.60 and the net amount paid was $792.40, which included the shipping fee.

SELF-CHECK 7.3

 Larry Blanton received an invoice dated March 9, with terms 2/10, n/30, amounting to $540. He paid the bill on March 12.

1. How much was the cash discount?

2. What is the net amount Larry will pay?

James Champion gets an invoice for $450 with terms 4/10, 1/15, n/30.

3. How much would James pay seven days after the invoice date?

4. How much would James pay 15 days after the invoice date?

5. How much would James pay 25 days after the invoice date?

Jana Turner, director of accounts, received a bill for $648, dated April 6, with sales terms 2/10, 1/15, n/30. A 3% penalty is charged for payment after 30 days.

6. Find the amount due if the bill is paid on or before April 16.

7. What amount is due if the bill is paid on or between April 17 and April 21?

8. What amount is due if Jana pays on or between April 22 and May 6?

9. If Jana pays on or after May 7, how much must she pay?

Grace Cox is an accounts payable officer for her company and must calculate cash discounts before paying invoices. She is paying bills on June 18 and has an invoice dated June 12 with terms 3/10, n/30.

10. If the net price of the invoice is $1,296.45, how much cash discount can she take?

11. What is the net amount Grace will need to pay?

12. Charlene Watson received a bill for $800 dated July 5, with sales terms of 2/10 EOM. She paid the bill on August 8. How much should Charlene pay?

13. An invoice for a camcorder that cost $1,250 is dated August 1, with sales terms of 2/10 EOM. If the bill is paid on September 8, how much is due?

14. Ruby Wossum received an invoice for $798.53 dated February 27 with sales terms of 3/10 EOM. How much should she pay if she pays the bill on April 15?

15. Sylvester Young received an invoice for a leaf blower for $493 dated April 15 with sales terms of 3/10 EOM. How much should he pay if he pays the bill on April 30?

 An invoice for $900 is dated October 15 and has sales terms of 2/10 ROG. The merchandise arrives October 21.

16. How much is due if the bill is paid October 27?

17. How much is due if the bill is paid on November 3?

18. Sharron Smith is paying an invoice showing a total of $5,835 and dated June 2. The invoice shows sales terms of 2/10 ROG. The merchandise delivery slip shows a receiving date of 6/5. How much is due if the bill for the merchandise is paid on June 12?

19. Kariem Salaam is directing the accounts payable office and is training a new accounts payable associate. They are processing an invoice for a credenza which is dated August 19 in the amount of $392.34. The delivery ticket for the credenza is dated August 23. If the sales terms indicated on the invoice are 3/10 ROG, how much needs to be paid if the bill is paid on September 5?

20. Clordia Patterson-Nathanial handles all accounts payable for her company. She has a bill for $730 and plans to make a partial payment of $400 within the discount period. If the terms of the transaction were 3/10, n/30, find the amount credited to the account and find the outstanding balance.

21. Robert Palinchak has an invoice for a complete computer system for $3,982.48. The invoice shows terms of 3/10, 2/15, n/30. He can afford to pay $2,000 within 10 days of the date on the invoice and the remainder within the 30-day period. How much should be credited to the account for the $2,000 payment, and how much is still due?

22. Ada Shotwell has been directed to pay all invoices in time to receive any discounts offered by vendors. However, she has an invoice with terms of 2/10, n/30 for $2,983 and the funds for accounts payable has a balance of $2,196.83. So she elects to pay $2,000 on the invoice within the 10-day discount period and the remainder within the 30-day period. How much should be credited to the account for the $2,000 payment and how much remains to be paid?

23. Dorothy Rogers' Bicycle Shop received a shipment of bicycles via truck from Better Bilt Bicycles. The bill of lading was marked FOB destination. Who paid the freight? To whom was the freight paid?

24. Joseph Denatti is negotiating the freight payment for a large shipment of office furniture and agrees to take a discount on the invoice offered by the vendor since the freight terms are FOB shipping point. Who is to pay the freight?

25. Phyllis Porter receives a shipment with the bill of lading marked "prepay and add." Who is responsible for freight charges? Who pays the freight company?

26. Explain the difference in the freight terms *FOB shipping point* and *prepay and add.*

Rebates and Bill-Backs

Misuse and abuse of trade discounts infringes on fair trade laws and can cost companies stiff fines and legal fees. One way to avoid misuse is to establish the same discount for everyone and give rebates based solely on volume. Beall Manufacturing Co. uses this policy for equipment sales to the railroad industry. For example, a "wear plate" (which goes on the wheel assembly of railroad cars) sells for about $3 to a company like Burlington Northern or Union Pacific who is currently buying 15,000 pieces per month. In an effort to run more cost-efficient large jobs and to capture market share, Beall will give an incentive for higher volume. They offer to rebate 5% for orders of 20,000 pieces per month, or rebate 17–18¢ per piece for orders of at least 22,000 pieces per month. The amount of increased volume needed for a rebate is determined after market research tells Beall mediating factors such as how much volume the customer is capable of ordering per month, what volume of the same part the customer is currently buying from other suppliers, and at what cost? The amount of the rebate discount is determined by Beall's profit margin, ability to acquire raw materials in sufficient quantity to produce the larger volume, and capability of current machinery/labor force to produce higher volumes without raising the fixed or variable production cost. In the grocery store industry, these rebates are called "bill-backs" because the customers receive credit on their next order instead of a rebate check.

Exercises

Use the above information to answer the following:

1. Suppose a railroad company currently orders 15,000 wear plates per month from Beall @ $3 each, which is about half of what they buy each month from other suppliers. If they move 5,000 pieces per month from another company to Beall, how much rebate will they receive on the total order? What will be the discounted cost per piece? (@ means "at")

2. If this same company increases its order to 22,000 pieces per month and negotiates an 18¢ per piece trade discount, how much rebate will it receive? What percentage discount does this amount to?

3. Impressed with Beall's quality, dependability, and pricing, this company gives Beall its entire order of 30,000 wear plates per month. Calculate its monthly rebate. Other than the 18¢ per piece rebate, give a reason why giving Beall its entire order could be beneficial. Give a reason *against* giving Beall its entire order.

4. If this company also receives a $\frac{1}{2}$% cash discount (for 10 days, net 30) calculate the total of its rebate and cash discount on its 30,000 piece per month order, and then find its net price.

5. A railway repair company currently orders about 6,000 wear plates per month from Beall @ $3 each. Beall's marketing manager believes this company is capable of expanding its business to 8,000 pieces per month and recommends a rebate of 17¢ per piece if they do so. Rounded to the nearest tenth, what percentage rebate does this amount to? Do you think this trade discount violates fair trade laws? Argue why and why not.

Answers

1. On the 20,000 piece order @ $3 each, the $60,000 sale will earn a rebate of $3,000. (5% × $60,000 = 0.05 × $60,000 = $3,000). The price per piece is $2.85 ($60,000 − $3,000 = $57,000; $57,000 ÷ $20,000 = $2.85).

2. On a 22,000 piece order @ $3 each (22,000 × $3 = $66,000), the $66,000 sale will earn a rebate of $3,960 (22,000 × $0.18 = $3,960). This amounts to a 6% discount ($3,960 ÷ $66,000 = 0.06 or 6%).

3. On a 30,000 piece order @ $3 each, the $90,000 sale will earn a rebate of $5,400 (30,000 × $3 = $90,000; 30,000 × 0.18 = $5,400). By giving Beall all its business, the company can save money in placing and processing orders, and possibly shipping costs. It may also gain clout with Beall and procure trade discounts for other parts Beall produces. The main disadvantage of "putting all your eggs in one basket" is that if anything happens to disrupt Beall's supply, it may be difficult and expensive to switch to another company on short notice.

4. The $\frac{1}{2}$% cash discount on the initial $90,000 order is $450 ($90,000 × 0.005 = $450). Combined with the rebate, the total trade allowance is $5,850 ($5,400 + $450 = $5,850), which gives a net price of $84,150 ($90,000 − $5,850 = $84,150).

5. A 17¢ rebate on a $3 part amounts to a 5.6% discount (8,000 × 0.17 = $450: $450 ÷ 8,000 = 0.05625 or 5.6%). Other Beall customers who pay a higher price for the same or higher volume may claim unfair trade practices. But Beall's marketing manager may argue that the $33\frac{1}{3}$% increase in volume from this customer is worth the 5.6% rebate incentive.

CHAPTER 7 OVERVIEW

Section Outcome	Important Points with Examples

Section 7.1

  Find the trade discount using a single trade discount rate; find the net price using the trade discount. (page 300)

Find the trade discount using a single trade discount rate. Multiply the list price by the single trade discount rate.

$$\text{Trade discount} = \text{single trade discount rate} \times \text{list price}$$

The list price of a laminating machine is $76 and the single trade discount rate is 25%. Find the trade discount.

$$\text{Trade discount} = 25\% \times \$76$$
$$= 0.25 \times 76$$
$$= \$19$$

Find the net price using the trade discount. Subtract the trade discount from the list price.

$$\text{Net price} = \text{list price} - \text{trade discount}$$

Find the net price when the list price is $76 and the trade discount is $19.

$$\text{Net price} = \$76 - \$19$$
$$= \$57$$

2   Find the net price using the complement of the single trade discount rate. (page 301)

1. Find the complement: subtract the single trade discount rate from 100%.

     Complement of single trade discount rate = 100% − single trade discount rate

2. Multiply the list price by the complement of the single trade discount rate.

     Net price = complement of single trade discount rate × list price

OR

     Net price = (100% − single trade discount rate) × list price

---

The list price is $480 and the single trade discount rate is 15%. Find the net price.

Net price = (100% − 15%) ($480)

           = 0.85 ($480)

           = $408

Section 7.2

1   Find the net price, applying a trade discount series and using the net decimal equivalent. (page 305)

1. Find the net decimal equivalent: multiply the complements of the trade discount rates, in decimal form, of all the rates in the series.

     Net decimal equivalent =

         product of complements of trade discount rates, in decimal form

2. Multiply the list price by the net decimal equivalent.

     Net price = net decimal equivalent × list price

The list price is $960 and the discount series is 10/5/2. Find the net price.

Net decimal equivalent = (0.9)(0.95)(0.98) = 0.8379

Net price = (0.8379)($960)

           = $804.38

2   Find the trade discount, applying a trade discount series and using the single discount equivalent. (page 307)

1. Find the single discount equivalent: subtract the net decimal equivalent from 1.

     Single discount equivalent = 1 − net decimal equivalent

2. Multiply the list price by the single discount equivalent.

     Trade discount = single discount equivalent × list price

OR   Trade discount = (1 − net decimal equivalent) × list price

---

The list price is $2,800 and the discount series is 25/15/10. Find the trade discount.

Net decimal equivalent = (0.75)(0.85)(0.9) = 0.57375

Single decimal equivalent = 1 − 0.57375 = 0.42625

Trade discount = (0.42625)($2,800)

                = $1,193.50

Section 7.3

Find the cash discount and the net amount using ordinary dating terms. (page 311)

Interpret ordinary dating terms. To find the last day to receive a discount, add to the invoice date the number of days specified in the terms. If this sum is greater than the number of days in the month the invoice is dated, subtract from the sum the number of days in the month the invoice is dated. The result is the last date the cash discount is allowed. Use the knuckle method to remember how many days are in each month, or use the days-in-a-month rhyme.

> **By what date must an invoice dated July 10 be paid if it is due in 10 days?**
>
> **July 10 + 10 days = July 20**
>
> **By what date must an invoice dated May 15 be paid if it is due in 30 days?**
>
> **May 15 + 30 = "May 45"**
>
> **May is a "knuckles" month, so it has 31 days.**
>
> **"May 45" − 31 days in May = June 14**
>
> **The invoice must be paid on or before June 14.**

1. Find the cash discount: multiply the cash discount rate by the net price.

   $$\text{Cash discount} = \text{cash discount rate} \times \text{net price}$$

2. Find the net amount using the cash discount: subtract the cash discount from the net price.

   $$\text{Net amount} = \text{net price} - \text{cash discount}$$

3. Find the net amount using the complement of the cash discount rate: multiply the net price by the complement of the cash discount rate.

   $$\text{Net amount} = \text{complement of cash discount rate} \times \text{net price}$$

   OR

   $$\text{Net amount} = (100\% - \text{cash discount rate}) \times \text{net price}$$

> **An invoice is dated July 17 with terms 2/10, n/30 on a $2,500 net price. What is the latest date a cash discount is allowed? What is the net amount due on that date? On what date may interest begin accruing? What is the net amount due one day earlier?**
>
> **Sale terms 2/10, n/30 mean the buyer takes a 2% cash discount if he or she pays within 10 days of the invoice date; interest may accrue after the 30th day.**
>
> **Latest discount date = July 17 + 10 days = July 27**
>
> **Net amount = (100% − 2%)($2,500)**
>
> $$= (0.98)(\$2,500)$$
>
> $$= \$2,450$$
>
> **Latest no-interest date = July 17 + 30 = "July 47"**
>
> **"July 47" − 31 days in July = Aug 16**
>
> **Interest begins accruing Aug 17. On Aug 16 the amount due is the net price of $2,500.**

2 Interpret and apply end-of-month (EOM) terms. (page 313)

To an invoice dated *before the 26th* day of the month: A cash discount is allowed when the bill is paid by the specified day of the *next month*. To an invoice dated *on or after the 26th* day of the month: A cash discount is allowed when the bill is paid by the specified day of the *month after the next month*.

> **An invoice dated November 5 shows terms of 2/10 EOM on an $880 net price. By what date does the invoice have to be paid in order to get the cash discount? What is the net amount due on that date?**
>
> **Sale terms 2/10 EOM for an invoice dated on or before the 26th day of a month mean that a 2% cash discount is allowed if the invoice is paid on or before the 10th day of the next month.**
>
> **Latest discount day = December 10**
>
> **Net amount = (100% − 2%)($880)**
>
> **= (0.98)($880)**
>
> **= $862.40**

3 Interpret and apply receipt-of-goods (ROG) terms. (page 314)

A cash discount is allowed when the bill is paid within the specified number of days from the *receipt of goods*, not from the date of the invoice.

> **What is the net amount due on April 8 for an invoice dated March 28 with terms of 1/10 ROG on a net price of $500? The shipment arrived April 1.**
>
> **Sales terms 1/10 ROG mean that a 1% cash discount is allowed if the invoice is paid within 10 days of the receipt of goods.**
>
> **April 8 is within 10 days of April 1, the date the shipment is received, so the cash discount is allowed.**
>
> **Net amount = (100% − 1%)($500)**
>
> **= (0.99)($500)**
>
> **= $495**

4 Find the amount credited and the outstanding balance from partial payments. (page 315)

1. Find the amount credited to the account: divide the partial payment by the complement of the cash discount rate.

$$\text{Amount credited} = \frac{\text{partial payment}}{\text{complement of cash discount rate}}$$

2. Find the outstanding balance: subtract the amount credited from the net price.

$$\text{Outstanding balance} = \text{net price} - \text{amount credited}$$

OR

$$\text{Outstanding balance} = \text{net price} - \frac{\text{partial payment}}{\text{complement of cash discount rate}}$$

> **Estrada's Restaurant purchased carpet for $1,568 with sales terms of 3/10, n/30 and paid $1,000 on the bill within the 10 days specified. How much was credited to Estrada's account and what balance remained?**
>
> **Amount credited to account = $1,000 ÷ 0.97 = $1,030.93**
> **Outstanding balance = $1,568 − $1,030.93 = $537.07**

If the bill of lading is marked FOB (free on board) *shipping point*, or freight collect, the buyer is responsible for paying freight expenses directly to the freight company. If the bill of lading is marked *FOB destination* or *freight paid*, the shipper is responsible for paying freight expenses directly to the freight company. If the bill of lading is marked *prepay and add*, the buyer is responsible for paying the freight expenses to the seller, who pays the freight company. Cash discounts do not apply to freight charges.

A shipment is sent from a manufacturer in Boston to a wholesaler in Dallas and is marked FOB destination. Who is responsible for the freight cost?

The manufacturer is responsible and pays the shipper.

WORDS TO KNOW

suggested retail price (p. 300)
catalog price (p. 300)
list price (p. 300)
trade discount (p. 300)
net price (p. 300)
discount rate (p. 300)
single discount rate (p. 300)
complement (p. 301)
trade discount series (p. 304)

net decimal equivalent (p. 305)
single discount equivalent (p. 307)
cash discount (p. 310)
net amount (p. 312)
end-of-month (EOM)
(p. 313)
receipt of goods (ROG) (p. 314)
partial payment (p. 315)
partial cash discount (p. 315)

amount credited (p. 315)
outstanding balance (p. 315)
bill of lading (p. 316)
manufacturer's price list (p. 316)
FOB shipping point (p. 316)
freight collect (p. 316)
FOB destination (p. 316)
freight paid (p. 316)
prepay and add (p. 316)

CHAPTER 7 · CONCEPTS ANALYSIS

1. Who generally pays the list price? Who generally pays the net price?

2. The net price can be found by first finding the trade discount as discussed in Outcome 1 in Section 7.1, then subtracting to get the net price. When is it advantageous to use the complement of the discount rate for finding the net price directly?

3. Use an example to illustrate that a trade discount series of 20/10 is not the same as a discount of 30%. Why are the discounts not the same?

4. When finding the amount to be credited for a partial payment that is made at a discounted rate, it is necessary to find the complement of the discount rate, then divide the partial payment by this complement. Explain why one cannot multiply the payment by the discount rate and add the product to the payment to determine the amount to be credited to the account balance.

5. If the rate of single discount is 20%, the complement is 80%. What does the complement represent?

6. Describe the calculations you would use to project a due date of 60 days from a date of purchase assuming the 60 days are within the same year. Verify your description by working an example using the calculation you described.

7. Illustrate the Tip suggestion for Ordinary Dating Terms across Months on page 311 by supplying an invoice date and credit terms and finding the last day to receive a discount.

8. Describe a procedure for mentally finding a 1% discount on an invoice. Illustrate with an example.

9. Expand the mental process for finding a 1% discount on an invoice to finding a 2% discount. Illustrate with an example.

10. Use the results of your investigations to develop a process for estimating a cash discount on an invoice. Illustrate with an example.

11. Why is it important to estimate the discount amount on an invoice?

Section 7.1

Complete the following table. Round results to the nearest cent.

List Price	Single Discount Rate	Trade Discount		List Price	Single Discount Rate	Trade Discount
1. $300	15%	_____		**2.** $48	10%	_____
3. $127.50	20%	_____		**4.** $100	12%	_____
5. $37.85	20%	_____		**6.** $425	15%	_____

7. Find the trade discount on a conference table listed at $1,025 less 10% (single discount rate).

8. The list price for velvet by Harris Fabrics is $6.25 per yard less 6%. What is the trade discount?

9. Find the trade discount on a suit listed at $165 less 12%.

10. Rocha Bros. offered a $12\frac{1}{2}$% trade discount on a tractor listed at $10,851. What was the trade discount?

11. Find the trade discount on an order of 30 lamps listed at $35 each less 9%.

12. The list price for a big screen TV is $1,480 and the trade discount is $301. What is the net price?

13. The list price on skirts is $22, and the list price on corduroy jumpers is $37. If Petitt's Clothing Store orders 30 skirts and 40 jumpers at a discount rate of 11%, what is the trade discount on the purchase?

14. A stationery shop bought 10 boxes of writing paper that were listed at $5 each and 200 greeting cards listed at $3.00 each. If the single discount rate for the purchase is 15%, find the trade discount.

Complete the following table. Round all results to the nearest cent.

List Price	Trade Discount	Net Price		List Price	Trade Discount	Net Price
15. $21	$3	_____		**16.** $24.62	$5.93	_____
17. $6.85	$0.72	_____		**18.** $0.89	$0.12	_____

19. A camera has a list price of $378.61 with a trade discount of $42.58. What is the net price?

20. The list price of carpeting from Marie's Mill Outlet is $19 per square yard. The trade discount is $2.50 per square yard. What is the net price per square yard?

Complete the following table. Round results to the nearest cent.

List Price	Single Discount Rate	Trade Discount	Net Price		List Price	Single Discount Rate	Trade Discount	Net Price
21. $25	5%	_____	_____		**22.** $1,263	12%	_____	_____
23. $0.89	2%	_____	_____		**24.** $27.50	3%	_____	_____
25. $2,100	17%	_____	_____		**26.** $8,952	18%	_____	_____

Complete the following table.

List Price	Single Discount Rate	Complement	Net Price	List Price	Single Discount Rate	Complement	Net Price
27. $15.97	4%	_____	_____	**28.** $421	5%	_____	_____
29. $138.54	6%	_____	_____	**30.** $721.18	3%	_____	_____
31. $16.97	11%	_____	_____	**32.** $3,983.00	8%	_____	_____

Section 7.2

Complete the following table. Round results to the nearest cent.

List Price	Trade Discount Series	Decimal Equivalents of Complements	Net Decimal Equivalent	Net Price
33. $200	20/10	_____	_____	_____
34. $50	10/7/5	_____	_____	_____
35. $1,500	20/15/10	_____	_____	_____
36. $35	20/15/5	_____	_____	_____
37. $400	15/5	_____	_____	_____
38. $2,834	5/10/10	_____	_____	_____

39. A trade discount series of 10/5 was given on ladies' scarves listed at $4. Find the net price of each scarf.

40. Find the net price of an item listed at $800 with a trade discount series of 25/10/5.

41. A trade discount series of 10/5/5 is offered on a printer, which is listed at $800. Also, a trade discount series of 5/10/5 is offered on a desk chair listed at $250. Find the total net price for the printer and the chair. Round to the nearest cent.

42. Five desks are listed at $400 each, with a trade discount series of 20/10/10. Also, 10 bookcases are listed at $200 each, discounted 10/20/10. Find the total net price for the desks and bookcases.

Complete the following table. Round results to the nearest hundredth of a percent when necessary.

Net Decimal Equivalent	Net Decimal Equivalent in Percent Form	Single Discount Equivalent in Percent Form	Net Decimal Equivalent	Net Decimal Equivalent in Percent Form	Single Discount Equivalent in Percent Form
43. 0.765	_____	_____	**44.** 0.82	_____	_____
45. 0.6835	_____	_____	**46.** 0.6502	_____	_____
47. 0.7434	_____	_____	**48.** 0.758	_____	_____

Find the single discount equivalent for the following discount series.

49. 20/10

50. 30/20/5

51. 10%, 5%, 2%

52. 10%, 10%, 5%

53. 10/5

54. 20/15

55. A television set is listed at $400 less 20%. The same set is listed by another manufacturer for $425 less 24%. Which is the better deal?

56. A hutch is listed at $650 with a trade discount of $65. The same hutch listed by another manufacturer is $595 with a trade discount of $25. Find the better deal.

57. One manufacturer lists an aquarium for $58.95 with a trade discount of $5.90. Another manufacturer lists the same aquarium for $60 with a trade discount of $9.45. Which is the better deal?

58. One manufacturer lists a table at $200 less 12%. Another manufacturer lists the same table at $190 less 10%. Which is the better deal?

59. One manufacturer lists picture frames at $20 each, discounted 10/10/10. Another manufacturer lists the same picture frames at $19 with a trade discount series of 10/5/10. Which is the better deal?

60. A trunk listed at $250 is discounted 10/10/5. The same trunk is listed by another manufacturer for $260 discounted 10/10/10. Which is the better deal?

Section 7.3

61. Isidore Quaranta received a bill dated March 1 with sales terms of 3/10, n/30. What percent discount will she receive if she pays the bill on March 5?

62. Chris Merillat received a bill dated September 3 with sales terms of 2/10, n/30. Did she receive a discount if she paid the bill on September 15?

63. An invoice dated February 13 had sales terms of 2/10, n/30. The bill was paid February 19. Was a cash discount allowed?

64. Ernest Pedalino received an invoice for $300 dated March 3 with sales terms of 1/10, n/30. He paid the bill on March 6. What was his cash discount?

65. Find the cash discount on an invoice for $270 dated April 17 with terms of 2/10, n/30 if the bill was paid April 22.

66. Find the cash discount on an invoice for $50 dated May 3 with terms 1/15, n/30 if the bill was paid May 14.

67. Nickolas Raisis received an invoice dated June 5 for $70 with terms of 2/10, n/30. He paid the bill on June 9. What was his cash discount and how much did he pay?

68. Emil Ramirez received an invoice dated July 3 for $165 with terms of 2/10, n/30. He paid the bill on July 7. How much did he pay?

69. How much would have to be paid on an invoice for $350 with terms of 2/10, 1/15, n/30, if the bill is paid (a) 7 days after the invoice date; (b) 15 days after the invoice date; (c) 25 days after the invoice date?

70. How much would have to be paid on an invoice for $28 with terms of 3/10 EOM if the bill dated June 8 is paid (a) July 2; (b) July 20?

71. Susan Rains received an invoice for $650 dated January 26. The sales terms in the invoice were 2/10 EOM. She paid the bill on March 4. How much did Susan pay?

72. How much would have to be paid on an invoice for $328 with terms of 2/10 ROG if the merchandise invoice is dated January 3, the merchandise arrives January 8, and the invoice is paid (a) January 11; (b) January 15; (c) January 25?

73. An invoice for $5,298 has terms of 3/10 ROG and is dated March 15. The merchandise is received on March 20. How much should be paid if the invoice is paid on March 25?

74. Find the amount credited and the outstanding balance on an invoice dated August 19 if a partial payment of $500 is paid on August 25 and has terms of 3/10, 1/15, n/30. The amount of the invoice is $826.

75. An invoice for $1,200 is dated June 3, and terms of 3/10, n/30 are offered. A payment of $800 is made on June 12, and the remainder is paid on July 2. Find the amount remitted on July 2 and the total amount paid.

76. Campbell Sales purchased merchandise worth $745 and made a partial payment of $300 on day 13. If the sales terms were 2/15, n/30, how much was credited to the account? What was the outstanding balance?

77. A. J. Rachide purchased roll vinyl floor covering for $1,150 with sales terms of 3/15, n/30. He paid $800 on the bill within 15 days. How much was credited to his account? What was his outstanding balance after the payment?

78. A shipment of trailer parts has a bill of lading marked "FOB destination." Does the purchaser or vendor (seller) pay the freight? Who first receives the freight expense, the purchaser, vendor, or freight company?

79. Ultra Products Manufacturing Company places a shipment with a trucking company to be shipped "FOB shipping point." Who pays the freight?

Spreadsheet Exercises

80. In most spreadsheet software, percent and decimal equivalents of percents are interchangeable. That is, you may enter a percent and the program will automatically calculate with the decimal equivalent. The result may then be displayed as a percent or decimal equivalent by appropriate formatting functions. In writing the formulas use the decimal equivalent notation.

(a) Write formulas to complete the spreadsheet showing the Net Decimal Equivalent for items in invoice 322510.

(b) Write formulas to complete the spreadsheet to give the Net Price for each item in Invoice 322510.

81. Complete the spreadsheet using the formulas.

	A	B	C	D	E	F	G	H	I
1				Invoice 322510 with Trade Discounts					
2	Item #	Item Description	Price	Discount1	Discount2	Discount3	Net Decimal	Net Price	
3	588243	Large Easel	$23.50	5%	7%	8%			
4	723468	Beveled Mirror	$45.99	3%	5%	8%			
5	347328	Hor Plate Rack	$12.15	2%	3%	4%			
6	65843	Ver Plate Rack	$12.15	5%	5%	5%			
7	477873	Doll Stand	$3.50	4%	5%	7%			
8	101453	Room Divider	$98.75	1%	3%	4%			
9	454789	Sconce Frosted	$44.28	3%	7%	0%			
10	267811	Sconce Gold	$48.50	3%	3%	3%			
11	115226	Floor Lamp	$46.50	6%	6%	6%			
12	525793	Desk Lamp	$19.98	5%	3%	1%			

Challenge Problems

82. Swift's Dairy Mart receives a shipment of refrigeration units totaling $2,386.50 including a shipping charge of $32. Swift's returns $350 worth of the units. Terms of the purchase are 2/10, n/30. If Swift's takes advantage of the discount, what is the net amount payable?

83. An important part of owning a business is the purchasing of equipment and supplies to run the office. Before paying an invoice, all items must be checked and amounts refigured before writing the check for payment. At this time the terms of the invoice can be applied.

Using the information on the invoice Figure 7-2, fill in the extended amount for each line, the merchandise total, the tax amount, and the total invoice amount. Locate the terms of the invoice and find how much you would write a check for to pay Harper on each of the following dates:

March 5, 20XX
March 12, 20XX
March 25, 20XX

INVOICE DATE	TERMS	DATE OF ORDER	ORDERED BY	PHONE NO.	REMIT TO ▶	HARPER General Accounting Office
02/27/XX	2/10, 1/15, n/30	02/27/XX		803-000-4488		

LINE NO.	MANUFACTURER PRODUCT NUMBER	QTY. ORD.	QTY. B.O.	QTY. SHP.	U/M	DESCRIPTION	UNIT PRICE	EXTENDED AMOUNT
001	REMYY370/02253	3	0	3	EA	TONER, F/ROYAL TA210 COP 1	11.90	
002	Sk 1230M402	5	2	3	EA	CORRECTABLE FILM RIBBON	10.95	
003	JRLM01023	10	0	10	EA	COVER-UP CORRECTION TAPE	9.90	
004	rTu123456	9	0	9	EA	PAPER, BOND, WHITE 8 1/2 x 11	58.23	

DATE REC'D.	01460900001		5%		$0.00	TOTAL INVOICE AMOUNT ▶	
	OUR ORDER NO.	MDSE. TOTAL	TAX RATE	TAX AMOUNT	FREIGHT AMOUNT		

Figure 7-2 Harper Invoice

84. Mary Stone saved $15.98 by taking advantage of a $3\frac{1}{2}\%$ cash discount on an invoice. What was the amount of the invoice?

85. A retail clothing store advertised an additional 30% of already reduced prices to result in a total savings of 45–60%. By what percent have the prices already been reduced to result in a net reduction of 45%?

86. Find the percent by which retail clothing prices in exercise 85 have already been reduced to result in a net reduction of 60%.

87. The store advertised an additional discount of 10% for opening a credit card account. Find the net discount rate for persons opening a credit card account if the total savings on an item is 45%.

CHAPTER 7 PRACTICE TEST

1. The list price of a refrigerator is $550. The retailer can buy the refrigerator at the list price minus 20%. Find the trade discount.

2. The list price of a television is $560. The trade discount is $27.50. What is the net price?

3. A retailer can buy a lamp that is listed at $36.55 for 20% less than the list price. How much does the retailer have to pay for the lamp?

4. A manufacturer lists a dress at $39.75 with a trade discount of $3.60. Another manufacturer lists the same dress at $42 with a trade discount of $6.75. Which is the better deal?

5. One manufacturer lists a chair for $250 less 20%. Another manufacturer lists the same chair at $240 less 10%. Which manufacturer offers the better deal?

6. Find the net price if a discount series of 20/10/5 is deducted from $70.

7. Find the net decimal equivalent of the series 20/10/5.

8. Find the single discount equivalent for the discount series 20/20/10.

9. What do the initials ROG represent?

10. A retailer buys 20 boxes of stationery at $4 each and 400 greeting cards at $0.50 each. The discount rate for the order is 15%. Find the trade discount.

11. A retailer buys 30 electric frying pans listed at $40 each for 10% less than the list price. How much does the retailer have to pay for the frying pans?

12. What is the complement of 15%?

13. What do the initials EOM represent?

14. Shareesh Raz received a bill dated September 1 with sales terms of 3/10, 1/15, n/30. What percent discount will she receive if she pays the bill on September 6?

15. Domingo Castro received an invoice for $200 dated March 6 with sales terms 1/10, n/30. He paid the bill on March 9. What was his cash discount?

16. Gladys Quaweay received a bill for $300 dated April 7. The sales terms on the invoice were 2/10 EOM. If she paid the bill on May 2, how much did she pay?

17. An invoice for $400 dated December 7 has sales terms of 2/10 ROG. The merchandise arrived December 11. If the bill is paid on December 18, what is the amount due?

18. If the bill in exercise 17 is paid on January 2, what is the amount due?

19. A trade discount series of 10% and 20% is offered on 20 dartboards that are listed at $14 each. Also, a trade discount series of 20% and 10% is offered on 10 bowling balls that are listed at $40 each. Find the total net price for the dartboards and bowling balls.

20. Zing Manufacturing lists artificial flower arrangements at $30 less 10% and 10%. Another manufacturer lists the same flower arrangements at $31 less 10%, 10%, and 5%. Which is the better deal?

21. The Dean Specialty Company purchased monogrammed items worth $895 and made a partial payment of $600 on day 12. If the sales terms were 3/15, n/30, how much was credited to the account? What was the outstanding balance?

22. The monogrammed items purchased by Dean Specialty Company are shipped by rail from the manufacturer. The bill of lading is marked "FOB destination." Who is responsible for paying freight expenses?

SELF-CHECK 7.1

1. $400 × 0.30 = $120

2. $400 − 120 = $280

3. $14.67 × 20 = $293.40 total cost
$293.40 × 0.2 = $58.68 trade discount

4. 30 × 6 = 180 one-gallon units
180 × $2.18 = $392.40
$392.40 × 0.18 = $70.63 trade discount

5. $293.40 − $58.68 = $234.72 net price

6. $392.40 − $70.63 = $321.77

7. Complement = 100% − 20% = 1 − 0.2 = 0.8
$293.40 × 0.8 = $234.72 net price

8. Complement = 100% − 18% = 1 − 0.18 = 0.82
$392.40 × 0.82 = $321.77

9. Answers will vary.

10. Complement method. The net price can be found using a direct series of calculations.

11. Notebooks: 15 × $1.50 = $22.50
Looseleaf paper: 10 × $0.89 = $8.90
Ballpoint pens: 30 × $0.79 = $23.70
Total list price = $22.50 + $8.90 + $23.70 = $55.10
40% trade discount = $55.10 × 0.4 = $22.04
Net price = $55.10 − $22.04 = $33.06

12. Complement = 100% − 40% = 1 − 0.4 = 0.6
Net price = $55.10 × 0.6 = $33.06

SELF-CHECK 7.2

1. 100% − 7% = 93% = 0.93
100% − 10% = 90% = 0.9
100% − 5% = 95% = 0.95
0.93 × 0.9 × 0.95 = 0.79515
100 × $215.00 = $21,500 list price of TVs
$21,500 × 0.79515 = $17,095.73 total net price of TVs

2. 100% − 5% = 95% = 0.95
100% − 5% = 95% = 0.95
100% − 10% = 90% = 0.90
(0.95)(0.95)(0.9) = 0.81225
36 × $1,599.00 = $57,564 total list price
$57,564 × 0.81225 = $46,756.36

3. 100% − 12% = 88% = 0.88
100% − 10% = 90% = 0.9
100% − 6% = 94% = 0.94
0.88 × 0.9 × 0.94 = 0.74448
$800 × 0.74448 = $595.58

4. 100% − 25% = 75% = 0.75
100% − 15% = 85% = 0.85
100% − 10% = 90% = 0.90
0.75 × 0.85 × 0.90 = 0.57375
1.0000 − 0.57375 = 0.42625
$2,200 × 0.42625 = $937.75

5. $100\% - 10\% = 90\% = 0.9$
$100\% - 10\% = 90\% = 0.9$
$100\% - 10\% = 90\% = 0.9$
$0.9 \times 0.9 \times 0.9 = 0.729$
$1 - 0.729 = 0.271$
$\$269 \times 0.271 = \$72.90$
$\$269 - \$72.90 = \$196.10$

7. $100\% - 5\% = 95\% = 0.95$
$100\% - 5\% = 95\% = 0.95$
$100\% - 10\% = 90\% = 0.90$
$0.95 \times 0.95 \times 0.9 = 0.81225$
$\$189.97 \times 0.81225 = \$154.30$
$100\% - 5\% = 95\% = 0.95$
$100\% - 10\% = 90\% = 0.9$
$100\% - 10\% = 90\% = 0.9$
$0.95 \times 0.9 \times 0.9 = 0.7695$
$\$210 \times 0.7695 = \$161.60$
The better deal is $189.97 with discounts 5/5/10.

9. $100\% - 5\% = 95\% = 0.95$
$100\% - 10\% = 90\% = 0.9$
$100\% - 10\% = 90\% = 0.9$
$0.95 \times 0.9 \times 0.9 = 0.7695$
$\$1,899 \times 0.7695 = \$1,461.28$
$100\% - 5\% = 95\% = 0.95$
$100\% - 5\% = 95\% = 0.95$
$100\% - 10\% = 90\% = 0.9$
$0.95 \times 0.95 \times 0.9 = 0.81225$
$\$1,800 \times 0.81225 = \$1,462.05$
The better deal is $1,899 with discounts of 5/10/10.

11. $100\% - 15\% = 85\%$
$100\% - 12\% = 88\%$
$100\% - 5\% = 95\%$
$0.85 \times 0.88 \times 0.95 = 0.7106$
Net price $= \$460 \times 0.7106 = \$326.88$
$100\% - 10\% = 90\%$
$100\% - 10\% = 90\%$
$100\% - 5\% = 95\%$
$0.9 \times 0.9 \times 0.95 = 0.7695$
Net price $= \$410 \times 0.7695 = \$315.50$
The better deal is $410 with a discount series of 10/10/5.

6. $100\% - 5\% = 95\% = 0.95$
$100\% - 5\% = 95\% = 0.95$
$100\% - 8\% = 92\% = 0.92$
$0.95 \times 0.95 \times 0.92 = 0.8303$
$1 - 0.8303 = 0.1697$
$\$395 \times 0.1697 = \$67.03$

8. $100\% - 8\% = 92\% = 0.92$
$100\% - 8\% = 92\% = 0.92$
$100\% - 5\% = 95\% = 0.95$
$0.92 \times 0.92 \times 0.95 = 0.80408$
$\$1,899 \times 0.80408 = \$1,526.95$
$100\% - 10\% = 90\% = 0.9$
$100\% - 5\% = 95\% = 0.95$
$100\% - 5\% = 95\% = 0.95$
$0.9 \times 0.95 \times 0.95 = 0.81225$
$\$2,000 \times 0.81225 = \$1,674.50$
$\$1,624.50 + \$50$ shipping $= \$1,674.50$
The better deal is $1,899 with discounts of 8/8/5 and no shipping charge.

10. $100\% - 20\% = 80\% = 0.8$
$100\% - 10\% = 90\% = 0.9$
$100\% - 5\% = 95\% = 0.95$
$0.8 \times 0.9 \times 0.95 = 0.684$
$1 - 0.684 = 0.316$ single discount equivalent for 20/10/5 series
Trade discount $= 0.316 \times \$1,000 = \$316$
$100\% - 5\% = 95\% = 0.95$
$100\% - 10\% = 90\% = 0.9$
$100\% - 20\% = 80\% = 0.8$
$0.95 \times 0.9 \times 0.8 = 0.684$
$1 - 0.684 = 0.316$ single discount equivalent for 5/10/20 series
Trade discount $= 0.316 \times \$1,000 = \$316$
Both series result in the same trade discount.

1. Invoice paid within 2% discount period.
   $540 \times 0.02 = \$10.80$ cash discount

2. $540 - \$10.80 = \$529.20$ net amount

3. Invoice paid within 4% discount period.
   $1 - 0.04 = 0.96$ complement
   $450 \times 0.96 = \$432$ net amount

4. Invoice paid within 1% discount period.
   $1 - 0.01 = 0.99$ complement
   $450 \times 0.99 = \$445.50$ net amount

5. No cash discount allowed.
   $450 is due.

6. Bill paid within 2% discount period.
   $1 - 0.02 = 0.98$ complement
   $648 \times 0.98 = \$635.04$ net amount

7. Bill paid within 1% discount period.
   $1 - 0.01 = 0.99$ complement
   $648 \times 0.99 = \$641.52$ net amount

8. No cash discount allowed.
   $648 is due.

9. 3% interest penalty charged
   $648 \times 0.03 = \$19.44$ interest penalty
   $648 + \$19.44 = \$667.44$ total bill

10. June 18 payment is within the 3% discount period.
    $1,296.45 \times 0.03 = \$38.89$ discount

11. $1,296.45 - \$38.89 = \$1,257.56$ net amount

12. Bill paid within 2% discount period.
    $1 - 0.02 = 0.98$ complement
    $800 \times 0.98 = \$784$ net amount

13. Bill paid within 2% discount period.
    $1 - 0.02 = 0.98$ complement
    $1,250 \times 0.98 = \$1,225$ net amount

14. No cash discount allowed.
    $798.53 is due.

15. April 30 is within the 3% discount period.
    $1 - 0.03 = 0.97$ complement
    $493 \times 0.97 = \$478.21$ net amount

16. October 27 is within the 2% discount period.
    $1 - 0.02 = 0.98$ complement
    $900 \times 0.98 = \$882$ net amount

17. No cash discount allowed.
    $900 is due.

18. June 12 is within the 2% discount period.
    $1 - 0.02 = 0.98$ complement
    $5,835 \times 0.98 = \$5,718.30$ net amount

19. No cash discount allowed.
    $392.34 is due.

20. $400 payment is within the 3% discount period.
    $1 - 0.03 = 0.97$ complement
    $\dfrac{400}{0.97} = \$412.37$ amount credited to account
    $730 - \$412.37 = \$317.63$ outstanding balance

21. $2,000 payment is within the 3% discount period.
    $1 - 0.03 = 0.97$ complement
    $\dfrac{\$2,000}{0.97} = \$2,061.86$ amount credited to account
    $3,982.48 - \$2,061.86 = \$1,920.62$ outstanding balance

22. $2,000 payment is within the 2% discount period.
    $1 - 0.02 = 0.98$ complement
    $\dfrac{\$2,000}{0.98} = \$2,040.82$ amount credited to account
    $2,983 - \$2,040.82 = \$942.18$ outstanding balance

23. Better Bilt Bicycles paid the freight to the freight company.

24. Joseph Denatti pays the freight to the freight company.

25. The vendor pays the shipping company and adds the charge to Phyllis's invoice.

26. FOB shipping point: Buyer pays shipping charges to the freight company upon receipt of the merchandise. Prepay and add: Vendor pays shipping charges to the freight company and adds these charges to the invoice. The receiving company pays shipping charges to the vendor.

Markup and Markdown

Good Decisions through Teamwork

Laundry detergent is one of the most stable selling items in a grocery store. Your team will investigate and report on the markup of one leading brand of a 50-oz. box of regular laundry detergent. In your team investigation include four types of grocery stores: (1) an independently owned grocery store that is not a member of a buying group, (2) an independently owned grocery store such as Piggly Wiggly that is a member of a local buying group of about 30 stores, (3) a company-owned store such as Albertsons that uses regional buying groups of at least 100 stores, and (4) Walmart, which buys for all its stores through its national buying group.

Interview the grocery pricer for each store regarding the current selling price of the selected product, the net price, amount of markup, and how the markup was calculated. Ask about their use of *"loss leaders."* Loss leaders are products that may be sold at a loss and are designed specifically to attract customers. Together, read, critique, and edit each member's findings and organize a final report. Be sure to include introductory and summary paragraphs; discuss the advantages and disadvantages of shopping at each type of grocery store from a consumer's viewpoint.

Any successful business must keep prices low enough to attract customers, yet high enough to pay expenses and make a profit.

The price at which a business purchases merchandise is called the **cost.** The merchandise is then sold at a higher price called the **selling price.** The difference between the selling price and the cost is the **markup** or **gross profit** or **margin.** Merchandise may also be reduced from the original selling price. The amount the selling price is reduced is called the **markdown.**

Markups and markdowns are an important part of operating a business.

8.1 Markup

1 Find the markup, cost, selling price, rate of markup, or rate of selling price when the markup is based on cost.

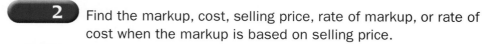

2 Find the markup, cost, selling price, rate of markup, or rate of cost when the markup is based on selling price.

3 Compare markup based on cost with markup based on selling price.

The markup rate can be calculated as a percentage of either the cost or the selling price of an item. Most manufacturers calculate markup as a percentage of *cost,* since they typically keep their records in terms of cost. Some wholesalers and a few retailers also use this method. Many retailers, however, use the *selling price* as a base in computing markup since they keep most of their records in terms of selling price.

Three basic formulas describe the relationship among cost, markup, and selling price, regardless of whether the markup rate is a percentage of cost or selling price. You can use these formulas to find the value of any one of the three amounts if you know the values of the other two.

$$\text{Selling price} = \text{cost} + \text{markup}, \qquad S = C + M$$
$$\text{Cost} = \text{selling price} - \text{markup}, \qquad C = S - M$$
$$\text{Markup} = \text{selling price} - \text{cost}, \qquad M = S - C$$

The first of the three formulas is the one referred to most often. The techniques we learned in solving equations can be applied in the first formula no matter which amount is unknown. Similarly, whether markup is based on cost or selling price, the *rate* of markup, the *rate* of selling price, and the *rate* of cost are related in the same way.

$$\text{Rate of } S = \text{rate of } C + \text{rate of } M$$
$$\text{Rate of } C = \text{rate of } S - \text{rate of } M$$
$$\text{Rate of } M = \text{rate of } S - \text{rate of } C$$

1 Find the markup, cost, selling price, rate of markup, or rate of selling price when the markup is based on cost

Most "markup problems" give you three facts and ask you to find additional facts. To organize the information you have and determine what you need to find, create a table using the cost (C) + markup (M) = selling price (S) formula.

C	\$____	rate of C	100%
$+M$	\$____	$+$rate of M	____%
S	\$____	rate of S	____%

When markup is based on cost, the rate of cost is always 100%, as noted in the table. The rest of the numbers, both percents and dollars, can be filled in according to the facts of the given situation.

HOW TO Find the Markup *M*, Cost *C*, Selling Price *S*, Rate of Markup, or Rate of Selling Price When the Markup Is *Based on Cost*

1. Put known information in the table.

C	$___	rate of *C*	100%
+*M*	$___	+rate of *M*	___%
S	$___	rate of *S*	___%

2. If one dollar value and two rates are missing:

  (a) Use one of the markup formulas to find the missing dollar value:

$$C = S - M \quad \text{if } C \text{ is missing}$$

$$M = S - C \quad \text{if } M \text{ is missing}$$

$$S = C + M \quad \text{if } S \text{ is missing}$$

  (b) Use the percentage formula $R = \frac{P}{B}$ to find a missing rate. *R* is a missing rate, *P* is its corresponding dollar value, and *B* is the dollar value of the cost.

  (c) Use one of the rate-of-markup formulas to find the other missing rate.

Rate of *M* = rate of *S* − rate of cost or

Rate of *M* = rate of *S* − 100% if rate of *M* is missing

Rate of *S* = rate of cost + rate of markup or

Rate of *S* = 100% + rate of *M* if rate of *S* is missing

3. If one rate and two dollar values are missing:

  (a) Do step 2c to find the missing rate.

  (b) Use one of the percentage formulas to find a missing dollar value. *P* is either markup *M* or selling price *S*, *R* is its corresponding rate, and *B* is cost *C*.

$$P = RB \quad \text{if } S \text{ or } M \text{ is missing but } C \text{ is not}$$

$$B = \frac{P}{R} \quad \text{if } C \text{ is missing}$$

  (c) Do step 2a to find the final dollar value.

EXAMPLE The Van Dyke's Hat Shoppe buys hats from Carroll Millinery for $6 each and sells them for $10 each. Find the markup and the rate of markup based on cost. Check by using the rate of the selling price based on cost.

First, use a table to set up the problem. Remember, when doing a markup based on cost, the rate of cost is always 100%. Fill in the other two amounts you know from the problem: cost = $6 and selling price = $10.

C	$ 6	rate of *C*	100%
+*M*	$___	+rate of *M*	___%
S	$10	rate of *S*	___%

Since *M* is what we want to find, we need to use the formula $M = S - C$ (Markup = selling price − cost). The markup is $4, since $4 = 10 - 6$.

Next, use the percentage formula to find the *rate* of markup based on cost. As you saw in Chapter 3, the percentage formula may be written $P = R \times B$, $R = \frac{P}{B}$, or $B = \frac{P}{R}$. When finding the rate of markup based on cost, use the cost as the *base B,* the markup as the *percentage P,* and the rate of markup as the *rate R.* The percentage formula diagram is shown in Figure 8-1.

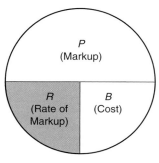

Figure 8-1 Percentage Formula Diagram

Use the form $R = \frac{P}{B}$ of the percentage formula to find the rate of markup based on the cost.

$$R = \frac{P}{B} = \frac{M}{C} = \frac{4}{6}$$

> **Divide the markup (percentage) by the cost (base) to find the rate of markup (rate).**

$$= \boxed{0.6666,} \text{ or } \boxed{67\%} \text{ (rounded)}$$

> **The rate of markup based on cost is 67%.**

Now use the relationship 100% + rate of markup = rate of selling price to find the rate of selling price: $\boxed{S\% = C\% + M\%}$

C	$ 6	rate of C	100%
$+M$	$ 4	+rate of M	67%
S	$10	rate of S	167%

Check:

$$P = R \times B$$
$$= \boxed{167\%} \times 6 = \boxed{1.67} \times 6$$

> **Cost ($10) is still the *base*.**

$$= \$10 \text{ (rounded)}$$

> **The answer is correct.**

The markup is $4 and the percent of markup based on cost is 67%.

In most instances, you may know the cost and the rate of markup based on cost and need to find the markup and the selling price. You can compute these amounts more easily if you use the table format.

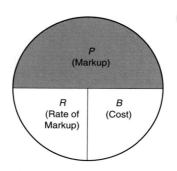

Figure 8-2 Markup = Rate of Markup × Cost

EXAMPLE A boutique pays $5 a pair for handmade earrings and sells them at a 50% markup rate based on cost. Find the markup and the selling price of the earrings.

Fill in the table with known data. $\boxed{S\% = C\% + M\%}$

C	$5	rate of C	100%
$+M$	$____	+rate of M	50%
S	$____	rate of S	____%

To find the selling price rate (150%), add the cost rate (100%) and the markup rate (50%).

Use the percentage formula $P = R \times B$ (Figure 8-2) to find the markup:

$$P = 0.5 \times 5$$

> **Multiply the rate of markup (rate) by the cost (base) to find the amount of markup (percentage).**

$$P = \$2.50$$

Now we add the cost and markup to find the selling price and complete the table:

$$S = C + M$$

C	$5	rate of C	100%
$+M$	$2.50	+rate of M	+50%
S	$7.50	rate of S	150%

> **The selling price is $7.50.**

Check:

$$P = R \times B$$
$$= \boxed{150\%} \times 5 = \boxed{1.5} \times 5 = \$7.50$$

> **The answer is correct.**

The markup is $2.50 and the selling price is $7.50.

To enhance sales, sometimes items are marked down from the selling price. Before making the decision to mark down merchandise, you want to know how much the item costs. When researching the cost through invoices is impractical, you can calculate the cost and markup by using the selling price when you know the standard markup rate.

EXAMPLE A camera sells for $20. The markup rate is 50% of the cost. Find the cost of the camera and the markup.

Fill in the table with known data. $S\% = C\% + M\%$

C	$\$\_\_\_$	rate of C	100%
$+ M$	$\$\_\_\_$	$+$rate of M	50%
S	$\$20$	rate of S	$\_\_\_\%$

To find the selling price rate (150%), add the cost rate (100%) and the markup rate (50%).

Now find the missing cost. Use the formula $B = \frac{P}{R}$ (Figure 8-3), since B is the base, or cost.

$$B = \frac{P}{R} = \frac{\text{selling price}}{\text{rate of selling price}} = \frac{20}{150\%} = \frac{20}{1.5}$$

$$= \$13.33, \text{ rounded to the nearest cent}$$

Thus, the cost is $13.33. To find the markup, use the markup formula $M = S - C$.

$$\$6.67 = \$20 - \$13.33$$

Complete the table and check:

C	$\$13.33$	rate of C	100%
$+M$	$\$6.67$	$+$rate of M	50%
S	$\$20.00$	rate of S	150%

Check:

$$P = R \times B$$

$$= 150\% \times 13.33 = 1.5 \times 13.33 = \$20 \text{ (rounded)}$$

The cost is $13.33 and the markup is $6.67.

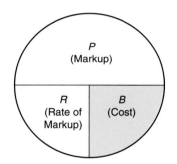

Figure 8-3

$$\text{Cost} = \frac{\text{Markup}}{\text{Rate of Markup}}$$

2 Find the markup, cost, selling price, rate of markup, or rate of cost when the markup is based on selling price.

As noted earlier, most retailers base markup on the selling price because this method works best with their other records such as inventory. When the *markup is based on cost,* the *cost* is the *base* and the rate of cost is 100%. Similarly, when the ***markup is based on selling price,*** the **selling price** is the *base* and the rate of selling price is 100%.

HOW TO Find the Markup *M*, Cost *C*, Selling Price *S*, Rate of Markup, or Rate of Cost When the Markup Is Based on Selling Price

1. Put known information in the table.

C	$____	rate of *C*	____%
+*M*	$____	+rate of *M*	____%
S	$____	rate of *S*	100%

2. If one dollar value and two rates are missing:

(a) Use one of the markup formulas to find the missing dollar value.

$C = S - M$	if *C* is missing
$M = S - C$	if *M* is missing
$S = C + M$	if *S* is missing

(b) Use the percentage formula $R = \frac{P}{B}$ to find a missing rate. *R* is a missing rate, *P* is its corresponding dollar value, and *B* is the selling price.

(c) Use one of the rate-of-markup formulas to find the other missing rate.

Rate of $C = 100\% -$ rate of *M*	if rate of *C* is missing
Rate of $M = 100\% -$ rate of *C*	if rate of *M* is missing

3. If one rate and two dollar values are missing:

(a) Do step 2c to find the missing rate.

(b) Use one of the percentage formulas to find a missing dollar value. *P* is either markup *M* or cost *C*, *R* is its corresponding rate, and *B* is the selling price *S*.

$P = RB$	if *C* or *M* is missing but *S* is not
$B = \dfrac{P}{R}$	if *S* is missing

(c) Do step 2a to find the final dollar value.

EXAMPLE A calculator costs $5 and sells for $10. Find the rate of markup based on selling price.

Fill in the table with known data.

C	$ 5	rate of *C*	____%
+*M*	$____	+rate of *M*	____%
S	$10	rate of *S*	100%

The markup is based on selling price, so you know the rate of selling price is 100%.

Use the formula $M = S - C$:

$10
−$ 5
$ 5

Subtract the cost from the selling price to find the markup.

Use the percentage formula $R = \frac{P}{B}$ (Figure 8-4) to find the rate of markup. The markup, $5 , is the percentage *P*, and the selling price, $10 , is the base *B*.

$$R = \frac{P}{B} = \frac{\text{markup}}{\text{selling price}} = \frac{5}{10} = 0.5 = 50\%$$

The rate of markup based on selling price is 50%.

Complete the table as a check of your work. To complete the table, you still need the rate of cost.

Figure 8-4 Rate of Markup $= \dfrac{\text{Markup}}{\text{Selling Price}}$

Use the formula $C\% = 100\% - M\%$.

C	\$ 5	rate of C	50%
$+M$	\$ 5	$+$rate of M	50%
S	\$10	rate of S	100%

Subtract the markup rate (50%) from the selling price rate (100%) to find the cost rate: 100% − 50% = 50%.

Check:

$$P = R \times B$$

$$= 50\% \times 10 = 0.5 \times 10 = \$5$$ **The answer is correct.**

The rate of markup based on selling price is 50%.

In some instances you may have records indicating the markup and the rate of markup but not the cost or the selling price. While the cost and selling price can be calculated from the markup and rate of markup, it is not likely that this situation will occur often.

EXAMPLE   Find the cost and selling price if a textbook is marked up \$5 with a 20% markup rate based on selling price.

If the selling price rate is 100% and the markup rate is 20%, then the cost rate equals 100% − 20%, or 80%. ($C\% = 100\% - M\%$).

C	\$___	rate of C	80%
$+M$	\$5	$+$rate of M	20%
S	\$___	rate of S	100%

Use the formula $B = \frac{P}{R}$ to find the base or selling price (Figure 8-5). The markup, \$5, is the percentage P, and the rate of markup, 20%, is the rate R or 0.2.

$$B = \frac{P}{R} = \frac{\text{markup}}{\text{rate of markup}} = \frac{\$5}{0.2} = \$25$$ **The base or selling price is \$25.**

Figure 8-5   Selling Price $= \dfrac{\text{Markup}}{\text{Rate of Markup}}$

Use the formula $C = S - M$ to find the cost and complete the table.

C	\$20	rate of C	80%
$+M$	\$ 5	$+$rate of M	20%
S	\$25	rate of S	100%

Check:

$$80\% \times \$25 = 0.08 \times \$25 = \$20$$ **The answer is correct.**

The cost is \$20 and the selling price is \$25.

EXAMPLE   Find the markup and cost of a box of pencils that sells for \$2.99 and is marked up 25% of the selling price.

The rate of cost is 100% − the rate of markup, or 100% − 25%, or 75% ($C\% = 100\% - M\%$).

C	\$___	rate of C	75%
$+M$	\$___	$+$rate of M	25%
S	\$2.99	rate of S	100%

Since you are looking for the markup, or percentage P, use the formula $P = RB$ (Figure 8–6). The selling price, or base B, is \$2.99, and the rate of markup, or rate R, is 25%.

$$P = RB$$

$$P = \text{rate of markup} \times \text{selling price}$$

$$P = 0.25 \ (2.99)$$

$$P = \$0.75$$

Round to the nearest cent. The markup is \$0.75.

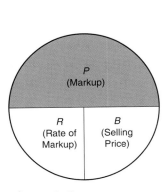

Figure 8-6   Markup = Rate of Markup × Selling Price

Use the formula $C = S - M$.
$$C = \$2.99 - \$0.75 = \$2.24$$

C	$2.24	rate of C	75%
$+M$	$0.75	+rate of M	25%
S	$2.99	rate of S	100%

Check:

$$75\% \times \$2.99 = 0.75 \times \$2.99$$
$$= \$2.24 \text{ (rounded)} \quad \textbf{The answer is correct.}$$

The markup is \$0.75 and the cost is \$2.24.

EXAMPLE Find the selling price and markup for a pair of jeans that costs the retailer \$28 and is marked up 30% of the selling price.

Since one of the known values is the cost, we should find the percent that the cost is of the selling price. $C\% = S\% - M\%$

$$70\% = 100\% - 30\% \quad \textbf{Cost rate equals selling price rate minus markup rate.}$$

C	$28	rate of C	70%
$+M$	$___	+rate of M	30%
S	$___	rate of S	100%

Use the formula $B = \frac{P}{R}$ (Figure 8-7) to find the selling price, or base B, given the cost, \$28, as the percentage P and the rate of cost, 70%, as the rate R.

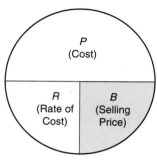

Figure 8-7
$$\text{Selling Price} = \frac{\text{Cost}}{\text{Rate of Cost}}$$

$$B = \frac{P}{R} = \frac{\text{cost}}{\text{rate of cost}} = \frac{\$28}{0.7} = \$40 \quad \textbf{The selling price is \$40.}$$

Use the formula $M = S - C$.

C	$28	rate of C	70%
$+M$	$12	+rate of M	30%
S	$40	rate of S	100%

($12 = $40 − $28)

Check:

$$30\% \times 40 = 0.3 \times 40 = \$12 \quad \textbf{The answer is correct.}$$

The selling price is \$40 and the markup is \$12.

 TIP! **Finding the Rate of Markup**

To help remember a strategy for finding missing amounts or rates in markup problems, use these tips:

1. When the markup is based on cost, it means that the rate of the cost is given, and is 100%.
   When the markup is based on selling price, it means that the rate of the selling price is given, and is 100%.
   Thus, at least one rate is given in each instance.
2. If two dollar amounts and one rate are given, first find the third dollar amount. Then find the missing rates.
3. If two rates and one dollar amount are given, first find the missing rate. Then find the missing dollar amounts.

All markup problems are solved in basically the same way. The key is that when the markup rate is based on selling price, the selling price is the base, so the selling price rate is 100%; when the markup rate is based on cost, the cost is the base, so the cost rate is 100%. You can then use the percentage formula or one of its variations, substitute in the known values, and solve for the missing value.

 TIP! Match the Rate and Percentage

Look again at the previous two examples and Figures 8-6 and 8-7. When the *percentage* is the markup, the *rate* is the rate of markup. When the *percentage* is the *cost,* the *rate* is the rate of cost.

 3 Compare markup based on cost with markup based on selling price.

If you go into a store and are told that the markup rate is 25%, you don't know whether that means markup based on cost or on selling price. What's the difference? Let's use a new computer as an example. The store pays $1,500 for it and sells it for $2,000. Here is the difference in rates of markup:

$$R = \frac{\$500 \text{ markup}}{\$2,000 \text{ selling price}} = 25\% \text{ markup based on selling price}$$

$$R = \frac{\$500 \text{ markup}}{\$1,500 \text{ cost}} = 33\frac{1}{3}\% \text{ markup based on cost}$$

Sometimes it is necessary to switch from a markup based on selling price to a markup based on cost, or vice versa. Here is how to do it.

 TIP! Convert a Markup Rate Based on Selling Price to a Markup Rate Based on Cost

1. Write the markup rate based on selling price in decimal form.
2. Subtract the markup rate (decimal form) based on selling price from 1.
3. Divide the markup rate (decimal form) based on selling price by the difference from step 2.

Markup rate (decimal form) based on cost

$$= \frac{\text{markup rate (decimalform) based on selling price}}{1 - \text{markup rate (decimal form) based on selling price}}$$

EXAMPLE A desk is marked up 25% based on selling price. What is the equivalent markup rate based on the cost?

$$25\% = 0.25 \qquad \textbf{Write the rate in decimal form.}$$

$$\text{Markup rate based on cost} = \frac{\text{markup rate based on selling price}}{1 - \text{markup rate of selling price}}$$

$$= \frac{0.25}{1 - 0.25} = \frac{0.25}{0.75} = 0.333 \text{ or } 33.3\%$$

The markup rate based on cost is 33.3%.

Use Memory Keys or Parentheses

Basic calculator using memory:

$\boxed{\text{AC}}$ $\boxed{\text{MC}}$ 1 $\boxed{-}$ .25 $\boxed{=}$ $\boxed{\text{M+}}$ $\boxed{\text{C}}$ .25 $\boxed{\div}$ $\boxed{\text{MR}}$ $\boxed{=}$

Display 0.33333333

Scientific calculator using parentheses:

$\boxed{\text{AC}}$ .25 $\boxed{\div}$ $\boxed{(}$ 1 $\boxed{-}$ .25 $\boxed{)}$ $\boxed{=}$

Display 0.33333333

 HOW TO Convert a Markup Rate Based on Cost to a Markup Rate Based on Selling Price

1. Write the markup rate based on cost in decimal form.
2. Add the markup rate (decimal form) based on cost to 1.
3. Divide the markup rate (decimal form) based on cost by the sum from step 2.

Markup rate (decimal form) based on selling price

$$= \frac{\textbf{markup rate (decimal form) based on cost}}{\textbf{1 + markup rate (decimal form) based on cost}}$$

EXAMPLE A VCR is marked up 40% based on cost. What is the markup percent based on selling price?

$$40\% = 0.4 \qquad \text{Convert the percent to a decimal and use the formula.}$$

$$\text{Markup rate based on selling price} = \frac{\text{markup rate based on cost}}{1 + \text{markup rate based on cost}}$$

$$\frac{0.4}{1 + 0.4} = \frac{0.4}{1.4}$$

$$= 0.2857, \text{ or } 28.57\%$$

The markup rate based on selling price is 28.57%.

TIP! Memory Tips for Equivalency Formulas

Here are some tips to help you remember the two formulas for converting between markup based on cost and markup based on selling price:

$$\text{Markup based on cost} = \frac{\text{original markup rate } (M\%)}{\text{original cost rate } (C\%)}$$

Since the original markup rate is based on the selling price, $S\% = 100\%$.

$$C\% = S\% - M\%$$
$$= 100\% - M\%$$
$$C\% = 1 - M\%$$

Similarly,

$$\text{Markup rate based on selling price} = \frac{\text{original markup rate } (M\%)}{\text{original selling price rate } (S\%)}$$

Since this original markup rate is based on the cost, $C\% = 100\%$.

$$\text{The original } S\% = C\% + M\%$$
$$= 100\% + M\%$$
$$S\% = 1 + M\%$$

SELF-CHECK 8.1

1

1. Bottoms Up buys mugs for $2 each and sells them for $6 each. Find the markup and the rate of markup based on cost.

2. It's a Cinch pays $4 each for handmade belts and sells them at a 60% markup rate based on cost. Find the markup and the selling price of the belts.

3. A compact disc player sells for $300. The markup rate is 40% of the cost. Find the cost of the CD player and the markup.

4. The Manie Luce Wholesale Show sells battery powered massagers for $8.50 if they are purchased in lots of 36 or more. The Gift Horse Shoppe purchased 48 and marked them up 65% based on the cost. Find the total cost of the massagers, the selling price of each one, and the total selling price for all 48 if none of them must be marked down to sell them.

5. Just The Right Thing, a gift and decorator shop, purchased 20 decorative enamel balls for $12.75 each and marked them up 75% of the wholesale price. Find the total cost, the amount of markup on each one, and the total amount of markup for the 20 balls.

2

6. A compact disc costs $4 and sells for $12. Find the rate of markup based on the selling price.

7. Find the cost and selling price if a hard hat is marked up $5 with a 40% markup rate based on the selling price.

8. Find the markup and cost of a magazine that sells for $3.50 and is marked up 50% of the selling price.

9. Find the selling price and markup if a box of photocopier paper costs $40 and is marked up 60% of the selling price.

10. A chair is marked up 60% based on selling price. What is the rate of markup based on cost?

11. A surround sound audio system is marked up 75% based on selling price. What is the rate of markup based on cost?

12. A lamp is marked up 120% based on cost. What is the rate of markup based on selling price?

13. A stereo TV is marked up 82% based on cost. What is the rate of markup based on selling price?

14. A computer desk is marked up 68% based on selling price. What is the rate of markup based on cost?

8.2 Markdown

 Find the markdown, reduced (new) price, original selling price, rate of markdown, or rate of reduced (new) price.

Merchants often have to reduce the price of merchandise from the price at which it was originally sold. There are many reasons for this. Sometimes merchandise is marked too high to begin with. Sometimes it gets worn or dirty or goes out of style. Flowers, fruits, vegetables, and baked goods that have been around a day or two must be sold for less than fresh items because the quality of the items is not as good. Competition from other stores may also require that a retailer mark down prices.

 Find the markdown, reduced (new) price, original selling price, rate of markdown, or rate of reduced (new) price.

No matter what the reason for the reduction in price, you can determine the **markdown** by subtracting the reduced price from the original selling price. You can then figure the rate of markdown by using a variation of the percentage formula, $R = \frac{P}{B}$. Unlike markups, which may be based on selling price *or* cost, markdowns, for all practical purposes, are always based on selling price. Applying the percentage formula, then, the base B is always the selling price.

The markup and rate of markup formulas we gave on page 338 actually apply to markdown situations, too. When we use the formulas for markdown situations, S is the original selling price, C is the reduced price, and M is the markdown. The How-To box on page 339 applies as well. Here, too, S is the original selling price, C is the reduced price, and M is the markdown. To reinforce these formulas and How-To steps, we repeat them here. Notice that the rate of the original selling price S is 100% because the base for markdowns is the original selling price.

Reduced (new) price = original selling price − markdown $\qquad N = S - M$

Markdown = original selling price − reduced (new) price $\qquad M = S - N$

Original selling price = reduced (new) price + markdown $\qquad S = N + M$

Rate of N = 100% − rate of M

Rate of M = 100% − rate of N

100% = rate of N + rate of M

HOW TO Find the Markdown, Reduced Price, Original Selling Price, Rate of Markdown, or Rate of Reduced Price

1. Place known information in the table

N	$\$\_\_\_$	rate of N	$\_\_\_\%$
$+M$	$\$\_\_\_$	$+$rate of M	$\_\_\_\%$
S	$\$\_\_\_$	rate of S	100%

2. If one dollar value and two rates are missing:

   (a) Use one of the markdown formulas to find the missing dollar value:

   $$N = S - M \qquad \text{if } N \text{ is missing}$$

   $$M = S - N \qquad \text{if } M \text{ is missing}$$

   $$S = N + M \qquad \text{if } S \text{ is missing}$$

   (b) Use the percentage formula $R = \frac{P}{B}$ to find a missing rate. R is missing rate, P is its corresponding dollar value, and B is original selling price.

   (c) Use one of the rate-of-markdown formulas to find the other missing rate:

   $$\text{Rate of } N = 100\% - \text{rate of } M \qquad \text{if rate of } N \text{ is missing}$$

   $$\text{Rate of } M = 100\% - \text{rate of } N \qquad \text{if rate of } M \text{ is missing}$$

3. If one rate and two dollar values are missing:

   (a) Do step 2c to find the missing rate.

   (b) Use one of the percentage formulas to find a missing dollar value. P is either markdown M or reduced price N, R is its corresponding rate, and B is original selling price.

   $$P = RB \qquad \text{if } N \text{ or } M \text{ is missing but } S \text{ is given}$$

   $$B = \frac{P}{R} \qquad \text{if } S \text{ is missing}$$

   (c) Do step 2a to find the final dollar value.

16.67%

EXAMPLE A lamp originally sold for $36 and was marked down to sell for $30. Find the *markdown* and the *rate of markdown* (to the nearest hundredth).

Fill in the table with known data.

N	$\$30$	rate of N	$\_\_\_\%$
$+M$	$\$\_\_\_$	$+$rate of M	$\_\_\_\%$
S	$\$36$	rate of S	100%

Use the formula: Markdown = original selling price − reduced (new) price.

$$M = \$36 - \$30 = \$6$$

The markdown is $6.

Now use the formula $R = \frac{P}{B}$ to find the rate of markdown. The original selling price, $36, is the base B, and the markdown, $6, is the percentage P.

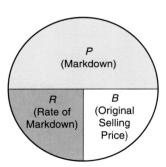

Figure 8-8 Rate of Markdown = $\dfrac{\text{Markdown}}{\text{Original Selling Price}}$

$$R = \frac{P}{B} = \frac{\text{markdown}}{\text{original selling price}} = \frac{\$6}{\$36} = 0.1667 = 16.67\% \qquad \textbf{(rounded)}$$

The lamp was marked down 16.67% of the original selling price.

To complete the table, use the formula $N\% = 100\% - M\%$. The rate of reduced price is $100\% - 16.67\%$ or 83.33% .

N	$30	rate of N	83.33%
$+M$	$ 6	$+$rate of M	16.67%
S	$36	rate of S	100%

Check:

$$83.33\% \times \$36 = 0.8333 \times \$36 = \$30 \qquad \textbf{The answer is correct.}$$

The amount of markdown is $6 and the rate of markdown is 16.67 %.

Learning Strategy Making Connections between Markup and Markdown

Some business processes use the same or similar terminology in different contexts. Examine the terms *original price* and *new price* when associated with markup and markdown.

Markup

Original price $=$ cost (C)
Upward change $=$ markup (M)
New price $=$ selling price (S)
$S = C + M$

Markdown

Original price $=$ selling price (S)
Downward change $=$ markdown (M)
New price $=$ reduced or sale price (N)
$N = S - M$

EXAMPLE   A wallet was originally priced at $12 and was reduced by 25%. Find the markdown and the sale (new) price.

Fill in the table with known data. $N\% = 100\% - M\%$

N	$____	rate of N	____%
$+M$	$____	$+$rate of M	25%
S	$12	rate of S	100%

Use the formula: Rate of $N = 100\%$ − rate of M.

$$\text{Rate of } N = 100\% - 25\% = 75\%$$

The rate of the sale or reduced (new) price is 75%.

Now use the percentage formula $P = RB$ (Figure 8-9) to find the markdown. The rate of markdown, 25%, is the rate R, and the original selling price, $12, is the base B.

$$P = RB = (\text{rate of markdown})(\text{selling price}) = 0.25 \times 12 = \$3$$

The markdown was $3.

Finally, to find the sale (new) price, use the formula: Reduced (new) price = original selling price − markdown.

$$\text{Reduced (new) price} = \$12 - \$3 = \$9$$

The sale (new) price was $9.

N	$ 9	rate of N	75%
$+M$	$ 3	$+$rate of M	25%
S	$12	rate of S	100%

Check:

$$75\% \times \$12 = 0.75 \times \$12 = 9$$

The markdown is $3 and the sale (new) price is $9.

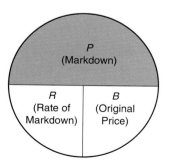

Figure 8-9 Markdown = Rate of Markdown × Original Price

1. A printer originally sold for $480 and was marked down to sell for $420. Find the markdown and the markdown rate.

2. A Sony handycam camcorder originally sold for $599.97 and was marked down to sell for $550. Find the markdown and the rate of markdown based on the original selling price.

3. An RCA 13″ TV with remote control originally sells for $169. It is marked down to sell for $139.97. Find the markdown and the rate of markdown.

4. Brand name walking shoes originally sell for $79.99. They are marked down to sell for $47.97. Find the markdown and the rate of markdown.

5. A Magnavox four-head Hi-Fi Stereo VCR originally sells for $549.99 and is marked down to sell for $509.99. Find the markdown and the rate of markdown.

6. A calculator that was originally priced at $115.95 was reduced by 15%. Find the markdown and the sale price (reduced price).

7. A Maytag super capacity washer originally priced at $529.99 is reduced by 23%. Find the markdown and the sale price.

8. A Quasar microwave oven originally priced at $368.00 has been placed on sale with a 25% markdown. Find the markdown and the sale price.

9. An Amana 25.0-cubic-foot refrigerator with cubed ice and water dispenser was originally priced at $1,899.97 and is included in a Harvest sale at a 21% discount. Find the markdown and the sale price.

10. A Motorola flip portable cellular phone weighing only 9.9 ounces is included in a Memorial Day sale. It was originally priced at $59.99 and is marked down by 19%. What sale price should be listed for the phone?

8.3 Markup and Markdown Series

> **1** Find the final selling price for a series of markups and markdowns.

> **2** Find the selling price to achieve a desired profit (markup).

Prices are in a continuous state of flux in the business world. Markups are made to cover increased costs. Markdowns are made to move merchandise more rapidly, to move dated or perishable merchandise, or to draw customers into a store.

> **1** Find the final selling price for a series of markups and markdowns.

Every business expects to mark down the price of seasonal and slow-moving merchandise. Sometimes prices are marked down several times or marked up between markdowns before the merchandise is sold. Calculating each stage of prices, markups, markdowns, and rates, we use exactly the same markup/markdown formulas and How-To steps as before. To apply these formulas and How-To steps, though, we must be sure we understand that both the markup and the markdown are based on the *previous selling price* in the series. So:

- For a stage that requires a *markdown*, identify the previous selling price as the *original selling price S* for this stage. Then use the How-To steps for markdown to find *the reduced or new price N*. This price is the selling price for this stage in the series.

- For a stage that requires a *markup,* identify the previous selling price as the *cost C* for this stage. Then use the How-To steps for markup *based on cost* to find the *selling price S.* This price is the selling price for this stage in the series.

HOW TO Find the Final Selling Price for a Series of Markups and Markdowns

1. For the first stage in the series, find the first selling price, if it isn't known already, using the first markup/markdown facts and the How-To steps for markup or markdown.

2. For each remaining stage in the series:

   (a) If the stage requires a **markdown,** identify the previous selling price as the *original selling price S* for this stage. Use the How-To steps for markdown to find the *reduced price N.* This price is the selling price for this stage.

   (b) If the stage requires a **markup,** identify the previous selling price as the *cost C* for this stage. Use the How-To steps for markup *based on cost* to find the *selling price S.* This price is the selling price for this stage.

3. Identify the selling price for the last stage as the *final selling price.*

EXAMPLE   Belinda's China Shop paid a wholesale price of $800 for a set of imported china. On August 8, Belinda marked up the china 50% based on the cost. On October 1, she marked the china down 25% for a special 10-day promotion. On October 11, she marked the china up 15%. The china was again marked down 30% for a preholiday sale. What was the final selling price of the china?

First Stage: August 8
Find the first selling price, using markup based on cost.

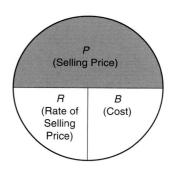

Figure 8-10 Selling Price = Rate of Selling Price × Cost

C	$800	rate of C	100%
$+M$	$___	+rate of M	50%
S	$___	rate of S	___%

The rate of selling price is 150% (100% + 50%) of the cost. Since the cost is $800, find the selling price as a percentage P of the $800 base cost (Figure 8-10).

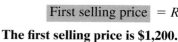

$$\text{First selling price} = RB = 150\% \times \$800 = 1.5 \times \$800 = \$1,200$$

The first selling price is $1,200.

Next Stage: October 1
The stage requires a 25% *markdown,* so identify the first selling price, $1,200, as the *original selling price S.* This is the base of the 25% markdown at this stage. Find the reduced price $N.$

N	$___	rate of N	___%
$+M$	$___	+rate of M	25%
S	$1,200	rate of S	100%

The rate of the reduced price is the rate of the original selling price minus the rate of markdown, or 100% − 25%, or 75%. Use the formula $P = RB$ to find the reduced price as a percentage P of the $1,200 base original selling price.

$$P = RB = 75\% \times \$1,200 = 0.75 \times \$1,200 = \$900$$

The reduced price is $900. This is the selling price at this stage.

Next Stage: October 11

The stage requires a 15% *markup,* so identify the previous selling price, $900, as the *cost C.* This is the base of the 15% markup at this stage. Find the selling price *S.*

$$
\begin{array}{lll}
C & \$900 & \text{rate of } C & 100\% \\
+M & \underline{\$\_\_\_} & +\text{rate of } M & \underline{15\%} \\
S & \$\_\_\_ & \text{rate of } S & \underline{\_\_\_}\%
\end{array}
$$

The rate of the selling price is 100% + 15%, or 115%. Use the formula $P = RB$ to find the selling price as a percentage *P* of the $900 base cost.

$$P = RB = 115\% \times \boxed{\$900} = 1.15 \times \boxed{\$900} = \$1{,}035$$

The selling price at this stage is $1,035.

Last stage

For the 30% markdown, we identify the selling price, $1,035 as the *original selling price S* and the base of the markdown (Figure 8-11).

$$
\begin{array}{lll}
N & \$\_\_\_ & \text{rate of } N & \underline{\_\_\_}\% \\
+M & \$\_\_\_ & +\text{rate of } M & 30\% \\
S & \$1{,}035 & \text{rate of } S & 100\%
\end{array}
$$

$$\text{Rate of } N = \text{rate of } S - \text{rate of } M = 100\% - 30\% = 70\%$$

$$P = RB = 70\% \times \boxed{\$1{,}035} = 0.7 \times \boxed{\$1{,}035} = \$724.50$$

The reduced price is $724.50 and is the final price in the series.

In many applications such as the previous example, the terms *cost, markdown, markup,* and *selling price* are not always used in the usual sense. For example, at the October 11 stage, the $900 price that is to be marked up is referred to as the cost. We are looking for a higher price that we will refer to as our selling price. Since we are making a change from $900, we consider $900 to be the base or 100%. The change is an increase or markup. The rate of change is the rate of markup and the rate of markup + 100% is the rate that the new (increase) price is when based on $900. Using a proportion we have the relationship:

$$\frac{\text{lower price}}{\text{higher price (H)}} = \frac{100\%}{100\% + 15\%}$$

Then,

$$\frac{\$900}{H} = \frac{1}{1.15}$$

$$H \times 1 = \$900 \times 1.15$$

$$H = \$1{,}035$$

In the last stage we reduce the price from $1,035. This price now becomes the base and the rate is 100%. Since the price is being decreased, we will refer to the price before the reduction as the selling price and the new reduced price as the cost or *N.* As a proportion:

$$\frac{\text{lower price}}{\text{higher price}} = \frac{100\% - 30\%}{100\%}$$

$$\frac{N}{\$1{,}035} = \frac{0.7}{1}$$

$$N \times 1 = \$1{,}035 \times 0.7$$

$$N = \$724.50$$

The Tip box that follows may help in clarifying this adaptation.

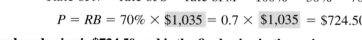

Figure 8-11   Reduced Price = Rate of Reduced Price × Current Selling Price

Sometimes in retail marketing the series of changes are all markdowns. We can adapt our procedure for finding the net price after applying a trade discount series, which was discussed in Chapter 7. Repricing individual items can be very time consuming, and many department stores have chosen to use a sign on an entire table or rack to indicate the same percent markdown on a variety of items. Also, as a further incentive to buy, they may publish a coupon that entitles you to "take an extra 10% off already reduced prices." This is a situation that can model the procedure for finding the net price after applying a trade discount series.

EXAMPLE   Burdines' has various sales racks throughout the store. Chloe Duke finds a coat that she would like to purchase from a rack labeled 50% off. She also has a newspaper coupon that reads "Take an additional 10% off any already reduced item." How much will a coat cost (net price) that was originally priced at $145? What is her total percent of reduction?

Discount rates are 50% and 10%. The net decimal equivalent is the decimal form of the rate she will have to pay.

$$0.5(0.9) = 0.45 \quad \text{net decimal equivalent}$$

$$\$145(.45) = \mathbf{\$65.25} \quad \text{net price or amount to be paid}$$

If Chloe pays 0.45 or 45% of the original price, **then the percent of reduction is 100% − 45% or 55%.**

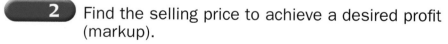 **2**   Find the selling price to achieve a desired profit (markup).

Most businesses anticipate that some seasonal merchandise will have to be marked down from the original selling price. Stores that sell perishable or strictly seasonal items (fresh fruits, vegetables, swimsuits, or coats, for example) usually anticipate from past experience how much merchandise will be marked down or discarded due to spoilage. For example, most retail stores mark down holiday items to 50% of the original price the day after the holiday. Thus, merchants set the original markup of such items to obtain the desired **profit** level based on the projected number of items sold at "full price" (the original selling price).

HOW TO Find the Selling Price to Achieve a Desired Profit

1. Establish the rate of profit (markup)—based on cost—desired on the sale of the merchandise.
2. Find the total cost of the merchandise: multiply the unit cost by the quantity of merchandise. Add in additional charges such as shipping.
3. Find the total desired profit (markup) based on cost: multiply the rate of profit (markup) by the total cost.
4. Find the total selling price: add the total cost and the total desired profit.
5. Establish the quantity expected to sell.
6. Divide the total selling price by the expect-to-sell quantity.

$$\text{Selling price to achieve desired profit (markup)} = \frac{\text{total selling price}}{\text{expect-to-sell quantity}}$$

EXAMPLE   Green's Grocery specializes in fresh fruits and vegetables. A portion of most merchandise must be reduced for quick sale, and some must be discarded because of spoilage. Hardy Green, the owner, must mark the selling price of incoming produce high enough to make the desired amount of profit while taking expected markdowns and spoilage into account. Hardy receives 400 pounds of bananas, for which he pays $0.15 per pound. On the average, 8% of the bananas will spoil. Find the selling price per pound to obtain a 175% markup on cost. The desired rate of profit (markup) is 175% based on cost.

$C = \$0.15 \times 400 = \$60$ **Find the total cost of the bananas.**

$M = 1.75 \times \$60 = \$105$ **Find the total profit (markup).**

$S = C + M = \$60 + \$105 = \boxed{\$165}$ **Find the total selling price.**

Hardy must receive $165 for the bananas he expects to sell. He expects 8% not to sell, or 92% to sell.

$0.92 \times 400 = \boxed{368}$ **Establish how many pounds he can expect to sell.**

He can expect to sell 368 pounds of bananas.

$$\text{Selling price per pound} = \frac{\text{total selling price}}{\text{number of pounds expected to sell}}$$

$$= \frac{\$165}{368} = \$0.448 \text{ or } \$0.45$$

Hardy must sell the bananas for $0.45 per pound to receive the profit he desires. If he sells more than 92% of the bananas, he will receive additional profit.

EXAMPLE   At the 7th Inning Sports Memorabilia Shop, Charlie has an opportunity to buy T-shirts with the 1999 University of Memphis basketball team imprinted on the shirt. The shirts will cost $6 each as long as he buys 200 shirts. He only expects to be able to sell 150 shirts before the end of the season; the other shirts will have little or no value. After doing marketing research, he thinks the shirts will sell only if they are priced at $10 or less. Of course, more shirts are likely to be sold if the price is significantly less than $10. Since he must have a 50% markup based on cost to cover overhead expenses and desired profit, should Charlie buy the shirts?

1 Decision needed   Should Charlie buy the University of Memphis T-shirts?

2 Known facts   Quantity of shirts to be purchased: 200 shirts
Quantity of shirts expected to be sold: 150 shirts
Cost per shirt: $6
Maximum selling price: $10 per shirt
Necessary rate of markup: 50% based on cost

3 Unknown fact   Selling price to achieve profit (markup)

4 Relationships   Total cost = cost per shirt × quantity purchased
Necessary markup = necessary rate of markup × total cost
Total selling price = total cost + necessary markup

$$\text{Selling price to achieve profit (markup)} = \frac{\text{total selling price}}{\text{expect-to-sell quantity}}$$

5 Estimation   If 150 shirts are sold at $10 each, the total selling price would be $1,500. If 200 shirts are purchased at $6 each, the total cost would be $1,200.

6 Calculation   Total cost = number of items × cost per item
Total cost = 200 × $6
Total cost = $1,200
Necessary markup = total cost × rate of necessary markup
Necessary markup = $1,200 × 50%
Necessary markup = $1,200 × 0.5
Necessary markup = $600
Total selling price = total cost + markup
Total selling price = $1,200 + $600
Total selling price = $1,800

$$\text{Selling price to achieve profit (markup)} = \frac{\text{total selling price}}{\text{expect-to-sell quantity}}$$

$$\text{Selling price} = \frac{\$1,800}{150 \text{ shirts}}$$

7 Interpretation   Selling price = $12 per shirt

8 Decision made   **The shirts should not be purchased** since Charlie would need to sell the shirts at $12 per shirt but, to sell, the shirts need to be priced at $10 or less.

1. The Splash Shop paid a wholesale price of $24 each for Le Paris swimsuits. On May 5 it marked up the suits 50% of this cost. On June 15 the swimsuits were marked down 15% for a two-day sale, and on June 17 they were marked up again by 10%. On August 30 the shop sold all remaining swimsuits for 40% off. What was the final selling price of a Le Paris swimsuit?

2. A ladies' suit selling for $135 is marked down 25% for a special promotion. It is later marked down 15% of the sale price. Since it still hasn't sold, it is marked down to a price 75% off the original selling price. What are the two sale prices of the suit? What is the final selling price of the suit?

3. Farmer Brown's fruit stand sells fresh fruits and vegetables. Becky Brown, the manager, must mark the selling price of incoming produce high enough to make the desired profit while taking expected markdowns and spoilage into account. Becky paid $0.35 per pound for 300 pounds of grapes. On the average, 12% of the grapes will spoil. Find the selling price per pound needed to achieve a 175% markup on cost.

4. Teddy Jeanfreau ordered 600 pounds of Red Delicious apples for the produce section of the supermarket. He paid $0.32 per pound for the apples and expected 15% of them to spoil. If the store wants to make a profit on cost of 90%, what should be the per-pound selling price?

5. The 7th Inning Sports Memorabilia Shop is considering buying T-shirts with the 2002 Salt Lake City Olympic emblem imprinted on them. The cost of the shirts, which includes permission fees paid to the Olympic Committee, will be $7.90 each if 1,000 shirts are purchased. Charlie projects that 800 shirts will sell before the Olympic games are over if he sells them at $15 each. However, Charlie calculates that he must have a 50% markup based on cost to justify handling them. Should Charlie buy the shirts?

Congressional Pay Raises

United States congressional salaries are determined by legislative act. A 1989 law was passed linking cost-of-living increases in legislators' salaries to the president's annual recommendation for all federal employees. This recommended increase for legislators takes effect automatically unless Congress votes to not accept the increase.

A pay raise essentially a "markup" in salary from the previous salary, and the amount is found in the same way as a markup of merchandise. The annual accounting period adopted by an enterprise is known as its fiscal year. The fiscal year ordinarily begins with the first day of the particular month selected, and ends on the last day of the twelfth month hence. The fiscal year period most commonly adopted is the calendar year, but other fiscal-year cycles are used in specialized businesses. The U.S. government's fiscal year begins on October 1 and ends on September 30. Pay increases ordinarily take place at the beginning of a fiscal year.

Examine the historical data regarding congressional salaries. Assume increases take place on October 1 unless otherwise noted.

Congressional Salaries Since 1789		
1789-1815—$6.00 per diem	1947-1955—$12,500 per annum	1990 (2/1)—$98,400 per annum
1815-1817—$1,500 per annum	1955-1965—$22,500 per annum	1991—$101,900 per annum
1817-1855—$8.00 per diem	1965-1969—$30,000 per annum	1991 (8/15)—$125,100 per annum
1855-1865—$3,000 per annum	1969-1975—$42,500 per annum	1992—$129,500 per annum
1865-1871—$5,000 per annum	1975-1977—$44,600 per annum	1993—$133,600 per annum
1871-1873—$7,500 per annum	1977-1978—$57,500 per annum	1994—$133,600 per annum
1873-1907—$5,000 per annum	1979-1983—$60,662.50 per annum	1995—$133,600 per annum
1907-1925—$7,500 per annum	1983—$69,800 per annum	1996—$133,600 per annum
1925-1932—$10,000 per annum	1984—$72,600 per annum	1997—$133,600 per annum
1932-1933—$9,000 per annum	1985-1986—$75,100 per annum	1998—$136,700 per annum
1933-1935—$8,500 per annum	1987 (1/1–2/3)—$77,400 per annum	1999—$136,700 per annum
1935-1947—$10,000 per annum	1987 (2/4)—$89,500 per annum	2000—$141,300 per annum

Note: Since the early 1980s, Congressional leaders (majority and minority leaders, the Speaker of the House and the Senate President *Pro Tempore*) have received slightly higher salaries than other members. In 2000 leaders earned $181,400 per year.

Source: Senate Historical Office and Senate Disbursing Office, "Salaries of Members of Congress: Payable Rates and Effective Dates, 1789-2000," Report No. 97-1011GOV, Congressional Research Service, Library of Congress, Washington, DC, Updated November 23, 1999. (*www.senate.gov*)

Exercises

1. What percent pay increase did legislators receive in 2000?
2. A pay increase was accepted for 1998. What was the percent of increase, to the nearest tenth of a percent, for 1998?

3. The recommended raise for 1994 was 3.7%; for 1995, 2.0%; for 1996, 2.4%; and for 1997, 2.1%. Congress did not accept the increase for each of these years. What would the 1997 salary have been if each of these increases had been accepted?

4. How much money per legislator can politicians say they have saved taxpayers by refusing pay raises in 1994 through 1997?

5. Find the percent of increase in legislative salaries from 1992 to 1993; from 1997 to 1998; and from 1999 to 2000

6. Find the percent of increase in legislative salaries from 1992 to 2000.

7. Compare the percent of increase from 1992 to 2000 (Exercise 6) to the sum of the percents of increase found in Exercise 5. Why are the two percents different?

8. By what percent does congressional leaders' salary exceed that of rank and file congress members?

9. George Washington's salary was $25,000. When adjusted for inflation, this amounts to $4.6 million in today's dollars. The current president earns $200,000. Today's president earns what percent of George Washington's salary adjusted to today's dollars?

10. The congress recently debated raising the president's salary to $400,000. How will this new salary compare as a percent of George Washington's salary adjusted to today's dollars?

11. How does the president's salary percent increase or decrease from 1789 to 2000 compare with the percent of increase or decrease in the salary of congress from 1815 to 2000, roughly the same period of time? Disregard any inflation factor in your calculations.

Answers

1. Legislators received a 3.4% increase in 2000.

2. The percent increase in 1998 was 2.3%

3. The 1994 salary would have been $138,543. The 1995 salary would have been $141,314. The 1996 salary would have been $144,706. The 1997 salary would have been $147,744. The 1998 salary would have been $151,142.

4. The savings per legislator is $14,442.

5. The percent increase from 1992 to 1993 was 3.2%. The precent increase from 1997 to 1998 was 2.3%. The percent increase from 1999 to 2000 was 3.4%

6. The percent increase from 1992 to 2000 was 9.1%

7. The sum of percents in Exercises 5 is 8.9% (3.2% + 2.3% + 3.4%) This is less than the percent of increase from 1992 to 2000 (9.1%). The overall percent of increase is more than the sum of the percents of the raises due to the compounding effect in which a worker earns a percent raise on each previous raise.

8. Congressional leaders' salaries exceed those of rank and file by 28.4%. $181,400 − $141,300 = $40,100 $40,100 ÷ $141,300 = 28.4%.

9. The current president's salary is 4.3% of George Washington's salary adjusted to today's dollars: $200,000 ÷ $4,600,000 = 4.3%

10. The proposed salary of $400,000 would be 8.7% of George Washington's salary adjusted to today's dollars.

11. The president's percent of salary increase (from $25,000 to $200,000) is 800%. The legislator's percent of salary increase (from $1,500 to $141,300) is 9,420%. (These figures disregard any inflation factor.)

Section
Outcome   Important Points with Examples

Section 8.1

Find the
markup, cost,
selling price,
rate of
markup, or
rate of selling
price when
the markup is
based on
cost.
(page 338)

1. Put known information in the table.

	C	$\$$___	rate of C	100%
$+M$		$\$$___	$+$rate of M	___%
S		$\$$___	rate of S	___%

2. If one dollar value and two rates are missing:
   (a) Use one of the markup formulas to find the missing dollar value:

   $$C = S - M \quad \text{if } C \text{ is missing}$$
   $$M = S - C \quad \text{if } M \text{ is missing}$$
   $$S = C + M \quad \text{if } S \text{ is missing}$$

   (b) Use the percentage formula $R = \frac{P}{B}$ to find a missing rate. R is a missing rate, P is its corresponding dollar value, and B is the dollar value of the cost.
   (c) Use one of the rate-of-markup formulas to find the other missing rate.

   $$\text{Rate of } M = \text{rate of } S - 100\% \quad \text{if rate of } M \text{ is missing}$$
   $$\text{Rate of } S = 100\% + \text{rate of } M \quad \text{if rate of } S \text{ is missing}$$

3. If one rate and two dollar values are missing:
   (a) Do step 2c to find the missing rate.
   (b) Use one of the percentage formulas to find a missing dollar value. P is either markup M or selling price S, R is its corresponding rate, and B is cost C.

   $$P = RB \quad \text{if } S \text{ or } M \text{ is missing but } C \text{ is not}$$

   $$B = \frac{P}{R} \quad \text{if } C \text{ is missing}$$

   (c) Do step 2a to find the final dollar value.

Find the markup and rate of markup based on a cost of $2 if the selling price is $4.

	C	$\$2$	rate of C	100%
$+M$		$\$$___	$+$rate of M	___%
S		$\$4$	rate of S	___%

Markup $= S - C = \$4 - \$2 = \$2$

Rate of markup $= \dfrac{P}{B} = \dfrac{\text{markup}}{\text{cost}} = \dfrac{2}{4} = 50\%$

Find the
markup, cost,
selling price,
rate of
markup, or
rate of cost
when the
markup is
based on
selling price.
(page 341)

1. Put known information in the table.

	C	$\$$___	rate of C	___%
$+M$		$\$$___	$+$rate of M	___%
S		$\$$___	rate of S	100%

2. If one dollar value and two rates are missing:
   (a) Use one of the markup formulas to find the missing dollar value:

   $$C = S - M \qquad \text{if } C \text{ is missing}$$
   $$M = S - C \qquad \text{if } M \text{ is missing}$$
   $$S = C + M \qquad \text{if } S \text{ is missing}$$

   (b) Use the percentage formula $R = \frac{P}{B}$ to find a missing rate. R is a missing rate, P is its corresponding dollar value, and B is the selling price.
   (c) Use one of the rate-of-markup formulas to find the other missing rate.

   $$\text{Rate of } C = 100\% - \text{rate of } M \qquad \text{if rate of } C \text{ is missing}$$
   $$\text{Rate of } M = 100\% - \text{rate of } C \qquad \text{if rate of } M \text{ is missing}$$

3. If one rate and two dollar values are missing:
   (a) Do step 2c to find the missing rate.
   (b) Use one of the percentage formulas to find a missing dollar value. P is either markup M or cost C, R is its corresponding rate, and B is the selling price S.

   $$P = RB \qquad \text{if } C \text{ or } M \text{ is missing but } S \text{ is given}$$
   $$B = \frac{P}{R} \qquad \text{if } S \text{ is missing}$$

   (c) Do step 2a to find the final dollar value.

Find the cost and the selling price on an item marked up \$50 if the rate of markup is 25% based on selling price.

C	\$___	**rate of** C	___%
$+M$	\$50	$+$**rate of** M	25%
S	\$___	**rate of** S	100%

$$\text{Selling price} = \frac{P}{R} = \frac{\text{markup}}{\text{rate of markup}} = \frac{50}{25\%} = \frac{50}{0.25} = \$200$$

$$\text{Cost} = \text{selling price} - \text{markup} = \$200 - \$50 = \$150$$

---

3 Compare markup based on cost with markup based on selling price. (page 345)

Convert a markup rate based on selling price to a markup rate based on cost.
1. Write the markup rate based on selling price in decimal form.
2. Subtract the markup rate (decimal form) based on selling price from 1.
3. Divide the markup rate (decimal form) based on selling price by the difference from step 2.

Markup rate (decimal form) based on cost
$$= \frac{\text{markup rate (decimal form) based on selling price}}{1 - \text{markup rate (decimal form) based on selling price}}$$

A fax machine is marked up 30% based on selling price. What is the rate of markup based on cost?

$$\text{Markup rate based on cost} = \frac{\text{markup rate based on selling price}}{1 - \text{markup rate based on selling price}}$$

$$= \frac{0.3}{1 - 0.3} = \frac{0.3}{0.7} = 0.429 = 42.9\%$$

Convert a markup rate based on cost to a markup rate based on selling price.
1. Write the markup rate based on cost in decimal form.
2. Add the markup rate (decimal form) based on cost to 1.
3. Divide the markup rate (decimal form) based on cost by the sum from step 2.

Markup rate (decimal form) based on selling price
$$= \frac{\text{markup rate (decimal form) based on cost}}{1 + \text{markup rate (decimal form) based on cost}}$$

> **A CD-ROM player is marked up 80% based on cost. What is the rate of markup based on selling price?**
>
> $$\text{Markup rate based on selling price} = \frac{\text{markup rate based on cost}}{1 + \text{markup rate based on cost}}$$
>
> $$= \frac{0.8}{1 + 0.8} = \frac{0.8}{1.8} = 0.444 = 44.4\%$$

Section 8.2

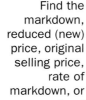

Find the markdown, reduced (new) price, original selling price, rate of markdown, or rate of reduced (new) price.
(page 348)

1. Place known information in the table.

N	\$___	rate of N	___%
$+M$	\$___	$+$rate of M	___%
S	\$___	rate of S	100%

2. If one dollar value and two rates are missing:
   (a) Use one of the markdown formulas to find the missing dollar value:

$N = S - M$	if N is missing
$M = S - N$	if M is missing
$S = N + M$	if S is missing

   (b) Use the percentage formula $R = \frac{P}{B}$ to find a missing rate. R is missing rate, P is its corresponding dollar value, and B is the original selling price.
   (c) Use one of the rate-of-markdown formulas to find the other missing rate:

Rate of $N = 100\% - $ rate of M	if rate of N is missing
Rate of $M = 100\% - $ rate of N	if rate of M is missing

3. If one rate and two dollar values are missing:
   (a) Do step 2c to find the missing rate.
   (b) Use one of the percentage formulas to find a missing dollar value. P is either markdown (M) or cheaper price (N) R is its corresponding rate, and B is the original selling price.

   $$P = RB \quad \text{if } N \text{ or } M \text{ is missing but } S \text{ is given}$$

   $$B = \frac{P}{R} \quad \text{if } S \text{ is missing}$$

   (c) Do step 2a to find the final dollar value.

> **Find the markdown and rate of markdown if the original selling price is \$4.50 and the sale (new) price is \$3.**
>
> | | | | |
> |---|---|---|---|
> | N | \$3.00 | rate of N | ___% |
> | $+M$ | \$___ | $+$rate of M | ___% |
> | S | \$4.50 | rate of S | 100% |

$$\text{Markdown} = S - N = \$4.50 - \$3 = \$1.50$$

$$\text{Rate of markdown} = \frac{P}{B} = \frac{\text{markdown}}{\text{original selling price}} = \frac{\$1.50}{\$4.50} = 0.33\frac{1}{3} = 33\frac{1}{3}\%$$

Section 8.3

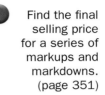

Find the final selling price for a series of markups and markdowns. (page 351)

1. For the first stage in the series, find the first selling price, if it isn't known already, using the first markup/markdown facts and the How-To steps for markup or markdown.
2. For each remaining stage in the series:
   (a) If the stage requires a **markdown,** identify the previous selling price as the *original selling price S* for this stage. Use the How-To steps for markdown to find the *reduced price N.* This price is the selling price for this stage.
   (b) If the stage requires a **markup,** identify the previous selling price as the *cost C* for this stage. Use the How-To steps for markup *based on cost* to find the *selling price S.* This price is the selling price for this stage.
3. Identify the selling price for the last stage as the *final selling price.*

An item costing $7 was marked up 70% on cost, then marked down 20%, marked up 10%, and finally marked down 20%. What was the final selling price?

First stage: Rate of selling price = 100% + 70% = 170%
Selling price = 170% × $7 = 1.7 × 7 = $11.90

Second stage: Rate of cheaper price = 100% − 20% = 80%
Cheaper price = 80% × 11.90 = 0.8 × 11.90 = $9.52

Third stage: Rate of selling price = 100% + 10% = 110%
Selling price = 110% × $9.52 = 1.1 × 9.52 = $10.47

Last stage: Rate of cheaper price = 100% − 20% = 80%
Cheaper price = 80% × $10.47 = 0.8 × 10.47 = $8.38

The final selling price is $8.38.

Find the selling price to achieve a desired profit (markup). (page 354)

1. Establish the rate of profit (markup)—based on cost—desired on the sale of the merchandise.
2. Find the total cost of the merchandise: multiply the unit cost by the quantity of merchandise.
3. Find the total profit (markup) based on cost: multiply the rate of profit (markup) by the total cost.
4. Find the total selling price: add the total cost and the total profit.
5. Establish the quantity expected to sell.
6. Divide the total selling price by the expect-to-sell quantity.

$$\text{Selling price to achieve profit (markup)} = \frac{\text{total selling price}}{\text{expect-to-sell quantity}}$$

At a total cost of $25, 25% of 400 lemons are expected to spoil before being sold. A 75% rate of profit (markup) on cost is needed. At what selling price must the lemons be sold to achieve the needed profit?

$$\text{Total profit (markup) based on cost} = 75\% \times \$25 = 0.75 \times 25 = \$18.75$$

$$\text{Total selling price} = \$18.75 + \$25 = \$43.75$$

$$\text{Expect-to-sell quantity} = (100\% - 25\%) \times 400 = 0.75 \times 400 = 300 \text{ lemons}$$

$$\text{Selling price} = \frac{\$43.75}{300 \text{ lemons}} = \$0.15 \text{ per lemon}$$

WORDS TO KNOW

cost (p. 338)
selling price (pp. 338, 341)

markup (pp. 338, 341, 363)
gross profit (p. 338)

margin (p. 338)
markdown (pp. 338, 348, 363)
profit (p. 354)

CHAPTER 8 CONCEPTS ANALYSIS

1. Explain why taking a series of markdowns of 25% and 30% is not the same as taking a single markdown of 55%. Illustrate your answer with a specific example.

2. Will the series markdown of 25% and 30% be more than or less than 55%? Explain why.

3. Under what circumstances would you be likely to base the markup for an item on cost?

4. Under what circumstances would you be likely to base the markup on an item on the selling price?

5. If you were a retailer, would you prefer to base your markup on selling price or cost? Why? Give an example to illustrate your preference.

6. What clues do you look for to determine whether the cost or selling price represents 100% in a markup problem?

7. Show by giving an example that the final reduced price in a series markdown can be found by doing a series of computations or by using the net decimal equivalent.

8. When given the rate of markup, describe at least one situation that leads to adding the rate to 100%. Describe at least one situation that leads to subtracting the rate from 100%.

9. Explain the mental process for finding a discount of 1% on an invoice.

10. Expand the mental process for finding a 1% discount on an invoice to finding a 2% discount on an invoice.

11. Use your responses to exercise 8 and 9 to develop a process for estimating a cash discount on an invoice for any discount rate.

CHAPTER 8 ASSIGNMENT EXERCISES

Section 8.1

Find the missing numbers in the table if the markup is based on the cost.

1.

C	$50	rate of C	100%
$+M$	$25	+rate of M	50%
S	$___	rate of S	___%

2.

C	$4	rate of C	___%
$+M$	$1	+rate of M	25%
S	$___	rate of S	___%

3.

C	$41	rate of C	____%
+M	$____	+rate of M	100%
S	$____	rate of S	____%

4.

C	$25	rate of C	____%
+M	$____	+rate of M	____%
S	$30	rate of S	____%

Find the missing numbers in the table if the markup is based on the selling price.

5.

C	$38	rate of C	42%
+M	____	+rate of M	____%
S	$____	rate of S	100%

6.

C	$86	rate of C	____%
+M	$____	+rate of M	50%
S	$____	rate of S	____%

7.

C	$____	rate of C	____%
+M	$8	+rate of M	15%
S	$____	rate of S	____%

8.

C	$16	rate of C	42%
+M	$____	+rate of M	____%
S	$____	rate of S	____%

Solve the problems. Be careful to notice whether markup is based on the cost or the selling price.

9. A hairdryer costs $15 and is marked up 40% of the cost. Find the markup and selling price.

10. A hairbrush costs $3 and is marked up 40% of the cost. Find the markup and selling price.

11. A blender is marked up $9 and sells for $45. Find the cost and rate of markup if the markup is based on cost.

12. A package of cassette tapes costs $12 and is marked up $7.20. Find the selling price and rate of markup based on the cost.

13. A computer table sells for $198.50 and costs $158.70. Find the markup and rate of markup based on the cost. Round to the nearest tenth percent.

14. Find the cost and markup on an office chair if the selling price is $75 and this item is marked up 100% of the cost.

15. If a flower arrangement is marked up $12, which is 50% of the cost, find the cost and selling price.

16. A toaster sells for $28.70 and has a markup rate of 50% based on selling price. Find the markup and the cost.

17. A briefcase is marked up $15.30, which is 30% of the selling price. Find the cost and selling price of the item.

18. A three-ringed binder costs $4.60 and is marked up $3.07. Find the selling price and the rate of markup based on selling price. Round percents to the nearest hundredth percent.

19. A hole punch costs $40 and sells for $58.50. Find the rate of markup based on selling price and the markup. Round to the nearest hundredth percent.

20. A pair of bookends sells for $15 and cost $10. Find the rate of markup based on selling price. Round to the nearest hundredth percent.

21. A desk organizer sells for $35, which includes a markup rate of 60% of the selling price. Find the cost and markup.

22. A pair of athletic shoes costs $38 and is marked up $20. Find the selling price, rate of markup based on cost and rate of markup based on selling price.

Fill in the blanks in exercises 23 through 32. Round rates to the nearest hundredth percent.

	Cost	Markup	Selling Price	Rate of Markup Based on Cost	Rate of Markup Based on Selling Price
23.	_____	$32	$89	_____	_____
24.	$486	_____	_____	_____	30%
25.	$1.56	_____	$2	_____	_____
26.	_____	$5.89	_____	15%	_____
27.	_____	$27.38	_____	40%	_____
28.	$25	_____	_____	_____	48%
29.	_____	_____	$124	150%	_____
30.	_____	$28	_____	_____	27%
31.	_____	_____	$18.95	_____	15%
32.	$16.28	$15.92	_____	_____	_____

33. Find the rate of markup based on cost of a textbook that is marked up 12% based on selling price.

34. A desk has an 83% markup based on selling price. What is the rate of markup based on cost?

35. A chest is marked up 63% based on cost. What is the rate of markup based on selling price?

36. A dining room suite is marked up 45% based on cost. What is the rate of markup based on selling price?

Section 8.2

37. A fiberglass shower originally sold for $379.98 and was marked down to sell for $341.98. Find the markdown and the rate of markdown.

38. A three-speed fan originally sold for $29.88 and was reduced to sell for $25.40. Find the markdown and the rate of markdown.

39. An area rug originally sold for $89.99 and was reduced to sell for $65. Find the markdown and the rate of markdown.

40. A room air conditioner that originally sold for $509.99 was reduced to sell for $400. Find the markdown and the rate of markdown.

41. A portable CD player was originally priced at $249.99 and was reduced by 20%. Find the markdown and the sale price (cheaper price).

42. A set of rollers was originally priced at $39.99 and was reduced by 30%. Find the markdown and the sale price.

43. A set of stainless steel cookware was originally priced at $79 and was reduced by 25%. Find the markdown and the sale price.

44. A down comforter was originally priced at $280 and was reduced by 64%. Find the markdown and the sale price.

Section 8.3

45. Crystal stemware originally marked to sell for $49.50 was reduced 20% for a special promotion. The stemware was then reduced an additional 30% to turn inventory. What were the markdown and the sale price for each reduction?

46. A camcorder that originally sold for $1,199 was reduced to sell for $999. It was then reduced an additional 40%. What were the markdown and markdown rate for the first reduction, and what was the final selling price for the camcorder?

47. James McDonell operates a vegetable store. He purchases 800 pounds of potatoes at a cost of $0.18 per pound. If he anticipates a spoilage rate of 20% of the potatoes and wishes to make a profit of 140% of the cost, for how much must he sell the potatoes per pound?

48. Elena Jimenez received a shipment of oranges that was shipped after a severe frost, so she expects losses to be high. She paid $0.26 per pound for the 500 pounds and expects to lose 35% of the oranges. If she wishes to make 125% markup on cost, find the selling price per pound.

Spreadsheet Exercises

49. In most spreadsheet software, percent and decimal equivalents of percents are interchangeable. That is, you may enter a percent and the program will automatically calculate with the decimal equivalent. The result may then be displayed as a percent or decimal equivalent by appropriate formatting functions. In the writing the formulas use the percent notation.

(a) Write formulas to complete the spreadsheet showing the Selling Price for items in the Tracking Report. Markup is based on Cost.

(b) Write formulas to complete the spreadsheet to give the Net Price for each item in the tracking report. Markdown is based on Selling Price.

(c) Write formulas to complete the spreadsheet to give the Gross Profit or Loss after Markdown for each item in the tracking report. Estimate which items may result in a loss.

50. Complete the spreadsheet using the formulas.

	A	B	C	D	E	F	G	H	I	J
1			Markup and Markdown Tracking for Appliances							
2	Item #	Item Description	Cost	% Markup	Selling Price	Markdown	Net Price	Gross Profit/Loss		
3	5023	Dirt Devil • Vacuum	$86.66	50%		30%				
4	2844	Fantom • Vacuum	$123.45	62%		25%				
5	6252	Eureka • Vacuum	$55.16	45%		50%				
6	1135	Bush • Entertainment Ctr	$170.58	70%		25%				
7	4456	Frigidaire • Dishwasher	$103.44	190%		40%				
8	2964	Maytag • Dishwasher	$180.29	125%		50%				
9	2974	Maytag • Dishwasher	$205.00	160%		40%				
10	2578	Oster • Blender	$26.31	52%		20%				
11	2367	Nokia • Cell Phone	$90.47	110%		40%				
12	3799	Samsung • Cell Phone	$99.99	100%		20%				

Challenge Problems

51. Pro Peds, a local athletic shoe manufacturer, makes a training shoe at a cost of $8.40 per pair. This cost includes raw materials and labor only. A check of previous factory runs indicates that 10% of the training shoes will be defective and must be sold to Odd Tops, Inc., as irregulars for $12 per pair. If Pro Peds produces 1,000 pairs of the training shoes and desires a markup of 100% on cost, find the selling price per pair of the regular shoes.

52. Pro Peds has implemented a quality improvement initiative that has reduced the percentage of defective training shoes by 6%. Recalculate the selling price per pair based on this new information.

CHAPTER 8 PRACTICE TEST

1. A calculator sells for $23.99 and costs $16.83. What is the markup?

2. A mixer sells for $109.98 and has a markup of $36.18. Find the cost.

3. A cookbook has a 34% markup rate based on cost. If the markup is $5.27, find the cost of the cookbook.

4. A computer stand sells for $385. What is the markup if it is 45% of the selling price?

5. A box of computer paper costs $16.80. Find the selling price if there is a 35% markup rate based on cost.

6. The reduced price of a dress is $54.99. Find the original selling price if a reduction of 40% has been taken.

7. A daily organizer that originally sold for $86.90 was marked down by 30%. What is the markdown?

8. What is the sale price of the organizer in exercise 7?

9. If a television cost $87.15 and was marked up $39.60, what is the selling price?

10. A refrigerator that sells for $387.99 was marked down $97. What is the sale price?

11. What was the rate of markdown for the refrigerator in exercise 10?

12. A wallet cost $16.05 to produce. The wallet sells for $25.68. What is the rate of markup based on cost?

13. A lamp costs $88. What is the selling price if the markup is 45% of the selling price?

14. A file cabinet originally sold for $215 but was damaged and had to be reduced. If the reduced cabinet sold for $129, what was the rate of markdown based on the original selling price?

15. A bookcase desk that originally sold for $129.99 was marked down 25%. During the sale it was damaged and had to be reduced by 50% more. What was the final selling price of the desk?

16. Donald Byrd, the accountant for Quick Stop Shop, calculates the selling price for all produce. If 400 pounds of potatoes were purchased for $0.13 per pound and 18% of the potatoes were expected to spoil before being sold, determine the price per pound that the potatoes must sell for if a profit of 120% of the purchase price is desired.

17. Loose-leaf paper in a college bookstore is marked up 30% of its cost. Find the cost if the selling price is $2.34 per package.

18. A $5\frac{1}{4}$-inch double-sided, double-density floppy disk costs $0.90 and sells for $1.50. Find the rate of markup based on selling price. Also find the rate of markup based on cost.

19. A radio sells for $45, which includes a markup rate of 65% of the selling price. Find the cost and the markup.

20. Laura Kee purchased a small refrigerator for her dorm room for $95.20, which included a markup of $27.20 based on the cost. Find the cost and the rate of markup based on cost.

SELF-CHECK 8.1

1.

C	$2	rate of C	100%
$+M$	$4	$+$rate of M	200%
S	$6	rate of S	300%

Markup $= S - C = \$6 - \$2 = \$4$

Rate of markup based on cost $= \dfrac{P \text{ (markup)}}{B \text{ (cost)}} = \dfrac{\$4}{\$2} = 2 = 200\%$

2.

C	$4.00	rate of C	100%
$+M$	$2.40	$+$rate of M	60%
S	$6.40	rate of S	160%

Markup $= R \text{ (rate of markup)} \times B \text{ (cost)}$

$= 0.6 \times \$4 = \$2.40$

Selling price $= C + M = \$4 + \$2.40 = \$6.40$

3.

C	$214.29	rate of C	100%
$+M$	$ 85.71	$+$rate of M	40%
S	$300.00	rate of S	140%

Rate of S = rate of C + rate of M

Rate of $S = 100\% + 40\% = 140\%$

$$\text{Cost} = \frac{P \text{ (selling price)}}{R \text{ (rate of selling price based on cost)}}$$

$$= \frac{\$300}{1.4} = \$214.29 \text{ (rounded)}$$

Markup $= S - C = \$300 - \$214.29 = \$85.71$

4. Total cost = 48 × $8.50 = $408.00

	C		rate of C	100%
+M	$ 5.53		+rate of M	65%
S	$14.03		rate of S	165%

Rate of S = 100% + 65% = 165%

Markup = R (rate of markup) × B (cost)

$$= 0.65 × 8.50 = \$5.525 \text{ or } \$5.53 \text{ (rounded)}$$

Selling price = C + M = $ 8.50 + $5.53 = $14.03

Total selling price = 48 × $14.03 = $673.44

5. Total cost = 20 × $12.75 = $255

	C	$12.75	rate of C	100%
+M		$ 9.56	+rate of M	75%
S		$22.31	rate of S	175%

Rate of S = 100% + 75% = 175%

Markup = R (rate of markup) × B (base)

$$= 0.75 × \$12.75$$

$$= \$ 9.5625 \text{ (\$9.56 rounded)}$$

Selling price = C + M = $12.75 + $9.56 = $22.31

Total markup = 20 × $9.56 = $191.20

6.

	C	$ 4	rate of C	33.33%
+M		$ 8	+rate of M	66.67%
S		$12	rate of S	100.00%

Find amount of markup first.

$$M = S - C = \$12 - \$4 = \$8$$

$$\text{Rate of markup based on selling price} = \frac{P \text{ (markup)}}{B \text{ (selling price)}} = \frac{\$8}{\$12}$$

$$= 0.6667$$

$$= 66.67\%$$

7.

	C	$ 7.50	rate of C	60%
+M		$ 5.00	+rate of M	40%
S		$12.50	rate of S	100%

Rate of C = rate of S − rate of M

Rate of C = 100% − 40% = 60%

$$\text{Selling price} = \frac{P \text{ (markup)}}{R \text{ (rate of markup based on selling price)}} = \frac{\$5}{0.4} = \$12.50$$

$$C = S - M = \$12.50 - \$5 = \$7.50$$

8.

	C	$1.75	rate of C	50%
+M		$1.75	+rate of M	50%
S		$3.50	rate of S	100%

Rate of C = rate of S − rate of M

Rate of C = 100% − 50% = 50%

Markup = R (rate of markup based on selling price) × B (selling price)

$$= 0.5 × \$3.50 = \$1.75$$

Since the rate of markup and the rate of cost are the same, the markup and the cost are the same.

9.

	C	$ 40	rate of C	40%
+M		$ 60	+ rate of M	60%
S		$100	rate of S	100%

Rate of C = rate of S − rate of M

Rate of C = 100% − 60% = 40%

$$\text{Selling price} = \frac{P \text{ (cost)}}{R \text{ (rate of cost based on selling price)}}$$

$$= \frac{\$40}{0.4} = \$100$$

$$M = S - C = \$100 - \$40 = \$60$$

10. Markup rate based on cost $= \dfrac{\text{markup rate based on selling price}}{1 - \text{markup rate based on selling price}} = \dfrac{0.6}{1 - 0.6} = \dfrac{0.6}{0.4} = 1.5,$ or 150%

11. Markup rate based on cost $= \dfrac{\text{markup rate based on selling price}}{1 - \text{markup percent based on selling price}} = \dfrac{0.75}{1 - 0.75} = \dfrac{0.75}{0.25} = 3,$ or 300%

12. Markup rate based on selling price $= \dfrac{\text{markup rate based on cost}}{1 + \text{markup percent based on cost}} = \dfrac{1.2}{1 + 1.2} = \dfrac{1.2}{2.2} = 0.5455,$ or 54.55%

13. Markup rate based on selling price $= \dfrac{\text{markup rate based on cost}}{1 + \text{markup rate based on cost}} = \dfrac{0.82}{1 + 0.82} = \dfrac{0.82}{1.82} = 0.45 = 45\%$

14. Markup rate based on cost $= \dfrac{\text{markup rate based on selling price}}{1 - \text{markup rate based on selling price}} = \dfrac{0.68}{1 - 0.68} = \dfrac{0.68}{0.32} = 2.125$ or 212.5%

SELF-CHECK 8.2

1. Markdown = original selling price − reduced price

   $= \$480 - \$420 = \$60$

   Rate of markdown $= \dfrac{P}{B} = \dfrac{\$60}{\$480} = 0.125 = 12.5\%$

2. Markdown = original selling price − reduced price $= \$599.97 - \$550 = \$49.97$

   Rate of markdown $= \dfrac{P}{B} = \dfrac{\$49.97}{\$599.97} = 0.083 = 8.3\%$

3. Markdown = original selling price − reduced price $= \$169.00 - \$139.97 = \$29.03$

   Rate of markdown $= \dfrac{P}{B} = \dfrac{\$29.03}{\$169.00} = 0.172 = 17.2\%$

4. Markdown = original selling price − reduced price $= \$79.99 - \$47.97 = \$32.02$

   Rate of markdown $= \dfrac{P}{B} = \dfrac{\$32.02}{\$79.99} = 0.4 = 40.0\%$

5. Markdown = original selling price − reduced price $= \$549.99 - \$509.99 = \$40.00$

   Rate of markdown $= \dfrac{P}{B} = \dfrac{\$40}{\$549.99} = 0.0727 = 7.3\%$

6. Markdown $= R \times B = 0.15 \times \$115.95 = \$17.39$

   Reduced price = original selling price − markdown $= \$115.95 - \$17.39 = \$98.56$

7. Markdown = markdown rate $\times$ original selling price $= 0.23 \times \$529.99 = \$121.90$

   Reduced price = original selling price − markdown $= \$529.99 - \$121.90 = \$408.09$

8. Markdown = markdown rate $\times$ original selling price $= 0.25 \times \$368.00 = \$92.00$

   Reduced price = original selling price − markdown $= \$368.00 - \$92.00 = \$276.00$

9. Markdown = markdown rate $\times$ original selling price $= 0.21 \times \$1,899.97 = \$398.99$

   Reduced price = original selling price − markdown $= \$1,899.97 - \$398.99 = \$1,500.98$

10. Markdown = markdown rate $\times$ original selling price $= 0.19 \times \$59.99 = \$11.40$

   Reduced price = original selling price − markdown $= \$59.99 - \$11.40 = \$48.59$

SELF-CHECK 8.3

1. *May 5 markup:*
   Markup $= R \times B = 0.5 \times \$24 = \$12$
   $S = C + M = \$24 + \$12 = \$36$ (original selling price)
   June 15 markdown:
   Markdown $= R \times B = 0.15 \times \$36 = \$5.40$
   Reduced price $= \$36 - \$5.40 = \$30.60 =$ selling price on June 15
   June 17 markup:
   Markup $= R \times B = 0.1 \times \$30.60 = \$3.06$
   Selling price $= \$30.60 + \$3.06 = \$33.66 =$ selling price on June 17
   August 30 markdown:
   Markdown $= R \times B = 0.4 \times \$33.66 = \$13.46$
   Reduced price $= \$33.66 - \$13.46 = \$20.20 =$ final selling price

2. Markdown $= \$135 \times 0.25 = \$33.75$
   Reduced price $= \$135 - \$33.75 = \$101.25 =$ first selling price
   Markdown $= \$101.25 \times 0.15 = \$15.19$
   Reduced price $= \$101.25 - \$15.19 = \$86.06 =$ second selling price
   Markdown $= \$135 \times 0.75 = \$101.25$
   Reduced price $= \$135 - \$101.25 = \$33.75 =$ final selling price

3.
$$\text{Cost} = 300 \times \$0.35 = \$105$$
$$\text{Markup} = 1.75 \times \$105 = \$183.75$$
$$\text{Total selling price} = C + M = \$105 + \$183.75 = \$288.75$$
$$\% \text{ of grapes expected to sell} = 100\% - 12\% = 88\%$$
$$\text{Pounds of grapes expected to sell} = 0.88 \times 300 = 264 \text{ pounds}$$
$$\text{Selling price} = \frac{\$288.75}{264 \text{ pounds}} = \$1.09 \text{ per pound}$$

4.
$$\text{Cost} = 600 \times \$0.32 - \$192$$
$$\text{Markup} = \$192 \times 0.9 = \$172.80$$
$$\text{Total selling price} = \$192 + \$172.80 = \$364.80$$
$$\text{Percent of apples expected to sell} = 100\% - 15\% = 85\%$$
$$\text{Pounds of apples expected to sell} = 600 \times 0.85 = 510$$
$$\text{Selling price} = \frac{\$364.80}{510 \text{ pounds}} = \$0.72 \text{ (rounded)}$$

5. Total cost $=$ quantity of items $\times$ cost per item
   Total cost $= 1{,}000 \times \$7.90 = \$7{,}900$
   Necessary markup $=$ total cost $\times 50\% = \$7{,}900 \times 0.5 = \$3{,}950$
   Total selling price $=$ total cost $+$ markup $= \$7{,}900 + \$3{,}950 = \$11{,}850$

   Selling price $=$ total selling price $\div$ quantity of items expected to sell $= \dfrac{\$11{,}850}{800 \text{ items}} = \$14.81$ per item

   Charlie should purchase the shirts and sell them for at least $14.81 each.

9

Simple Interest and Simple Discount

9.1 The Simple Interest Formula

1 Find simple interest using the simple interest formula.

2 Find the maturity value of a loan.

3 Convert months to a fractional or decimal part of a year.

4 Find the principal, rate, or time using the simple interest formula.

9.2 Ordinary and Exact Time and Interest

1 Find ordinary and exact time.

2 Find the due date.

3 Find the interest using the ordinary and exact interest rates.

4 Find simple interest using a table.

9.3 Promissory Notes

1 Find the bank discount and proceeds for a simple discount note.

2 Find the bank discount and proceeds for a third-party discount note.

Good Decisions through Teamwork

With members of your team, investigate loan deals by researching the options available for the purchase of an engraving machine that costs $15,000 if the loan can be repaid in a lump sum in 18 months. List types of lending institutions that provide business loans and find local examples of each through newspapers and phone directories. Specify aspects of each institution's lending policies that should be compared in order to make the best decision for acquiring the loan, including:

- Rate. Is the rate simple interest or simple discount? What is the rate? Is the rate affected by any factors such as length of finance contract or the company's or owner's credit rating?
- Requirements for loan. What information must be provided to the institution in order to obtain a loan? Is a cosigner required? Is collateral in addition to the machine required?

Individually, select a type of lending institution and obtain the comparative information by reading published brochures or interviewing loan officers of selected institutions. After comparing the resulting information, as a team calculate the total cost of financing the purchase using two of the financing sources selected by team members. Select the deal that is the wisest choice for the loan. Prepare an oral report employing visual aids in which all team members participate.

Every business and every person at some time borrows or invests money. A person (or business) who borrows money must pay for the use of the money. A person who invests money must be paid by the person or firm who uses the money. The price paid for using money is called **interest.**

In the business world, we encounter two basic kinds of interest, *simple* and *compound.* **Simple interest** applies when a loan or investment is repaid in a lump sum. The person using the money has use of the full amount of money for the entire time of the loan or investment. **Compound interest,** which is explained in Chapter 10, most often applies to savings accounts, installment loans, and credit cards.

Both types of interest take into account three factors: the principal, the interest rate, and the time period involved. **Principal** is the amount of money borrowed or invested. **Rate** is the percent of the principal paid as interest per time period. **Time** is the number of days, months, or years that the money is borrowed or invested.

9.1 The Simple Interest Formula

1 Find simple interest using the simple interest formula.

2 Find the maturity value of a loan.

3 Convert months to a fractional or decimal part of a year.

4 Find the principal, rate, or time using the simple interest formula.

1 Find simple interest using the simple interest formula.

The interest formula (Figure 9-1) shows how interest, principal, rate, and time are related and gives us a way of finding one of these values if the other three values are known.

HOW TO Find Simple Interest Using the Simple Interest Formula

Multiply the principal by the rate and time.

Interest = Principal × Rate × Time

$$I = PRT$$

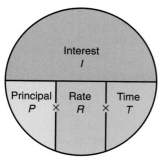

Figure 9-1 Simple Interest Formula $I = PRT$

The simple interest formula is another application of the percentage formula $P = RB$. The interest, I, is the part or percentage, P. The rate of interest is also the rate in the percentage formula. The principal is the amount invested or loaned or the base. The rate is expressed for a particular unit of time; when the amount of time is just one time period, the formulas are equivalent. $I = PR$ and $P = RB$ for one time period. When the time is different from one time period, multiply by the number of time periods or the fraction of a time period.

The rate of interest is a percent for a given time period, usually one year. The time in the interest formula must be expressed in the same unit of time as the rate. If the rate is a percent per year, the time must be expressed in years or a decimal or fractional part of a year. Similarly, if the rate is a percent per month, the time must be expressed in months.

EXAMPLE Find the interest paid on a loan of $1,500 for one year at a simple interest rate of 12% per year.

$I = PRT$　　　　　　　　　　Use the simple interest formula.

$I = (\$1,500)(12\%)(1)$　　　Principal P is $1,500, rate R is 12% per year, time T is one year.

$I = (\$1,500)(0.12)(1)$　　　Write 12% as a decimal.

$I = \$180$

The interest on the loan is $180.

Learning Strategy Using Color to Track Components

Color highlighting can be very useful when a problem has several different components. In this chapter the following color pattern is used in formulas and examples.

Interest Principal Rate Time

Watch for other words that have the same role as one of these key words. For example, bank discount has the same role as interest . Face value and maturity value of original note have the same role as principal .

　　This same learning strategy can be applied to note taking in this and other classes.

EXAMPLE Kanette's Salon borrowed $5,000 at $12\frac{1}{2}\%$ per year simple interest for two years to buy new hair dryers. How much interest must be paid?

$I = PRT$　　　　　　　　　　Use the simple interest formula.

$I = (\$5,000)(12\frac{1}{2}\%)(2)$　　Principal P is $5,000, rate R is $12\frac{1}{2}\%$ per year, time T is two years.

$I = (\$5,000)(0.125)(2)$　　Write $12\frac{1}{2}\%$ as a decimal.

$I = \$1,250$

Kanette's Salon will pay $1,250 interest.

A loan that is made using simple interest is to be repaid in a lump sum at the end of the time of the loan. Banks and lending institutions make loans at a variety of different rates based on factors such as prime interest rate and the amount of risk that the loan will be repaid. The **prime interest rate** is the lowest rate at which money is loaned to the most preferred borrowers. Banks borrow money from the Federal Reserve Bank at the prime rate. Banks establish the rate of a loan based on the current prime rate and the likelihood that it will not change significantly over the time of the loan. During the 1980s the prime rate fluctuated significantly from 7% to more than 15%. However, during the 1990s the prime rate was relatively stable between 7% and $9\frac{1}{2}\%$.

Loans are made at the prime rate or higher, often significantly higher. Investments such as savings accounts and certificates of deposit earn interest at a rate less than prime. Lending institutions make a profit based on the difference between the rate of interest charged for loans and the rate of interest given for investments.

2 Find the maturity value of a loan.

The *total* amount of money due by the end of a loan period—the amount of the loan *and* the interest—is called the **maturity value** of the loan. When the principal and interest of a loan are known, the maturity value is found by adding the principal and the interest. The maturity value can also be found directly from the principal, rate, and time.

HOW TO Find the Maturity Value of a Loan

1. If the principal and interest are known, add them.

$$\text{Maturity values} = \boxed{\text{principal}} + \boxed{\text{interest}}$$
$$MV = \boxed{P} + \boxed{I}$$

2. If the principal, rate, and time are known:
   (a) Add 1 to the product of rate and time.
   (b) Multiply the principal by the sum from step 2a.

$$\text{Maturity value} = \boxed{\text{principal}} (1 + \boxed{\text{rate decimal equivalent}} \times \boxed{\text{time}})$$
$$MV = \boxed{P}(1 + \boxed{R}\boxed{T})$$

TIP! Why Add 1?

In the formula for finding the maturity values directly, we multiply the principal by 1 plus the product of the rate and time. Where did the 1 come from? The maturity value is the principal plus the interest. The interest is the product of the principal, the rate, and the time.
Thus, $MV = P + PRT$.

The variation $MV = P(1 + RT)$ is an application of the distributive property.

The distributive property allows two ways for performing the multiplication and addition steps.

$$5(1 + 3) \quad \text{or} \quad 5 \times 1 + 5 \times 3$$
$$5(4) \qquad\qquad 5 + 15$$
$$20 \qquad\qquad\quad 20$$

Similarly, $P(1 + RT)$ is the same as $P + PRT$.

The variation of the formula for finding the maturity value when the principal, rate, and time are known requires that the operations be performed according to the standard order of operations. To review briefly, when more than one operation is to be performed, perform operations within parentheses first. Perform multiplications and divisions before additions and subtractions. Perform additions and subtractions last.

EXAMPLE   How much money will Kanette's Salon (from the previous example) pay at the end of two years?

$$\text{Maturity value} = \boxed{\text{principal}} + \boxed{\text{interest}}$$

$$MV = P + \boxed{I}$$

$$= \boxed{\$5,000} + \boxed{\$1,250} = \$6,250$$

or, using the second formula given in the How-To box,

$$\text{Maturity value} = \boxed{\text{principal}}\,(1 + \boxed{\text{rate}} \times \boxed{\text{time}})$$

$$MV = P(1 + \boxed{R}\;\boxed{T})$$

$MV = \boxed{\$5,000}\,(1 + \boxed{0.125} \times \boxed{2})$ **Follow the standard order of operations.**

$MV = \boxed{\$5,000}\,(1 + 0.25)$ **Multiply 0.125 × 2.**

$MV = \boxed{\$5,000}\,(1.25)$ **Add 1 + 0.25.**

$MV = \$6,250$

Kanette's Salon will pay $6,250 at the end of the loan period.

> ## TIP! Order Is Important
>
> It is important to follow the standard order of operations carefully. In the preceding example, the maturity value formula $MV = P(1 + RT)$ requires that the operations within the parentheses be done first. However, within the parentheses both addition and multiplication are indicated. Within the parentheses, perform the multiplication, then the addition.
>
> $MV = \$5,000(1 + \boxed{0.125 \times 2})$ **Multiply within parentheses.**
>
> $MV = \$5,000(1 + \boxed{0.25})$ **Add within parentheses.**
>
> $MV = \$5,000(1.25)$
>
> Finally, the multiplication that is indicated from outside the parentheses is performed.
>
> $MV = \$6,250$

Does a Calculator Know the Proper Order of Operations? Some Do, Some Don't.

Using a basic calculator, you enter calculations as they should be performed according to the standard order of operations.

$\boxed{\text{AC}}\ .125\ \boxed{\times}\ 2\ \boxed{=}\ \boxed{+}\ 1\ \boxed{=}\ \boxed{\times}\ 5000\ \boxed{=} \Rightarrow 6250$

Using an office calculator the calculations are still entered as they should be performed according to the standard order of operations, but using a different key sequence.

$\boxed{\text{AC}}\ .125\ \boxed{\times}\ 2\ \boxed{=}\ \boxed{1}\ \boxed{+}\ \boxed{\times}\ 5000\ \boxed{=} \Rightarrow 6250$

Using a scientific calculator with parentheses keys allows you to enter values for the maturity value formula as they appear. The calculator is programmed to perform the operations in the standard order. The calculator has special keys for entering parentheses $\boxed{(}\,\boxed{)}$.

$\boxed{\text{AC}}\ 5000\ \boxed{\times}\ \boxed{(}\ 1\ \boxed{+}\ .125\ \boxed{\times}\ 2\ \boxed{)}\ \boxed{=} \Rightarrow 6250$

Convert months to a fractional or decimal part of a year.

Not all loans or investments are made for a whole number of years, but since the interest rate is most often given per year, the time must also be expressed in the same unit of time as the rate.

 HOW TO Convert Months to a Fractional or Decimal Part of a Year

1. Write the number of months as the numerator of a fraction.
2. Write 12 as the denominator of the fraction.
3. Reduce the fraction to lowest terms if using the fractional equivalent.
4. Divide the numerator by the denominator to get the decimal equivalent of the fraction.

EXAMPLE Convert (a) 5 months and (b) 15 months to years, expressed in both fraction or mixed number and decimal form.

(a) 5 months $= \dfrac{5}{12}$ year

> 5 months equal $\frac{5}{12}$ year.

$$12\overline{)5.0000000}\quad 0.4166666 \text{ year} = 0.42 \text{ year}$$

> To write the fraction as a decimal, divide the number of months (the numerator) by the number of months in a year (the denominator).

5 months = 0.42 year (rounded)

(b) 15 months $= \dfrac{15}{12}$ years $= \dfrac{5}{4}$ or $1\frac{1}{4}$ years

> 15 months equal $\frac{15}{12}$ years.

$$4\overline{)5.00}\quad 1.25 \text{ years}$$

> To write the fraction as a decimal, divide the number of months (the numerator) by the number of months in a year (the denominator).

15 months $= 1\frac{1}{4}$ years or 1.25 years

EXAMPLE To save money for a shoe repair shop, Stan Wright invested $2,500 for 45 months at $12\frac{1}{2}\%$ interest per year. How much interest did he earn?

$T =$ 45 months $= \dfrac{45}{12}$ years $= 3\frac{3}{4}$ or 3.75 years

> Write the time in terms of years.

$I = PRT$

> Use the simple interest formula.

$I =$ $2,500 (0.125)(3.75)

> Principal P is $2,500, rate R is 0.125, and time T is $\frac{45}{12}$ or 3.75.

$I = \$1,171.88$

> Rounded to the nearest cent.

Stan Wright earned $1,171.88 in interest.

When time is expressed in months, the calculator sequence is the same as when time is expressed in years, except that we do not enter a whole number for the time. Months can be changed to years in the sequence rather than as a separate calculation. All other steps are the same. To solve the equation using a calculator without the percent key, use the decimal equivalent of $12\frac{1}{2}\%$.

$$\boxed{AC} \; 2500 \; \boxed{\times} \; .125 \; \boxed{\times} \; 45 \; \boxed{\div} \; 12 \; \boxed{=} \; \Rightarrow 1171.875$$

The percent key on a calculator serves as an equal key *and* changes the percent to a decimal equivalent.

To solve the equation using a calculator with a percent key, enter

$$\boxed{AC} \; 2500 \; \boxed{\times} \; 12.5 \; \boxed{\%} \; \boxed{\times} \; 45 \; \boxed{\div} \; 12 \; \boxed{=} \; \Rightarrow 1171.875$$

It is not necessary to find the decimal equivalent of $\frac{45}{12}$ or to reduce $\frac{45}{12}$. However, you will get the same result if you do.

$$\boxed{AC} \; 2500 \; \boxed{\times} \; 12.5 \; \boxed{\%} \; \boxed{\times} \; 3.75 \; \boxed{=} \; \Rightarrow 1171.875$$

 TIP! **Check Calculations by Estimating**

As careful as we are, there will always be times that we hit an incorrect key or use an improper sequence of steps and produce an incorrect solution. You can catch most of these mistakes by first anticipating what a reasonable answer should be.

In the preceding example, 10% interest for one year would be $250. At that rate the interest for four years would be $1,000. The actual rate is more than 10% and the time is less than four years, so $1,000 is a reasonable estimate.

---

4 Find the principal, rate, or time using the simple interest formula.

So far in this chapter, we have used the formula $I = PRT$ to find the simple interest on a loan. However, sometimes you need to find the principal or the rate or the time instead of the interest. You can remember the different forms of this formula with a circle diagram (see Figure 9-2) like the one used for the percentage formula. Cover the unknown term to see the form of the simple interest formula needed to find the missing value.

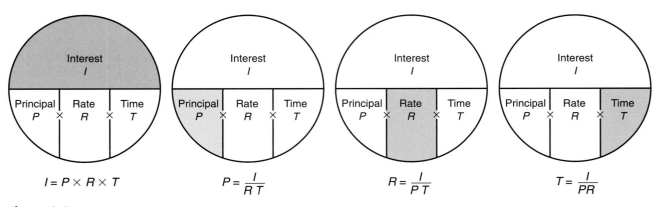

$$I = P \times R \times T \qquad P = \frac{I}{RT} \qquad R = \frac{I}{PT} \qquad T = \frac{I}{PR}$$

Figure 9-2   Various Forms of the Simple Interest Formula

HOW TO Find the Principal, Rate, or Time Using the Simple Interest Formula

1. Select the appropriate form of the formula.
   (a) If the principal is unknown, use

   $$P = \frac{I}{RT}$$

   (b) If the rate is unknown, use

   $$R = \frac{I}{PT}$$

   (c) If the time is unknown, use

   $$T = \frac{I}{PR}$$

2. Replace letters with known values and perform the indicated operations.

EXAMPLE To buy new knives for his restaurant, Clarence Cooke borrowed $800 for $3\frac{1}{2}$ years and paid $348 simple interest on the loan. What rate of interest did he pay?

$R = \dfrac{I}{PT}$ **R is unknown. Select the correct form of the simple interest formula.**

$I = \boxed{\$348}$

$P = \$800$

$T = \boxed{3.5}$ years

$R = \dfrac{348}{(800)\,(3.5)}$ **Replace letters with known values: I is $348, P is $800, T is 3.5 years. Perform the operations.**

$R = 0.124$ **Write the rate in percent form by moving the decimal point two places to the right and attaching a % symbol.**

$\boxed{R = 12.4\%}$

He paid 12.4% interest.

Using Memory Functions versus Repeated Division

There are several efficient ways to perform the calculations in the preceding example. With a basic calculator and using memory: multiply 800×3.5, store the result in memory and clear display, enter 348 and divide by the stored product:

$\boxed{\text{AC}}\ 800\ \boxed{\times}\ 3.5\ \boxed{=}\ \boxed{\text{M}^+}\ \boxed{\text{CE/C}}\ 348\ \boxed{\div}\ \boxed{\text{MRC}}\ \boxed{=} \Rightarrow 0.1242857$

Using repeated division: divide 348 by both 800 and 3.5:

$\boxed{\text{AC}}\ 348\ \boxed{\div}\ 800\ \boxed{\div}\ 3.5\ \boxed{=} \Rightarrow 0.1242857$

With a scientific calculator and parentheses: group the calculations in the denominator using parentheses:

$\boxed{\text{AC}}\ 348\ \boxed{\div}\ \boxed{(}\ 800\ \boxed{\times}\ 3.5\ \boxed{)}\ \boxed{=} \Rightarrow 0.1242857$

EXAMPLE   Phyllis Cox wanted to borrow some money to expand her egg farm. She was told she could borrow a sum of money for 18 months at 18% simple interest per year. She thinks she can afford to pay as much as $540 in interest charges. How much money could she borrow?

$$P = \frac{I}{RT}$$

P is unknown. Select the correct form of the simple interest formula.

$I = \boxed{\$540}$

$R = \boxed{18\%} = 0.18$

$T = \boxed{18} \text{ months} = \frac{18}{12}$

The interest rate is per year, so write 18 months as 1.5 years.

$\qquad\qquad = \boxed{1.5} \text{ years}$

$$P = \frac{540}{0.18\,(1.5)}$$

Replace letters with known values: I is $540, R is 0.18, T is 1.5.

$P = \$2,000$

Perform the operations.

The principal is $2,000.

Numerator Divided by Denominator

When a series of calculations has fractions and a calculation in the denominator, the numerator must be divided by the entire denominator.

With a basic calculator and using memory: multiply 0.18×1.5, store the result in memory and clear the display, and divide 540 by the stored product:

$$\boxed{AC}\ .18\ \boxed{\times}\ 1.5\ \boxed{=}\ \boxed{M^+}\ \boxed{CE/C}\ 540\ \boxed{\div}\ \boxed{MRC}\ \boxed{=}\ \Rightarrow 2000$$

Using repeated division: divide 540 by both 0.18 and 1.5:

$$\boxed{AC}\ 540\ \boxed{\div}\ .18\ \boxed{\div}\ 1.5\ \boxed{=}\ \Rightarrow 2000$$

With a scientific calculator and parentheses: group the calculation in the denominator using parentheses:

$$\boxed{AC}\ 540\ \boxed{\div}\ \boxed{(}\ .18 \times 1.5\ \boxed{)}\ \boxed{=}\ \Rightarrow 2000$$

EXAMPLE   Lee's Tree Service borrowed $2,400 at 14% simple interest per year to repair its tree-topper. If it paid $840 interest, what was the duration of the loan?

$$T = \frac{I}{PR}$$

T is unknown. Select the correct form of the simple interest formula.

$$T = \frac{840}{2,400\,(0.14)} = 2.5 \text{ years}$$

Replace letters with known values: I = $840, P = $2,400, R = 0.14. Perform the operations.

The duration of the loan is 2.5 years.

TIP! Is the Answer Reasonable?

Suppose in the previous example we had mistakenly made the following calculations:

$$840 \div 2400 \times 0.14 = \Rightarrow 0.049$$

Is it reasonable to think that $840 in interest would be paid on a $2,400 loan that is made for such a small portion of a year? The interest on a 10% loan for one year would be $240. The interest on a 20% loan for one year still would be only $480. This type of reasoning draws attention to a totally unreasonable answer.

You can reexamine your steps to discover that you should have used your memory function, repeated division, or your parentheses keys.

SELF-CHECK 9.1

1

1. Find the interest paid on a loan of $2,400 for one year at a simple interest rate of 11% per year.
2. Find the interest paid on a loan of $800 at $8\frac{1}{2}$% annual simple interest for two years.
3. How much interest will have to be paid on a loan of $7,980 for two years at a simple interest rate of 6.2% per year?

2

4. Find the total amount of money (maturity value) that the borrower will pay back on a loan of $1,400 at $12\frac{1}{2}$% annual simple interest for three years.
5. Find the maturity value of a loan of $2,800 after three years. The loan carries a simple interest rate of 7.5% per year.
6. Susan Duke borrowed $20,000 for four years to purchase a car. The simple interest loan has a rate of 8.2% per year. What is the maturity value of the loan?

3 *Convert to years, expressed in decimal form.*

7. 8 months
8. 40 months
9. A loan is made for 18 months. Convert the time to years.
10. Express 28 months in decimal form.

4

11. Alexa May took out a $42,000 construction loan to remodel a house. The loan rate is 8.3% simple interest per year and will be repaid in six months. How much is paid back?
12. Madison Duke needed start-up money for her bakery. She borrowed $1,200 for 30 months and paid $360 simple interest on the loan. What interest rate did she pay?
13. Raul Fletes needed money to buy lawn equipment. He borrowed $500 for seven months and paid $53.96 in interest. What was the rate of interest?
14. Linda Davis agreed to lend money to Alex Luciano at a special interest rate of 9% per year, on the condition that he borrow enough that he would pay her $500 in interest over a two-year period. What was the minimum amount Alex could borrow?
15. Jake McAnally needed money for college. He borrowed $6,000 at 12% simple interest per year. If he paid $360 interest, what was the duration of the loan?
16. Keaton Smith borrowed $25,000 to purchase stock for his baseball card shop. He repaid the simple interest loan after three years. He paid interest of $6,750. What was the interest rate?

9.2 Ordinary and Exact Time and Interest

 1 Find ordinary and exact time.

2 Find the due date.

3 Find the interest using the ordinary and exact interest rates.

4 Find simple interest using a table.

Sometimes the time period of a loan is indicated by the beginning date and the due date of the loan rather than by a specific number of months or days. In such cases, you must first determine the time of the loan. There are two commonly used ways to determine the time in days of a loan. The first is called **ordinary time** and it is based on counting 30 days in each month. The other is called **exact time** and it is based on counting the exact number of days in a time period.

> **?** **HOW TO** Change Months and Years to Ordinary or Exact Time in Days
>
> **1.** For ordinary time use:
> $$1 \text{ month} = 30 \text{ days}$$
> $$1 \text{ year} = 360 \text{ days}$$
>
> **2.** For exact time use:
> $$1 \text{ month} = \text{exact number of days in the month}$$
> $$1 \text{ year} = 365 \text{ days (or 366 days in a leap year)}$$

Suppose you take out a loan on July 12 that is due September 12. If you use ordinary time, you figure each of the two months to have 30 days, so the total days are 2×30, or 60 days. If you use the exact time, you must figure the exact number of days from July 12 to September 12 and add the 19 days remaining in July, the 31 days in August, and the 12 days in September to get the total of 62 days. This calculation is much quicker if you use Table 9-1, which numbers each day of the year in sequence beginning with January 1.

 1 Find ordinary and exact time.

To use Table 9-1 to find the exact time of a loan from July 12 to September 12, note that July 12 is the 193rd day of the year and September 12 is the 255th day. Subtract 193 from 255 to find the total number of days.

$$
\begin{array}{ll}
255 & \textbf{Sequence number for September 12} \\
\underline{193} & \textbf{Sequence number for July 12} \\
62 \text{ days} &
\end{array}
$$

If the period of a loan includes February, count it as 30 days for ordinary time but 28 days for exact time. In leap years, February has 29 days, so the exact time is determined by counting 28 days and adding 1 to the total number of days if February 29 is within the loan period.

To determine if a year is a leap year, see if the year is divisible by 4. (Recall the rule for divisibility by 4: If the last *two* digits form a number that is divisible by 4, the entire number is divisible by 4.) The year 2004 will be a leap year because it is divisible by 4. The year 2000 was a leap year. See the note at the bottom of Table 9-1 for other centennial years.

Table 9-1 Sequential Numbers for Dates of the Year

Day of Month	Jan.	Feb.	Mar.	Apr.	May	June	July	Aug.	Sept.	Oct.	Nov.	Dec.
1	1	32	60	91	121	152	182	213	244	274	305	335
2	2	33	61	92	122	153	183	214	245	275	306	336
3	3	34	62	93	123	154	184	215	246	276	307	337
4	4	35	63	94	124	155	185	216	247	277	308	338
5	5	36	64	95	125	156	186	217	248	278	309	339
6	6	37	65	96	126	157	187	218	249	279	310	340
7	7	38	66	97	127	158	188	219	250	280	311	341
8	8	39	67	98	128	159	189	220	251	281	312	342
9	9	40	68	99	129	160	190	221	252	282	313	343
10	10	41	69	100	130	161	191	222	253	283	314	344
11	11	42	70	101	131	162	192	223	254	284	315	345
12	12	43	71	102	132	163	193	224	255	285	316	346
13	13	44	72	103	133	164	194	225	256	286	317	347
14	14	45	73	104	134	165	195	226	257	287	318	348
15	15	46	74	105	135	166	196	227	258	288	319	349
16	16	47	75	106	136	167	197	228	259	289	320	350
17	17	48	76	107	137	168	198	229	260	290	321	351
18	18	49	77	108	138	169	199	230	261	291	322	352
19	19	50	78	109	139	170	200	231	262	292	323	353
20	20	51	79	110	140	171	201	232	263	293	324	354
21	21	52	80	111	141	172	202	233	264	294	325	355
22	22	53	81	112	142	173	203	234	265	295	326	356
23	23	54	82	113	143	174	204	235	266	296	327	357
24	24	55	83	114	144	175	205	236	267	297	328	358
25	25	56	84	115	145	176	206	237	268	298	329	359
26	26	57	85	116	146	177	207	238	269	299	330	360
27	27	58	86	117	147	178	208	239	270	300	331	361
28	28	59	87	118	148	179	209	240	271	301	332	362
29	29	*	88	119	149	180	210	241	272	302	333	363
30	30		89	120	150	181	211	242	273	303	334	364
31	31		90		151		212	243		304		365

*See the discussion on leap year. For centennial years (those at the turn of the century), leap years occur only when the number of the year is divisible by 400. Thus, 2000 was a leap year (2000/400 divides exactly), but 1700, 1800, and 1900 were not leap years.

? HOW TO Find the Exact Time of a Loan Using the Sequential Numbers Table (Table 9-1)

1. If the beginning and due dates of the loan fall within the same year, subtract the beginning date's sequential number from the due date's sequential number.

   From May 15 to Oct. 15
   288 − 135 = 153 days

2. If the beginning and due dates of the loan do not fall within the same year:

   From May 15 to March 15

   (a) Subtract the beginning date's sequential number from 365.

   365 − 135 = 230

   (b) Add the due date's sequential number to the difference from step 2a.

   230 + 74 = 304 days (non-leap year)

3. If February 29 is between the beginning and due dates, add 1 to the difference from step 1 or the sum from step 2b.

   304 + 1 = 305 days (leap year)

EXAMPLE   A loan made on September 5 is due July 5 of the *following year.* Find (a) the ordinary time, (b) the exact time for the loan in a non-leap year, and (c) the exact time in a leap year.

(a) *Ordinary time*

There are 10 months from September to July.
10 months × 30 days/month = 300 days

(b) *Exact time in a non-leap year*

From Table 9-1, September 5 is the 248th day.

$$\begin{array}{r} 365 \\ 248 \\ \hline 117 \text{ days} \end{array}$$

> Subtract 248 from 365.
> Days from September 5 through December 31

July 5 is the 186th day.

117 + 186 = 303 days

> Add 117 and 186 to find the exact time of the loan.

(c) *Exact time in a leap year*

303 + 1 = 304 days

> Since Feb. 29 is between the beginning and due dates, add 1 to the non-leap year total.

Ordinary time is 300 days. Exact time is 303 days in a non-leap year and 304 days in a leap year.

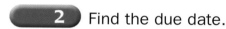 **2** Find the due date.

Sometimes the beginning date of a loan and the time period of the loan are known, and the due date must be determined.

HOW TO   Find the Due Date of a Loan Given the Beginning Date and the Time Period in Days

1. For ordinary time:

  (a) Determine the number of months of the loan, counting each month as 30 days.

> 60 days from July 1
> 60 ÷ 30 = 2 months

  (b) Count forward from the beginning date the number of months from step 1a. Add extra days for a part of a month if necessary.

> August, September
> Due September 1

2. For exact time:

  (a) Add the sequential number of the beginning date to the number of days in the time period.

> July = Day 182
> 182 + 60 = 242

  (b) If the sum is less than or equal to 365, find the date (Table 9-1) corresponding to the sum.

> 242nd day = August 30

  (c) If the sum is more than 365, subtract 365 from the sum. Then find the date (Table 9-1) in the following year corresponding to the difference.

  (d) Adjust for February 29 on a leap year if appropriate by *subtracting* one from the result in step 2b or 2c.

EXAMPLE   Figure the due date using (a) ordinary time and (b) exact time for a 90-day loan made on November 15.

(a) *Ordinary time*

In ordinary time, there are 30 days in a month, and 90 days is the same as 3 months.

Count 3 months from November 15 to find a due date of February 15.

(b) *Exact time*

From Table 9-1, November 15 is the 319th day.

$$\begin{array}{r} 319 \\ + 90 \\ \hline 409 \end{array}$$ **Add 319 to 90 days in the time period.**

409 is greater than 365, so the loan is due in the following year.

$$\begin{array}{r} 409 \\ -365 \\ \hline 44 \end{array}$$ **Subtract 365 from 409.**

In Table 9-1, day 44 corresponds to February 13.

The loan using ordinary time is due February 15 and using exact time is due February 13.

 TIP! Time Periods That Involve Parts of Months

When the number of days in ordinary time is not a multiple of 30, the extra days are used to adjust the due date. For a time period of 100 days, 90 days are three months in ordinary time. The extra 10 days advance the due date by 10 days. If the beginning date on a 100-day loan is July 25, three months advance the due date to October 25. Five of the extra days advance the due date to the end of the month (30 days). Then, the remaining extra five days advance the due date to November 5.

 3 Find the interest using the ordinary and exact interest rates.

An interest rate is normally given as a rate *per year*. But if the time period of the loan is in days, then using the simple interest formula requires that the rate *also* be expressed as a rate *per day*. We convert a rate per year to a rate per day in two different ways, depending on whether the rate per day is to be an **ordinary interest** rate or an **exact interest** rate. An ordinary interest rate assumes 360 days per year; an exact interest rate assumes 365 days per year.

 HOW TO Find the Ordinary Interest Rate Per Day and the Exact Interest Rate Per Day

1. For ordinary interest, divide the annual interest rate by 360.

$$\text{Ordinary interest rate per day} = \frac{\text{interest rate per year}}{360}$$

2. For exact interest, divide the annual interest rate by 365.

$$\text{Exact interest rate per day} = \frac{\text{interest rate per year}}{365}$$

EXAMPLE Use ordinary time to find the ordinary interest on a loan of $500 at 17% annual interest rate. The loan was made on March 15 and is due May 15.

Ordinary interest rate per day $= \dfrac{17\%}{360}$

> Divide the annual rate by 360.

Ordinary time $= 2 \times 30 = 60$ days

> Multiply the number of days per month by 2.

$I = P\,R\,T$

$I = \$500\left(\dfrac{0.17}{360}\right)60$

> Replace with known values.

$I = \$14.17$

> Perform the operations.

The interest is $14.17.

EXAMPLE Find the ordinary interest using exact time for the loan in the preceding example.

Ordinary interest rate per day $= \dfrac{17\%}{360}$

Exact time $= 135 - 74 = 61$ days

> Find each date's sequential number in Table 9–1 and subtract.

$I = P\,R\,T$

$I = \$500\left(\dfrac{0.17}{360}\right)61$

> Replace with known values.

$I = \$14.40$

> Perform the operations.

The interest is $14.40.

EXAMPLE Find the exact interest using exact time on the loan in the first example on this page.

Exact interest $= \dfrac{17\%}{365}$

> Divide the annual rate by 365.

Exact time $= 61$ days

$I = P\,R\,T$

$I = \$500\left(\dfrac{0.17}{365}\right)61$

> Replace with known values.
> Perform the operations.

$I = \$14.21$

The interest is $14.21.

The three preceding examples can be calculated and compared using the memory function of a calculator:

Be sure memory is clear or equal to 0 before you begin.

$\boxed{\text{AC}}$ 500 $\boxed{\times}$ .17 $\boxed{=}$ $\boxed{\text{M}^+}$ $\boxed{\times}$ 60 $\boxed{\div}$ 360 $\boxed{=}$ ⟹ 14.166666

$\boxed{\text{AC}}$ $\boxed{\text{MR}}$ $\boxed{\times}$ 61 $\boxed{\div}$ 360 $\boxed{=}$ ⟹ 14.402777

$\boxed{\text{AC}}$ $\boxed{\text{MR}}$ $\boxed{\times}$ 61 $\boxed{\div}$ 365 $\boxed{=}$ ⟹ 14.205479

Note that the interest varies in each case. The second method illustrated, *ordinary interest using exact time,* is most often used by bankers when they are *lending* money because it yields a slightly higher amount of interest. It is sometimes called the **banker's rule.** On the other hand, when bankers *pay* interest on savings accounts, they normally use a 365-day year—an exact interest rate—which yields the most accurate amount of interest but is less than the amount yielded by the banker's rule.

EXAMPLE Borrowing money to pay cash for large purchases is sometimes profitable when a cash discount is allowed on the purchases. Joann Jimanez purchased a computer, printer, copier, and fax machine for her consulting firm that regularly sold for $5,999. A special promotion offered the equipment for $5,890, with cash terms of 3/10, n/90. She does not have the cash to pay the bill now, but she will within the next three months. She finds a bank that will loan her the money for the equipment at 13% (using ordinary interest) for 80 days. Should she take out the loan to take advantage of the special promotion and cash discount?

1 Decision needed

Should Joann Jimanez take out the loan?

2 Unknown facts

Cash discount on special price, compared with interest on loan

3 Known facts

Since Joann would have the money by the 90-day net period, she can take advantage of the special price with either choice.
Special price: $5,890
Cash discount rate: 0.03

Ordinary interest rate of loan: $\dfrac{0.13}{360}$ per day

Exact term of loan: 80 days

4 Relationships

Cash discount = special price × discount rate
Cash discount = $5,890 × 0.03
Interest on loan = principal × rate × time

The principal is the net amount Joann would pay, once the cash discount is allowed. Net amount is the special price, $5,890, multiplied by the complement of the cash discount rate.

$$\text{Interest on loan} = (\$5,890 \times 0.97) \times \frac{0.13}{360} \times 80$$

5 Estimation

Both the cash discount and the interest on the loan are a percentage of the special price. That is, both are $5,890 multiplied by some factor.

$$\text{Cash discount} = \$\,5,890 \times \boxed{0.03}$$

$$\text{Interest on loan} = \$5,890 \times \boxed{0.97 \times \frac{0.13}{360} \times 80}$$

One way to compare the interest and cash discount, then, is to compare these factors. We estimate

$$\text{Cash discount factor} = 0.03 = \frac{3}{100} \approx \frac{1}{33}$$

$$\text{Interest factor} \approx 1 \times \frac{0.12}{360} \times 100 = \frac{12}{360} = \frac{1}{30}$$

The cash discount factor looks to be slightly smaller than the interest factor, so that the cash discount may not be large enough to offset the interest on the loan. In any case, whatever dollar benefit there may be is likely to be small.

6 Calculation

$$\text{Cash discount} = \$5{,}890 \times 0.03$$

$$= \$176.70$$

$$\text{Interest on loan} = \$5{,}890 \times 0.97 \times \frac{0.13}{360} \times 80$$

$$= \$165.05$$

7 Interpretation

The interest on the loan is $165.05, slightly less than the cash discount of $176.70.

8 Decision made

Since the cash discount is about $10 more than the interest on the loan, Joann will not lose money by borrowing to take advantage of the discount terms of sale. But other factors—the time she spends to take out the loan, for example—may weigh her decision against the loan. Instead she may settle for paying a slightly higher price, forgoing the cash discount.

4 Find simple interest using a table.

Many tables are available for finding ordinary and exact interest. Notes on the table will explain how to interpret table values. The values in Table 9-2 give the exact interest for $100 for a specific number of days.

? HOW TO Find Simple Interest Using a Table

1. Identify the amount of money that the table uses as the principal. (A typical table principal is $1, $100, or $1,000.)
2. Divide the loan principal by the table principal.
3. Select the days row corresponding to the time period (in days) of the loan.
4. Select the annual rate column corresponding to the annual interest rate of the loan.
5. Locate the value in the cell where the annual rate column intersects the days row.
6. Multiply the quotient from step 2 by the value from step 5.

EXAMPLE Find the exact interest on a loan of $6,500 at 11.75% annually for 45 days.

Use Table 9-2 (on page 392) to find the interest for $100. Move across the 45 days row to the 11.75% column. The number 1.448630 is the interest on $100 for 45 days. The interest on $6,500 is

$$\frac{\$6{,}500}{\$100} \times 1.448630 = 65 \times 1.448630 = \$94.16 \text{ (to nearest cent)}$$

Table 9-2 Simple Exact Interest on $100 for Indicated Number of Days (Exact Time, Exact Interest Basis)

Days	Annual Rate 11.5%	11.75%	12.00%	12.25%	12.50%	12.75%
1	0.031507	0.032192	0.032877	0.033562	0.034247	0.034932
2	0.063014	0.064384	0.065753	0.067123	0.068493	0.069863
3	0.094521	0.096575	0.098630	0.100685	0.102740	0.104795
4	0.126027	0.128767	0.131507	0.134247	0.136986	0.139726
5	0.157534	0.160959	0.164384	0.167808	0.171233	0.174658
6	0.189041	0.193151	0.197260	0.201370	0.205479	0.209589
7	0.220548	0.225342	0.230137	0.234932	0.239726	0.244521
8	0.252055	0.257534	0.263014	0.268493	0.273973	0.279452
9	0.283562	0.289726	0.295890	0.302055	0.308219	0.314384
10	0.315068	0.321918	0.328767	0.335616	0.342466	0.349315
11	0.346575	0.354110	0.361644	0.369178	0.376712	0.384247
12	0.378082	0.386301	0.394521	0.402740	0.410959	0.419178
13	0.409589	0.418493	0.427397	0.436301	0.445205	0.454110
14	0.441096	0.450685	0.460274	0.469863	0.479452	0.489041
15	0.472603	0.482877	0.493151	0.503425	0.513699	0.523973
16	0.504110	0.515068	0.526027	0.536986	0.547945	0.558904
17	0.535616	0.547260	0.558904	0.570548	0.582192	0.593836
18	0.567123	0.579452	0.591781	0.604110	0.616438	0.628767
19	0.598630	0.611644	0.624658	0.637671	0.650685	0.663699
20	0.630137	0.643836	0.567534	0.671233	0.684932	0.698630
21	0.661644	0.676027	0.690411	0.704795	0.719178	0.733562
22	0.693151	0.708219	0.723288	0.738356	0.753425	0.768493
23	0.724658	0.740411	0.756164	0.771918	0.787671	0.803425
24	0.756164	0.772603	0.789041	0.805479	0.821918	0.838356
25	0.787671	0.804795	0.821918	0.839041	0.856164	0.873288
26	0.819178	0.836986	0.854795	0.872603	0.890411	0.908219
27	0.850685	0.869178	0.887671	0.906164	0.924658	0.943151
28	0.882192	0.901370	0.920548	0.939726	0.958904	0.978082
29	0.913699	0.933562	0.953425	0.973288	0.993151	1.013014
30	0.945205	0.965753	0.986301	1.006849	1.027397	1.047945
31	0.976712	0.997945	1.019178	1.040411	1.061644	1.082877
32	1.008219	1.030137	1.052055	1.073973	1.095890	1.117808
33	1.039726	1.062329	1.084932	1.107534	1.130137	1.152740
34	1.071233	1.094521	1.117808	1.141096	1.164384	1.187671
35	1.102740	1.126712	1.150685	1.174658	1.198630	1.222603
36	1.134247	1.158904	1.183562	1.208219	1.232877	1.257534
37	1.165753	1.191096	1.216438	1.241781	1.267123	1.292466
38	1.197260	1.223288	1.249315	1.275342	1.301370	1.327397
39	1.228767	1.255479	1.282192	1.308904	1.385616	1.362329
40	1.260274	1.287671	1.315068	1.342466	1.369863	1.397260
41	1.291781	1.319863	1.347945	1.376027	1.404110	1.432192
42	1.323288	1.352055	1.380822	1.409589	1.438356	1.467123
43	1.354795	1.384247	1.413699	1.443151	1.472603	1.502055
44	1.386301	1.416438	1.446575	1.476712	1.506849	1.536986
45	1.417808	1.448630	1.479452	1.510274	1.541096	1.571918
46	1.449315	1.480822	1.512329	1.543836	1.575342	1.606849
47	1.480822	1.513014	1.545205	1.577397	1.609589	1.641781
48	1.512329	1.545205	1.578082	1.610959	1.643836	1.676712
49	1.543836	1.577397	1.610959	1.644521	1.678082	1.711644
50	1.575342	1.609589	1.643836	1.678082	1.712329	1.746575

Table shows exact interest on $100 at a rate of R for a given number of days D. Table values can be generated using the formula

$$\$100\left(R \times \frac{D}{365}\right).$$

To check this answer, we use the formula $I = PRT$.

Check:

$$I = P \: R \: T$$

$$I = \$6{,}500 \times \left(\frac{0.1175}{365} \right) \times 45 = \$94.16$$

The interest is \$94.16.

SELF-CHECK 9.2

1. A loan made on March 10 is due September 10 of the *following year*. Find the ordinary time and exact time for the loan in a non-leap year and a leap year.

2. Find the ordinary and exact time of a loan made on March 25 and due on November 15 of the same year.

3. A loan is made on January 15 and has a due date of October 20 during a leap year. Find the ordinary time and the exact time of the loan.

4. Find the due date using ordinary time and exact time for a loan made on October 15 for 120 days.

5. A loan is made on March 20 for 180 days. Find the due date using ordinary time and exact time.

6. Use exact time to find the due date of a loan that is made on February 10 of a leap year and is due in 60 days.

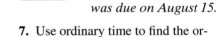 *Exercises 7–9: A loan for \$3,000 with a simple annual interest rate of 15% was made on June 15 and was due on August 15.*

7. Use ordinary time to find the ordinary interest on the loan.

8. Find the exact interest using exact time.

9. Find the ordinary interest using exact time.

 For exercises 10–12, use Table 9–2.

10. Find the exact interest on a loan of \$3,500 at $12\frac{1}{2}\%$ annual simple interest for 45 days.

11. Find the exact interest on a loan of \$1,000 at 12% annual simple interest for 10 days.

12. Find the exact interest on a loan of \$1,850 at $11\frac{1}{2}\%$ annual simple interest for 21 days.

13. Discuss the practicality of using tables versus a calculator for finding interest.

9.3 Promissory Notes

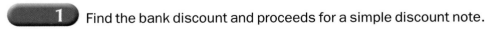

Find the bank discount and proceeds for a simple discount note.

Find the bank discount and proceeds for a third-party discount note.

When a business or individual borrows money, it is customary for the borrower to sign a legal document promising to repay the loan. The document is called a **promissory**

note. The note includes all necessary information about the loan. The **maker** is the person borrowing the money. The **payee** is the person loaning the money. The **term** of the note is the length of time for which the money is borrowed; the **maturity date** is the date on which the loan is due to be repaid. The **face value** of the note is the amount borrowed. Figure 9-3 shows a sample promissory note signed by Mary Fisher.

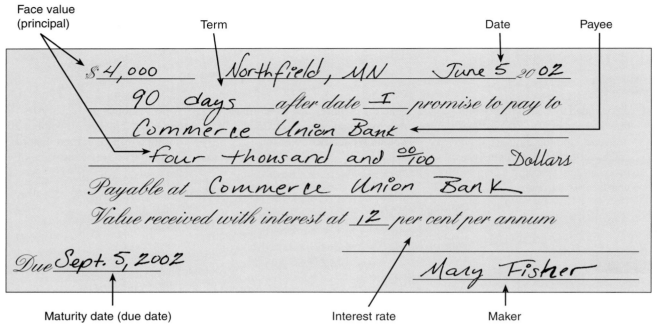

Figure 9-3   A promissory note

1   Find the bank discount and proceeds for a simple discount note.

If money is borrowed from a bank at a simple interest rate, the bank often collects the interest, which is also called the **bank discount,** at the time the loan is made. Thus, the maker receives the face value of the loan minus the bank discount. This difference is called the **proceeds.** Such a loan is called a **simple discount note.** Loans of this type allow the bank or payee of the loan to receive all fees and interest at the time the loan is made. This increases the yield on the loan since the interest and fees can be reinvested immediately. Besides increased yields, a bank may require this type of loan when the maker of the loan has an inadequate or poor credit history. This decreases the amount of risk to the bank or lender.

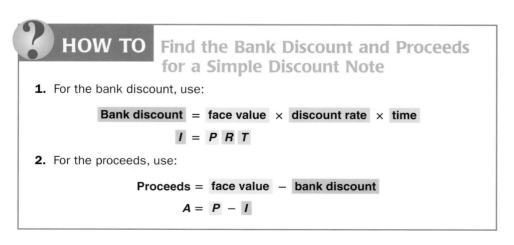

? HOW TO Find the Bank Discount and Proceeds for a Simple Discount Note

1. For the bank discount, use:

Bank discount = **face value** × **discount rate** × **time**

$$I = P \ R \ T$$

2. For the proceeds, use:

Proceeds = **face value** − **bank discount**

$$A = P - I$$

EXAMPLE Find the (a) bank discount and (b) proceeds using ordinary interest and ordinary time on the promissory note shown in Figure 9-3. It is a loan to Mary Fisher of $4,000 at 12% annual simple interest from June 5 to September 5.

(a) Bank discount = $P \times R \times T$

Bank discount = $\$4,000 \times \dfrac{0.12}{360} \times 90$

Bank discount = $120

The bank discount is $120.

(b) Proceeds = $A = P - I$

Proceeds = $4,000 − $120

Proceeds = $3,880

Subtract the bank discount from the face value of the note.

The proceeds are $3,880.

The difference between the simple interest note, which is also called an **undiscounted note,** and the simple discount note is the amount of money the borrower has use of for the length of the loan, and also the maturity value of the loan, the amount owed at the end of the loan term. Interest is paid on the same amount for the same period of time in both cases. In the simple interest note, the borrower has use of the full principal of the loan, but the maturity value is principal plus interest. In the simple discount note, the borrower has use of only the proceeds (face value − discount), but the maturity value is just the face value, since the interest (the discount) was paid "in advance." Thus, if Bill borrows $5,000 with a discount (interest) rate of 18%, the discount is 18% × $5,000, or $900, so he gets the use of only $4,100, though the bank charges interest on the full $5,000. The maturity value is $5,000.

Here is a comparison of simple interest notes versus simple discount notes:

	Simple Interest Note	Simple Discount Note
Face value	$5,000	$5,000
Discount or interest	900	900
Proceeds or amount available to borrower	5,000	4,100
Maturity value	5,900	5,000

2 Find the bank discount and proceeds for a third-party discount note.

Many businesses agree to be the payee for a promissory note as payment for the sale of goods. If these businesses in turn need cash, they may sell such a note to a bank who is the **third party** of the note. Selling a note to a bank in return for cash is called discounting a note. The note is called a **third-party discount note.**

When the third-party bank discounts a note, it gives the business owning the note the maturity value of the note minus a bank discount. The bank's discount is based on how long it holds the note, called the **discount period.** The bank receives the full maturity value of the note from the maker when it comes due. From the standpoint of the note maker (the borrower), the term of the note is the same because the maturity (due) date is the same, and the maturity value is the same.

The following diagram shows how the discount period is figured:

Original date
of loan
July 14 —————————————————→ Sept. 12

Date loan is
discounted

Maturity date
Sept. 12

Aug. 3 ——————————→ Sept. 12

Discount period

HOW TO   Find the Bank Discount and Proceeds for a Third-Party Discount Note

1. For the bank discount, use:

Bank discount = maturity value of original note × discount rate × discount period

$$I = P\ R\ T$$

2. For the proceeds, use:

Proceeds = maturity value of original note − bank discount

$$A = P - I$$

EXAMPLE   Alpine Pleasures, Inc., delivers ski equipment to retailers in July but does not expect payment until mid-September, so the retailers agree to sign promissory notes for the equipment. These notes are based on exact interest and exact time, with a 10% annual simple interest rate. One promissory note held by Alpine is for $8,000, was made on July 14, and is due September 12. Alpine needs cash, so it takes the note to its bank. On August 3, the bank agrees to buy the note at a 12% discount rate using the banker's rule (ordinary interest, exact time). Find the proceeds for the note.

A table can help you organize the facts:

Date of Original Note	Principal of Note	Simple Interest Rate	Date of Discount Note	Bank Discount Rate	Maturity Date
July 14	$8,000	10%	Aug. 3	12%	Sept. 12

Calculate the time and maturity value of the original note. From Table 9–1, September 12 is the 255th day of the year, July 14 is the 195th day.

$$\begin{array}{r} 255 \\ \underline{195} \\ 60 \text{ days} \end{array}$$

$$I = P \times R \times T$$

> Use the simple interest equation to find exact interest using exact time.

$$I = \$8{,}000 \times \frac{0.1}{365} \times 60$$

$$I = \$131.51 \text{ (rounded)}$$

The simple interest for the original loan is $131.51.

To find the maturity value, add the principal and interest.

$$\text{Maturity value} = \text{principal} + \text{interest}$$
$$\text{Maturity value} = \$8{,}000 + \$131.51$$
$$\text{Maturity value} = \$8{,}131.51$$

The maturity value of the original loan is $8,131.51.

Now calculate the discount period.

Discount period = number of days from August 3 to September 12

August 3 is the 215th day.

$$\begin{array}{r} 255 \\ \underline{215} \\ 40 \text{ days} \end{array}$$

The discount period for the discount note is 40 days.

Now calculate the bank discount based on the banker's rule (ordinary interest using exact time).

Bank discount = maturity value × bank discount rate × discount period

$$\text{Bank discount} = \$8,131.51 \times \frac{0.12}{360} \times 40$$

Ordinary interest (discount) rate is $\frac{12\%}{360}$.

Bank discount = $108.42

The bank discount is $108.42.

Now calculate the proceeds that will be received by Alpine.

Proceeds = maturity value − bank discount

Proceeds = $8,131.51 − $108.42

Proceeds = $8,023.09

The proceeds to Alpine are $8,023.09.

 TIP! **Interest-Free Money**

A non-interest-bearing note is very uncommon but sometimes available. This means that you borrow a certain amount and pay that same amount back later. The note itself carries no interest, and the maturity value of the note is the same as the face value or principal. The payee or person loaning the money only wants the original amount of money at the maturity date.

What happens if a non-interest-bearing note is discounted? Use the information from the preceding example, without the simple interest on the original loan.

Bank discount = maturity value × discount rate × discount period

$$\text{Bank discount} = \$8,000 \times \frac{0.12}{360} \times 40$$

The maturity value is the face value, or $8,000, rather than $8,131.51, which included interest.

Bank discount = $106.67

The bank discount is $106.67.

Proceeds = maturity value − bank discount

Proceeds = $8,000 − $106.67

The maturity value is $8,000.

Proceeds = $7,893.33

The proceeds are $7,893.33.

The original payee loans $8,000 and receives $7,893.33 in cash from the third-party bank.

Use the banker's rule unless otherwise specified.

1

1. José makes a simple discount note with a face value of $2,500, a term of 120 days, and a 16% discount rate. Find the discount.

2. Find the proceeds for exercise 1.

3. Find the discount and proceeds on a $3,250 face-value note for six months if the discount rate is 9.2%.

2

4. Find the maturity value of the undiscounted promissory note shown in Figure 9-4.

5. Carter Manufacturing holds a note of $5,000 that has an interest rate of 11% annually. The note was made on March 18 and is due November 13. Carter sells the note to a bank on June 13 at a discount rate of 14% annually. Find the proceeds on the third-party discount note.

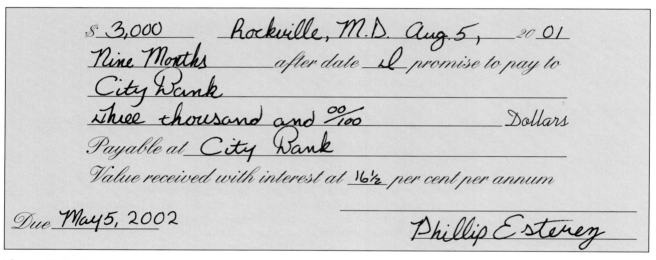

$ 3,000   Rockville, M.D. Aug. 5,   20 01

Nine Months _____ after date _I_ promise to pay to

City Bank _____

three thousand and 00/100 _____ Dollars

Payable at _City Bank_____

Value received with interest at _16½_ per cent per annum

Due _May 5, 2002_

Phillip Esterey

Figure 9-4 Promissory Note

6. Discuss some reasons a payee might agree to a non-interest-bearing note.

7. Discuss some reasons a payee would sell a note to a bank and lose money in the process.

90 Days Same as Cash! Deals

Just before Christmas, Kwanza, and Hanukkah, stores advertise "90 days—same as cash!" deals on home appliances, furniture, electronics, and so on, with a minimum purchase of $500. The customer must be approved for credit and must sign a contract before purchase agreeing to the following terms: If the customer pays in full within 90 days, he or she pays only the sales price plus tax. But if payment is not made *in full* within 90 days, 26.8% annual simple interest is added to the sales price plus tax for the first 90 days, plus 2% simple interest per month on the unpaid balance, with minimum payments of $50 per month. Finance companies, with their established methods of credit approval, collection, repossession, and litigation, usually handle these contracts for the stores. Research shows that only about 30% of customers pay off these bills within 90 days, and most customers become continuous or repeat customers of the finance company after the initial loan is paid off.

On December 15, a single mother of three children purchases a washer/dryer set under these terms for $699 plus 8.25% sales tax. She plans to pay it off within 90 days with her anticipated $1,000 IRS refund. Her refund doesn't arrive until April 1.

Exercises

Use the above information to answer the following:

1. What is the total of her "90 days—same as cash" purchase? Round to the nearest cent.

2. Using the exact time, what is her deadline for paying no interest in a non-leap year? In a leap year? Find the dates in ordinary time. Which time is the finance company likely to use and why?

3. Using ordinary time in a non-leap year, how much interest does she pay for the first 90 days? Assuming she makes no payments, what is her unpaid balance on March 15?

4. Find her payoff on April 1.

5. How much did it cost her to pay off this loan 15 days late? What annual simple interest rate does this amount to?

Answers

1. $699 plus sales tax totals $756.67.

2. In a non-leap year, her deadline is March 15, March 14 in a leap year. These dates are the same for ordinary time. Money lenders typically use ordinary time for loans to earn slightly higher interest.

3. She owes $50.70 in interest for the first 90 days, so her unpaid balance on March 15 is $807.37.

4. She owes $8.07 in interest for the next 15 days on the $807.37 unpaid balance, so her April 1 payoff is $815.44.

5. It cost her $58.77 to pay off her loan 15 days late! Since interest is paid on interest and keeping the original amount of $756.67 as the base, this amounts to 26.6% annual simple interest.

OVERVIEW

Section Outcome	Important Points with Examples

Section 9.1

1 Find simple interest using the simple interest formula. (page 376)

Multiply the principal by the rate and time.

$$\text{Interest} = \text{principal} \times \text{rate} \times \text{time}$$

$$I = P R T$$

Find the interest paid on a loan of \$8,400 for one year at $9\frac{1}{2}\%$ annual simple interest rate.	**Find the interest paid on a loan of \$4,500 for two years at a simple interest rate of 12% per year.**
Interest = principal × rate × time = \$8,400 × 0.095 × 1 = \$798	Interest = principal × rate × time = \$4,500 × 0.12 × 2 = \$1,080

2 Find the maturity value of a loan. (page 378)

1. If the principal and interest are known, add them.

$$\text{Maturity value} = \text{principal} + \text{interest}$$

$$MV = P + I$$

2. If the principal, rate, and time are known:
   (a) Add 1 to the product of the rate and time.
   (b) Multiply the principal by the sum from step 2a.

$$\text{Maturity value} = \text{principal} \times (1 + \text{rate} \times \text{time})$$

$$MV = P(1 + R T)$$

Find the maturity value of a loan of \$8,400 with \$798 interest rate of 12% per year.	**Find the maturity value of a loan of \$4,500 for two years at a single interest**
$MV = P + I$ $MV = \$8,400 + \$798$ $MV = \$9,198$	$MV = P(1 + RT)$ $MV = \$4,500(1 + 0.12 \times 2)$ $MV = \$4,500(1.24)$ $MV = \$5,580$

3 Convert months to a fractional or decimal part of a year. (page 380)

1. Write the number of months as the numerator of a fraction.
2. Write 12 as the denominator of the fraction.
3. Reduce the fraction to lowest terms.
4. Divide the numerator by the denominator to get the decimal equivalent of the fraction.

Convert 42 months to years.	**Convert 3 months to years.**
$\dfrac{42}{12} = \dfrac{7}{2} = 3.5 \text{ years}$	$\dfrac{3}{12} = \dfrac{1}{4} = 0.25 \text{ years}$

4

Find the principal, rate, or time using the simple interest formula.
(page 381)

1. Select the appropriate form of the formula.

   (a) If the principal is unknown, use $P = \dfrac{I}{RT}$

   (b) If the rate is unknown, use $R = \dfrac{I}{PT}$

   (c) If the time is unknown, use $T = \dfrac{I}{PR}$

2. Replace letters with known values and perform the indicated operations.

Nancy Jeggle borrowed $6,000 for $3\frac{1}{2}$ years and paid $2,800 simple interest. What was the annual interest rate?	R is unknown. $$R = \frac{I}{PT}$$ $$R = \frac{\$2,800}{(\$6,000)(3.5)}$$ $$R = 0.133$$ $$R = 13.3\% \text{ annually}$$
Donna Ruscitti paid $675 interest on an 18-month loan at 18% annual simple interest. What was the principal?	P is unknown. $$P = \frac{I}{RT}$$ $$P = \frac{\$675}{0.18(1.5)}$$ $$P = \$2,500$$
Ashish Paranjape borrowed $1,500 at 16.5% annual simple interest. If he paid $866.25 interest, what was the time period of the loan?	T is unknown. $$T = \frac{I}{PR}$$ $$T = \frac{\$866.25}{\$1,500(0.165)}$$ $$T = 3.5 \text{ years}$$

Section 9.2

1

Find ordinary and exact time.
(page 385)

Change months and years to ordinary or exact time in days.
1. For ordinary time use:

$$1 \text{ month} = 30 \text{ days and } 1 \text{ year} = 360 \text{ days}$$

2. For exact time use:

$$1 \text{ month} = \text{exact number of days in the month}$$

$$1 \text{ year} = 365 \text{ days (or 366 days in a leap year)}$$

Find the ordinary time of a loan made on October 1 and due May 1 (non-leap year).	Find the exact time of a loan made October 1 and due May 1 (non-leap year).
October 1 to May 1 = 7 months 7 months = 7 × 30 days = 210 days	October, December, January, and March have 31 days. November and April have 30 days. February has 28 days. 4(31) + 2(30) + 28 = 212 days

Find the exact time of a loan using the sequential numbers table (Table 9–1).
1. If the beginning and due dates of the loan fall within the same year, subtract the beginning date's sequential number from the due date's sequential number.
2. If the beginning and due dates of the loan do not fall within the same year:
   (a) Subtract the beginning date's sequential number from 365.
   (b) Add the due date's sequential number to the difference from step 2a.
3. If February 29 is between the beginning and due dates, add 1 to the difference from step 1 or to the sum from step 2b.

Find the exact time of a loan made on March 25 and due on October 10.	Find the exact time of a loan made on June 7 and due the following March 7 in a non-leap year.

October 10 = day 283
  March 25 = day 84
          199 days
 	
The loan is made for 199 days.
	December 31 = day 365
	    June 7 = day 158
	         207 days
	March 7 = + 66 days
	        273 days
	
	The loan is made for 273 days in all.

2   Find the due date. (page 387)

Find the due date of a loan given the beginning date and the time period in days.
1. **For ordinary time:**
   (a) Determine the number of months of the loan, counting each month as 30 days.
   (b) Count forward from the beginning date the number of months. Add extra days for a part of a month if necessary.
2. **For exact time:**
   (a) Add the sequential number of the beginning date to the number of days in the time period.
   (b) If the sum is less than or equal to 365, find the date (Table 9–1) corresponding to the sum.
   (c) If the sum is more than 365, subtract 365 from the sum. Then find the date (Table 9–1) in the following year corresponding to the difference.
   (d) Adjust for February 29 on a leap year if appropriate.

Figure the due date using ordinary time and exact time for a 60-day loan made on August 12.

Ordinary time:
60 days is two months. Two months from August 12 is October 12.

Exact time:
August 12 = day 224
        + 60
          284
Day 284 is October 11.

3 Find interest using the ordinary and exact interest rates. (page 388)

1. For the ordinary interest rate per day, divide the annual interest rate by 360.

$$\text{Ordinary interest rate per day} = \frac{\text{interest rate per year}}{360}$$

2. For the exact interest rate per day, divide the annual interest rate by 365.

$$\text{Exact interest rate per day} = \frac{\text{interest rate per year}}{365}$$

On May 15, Roberta Krech borrowed $6,000 at 12.5% annual simple interest. The loan was due on November 15. Use ordinary time to find the ordinary interest due on the loan.

Time is 6 months, 30 days each, or 6 × 30 days. Interest rate is $\frac{12.5\%}{360}$ per day.

$$I = PRT$$

$$I = (\$6,000)\left(\frac{0.125}{360}\right)(6 \times 30)$$

$$I = \$375$$

Use exact interest and exact time to find the interest due on Roberta's loan (see above).

Use Table 9-1 to find exact time. November 15 is day 319. May 15 is day 135. So time is 319 − 135 days. Interest is $\frac{12.5\%}{365}$ per day.

$$I = PRT$$

$$I = (\$6,000)\left(\frac{0.125}{365}\right)(319 - 135)$$

$$I = \$378.08$$

4 Find simple interest using a table. (page 391)

1. Identify the amount of money that the table uses as the principal. (A typical table principal is $1, $100, or $1,000.)
2. Divide the loan principal by the table principal.
3. Select the days row corresponding to the time period (in days) of the loan.
4. Select the annual rate column corresponding to the annual interest rate of the loan.
5. Locate the value in the cell where the annual rate column intersects the days row.
6. Multiply the quotient from step 2 by the value from step 5.

Use Table 9-2 to find the exact interest on a loan of $2,500 at a 12.5% annual interest rate for 40 days.

The table uses $100 as the principal.

$$\frac{\$2,500}{\$100} = 25$$

Interest = 25 × 1.369863

Interest = $34.25

Use Table 9-2 to find the exact interest on a loan of $4,875 at an annual rate of 12.75% for 30 days.

The table uses $100 as the principal.

$$\frac{\$4,875}{\$100} = \$48.75$$

Interest = 48.75 × 1.047945

Interest = $51.09

Chapter 9 Simple Interest and Simple Discount **403**

1 Find the bank discount and proceeds for a simple discount note.
(page 394)

1. For the bank discount, use:

$$\boxed{\text{Bank discount}} = \boxed{\text{face value}} \times \boxed{\text{discount rate}} \times \boxed{\text{time}}$$
$$\boxed{I} = \boxed{P}\,\boxed{R}\,\boxed{T}$$

2. For the proceeds, use:

$$\text{Proceeds} = \boxed{\text{face value}} - \boxed{\text{bank discount}}$$
$$A = \boxed{P} - \boxed{I}$$

> The bank charged Robert Milewsky a 16.5% annual discount rate on a bank note of $1,500 for 120 days. Find the proceeds of the note using banker's rule.
>
> First find the discount, then subtract the discount from the face value of $1,500.
>
> $$\text{Discount} = I = PRT$$
>
> $$\text{Discount} = \$1{,}500\left(\frac{0.165}{360}\right)(120) \qquad \textbf{Rate is ordinary; time is exact.}$$
>
> $$\text{Discount} = \$82.50$$
>
> $$\text{Proceeds} = A = P - I$$
>
> $$\text{Proceeds} = \$1{,}500 - \$82.50$$
>
> $$\text{Proceeds} = \$1{,}417.50$$

2 Find the bank discount and proceeds for a third-party discount note.
(page 395)

1. For the bank discount, use:

$$\boxed{\text{Bank discount}} = \boxed{\text{maturity value of original note}} \times \boxed{\text{discount rate}} \times \boxed{\text{discount period}}$$
$$\boxed{I} = \boxed{P}\,\boxed{R}\,\boxed{T}$$

2. For the proceeds, use:

$$\text{Proceeds} = \boxed{\text{maturity value of original note}} - \boxed{\text{bank discount}}$$
$$A = \boxed{P} - \boxed{I}$$

> Mihoc Trailer Sales made a note of $10,000 with Darcy Mihoc, company owner, at 9% simple interest based on exact interest and exact time. The note is made on August 12 and due on November 10. However, Mihoc Trailer Sales needs cash, so the note is taken to the bank on September 5. The bank agrees to accept the note with a 13% annual discount rate using banker's rule. Find the proceeds of the note.
>
> To find the proceeds, we find the maturity value of the original note then find the bank discount. Exact time is 90 days ($314 - 224$). Exact interest rate is $\frac{9\%}{365}$.
>
> $$\text{Maturity value} = P(1 + RT)$$
>
> $$\text{Maturity value} = \$10{,}000\left(1 + \frac{0.09}{365} \times 90\right)$$
>
> $$\text{Maturity value} = \$10{,}221.92$$

Exact time of the discount period is 66 days (314 − 248). Ordinary discount rate is $\frac{13\%}{360}$.

$$\text{Bank discount} = I = PRT$$

$$\text{Bank discount} = \$10,221.92\left(\frac{0.13}{360}\right)(66)$$

$$\text{Bank discount} = \$243.62$$

$$\text{Proceeds} = A = P - I$$

$$\text{Proceeds} = \$10,221.92 - \$243.62$$

$$\text{Proceeds} = \$9,978.30$$

WORDS TO KNOW

interest (p. 376)
simple interest (p. 376)
compound interest (p. 376)
principal (p. 376)
rate (p. 376)
time (p. 376)
prime interest rate (p. 377)
maturity value (p. 378)
ordinary time (p. 385)

exact time (p. 385)
ordinary interest (p. 388)
exact interest (p. 388)
banker's rule (p. 390)
promissory note (p. 393)
maker (p. 394)
payee (p. 394)
term (p. 394)
maturity date (p. 394)

face value (p. 394)
bank discount (p. 394)
proceeds (p. 394)
simple discount note (p. 394)
undiscounted note (p. 395)
third party (p. 395)
third-party discount note (p. 395)
discount period (p. 395)

CHAPTER 9 CONCEPTS ANALYSIS

1. In applying most formulas involving a rate, a fractional or decimal equivalent of the rate is used. Explain how a rate can be mentally changed to a decimal.

2. A good thing to do when solving problems is first to devise a method to estimate the solution or answer to the question. Describe a strategy for estimating the interest in the first example of section 9.1.

3. Explain how the rate can be estimated in the sixth example of section 9.1.

4. Use the knuckle method introduced in section 7.3 to verify three entries in Table 9–1.

5. Use the formula $I = \$100\left(R \times \dfrac{D}{365}\right)$ to verify three entries in Table 9–2.

6. Find the corresponding entries for the first three rows of a table similar to Table 9–2 if the table values are based on a principal of $1,000.

7. The ordinary interest using exact time (banker's rule) will always be higher than ordinary interest using ordinary time and exact interest using exact time. Explain why this is true.

8. In section 9.1, three variations are given for the formula $I = PRT$. Explain how these formulas are derived from $I = PRT$.

9. Show how the formulas $I = PRT$ and $MV = P + I$ lead to the formula $MV = P(I + RT)$.

10. The maturity value for a loan of $2,000 at 9% interest for two years was found to be $4,360. This answer is not reasonable. Examine the solution to identify the incorrect mathematical process. Explain the correct process and rework the problem correctly.

$$MV = P(1 + RT)$$
$$MV = \$2,000(1 + 0.09 \times 2)$$
$$MV = \$2,000(1.09 \times 2)$$
$$MV = \$2,000(2.18)$$
$$MV = \$4,360$$

Section 9.1

Find the simple interest. Round to the nearest cent when necessary.

	Principal	Annual Rate	Time	Interest
1.	$500	12%	2 years	_____
2.	$1,000	$9\frac{1}{2}$%	3 years	_____
3.	$3,575	21%	3 years	_____
4.	$2,975	$12\frac{1}{2}$%	2 years	_____
5.	$800	18%	1 year	_____
6.	$25,000	6.9%	2 years	_____

7. Capco, Inc., borrowed $4,275 for three years at 15% interest. (a) How much simple interest did the company pay? (b) What is the maturity value?

8. Legan Company borrowed $15,280 at $16\frac{1}{2}$% for 12 years. How much simple interest did the company pay? What was the total amount paid back?

Find the rate of annual simple interest in each of the following problems.

	Principal	Interest	Time	Rate
9.	$800	$124	1 year	_____
10.	$1,280	$256	2 years	_____
11.	$1,000	$375	3 years	_____
12.	$40,000	$64,000	10 years	_____
13.	$175	$52.50	2 years	_____
14.	$423	$355.32	4 years	_____

Find the time period of the loan using the formula for simple interest.

	Principal	Annual Rate	Interest	Time
15.	$450	10%	$135	_____
16.	$700	18%	$252	_____
17.	$1,500	$21\frac{1}{2}$%	$483.75	_____
18.	$2,000	$16\frac{1}{2}$%	$825	_____
19.	$800	$15\frac{3}{4}$%	$252	_____
20.	$3,549	9.2%	$979.52	_____

21. Madewell Manufacturing paid back a loan of $7,500 at $16\frac{1}{2}$% annual rate with $618.75 simple interest. How long was the loan outstanding?

22. Ronald Cox received $1,440 on an investment of $12,000 at 16% annual simple interest rate. How long was the money invested?

In each of the following problems, find the principal, based on simple interest.

	Interest	Annual Rate	Time	Principal
23.	$100	10%	2 years	_____
24.	$281.25	$12\frac{1}{2}$%	3 years	_____
25.	$90	9%	1 year	_____
26.	$180	11.25%	2 years	_____
27.	$661.50	8.82%	5 years	_____
28.	$304.64	$3\frac{3}{5}$%	4 years	_____

29. A loan for three years with an annual simple interest rate of 18% cost $486 interest. Find the principal.

30. An investor earned $1,530 interest on funds invested at $12\frac{3}{4}$% annual simple interest for four years. How much was invested?

Write a fraction expressing each amount of time as a part of a year (12 months = 1 year).

31. 7 months

32. 18 months

33. 16 months

34. 9 months

35. 3 months

36. 42 months

37. Draw the circle showing the four parts of an interest problem.

38. Write the formula for finding each part of the interest formula.

39. Robert Ellis made a car loan for $2,500 to be paid off in $3\frac{1}{2}$ years. The simple interest rate for the loan was 12% annually. How much interest did he pay?

40. Rob Farinelli bought a dining room suite and paid for the furniture in full after one month, with a finance charge of $18.75. If he was charged 18% annual interest, how much did the suite cost?

41. Carol Stoy invested $500 at 8% annually for six months. How much interest did she receive?

42. Alpha Hodge borrowed $500 for three months and paid $12.50 interest. What was the annual rate of interest?

43. Find the interest paid on a loan of $1,200 for 60 days at a simple interest rate of 6% annually.

44. Find the interest paid on a loan of $2,100 for 90 days at a simple interest rate of 4% annually.

45. Find the interest paid on a loan of $800 for 120 days at a simple interest rate of 6% annually.

46. Find the interest paid on a loan of $15,835 for 45 days at a simple interest rate of 8.1% annually.

Section 9.2

47. Time figured using 30 days per month is called what kind of time?

48. When the exact number of days in each month is used to figure time, it is called what kind of time?

Use Table 9–1 to find the exact time from the first date to the second date for non-leap years unless a leap year is identified.

49. March 15 to July 10

50. April 12 to November 15

51. January 18 to October 6

52. November 12 to April 15 of the next year

53. January 5 to June 7

54. April 7, 2003, to August 15, 2003

55. January 12, 2002, to June 28, 2002

56. February 3, 2004, to August 12, 2004

57. January 27, 2004, to September 30, 2004

58. February 15, 2003, to June 15, 2003

59. April 5, 2004 to September 15, 2004

If a loan is made on the given date, find the date it is due, using both ordinary time and exact time.

60. March 15 for 30 days

61. January 10 for 210 days

62. May 30 for 240 days

63. August 12 for 60 days

64. June 13 for 90 days

65. December 28 for 60 days

For each of the following problems, find (a) the ordinary interest using ordinary time, (b) the exact interest using exact time, and (c) the ordinary interest using exact time. Round answers to the nearest cent.

66. $5,000 at 17% annually for 90 days

67. $3,500 at 18% annually for 60 days

68. A loan of $4,225 at 8% annually made on March 5 and due on May 5 of the same year

69. A loan of $1,200 at 10% annually made on October 15 and due on March 20 of the following year

Section 9.3

Use the following note for exercises 70–76.

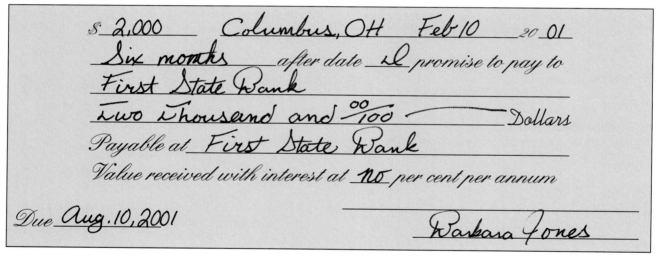

Figure 9-5 Promissory Note

70. Who is the maker of the note shown in Figure 9-5?

71. Who is the payee?

72. What is the face value of the note?

73. What is the due date?

74. If the bank charged 9%, find the discount on the note.

75. Find the proceeds of the note in exercise 74.

76. If the bank charged 14% annually, find the discount on the note. Find the proceeds of the note. Compare the proceeds at 14% annual interest with the proceeds at 9% (exercise 75).

Use Table 9-2.

77. Find the exact interest on a loan of $3,700 at $12\frac{1}{4}\%$ annually for 15 days.

78. Find the exact interest on a loan of $2,100 at $11\frac{1}{2}\%$ annual interest for 40 days.

79. Find the exact interest on a loan of $3,600 at 12.75% annual interest for 18 days.

80. Find the exact interest on a loan of $8,972 at 12% annually for 45 days.

81. MAK, Inc., accepted an interest-bearing note for $10,000 with 9% annual ordinary interest. The note was made on April 10 and was due December 6. MAK needed cash and took the note to First United Bank, which offered to buy the note at a discount rate of $12\frac{1}{2}\%$. The transaction was made on July 7. How much cash did MAK receive for the note?

82. Allan Stojanovich can purchase an office desk for $1,500 with cash terms of 2/10, n/30. If he can borrow the money at 12% annual simple interest for 20 days, will he save money by taking advantage of the cash discount offered?

Spreadsheet Exercises

83. Spreadsheet software like Excel™ performs many common tasks in business mathematics. For example, a function named YEARFRAC calculates the number of days between a beginning and an ending date. Other options allow you to select an appropriate fraction for exact or ordinary time.

(a) Write formulas to complete the spreadsheet showing the Time for the four loans shown. For each loan find (a) the ordinary interest using ordinary time, (b) the exact interest using exact time, and (c) the ordinary interest using exact time. You can use a spreadsheet function to find the time decimal or you can calculate the time using your calculator.

If you are using Excel™ you may have to run Setup and install Analysis ToolPak. After ToolPak is installed, enable it by clicking on the Tools menu and then clicking on Add-Ins. Check Analysis ToolPak, then click OK. Next, click on the equal sign in the formula bar to get the dropdown formula bar on the left. Click on the down arrow, then click on More functions... at the bottom. This brings up a "Paste function" screen. Highlight "Date & Time" on the left screen and "YEARFRAC" on the right screen. Then click OK. The syntax for this function is YEARFRAC(start_date,end_date,basis). The dates can be entered by referencing the appropriate cell in the worksheet and the "basis" depends on the type of time fraction being used. The table gives the basis numbers.

Basis	Day Count Basis
0 or omitted	30/360
1	Actual/Actual
2	Actual/360
3	Actual/365

(b) Write formulas to complete the spreadsheet to give the Interest for each loan amount in (a).

(c) Write formulas to complete the spreadsheet to give the Total Payback for each loan amount in (a).

84. Complete the spreadsheet using the formulas.

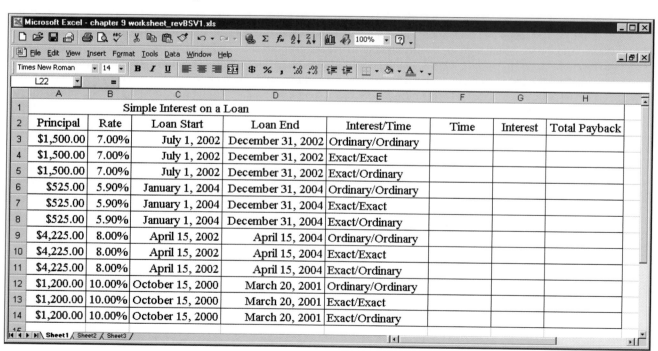

	Principal	Rate	Loan Start	Loan End	Interest/Time	Time	Interest	Total Payback
1			Simple Interest on a Loan					
2	Principal	Rate	Loan Start	Loan End	Interest/Time	Time	Interest	Total Payback
3	$1,500.00	7.00%	July 1, 2002	December 31, 2002	Ordinary/Ordinary			
4	$1,500.00	7.00%	July 1, 2002	December 31, 2002	Exact/Exact			
5	$1,500.00	7.00%	July 1, 2002	December 31, 2002	Exact/Ordinary			
6	$525.00	5.90%	January 1, 2004	December 31, 2004	Ordinary/Ordinary			
7	$525.00	5.90%	January 1, 2004	December 31, 2004	Exact/Exact			
8	$525.00	5.90%	January 1, 2004	December 31, 2004	Exact/Ordinary			
9	$4,225.00	8.00%	April 15, 2002	April 15, 2004	Ordinary/Ordinary			
10	$4,225.00	8.00%	April 15, 2002	April 15, 2004	Exact/Exact			
11	$4,225.00	8.00%	April 15, 2002	April 15, 2004	Exact/Ordinary			
12	$1,200.00	10.00%	October 15, 2000	March 20, 2001	Ordinary/Ordinary			
13	$1,200.00	10.00%	October 15, 2000	March 20, 2001	Exact/Exact			
14	$1,200.00	10.00%	October 15, 2000	March 20, 2001	Exact/Ordinary			

Challenge Problems

85. A data entry clerk at Third Federal Savings and Loan spilled coffee on a diskette, wiping out some critical loan data for several of S&L's customers. Your assignment, as chief accounting department troubleshooter, is to reconstruct the missing data from the data fragment below. Express all dollar amounts correct to the nearest cent, interest rates to one decimal place, and time to the nearest day.

What methods do banks use to protect themselves from the loss of vital financial data?

Customer	Interest	Principal	Annual Rate	Time (Ordinary)
Rocky's Market	$7.00		10%	30 days
David's Art Gallery	85.00		12%	100 days
Fortune Hardware	209.00	5,500		180 days
M. Converse & Son	22.63	1,460		90 days
Sun Twins Jai Alai	72.00	2,560	13.5%	
Sun Coast Brokerage	1,711.11	28,000	11%	

86. Are you interested in buying a "new" used car or installing a pool? A simple interest loan with a low monthly payment sounds good, but be sure you understand what this monthly payment means.

A simple interest loan with a final "balloon payment" can be a good deal for both the consumer and the banker. For the banker, this loan reduces the rate risk, since the loan rate is actually locked in for a short period of time. For the consumer, this loan allows you to make lower monthly payments.

Example: You borrow $5,000 at 13% simple interest rate for a year.

For 12 monthly payments:

$$\$5,000 \times 13\% \times 1 = \$650 \text{ interest}$$

$$\frac{\$5,650}{12} = \$470.83 \text{ monthly payment}$$

Your banker will offer to make the loan as if it is to be extended over five years, or 60 monthly payments but with a final balloon payment on the 12th payment. This means a much lower monthly payment.

For 60 monthly payments:

$$\frac{\$5,650}{60} = \$94.17 \text{ monthly payment}$$

The lower monthly payment is tempting! The banker will expect you to make these lower payments for a year. You will actually make 11 payments of $94.17: $94.17 \times 11 = \$1,035.87$ amount paid during the first 11 months.

The 12th and final payment, the *balloon payment,* is the *remainder* of the loan.

$$\$5,650 - \$1,035.87 = \$4,614.13$$

At this time you are expected to pay the balance of the loan in the balloon payment shown above. Don't panic! Usually the loan is refinanced for another year. But beware—you may have to pay a higher interest rate for the next year.

(a) Find the monthly payment for a $2,500 loan at 12% interest for one year extended over a three-year period.

(b) What is the amount of the final balloon payment for a $1,000 loan at 10% interest for one year, extended over five years?

(c) You need a loan of $5,000 at 10% interest for one year. What is the amount of the monthly payment?

(d) If your banker agrees to extend the monthly payments over two years for the loan described in part (c) how much will your monthly payments be? How much will the final balloon payment be?

1. Find the simple interest on $500 invested at 14% annually for three years.

2. How much money was borrowed at 17% annually for six months if the interest was $85?

3. A loan of $3,000 was made for 210 days. If ordinary interest is $350, find the rate.

4. A loan of $5,000 at 16% annually requires $1,200 interest. For how long is the money borrowed?

5. Find the exact time from February 13 to November 27 in a non-leap year.

6. Find the exact time from October 12 to March 28 of the following year (a leap year).

7. Find the exact time from January 28, 2004, to July 5, 2004.

8. Find the ordinary time from April 5 to December 20.

9. Find the simple interest on a loan of $20,000 at 21% annual interest for two years.

10. Use ordinary time to find the ordinary interest on a loan of $2,800 at 10% annually made on March 15 for 270 days.

11. Find the interest on a loan of $469 if the simple interest rate charged is 12% annually for six months.

12. A bread machine with a cash price of $188 can be purchased with a one-year loan at 10% annual simple interest. Find the total amount to be repaid.

13. An investment of $7,000 is made for six months at the rate of 19% annual simple interest. How much interest will the investor earn?

14. A copier that originally cost $300 was purchased with a loan for 12 months at 15% annual simple interest. What was the *total* cost of the copier?

15. Find the ordinary interest on a loan of $850 at 15% annually. The loan was made January 15 and was due March 15. Use ordinary time.

16. Find the exact interest in exercise 15. Use exact time in a non-leap year. Round to the nearest cent.

17. Find the duration of a loan of $3,000 if the loan required interest of $416.25 and was at a rate of $18\frac{1}{2}\%$ annual simple interest.

18. Find the simple interest on a loan of $165 if the interest rate is 16% annually over a three-month period.

19. Find the rate of simple interest on a $1,200 loan that requires the borrower to repay a total of $1,440 after one year.

20. Find the rate of simple interest on a $600 loan with total interest of $40.50 if the loan is paid in six months.

21. A promissory note has a face value of $5,000 and is discounted by the bank at the rate of $18\frac{1}{2}\%$. If the note is made for 180 days, find the discount of the note.

22. A promissory note with a face value of $3,500 is discounted by the bank at the rate of $19\frac{1}{2}\%$. The term of the note is six months. Find the proceeds of the note.

23. Find the ordinary interest paid on a loan of $1,600 for 90 days at a simple interest rate of 16% annually.

24. Jerry Brooks purchases office supplies totaling $1,890. He can take advantage of cash terms of 2/10, n/30 if he obtains a short-term loan. If he can borrow the money at $10\frac{1}{2}\%$ annual simple ordinary interest for 20 days, will he save money if he borrows to take advantage of the cash discount? How much will he save?

25. Find the exact interest on a loan of $25,000 at $11\frac{3}{4}\%$ annually for 21 days.

26. Find the exact interest on a loan of $1,510 at $12\frac{3}{4}\%$ annual interest for 27 days.

27. Find the exact interest on a loan of $4,300 at 11.75% annual interest for 32 days.

CHAPTER 9 | **SELF-CHECK SOLUTIONS**

SELF-CHECK 9.1

1. $I = PRT$
$I = \$2,400 \times 0.11 \times 1$
$I = \$264$

2. $I = PRT$
$I = \$800 \times 0.085 \times 2$
$I = \$136$

3. $I = PRT$
$I = \$7,980 \times 0.062 \times 2$
$I = \$989.52$

4. $MV = P(1 + RT)$
$MV = \$1,400(1 + 0.125 \times 3)$
$MV = \$1,925$

5. $MV = P(1 + RT)$
$MV = \$2,800 (1 + 0.075 \times 3)$
$MV = \$3,430$

6. $MV = P(1 + RT)$
$MV = \$20,000 (1 + 0.082 \times 4)$
$MV = \$26,560$

7. 8 months $= \dfrac{8}{12}$ year
$= 0.6666666,$
or 0.67 year

8. 40 months $= \dfrac{40}{12}$ years
$= 3.333333,$ or
3.33 years

9. $18 \div 12 = 1.5$ years

10. $28 \div 12 = 2.3333333$ or 2.33

11. $MV = P(1 + RT)$
$MV = \$42,000(1 + 0.083 \times 0.5)$
$MV = \$43,743$

12. $R = \dfrac{I}{PT}$ $T = 30$ months $= \dfrac{30}{12}$ Years $= 2.5$ years

$R = \dfrac{\$360}{\$1,200 \times 2.5}$

$R = \dfrac{360}{3,000}$

$R = 0.12,$ or 12% per year

13. $R = \dfrac{I}{PT}$ $T = \dfrac{7}{12}$ year

$R = \dfrac{\$53.96}{\$500 \times \frac{7}{12}}$ $\left(\$500 \times \dfrac{7}{12} = \$291.6667\right)$

$R = \dfrac{\$53.96}{\$291.6667}$

$R = 0.185,$ or 18.5% per year

14. $P = \dfrac{I}{RT}$

$P = \dfrac{\$500}{0.09 \times 2}$

$P = \dfrac{\$500}{0.18}$

$P = \$2,777.78$

15. $T = \dfrac{I}{PR}$

$T = \dfrac{\$360}{\$6,000 \times 0.12}$

$T = \dfrac{360}{720}$

$T = 0.5 = \dfrac{1}{2}$ year, or six months

16. $R = \dfrac{I}{PT}$

$R = \dfrac{\$6,750}{\$25,000 \times 3}$

$R = 0.09$ or 9% per year

1. *Non-leap year*
   Ordinary time: March 10 to March 10 is 12 months, or 12 × 30 days = 360 days.
   March 10 to September 10 is 6 months, or 6 × 30 days = 180 days.
   360 days + 180 days = 540 days
   Exact time: March 10 to March 10 of the following year is 1 year, or 365 days.
   September 10 = day 253
   $\quad$ March 10 = day $\underline{\quad 69}$
   $\qquad\qquad\qquad$ 184 days
   365 + 184 = 549 days
   Leap year
   1 + 549 days = 550 days

2. Ordinary time: March 25 to November 25 is 8 × 30 days = 240 days.
   November 15 = November 25 − 10 days
   $\qquad\qquad$ = 240 − 10
   $\qquad\qquad$ = 230 days
   Exact time: November 15 = day 319
   $\qquad\qquad$ March 25 = day $\underline{\quad 84}$
   $\qquad\qquad\qquad\qquad$ 235 days

3. Ordinary time: January 15 to October 15 is 9 × 30 days = 270 days.
   October 20 = October 15 + 5 days
   $\qquad\qquad$ = 270 + 5
   $\qquad\qquad$ = 275 days
   Exact time: October 20 = day 293
   $\qquad\qquad$ January 15 = day $\underline{\quad 15}$
   $\qquad\qquad\qquad\qquad$ 278 days
   $\qquad$ 278 + leap day = 279 days

4. Ordinary time: 120 days is $\frac{120}{30}$ months, or 4 months.
   4 months from October 15 is February 15.
   Exact time: October 15 = day 288
   $\qquad\qquad\qquad\qquad \underline{+120}$
   $\qquad\qquad\qquad\qquad\quad 408$
   408 − 365 = 43 days
   The 43rd day is February 12.

5. Ordinary time:
   180 ÷ 30 = 6 months
   Six months from March 20 is September 20.
   Exact time:
   March 20 = day 79
   $\qquad\qquad \underline{+180}$
   $\qquad\qquad\quad 259$
   Day 259 is September 16.

6. Exact time:
   February 10 = day 41
   $\qquad\qquad\quad \underline{+60}$
   $\qquad\qquad\quad\ 101$
   Day 101 is April 11, but adjusting for one leap day makes this April 10.

7. Ordinary time = 2 months, or 2 × 30 days = 60 days
   $$I = \$3{,}000 \times \frac{0.15}{360} \times 60 = \$75$$

8. Exact time: August 15 = day 227
   $\qquad\qquad\quad$ June 15 = day $\underline{166}$
   $\qquad\qquad\qquad\qquad\quad$ 61 days
   $$I = \$3{,}000 \times \frac{0.15}{365} \times 61 = \$75.21$$

9. $I = \$3,000 \times \dfrac{0.15}{360} \times 61 = \$76.25$

10. $I = \dfrac{\$3,500}{100} \times 1.541096 = \$53.94$

11. $I = \dfrac{\$1,000}{100} \times 0.328767 = \$3.29$

12. $I = \dfrac{\$1,850}{100} \times 0.661644 = \$12.24$

13. Answers will vary.

SELF-CHECK 9.3

1. $I = \$2,500 \times \dfrac{0.16}{360} \times 120 = \$133.33$

2. Proceeds $= \$2,500 - \$133.33 = \$2,366.67$

3. $I = \$3,250 \times \dfrac{0.092}{360} \times 180$

$I = \$149.50$

Proceeds $= \$3,250 - \$149.50 = \$3,100.50$

4. Calculate time: December 31 = day 365

August 5 = $\underline{\text{day } 217}$

148 days

May 5 = $\underline{\text{day } 125}$

273 days

$I = \$3,000 \times \dfrac{0.165}{360} \times 273 = \$375.38$

Maturity value of note $= \$3,000 + \$375.38 = \$3,375.38$

5. Time: November 13 = day 317

March 18 = $\underline{\text{day \ \ } 77}$

240 days

$I = \$5,000 \times \dfrac{0.11}{360} \times 240 = \$366.67$

Maturity value $= \$5,000 + \$366.67 = \$5,366.67$

Bank discount: November 13 = day 317

June 13 = $\underline{\text{day } 164}$

153 days

$I = \$5,366.67 \times \dfrac{0.14}{360} \times 153 = \$319.31$

Proceeds $= \$5,366.67 - \$319.31 = \$5,047.36$

6. Answers will vary.

7. Answers will vary.

CHAPTER

10

Compound Interest, Future Value, and Present Value

10.1 Compound Interest and Future Value

1 Use the simple interest formula to find the future value.

2 Find the future value using a $1.00 future value table.

3 Find the effective interest rate.

4 Find the interest compounded daily using a table.

10.2 Present Value

1 Find the present value based on annual compounding for one year.

2 Find the present value using a $1.00 present value table.

Good Decisions through Teamwork

With your team members, select several financial institutions in your area. Individually, contact one company to determine that lender's policies related to investing. Determine the types of investment opportunities available, the restrictions that apply, the risks involved, and the rate of return for each type of investment.

With members of your team, analyze the information gathered by each team member from the various financial institutions and use the information to calculate the maximum amount of interest or dividends that could be earned on $5,000 invested for five years. Make a presentation to the class explaining how the team selected the best investment option for the $5,000.

For most loans made on a short-term basis, interest is computed once, using the simple interest formula. For longer-term loans, interest may be *compounded:* interest is calculated more than once during the term of the loan or investment and this interest is added to the principal. This sum (principal + interest) then becomes the principal for the next calculation of interest, and interest is charged or paid on this new amount.

This process of adding interest to the principal before interest is calculated for the next period is called *compounding interest.* Compounding interest has several uses in the business world. The one with which you are probably familiar is used in a savings account, where you "earn interest on your interest."

10.1 Compound Interest and Future Value

1 Use the simple interest formula to find the future value.

2 Find the future value using a $1.00 future value table.

3 Find the effective interest rate.

4 Find the interest compounded daily using a table.

Whether the interest rate is simple or compound, interest is calculated for each **interest period.** When the interest rate is simple, there is only one interest period: The entire period of the loan or investment is the single, simple interest period. When the interest is compound, there are two or more interest periods, each of the same duration. The interest period may be one day, one week, one month, one quarter, one year, or some other designated period of time. The greater the number of interest periods in the time period of the loan or investment, the greater the total interest that accumulates during the time period. The total interest that accumulates is the **compound interest.** The sum of the compound interest and the original principal is the **future value** or **maturity value** or **compound amount** in the case of an investment, or the compound amount in the case of a loan. In this chapter we may use the term *future value to* mean future value *or* compound amount, depending on whether the principal is an investment or a loan.

1 Use the simple interest formula to find the future value.

We can calculate the future value of principal using the simple interest formula method. The terms of a loan or investment indicate the annual number of interest periods and the annual interest rate. Dividing the annual interest rate by the annual number of interest periods gives us the **period interest rate** or interest rate per period. We can use the period interest rate to calculate the interest that accumulates for each period using the familiar simple interest formula: $I = PRT$. I is the interest for the period, P is the principal at the beginning of the period, R is the period interest rate, and T is the length of the period. Since we are calculating the interest for only one period, the length of time is one period. So the value of T in the formula is one period, and the formula is simplified to $I = P \times R \times 1$, or $I = P \times R$. The value of P is different for each period in turn because the principal at the beginning of each period includes the original principal and all the interest so far accumulated. Calculating the principal for each interest period in turn is our goal in calculating the future value of a loan or investment.

HOW TO Find the Period Interest Rate

Divide the annual interest rate by the number of interest periods per year.

$$\text{Period interest rate} = \frac{\textbf{annual interest rate}}{\textbf{number of interest periods per year}}$$

HOW TO Find the Future Value Using the Simple Interest Formula Method

1. Find the first end-of-period principal: multiply the original principal by the sum of 1 and the period interest rate.

   First end-of-period principal = original principal × (1 + period interest rate)

   $$A = P(1 + R)$$

2. For each remaining period in turn, find the next end-of-period principal: multiply the previous end-of-period principal by the sum of 1 and the period interest rate.

   End-of-period principal = previous end-of-period principal
   × (1 + period interest rate)

3. Identify the last end-of-period principal as the future value.

   Future value = last end-of-period principal

The future value is calculated before the compound interest can be calculated.

HOW TO Find the Compound Interest

Subtract the original principal from the future value.

Compound interest = future value − original principal

EXAMPLE A loan of $800 at 13% annually is made for three years, compounded annually. Find (a) the future value (compound amount) and (b) the compound interest paid on the loan. (c) Compare the compound interest with simple interest for the same loan period, original principal, and annual interest rate.

$$\text{Period interest rate} = \frac{\text{rate per year}}{\text{number of interest periods per year}}$$

(a) Since the loan is compounded annually, there is one interest period per year. So the period interest rate is $\frac{13}{100}$ or 0.13. There are three interest periods, one for each of the three years.

First end-of-period principal = $800 (1 + 0.13)   **800(1.13) = 904**

= $904

Next end-of-period principal = $904(1 + 0.13)   **904(1.13) = 1,021.52**

= $1,021.52

Third end-of-period principal = $1,021.52(1 + 0.13)$

$\qquad\qquad\qquad\qquad\qquad\qquad$ **1,021.52(1.13) = 1,154.32**

$\qquad\qquad\qquad\qquad\quad = \$1,154.32$

The future value is \$1,154.32.

(b) Compound interest is the future value (compound amount) minus the original principal.

$ 1,154.32	**Compound amount**
− 800.00	**Original principal**
$ 354.32	**Compound interest**

The compound interest is \$354.32.

(c) Use the simple interest formula to find the simple interest on \$800 at 13% annually for three years.

$$I = PRT$$
$$I = \boxed{\$800.00} \times 0.13 \times 3$$
$$\boxed{I = \$312.00}$$
$$\boxed{\$354.32} - \boxed{\$312.00} = \$42.32$$

The simple interest is \$312, which is \$42.32 less than the compound interest. This difference would be even greater if the interest were compounded more frequently.

EXAMPLE   Find the future value of a \$10,000 investment at 8% annual interest compounded semiannually for three years.

$$\text{Period interest rate} = \frac{8\% \text{ annually}}{2 \text{ periods annually}} = \frac{0.08}{2} = 0.04$$

First end-of-period principal = $10,000(1 + 0.04)$

$\qquad\qquad\qquad\qquad\qquad\qquad$ **10,000(1.04) = 10,400**

$\qquad\qquad\qquad\qquad\quad = \$10,400$

Second end-of-period principal = $10,400(1 + 0.04)$

$\qquad\qquad\qquad\qquad\qquad\qquad$ **10,400(1.04) = 10,816**

$\qquad\qquad\qquad\qquad\quad = \$10,816$

Third end-of-period principal = $11,248.64$

$\qquad\qquad\qquad\qquad\qquad\qquad$ **10,816(1.04) = 11,248.64**

Fourth end-of-period principal = $11,698.59$

$\qquad\qquad\qquad\qquad\qquad\qquad$ **11,248.64(1.04) = 11,698.59**

Fifth end-of-period principal = $12,166.53$

$\qquad\qquad\qquad\qquad\qquad\qquad$ **11,698.59(1.04) = 12,166.53**

Sixth end-of-period principal = $12,653.19$

$\qquad\qquad\qquad\qquad\qquad\qquad$ **12,166.53(1.04) = 12,653.19**

Since there are two interest periods for each of the three years, the sixth period (2×3) is the last.

The future value is \$12,653.19.

2 Find the future value using a \$1.00 future value table.

As you may have guessed from the previous examples, compounding interest for a large number of periods is very time consuming. This task is done more quickly if you use a compound interest table, as shown in Table 10-1.

Table 10-1 gives the future value of \$1.00, depending on the number of interest periods per year and the interest rate per period.

EXAMPLE   Use Table 10-1 to compute the compound interest on a \$500 loan for six years compounded annually at 8%.

$$\text{Interest periods} = \text{years} \times \text{interest periods per year}$$
$$= 6 \times 1 = 6 \text{ periods}$$
$$\text{Period interest rate} = \frac{\text{annual interest rate}}{\text{interest periods per year}}$$
$$= \frac{8\%}{1} = 8\% = 0.08$$

Find period row 6 of the table and the 8% rate column. The value in the intersecting cell is 1.58687. This means that $1 would be worth $1.58687 or $1.59 rounded, compounded annually at the end of six years.

$$\$500 \times 1.58687 = \boxed{\$793.44}$$

The loan is for $500, so multiply $500 by 1.58687 to find the future value of the loan.

The compound amount is $793.44.

$$\boxed{\$793.44} - \$500 = \$293.44$$

The compound amount minus the principal is the compound interest.

The compound interest on $500 for six years compounded annually at 8% is $293.44.

Table 10-1 Future Value or Compound Amount of $1.00

Periods	1%	1.5%	2%	2.5%	3%	4%	5%	6%	8%	10%	12%
1	1.01000	1.01500	1.02000	1.02500	1.03000	1.04000	1.05000	1.06000	1.08000	1.10000	1.12000
2	1.02010	1.03023	1.04040	1.05063	1.06090	1.08160	1.10250	1.12360	1.16640	1.21000	1.25440
3	1.03030	1.04568	1.06121	1.07689	1.09273	1.12486	1.15763	1.19102	1.25971	1.33100	1.40493
4	1.04060	1.06136	1.08243	1.10381	1.12551	1.16986	1.21551	1.26248	1.36049	1.46410	1.57352
5	1.05101	1.07728	1.10408	1.13141	1.15927	1.21665	1.27628	1.33823	1.46933	1.61051	1.76234
6	1.06152	1.09344	1.12616	1.15969	1.19405	1.26532	1.34010	1.41852	1.58687	1.77156	1.97382
7	1.07214	1.10984	1.14869	1.18869	1.22987	1.31593	1.40710	1.50363	1.71382	1.94872	2.21068
8	1.08286	1.12649	1.17166	1.21840	1.26677	1.36857	1.47746	1.59385	1.85093	2.14359	2.47596
9	1.09369	1.14339	1.19509	1.24886	1.30477	1.42331	1.55133	1.68948	1.99900	2.35795	2.77308
10	1.10462	1.16054	1.21899	1.28008	1.34392	1.48024	1.62889	1.79085	2.15892	2.59374	2.10585
11	1.11567	1.17795	1.24337	1.31209	1.38423	1.53945	1.71034	1.89830	2.33164	2.85312	3.47855
12	1.12683	1.19562	1.26824	1.34489	1.42576	1.60103	1.79586	2.01220	2.51817	3.18343	3.89598
13	1.13809	1.21355	1.29361	1.37851	1.46853	1.66507	1.88565	2.13293	2.71962	3.45227	4.36349
14	1.14947	1.23176	1.31948	1.41297	1.51259	1.73168	1.97993	2.26090	2.93719	3.79750	4.88711
15	1.16097	1.25023	1.34587	1.44830	1.55797	1.80094	2.07893	2.39656	3.17217	4.17725	5.47357
16	1.17258	1.26899	1.37279	1.48451	1.60471	1.87298	2.18287	2.54035	3.42594	4.59497	6.13039
17	1.18430	1.28802	1.40024	1.52162	1.65284	1.94790	2.29202	2.69277	3.70002	5.05447	6.86604
18	1.19615	1.30734	1.42825	1.55966	1.70243	2.02582	2.40662	2.85434	3.99602	5.55992	7.68997
19	1.20811	1.32695	1.45681	1.59865	1.75351	2.10685	2.52695	3.02560	4.31570	6.11591	8.61276
20	1.22019	1.34686	1.48595	1.63862	1.80611	2.19112	2.65330	3.20714	4.66096	6.72750	9.64629
21	1.23239	1.36706	1.51567	1.67958	1.86029	2.27877	2.78596	3.39956	5.03383	7.40025	10.80385
22	1.24472	1.38756	1.54598	1.72157	1.91610	2.36992	2.92526	3.60354	5.43654	8.14027	12.10031
23	1.25716	1.40838	1.57690	1.76461	1.97359	2.46472	3.07152	3.81975	5.87146	8.95430	13.55235
24	1.26973	1.42950	1.60844	1.80873	2.03279	2.56330	3.22510	4.04893	6.34118	9.84973	15.17863
25	1.28243	1.45095	1.64061	1.85394	2.09378	2.66584	3.38635	4.29187	6.84848	10.83471	17.00006
26	1.29526	1.47271	1.67342	1.90029	2.15659	2.77247	3.55567	4.54938	7.39635	11.91818	19.04007
27	1.30821	1.49480	1.70689	1.94780	2.22129	2.88337	3.73346	4.82235	7.98806	13.10999	21.32488
28	1.32129	1.51722	1.74102	1.99650	2.28793	2.99870	3.92013	5.11169	8.62711	14.42099	23.88387
29	1.33450	1.53998	1.77584	2.04641	2.35657	3.11865	4.11614	5.41839	9.31727	15.86309	26.74993
30	1.34785	1.56308	1.81136	2.09757	2.42726	3.24340	4.32194	5.74349	10.06266	17.44940	29.95992

Rate per Period

Note: The values listed in the table have been rounded.
Table shows future value (*FV*) of $1.00 compounded for *N* periods at *R* rate per period.
Table values can be generated using the formula: $FV = \$1(1 + R)^N$.

Chapter 10 Compound Interest, Future Value, and Present Value   **421**

HOW TO Find the Future Value Using a $1.00 Future Value Table

1. Find the number of interest periods: multiply the number of years by the number of interest periods per year.

   Interest periods = number of years × number of interest periods per year

2. Find the period interest rate: divide the annual interest rate by the number of interest periods per year.

   $$\text{Period interest rate} = \frac{\text{annual interest rate}}{\text{number of interest periods per year}}$$

3. Select the periods row corresponding to the number of interest periods.
4. Select the rate-per-period column corresponding to the period interest rate.
5. Locate the value in the cell where the periods row intersects the rate-per-period column. This value is sometimes called the *i-factor*.
6. Multiply the original principal by the value from step 5.

EXAMPLE An investment of $300 at 8% annually is compounded *quarterly* (four times a year) for three years. Find the future value and the compound interest.

Interest periods = number of years × number of interest periods per year

$$= 3 \times 4 = 12$$ **The investment is compounded four times a year for three years.**

$$\text{Period interest rate} = \frac{\text{annual interest rate}}{\text{number of interest periods per year}}$$

$$= \frac{8\%}{4} = 2\% = 0.02$$ **Divide the annual rate of 8% by the number of periods per year to find the period interest rate.**

Future value of $1 = 1.26824   **Find the 12 periods row in Table 10–1. Move across to the 2% column.**

$$\$300 \times 1.26824 = \$380.47$$ **The principal times the future value per dollar equals the total future value.**

$380.47 is the future value.

Compound interest = future value − original principal

$$= \$380.47 - \$300$$

$$= \$80.47$$

The compound interest is $80.47.

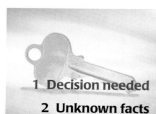

EXAMPLE Joe Gallegos can invest $10,000 at 8% compounded quarterly for two years. Or he can invest the same $10,000 at 8.2% compounded annually for the same two years. If all other conditions (such as early withdrawal penalty, etc.) are the same, which deal should he take?

1 Decision needed Which deal should Joe take?

2 Unknown facts Future value for each investment

3 Known facts
Principal: $10,000
Time period: 2 years
Deal 1 annual rate: 8%
Deal 1 interest periods per year: 4
Deal 2 annual rate: 8.2%
Deal 2 interest periods per year: 1

4 Relationships
Number of interest periods = number of years × number of interest periods per year
Deal 1 interest periods = 2 × 4
Deal 2 interest periods = 2 × 1

$$\text{Period interest rate} = \frac{\text{annual interest rate}}{\text{number of interest periods per year}}$$

Deal 1 period interest rate = $\dfrac{8\%}{4}$

Deal 2 period interest rate = $\dfrac{8.2\%}{1}$

5 Estimation
Simple interest on $10,000 at 8% for two years is $1,600, and future value is $11,600. Thus, future value on either deal should be more than $11,600.

6 Calculation
Deal 1: Use the table method.
Interest periods = 2 × 4 = 8

$$\text{Period interest rate} = \frac{8\%}{4} = 2\% = 0.02$$

The Table 10-1 value is 1.17166.
Future value = $10,000 × 1.17166 = $11,716.60
Deal 1 future value is $11,716.60.

Deal 2: Use the simple interest formula method (since the table does not include values for 8.2%).
Interest periods = 2 × 1 = 2

$$\text{Period interest rate} = \frac{8.2\%}{1} = 8.2\% = 0.082$$

First end-of-period principal = $10,000 × (1 + 0.082) = $10,820
Second end-of-period principal = $10,820 × (1.082) = $11,707.24

7 Interpretation **Deal 2 future value is $11,707.24, which is less than deal 1.**

8 Decision made **Deal 1, the lower interest rate of 8% compounded more frequently (quarterly), is a slightly better deal because it yields the greater future value.**

TIP! **Formula for Finding Future Value of $1.00**

Table 10-1 is generated using the formula $FV = \$1.00(1 + R)^N$, where FV represents the future value, R represents the rate per period, and N represents the number of periods. Using a scientific calculator and the general power key, $\boxed{x^y}$, you can calculate these table values and other values not on the table. Find the future value for $1.00 at 3% per period for five periods.

$$FV = \$1.00(1 + 0.03)^5 = 1(1.03)^5 = \$1.15927 \text{ (rounded)}$$

For any amount of money, substitute P for $1.00 in the formula, $FV = P(1 + R)^N$. Find the future value of $250 at 3% interest per year for five years.

$$FV = \$250(1 + 0.03)^5 = 250(1.15927) = \$289.82.$$

If you have access to a scientific, graphing, or business calculator, results from manual or table calculations can be verified using the calculator and the formula.

---

 3 Find the effective interest rate.

If the investment in the example on page 423 is compounded annually instead of quarterly for three years—three periods at 8% per period—the future value would be $377.91 (using table value 1.25971), and the compound interest would be $77.91. The simple interest at the end of three years is $300 × 8% × 3, or $72. You can see from these comparisons that a loan or investment with an interest rate of 8%, compounded quarterly, carries higher interest than a loan with an interest rate of 8%, compounded annually, or a loan with an annual simple interest rate of 8%. When you compare interest rates, you need to know the actual or **effective rate** of interest. The effective rate of interest equates compound interest rates to equivalent simple interest rates so that comparisons can be made.

The effective rate of interest is also referred to as the **annual percentage yield (APY)** when identifying the rate of earnings on an investment. It is referred to as **annual percentage rate (APR)** when identifying the rate of interest on a loan.

 HOW TO Find the Effective Interest Rate of a Compound Interest Rate

Using the simple interest formula method: divide the compound interest for the first year by the principal.

$$\text{Effective interest rate} = \frac{\text{compound interest for first year}}{\text{principal}}$$

Using the table method: find the future value of $1.00 by using the future value table, Table 10-1. Subtract $1.00 from the future value of $1.00 after one year and divide by $1.00 to remove the dollar sign.

$$\text{Effective interest rate} = \frac{\text{future value of \$1.00 after 1 year} - \$1.00}{\$1.00}$$

EXAMPLE Marcia borrowed $600 at 10% compounded semiannually. What is the effective interest rate?

Using the simple interest formula method

$$\text{Period interest rate} = \frac{10\%}{2} = 5\% = 0.05$$

$$\text{First end-of-period principal} = \$600\,(1 + 0.05)$$
$$= \$630$$

$$\text{Second end-of-period principal} = \$630(1 + 0.05)$$
$$= \$661.50$$

$$\text{Compound interest after first year} = \$661.50 - \$600 = \$61.50$$

$$\text{Effective interest rate} = \frac{\$61.50}{\$600}$$
$$= 0.1025$$
$$= 10.25\%$$

Using the table method

10% compounded semiannually means two periods in the first (and every) year and a period interest rate of 5%. The Table 10-1 value is 1.10250. Subtract 1.00.

$$\text{Effective interest rate} = 1.10250 - 1.00$$
$$= 0.10250$$
$$= 10.25\%$$

The effective interest rate is 10.25%.

Using the Power Key on a Scientific or Graphing Calculator

The effective interest rate also can be calculated using a calculator or computer program that is capable of finding powers of numbers. Use the formula

$E = \left(1 + \dfrac{R}{N}\right)^{N} - 1$ where E is the effective intereste rate, R is the stated rate per year,

and N is the number of periods per year. Using this formula for the compound

interest rate for deal 1 in the example on page 423, we have $E = \left(1 + \dfrac{0.08}{4}\right)^{4} - 1$

$$= (1 + 0.02)^4 - 1 = (1.02)^4 - 1 = 1.082432159 - 1 = 0.082432159 \text{ or } 8.24\%$$

$$\boxed{\text{AC}}\;\boxed{(}\; 1 + .08 \;\boxed{\div}\; 4 \;\boxed{)}\; \boxed{x^y}\; 4 \;\boxed{-}\; 1 \;\boxed{=}\; \Rightarrow 0.082432159$$

In the example on page 424, we have $E = \left(1 + \dfrac{0.1}{2}\right)^{2} - 1$

$$= (1.05)^2 - 1 = 1.1025 - 1 = 0.1025 = 10.25\%$$

---

4 Find the interest compounded daily using a table.

Some banks compound interest daily and others use continuous compounding to compute interest on savings accounts. There is no significant difference in the interest earned on money using interest compounded daily and compounded continuously. A computer is generally used in calculating interest if either daily or continuous compounding is used.

Table 10–2 gives compound interest for $100 compounded daily (using 365 days as a year). Notice that this table gives the *compound interest* rather than the future value of the principal, as is given in Table 10–1.

Table 10-2 Compound Interest on $100, Compounded Daily (365 Days)
(Exact Time, Exact Interest Basis)

Days	5.00%	5.25%	5.50%	5.75%	6.00%	6.25%	6.50%	6.75%	7.00%
					Annual Rate				
1	0.0136986	0.0143836	0.0150685	0.0157534	0.0164384	0.0171233	0.0178082	0.0184932	0.0191781
2	0.0273991	0.0287692	0.0301393	0.0315093	0.0328794	0.0342495	0.0356196	0.0369897	0.0383598
3	0.0411015	0.0431569	0.0452123	0.0472677	0.0493232	0.0513787	0.0534342	0.0554897	0.0575453
4	0.0548058	0.0575467	0.0602876	0.0630286	0.0657696	0.0685107	0.0712519	0.0739931	0.0767344
5	0.0685119	0.0719385	0.0753652	0.0787919	0.0822188	0.0856458	0.0890728	0.0925000	0.0959272
6	0.0822199	0.0863324	0.0904450	0.0945578	0.0986707	0.1027837	0.1068969	0.1110102	0.1151237
7	0.0959298	0.1007284	0.1055271	0.1103261	0.1151253	0.1199246	0.1247242	0.1295239	0.1343238
8	0.1096416	0.1151264	0.1206115	0.1260969	0.1315825	0.1370684	0.1425546	0.1480410	0.1535277
9	0.1233552	0.1295266	0.1356982	0.1418702	0.1480425	0.1542152	0.1603882	0.1665615	0.1727352
10	0.1370708	0.1439288	0.1507871	0.1576460	0.1645052	0.1713649	0.1782250	0.1850855	0.1919464
11	0.1507882	0.1583330	0.1658784	0.1734242	0.1809706	0.1885175	0.1960649	0.2036129	0.2111613
12	0.1645075	0.1727394	0.1809719	0.1892050	0.1974387	0.2056731	0.2139081	0.2221437	0.2303799
13	0.1782286	0.1871478	0.1960676	0.2049882	0.2139095	0.2228316	0.2317544	0.2406779	0.2496022
14	0.1919517	0.2015582	0.2111657	0.2207739	0.2303830	0.2399930	0.2496039	0.2592156	0.2688281
15	0.2056766	0.2159708	0.2262660	0.2365621	0.2468593	0.2571574	0.2674565	0.2777566	0.2880577
16	0.2194034	0.2303854	0.2413686	0.2523528	0.2633382	0.2743247	0.2853124	0.2963012	0.3072911
17	0.2331321	0.2448021	0.2564734	0.2681460	0.2798199	0.2914950	0.3031714	0.3148491	0.3265281
18	0.2468627	0.2592209	0.2715806	0.2839417	0.2963042	0.3086682	0.3210336	0.3334005	0.3457688
19	0.2605951	0.2736417	0.2866900	0.2997398	0.3127913	0.3258443	0.3388990	0.3519553	0.3650132
20	0.2743294	0.2880647	0.3018017	0.3155405	0.3292810	0.3430234	0.3567676	0.3705135	0.3842613
21	0.2880656	0.3024897	0.3169156	0.3313436	0.3457735	0.3602054	0.3746393	0.3890752	0.4035130
22	0.3018037	0.3169167	0.3320319	0.3471492	0.3622687	0.3773904	0.3925143	0.4076403	0.4227685
23	0.3155437	0.3313459	0.3471504	0.3629573	0.3787666	0.3945783	0.4103924	0.4262088	0.4420277
24	0.3292856	0.3457771	0.3622712	0.3787679	0.3952673	0.4117692	0.4282737	0.4447808	0.4612905
25	0.3430293	0.3602104	0.3773943	0.3945810	0.4117706	0.4289630	0.4461582	0.4633562	0.4805571
26	0.3567749	0.3746458	0.3925197	0.4103966	0.4282766	0.4461597	0.4640458	0.4819351	0.4998273
27	0.3705224	0.3890832	0.4076473	0.4262147	0.4447854	0.4633594	0.4819367	0.5005173	0.5191013
28	0.3842718	0.4035227	0.4227772	0.4420353	0.4612969	0.4805620	0.4998308	0.5191030	0.5383789
29	0.3980231	0.4179643	0.4379094	0.4578583	0.4778110	0.4977676	0.5177280	0.5376922	0.5576602
30	0.4117762	0.4324080	0.4530439	0.4736839	0.4943279	0.5149761	0.5356284	0.5562848	0.5769453
35	0.4805703	0.5046576	0.5287505	0.5528490	0.5769532	0.6010629	0.6251783	0.6492993	0.6734259
40	0.5494114	0.5769591	0.6045142	0.6320766	0.6596464	0.6872235	0.7148080	0.7423999	0.7699991
45	0.6182998	0.6493127	0.6803349	0.7113666	0.7424075	0.7734578	0.8045175	0.8355865	0.8666649
50	0.6872353	0.7217183	0.7562129	0.7907190	0.8252367	0.8597660	0.8943069	0.9288594	0.9634235
55	0.7562181	0.7941760	0.8321480	0.8701340	0.9081340	0.9461481	09841763	1.0222186	1.0602749
60	0.8252481	0.8666858	0.9081403	0.9496115	0.9910995	1.0326042	1.0741258	1.1156641	1.1572192
90	1.2404225	1.3028414	1.3652984	1.4277935	1.4903267	1.5528980	1.6155075	1.6781551	1.7408410
120	1.6573065	1.7408830	1.8245277	1.9082406	1.9920218	2.0758712	2.1597890	2.2437752	2.3278299
150	2.0759071	2.1808188	2.2858375	2.3909635	2.4961968	2.6015376	2.7069859	2.8125418	2.9182055
180	2.4962314	2.6226568	2.7492373	2.8759730	3.0028642	3.1299110	3.2571136	3.3844723	3.5119872
240	3.3420796	3.5120728	3.6823445	3.8528951	4.0237250	4.1948348	4.3662249	4.5378957	4.7098477
360	5.0547746	5.3140969	5.5740576	5.8346582	6.0959003	6.3577854	6.6203152	6.8834911	7.1473149
365	5.1267496	5.3898583	5.6536237	5.9180474	6.1831311	6.4488763	6.7152849	6.9823583	7.2500983
790	11.4283688	12.0328522	12.6406107	13.2516619	13.8660238	14.4837141	15.1047510	15.7291526	16.3569369
1095	16.1822307	17.0567500	17.9378459	18.8255677	19.7199653	20.6210888	21.5289888	22.4437161	23.3653221
1825	28.4003432	30.0151925	31.6503400	33.3060407	34.9825527	36.6801376	38.3990600	40.1395879	41.9019929
3650	64.8664814	69.0395029	73.3181203	77.7050049	82.2028955	86.8146001	91.5429980	96.3910411	101.3617560

Table shows interest (I) on $100 compounded daily for N days at an annual rate of R. Table values
can be generated using the formula: $I = 100\left(1 + \dfrac{R}{365}\right)^N - 100$.

Table 10-2 Compound Interest on $100, Compounded Daily (365 Days)
(Exact Time, Exact Interest Basis)

Days	Annual Rate 7.25%	7.50%	7.75%	8.00%	8.25%	8.50%	8.75%	9.00%
1	0.0198630	0.0205479	0.0212329	0.0219178	0.0226027	0.0232877	0.0239726	0.0246575
2	0.0397300	0.0411001	0.0424703	0.0438404	0.0452106	0.0465808	0.0479510	0.0493211
3	0.0596009	0.0616565	0.0637122	0.0657678	0.0678235	0.0698793	0.0719351	0.0739908
4	0.0794757	0.0822171	0.0849586	0.0877001	0.0904416	0.0931832	0.0959249	0.0986666
5	0.0993545	0.1027820	0.1062095	0.1096371	0.1130648	0.1164926	0.1199205	0.1233485
6	0.1192373	0.1233510	0.1274649	0.1315789	0.1356931	0.1398074	0.1439218	0.1480364
7	0.1391240	0.1439243	0.1487248	0.1535256	0.1583265	0.1631276	0.1679290	0.1727305
8	0.1590146	0.1645018	0.1699893	0.1754770	0.1809650	0.1864533	0.1919418	0.1974306
9	0.1789092	0.1850836	0.1912583	0.1974333	0.2036087	0.2097844	0.2159604	0.2221368
10	0.1988078	0.2056696	0.2125318	0.2193944	0.2262574	0.2331209	0.2399848	0.2468491
11	0.2187103	0.2262598	0.2338098	0.2413603	0.2489113	0.2564629	0.2640149	0.2715675
12	0.2386167	0.2468542	0.2550923	0.2633310	0.2715703	0.2798103	0.2880508	0.2962920
13	0.2585271	0.2674529	0.2763793	0.2853065	0.2942344	0.3031631	0.3120925	0.3210226
14	0.2784415	0.2880558	0.2976709	0.3072869	0.3169037	0.3265214	0.3361399	0.3457593
15	0.2983598	0.3086629	0.3189670	0.3292720	0.3395780	0.3498851	0.3601931	0.3705021
16	0.3182821	0.3292743	0.3402676	0.3512620	0.3622575	0.3732542	0.3842520	0.3952510
17	0.3382083	0.3498899	0.3615727	0.3732568	0.3849422	0.3966288	0.4083168	0.4200060
18	0.3581385	0.3705097	0.3828823	0.3952564	0.4076319	0.4200089	0.4323872	0.4447671
19	0.3780727	0.3911338	0.4041965	0.4172608	0.4303268	0.4433943	0.4564635	0.4695343
20	0.3980108	0.4117621	0.4255152	0.4392701	0.4530268	0.4667853	0.4805455	0.4943076
21	0.4179529	0.4323947	0.4468384	0.4612842	0.4757319	0.4901816	0.5046333	0.5190870
22	0.4378989	0.4530315	0.4681662	0.4833031	0.4984422	0.5135835	0.5287269	0.5438725
23	0.4578489	0.4736725	0.4894985	0.5053268	0.5211576	0.5369907	0.5528263	0.5686642
24	0.4778028	0.4943178	0.5108353	0.5273554	0.5438781	0.5604035	0.5769314	0.5934619
25	0.4977608	0.5149673	0.5321766	0.5493888	0.5666038	0.5838216	0.6010423	0.6182658
26	0.5177226	0.5356210	0.5535225	0.5714270	0.5893346	0.6072453	0.6251590	0.6430758
27	0.5376885	0.5562790	0.5748729	0.5934701	0.6120706	0.6306744	0.6492815	0.6678919
28	0.5576583	0.5769413	0.5962278	0.6155180	0.6348116	0.6541089	0.6734097	0.6927141
29	0.5776321	0.5976078	0.6175873	0.6375707	0.6575579	0.6775489	0.6975437	0.7175424
30	0.5976098	0.6182785	0.6389513	0.6596282	0.6803092	0.7009943	0.7216836	0.7423769
35	0.6975581	0.7216960	0.7458394	0.7699885	0.7941432	0.8183036	0.8424695	0.8666411
40	0.7976057	0.8252197	0.8528411	0.8804698	0.9081059	0.9357494	0.9634003	0.9910586
45	0.8977527	0.9288498	0.9599563	0.9910722	1.0221975	1.0533321	1.0844761	1.1156295
50	0.9979992	1.0325865	1.0671854	1.1017959	1.1364180	1.1710517	1.2056971	1.2403541
55	1.0983453	1.1364297	1.1745283	1.2126410	1.2507677	1.2889085	1.3270635	1.3652326
60	1.1987911	1.2403797	1.2819852	1.3236075	1.3652467	1.4069026	1.4485754	1.4902650
90	1.8035650	1.8663273	1.9291278	1.9919667	2.0548438	2.1177593	2.1807131	2.2437053
120	2.4119531	2.4961449	2.5804053	2.6647345	2.7491323	2.8335990	2.9181345	3.0027390
150	3.0239770	3.1298566	3.2358442	3.3419400	3.4481442	3.5544567	3.6608778	3.7674075
180	3.6396585	3.7674863	3.8954710	4.0236126	4.1519114	4.2803676	4.4089813	4.5377528
240	4.8820814	5.0545972	5.2273956	5.4004770	5.5738419	5.7474908	5.9214241	6.0956423
360	7.4117881	7.6769122	7.9426889	8.2091198	8.4762066	8.7439507	9.0123538	9.2814175
365	7.5185065	7.7875846	8.0573343	8.3277572	8.5988550	8.8706293	9.1430819	9.4162145
790	16.9881224	17.6227275	18.2607706	18.9022704	19.5472455	20.1957148	20.8476971	21.5032115
1095	24.2938584	25.2293771	26.1719307	27.1215720	28.0783543	29.0423311	30.0135567	30.9920853
1825	43.6865497	45.4935366	47.3232354	49.1759314	51.0519134	52.9514740	54.8749093	56.8225193
3650	106.4582457	111.6836920	117.0413569	122.5345850	128.1668053	133.9415338	139.8623753	145.9330256

Table shows interest (I) on $100 compounded daily for N days at an annual rate of R. Table values
can be generated using the formula: $I = 100\left(1 + \dfrac{R}{365}\right)^{N} - 100.$

Using Table 10–2 is exactly like using Table 9–2, which gives the *simple* interest, rather than the compound interest, on $100:

HOW TO Find the Compounded Daily Interest Using a Table

1. Determine the amount of money the table uses as the principal ($1, $100, or $1,000).
2. Divide the loan principal by the table principal.
3. Select the days row corresponding to the time period (in days) of the loan.
4. Select the interest column corresponding to the interest rate of the loan.
5. Locate the value in the cell where the interest column intersects the days row.
6. Multiply the quotient from step 2 by the value from step 5.

TIP! Examine Table Title Carefully!

All tables are not alike! Different reference sources may approach finding the same information using different methods.

In working with compound interest, you more frequently want to know the accumulated amount than the accumulated interest, or vice versa. A table can be designed to give a factor for finding either amount directly.

- Determine whether the table will help you find the compound amount or the compound interest. Table 10–1 finds the compound amount and Table 10–2 finds the compound interest. Also, the principal that is used to determine the table value may be $1, $10, $100, or some other amount.

- Determine the principal amount used in calculating table values. Table 10–1 uses $1 as the principal amount and Table 10–2 uses $100 as the principal.

EXAMPLE Find the interest on $800 at 7.5% annually, compounded daily, for 28 days.

$800 ÷ $100 = 8

> Find the number of $100 units in the principal. Find the 28 days row in Table 10–2. Move across to the 7.5% column and find the interest for $100.

8 × $0.5769413 = $4.62

> Multiply the table value by 8, the number of $100 units.

The interest is $4.62.

Evaluating a Compound Interest Formula Using a Scientific, Business, or Graphing Calculator

Table 10–2 shows the interest per $100 of principal since most of the table values for $1.00 of principal would round to $0.00.

The formula for calculating daily interest is more cumbersome; thus, tables, scientific or financial calculators, or computers are generally used to calculate daily interest.

The formula used to generate the table is $I = \$100\left(1 + \dfrac{R}{365}\right)^N - 100$, where I is the interest, R is the annual rate, and N is the number of days.

To verify the table value from the previous example with the formula we would calculate

$$I = \$100\left(1 + \frac{0.075}{365}\right)^{28} - 100.$$ Using a scientific, business, or graphing calculator,

$\boxed{AC}$ 100 $\boxed{\times}$ $\boxed{(}$ 1 + .075 ÷ 365 $\boxed{)}$ $\boxed{x^y}$ 28 $\boxed{=}$ $\boxed{-}$ 100 $\boxed{=}$ $\Rightarrow$ 0.5769413

If the \$100 in the formula is replaced with any amount of principal, the interest can

be found without using tables. $I = P\left(1 + \dfrac{R}{365}\right)^{N} - P.$ Find the compound

interest for \$300 at 9% per year compounded daily for 45 days.

$$I = \$300\left(1 + \frac{0.09}{365}\right)^{45} - 300$$

$\boxed{AC}$ 300 $\boxed{\times}$ $\boxed{(}$ 1 + .09 ÷ 365 $\boxed{)}$ $\boxed{x^y}$ 45 $\boxed{=}$ $\boxed{-}$ 300 $\boxed{=}$

$\Rightarrow$ 3.346888494 or \$3.35

SELF-CHECK 10.1

 Use the simple interest formula method for exercises 1–4.

1. Thayer Farm Trust made a farmer a loan of \$1,200 at 16% for three years, compounded annually. Find the future value and the compound interest paid on the loan. Compare the compound interest with simple interest for the same period.

2. Maeola Killebrew invests \$3,800 at 7%, compounded semiannually for two years. What is the future value of the investment, and how much interest will she earn over the two-year period?

3. Carolyn Smith borrowed \$6,300 at $8\frac{1}{2}$% for three years, compounded annually. What is the compound amount of the loan and how much interest will she pay on the loan?

4. Margaret Hillman invested \$5,000 at 6%, compounded quarterly for one year. Find the future value and the interest earned for the year.

 Use Table 10–1 for exercises 5–10.

5. First State Bank loaned Doug Morgan \$2,000 for four years compounded annually at 8%. How much interest was Doug required to pay on the loan?

6. A loan of \$8,000 for two acres of woodland is compounded quarterly at an annual rate of 12% for five years. Find the compound amount and the compound interest.

7. Compute the compound amount and the interest on a loan of \$10,500 compounded annually for four years at 10%.

8. Find the future value of an investment of \$10,500 if it is invested for four years and compounded quarterly at an annual rate of 8%.

9. You have $8,000 that you plan to invest in a compound-interest-bearing instrument. Your investment agent advises you that you can invest the $8,000 at 8% compounded quarterly for three years or you can invest the $8,000 at $8\frac{1}{4}$% compounded annually for three years. Which investment should you choose to receive the most interest?

10. Find the future value of $50,000 at 6%; compounded semiannually for 10 years.

11. Find the effective interest rate for the loan described in exercise 8. Use the table method.

12. What is the effective interest rate for a loan of $5,000 at 10%, compounded semiannually for three years? Use the simple interest formula method.

13. Ross Land has a loan of $8,500, compounded quarterly for four years at 6%. What is the effective interest rate for the loan? Use the table method.

14. What is the effective interest rate for a loan of $20,000 for three years if the interest is compounded quarterly at a rate of 12%?

4   *Use Table 10–2 for Exercises 15–18.*

15. Find the compound interest on $2,500 at $6\frac{3}{4}$%, compounded daily by Leader Financial Bank for 20 days.

16. How much compound interest is earned on a deposit of $1,500 at 6.25%, compounded daily for 30 days?

17. John McCormick has found a short-term investment opportunity. He can invest $8,000 at 8.5% interest for 15 days. How much interest will he earn on this investment if the interest is compounded daily?

18. What is the compound interest on $8,000 invested at 8% for 180 days if it is compounded daily?

10.2   Present Value

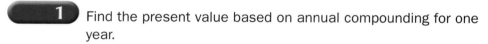 Find the present value based on annual compounding for one year.

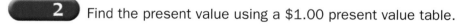 Find the present value using a $1.00 present value table.

In section 1 of this chapter we learned how to find the future value of money invested at the present time. Sometimes businesses and individuals need to know how much to invest at the present time to yield a certain amount at some specified future date. For example, a business may want to set aside a lump sum of money to provide pensions for employees in years to come. Individuals may want to set aside a lump sum of money now to pay for a child's college education or for a vacation. You can use the concepts of compound interest to determine the amount of money that must be set aside at present and compounded periodically to yield a certain amount of money at some specific time in the future. The amount of money set aside now is called **present value.**

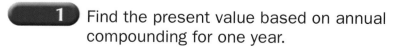 Find the present value based on annual compounding for one year.

Finding the present value of $100 means finding the *principal* that we must invest today so that $100 is its future value. We know that the future value of principal depends on the period interest rate and the number of interest periods. Just as calculating future value by hand is time consuming when there are many interest periods, so is calculating present value by hand. A present value table is more efficient. For now, we find present value based on the simplest case—annual compounding for one year. In this case, the number of interest periods is 1, and the period interest rate is the annual interest rate. Thus, in this case,

$$\text{Future value} = \text{principal}(1 + \text{annual interest rate})$$

and, using algebra to find present value,

$$\text{Principal (present value)} = \frac{\text{future value}}{1 + \text{annual interest rate}}$$

? HOW TO Find the Present Value Based on Annual Compounding for One Year

Divide the future value by the sum of 1 and the annual interest rate.

$$\text{Present value (principal)} = \frac{\text{future value}}{1 + \text{annual interest rate}}$$

 **EXAMPLE**   Find the amount of money that Tinquist Editorial Services needs to set aside today to ensure that $10,000 will be available to buy a new desktop publishing system in one year if the annual interest rate is 8% compounded annually.

$$1 + 0.08 = \boxed{1.08}$$
Convert the annual interest rate to a decimal and add to 1.

$$\frac{\$10,000}{1.08} = \$9,259.26$$
Divide the future value by 1.08 to get the present value.

An investment of $9,259.26 at 8% would have a value of $10,000 in one year.

2 Find the present value using a $1.00 present value table.

If the interest in the preceding example had been compounded more than once a year, you would have to make calculations for each time the money was compounded. It is more efficient to use Table 10–3, which shows the present value of $1.00 at different interest rates for different periods.

Table 10–3 is used like Table 10–1, which gives the future value of $1.00: Locate the value in the cell where the applicable periods row intersects the applicable rate-per-period column. This value is the present value of $1.00, so multiply this value by the desired future value.

EXAMPLE   The Absorbent Diaper Company needs $20,000 in 10 years to buy a new diaper edging machine. How much must the firm invest at the present if it receives 10% interest compounded annually?

$R = 10\%$ and $N = 10$ years.

Table value = 0.38554

The money is to be compounded for 10 periods, so we find periods row 10 in Table 10–3 and the 10% rate column to find the present value of $1.00.

$\$20,000 \times 0.38554 = \$7,710.80$

Multiply the present value factor times the desired future value to find the amount that must be invested at the present.

The Absorbent Diaper Company should invest $7,710.80 today to have $20,000 in 10 years.

Table 10–3 Present Value of $1.00

Periods	1%	1.5%	2%	2.5%	3%	4%	5%	6%	8%	10%	12%
1	0.99010	0.98522	0.98039	0.97561	0.97087	0.96154	0.95238	0.94340	0.92593	0.90909	0.89286
2	0.98030	0.97066	0.96117	0.95181	0.94260	0.92456	0.90703	0.89000	0.85734	0.82645	0.79719
3	0.97059	0.95632	0.94232	0.92860	0.91514	0.88900	0.86384	0.83962	0.79383	0.75131	0.71178
4	0.96098	0.94218	0.92385	0.90595	0.88849	0.85480	0.82270	0.79209	0.73503	0.68301	0.63552
5	0.95147	0.92826	0.90573	0.88385	0.86261	0.82193	0.78353	0.74726	0.68058	0.62092	0.56743
6	0.94205	0.91454	0.88797	0.86230	0.83748	0.79031	0.74622	0.70496	0.63017	0.56447	0.50663
7	0.93272	0.90103	0.87056	0.84127	0.81309	0.75992	0.71068	0.66506	0.58349	0.51316	0.45235
8	0.92348	0.88771	0.85349	0.82075	0.78941	0.73069	0.67684	0.62741	0.54027	0.46651	0.40388
9	0.91434	0.87459	0.83676	0.80073	0.76642	0.70259	0.64461	0.59190	0.50025	0.42410	0.36061
10	0.90529	0.86167	0.82035	0.78120	0.74409	0.67556	0.61391	0.55839	0.46319	0.38554	0.32197
11	0.89632	0.84893	0.80426	0.76214	0.72242	0.64958	0.58468	0.52679	0.42888	0.35049	0.28748
12	0.88475	0.83639	0.78849	0.74356	0.70138	0.62460	0.55684	0.49697	0.39711	0.31863	0.25668
13	0.87866	0.82403	0.77303	0.72542	0.68095	0.60057	0.53032	0.46884	0.36770	0.28966	0.22917
14	0.86996	0.81185	0.75788	0.70773	0.66112	0.57748	0.50507	0.44230	0.34046	0.26333	0.20462
15	0.86135	0.79985	0.74301	0.69047	0.64186	0.55526	0.48102	0.41727	0.31524	0.23939	0.18270
16	0.85282	0.78803	0.72845	0.67362	0.62317	0.53391	0.45811	0.39365	0.29189	0.21763	0.16312
17	0.84438	0.77639	0.71416	0.65720	0.60502	0.51337	0.43630	0.37136	0.27027	0.19784	0.14564
18	0.83602	0.76491	0.70016	0.64117	0.58739	0.49363	0.41552	0.35034	0.25025	0.17986	0.13004
19	0.82774	0.75361	0.68643	0.62553	0.57029	0.47464	0.39573	0.33051	0.23171	0.16351	0.11611
20	0.81954	0.74247	0.67297	0.61027	0.55368	0.45639	0.37689	0.31180	0.21455	0.14864	0.10367
21	0.81143	0.73150	0.65978	0.59539	0.53755	0.43883	0.35894	0.29416	0.19866	0.13513	0.09256
22	0.80340	0.72069	0.64684	0.58086	0.52189	0.42196	0.34185	0.27751	0.18394	0.12285	0.08264
23	0.79544	0.71004	0.63416	0.56670	0.50669	0.40573	0.32557	0.26180	0.17032	0.11168	0.07379
24	0.78757	0.69954	0.62172	0.55288	0.49193	0.39012	0.31007	0.24698	0.15770	0.10153	0.06588
25	0.77977	0.68921	0.60953	0.53939	0.47761	0.37512	0.29530	0.23300	0.14602	0.09230	0.05882
26	0.77205	0.67902	0.59758	0.52623	0.46369	0.36069	0.28124	0.21981	0.13520	0.08391	0.05252
27	0.76440	0.66899	0.58586	0.51340	0.45019	0.34682	0.26785	0.20737	0.12519	0.07628	0.04689
28	0.75684	0.65910	0.57437	0.50088	0.43708	0.33348	0.25509	0.19563	0.11591	0.06934	0.04187
29	0.74934	0.64935	0.56311	0.48866	0.42435	0.32065	0.24295	0.18456	0.10733	0.06304	0.03738
30	0.74192	0.63976	0.55207	0.47674	0.41199	0.30832	0.23138	0.17411	0.09938	0.05731	0.03338

Table shows the lump sum amount of money, present value (PV), that should be invested now so that the accumulated amount will be $1.00 after a specified number of periods, N, at a specified rate per period, R. Table values can be generated using the formula: $PV = \dfrac{\$1.00}{(1 + R)^N}$.

TIP! **Which Table Do I Use?**

Tables 10-1 and 10-3 have entries that are reciprocal. Except for minor rounding discrepancies, the product of corresponding entries is 1. And 1 divided by a table value equals its comparable table value in the other table.

Look at period row 1 at 1% on each table.

Table 10-1: 1.01000
Table 10-3: 0.99010

The product $1.01000 \times 0.99010 = 1.000001$
Look at period row 16 at 4% on each table.

Table 10-1: 1.87298
Table 10-3: 0.53391

The product $1.87298 \times 0.53391 = 1.000002752$
Now, look at the formulas that were used to generate each table.

Table 10-1: $FV = \$1.00(1 + R)^N$

Table 10-3: $PV = \dfrac{\$1.00}{(1 + R)^N}$

The formulas are also reciprocals. One way to select the appropriate table is to anticipate whether you expect a larger or smaller amount. You expect a future value to be larger than what you start with. All entries in Table 10-1 are greater than 1 and produce a larger product.

You expect a present value to require a smaller investment to reach a desired amount. All entries in Table 10-3 are less than 1 and produce a smaller product.

SELF-CHECK 10.2

 1

1. Compute the amount of money to be set aside today to ensure a future value of $2,500 in one year if the interest rate is 11% annually, compounded annually.

2. How much should Linda Bryan set aside now to buy equipment that costs $8,500 in one year? The current interest rate is 7.5% annually, compounded annually.

3. Ronnie Cox has just inherited $27,000. How much of this money should he set aside today to have $21,000 to pay cash for a Ventura Van, which he plans to purchase in one year? He can invest at 7.9% annually, compounded annually.

4. Shirley Riddle received a $10,000 gift from her mother and plans a minor renovation to her home and an investment for one year, at which time she plans to take a trip projected to cost $6,999. The current interest rate is 8.3% annually, compounded annually. How much should be set aside today for her trip?

 2

5. Rosa Burnett needs $2,000 in three years to make the down payment on a new car. How much must she invest today if she receives 8% interest annually, compounded annually? Use Table 10-3.

6. Use Table 10-3 to calculate the amount of money that must be invested now at 6% annually, compounded quarterly, to obtain $1,500 in three years.

7. Dewey Sykes plans to open a business in four years when he retires. How much must he invest today to have $10,000 when he retires if the bank pays 10% annually, compounded quarterly.

8. Charlie Bryant has a child who will be college age in five years. How much must he set aside today to have $20,000 for college tuition in five years if he gets 8% annually, compounded annually?

Maximize Your Investments: Start Early!

Many young adults do not realize the importance of starting an investment strategy early. The greater benefits of compound interest are realized over longer periods of time. For instance, suppose by age 35 you have accumulated $25,000 in savings and invest it in a long-term program that is compounded annually at 8%. At age 65, this investment will have accumulated to $251,566.50. Use factors from Table 10-1.

$$\$25,000 \times 10.06266 = \$251,566.60$$

If it takes you until age 45 to accumulate $25,000 in savings and you invest it in a long-term program that is compounded annually at 8%, at age 65 this investment will have accumulated to only $116,524.00.

$$\$25,000 \times 4.66096 = \$116,524.00$$

Even if you have accumulated $50,000 by age 45 and invest it in a long-term program that is compounded annually at 8%, this investment will have accumulated to only $233,048.00 by the time you are 65.

$$\$50,000 \times 4.66096 = \$233,048.00$$

Even a modest investment plan, started early and continued consistently, will reap significant benefits.

Exercises

1. You purchase a $2,000 Roth Individual Retirement Account (Roth IRA) when you are 25 years old. You expect to earn an average of 6% per year, compounded annually over 35 years (until age 60). What will be the accumulated amount of your investment?

2. The same $2,000 Roth Individual Retirement Account is invested age age 35 for a 25-year period (until age 60). If the IRA grows at a rate of 6% per year compounded annually, what will be the accumulated amount of the investment?

3. The same $2,000 Roth Individual Retirement Account is invested at age 45 for a 15-year period (until age 60). If the IRA grows at a rate of 6% per year compounded annually, what will be the accumulated amount of the investment?

4. Draw a bar graph illustrating the accumulated amounts of the investments in exercises 1, 2, and 3.

5. What are the differences in the accumulated amounts for the investments in exercises 1, 2 and 3?

6. What is the percent increase of the original $2,000 for each investment in exercises 1, 2 and 3?

7. How much would you accumulate by age 67 if you invested $1,000 today at 8% compounded annually. Compare your accumulated amount with a classmate of a different age to determine which of you will have accumulated more.

8. Interest rate is critical to the speed at which your investment grows. If $1 is invested at 2%, it takes 34.9 years to double. If $1 is invested at 5%, it takes 14.2 years to double. Use Table 10-1 to determine how many years it takes $1 to double if invested at 10%; at 12%.

9. At what interest rate would you need to invest to have your money double in 10 years?

Answers

1. Use the formula at the bottom of Table 10-1 to find the table value of 7.688609: $2,000 × 7.688609 = $15,372.18

2. $2,000 × 4.29187 = $8,583.74

3. $2,000 × 2.39656 = $4,793.12

4.

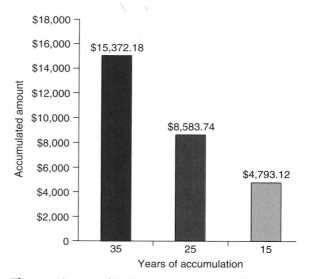

Figure 10-1   A $2,000 Investment @ 6%

5. Amount of increase:
   15 years to 25 years: $8,583.74 − $4,793.12 = $3,790.62
   25 years to 35 years: $15,372.18 − $8,583.74 = $6,788.44
   15 years to 35 years: $15,372.18 − $4,793.12 = $10,569.06

6. Percent increase:
   15 years to 25 years: $3,790.62 ÷ $4,793.12 = 79.1%
   25 years to 35 years: $6,788.44 ÷ $8,583.74 = 79.1%
   15 years to 35 years: $10,579.06 ÷ $8,583.74 = 123.2%

7. Answers will vary. Younger persons will have accumulated more than older persons.

8. At 10%, $1 takes slightly more than 7 years to double. At 12%, it takes slightly more than six years. To find the number of years it takes for $1 to double, go across the top row of the table to find the desired percent. Then move down the column until you find the table value nearest 2 (because it doubles) and read across to the left to find the number of years.

9. 8%. In Table 10-1, move down the periods column on the left to find 10, then move across to find the number closest to 2 (since you want to *double* your investment). This value is 2.15892. Then read up the column to find 8%.

Section Outcome **Important Points with Examples**

Section 10.1

Use the simple interest formula to find the future value (page 418)

Find the period interest rate. Divide the annual interest rate by the number of interest periods per year.

$$\text{Period interest rate} = \frac{\text{annual interest rate}}{\text{number of interest periods per year}}$$

Find the future value using the simple interest formula method.

1. Find the first end-of-period principal: multiply the original principal by the sum of 1 and the period interest rate.

   First end-of-period principal = original principal × (1 + period interest rate)

2. For each remaining period in turn, find the next end-of-period principal: multiply the previous end-of-period principal by the sum of 1 and the period interest rate.

   End-of-period principal = previous end-of-period principal

   × (1 + period interest rate)

3. Identify the last end-of-period principal as the future value.

   Future value = last end-of-period principal

Find the compound interest. Subtract the original principal from the future value.

Compound interest = future value − original principal

Find the compound amount and compound interest on $500 at 7%, compounded annually for two years.

$500 × (1 + 0.07) = $535 end-of-first-period principal
$535 × (1 + 0.07) = $572.45 end-of-last-period principal (future value)
Compound amount = $572.45
Compound interest = $572.45 − $500 = $72.45

Find the compound amount (future value) and compound interest on $1,500 at 8%, compounded semiannually for two years.

Number of interest periods = 2 × 2 = 4 periods
Period interest rate = $\dfrac{8\%}{2}$ = 4% or 0.04

$1,500 × (1 + 0.04) = $1,560 (first period)
$1,560 × (1 + 0.04) = $1,622.40 (second period)
$1,622.40 × (1 + 0.04) = $1,687.30 (third period)
$1,687.30 × (1 + 0.04) = $1,754.79 (fourth period)
Compound amount = $1,754.79
Compound interest = $1,754.79 − $1,500 = $254.79

Find the future value using a $1.00 future value table. (page 420)

1. Find the number of interest periods: multiply the time period, in years, by the number of interest periods per year.

   Interest periods = number of years × number of interest periods per year

2. Find the period interest rate: divide the annual interest rate by the number of interest periods per year.

$$\text{Period interest rate} = \frac{\text{annual interest rate}}{\text{number of interest periods per year}}$$

3. Select the periods row corresponding to the number of interest periods.
4. Select the rate-per-period column corresponding to the period interest rate.
5. Locate the value in the cell where the periods row intersects the rate-per-period column.
6. Multiply the original principal by the value from step 5 to find future value or compound amount.

$$\text{Compound interest} = \text{future value} - \text{original principal}$$

Find the future value of $2,000 at 12%, compounded semiannually for four years.

$4 \times 2 = 8$ periods

$\dfrac{12\%}{2} = 6\%$ period interest rate

Find periods row 8 in Table 10-1 and move across to the 6% rate column: 1.59385.

$2,000 \times 1.59385 = \$3,187.70$ future value or compound amount

Find the compound interest on $800 at 8%, compounded annually for four years.
Annually indicates one period per year. Period interest rate is 8%.

Find periods row 4 in Table 10-1.

Move across to the 8% rate column and find the compound amount per dollar of principal: 1.36049.

$800 \times 1.36049 = \$1,088.39$ compound amount

$1,088.39	compound amount or future value
−800.00	principal
$288.39	compound interest

3 Find the effective interest rate. (page 424)

Use the simple interest formula method: divide the interest compounded for the first year by the principal.

$$\text{Effective interest rate} = \frac{\text{interest compounded for first year}}{\text{principal}}$$

Use the table method: use Table 10-1 to find the future value of $1.00 of the investment. Subtract $1.00 from the future value of $1.00 after one year and divide by $1.00 to remove the dollar sign.

$$\text{Effective interest rate} = \frac{\text{future value of } \$1.00 \text{ after 1 year} - \$1.00}{\$1.00}$$

Betty Padgett earned $247.29 interest on an investment of $3,000 at 8% annually, compounded quarterly. Find the effective interest rate.

Using the simple interest formula method:

$$\text{Effective interest} = \frac{\$247.29}{\$3,000} = 0.08243 = 8.24\%$$

Using Table 10-1: Periods per year = 4

$$\text{Rate per period} = \frac{8\%}{4} = 2\%$$

Table value = 1.08243 (from Table 10-1)

Effective interest rate = 1.08243 − 1.00 = 0.08243 = 8.24%

Find the interest compounded daily using a table. (page 425)

1. Determine the amount of money the table uses as the principal. (A typical table principal is $1, $100, or $1,000.)
2. Divide the loan principal by the table principal.
3. Select the days row corresponding to the time period (in days) of the loan.
4. Select the interest column corresponding to the interest rate of the loan.
5. Locate the value in the cell where the interest column intersects the days row.
6. Multiply the quotient from step 2 by the value from step 5.

Find the interest on a $300 loan borrowed at 9%, compounded daily for 21 days.

Select the 21 days row of Table 10-2; then move across to the 9% rate column. The table value is 0.5190870.

$$\frac{\$300}{100} \times 0.5190870 = \$1.56$$

The interest on $300 is $1.56.

Section 10.2

Find the present value based on annual compounding for one year. (page 430)

Divide the future value by the sum of 1 and the annual interest rate.

$$\text{Present value (principal)} = \frac{\text{future value}}{1 + \text{annual interest rate}}$$

Find the amount of money that must be invested to produce $4,000 in one year if the interest rate is 7% annually, compounded annually.

$$\text{Present value} = \frac{\$4,000}{1 + 0.07} = \frac{\$4,000}{1.07} = \$3,738.32$$

How much must be invested to produce $30,000 in one year if the interest rate is 6% annually, compounded annually?

$$\text{Present value} = \frac{\$30,000}{1 + 0.06} = \frac{\$30,000}{1.06} = \$28,301.89$$

Find the present value using a $1.00 present value table. (page 431)

1. Find the number of interest periods: multiply the time period, in years, by the number of interest periods per year.

   Interest periods = number of years × number of interest periods per year

2. Find the period interest rate: divide the annual interest rate by the number of interest periods per year.

   $$\text{Period interest rate} = \frac{\text{annual interest rate}}{\text{number of interest periods per year}}$$

3. Select the periods row corresponding to the number of interest periods.
4. Select the rate-per-period column corresponding to the period interest rate.
5. Locate the value in the cell where the periods row intersects the rate-per-period column.
6. Multiply the future value by the value from step 5.

Find the amount of money that must be deposited to ensure $3,000 at the end of three years if the investment earns 6%, compounded semiannually.

3 × 2 = 6 periods

$$\frac{6\%}{2} = 3\%\ \text{rate per period}$$

Find periods row 6 in Table 10-3 and move across to the 3% rate column: 0.83748.

$3,000 × 0.83748 = $2,512.44
The amount that must be invested now to have $3,000 in three years is $2,512.44.

WORDS TO KNOW

interest period (p. 418)
compound interest (p. 418)
future value (p. 418)
maturity value (p. 418)

compound amount (p. 418)
period interest rate (p. 418)
effective rate (p. 424)
annual percentage yield (APY)
  (p. 424)

annual percentage rate (APR)
  (p. 424)
present value (p. 430)

CHAPTER 10   CONCEPTS ANALYSIS

1. The compound amount or future value can be found using two formulas: $I = PR$ (assuming $T = 1$) and $A = P + I$. Show how these two formulas relate to the single formula $A = P(1 + R)$.

2. Find the future value of $1,000 at 6% compounded annually for one year using the two formulas $I = PR$ and $A = P + I$. Compare this result with the result found when using the formula $A = P(1 + R)$.

3. In finding a future value, how will your result compare in size to your original investment?

4. In finding a present value, how will your result compare in size to your desired goal?

5. Since the entries in the present value table (Table 10-3) are reciprocals of the corresponding entries in the future value table (Table 10-1), how can Table 10-3 be used to find the future value of an investment?

6. Illustrate the procedure you described in exercise 5 to find the future value of $500 invested at 8% for two years if it is compounded quarterly. Check your result using the future value table (Table 10-1).

7. How can the future value table (Table 10-1) be used to find the present value of a desired goal?

8. Illustrate the procedure described in exercise 7 to find the present value of an investment if you want to have $500 at the end of two years. The investment earns 8%, compounded quarterly. Check your result using the present value table.

9. Banking regulations require that the effective interest rate (APR or APY) be stated on all loan or investment contracts. Why?

10. How does the effective interest rate compare with the compounded rate on a loan or investment? Illustrate your answer with an example that shows the compounded rate and the effective rate.

Section 10.1

1. Calculate the compound interest on a loan of $1,000 at 8%, compounded annually for two years.

2. Calculate the compound interest on a loan of $200 at 6%, compounded annually for four years.

3. Calculate the compound interest on a 13% loan of $1,600 for three years if the interest is compounded annually.

4. Calculate the compound interest on a loan of $6,150 at $11\frac{1}{2}$% annual interest, compounded annually for three years.

5. Maria Sanchez invested $2,000 for two years at 12% annual interest, compounded semiannually. Calculate the interest she earned on her investment.

6. EZ Loan Company loaned $500 at 8% annual interest, compounded quarterly for one year. Calculate the amount the loan company will earn in interest.

7. Use Table 10-1 to find the future value on an investment of $3,000 made by Ling Lee for five years at 12% annual interest, compounded semiannually.

8. Use Table 10-2 to find the daily interest on $2,500 invested for 21 days at 8.75%, compounded annually.

9. Use Table 10-1 to find the interest on a certificate of deposit (CD) of $10,000 for five years at 4%, compounded semiannually.

10. How much more interest is paid on the CD in exercise 9 than if simple interest had been used?

Use Table 10-1 for Exercises 11–18. Find the compound interest on the following loans:

	Principal	Term (Years)	Rate of Compound Interest	Compound Interest	Compounded
11.	$2,000	3	3%	_____	Annually
12.	$3,500	4	10%	_____	Semiannually
13.	$800	2	6%	_____	Quarterly

14. Find the factor for compounding an amount for 25 periods at 8% per period.

15. Find the future value on an investment of $8,000, compounded quarterly for seven years at 8%.

16. Find the compound interest on $5,000 for two years if the interest is compounded semiannually at 12%.

17. Find the compound interest on $5,000 for two years if the interest is compounded quarterly at 12%.

18. An investment of $1,000 made at the beginning of each year for two years is compounded semiannually at 10%. Find the compound amount and compound interest at the end of the two years.

19. Mario Piazza was offered $900 now for one of his salon photographs or $1,100 in one year for the same photograph. Which would give Mr. Piazza a greater yield if he could invest the $900 for one year at 16% compounded quarterly? Use Table 10-1.

20. Find the effective interest rate for the loan described in exercise 16.

21. Find the effective interest rate for the loan described in exercise 17.

22. Use Table 10-2 to find the accumulated daily interest on an investment of $5,000 invested for 30 days at 9%.

23. Use Table 10-2 to find the amount of interest on $100 invested for 10 days at 8.5%, compounded daily.

24. Use Table 10-2 to find the compound interest and the compound amount on an investment of $24,982 if it is invested for 28 days at 7%, compounded daily.

25. Use Table 10-2 to find the compound interest and the compound amount on an investment of $2,000 if it is invested for 21 days at 8%, compounded daily.

26. Find the interest on an investment of $1,000 for 30 days if it is invested at an annual rate of 7.25%, compounded monthly. Compare this interest to the interest earned on $1,000 for 30 days at an annual rate of 7.25% compounded daily. (Use Tables 10-1 and 10-2.)

27. Lauren McAnally invests $2,000 at 8% compounded semiannually for two years, and Inez Everett invests an equal amount at 8% compounded quarterly for 18 months. Use Table 10-1 to determine which investment yields the greater interest.

28. What is the effective interest rate of each investment in exercise 27?

SECTION 10.2

29. How much money should Brienne Smith set aside today to have $5,000 in one year for an international trip? Today's annual interest rate is 7.9%.

30. Miranda Bolden wishes to have $8,000 one year from now to make a down payment on a lake house. How much should she invest at 9.5% annual interest to have her payment in one year?

In the following exercises, find the amount of money that should be invested (present value) at the stated interest rate to yield the given amount (future value) after the indicated amount of time. Use Table 10-3.

31. $1,500 in three years at 10%, compounded annually

32. $2,000 in five years at 10%, compounded semiannually

33. $1,000 in seven years at 8%, compounded quarterly

34. $3,500 in 12 years at 12%, compounded annually

35. $4,000 in two years at 12% annual interest, compounded quarterly

36. $10,000 in seven years at 16% annual interest, compounded quarterly

37. $500 in 15 years at 8% annual interest, compounded semiannually

38. $800 in four years at 10% annual interest, compounded annually

39. $1,800 in one year at 12% annual interest, compounded monthly

40. $700 in six years at 8% annual interest, compounded quarterly

41. Myrna Lewis wished to have $4,000 in four years to tour Europe. How much must she invest today at 8% annual interest, compounded quarterly, to have the $4,000 in four years?

42. Louis Banks was offered $15,000 cash or $19,500 to be paid in two years for a resort cabin. If money can be invested in today's market for 12% annual interest, compounded quarterly, which offer should Louis accept?

43. An art dealer offered a collector $8,000 for a painting. The collector could sell the painting to an individual for $11,000 to be paid in 18 months. Currently investments yield 12% annual interest, compounded monthly. Which is the better deal for the collector?

44. If you were offered $700 today or $800 in two years, which would you accept if money can be invested at 12% annual interest, compounded monthly?

45. How much should a family invest now at 10% compounded annually to have a $7,000 house down payment in four years.

46. (a) Write formulas to complete the spreadsheet showing the Accumulated Amount for each of exercises 4–8 in Self-Check 10.1 and exercises 11–13 in Assignment Exercises. Compare your spreadsheet results with the results of calculations using Table 10-1. You will need to use the formula referenced in Table 10.1. The formula written for the spreadsheet is: $= P*(1+r)^t$, where P is principal, r is rate per period, and t is number of periods.

(b) Write formulas to complete the spreadsheet to give the Interest for each loan amount in (a).

47. Complete the spreadsheet using the formulas.

	Microsoft Excel - chapter 10 worksheet.xls								
	A	B	C	D	E	F	G	H	
1		Accumulated Amount and Compound Interest							
2	Exercise	Principal	Periodic Rate	Periods	Accumulated Amount	Interest			
3	4	$2,000.00	8.00%	4.000000					
4	5	$8,000.00	3.00%	20.000000					
5	6	$10,500.00	10.00%	4.000000					
6	7	$10,500.00	2.00%	16.000000					
7	8	$8,000.00	2.00%	12.000000					
8	8	$8,000.00	8.25%	3.000000					
9	11	$2,000.00	3.00%	3.000000					
10	12	$3,500.00	5.00%	8.000000					
11	13	$800.00	1.50%	8.000000					

Challenge Problems

48. An investment of $2,000 is made at the beginning of each year for three years and compounded annually at 8%. Find the future value and compound interest at the end of three years.

49. Your company plans to enter several short-term financing agreements. You are assigned to compute interest for monthly compounding at the nominal annual rate of 8%. Construct an interest rate table showing the current principal and the interest earned for each of the 12 months for $1.00, compounded monthly. What is the effective rate of this financing agreement?

50. One real estate sales technique is to encourage customers or clients to buy today because the value of the property will probably increase during the next few years. "Buy this lot today for $30,000. In two years, I project it will sell for $32,500." Let's see if this is a wise investment.

In two years the future value is projected to be $32,500. If the interest rate is 12%, compounded annually, what amount should you invest today to have the $32,500 in two years?

Using Table 10-3, the factor for 12% and two periods is 0.79719.

Present value = $32,500 × 0.79719 = $25,908.68

By investing only $25,908.68 today at 12% for two years, you will have the $32,500 needed to purchase the land. You have actually paid only $25,908.68 for the lot, a savings of $4,091.32 on the $30,000 price. Of course, there can be problems with waiting to buy.

(a) What are some of the problems with waiting to buy land?

(b) What are some of the advantages of waiting?

(c) Lots in a new subdivision sell for $15,600. If you invest your money today in an account earning 8% quarterly, how much will the lot actually cost you in a year assuming the price does not go up? How much do you save?

(d) 1) You have inherited $60,000 and plan to buy a home. If you invest the $60,000 today at 10%, compounded annually, how much could you spend on the house in one year?

2) If you intend to spend $60,000 on a house in one year, how much of your inheritance should you invest today at 10%, compounded annually? How much do you have left to spend on a car?

1. Calculate the compound interest on a loan of $2,000 at 7%, compounded annually for three years.

2. Calculate the compound interest on a 14% annual interest loan of $3,000 for four years if interest is compounded annually.

3. Use Table 10-1 to find the interest on a loan of $5,000 for six years at 10% annual interest if interest is compounded semiannually.

4. Use Table 10-1 to find the compound amount on an investment of $12,000 for seven years at 12% annual interest, compounded quarterly.

5. An investment of $1,500 is made at the beginning of each year for two years at 12% annual interest, compounded semiannually. Find the compound amount and the compound interest at the end of two years.

6. Use Table 10-1 to find the compound interest on a loan of $3,000 for one year at 12% annual interest if the interest is compounded quarterly.

7. Find the effective interest rate for the loan described in exercise 6.

8. Use Table 10-2 to find the daily interest on an investment of $2,000 invested at 5.75% for 28 days.

9. Use Tables 10-1 and 10-2 to compare the interest on an investment of $3,000 that is invested at 8% annual interest compounded quarterly and daily for one year.

Find the amount that should be invested today (present value) at the stated interest rate to yield the given amount (future value) after the indicated amount of time.

10. $3,400 in four years at 8% annual interest, compounded annually

11. $5,000 in eight years at 8% annual interest, compounded semiannually

12. $8,000 in 12 years at 12% annual interest, compounded annually

13. $6,000 in six years at 12% annual interest, compounded quarterly

14. Jamie Juarez needs $12,000 in 10 years for her daughter's college education. How much must be invested today at 8% annual interest, compounded semiannually, to have the needed funds?

15. If you were offered $600 today or $680 in one year, which would you accept if money can be invested at 12% annual interest, compounded monthly?

16. Derek Anderson plans to buy a house in four years. He will make an $8,000 down payment on the property. How much should he invest today at 6% annual interest, compounded quarterly, to have the required amount in four years?

17. Which of the two options yields the greatest return on your investment of $2,000?
Option 1: 8% annual interest compounded quarterly for four years
Option 2: $8\frac{1}{4}$% annual interest compounded annually for four years

18. If you invest $2,000 today at 8% annual interest, compounded quarterly, how much will you have after three years? (Table 10-1)

19. If you invest $1,000 today at 12% annual interest compounded daily, how much will you have after 20 days? (Table 10-2)

20. How much money should Bryan Trailer Sales set aside today to have $15,000 in one year to purchase a forklift if the interest rate is 10.4%, compounded annually?

SELF-CHECK 10.1

1. $1,200 × (1 + 0.16) = $1,392 (first year)
$1,392 × (1.016) = $1,614.72 (second year)
$1,614.72 × (1 + 0.16) = $1,873.08 (third year)
future value
Compound interest = $1,873.08 − $1,200
= $673.08
Simple interest = $1,200 × 0.16 × 3 = $576

2. Period interest rate = $\dfrac{7\%}{2}$ = 0.035
$3,800 × (1 + 0.035) = $3,933 (first period)
$3,933 × (1 + 0.035) = $4,070.66 (second period)
$4,070.66 × (1 + 0.035) = $4,213.13 (third period)
$4,213.13 × (1 + 0.035) = $4,360.59 (last period)
Future value = $4,360.59
Compound interest = $4,360.59 − $3,800 = $560.59

3. $6,300 × (1 + 0.085) = $6,835.50 (first year)
$6,835.50 × (1 + 0.085) = $7,416.52 (second year)
$7,416.52 × (1 + 0.085) = $8,046.92 (last year)
Compound amount = $8,046.92
Compound interest = $8,046.92 − $6,300 =
$1,746.92

4. $5,000 × $\left(1 + \dfrac{0.06}{4}\right)$ = $5,075 (first period)

$5,075 × $\left(1 + \dfrac{0.06}{4}\right)$ = $5,151.13 (second period)

$5,151.13 × $\left(1 + \dfrac{0.06}{4}\right)$ = $5,228.40 (third period)

$5,228.40 × $\left(1 + \dfrac{0.06}{4}\right)$ = $5,306.83

Future value (compound amount) = $5,306.83
Compound interest = $5,306.83 − 5,000 = $306.83

5. Find periods row 4 (Table 10-1). Move across to
the 8% rate column.
Table value = 1.36049
$2,000(1.36049) = $2,720.98 compound amount
$2,720.98 − $2,000 = $720.98 compound interest

6. 5 years × 4 quarters per year = 20 periods
12% ÷ 4 quarters = 3% per period
Table value = 1.80611 (Table 10-1)
$8,000(1.80611) = $14,448.88 compound amount
$14,448.88 − $8,000 = $6,448.88 compound interest

7. Find the table value for 4 periods and 10% per period.
Table value = 1.46410
$10,500 × 1.46410 = $15,373.05 compound amount
Interest = $15,373.05 − $10,500 = $4,873.05

8. 4 years × 4 quarters = 16 periods
8% ÷ 4 quarters = 2% per period
Table value = 1.37279
$10,500 × 1.37279 = $14,414.30

9. 8% quarterly; 12 periods at 2% per period
Table value = 1.26824
$8,000 × 1.26824 = $10,145.92
$8\frac{1}{4}$% annually (not on table)
$8,000 × 1.0825 = $8,660
$8,660 × 1.0825 = $9,374.45
$9,374.45 × 1.0825 = $10,147.84
$8\frac{1}{4}$% annually is the better deal.

10. 6% semiannually; 20 periods @ 3% per period.
Table value = 1.80611
$50,000 × 1.80611 = $90,305.50

11. Compounded quarterly = 4 periods in year 1
$\dfrac{8\% \text{ annual}}{4}$ = 2% per period
Table value = 1.08243
Effective rate = 1.08243 − 1
= .08243
= 8.24%

12. Period interest rate = $\dfrac{10\%}{2}$ = 0.05
$5,000 × (1 + 0.05) = $5,250 (first period)
$5,250 × (1 + 0.05) = $5,512.50 (second period)
Compound interest = $5,512.50 − $5,000 = $512.50
Effective rate = $\dfrac{\$512.50}{\$5,000}$
= 0.1025
= 10.25%

13. Compounded quarterly = 4 periods in year 1

$\dfrac{6\%}{4} = 1.25\%$ per period

Table value = 1.06136

Effective rate = 1.06136 − 1

$\qquad\qquad$ = 0.06136

$\qquad\qquad$ = 6.14%

14. Compounded quarterly = 4 periods in 1 year

$\dfrac{12\% \text{ annual}}{4} = 3\%$ per period

Table value $\;=$ 1.12551

Effective rate = 1.12551 − 1

$\qquad\qquad$ = 0.12551

$\qquad\qquad$ = 12.55%

15. 20 days; $6\frac{3}{4}\%$ annual rate

Table value = 0.3705135

$\dfrac{\$2,500}{\$100} = 25$ \$100-units

Compound interest = 25(0.3705135)

$\qquad\qquad\qquad\quad$ = \$9.26

16. 30 days; 6.25% annual rate

Table value = 0.5149761

$\dfrac{\$1,500}{\$100} = 15$ \$100-units

Compound interest = 15(0.5149761)

$\qquad\qquad\qquad\quad$ = \$7.72

17. 15 days; 8.5% annual rate

Table value = 0.3498851

$\dfrac{\$8,000}{\$100} = 80$ \$100-units

Compound interest = 80(0.3498851)

$\qquad\qquad\qquad\quad$ = \$27.99

18. 180 days; 8% annual rate

Table value = 4.0236126

$\dfrac{\$8,000}{\$100} = 80$ \$100 units

Compound interest = 80 (4.0236126) = \$321.89

SELF-CHECK 10.2

1. Present value $= \dfrac{\$2,500}{1 + 0.11} = \dfrac{\$2,500}{1.11} = \$2,252.25$

2. $\dfrac{\$8,500}{1.075} = \$7,906.98$

3. $\dfrac{\$21,000}{1.079} = \$19,462.47$

4. $\dfrac{\$6,999}{1.083} = \$6,462.60$

5. 3 periods; 8% per period

Table value = 0.79383

\$2,000(0.79383) = \$1,587.66

6. $3 \times 4 = 12$ periods

$6\% \div 4 = 1\frac{1}{2}\%$ per period

Table value = 0.83639

\$1,500(0.83639) = \$1,254.59

7. $4 \times 4 = 16$ periods

$10\% \div 4 = 2\frac{1}{2}\%$ per period

Table value = 0.67362

\$10,000(0.67362) = \$6,736.20

8. 5 periods; 8% per period

Table value = 0.68058

\$20,000(0.68058) = \$13,611.60

11

Annuities and Sinking Funds

11.1 Future Value of an Annuity

1 Find the future value of an ordinary annuity using the simple interest formula method.

2 Find the future value of an ordinary annuity using a $1.00 ordinary annuity future value table.

3 Find the future value of an annuity due using the simple interest formula method.

4 Find the future value of an annuity due using a $1.00 ordinary annuity future value table.

11.2 Sinking Funds and the Present Value of an Annuity

1 Find the sinking fund payment using a $1.00 sinking fund payment table.

2 Find the present value of an ordinary annuity using a $1.00 ordinary annuity present value table.

Good Decisions through Teamwork

The biggest, smartest companies are using their economic sophistication and the clout of their huge retirement funds to negotiate low-cost deals, while smaller and less aggressive employers often unwittingly agree to high fees, which are paid out of their workers' 401(k) savings. Administration fees cover investment management, record-keeping, issuing statements, and complying with federal regulations; with more than 90% of these costs paying for investment management.

When 401(k)s were first established, the employer typically paid all or most of the administrative fees, but recently workers are forced to pay a growing portion of these fees, which have also steadily increased in cost per $100. Workers typically do not even know what fees they pay because federal law does not require disclosure on the periodic statements they receive. Although most U.S. workers have about $1.00 per $100 taken from their 401(k) account in fees, this can vary from 0¢ to $2.00 per $100. Large corporations can easily negotiate a 5¢ per $100 fee, while the small to medium size firms are the ones that may not be able to negotiate a good deal for their employees.

The difference between paying a nickel and paying $2.00 out of every $100 may seem small, but over time (and many compounding periods) the difference is enormous! For example, after 30 years the worker who saves $5,000 annually in a 401(k) stocks fund earning 10.9% annual interest compounded quarterly and pays the nickel fee will have more than $1 million. That is 53% more than someone in the same situation who pays fees at the $2.00 rate! Leaders of the mutual fund industry, large trade organizations, and consultants who advise small companies on retirement plans have urged the Labor Department to require full disclosure of 401(k) funds' administrative fees.

Your team will investigate and report on the 401(k) plan(s) offered through three different employers: (1) the largest corporate employer within a 100-mile radius of your home, (2) an employer in your city with fewer than 10 employees, and (3) the educational institution at which you are using this course textbook. For each employer, include

- the name and type of each 401(k) fund offered,
- the fund's cost per $100 paid by the worker,
- the fund's rate of return for the previous year, and
- whether the fund's administrative fee rate is disclosed to employees.

So far we have discussed interest accumulated from one *lump sum investment*. But an individual or business may also make *periodic investments*, or payments, to a compound interest account. If the payment each period is the same, and the rate of interest does not change, the payment is called an **annuity** payment or **sinking fund** payment. The growing account is called an annuity or sinking fund. Retirement funds, saving for a college education or vacation, a company putting away money periodically now to pay for new equipment and buildings or to retire a bond debt in the future are all examples of an annuity or sinking fund.

11.1 Future Value of an Annuity

1 Find the future value of an ordinary annuity using the simple interest formula method.

2 Find the future value of an ordinary annuity using a $1.00 ordinary annuity future value table.

3 Find the future value of an annuity due using the simple interest formula method.

4 Find the future value of an annuity due using a $1.00 ordinary annuity future value table.

An annuity paid over a guaranteed number of periods, is an **annuity certain.** An annuity paid over an uncertain number of periods, is a **contingent annuity.** A mortgage payment is an annuity certain, whereas a life insurance premium is a contingent annuity.

We can also categorize annuities according to when payment is made. For an **ordinary annuity,** payment is made at the *end* of the period. For an **annuity due,** payment is made at the *beginning* of the period.

1 Find the future value of an ordinary annuity using the simple interest formula method.

Finding the future value of an annuity is similar to finding the future value of a lump sum. The significant difference is that, for each interest period, more principal—the annuity payment—is added to the amount on which interest is earned. Nonetheless, the simple interest formula $I = PRT$ is still the basis of calculating interest.

HOW TO Find the Future Value of an Ordinary Annuity Using the Simple Interest Formula Method

1. Find the first end-of-period principal.

> First end-of-period principal = annuity payment

2. For each remaining period in turn, find the next end-of-period principal:
   (a) Multiply the previous end-of-period principal by the sum of 1 and the period interest rate.
   (b) Add the product from step 2a and the annuity payment.

> End-of-period principal = previous end-of-period principal
> × (1 + period interest rate) + annuity payment

3. Identify the last end-of-period principal as the future value.

> Future value = last end-of-period principal

For an ordinary annuity, no interest accumulates on the annuity payment during the month in which it is paid because the payment is made at the *end* of the period. For the first period, this means no interest accumulates at all.

EXAMPLE   What is the future value of an annual ordinary annuity of $1,000 for three years at 8% annual interest?

The period interest rate is 0.08. The annuity is $1,000.

$$\text{End-of-year value} = (\text{previous end-of-year value})(1 + 0.08) + 1,000$$

$$\text{End-of-year 1} = \$1,000.00 \quad \text{\textbf{No interest earned the first year.}}$$

$$\text{End-of-year 2} = \$1,000.00\ (1.08) + \$1,000.00$$

$$= \$1,080.00 + \$1,000.00$$

$$= \$2,080.00$$

$$\text{End-of-year 3} = \$2,080.00\ (1.08) + \$1,000.00$$

$$= \$2,246.40 + \$1,000.00$$

$$= \$3,246.40$$

The future value is $3,246.40.

To find the total amount of interest earned, subtract the total of the annuity payments from the future value. In the previous example, three payments of $1,000 each were made for a total of $3,000. The interest is $3,246.40 − $3,000 or $246.40.

2   Find the future value of an ordinary annuity using a $1.00 ordinary annuity future value table.

Calculating the future value of an ordinary annuity can become quite tedious if the number of periods is large. For example, a monthly annuity such as a monthly savings plan running for five years has 60 periods and 60 calculation sequences. For this reason, most businesspeople rely on prepared tables or computers.

? HOW TO Find the Future Value of an Ordinary Annuity Using a $1.00 Ordinary Annuity Future Value Table

1. Select the periods row corresponding to the number of interest periods.
2. Select the rate-per-period column corresponding to the period interest rate.
3. Locate the value in the cell where the periods row intersects the rate-per-period column.
4. Multiply the annuity payment by the table value from step 3.

Future value = annuity payment × table value

EXAMPLE   Use Table 11-1 to find the future value of a semiannual ordinary annuity of $6,000 for five years at 12% annual interest, compounded semiannually.

$$5 \text{ years} \times 2 \text{ periods per year} = 10 \text{ periods}$$

$$\frac{12\% \text{ annual interest rate}}{2 \text{ periods per year}} = 6\% \text{ period interest rate}$$

Table 11-1 value for 10 periods at 6% is 13.181.

$$\text{Future value of annuity} = \text{annuity payment} \times \text{table value}$$

$$= \$6{,}000 \times 13.181$$

$$= \$79{,}086$$

The future value of the ordinary annuity is \$79,086.

Table 11-1 Future Value of \$1.00 Ordinary Annuity

	Rate per Period									
Periods	2%	3%	4%	5%	6%	7%	8%	9%	10%	12%
1	1.000	1.000	1.000	1.000	1.000	1.000	1.000	1.000	1.000	1.000
2	2.020	2.030	2.040	2.050	2.060	2.070	2.080	2.090	2.100	2.120
3	3.060	3.091	3.122	3.153	3.184	3.215	3.246	3.278	3.310	3.374
4	4.122	4.184	4.246	4.310	4.375	4.440	4.506	4.573	4.641	4.779
5	5.204	5.309	5.416	5.526	5.637	5.751	5.867	5.985	6.105	6.353
6	6.308	6.468	6.633	6.802	6.975	7.153	7.336	7.523	7.716	8.115
7	7.434	7.662	7.898	8.142	8.394	8.654	8.923	9.200	9.487	10.089
8	8.583	8.892	9.214	9.549	9.897	10.260	10.637	11.028	11.436	12.300
9	9.755	10.159	10.583	11.027	11.491	11.978	12.488	13.021	13.579	14.776
10	10.950	11.464	12.006	12.578	13.181	13.816	14.487	15.193	15.937	17.549
11	12.169	12.808	13.486	14.207	14.972	15.784	16.645	17.560	18.531	20.655
12	13.412	14.192	15.026	15.917	16.870	17.888	18.977	20.141	21.384	24.133
13	14.680	15.618	16.627	17.713	18.882	20.141	21.495	22.523	24.523	28.029
14	15.974	17.086	18.292	19.599	21.015	22.550	24.215	26.019	27.975	32.393
15	17.293	18.599	20.024	21.579	23.276	25.129	27.152	29.361	31.772	37.280
16	18.639	20.157	21.825	23.657	25.673	27.888	30.324	33.003	35.950	42.753
17	20.012	21.762	23.698	25.840	28.213	30.840	33.750	36.974	40.545	48.884
18	21.412	23.414	25.645	28.132	30.906	33.999	37.450	41.301	45.599	55.750
19	22.841	25.117	27.671	30.539	33.760	37.379	41.446	46.018	51.159	63.440
20	24.297	26.870	29.778	33.066	36.786	40.995	45.762	51.160	57.275	72.052
21	25.783	28.676	31.969	35.719	39.993	44.865	50.423	56.765	64.002	81.699
22	27.299	30.537	34.248	38.505	43.392	49.006	55.457	62.873	71.403	92.503
23	28.845	32.453	36.618	41.430	46.996	53.436	60.893	69.532	79.543	104.603
24	30.422	34.426	39.083	44.502	50.816	58.177	66.765	76.790	88.497	118.155
25	32.030	36.459	41.646	47.727	54.865	63.249	73.106	84.701	98.347	133.334
26	33.671	38.553	44.312	51.113	59.156	68.676	79.954	93.324	109.182	150.334
27	35.344	40.710	47.084	54.669	63.706	74.484	87.351	102.723	121.100	169.374
28	37.051	42.931	49.968	58.403	68.528	80.698	95.339	112.968	134.210	190.699
29	38.792	45.219	52.966	62.323	73.640	87.347	103.966	124.135	148.631	214.583
30	40.568	47.575	56.085	66.439	79.058	94.461	113.283	136.308	164.494	241.333
35	49.994	60.462	73.652	90.320	111.435	138.237	172.317	215.711	271.024	431.663
40	60.402	75.401	95.026	120.800	154.762	199.635	259.057	337.882	442.593	767.091
45	71.893	92.720	121.029	159.700	212.744	285.749	386.506	525.859	718.905	1358.230
50	84.579	112.797	152.667	209.348	290.336	406.529	573.770	815.084	1163.909	2400.018
55	98.587	136.072	191.159	272.713	394.172	575.929	848.923	1260.092	1880.591	4236.005
60	114.052	163.053	237.991	353.584	533.128	813.520	1253.213	1944.792	3034.816	7471.641
65	131.126	194.333	294.968	456.798	719.083	1146.755	1847.248	2998.288	4893.707	13173.937
70	149.978	230.594	364.290	588.529	967.932	1614.134	2720.080	4619.223	7887.470	23223.332
75	170.792	272.631	448.631	756.654	1300.949	2269.657	4002.557	7113.232	12708.954	40933.799
80	193.772	321.363	551.245	971.229	1746.600	3189.063	5886.935	10950.574	20474.002	72145.693
85	219.144	377.857	676.090	1245.087	2342.982	4478.576	8655.706	16854.800	32979.690	127151.714
90	247.157	443.349	827.983	1594.607	3141.075	6287.185	12723.939	25939.184	53120.226	224091.119
95	278.085	519.272	1012.785	2040.694	4209.104	8823.854	18701.507	39916.635	85556.760	394931.472
100	312.232	607.288	1237.624	2610.025	5638.368	12381.662	27484.516	61422.675	137796.123	696010.548

Table values show the future value, or accumulated amount of the investment and interest, of a \$1.00 investment for a given number of periods at a given rate per period. Table values can be generated

using the formula: FV of \$1.00 per period $= \left(\dfrac{(1 + R)^N - 1}{R} \right)$, when FV is the future value, R is the rate

per period, and N is the number of periods.

To calculate the future value of an ordinary annuity or to verify the table-value calculations, use the formula

$$FV = P\left(\frac{(1 + R)^N - 1}{R}\right),$$ where FV is future value, P is the annuity payment, R is the

rate per period, and N is the number of periods. The value in the parentheses represents the table value.

To verify the results of the preceding example

$$FV = 6000\left(\frac{(1.06)^{10} - 1}{0.06}\right)$$

Make the calculations inside the parentheses first.

$\boxed{AC}$ 1.06 $\boxed{x^y}$ 10 $\boxed{=}$ $- 1$ $\boxed{=}$ $\boxed{\div}$ $.06$ $\boxed{=}$ $\boxed{\times}$ 6000 $\boxed{=}$ $\Rightarrow 79084.76965$ or $79,084.77

The slight variation in the future value of the annuity is due to the increased accuracy when using full calculator values in calculations.

How much interest was earned on the annuity in the previous example? Ten payments were made at $6,000 each for a total of $60,000. So, the total interest earned was $79,086 − $60,000 or $17,086.

 3 Find the future value of an annuity due using the simple interest formula method.

Because an annuity due is paid at the *beginning* of each period, rather than at the end, the annuity due payment earns interest throughout the period in which it is paid. To find the interest earned for any given period, the annuity payment is added to the previous accumulation and the sum is multiplied by the period interest rate. The future value of an annuity due, then, is greater than the future value of the corresponding ordinary annuity: given the same number of periods, the same period interest rate, and the same annuity payment, the difference in the future values of an ordinary annuity and an annuity due is exactly one period's worth of interest on what amounts to the future value of the ordinary annuity.

 HOW TO Find the Future Value of an Annuity Due Using the Simple Interest Formula Method

1. Find the first end-of-period principal: multiply the annuity payment by the sum of 1 and the period interest rate.

First end-of-period principal = annuity payment × (1 + period interest rate)

2. For each remaining period in turn, find the next end-of-period principal:
   (a) Add the previous end-of-period principal and the annuity payment.
   (b) Multiply the sum from step 2a by the sum of 1 and the period interest rate.

End-of-period principal = (previous end-of-period principal
                             + annuity payment) × (1 + period interest rate)

3. Identify the last end-of-period principal as the future value.

Future value = last end-of-period principal

EXAMPLE   What is the future value of a quarterly annuity due of $100 for one year at 10% annual interest, compounded quarterly? Find the total investment and the total interest earned.

The annuity is $100; the period interest rate is:

$$\frac{10\% \text{ annual interest rate}}{4 \text{ periods per year}} = 2.5\% = 0.025 \text{ period interest rate}$$

End-of-quarter value = (previous end-of-quarter + $100)(1 + 0.025)

End-of-quarter 1 = $100(1.025)   **The annuity earns interest during the first period.**

= $102.50

End-of-quarter 2 = ($102.50 + $100)(1.025)   **Second payment is made.**

= $202.50(1.025)

= $207.56

End-of-quarter 3 = ($207.56 + $100)(1.025)   **Third payment is made.**

= $307.56(1.025)

= $315.25

End-of-quarter 4 = ($315.25 + $100)(1.025)   **Fourth payment is made.**

= $415.25(1.025)

= $425.63 (future value of annuity due)

Total investment = investment per period × total periods

= $100 × 4

= $400

Total interest earned = future value − total investment

= $425.63 − $400

= $25.63

The future value of the annuity due is $425.63, the total investment is $400, and the total interest earned is $25.63.

 TIP! **Ordinary Annuity versus Annuity Due**

One difference between an ordinary annuity and an annuity due is whether you make the first payment immediately or at the end of the first period.

If you are establishing your own annuity plan through a savings account, you begin your annuity with your first payment or deposit (annuity due).

If you are entering a payroll deduction plan, a 401(k) plan, or an annuity plan with an insurance company, you may complete the paperwork to establish the plan, and the first payment will be made at a later time.

 Find the future value of an annuity due using a $1.00 ordinary annuity future value table.

Because the future value of an annuity due is so closely related to the future value of the corresponding ordinary annuity, we can also use Table 11-1 to find the future valve of an annuity due. An annuity due accumulates interest one period more than does the ordinary annuity, but has the same number of payments. Thus, we adjust Table 11-1 values by multiplying by the sum of 1 and the period interest rate.

 HOW TO Find the Future Value of an Annuity Due Using a $1.00 Ordinary Annuity Future Value Table

1. Select the periods row corresponding to the number of interest periods.
2. Select the rate-per-period column corresponding to the period interest rate.
3. Locate the value in the cell where the periods row intersects the rate-per-period column.
4. Multiply the annuity payment by the table value from step 3 and the sum of 1 and the period interest rate.

Future value = annuity payment × table value
× (1 + period interest rate)

EXAMPLE   Use Table 11-1 to find the future value of a quarterly annuity due of $2,800 for four years at 12% annual interest, compounded quarterly.

$$4 \text{ years} \times 4 \text{ periods per year} = 16 \text{ periods}$$

$$\frac{12\% \text{ annual interest rate}}{4 \text{ periods per year}} = 3\% \text{ period interest rate}$$

The Table 11-1 value for 16 periods at 3% is 20.157.

$$\text{Future value} = \text{annuity payment} \times \text{table value} \times (1 + \text{period interest rate})$$

$$= \$2,800 \times 20.157 \times 1.03$$

$$= \$58,132.79$$

The future value is $58,132.79.

Calculate the Future Value of an Annuity Due Using a Formula

To calculate the future value of an annuity due or to verify the calculations using a table value, use the formula $FV = P\left(\dfrac{(1 + R)^N - 1}{R}\right)(1 + R)$, where FV is future value, P is the annuity payment, R is the rate per period, and N is the number of periods. The value in the first set of parentheses represents the table value.

To verify the results of the previous example,

$$FV = \$2,800\left(\frac{(1.03)^{16} - 1}{0.03}\right)(1.03)$$

Start by making the calculations in the first set of parentheses.

$\boxed{\text{AC}}$ 1.03 $\boxed{x^y}$ 16 $\boxed{=}$ $\boxed{-}$ 1 $\boxed{=}$ $\boxed{\div}$ .03 $\boxed{=}$ $\boxed{\times}$ 1.03 $=$ $\boxed{\times}$ 2800 $\boxed{=}$ $\Rightarrow$ 58132.44568

What is the total interest earned on the annuity in the previous example? Sixteen payments of $2,800 each were made for a total investment of $44,800. The total interest earned was $58,132.79 − $44,800 or $13,332.79.

EXAMPLE Sarah Smith wants to select the best annuity plan. She plans to invest a total of $8,000 over two-years' time at 8% annual interest. Annuity 1 is a quarterly ordinary annuity of $1,000; interest is compounded quarterly. Annuity 2 is a semiannual annuity of $2,000; interest is compounded semiannually. Annuity 3 is a quarterly annuity due of $1,000; interest is compounded quarterly. Annuity 4 is a semiannual annuity due of $2,000; interest is compounded semiannually. Which annuity yields the greatest future value?

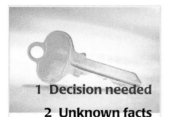

1 Decision needed

Which annuity yields the greatest future value?

2 Unknown facts

Future value of each annuity

3 Known facts

Annuity 1: Ordinary annuity of $1,000 quarterly for two years at 8% annual interest, compounded quarterly
Annuity 2: Ordinary annuity of $2,000 semiannually for two years at 8% annual interest, compounded semiannually
Annuity 3: Annuity due of $1,000 quarterly for two years at 8% annual interest, compounded quarterly
Annuity 4: Annuity due of $2,000 semiannually for two years at 8% annual interest, compounded semiannually.

4 Relationships

Future value of ordinary annuity = annuity payment × Table 11-1 value
Future value of annuity due = annuity payment × Table 11-1 value × (1 + period interest rate)
Number of periods = years × periods per year
Period interest rate = $\dfrac{\text{annual interest rate}}{\text{periods per year}}$

5 Estimation

An annuity due yields a greater future value than a corresponding ordinary annuity since the annuity payment earns interest during the period in which it is paid. So annuity 3 should be better than annuity 1, and annuity 4 should be better than annuity 2.

6 Calculation

Annuity 1
Number of periods = years × periods per year
$$= 2 \times 4$$
$$= 8$$
Period interest rate = $\dfrac{\text{annual interest rate}}{\text{periods per year}}$
$$= \dfrac{8\%}{4} = 2\%$$
$$= 0.02$$
Table value = 8.583
Future value = annuity payment × table value
Future value = ($1,000)(8.583)
$$= \$8,583$$

Annuity 2
Number of periods = years × periods per year
$$= 2 \times 2$$
$$= 4$$
Period interest rate = $\dfrac{\text{annual interest rate}}{\text{periods per year}}$
$$= \dfrac{8\%}{2} = 4\%$$
$$= 0.04$$

Table value = 4.246
Future value = annuity payment × table value
= $2,000 × 4.246
= $8,492

Annuity 3

The number of periods and period interest rate are the same as those for annuity 1.
Future value = annuity payment × table value × (1 + period interest rate)
= $1,000 × 8.583 × 1.02
= $8,754.66

Annuity 4

The number of periods and period interest rate are the same as those for annuity 2.
Future value = annuity payment × table value × (1 + period interest rate)
= $2,000 × 4.246 × 1.04
= $8,831.68

7 Interpretation **The future values for the four annuities are $8,583, $8,492, $8,754.66, and $8,831.68.**

8 Decision made **Annuity 4, with the larger annuity due payment, yields the greatest future value.** Notice that the ordinary annuity with fewer periods per year yields the least future value of all four annuities. If the total investment is the same, the number of years is the same, and the annual rate of interest is the same, any annuity due yields a larger future value than any corresponding ordinary annuity. The annuity due with the largest payment is the most profitable, while the ordinary annuity paid most frequently is the most profitable ordinary annuity.

SELF-CHECK 11.1

 Use the simple interest formula method for exercises 1–4.

1. Find the future value of an ordinary annuity of $3,000 annually for two years at 9% annual interest. Find the total interest earned.

2. Len and Sharron Smith are saving money for their daughter Heather to attend college. They set aside an ordinary annuity of $4,000 annually for two years at 7% annual interest. How much will Heather have for college when she graduates from high school in two years? Find the total interest earned.

3. Harry Taylor plans to pay an ordinary annuity of $5,000 annually for three years so he can take a year's sabbatical to study for a master's degree in business. The annual rate of interest is 8%. How much will Harry have at the end of three years? How much interest will he earn on the investment?

4. Scott Martin is planning to establish a small business to provide consulting services in computer networking. He is committed to an ordinary annuity of $3,000 annually at 8.5% annual interest. How much will Scott have to establish the business after three years? How much interest will he earn?

2 *Use Table 11-1 for exercises 5–9.*

5. Find the future value of an ordinary annuity of $6,500 semiannually for seven years at 10% annual interest, compounded semiannually. How much was invested? How much interest was earned?

6. Pat Lechleiter pays an ordinary annuity of $2,500 quarterly at 8% annual interest, compounded quarterly, to establish supplemental income for retirement. How much will Pat have available at the end of five years?

7. Latanya Brown established an ordinary annuity of $1,000 annually at 7% annual interest. What is the future value of the annuity after 15 years? How much of her own money will Latanya have invested during this time period? By how much will her investment have grown?

8. You invest in an ordinary annuity of $500 annually at 8% annual interest. Find the future value of the annuity at the end of 10 years. How much have you invested? How much interest has your annuity earned?

9. You invest in an ordinary annuity of $2,000 annually at 8% annual interest. What is the future value of the annuity at the end of five years? How much have you invested? How much interest has your annuity earned?

10. Make a chart comparing your results for exercises 8 and 9. Use these headings: Years, Total Investment, Total Interest. What general conclusion might you draw about effective investment strategy?

3 *Use the simple interest formula method for exercises 11–14.*

11. Find the future value of an annuity due of $12,000 annually for three years at 14% annual interest. How much was invested? How much interest was earned?

12. Bernard McGhee has decided to establish an annuity due of $2,500 annually for 15 years at 7.2% annual interest. How much is the annuity due worth after two years? How much was invested? How much interest was earned?

13. Find the future value of an annuity due of $7,800 annually for two years at 8.1% annual interest. Find the total amount invested. Find the interest.

14. Find the future value of an annuity due of $400 annually for two years at 6.8% annual interest compounded annually.

4 *Use Table 11-1 for exercises 15–18.*

15. Find the future value of a quarterly annuity due of $4,400 for three years at 8% annual interest, compounded quarterly. How much was invested? How much interest was earned?

16. Find the future value of an annuity due of $750 semi-annually for four years at 8% annual interest, compounded semiannually. What is the total investment? What is the interest?

17. Which annuity earns more interest: an annuity due of $300 quarterly for one year at 8% annual interest, compounded quarterly, or an annuity due of $600 semiannually for one year at 8% annual interest, compounded semiannually?

18. You have carefully examined your budget and determined that you can manage to set aside $250 per year. So you set up an annuity due of $250 annually at 7% annual interest. How much will you have contributed after 20 years? What is the future value of your annuity after 20 years? How much interest will you earn?

11.2 Sinking Funds and the Present Value of an Annuity

1 Find the sinking fund payment using a $1.00 sinking fund payment table.

2 Find the present value of an ordinary annuity using a $1.00 ordinary annuity present value table.

Businesses and individuals often use sinking funds to accumulate a desired amount of money by the end of a certain period of time to pay off a financial obligation, for a vacation or college fund, or to reach a specific goal such as retiring a bond issue or paying for equipment replacement and modernization. Essentially, a **sinking fund** is payment into an ordinary annuity to yield a desired future value.

In general, you are finding the *future value of an annuity* when you know how much you can set aside per period at a given rate and you want to know how much you will have accumulated after a certain amount of time. You are finding the *sinking fund payment* when you know in advance how much future value you want after a certain amount of time at a given rate and you want to know how much you should set aside each period to reach that goal.

1 Find the sinking fund payment using a $1.00 sinking fund payment table.

A sinking fund payment is made at the *end* of each period, so a sinking fund payment is an ordinary annuity payment. These payments, along with the interest, accumulate over a period of time in order to provide the desired future value.

To calculate the *payment* required to yield a desired future value, use Table 11-2.

The procedure for locating a value in Table 11-2 is similar to the procedure used for Table 11-1.

? HOW TO Find the Sinking Fund Payment Using a $1.00 Sinking Fund Payment Table

1. Select the periods row corresponding to the number of interest periods.
2. Select the rate-per-period column corresponding to the period interest rate.
3. Locate the value in the cell where the periods row intersects the rate-per-period column.
4. Multiply the table value from step 3 by the desired future value.

Sinking fund payment = future value × Table 11-2 value

Table 11-2 $1.00 Sinking Fund Payments

	Rate per Period						
Periods	**1%**	**2%**	**3%**	**4%**	**6%**	**8%**	**12%**
1	1.0000000	1.0000000	1.0000000	1.0000000	1.0000000	1.0000000	1.0000000
2	0.4975124	0.4950495	0.4926108	0.4901961	0.4854369	0.4807692	0.4716981
3	0.3300221	0.3267547	0.3235304	0.3203485	0.3141098	0.3080335	0.2963490
4	0.2462881	0.2426238	0.2390271	0.2354901	0.2285915	0.2219208	0.2092344
5	0.1960398	0.1921584	0.1883546	0.1846271	0.1773964	0.1704565	0.1574097
6	0.1625484	0.1585258	0.1545975	0.1507619	0.1433626	0.1363154	0.1232257
7	0.1386283	0.1345120	0.1305064	0.1266096	0.1191350	0.1120724	0.0991177
8	0.1206903	0.1165098	0.1124564	0.1085278	0.1010359	0.0940148	0.0813028
9	0.1067404	0.1025154	0.0984339	0.0944930	0.0870222	0.0800797	0.0676789
10	0.0955821	0.0913265	0.0872305	0.0832909	0.0758680	0.0690295	0.0569842
11	0.0864541	0.0821779	0.0780775	0.0741490	0.0667929	0.0600763	0.0484154
12	0.0788488	0.0745596	0.0704621	0.0675522	0.0592770	0.0526950	0.0414368
13	0.0724148	0.0681184	0.0670295	0.0601437	0.0529601	0.0465218	0.0356772
14	0.0669012	0.0626020	0.0585263	0.0546690	0.0475849	0.0412969	0.0308712
15	0.0621238	0.0578255	0.0537666	0.0499411	0.0429628	0.0368295	0.0268242
16	0.0579446	0.0536501	0.0496109	0.0458200	0.0389521	0.0329769	0.0233900
17	0.0542581	0.0499698	0.0459525	0.0421985	0.0354448	0.0296294	0.0204567
18	0.0509821	0.0467021	0.0427087	0.0389933	0.0323565	0.0267021	0.0179373
19	0.0480518	0.0437818	0.0398139	0.0361386	0.0296209	0.0241276	0.0157630
20	0.0454153	0.0411567	0.0372157	0.0335818	0.0271846	0.0218522	0.0138788
25	0.0354068	0.0312204	0.0274279	0.0240120	0.0182267	0.0136788	0.0075000
30	0.0287481	0.0246499	0.0210193	0.0178301	0.0126489	0.0088274	0.0041437
40	0.0204556	0.0165558	0.0132624	0.0105235	0.0064615	0.0038602	0.0013036
50	0.0155127	0.0118232	0.0088655	0.0065502	0.0034443	0.0017429	0.0004167

Table values show the sinking fund payment earning a given rate for a given number of periods so that the accumulated amount at the end of the time will be $1.00. The formula for generating the table values is $TV = \dfrac{R}{(1 + R)^N - 1}$ where TV is the table value, R is the rate per period, and N is the number of periods or payments.

EXAMPLE   Use Table 11-2 to find the annual sinking fund payment required to accumulate $140,000 in 12 years at 8% annual interest.

$$12 \text{ years} \times 1 \text{ period per year} = 12 \text{ periods}$$

$$\text{interest rate} \quad \frac{8\% \text{ annual interest rate}}{1 \text{ period per year}} = 8\% \text{ period}$$

The Table 11-2 value for 12 periods at 8% is 0.0526950.

$$\text{sinking fund payment} = \text{desired future value} \times \text{table factor}$$

$$= \$140,000 \times 0.0526950$$

$$= \$7,377.30$$

A sinking fund payment of $7,377.30 is required at the end of each year for 12 years at 8% to yield the desired $140,000.

Calculate the Sinking Fund Payment Using a Formula

A scientific, business, or graphing calculator can be used to find the sinking fund payment using the formula $P = FV\left(\dfrac{R}{(1 + R)^N - 1}\right)$, where P is the sinking fund payment, FV is the future value of the sinking fund, R is the rate per period, and N is the number of periods. The value in the parentheses represents the table value.

To verify the results of the preceding example,

$$P = 140{,}000\left(\frac{0.08}{(1.08)^{12} - 1}\right)$$

Make the calculations inside the parentheses first.

$$\boxed{AC}\; .08 \;\boxed{\div}\;\boxed{(}\;1.08\;\boxed{x^y}\;12\;\boxed{-}\;1\;\boxed{)}\;\boxed{=}\;\boxed{\times}\;140000\;\boxed{=}\;\Rightarrow 7377.302369$$

EXAMPLE Find the total interest earned on the sinking fund in the previous example.

$$FV = \$140{,}000 \qquad \text{Number of payments} = 12$$

$$\text{Total investment} \quad = \text{amount of payment} \times 12$$

$$= \$7{,}377.30 \times 12$$

$$= \$88{,}527.60$$

$$\text{Total interest earned} = \$140{,}000 - \$88{,}527.60$$

$$= \mathbf{\$51{,}472.40}$$

2 Find the present value of an ordinary annuity using a $1.00 ordinary annuity present value table.

An annuity allows you to make periodic payments that will accumulate with interest over a period of time to reach a future value. For comparative purposes a business or individual may want to know what lump sum investment with compound interest made now at the same rate for the same length of time would yield the same future value. The **present value of an annuity** is the lump sum that must be invested now to achieve the future value of the annuity started now.

Table 11-3 Present Value of a $1.00 Ordinary Annuity

Periods	2%	3%	4%	5%	6%	7%	8%	9%	10%	12%
1	0.980	0.971	0.962	0.952	0.943	0.935	0.926	0.917	0.909	0.893
2	1.942	1.913	1.886	1.859	1.833	1.808	1.783	1.759	1.736	1.690
3	2.884	2.829	2.775	2.723	2.673	2.624	2.577	2.531	2.487	2.402
4	3.808	3.717	3.630	3.546	3.465	3.387	3.312	3.240	3.170	3.037
5	4.713	4.580	4.452	4.329	4.212	4.100	3.993	3.890	3.791	3.605
6	5.601	5.417	5.242	5.076	4.917	4.767	4.623	4.486	4.355	4.111
7	6.472	6.230	6.002	5.786	5.582	5.389	5.206	5.033	4.868	4.564
8	7.325	7.020	6.733	6.463	6.210	5.971	5.747	5.535	5.335	4.968
9	8.162	7.786	7.435	7.108	6.802	6.515	6.247	5.995	5.759	5.328
10	8.983	8.530	8.111	7.722	7.360	7.024	6.710	6.418	6.145	5.650
11	9.787	9.253	8.760	8.306	7.887	7.499	7.139	6.805	6.495	5.938
12	10.575	9.954	9.385	8.863	8.384	7.943	7.536	7.161	6.814	6.194
13	11.348	10.635	9.986	9.394	8.853	8.358	7.904	7.487	7.103	6.424
14	12.106	11.296	10.563	9.899	9.295	8.745	8.244	7.786	7.367	6.628
15	12.849	11.939	11.118	10.380	9.712	9.108	8.559	8.061	7.606	6.811
16	13.578	12.561	11.652	10.838	10.106	9.447	8.851	8.313	7.824	6.974
17	14.292	13.166	12.166	11.274	10.477	9.763	9.122	8.544	8.022	7.102
18	14.992	13.754	12.659	11.690	10.828	10.059	9.372	8.756	8.201	7.250
19	15.678	14.324	13.134	12.085	11.158	10.336	9.604	8.950	8.365	7.366
20	16.351	14.877	13.590	12.462	11.470	10.594	9.818	9.129	8.514	7.469
25	19.523	17.413	15.622	14.094	12.783	11.654	10.675	9.823	9.077	7.843
30	22.396	19.600	17.292	15.372	13.765	12.409	11.258	10.274	9.427	8.055
40	27.355	23.115	19.793	17.159	15.046	13.332	11.925	10.757	9.779	8.244
50	31.424	25.730	21.482	18.256	15.762	13.801	12.233	10.962	9.915	8.304

Table values show the present value of a $1.00 ordinary annuity, or the lump sum amount that, invested now, yields the same compounded amount as an annuity of $1.00 at a given rate per period for a given number of periods. The formula for generating the table values is $TV = \dfrac{(1 + R)^N - 1}{R(1 + R)^N}$ where TV is the table value, R is the rate per period, and N is the number of periods.

To find the present value of an annuity, we use Table 11-3: locate the table value for the given number of periods and the given rate per period and multiply by the annuity payment.

 HOW TO Find the Present Value of an Annuity Using a Table Value.

1. Use a present value table to locate the table value for the given number of periods and the given rate per period.
2. Multiply the table value times the periodic annuity payment.

Present value of annuity = periodic annuity payment × table value.

EXAMPLE Use Table 11-3 to find the present value of a semiannual ordinary annuity of $3,000 for seven years at 12% annual interest, compounded semiannually.

$$7 \text{ years} \times 2 \text{ periods per year} = 14 \text{ periods}$$

$$\frac{12\% \text{ annual interest}}{2 \text{ periods per year}} = 6\% \text{ period interest rate}$$

The Table 11-3 value for 14 periods at 6% is 9.295.

$$\text{Present value of annuity} = \text{annuity payment} \times \text{table factor}$$
$$= \$3,000 \times 9.295$$
$$= \$27,885$$

By investing \$27,885 now at 12% interest, compounded semiannually, you will accumulate after seven years the same amount of money as you would if you paid an annuity of \$3,000 twice a year instead.

Calculate the Present Value of an Annuity Using a Formula

To calculate the present value of an ordinary annuity or to verify the calculations using a table value, use the formula $PV = P\left(\dfrac{(1 + R)^N - 1}{R(1 + R)^N}\right)$, where PV is present value, P is the annuity, R is the rate per period, and N is the number of periods. The value in the parentheses represents the table value. A scientific, business, or graphing calculator is needed.
To verify the results of the preceding example

$$PV = 3000 \left(\frac{(1.06)^{14} - 1}{0.06(1.06)^{14}}\right)$$

Make the calculations inside the parentheses first.

$\boxed{AC}\,\boxed{(}\,\boxed{(}\,1.06\,\boxed{x^y}\,14 - 1\,\boxed{)}\,\div\,\boxed{(}\,.06\,\boxed{\times}\,1.06\,\boxed{x^y}\,14\,\boxed{)}\,\boxed{=}\,\boxed{\times}\,3000\,\boxed{=} \Rightarrow 27884.95178$

Additional parentheses could be used.

$\boxed{AC}\,\boxed{(}\,\boxed{(}\,\boxed{(}\,1.06\,\boxed{x^y}\,14 - 1\,\boxed{)}\,\div\,\boxed{(}\,.06\,\boxed{\times}\,1.06\,\boxed{x^y}\,14\,\boxed{)}\,\boxed{)}\,\boxed{\times}\,3000\,\boxed{=} \Rightarrow 27884.95178$

SELF-CHECK 11.2

1

1. What semiannual sinking fund payment would be required to yield \$48,000 nine years from now? The annual interest rate is 6%, compounded semiannually.

2. The Bamboo Furniture Company manufactures rattan patio furniture. It has just purchased a machine for \$13,500 to cut and glue the pieces of wood. The machine is expected to last five years. If the company establishes a sinking fund to replace this machine, what annual payments must be made if the annual interest rate is 8%?

3. Tristin and Kim Denley are establishing a college fund for their one-year-old daughter Chloe. They want to save enough now to pay college tuition at the time she enters college (17 years from now). If her tuition is projected to be \$35,000 for a two-year degree, what annual sinking fund payment should they establish if the annual interest is 8%?

4. Michelle and Joe Hanover have a 12-year-old daughter and are now in a financial position to begin saving for her college education. What annual sinking fund payment should they make to have her entire college expenses paid at the time she enters college six years from now? Her college expenses are projected to be \$30,000 and the annual interest rate is 6%.

5. Bertha Looney recognizes the value of saving part of her income. She has set a goal to have $25,000 in cash available for emergencies. How much should she invest semiannually to have $25,000 in 10 years if the sinking fund she has selected pays 8% annually, compounded semiannually?

6. Stein and Company has established a sinking fund to retire a bond issue of $500,000, which is due in 10 years. How much is the quarterly sinking fund payment if the account pays 8% annual interest, compounded quarterly?

2

7. What is the present value of an annual ordinary annuity of $680 at 9% annual interest for 25 years?

8. Cindy Meziere plans to set aside $2,500 at the end of each year for two years at 8% annual interest to pay her college tuition and expenses at a local community college. What lump sum should she invest today to achieve the same value at the end of two years?

9. Laura Kleinaitis is setting up an annuity for a memorial scholarship. She can set aside $3,000 at the end of each year for the next 10 years and it will earn 7% annual interest. What lump sum does she need to set aside today at 7% annual interest to have the same scholarship fund available 10 years from now? Use the compound interest formula to find the value of the investment at the end of 10 years. Verify the investment value by using the future value table for an ordinary annuity. To what can you attribute the small difference in the two future values you found?

10. JoAnna Helba, a nationally recognized philanthropist, set up an annuity by depositing $1,600 at the end of each year for 10 years at 9% annual interest. The Helba Fund would be used to reward faculty for teaching, service, and research at a major two-year community/technical college. How much would Helba have to deposit today at an annual interest rate of 9% to have the same amount as the annuity yields after the 10 years?

11. Steve and Mary Kay Helba have agreed to pay for their granddaughter's college education. Melanie will be ready to attend college seven years from now. Steve and Mary Kay are trying to decide whether to deposit $2,300 at the end of each year for the seven years into an annuity at 7% annual interest, or make a lump sum deposit now at 7% annual interest. What lump sum should be deposited now to have the same amount as the annuity after seven years?

12. Janice and Terry Van Dyke are investigating retirement. Since they have 10 more years until retirement, they have decided to establish a quarterly ordinary annuity of $3,000 for the next 10 years at 8% annual interest, compounded quarterly. What will be the value of this annity at the end of 10 years? How much should they invest in a lump sum now at 8% annual interest, compounded quarterly, if they want to have the same amount as the annuity yields after 10 years? How much of their own money was invested in the annuity? Discuss the positive and negative aspects of making a lump sum investment versus periodic payments.

Around The Business World

Even YOU Can Become a Millionaire

The real secret to becoming a millionaire is not being a sports superstar, nor is it answering questions on a national television game show. According to Thomas Stanley and William Danko in *The Millionaire Next Door*, most millionaires make their money the old-fashioned way. They work hard, spend modestly, save aggressively, and invest wisely. Most millionaires live below their means. They watch for sales, clip coupons, and avoid impulse purchases. Most importantly, a significant amount of their time is devoted to studying investment options and consulting tax experts to take advantage of tax strategies to help them keep their wealth.

You may think that you don't earn enough to be able to save even $10 a week. But by carefully assessing your needs and determining the difference in *needs* and *wants,* you will find that you can save. A typical family in America spends from $6,000 to $10,000 a year on food and household supplies. Reducing that one expenditure by 10 percent gives $600 to $1,000 a year to invest. And, if you begin at an early age, as you saw in Chapter 10, that investment grows much more because of compound interest than investing far more when you are older. Instead of examining lump-sum investments as in Chapter 10, let's examine periodic investments for a long period of time.

Exercises

1. Savannah Byrd plans to save $100 a quarter for the next 5 years. She will put the money in a money market fund that earns 2% interest per quarter compounded quarterly. How much of her own money will she have invested and what will be the value of the fund at the end of the 5 years?

2. Raise time is an excellent time for you to consider increasing your investment commitment. For the first 2 years of your work career, you have saved $10 a month. After a salary increase, you determine that you can now save $25 per month and expect to save that much for the next 5 years. Both investments yield a return of 6% interest per year compounded monthly. How much have you invested? What is your accumulated investment worth at the end of 7 years?

3. Louise and Larry Vaughan have been consistent savers. They have set aside some amount of money each month faithfully from the time of their marriage and have regularly increased the per-month amount set aside. For the first 3 years they saved $10 monthly at 8% annual interest compounded monthly. For the next 2 years they saved $15 monthly at 12% annual interest compounded monthly. Even though they had children (an added expense), because of work promotions and significant salary increases, they were able to save $30 per month compounded monthly at 9% annual interest for the next 8 years. For the next 6 years they saved $50 per month compounded monthly at 8% annual interest. The next 5 years they were able to save only $40 a month compounded monthly at 7% annual interest. For the next 8 years they saved $80 a month and it was compounded monthly at 8% annual interest. Find the total amount of the Vaughans' own money that was saved over their 32 years of financial planning. What is the accumulated value of their investing plan?

4. Charles and Maxine Atmore thought they didn't earn enough to save any money until they had been working for 20 years and met with a financial planner who helped them see the urgency of their financial future. They immediately developed a plan to build their financial security over the next 15 years. They stopped taking their annual trip abroad, made a list of items they needed when shopping in order to avoid impulse purchases, and

Chapter 11 Annuities and Sinking Funds **465**

watched for sales and specials to reduce their expenditures so they could use the money for building their financial future. By taking these actions, they were able to free up $200 a month and invested it at 8% annual interest compounded monthly. How much of their own money have they invested? What will be the value of their investment in 15 years?

5. Compare the financial plans for the Vaughans and the Atmores (Exercises 3 and 4).

6. Suppose that at age 25 you decide that you want to have one million dollars in an investment fund at age 65. How much should you invest each month at 10% annual interest compounded monthly to reach your goal? (Use the generating formula for Table 11-2.)

Answers

1. Amount invested: $2,000; fund value after 5 years: $2,429.70
2. Amount invested: $6,240; accumulated investment value after 22 years: $11,791.02
3.

Time	Monthly deposit	Annual rate	Amount Invested	Investment value for period	Cumulative investment
3 yrs	$10	8%	$360	$405.36	$405.36
2 yrs	$15	12%	$360	$404.60	$919.30
8 yrs	$30	9%	$2,880	$4,195.68	$6,079.25
6 yrs	$50	8%	$3,600	$4,601.27	$14,410.15
5 yrs	$40	7%	$2,400	$2,863.72	$23,291.46
8 yrs	$80	8%	$7,680	$10,709.49	$44,078.09
32 yrs			$17,280		$67,258.21

Amount invested: $17,280
Investment value = $67,258.21

4. Amount invested: 15 years × 12 months per year × $200 = $36,000
   Investment value = $200 × 346.0382216 (from formula) = $69,207.64

5. The Vaughans invested less than half the amount the Atwoods invested, yer they accumulated nearly the same amount by investing early. The Vaughns were also able to take advantage of higher interest rates for some periods of their investment.

6. $158.13 per month

Section Outcome   **Important Points with Examples**

Section 11.1

Find the future value of an ordinary annuity using the simple interest formula method. (page 450)

1. Find the first end-of-period principal.

$$\text{First end-of-period principal} = \text{annuity payment}$$

2. For each remaining period in turn, find the next end-of-period principal:
    (a) Multiply the previous end-of-period principal by the sum of 1 and the period interest rate.
    (b) Add the product from step 2a and the annuity payment.

$$\begin{aligned}\text{End-of-period principal} = {} & \text{previous end-of-period principal} \\ & \times (1 + \text{period interest rate}) + \text{annuity payment}\end{aligned}$$

3. Identify the last end-of-period principal as the future value.

$$\text{Future value} = \text{last end-of-period principal}$$

Find the future value of an annual ordinary annuity of $2,000 for two years at 9% annual interest.

$$\text{End-of-year 1} = \$2,000$$

$$\text{End-of-year 2} = \$2,000(1.09) + \$2,000$$

$$= \$2,180 + \$2,000$$

$$= \$4,180$$

The future value is $4,180.

Find the future value of a semiannual ordinary annuity of $300 for one year at 9% annual interest, compounded semiannually.

$$\frac{9\% \text{ annual interest rate}}{2 \text{ periods per year}} = 4.5\% = 0.045 \text{ period interest rate}$$

$$\text{End-of-period 1} = \$300$$

$$\text{End-of-period 2} = \$300(1.045) + \$300$$

$$= \$313.50 + \$300$$

$$= \$613.50$$

The future value is $613.50.

Find the future value of an ordinary annuity using a $1.00 ordinary annuity future value table. (page 451)

1. Select the periods row corresponding to the number of interest periods.
2. Select the rate-per-period column corresponding to the period interest rate.
3. Locate the value in the cell where the periods row intersects the rate-per-period column.
4. Multiply the annuity payment by the table value from step 3.

$$\text{Future value} = \text{annuity payment} \times \text{table value}$$

> Find the future value of an ordinary annuity of $5,000 semiannually for four years at 12% annual interest, compounded semiannually.
>
> $$4 \text{ years} \times 2 \text{ periods per year} = 8 \text{ periods}$$
>
> $$\frac{12\% \text{ annual interest rate}}{2 \text{ periods per year}} = 6\% \text{ period interest rate}$$
>
> The Table 11-1 value for eight periods and 6% is 9.897.
>
> $$\text{Future value} = \$5,000 \times 9.987$$
> $$= \$49,485$$
>
> The future value is $49,485.

3 Find the future value of an annuity due using the simple interest formula method. (page 453)

1. Find the first end-of-period principal: multiply the annuity payment by the sum of 1 and the period interest rate.

   First end-of-period principal = annuity payment $\times$ (1 + period interest rate)

2. For each remaining period in turn, find the next end-of-period principal:
   (a) Add the previous end-of-period principal and the annuity payment.
   (b) Multiply the sum from step 2a by the sum of 1 and the period interest rate.

   End-of-period principal = (previous end-of-period principal + annuity payment) $\times$ (1 + period interest rate)

3. Identify the last end-of-period principal as the future value.

   Future value = last end-of-period principal

> Find the future value of an annual annuity due of $3,000 for two years at 10% annual interest.
>
> $$\text{End-of-year 1} = \$3,000(1.1)$$
> $$= \$3,300$$
> $$\text{End-of-year 2} = (\$3,300 + \$3,000)(1.1)$$
> $$= \$6,300(1.1)$$
> $$= \$6,930$$
>
> Find the future value of a semiannual annuity due of $400 for one year at 8% annual interest, compounded semiannually.
>
> $$\frac{8\% \text{ annual interest rate}}{2 \text{ periods per year}} = 4\% = 0.04 \text{ period interest rate}$$
>
> $$\text{End-of-period 1} = \$400(1.04)$$
> $$= \$416$$
> $$\text{End-of-period 2} = (\$416 + \$400)(1.04)$$
> $$= (\$816)(1.04)$$
> $$= \$848.64$$
>
> The future value is $848.64.

4 Find the future value of an annuity due using a $1.00 ordinary annuity future value table. (page 454)

1. Select the periods row corresponding to the number of interest periods.
2. Select the rate-per-period column corresponding to the period interest rate.
3. Locate the value in the cell where the periods row intersects the rate-per-period column.
4. Multiply the table value from step 3 by the sum of 1 and the period interest rate.
5. Multiply the annuity payment by the product from step 4.

Future value = annuity payment × table value × (1 + period interest rate)

Find the future value of a quarterly annuity due of $1,500 for three years at 12% annual interest, compounded quarterly.

3 years × 4 periods per year = 12 periods

$$\frac{12\% \text{ annual interest rate}}{4 \text{ periods per year}} = 3\% \text{ period interest rate}$$

The Table 11-1 value for 12 periods and 3% is 14.192.

Future value = $1,500 × 14.192 × 1.03

= $21,926.64

The future value is $21,926.64.

Section 11.2

1 Find the sinking fund payment using a $1.00 sinking fund payment table. (page 459)

1. Select the periods row corresponding to the number of interest periods.
2. Select the rate-per-period column corresponding to the period interest rate.
3. Locate the value in the cell where the periods row intersects the rate-per-period column.
4. Multiply the table value from step 3 by the desired future value.

Sinking fund payment = future value × Table 11-2 value

Find the quarterly sinking fund payment required to yield $15,000 in five years if interest is 12%, compounded quarterly.

5 years × 4 periods per year = 20 periods

$$\frac{12\% \text{ annual interest rate}}{4 \text{ periods per year}} = 3\% \text{ period interest rate}$$

The Table 11-2 value for 20 periods and 3% is 0.0372157.

Sinking fund payment = 15,000 × 0.0372157

= $558.24

The required quarterly payment is $558.24.

Find the present value of an ordinary annuity using a $1.00 ordinary annuity present value table. (page 461)

1. Select the periods row corresponding to the number of interest periods.
2. Select the rate-per-period column corresponding to the period interest rate.
3. Locate the value in the cell where the periods row intersects the rate-per-period column.
4. Multiply the table value from step 3 by the annuity payment.

Present value of annuity = periodic annuity payment × table value

Find the lump sum required for deposit today earning 8% annual interest compounded semiannually, to yield the future value of a semiannual ordinary annuity of $2,500 at 8% annual interest, compounded semiannually for 15 years.

15 years × 2 periods per year = 30 periods

$$\frac{8\% \text{ annual interest rate}}{2 \text{ periods per year}} = 4\% \text{ period interest rate}$$

The Table 11-3 value for 30 periods and 4% is 17.292.

Present value = $2,500 × 17.292

= $43,230

The lump sum required for deposit today is $43,230.

WORDS TO KNOW

annuity (p. 450)
sinking fund (pp. 450, 459)
annuity certain (p. 450)

contingent annuity (p. 450)
ordinary annuity (p. 450)
annuity due (p. 450)

present value of an annuity (p. 461)

CHAPTER 11 CONCEPTS ANALYSIS

1. Select three table values from Table 11-1 and verify them using the formula

$$FV = \frac{(1 + R)^N - 1}{R}$$

2. To find the future value of an annuity due, you can multiply the future value of an ordinary annuity by the sum of 1 + the period interest rate. Explain why this is the same as adding the simple interest earned on the first payment for the entire length of the annuity.

3. In the example on page (456), we found that the annuity due with semiannual payments had the greater future value. Also, the ordinary annuity with the quarterly payments was more than the ordinary annuity with semiannual payments. Why?

4. How are future value of a lump sum and future value of an annuity similar?

5. How are future value of a lump sum and future value of an annuity different?

6. How are the present value of a lump sum and the periodic payment of a sinking fund similar? How are they different?

7. How are annuities and sinking funds similar? How are they different?

8. Select three table values from Table 11-2 and verify them using the formula

$$TV = \frac{R}{(1 + R)^N - 1}$$

9. Select three table values from Table 11-3 and verify them using the formula

$$TV = \frac{(1 + R)^N - 1}{R (1 + R)^N}$$

10. The Calculator box on page 463 gives two different sequences of calculator steps. Why does the insertion of the additional set of parentheses make the first equal sign unnecessary?

CHAPTER 11 ASSIGNMENT EXERCISES

Section 11.1

Use Table 11-1 to complete the table below.

	Annuity Payment	Annual Rate	Annual Interest	Years	Type of Annuity	Future Value of Annuity
1.	$1,400	12%	Compounded quarterly	5	Quarterly ordinary	_____
2.	$2,900	9%	Compounded annually	12	Annual ordinary	_____
3.	$125	24%	Compounded monthly	$1\frac{1}{2}$	Monthly annuity due	_____
4.	$800	7%	Compounded annually	15	Annual annuity due	_____

Use the simple interest formula method for exercises 5 and 6.

5. Roni Sue deposited $1,500 at the beginning of each year for three years at an annual interest rate of 9%. Find the future value.

6. Find the future value if Roni Sue in exercise 5 had deposited the money at the end of each year rather than at the beginning.

Use Table 11-1 for exercises 7–12.

7. Barry Michael plans to deposit $2,000 at the end of every six months for the next five years to save up for a boat. If the interest rate is 12% annually, compounded semiannually, how much money will Barry have in his boat fund after five years?

8. Sam and Jane Crawford had a baby in 1988. At the end of that year they began putting away $900 per year at 10% annual interest for a college fund. When their child is 18 years old in 2006, the cost for four years of college is estimated to be about $20,000 per year.
(a) How much money will be in the account when the child is 18 years old?
(b) Will the Crawfords have enough saved to send their child to college for four years?

9. Bob Paris is 46 years old when he opens a retirement income account paying 9% annually. He deposits $3,000 at the beginning of each year.
(a) How much will be in the account after 10 years?
(b) When Bob retires at age 65, in 19 years, how much will be in the account?

10. A business deposits $4,500 at the end of each quarter in an account that earns 8% annual interest, compounded quarterly. What is the value of the annuity in five years?

11. The Shari Joy Corporation decided to set aside $3,200 at the beginning of every six months to provide donation funds for a new Little League baseball field scheduled to be built in 18 months. If money earns 12% annual interest, compounded semiannually, how much will be available as a donation for the field?

12. University Trailers is setting aside $800 at the beginning of every quarter to purchase a forklift in 30 months. The annual interest will be 8%, compounded quarterly. How much will be available for the purchase?

Section 11.2

Use Table 11-2 to complete the following table.

	Desired Future Value	Annual Interest Rate	Years	Annual Sinking Fund Payment
13.	$240,000	6%	15	_____
14.	$3,000,000	8%	10	_____
15.	$50,000	12%	5	_____
16.	$45,000	4%	8	_____

Use Table 11–2 for Exercises 17–23.

17. How much must be set aside at the end of each six months by the Fabulous Toy Company to replace a $155,000 piece of equipment at the end of eight years if the account pays 8% annual interest, compounded semiannually?

18. Tasty Food Manufacturers, Inc., has a bond issue of $1,400,000 due in 30 years. If they want to establish a sinking fund to meet this obligation, how much must be set aside at the end of each year if the annual interest rate is 6%?

19. Lausanne Private School System needs to set aside funds for a new computer system. What monthly sinking fund payment would be required to amount to $45,000, the approximate cost of the computer, in $1\frac{1}{2}$ years at 12% annual interest, compounded monthly?

20. Zachary Alexander owns a limousine that will need to be replaced in four years at a cost of $65,000. How much must he put aside each year in a sinking fund at 8% annual interest to be able to afford the new limousine?

21. Goldie's Department Store has a fleet of delivery trucks that will last for three years of heavy use and then need to be replaced at a cost of $75,000. How much must they set aside every three months in a sinking fund at 8% annual interest, compounded quarterly, to have enough money to replace the trucks?

22. Danny Lawrence Properties, Inc., has a bond issue that will mature in 25 years for $1 million. How much must the company set aside each year in a sinking fund at 12% annual interest to meet this future obligation?

23. Linda Zuk wants to save $25,000 for a new boat in six years. How much must be put aside in equal payments each year in an account earning 8% annual interest for Linda to be able to purchase the boat?

24. How much money needs to be set aside today at 10% annual interest, compounded semiannually, to have the same amount as a semiannual ordinary annuity of $500 for five years at 10% annual interest, compounded semiannually?

25. What is the present value of an annual ordinary annuity of $3,400 at 5% annual interest for seven years?

26. You are starting an annual ordinary annuity of $680 for 25 years at 9% annual interest. What lump sum amount would have to be set aside today earning 9% annual interest to have the same amount accumulated as the annuity?

27. An annual ordinary annuity of $2,500 for five years at 8% annual interest is equivalent to what lump sum earning 8% annual interest for the same period of time?

28. Your parents are trying to get you to form the habit of investing part of your paycheck and have agreed to set aside a lump sum of money today earning 12% annual interest, compounded quarterly, that will have the same value after five years as an annuity you begin now and continue for five years. Your ordinary annuity requires you to pay $500 quarterly at an annual interest rate of 12%, compounded quarterly. What lump sum will your parents set aside today?

29. Bret Workman is committed to creating a scholarship fund to be available when he retires from the faculty in eight years. How much does he need to set aside today earning 10% annual interest, compounded semiannually, to have an amount equivalent to the future value of a semiannual ordinary annuity of $700 at 10% annual interest, compounded semiannually?

30. Ted Davis has set the goal of accumulating $80,000 for his son's college fund, which will be needed 18 years in the future. How much should he deposit each year in a sinking fund that earns 8% annual interest? How much should he deposit each year if he waits until his son starts school (at age six) to begin saving? Compare the two payment amounts.

Spreadsheet Exercises

31. Most spreadsheet programs have a future value function that calculates the future value of an investment based on periodic payments of a constant amount invested and a constant interest rate. In Excel ^{TM} the function is FV. The syntax for this function is **FV(rate,nper,pmt,pv,type),** where *rate* is the interest rate per period, *nper* is the total number of payment periods in the annuity, *pmt* is the payment amount made each period, *pv* is the present (or beginning) value of the annuity. If *pv* is omitted from the formula, it is assumed to be 0. *Type* is 0 if the payments are due at the end of the period (ordinary annuity) and 1 if the payments are due at the beginning of the period (annuity due). When type is omitted, it is assumed to be 0. Note, using the Excel ^{TM} FV function, that deposits to savings (cash you pay out) are represented by negative numbers. This appears as a "red" number in parentheses.

(a) Write formulas for Future Value of the periodic payments (ordinary annuity) shown in column A if the number of periods and periodic rate are given in columns B and C, respectively.

(b) Copy columns A, B, and C to columns F, G, and H and write the ordinary annuity formula as spreadsheet formulas to calculate the future value of the ordinary annuities in rows 3-8 of the sheet. Compare and discuss the results of both calculations. The accumulated amount computed with the FV function in Excel ^{TM} shows up as a negative amount, but is the same dollar value as the amount calculated using the future value formula.

32. Complete the spreadsheet using the formulas.

	A	B	C	D	E	F	G	H	I	J	K
1	Future Value of an Annuity with FV Function					Future Value of an Annuity with the Formula					
2	Annuity Value	Periods	Period Rate	Future Value		Annuity Value	Periods	Period Rate	Future Value		
3	6,500.00	14.00	5.00%								
4	100.00	10.00	8.00%								
5	250.00	20.00	9.00%								
6	300.00	16.00	2.00%								
7	592.22	30.00	1.00%								
8	1,000.00	48.00	3.00%								

Challenge Problems

33. Carolyn Ellis is setting up an annuity for her retirement. She can set aside $2,000 at the end of each year for the next 20 years and it will earn 6% annual interest. What lump sum will she need to set aside today at 6% annual interest to have the same retirement fund available 20 years from now? Use the future value of an ordinary annuity table to find the amount in her retirement fund in 20 years. Use the compound interest formula to verify her retirement fund balance in 20 years. How much more will Carolyn need to invest in periodic payments than she will if she makes a lump sum payment if she intends to accumulate the same retirement balance?

34. Discuss the pros and cons of investing in a lump sum versus investing in regular periodic payments.

1. Use the simple interest formula method to find the future value of an ordinary annuity of $9,000 per year for two years at 15% annual interest.

2. Use the simple interest formula method to find the future value of an annuity due of $2,700 per year for three years at 11% annual interest.

3. What is the future value of an annuity due of $5,645 every six months for three years at 12% annual interest, compounded semiannually?

4. What is the future value of an ordinary annuity of $300 every three months for four years at 8% annual interest, compounded quarterly?

5. What is the sinking fund payment required at the end of each year to accumulate to $125,000 in 16 years at 4% annual interest?

6. What is the present value of an ordinary annuity of $985 every six months for eight years at 8% annual interest, compounded semiannually?

7. Mike's Sport Shop deposited $3,400 at the end of each year for 12 years at 7% annual interest. How much will Mike have in the account at the end of the time period?

8. How much would the annuity amount to in exercise 7 if Mike had deposited the money at the beginning of each year instead of at the end of each year?

9. How much must be set aside at the end of each year by the Caroline Cab Company to replace four taxicabs at a cost of $90,000? The current interest rate is 6% annually. The existing cabs will wear out in three years.

10. How much must Johnny Williams invest today to have an amount equivalent to investing $2,800 at the end of every six months for the next 15 years if interest is earned at 8% annually, compounded semiannually?

11. Maurice Eftink owns a lawn maintenance business. His riding lawnmower cost $850 and should last for six years. Maurice wants to establish a sinking fund to buy a new mower. How much must he set aside at the end of each year at 12% annual interest to have enough money to buy the new equipment?

12. Read and Sondra Davis want to know how much they must deposit in a retirement savings account today that would be equivalent to depositing $1,500 at the end of every six months for 15 years. The retirement account is paying 10% annual interest, compounded semiannually.

13. Morris Stocks wants to save $2,200 at the end of each year for 11 years in an account paying 7% annual interest. What is the future value of the annuity at the end of this period of time?

14. Maura Helba is saving for her college expenses. She sets aside $175 at the beginning of each three months in an account paying 12% annual interest, compounded quarterly. How much will Maura have accumulated in the account at the end of four years?

15. What is the present value of a semiannual ordinary annuity of $2,500 for seven years at 6% annual interest, compounded semiannually?

16. How much will you need to invest today to have the same amount after five years as a quarterly ordinary annuity of $800 if both interest rates are 8% annually, compounded quarterly?

SELF-CHECK 11.1

1. End-of-year 1 = $3,000
   End-of-year 2 = $3,000(1.09) + $3,000
   $\qquad$ = $3,270 + $3,000
   $\qquad$ = $6,270
   The future value is $6,270.
   Interest earned = $6,270 − $6,000 = $270

2. End-of-year 1 = $4,000
   End-of-year 2 = $4,000(1.07) + $4,000
   $\qquad$ = $4,280 + $4,000
   $\qquad$ = $8,280
   Heather will have $8,280 for college.
   Interest earned = $8,280 − $8,000 = $280

3. End-of-year 1 = $5,000
   End-of-year 2 = $5,000(1.08) + $5,000
   $\qquad$ = $5,400 + $5,000
   $\qquad$ = $10,400
   End-of-year 3 = $10,400(1.08) + $5,000
   $\qquad$ = $11,232 + $5,000
   $\qquad$ = $16,232
   Harry will have $16,232 at the end of three years.
   Interest = $16,232 − $15,000 = $1,232

4. End-of-year 1 = $3,000
   End-of-year 2 = $3,000(1.085) + $3,000
   $\qquad$ = $3,255 + $3,000
   $\qquad$ = $6,255
   End-of-year 3 = $6,255(1.085) + $3,000
   $\qquad$ = $6,786.68 + $3,000
   $\qquad$ = $9,786.68
   Scott will have $9,786.68 after three years.
   Interest = $9,786.68 − $9,000 = $786.68

5. 7 years $\times$ 2 periods per year = 14 periods

$$\frac{10\% \text{ annual interest rate}}{2 \text{ periods per year}} = 5\% \text{ period interest rate}$$

The Table 11-1 value for 14 periods at 5% is 19.599.
Future value = annuity payment $\times$ table value
Future value = $6,500 \times 19.599$
Future value = $127,393.50
Amount invested = $6,500 \times 2 \times 7 = \$91,000$
Interest = $127,393.50 - \$91,000$
$\qquad = \$36,393.50$

7. The Table 11-1 value for 15 periods at 7% is 25.129.
Future value = $1,000 \times 25.129$
Future value = $25,129
The future value is $25,129. Latanya will have invested 15 $\times$ $1,000, or $15,000, of her own money and will have received $10,129 in interest.

9. The table value for five periods at 8% is 5.867.
$2,000 \times 5.867 = \$11,734$
The future value of the annuity is $11,734.
Your investment = $2,000 \times 5 = \$10,000$
Your interest = $11,734 - \$10,000 = \$1,734$

11. End-of-year 1 = $12,000(1.14)
$\qquad = \$13,680$
End-of-year 2 = ($13,680 + $12,000)(1.14)
$\qquad = \$25,680(1.14)$
$\qquad = \$29,275.20$
End-of-year 3 =($29,275.20 + $12,000)(1.14)
$\qquad = \$41,275.20(1.14)$
$\qquad = \$47,053.73$
The future value is $47,053.73
Investment = $12,000 \times 3 = \$36,000$
Interest = $47,053.73 - \$36,000 = \$11,053.73$

13. End-of-year 1 = $7,800(1.081)
$\qquad = \$8,431.80$
End-of-year 2 = ($8,431.80 + $7,800)(1.081)
$\qquad = \$16,231.80(1.081)$
$\qquad = \$17,546.58$
The future value is $17,546.58.
Investment = $7,800 \times 2 = \$15,600$
Interest = $17,546.58 - \$15,600 = \$1,946.58$

15. 3 years $\times$ 4 periods per year = 12 periods

$$\frac{8\% \text{ annual interest rate}}{4 \text{ periods per year}} = 2\% \text{ period interest rate}$$

The Table 11-1 value for 12 periods at 2% is 13.412.
Future value = $4,400 \times 13.412 \times 1.02$
$\qquad = \$60,193.06$
Investment = $4,400 \times 4 \times 3 = \$52,800$
Interest = $60,193.06 - \$52,860 = \$7,333.06$

6. 5 years $\times$ 4 periods per year = 20 periods

$$\frac{8\% \text{ annual interest rate}}{4 \text{ periods per year}} = 2\% \text{ period interest rate}$$

The Table 11-1 value for 20 periods at 2% is 24.297.
Future value = $2,500 \times 24.297$
Future value = $60,742.50
Pat will have $60,742.50 after five years.

8. Table 11-1 value for 10 periods at 8% is 14.487.
$500 \times 14.487 = \$7,243.50$
The annuity is worth $7,243.50 after 10 years.
Your investment = $500 \times 10 = \$5,000$
Your interest = $7,243.50 - \$5,000 = \$2,243.50$

10.

Years	Total Investment	Total Interest
Ten-year	$5,000	$2,243.50
Five-year	$10,000	$1,734

The 10-year investment earned more interest even though half as much money was invested. At the same period interest rate, investing for twice as long gives a better yield on your investment than investing twice as much for half as long. Thus, the earlier you start saving, the better.

12. End-of-year 1 = $2,500(1.072)
$\qquad = \$2,680$
End-of-year 2 = ($2,650 + $2,500)(1.072)
$\qquad = \$5,150(1.072)$
$\qquad = \$5,552.96$
The annuity is worth $5,552.96 after two years.
Investment = $2,500 \times 2 = \$5,000$
Interest = $5,552.96 - \$5,000 = \$552.96$

14. End-of-year 1 = $400(1.068)
$\qquad = \$427.20$
End-of-year 2 = ($427.20 + $400)(1.068)
$\qquad = \$827.20(1.068)$
$\qquad = \$883.45$
The future value is $883.45.

16. 4 years $\times$ 2 periods per year = 8 periods

$$\frac{8\% \text{ annual interest rate}}{2 \text{ periods per year}} = 4\% \text{ period interest rate}$$

The Table 11-1 value for eight periods at 4% is 9.214.
Future value = $750(9.214)(1.04)
$\qquad = \$7,186.92$
Investment = $750 \times 2 \times 4 = \$6,000$
Interest = $7,186.92 - \$6,000 = \$1,186.92$

17. *Quarterly annuity due*

1 year × 4 periods = 4 periods

$$\frac{8\% \text{ annual interest rate}}{4 \text{ periods per year}} = 2\% \text{ period interest rate}$$

The Table 11-1 value for 4 periods at 2% is 4.122.

Future value = $300 × 4.122 × 1.02 = $1,261.33

Semiannual annuity due

1 year × 2 periods per year = 2 periods

$$\frac{8\% \text{ annual interest rate}}{2 \text{ periods per year}} = 4\% \text{ period interest rate}$$

The Table 11-1 value for 2 periods at 4% is 2.040.

Future value = $600 × 2.040 × 1.04 = $1,272.96

The semiannual annuity yields more interest.

18. Your contribution = $250 × 20 = $5,000

The Table 11-1 value for 20 periods at 7% is 40.995.

Future value = $250 × 40.995 × 1.07 = $10,966.16.

Earned interest = $10,966.16 − $5,000 = $5,966.16

SELF-CHECK 11.2

1. 9 years × 2 periods per year = 18 periods

$$\frac{6\% \text{ annual interest rate}}{2 \text{ periods per year}} = 3\% \text{ period interest rate}$$

The Table 11-2 value for 18 periods at 3% is 0.0427087.

Sinking fund payment = $48,000 × 0.0427087
= $2,050.02

2. 5 years × 1 period per year = 5 periods

$$\frac{8\% \text{ annual interest rate}}{1 \text{ period per year}} = 8\% \text{ period interest rate}$$

The Table 11-2 value for 5 periods at 8% is 0.1704565.

Sinking fund payment = $13,500 × 0.1704565
= $2,301.16

3. 17 years × 1 period per year = 17 periods

$$\frac{8\% \text{ annual interest rate}}{1 \text{ period per year}} = 8\% \text{ period interest rate}$$

The Table 11-2 value for 17 periods at 8% is 0.0296294.

Sinking fund payment = $35,000 × 0.0296294
= $1,037.03

4. 6 years × 1 period per year = 6 periods

$$\frac{6\% \text{ annual interest rate}}{1 \text{ period per year}} = 6\% \text{ period interest rate}$$

The Table 11-2 value for 6 periods at 6% is 0.1433626.

Sinking fund payment = $30,000 × 0.1433626
= $4,300.88

5. 10 years × 2 periods per year = 20 periods

$$\frac{8\% \text{ annual interest rate}}{2 \text{ periods per year}} = 4\% \text{ period interest rate}$$

The Table 11-2 value for 20 periods at 4% is 0.0335818.

Sinking fund payment = $25,000 × 0.0335818
= $839.55

6. 10 years × 4 periods per year = 40 periods

$$\frac{8\% \text{ annual interest rate}}{4 \text{ periods per year}} = 2\% \text{ period interest rate}$$

The Table 11–2 value for 40 periods at 2% is 0.0165558.

Sinking fund payment = $500,000 × 0.0165558
= $8,277.90

7. 25 years × 1 period per year = 25 periods

$$\frac{9\% \text{ annual interest rate}}{1 \text{ period per year}} = 9\% \text{ period interest rate}$$

The Table 11-3 value for 25 periods at 9% is 9.823.

Present value = $680 × 9.823
= $6,679.64

8. The Table 11-3 value for 2 periods at 8% is 1.783.

Present value = $2,500 × 1.783
= $4,457.50

9. The Table 11-3 value for 10 periods at 7% is 7.024.

Present value = $3,000 × 7.024
= $21,072

Compound interest = $P(1 + R)^N$
= $21,072(1 + 0.07)^{10}$
= $21,072(1.07)^{10}$
= $41,451.81

Future value (Table 11–1) = $3,000 × 13.816
= $41,448

The difference can be attributed to rounding differences.

10. The Table 11-3 value for 10 periods at 9% is 6.418.

Present value = $1,600 × 6.418
= $10,268.80

11. The Table 11-3 value for 7 periods at 7% is 5.389.
Present value = $2,300 × 5.389
= $12,394.70

12. For annuity yield, the Table 11-1 value for 40 periods at 2% is 60.402.

Annuity yield = $3,000 × 60.402
= $181,206

Accumulated investment = $3,000 × 4 × 10 = $120,000

10 years × 4 periods per year = 40 periods

$$\frac{8\% \text{ annual interest rate}}{4 \text{ periods per year}} = 2\% \text{ period interest rate}$$

For an equivalent lump sum investment, the Table 11-3 value for 40 periods at 2% is 27.355.

Equivalent lump sum = $3,000 × 27.355
= $82,065.00

The Van Dykes may not have the lump sum to invest. If they do have it, they may want to consider investing the lump sum since it is significantly less than the amount of their money that would need to be invested periodically to achieve the same financial goal. (Answers will vary.)

12

Consumer Credit

12.1 Installment Loans

1 Find the installment price given the installment payment.

2 Find the installment payment given the installment price.

12.2 Paying a Loan Before It Is Due: The Rule of 78

1 Find the interest refund using the rule of 78.

12.3 Open-End Credit

1 Find the unpaid balance using the unpaid balance method.

2 Find the unpaid balance using the average daily balance method.

12.4 Annual Percentage Rates

1 Estimate the annual percentage rate using the constant ratio formula.

2 Find the annual percentage rate using a table.

12.5 Home Mortgages

1 Find the monthly mortgage payment and total interest.

2 Complete a monthly amortization schedule.

Good Decisions through Teamwork

Many credit unions and some other types of lending institutions offer car loans in which interest is applied on a monthly basis to the unpaid balance. With your team members, select a low- to moderately priced new car to purchase and investigate current new car loan rates for a three-year loan and for a four-year loan at a local credit union. For each loan, prepare a spreadsheet showing the beginning monthly balance, the portion of the payment applied to interest, the portion of the payment applied to the principal, and the ending monthly balance for each month of the loan period. Decide which option you would choose and state your reasons for choosing that option.

If you have access to an electronic spreadsheet, include in your report the total interest paid for the various options. Also, investigate the effects of increasing the monthly payments by $10 over the required payment.

Many individuals and businesses make purchases for which they do not pay the full amount at the time of purchase. These purchases are paid for by paying a portion of the amount owed in regular payments. This type of loan or credit, by which many of us are able to purchase equipment, supplies, and other items we need in our businesses or personal lives, is called **consumer credit.**

In the preceding chapters we discussed the interest to be paid on loans that are paid in full on the date of maturity of the loan. Many times loans are made so that the maker (the borrower) pays a given amount in regular payments. This means that the borrower does not have use of the full amount of money borrowed for the full length of time it was borrowed. Instead, a certain portion of it has to be paid back with each regular payment. Loans with regular payments are called **installment loans.**

There are two kinds of installment loans. **Basic installment loans** are loans in which the amount borrowed plus interest is repaid in a specified number of equal payments. Examples include bank loans and loans for large purchases such as cars and appliances. **Open-end loans** are loans in which there is no fixed number of payments—the person keeps making payments until the amount is paid off, and the interest is computed on the unpaid balance at the end of each payment period. Credit card accounts, retail store accounts, and line-of-credit accounts most often use the open-end type of loan.

In this chapter we will consider both installment and open-end loans, as well as the annual percentage rate at which most such loans are made.

12.1 Installment Loans

1 Find the installment price given the installment payment.

2 Find the installment payment given the installment price.

Should you or your business take out an installment loan? That depends on the interest you will pay and how it is computed. The interest associated with an installment loan is part of the charges referred to as **finance charges** or **carrying charges.** In addition to accrued interest charges, installment loans often include charges for insurance, credit-report fees, or loan fees. Under the truth-in-lending law, all of these charges must be disclosed in writing to the consumer.

1 Find the installment price given the installment payment.

The **cash price** is the price you pay if you pay all at once at the time of sale. If you pay on an installment basis instead, the **down payment** is a partial payment of the cash price at the time of sale. The **amount financed** is the total amount you pay in regular payments to pay off the balance of the loan. The **installment payment** is the amount you pay each period, including interest, to pay off the loan. The **installment price** is the total paid, including all of the installment payments, the finance charges, and the down payment.

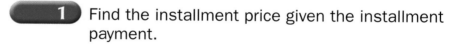

HOW TO Find the Installment Price

1. Find the total of the installment payments: multiply the number of installment payments by the amount of the installment payment.

Total of installment payments = number of installment payments
× installment payment

2. Add the down payment to the total of the installment payments.

Installment price = total of installment payments + down payment

EXAMPLE A printer was purchased on the installment plan with a $60 down payment and 12 payments of $45.58. Find the installment price of the printer.

$$\text{Total of installment payments} = \begin{pmatrix} \text{number of} \\ \text{installments} \end{pmatrix} \times \begin{pmatrix} \text{installment} \\ \text{payment} \end{pmatrix}$$

$$= \quad 12 \quad \times \quad \$45.58$$

$$= \boxed{\$546.96}$$

Installment price = total of installment payments + down payment

$$= \boxed{\$546.96} + \$60$$

$$= \$606.96$$

The installment price is $606.96.

TIP! **Where Is the Finance Charge?**

When the terms of a loan are given as a certain amount down with a given number of payments of a given amount, where is the finance charge? Fortunately, even though advertisements do not always itemize the finance charge, the lending institution or a business that sets up its own repayment terms is required to disclose in writing all charges associated with making a loan. Even though the finance charge may be stated as a lump sum, it must also be given as an effective interest rate or APR (annual percentage rate). The APR is discussed in more detail in section 12.4.

2 Find the installment payment given the installment price.

Since the installment price is the total of the installment payments plus the down payment, we can find the installment payment if we know the installment price, the down payment, and the number of payments.

HOW TO Find the Installment Payment Given the Installment Price, the Down Payment, and the Number of Payments

1. Find the total of the installment payments: subtract the down payment from the installment price.

Total of installment payments = installment price − down payment

2. Divide the total of the installment payments by the number of installment payments.

$$\text{Installment payment} = \frac{\text{total of installment payments}}{\text{number of payments}}$$

EXAMPLE The installment price of a drafting table with built-in lighting was $627 for a 12-month loan. If a $75 down payment had been made, find the installment payment.

$$\text{Total of installment payments} = \text{installment price} - \text{down payment}$$

$$= \$627 - \$75 = \boxed{\$552}$$

$$\text{Installment payment} = \frac{\text{total of installment payments}}{\text{number of payments}} = \frac{\boxed{\$552}}{12} = \$46$$

The installment payment is $46.

Sometimes the finance charge is given as a percent of the cash price. In such a case, you use the simple interest formula ($I = PRT$), with the cash price being the principal, the percent of interest charged being the rate per year, and the time being expressed in number of years or fraction of a year.

EXAMPLE   Pyramid Realty can recarpet its office for $4,000 in cash. If they choose to pay for it in 24 monthly installment payments, a 12% annual finance charge will be assessed for the total amount for the entire 24 months. Find the amount of the finance charge, the installment price, and the monthly payment if no down payment is made.

$$I = PRT$$

$$I = \$4,000 \times 0.12 \times 2$$

$$I = \boxed{\$960}$$

> Compute the finance charge as simple interest.
>
> The finance charge is $960.

$$\text{Installment price} = \text{amount of purchase} + \text{finance charge}$$

$$= \$4,000 + \boxed{\$960}$$

$$= \boxed{\$4,960}$$

> The total amount of loan is $4,960.

$$\text{Monthly payment} = \frac{\text{installment price} - \text{down payment}}{\text{number of monthly payments}}$$

$$= \frac{\boxed{\$4,960} - \$0}{24} = \frac{\boxed{\$4,960}}{24} = \$206.67 \quad \text{(rounded to the nearest cent)}$$

The finance charge is $960, the installment price is $4,960, and the monthly payment is $206.67.

SELF-CHECK 12.1

1. Find the installment price of a recliner bought on the installment plan with a down payment of $100 and six payments of $108.20.

2. Find the amount financed if a $125 down payment is made on a TV with a cash price of $579.

3. Stephen Helba purchased a TV with surround sound and remote control on an installment plan with $100 down and 12 payments of $106.32. Find the installment price of the TV.

4. A queen-size bedroom suite can be purchased on an installment plan with 18 payments of $97.42 if an $80 down payment is made. What is the installment price of the suite?

5. Zack's Trailer Sales will finance a 16-foot utility trailer with ramps and electric brakes. If a down payment of $100 and eight monthly payments of $82.56 are required, what is the installment price of the trailer?

6. A forklift is purchased for $10,000. The forklift is used as collateral and no down payment is required. Twenty-four monthly payments of $503 are required to repay the loan. What is the installment price of the forklift?

7. A computer with software costs $2,987, and Docie Johnson has agreed to pay a 19% per year finance charge on the cash price. If she contracts to pay the loan in 18 months, how much will she pay each month?

8. The cash price of a bedroom suite is $2,590. There is a 24% finance charge on the cash price, and 12 monthly payments. Find the monthly payment.

9. Find the monthly payment on a VCR with an installment price of $929, 12 monthly payments, and a down payment of $100.

10. The installment price of a teakwood extension table and four chairs is $625 with 18 monthly payments and a down payment of $75. What is the monthly payment?

11. An entertainment center is financed at a total cost of $2,357 including a down payment of $250. If the center is financed over 24 months, find the monthly payment.

12. A Hepplewhite sofa costs $3,780 in cash. Jaquanna Wilson will purchase the sofa in 36 monthly installment payments. A 13% per year finance charge will be assessed on the amount financed. Find the finance charge, the installment price, and the monthly payment.

12.2 Paying a Loan Before It Is Due: The Rule of 78

1 Find the interest refund using the rule of 78.

If an installment loan is paid entirely before the last payment is actually due, is part of the interest refundable? In most cases it is, but not always at the rate you might hope. If you paid a 12-month loan in six months, you might expect a refund of half the total interest. However, this is often not the case because the portion of the monthly payment that is interest is not the same from month to month. In many cases, interest or finance charge refunds are made according to the **rule of 78.**

1 Find the interest refund using the rule of 78.

Where does 78 come from in the rule of 78? Imagine that a loan is made for 12 months. We consider the principal to be divided into 12 equal parts and assume that one part is paid each month. If interest accrues on the parts of the principal that are left to be paid, then interest accrues on all 12 parts for the first month, on only 11 parts for the second month, on 10 parts for the third month, and so on.

Month **1**	Interest accrues on **12** parts of principal
Month **2**	Interest accrues on **11** parts of principal
Month **3**	Interest accrues on **10** parts of principal
Month **4**	Interest accrues on **9** parts of principal
Month **5**	Interest accrues on **8** parts of principal
Month **6**	Interest accrues on **7** parts of principal
Month **7**	Interest accrues on **6** parts of principal
Month **8**	Interest accrues on **5** parts of principal
Month **9**	Interest accrues on **4** parts of principal

Month **10**   Interest accrues on **3** parts of principal
Month **11**   Interest accrues on **2** parts of principal
Month **12**   Interest accrues on **1** part of principal

The sum of all the parts accruing interest for a 12-month loan is $12 + 11 + 10 + 9 + 8 + 7 + 6 + 5 + 4 + 3 + 2 + 1$, or 78.

Thus, 78 equal parts accrue interest. The interest each part accrues is the same because the rate is the same and the parts are the same (each is $\frac{1}{12}$ of the principal). Since 78 equal parts each accrue equal interest, the interest each part accrues must be $\frac{1}{78}$ of the total interest for the one-year loan. So if all 12 monthly payments are paid early, say, with three months remaining, then the interest that would have accrued in the 10th, 11th, and 12th months may be refunded. In the 10th month, three parts each accrue $\frac{1}{78}$ of the total interest, in the 11th month, two parts each accrue $\frac{1}{78}$ of the total interest, and in the 12th month, one part accrues $\frac{1}{78}$ of the total interest. So $3 + 2 + 1$ parts, or 6 parts each accrue $\frac{1}{78}$ of the total interest. Thus $\frac{6}{78}$ of the total interest must be refunded. The fraction $\frac{6}{78}$ is called the **refund fraction.**

All installment loans are not for 12 months, but the rule of 78 gives us a pattern that we can apply to loans of any length. We find the *numerator* of the refund fraction by adding the sequence numbers for the periods that a refund is due. For example, the numerator of the refund fraction for a six-month loan paid two months early would be $2 + 1$ or 3. We find the *denominator* by adding the sequence numbers for *all* the periods of the loan. The six-addend sum for a six-month loan is $6 + 5 + 4 + 3 + 2 + 1$, or 21. The refund fraction, then, is $\frac{3}{21}$.

 HOW TO Find the Interest Refund Using the Rule of 78

1. Find the period sequence numbers: number the periods of the loan so that the last period is 1, the next to the last is 2, and so on.
2. Find the numerator of the refund fraction: add the sequence numbers of the periods for which an interest refund is due.
3. Find the denominator of the refund fraction: add the sequence numbers of all the periods.
4. Multiply the total interest by the refund fraction.

Interest refund = total interest × refund fraction

EXAMPLE   A loan for 12 months with a finance charge of $117 is paid in full with four payments remaining. Find the amount of the finance charge (interest) refund.

$$\text{Refund fraction} = \frac{\text{sum of sequence numbers of payments remaining}}{\text{sum of all payment sequence numbers}}$$

$$= \frac{1 + 2 + 3 + 4}{1 + 2 + 3 + 4 + 5 + 6 + 7 + 8 + 9 + 10 + 11 + 12}$$

$$= \frac{10}{78}$$

$$\text{Interest refund} = \text{total interest or finance charge} \times \text{refund fraction}$$

$$= \$117 \times \frac{10}{78}$$

$$= \$15$$

The finance charge refund is $15.

If there are, say, 24 periods in the loan, finding the refund fraction requires adding the numbers from 1 to 24. The greater the number of periods, the more tedious this adding becomes. But there is a shortcut.

Examine the following illustrations for finding *twice* the sum of consecutive numbers beginning with 1.

Add the numbers from 1 to 4 twice.	$\begin{aligned} 1 + 2 + 3 + 4 & \quad \text{ascending order} \\ + \underline{4 + 3 + 2 + 1} & \quad \text{descending order} \\ 5 + 5 + 5 + 5 &= 4 \times 5 = 20 \end{aligned}$
Add the numbers from 1 to 5 twice.	$\begin{aligned} 1 + 2 + 3 + 4 + 5 & \quad \text{ascending order} \\ + \underline{5 + 4 + 3 + 2 + 1} & \quad \text{descending order} \\ 6 + 6 + 6 + 6 + 6 &= 5 \times 6 = 30 \end{aligned}$
Add the numbers from 1 to 6 twice.	$\begin{aligned} 1 + 2 + 3 + 4 + 5 + 6 & \quad \text{ascending order} \\ \underline{6 + 5 + 4 + 3 + 2 + 1} & \quad \text{descending order} \\ 7 + 7 + 7 + 7 + 7 + 7 &= 6 \times 7 = 42 \end{aligned}$

Do you see a pattern developing? In each case, twice the sum is the product of the largest number and 1 more than the largest number. Twice the sum of 1 to 7, then, we predict is $7 \times (7 + 1)$, or 7×8, or 56. Let's see if our prediction is correct:

$$\begin{aligned} 1 + 2 + 3 + 4 + 5 + 6 + 7 & \quad \text{ascending order} \\ + \underline{7 + 6 + 5 + 4 + 3 + 2 + 1} & \quad \text{descending order} \\ 8 + 8 + 8 + 8 + 8 + 8 + 8 &= 7 \times 8 = 56 \end{aligned}$$

It is correct: *Twice* the sum of consecutive numbers beginning with 1 is the product of the largest number and 1 more than the largest number. But we are really interested not in *twice* the sum, but *only* the sum. So we divide twice the sum by 2, leaving only the sum.

Our shortcut for finding the sum of consecutive numbers beginning with 1 is: Multiply the largest number by 1 more than the largest number and divide the product by 2. You may be interested to know that a young boy in elementary school discovered this shortcut in the late 18th century. He later went on to be one of the greatest mathematicians of all time. His name was Carl Friedrich Gauss (1777–1855).

? HOW TO Find the Sum of Consecutive Numbers Beginning with 1

Multiply the largest number by 1 more than the largest number and divide the product by 2.

$$\frac{\text{Sum of consecutive numbers}}{\text{beginning with 1}} = \frac{\text{largest number} \times (\text{largest number} + 1)}{2}$$

EXAMPLE A loan for 36 months, with a finance charge of \$1,276.50, is paid in full with 15 payments remaining. Find the finance charge to be refunded.

$$\text{Refund fraction} = \frac{\text{sum of sequence numbers of payments remaining}}{\text{sum of all payment sequence numbers}}$$

$$\text{Sum of the sequence numbers of 15 payments remaining} = \frac{15\,(15+1)}{2}$$

The sum of consecutive numbers from 1 to 15.

$$= \frac{15 \times 16}{2}$$

$$= 120$$

$$\text{Sum of all 36 payment sequence numbers} = \frac{36\,(36+1)}{2}$$

The sum of consecutive numbers from 1 to 36.

$$= \frac{36 \times 37}{2}$$

$$= 666$$

$$\text{Refund fraction} = \frac{120}{666} = \frac{20}{111}$$

$$\text{Finance charge refund} = \text{finance charge} \times \text{refund fraction}$$

$$= \$1{,}276.50 \times \frac{20}{111}$$

$$= \$230$$

The finance charge refund is \$230.

TIP! Shortcut for Finding the Refund Fraction

The calculations for the refund fraction in the preceding example can be further simplified by writing all the calculations in a complex fraction.

$$\text{Refund fraction} = \frac{\text{sum of sequence numbers of 15 payments remaining}}{\text{sum of all 36 payment sequence numbers}}$$

$$= \frac{\dfrac{15 \times (15+1)}{2}}{\dfrac{36 \times (36+1)}{2}}$$

A complex fraction is simplified by rewriting it as the division of two fractions.

$$= \frac{15 \times (15+1)}{2} \div \frac{36 \times (36+1)}{2}$$

To divide fractions, invert the second fraction and multiply.
Reduce or cancel.

$$= \frac{15 \times (15+1)}{2} \times \frac{2}{36 \times (36+1)}$$

$$= \frac{15 \times (15+1)}{36 \times (36+1)}$$

Compare this common fraction with the complex fraction we started with. The 2s in the denominators of the complex fraction are reduced. This pattern holds true for every refund fraction. For instance, we can apply this pattern to a refund fraction for eight months remaining on a 24-month loan paid in full.

$$\text{Refund fraction} = \frac{\text{sum of sequence numbers of eight payments remaining}}{\text{sum of all 24 payment sequence numbers}}$$

$$\text{Refund fraction} = \frac{\dfrac{8 \times 9}{2}}{\dfrac{24 \times 25}{2}} = \frac{8 \times 9}{24 \times 25} = \frac{72}{600} = \frac{3}{25}$$

Can a Decimal Equivalent Be Used Instead of the Refund Fraction?

Even though we use the terminology *refund fraction,* we can use a decimal equivalent of the fraction instead. In finding the decimal equivalent using a scientific, business, or graphing calculator, we can use a continuous series of calculations. Remember, the fraction bar indicates division. Using the division symbol instead, we must enclose the denominator in parentheses. For instance, use a calculator to

find $\dfrac{8 \times 9}{24 \times 25}$. $\boxed{AC}\ 8\ \boxed{\times}\ 9\ \boxed{\div}\ \boxed{(}\ 24\ \boxed{\times}\ 25\ \boxed{)}\ \boxed{=} \Rightarrow 0.12$

In the preceding example, $\frac{20}{111} = 0.1801801802$ and $\$1,276.50 \times 0.1801801802 = \$230.$

SELF-CHECK 12.2

1. Find the refund fraction on an 18-month loan if it is paid off with eight months remaining.

2. Stephen Helba took out a loan to purchase a computer. He originally agreed to pay off the loan in 18 months with a finance charge of $205. He paid the loan in full after 12 payments. How much finance charge refund should he get?

3. John Paszel took out a loan for 48 months, but paid it in full after 28 months. Find the refund fraction he should use to calculate the amount of his refund.

4. If the finance charge on a loan made by Marjorie Young is $1,645 and the loan is to be paid in 48 monthly payments, find the finance charge refund if the loan is paid in full with 28 months remaining.

5. Phillamone Berry has a car loan with a company that refunds interest using the rule of 78 when loans are paid in full ahead of schedule. He is using an employee bonus to pay off his Taurus, which is on a 42-month loan. The total interest for the loan is $2,397, and he has 15 more payments to make. How much finance charge will he get credit for if he pays the loan in full immediately?

6. Dwayne Moody purchased a four-wheel drive vehicle and is using severance pay from his current job to pay off the vehicle loan before moving to his new job. The total interest on the 36-month loan is $3,227. How much finance charge refund will he receive if he pays the loan with 10 more payments left?

12.3 Open-End Credit

 Find the unpaid balance using the unpaid balance method.

 Find the unpaid balance using the average daily balance method.

Open-end loans are often called **line-of-credit accounts.** While a person or company is paying off loans, that person or company may also be adding to the total loan account by making a new purchase or otherwise borrowing money on the account.

For example, you may want to use your Visa card to buy new textbooks even though you still owe for clothes bought last winter. Likewise, a business may use an open-end credit account to buy a new machine this month even though it still owes the bank for funds used to pay a major supplier six months ago.

Nearly all open-end accounts are billed monthly. Interest rates are most often stated as annual rates compounded monthly. Therefore, interest accrued for the month will itself accrue interest the next month if it has not been paid. Interest on open-end credit accounts is figured according to the *unpaid balance method* or the *average daily balance method*.

1 Find the unpaid balance using the unpaid balance method.

Using the **unpaid balance method,** interest accrues on the unpaid balance as of the first day of the monthly period, regardless of the charges or payments made to the account during the month. Interest is calculated by multiplying the unpaid balance on the first day of the monthly period by the monthly rate of interest.

$$I = P\,R\,T$$

$$\text{Interest for one month} = \text{unpaid balance on first day} \times \text{annual rate} \times \tfrac{1}{12} \text{ year}$$

$$= \text{unpaid balance on first day} \times \text{monthly rate}$$

For example, if the unpaid balance on the first day is $147 and the interest rate is $1\frac{1}{2}\%$ monthly, the interest for the monthly period is 147×0.015, or $2.21 rounded to the nearest cent.

To find the unpaid balance as of the first day of the monthly period, we begin with the unpaid balance for the first day of the previous monthly period, add the previous monthly period's accrued interest, add purchases made during the previous monthly period, and subtract payments made during the previous monthly period.

 HOW TO Find the Unpaid Balance Using the Unpaid Balance Method

1. Find the interest for the previous monthly period: multiply the unpaid balance of the first day of the previous monthly period by the monthly interest rate.

Interest = unpaid balance × monthly interest rate

2. Find the total purchases and cash advances during the previous monthly period: add all purchases or cash advances charged to the account during the previous monthly period.

3. Find the total payments for the previous monthly period: add all payments and adjustments credited to the account during the previous monthly period.

4. To the unpaid balance at the beginning of the previous monthly period, add the interest for the previous monthly period from step 1, and add the total purchases and cash advances from step 2. Then, subtract the total payments and credits from step 3.

Unpaid balance at the beginning of the monthly period = unpaid balance at the beginning of previous monthly period + interest for previous monthly period + total purchases and cash advances during previous monthly period − total payments during previous monthly period

---

EXAMPLE   Strong's Mailing Service has an open-end credit account at a local business supply store. On September 1, Strong's account had an unpaid balance of $150. During September, Strong's made purchases totaling $356.20 and a payment of $42.50. The supply store charges 1.7% interest per month on any unpaid balance. In October, Strong's made a payment of $200 and made purchases of $50. Find the unpaid balance on (a) October 1 and (b) November 1.

(a) Find the finance charge on the unpaid balance as of September 1.

$$\text{Finance charge} = \text{previous unpaid balance} \times \text{rate}$$
$$= \$150 \times 0.017$$
$$= \$2.55$$

$$\text{October 1 unpaid balance} = \text{September 1 unpaid balance} + \text{interest for September 1 unpaid balance} + \text{September charges} - \text{September payments}$$
$$= \$150 + \$2.55 + \$356.20 - \$42.50$$
$$= \$466.55$$

(b) Find the finance charge on the unpaid balance as of October 1.

$$\text{Finance charge} = \text{unpaid balance} \times \text{rate}$$
$$= \$466.55 \times 0.017$$
$$= \$7.93$$

$$\text{November 1 unpaid balance} = \text{October 1 unpaid balance} + \text{interest on October 1 unpaid balance} + \text{October charges} - \text{October payments}$$
$$= \$466.55 + \$7.93 + \$50 - \$200$$
$$= \$324.18$$

The October 1 unpaid balance is $466.25. The November 1 unpaid balance is $324.18.

 2 Find the unpaid balance using the average daily balance method.

Rather than basing interest on the unpaid balance as of the first day of the monthly period, many lenders determine the finance charge using the **average daily balance method.** In this method, the daily balances of the account are determined, and then the sum of these balances is divided by the number of days in the billing cycle. This average daily balance is then multiplied by the monthly interest rate to find the finance charge for the month.

? HOW TO **Find the Average Daily Balance**

1. Find the daily unpaid balance for each day in the billing cycle.
   (a) Find the total purchases and cash advances for the day: add all the purchases and cash advances charged to the account during the day.
   (b) Find the total credits for the day: add all the payments and adjustments credited to the account during the day.
   (c) To the previous daily unpaid balance, add the total purchases and cash advances for the day (from step 1a). Then, subtract the total credits for the day (from step 1b).

   Daily unpaid balance = previous daily unpaid balance
   + total purchases and cash advances for the day
   − total credits for the day

2. Add the unpaid balances from step 1 for each day and divide the sum by the number of days in the monthly period.

   Average daily balance = $\dfrac{\text{sum of daily unpaid balances}}{\text{number of days in billing cycle}}$

TIP! **When Does the Balance Change?**

In most cases, if a transaction reaches a financial institution at any time during the day, the transaction is posted and the balance is updated at the end of the business day. Thus, the new balance takes effect at the beginning of the next day. **Calculations on the day's unpaid balance are made on the end-of-day amount.**

EXAMPLE Use the chart showing May activity in the Hodge's Tax Service charge account to determine the average daily balance and finance charge for the month. The bank's finance charge is 1.5% per month on the average daily balance.

Date Transaction Posted	Transaction	Amount
May 1	Billing date	Balance $122.70
May 7	Payment	25.00
May 10	Purchase (pencils)	12.00
May 13	Purchase (envelopes)	20.00
May 20	Cash advance	50.00
May 23	Purchase (business forms)	100.00

To find the average daily balance, we must find the unpaid balance for each day, add these balances, and divide by the number of days.

Day	Balance		Day	Balance		Day	Balance	
1	122.70		11	109.70		21	179.70	
2	122.70		12	109.70		22	179.70	
3	122.70		13	129.70	(109.70 + 20)	23	279.70	(179.70 + 100)
4	122.70		14	129.70		24	279.70	
5	122.70		15	129.70		25	279.70	
6	122.70		16	129.70		26	279.70	
7	97.70	(122.70 − 25)	17	129.70		27	279.70	
8	97.70		18	129.70		28	279.70	
9	97.70		19	129.70		29	279.70	
10	109.70	(125.70 + 12)	20	179.70	(129.70 + 50)	30	279.70	
						31	279.70	

Total: $5,322.70   Average Daily Balance: $171.70

The average daily balance can also be determined by grouping days that have the same balance.

For the first six days, May 1–May 6, there is no activity, so the daily unpaid balance is the previous unpaid balance of $122.70. The sum of daily unpaid balances for these six days, then, is 122.70 × 6.

$$\$122.70 \times 6 = \$736.20$$

On May 7 there is a payment of $25, which reduces the daily unpaid balance.

$$\$122.70 - \$25 = \$97.70$$

The new balance of $97.70 holds for the three days (May 7, 8, and 9) until May 10.

$$\boxed{\$97.70} \times 3 = \$293.10$$

Continue doing this until you get to the end of the cycle. The calculations can be organized in a chart.

Date	Daily Unpaid Balance	Number of Days	Partial Sum
May 1–May 6	$122.70	6	$ 736.20
May 7–May 9	97.70	3	293.10
May 10–May 12	109.70	3	329.10
May 13–May 19	129.70	7	907.90
May 20–May 22	179.70	3	539.10
May 23–May 31	279.70	9	2,517.30
		Total 31	$5,322.70

Now divide the sum of $5,322.70 by the 31 days.

$$\text{Average daily balance} = \frac{\text{sum of daily unpaid balances}}{\text{number of days}}$$

$$= \frac{\$5,322.70}{31} = \boxed{\$171.70}$$

To find the interest, multiply the average daily balance by the monthly interest rate of 1.5%.

$$\text{Finance charge} = \boxed{\$171.70} \times 0.015$$

$$= \$2.58$$

The average daily balance is $171.70 and the finance charge is $2.58.

 TIP! Unpaid Monthly Balance versus Unpaid Daily Balance

The unpaid balance on an account for a billing cycle is the unpaid daily balance for the *last* day of the billing cycle. The beginning balance for the next cycle is the unpaid balance for the previous cycle.

The unpaid balance for the May billing cycle in the preceding example is $279.70. This is also the beginning balance for the June billing cycle.

SELF-CHECK 12.3

 1

1. What is the finance charge on an unpaid balance of $275.69 if the interest rate per month is 2.3%?

2. Find the new unpaid balance on an account with an interest rate of 1.6% per month if the previous unpaid balance was $176.95 and a payment of $45 was made.

3. Chang's grocery has an open-end credit account with Great China Wholesale Distributor. Interest is charged on the unpaid balance on the 15th of each month at a rate of 1.2%. On June 15 Chang's unpaid balance was $3,805. How much interest was charged?

4. Between June 15 and July 15, Chang charged $4,983 worth of merchandise and paid $7,000 on the account. What was Chang's unpaid balance on July 15?

5. How much interest was charged to Chang's account on July 15? What was the unpaid balance on August 15 if Chang made a payment of $500 on August 1 but charged $75 on the same day?

6. Rosa Burnett has a revolving charge account that charges 1% of the unpaid balance on the last day of the billing cycle. Her balance was $897.52. How much interest was charged?

7. Jim Riddle has a credit card that charges 10% annual interest on the monthly average daily balance for the billing cycle. The current billing cycle has 29 days. For 15 days his balance was $2,534.95. For seven days the balance was $1,534.95. And for seven days the balance was $1,892.57. Find the average daily balance. Find the amount of interest.

8. Suppose the charge account of Strong's Mailing Service at the local supply store had a 1.8% interest rate per month on the average daily balance. Find the average daily balance if Strong's had an unpaid balance on March 1 of $128.50, a payment of $20 posted on March 6, and a purchase of $25.60 posted on March 20. The billing cycle ends March 31.

9. Using exercise 8, find Strong's finance charge on April 1.

10. Make a chart to show the transactions for Rick Schiendler's credit card account in which interest is charged on the average daily balance. The cycle begins on May 4, and the cycle ends on June 3. The beginning balance is $283.57. A payment of $200 is posted on May 18. A charge of $19.73 is posted on May 7. A charge of $53.82 is posted on May 12. A charge of $115.18 is posted on May 29. How many days are in the cycle? What is the average daily balance?

11. Rick is charged 1.42% per period. What is the finance charge for the cycle?

12. What is the beginning balance for the next cycle of Rick's credit card account?

12.4 Annual Percentage Rates

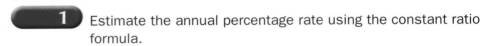

1 Estimate the annual percentage rate using the constant ratio formula.

2 Find the annual percentage rate using a table.

In 1969 the federal government passed the Truth-in-Lending Act, which requires that a lending institution tell the borrower, in writing, what the actual annual rate of interest is as it applies to the balance due on the loan each period. This interest rate tells the borrower what the true cost of the loan is.

For example, if you borrowed $1,500 for a year and paid an interest charge of $165, you would be paying an interest rate of 11% annually on the entire $1,500 ($165 ÷ $1,500 = 0.11 = 11\%$). But if you paid the money back in 12 monthly installments of $138.75 ([$1,500 + $165] ÷ 12 = $138.75), you would not have the use of the $1,500 for a full year. Instead, you would be paying it back in 12 payments of $138.75 each. Thus, you are losing the use of some of the money every month, but are still paying interest at the rate of 11% of *the entire amount*. This means that you are actually paying *more than* 11% interest. The true **annual percentage rate (APR)** is the effective interest rate discussed in Chapter 10. Applied to installment loans, the APR, or effective rate, is the *annual simple interest rate equivalent* that is actually being paid on the unpaid balances. The APR can be calculated using a government-issued table, or estimated by a formula.

Estimate the annual percentage rate using the constant ratio formula.

You can use the **constant ratio formula** to estimate the annual percentage rate on any loan that is paid back in equal quarterly, monthly, or weekly installments. This formula gives a close approximation of the APR if the time of the loan is short. On loans made for 10 years or more, this formula will not give a fair approximation of the APR.

 HOW TO Estimate the Annual Percentage Rate Using the Constant Ratio Formula

1. Substitute known values into the formula.

Approximate annual percentage rate

$$= \frac{2 \times \text{number of payments per year} \times \text{total interest}}{\text{amount financed} \times (\text{total number of payments} + 1)}$$

$$\text{APR} = \frac{2NI}{P(T+1)}$$

2. Solve the formula for the unknown.

EXAMPLE A loan of $6,000, borrowed for three years, required interest of $1,440. Find the annual percentage rate if the loan was repaid in monthly installments.

Total number of payments on the loan = 3 years × 12 payments per year

= 36 payments

Annual percentage rate

$$\text{APR} = \frac{2 \times \text{number of payments per year} \times \text{total interest}}{\text{amount financed} \times (\text{total number of payments} + 1)}$$

$$\text{APR} = \frac{(2)(12)(\$1,440)}{(\$6,000)(36+1)} = 0.1556756, \text{ which rounds to } 0.156, \text{ or } 15.6\%$$

The approximate annual percentage rate is 15.6%. Thus, each month the borrower is paying approximately $\frac{15.6}{12}$% or 1.3% of the remaining balance in interest.

 TIP! Your Mind Is Quicker Than Your Fingers!

In the series of calculations $\frac{2(12)(\$1,440)}{(\$6,000)(36+1)}$, you can work more quickly and you generally make fewer mistakes if you do some of the calculations mentally.

$\left.\begin{array}{l} 2 \times 12 = 24 \\ 36 + 1 = 37 \end{array}\right\}$ Work mentally.

Then, $\frac{24(1,400)}{6000(37)}$ is a shorter series of calculations.

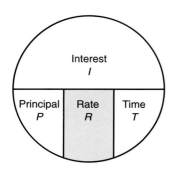

Figure 12-1 Interest
Formula for Finding Rate

$$R = \frac{I}{PT}$$

Compare the APR for the preceding example to the simple interest rate if the loan was repaid in a lump sum at the end of the three years. Use the formula for finding the rate (Fig. 12-1).

$$R = \frac{I}{PT} = \frac{\$1,440}{\$6,000(3)} = \frac{\$1,440}{\$18,000} = 0.08 = 8\%$$

The loan rate might have been advertised as 8% based on the simple interest rate for the entire time of the loan.

2 Find the annual percentage rate using a table.

While the formula provides a good approximation in many cases, the federal government issues annual percentage rate tables, which are used to find *exact* APR rates (within $\frac{1}{4}$%, which is the federal standard). A portion of one of these tables, based on monthly payments, is shown in Table 12-1.

? HOW TO Find the Annual Percentage Rate Using a per $100 of Amount Financed Table

1. Find the interest per $100 of amount financed: multiply the finance charges including interest by $100 and divide by the amount financed.

$$\text{Interest per }\$100 = \frac{\text{finance charge} \times \$100}{\text{amount financed}}$$

2. Find the row corresponding to the number of monthly payments. Move across the row to find the number closest to the value from step 1. Read up the column to find the annual percentage rate for that column. If the result in step 1 is exactly halfway between two table values, a rate halfway between the two rates can be used.

EXAMPLE Lewis Strang bought a motorcycle for $3,000, which was financed at $142 per month for 24 months. There was no down payment. Find the APR.

$$\text{Total paid} = 24 \times \$142$$
$$= \$3,408$$
$$\text{Interest} = \$3,408 - \$3,000$$
$$= \$408$$

$$\text{Interest per }\$100 = \frac{\text{finance charge} \times \$100}{\text{amount financed}} = \frac{\$408 \times \$100}{\$3,000} = \$13.60$$

Find the row for 24 monthly payments. Move across to find the number nearest to $13.60. $13.60 is between $13.54 and $13.82. $13.60 − $13.54 = $0.06; $13.82 − $13.60 = $0.22. Thus, $13.60 is closer to $13.54. Move up to the top of that column to find the **annual percentage rate, which is 12.50%.**

Table 12-1 Interest per $100 of Amount Financed

Number of Monthly Payments	APR (Annual Percentage Rate)															
	10.00%	10.25%	10.50%	10.75%	11.00%	11.25%	11.50%	11.75%	12.00%	12.25%	12.50%	12.75%	13.00%	13.25%	13.50%	13.75%
1	0.83	0.85	0.87	0.90	0.92	0.94	0.96	0.98	1.00	1.02	1.04	1.06	1.08	1.10	1.12	1.15
2	1.25	1.28	1.31	1.35	1.38	1.41	1.44	1.47	1.50	1.53	1.57	1.60	1.63	1.66	1.69	1.72
3	1.67	1.71	1.76	1.80	1.84	1.88	1.92	1.96	2.01	2.05	2.09	2.13	2.17	2.22	2.26	2.30
4	2.09	2.14	2.20	2.25	2.30	2.35	2.41	2.46	2.51	2.57	2.62	2.67	2.72	2.78	2.83	2.88
5	2.51	2.58	2.64	2.70	2.77	2.83	2.89	2.96	3.02	3.08	3.15	3.21	3.27	3.34	3.40	3.46
6	2.94	3.01	3.08	3.16	3.23	3.31	3.38	3.45	3.53	3.60	3.68	3.75	3.83	3.90	3.97	4.05
7	3.36	3.45	3.53	3.62	3.70	3.78	3.87	3.95	4.04	4.12	4.21	4.29	4.38	4.47	4.55	4.64
8	3.79	3.88	3.98	4.07	4.17	4.26	4.36	4.46	4.55	4.65	4.74	4.84	4.94	5.03	5.13	5.22
9	4.21	4.32	4.43	4.53	4.64	4.75	4.85	4.96	5.07	5.17	5.28	5.39	5.49	5.60	5.71	5.82
10	4.64	4.76	4.88	4.99	5.11	5.23	5.35	5.46	5.58	5.70	5.82	5.94	6.05	6.17	6.29	6.41
11	5.07	5.20	5.33	5.45	5.58	5.71	5.84	5.97	6.10	6.23	6.36	6.49	6.62	6.75	6.88	7.01
12	5.50	5.64	5.78	5.92	6.06	6.20	6.34	6.48	6.62	6.76	6.90	7.04	7.18	7.32	7.46	7.60
13	5.93	6.08	6.23	6.38	6.53	6.68	6.84	6.99	7.14	7.29	7.44	7.59	7.75	7.90	8.05	8.20
14	6.36	6.52	6.69	6.85	7.01	7.17	7.34	7.50	7.66	7.82	7.99	8.15	8.31	8.48	8.64	8.81
15	6.80	6.97	7.14	7.32	7.49	7.66	7.84	8.01	8.19	8.36	8.53	8.71	8.88	9.06	9.23	9.41
16	7.23	7.41	7.60	7.78	7.97	8.15	8.34	8.53	8.71	8.90	9.08	9.27	9.46	9.64	9.83	10.02
17	7.67	7.86	8.06	8.25	8.45	8.65	8.84	9.04	9.24	9.44	9.63	9.83	10.03	10.23	10.44	10.63
18	8.10	8.31	8.52	8.73	8.93	9.14	9.35	9.56	9.77	9.98	10.19	10.40	10.61	10.82	11.03	11.24
19	8.54	8.76	8.98	9.20	9.42	9.64	9.86	10.08	10.30	10.52	10.74	10.96	11.18	11.41	11.63	11.85
20	8.98	9.21	9.44	9.67	9.90	10.13	10.37	10.60	10.83	11.06	11.30	11.53	11.76	12.00	12.23	12.46
21	9.42	9.66	9.90	10.15	10.39	10.63	10.88	11.12	11.36	11.61	11.85	12.10	12.34	12.59	12.84	13.08
22	9.86	10.12	10.37	10.62	10.88	11.13	11.39	11.64	11.90	12.16	12.41	12.67	12.93	13.19	13.44	13.70
23	10.30	10.57	10.84	11.10	11.37	11.63	11.90	12.17	12.44	12.71	12.97	13.24	13.51	13.78	14.05	14.32
24	10.75	11.02	11.30	11.58	11.86	12.14	12.42	12.70	12.98	13.26	13.54	13.82	14.10	14.38	14.66	14.95
25	11.19	11.48	11.77	12.06	12.35	12.64	12.93	13.22	13.52	13.81	14.10	14.40	14.69	14.98	15.28	15.57
26	11.64	11.94	12.24	12.54	12.85	13.15	13.45	13.75	14.06	14.36	14.67	14.97	15.28	15.59	15.89	16.20
27	12.09	12.40	12.71	13.03	13.34	13.66	13.97	14.29	14.60	14.92	15.24	15.56	15.87	16.19	16.51	16.83
28	12.53	12.86	13.18	13.51	13.84	14.16	14.49	14.82	15.15	15.48	15.81	16.14	16.47	16.80	17.13	17.46
29	12.98	13.32	13.66	14.00	14.33	14.67	15.01	15.35	15.70	16.04	16.38	16.72	17.07	17.41	17.75	18.10
30	13.43	13.78	14.13	14.48	14.83	15.19	15.54	15.89	16.24	16.60	16.95	17.31	17.66	18.02	18.38	18.74
31	13.89	14.25	14.61	14.97	15.33	15.70	16.06	16.43	16.79	17.16	17.53	17.90	18.27	18.63	19.00	19.38
32	14.34	14.71	15.09	15.46	15.84	16.21	16.59	16.97	17.35	17.73	18.11	18.49	18.87	19.25	19.63	20.02
33	14.79	15.18	15.57	15.95	16.34	16.73	17.12	17.51	17.90	18.29	18.69	19.08	19.47	19.87	20.26	20.66
34	15.25	15.65	16.05	16.44	16.85	17.25	17.65	18.05	18.46	18.86	19.27	19.67	20.08	20.49	20.90	21.31
35	15.70	16.11	16.53	16.94	17.35	17.77	18.18	18.60	19.01	19.43	19.85	20.27	20.69	21.11	21.53	21.95
36	16.16	16.58	17.01	17.43	17.86	18.29	18.71	19.14	19.57	20.00	20.43	20.87	21.30	21.73	22.17	22.60
37	16.62	17.06	17.49	17.93	18.37	18.81	19.25	19.69	20.13	20.58	21.02	21.46	21.91	22.36	22.81	23.25
38	17.08	17.53	17.98	18.43	18.88	19.33	19.78	20.24	20.69	21.15	21.61	22.07	22.52	22.99	23.45	23.91
39	17.54	18.00	18.46	18.93	19.39	19.86	20.32	20.79	21.26	21.73	22.20	22.67	23.14	23.61	24.09	24.56
40	18.00	18.48	18.95	19.43	19.90	20.38	20.86	21.34	21.82	22.30	22.79	23.27	23.76	24.25	24.73	25.22
41	18.47	18.95	19.44	19.93	20.42	20.91	21.40	21.89	22.39	22.88	23.38	23.88	24.38	24.88	25.38	25.88
42	18.93	19.43	19.93	20.43	20.93	21.44	21.94	22.45	22.96	23.47	23.98	24.49	25.00	25.51	26.03	26.55
43	19.40	19.91	20.42	20.94	21.45	21.97	22.49	23.01	23.53	24.05	24.57	25.10	25.62	26.15	26.68	27.21
44	19.86	20.39	20.91	21.44	21.97	22.50	23.03	23.57	24.10	24.64	25.17	25.71	26.25	26.79	27.33	27.88
45	20.33	20.87	21.41	21.95	22.49	23.03	23.58	24.12	24.67	25.22	25.77	26.32	26.88	27.43	27.99	28.55
46	20.80	21.35	21.90	22.46	23.01	23.57	24.13	24.69	25.25	25.81	26.37	26.94	27.51	28.08	28.65	29.22
47	21.27	21.83	22.40	22.79	23.53	24.10	24.68	25.25	25.82	26.40	26.98	27.56	28.14	28.72	29.31	29.89
48	21.74	22.32	22.90	23.48	24.06	24.64	25.23	25.81	26.40	26.99	27.58	28.18	28.77	29.37	29.97	30.57
49	22.21	22.80	23.39	23.99	24.58	25.18	25.78	26.38	26.98	27.59	28.19	28.80	29.41	30.02	30.63	31.24
50	22.69	23.29	23.89	24.50	25.11	25.72	26.33	26.95	27.56	28.18	28.80	29.42	30.04	30.67	31.29	31.92
51	23.16	23.78	24.40	25.02	25.64	26.26	26.89	27.52	28.15	28.78	29.41	30.05	30.68	31.32	31.96	32.60
52	23.64	24.27	24.90	25.53	26.17	26.81	27.45	28.09	28.73	29.38	30.02	30.67	31.32	31.98	32.63	33.29
53	24.11	24.76	25.40	26.05	26.70	27.35	28.00	28.66	29.32	29.98	30.64	31.30	31.97	32.63	33.30	33.97
54	24.59	25.25	25.91	26.57	27.23	27.90	28.56	29.23	29.91	30.58	31.25	31.93	32.61	33.29	33.98	34.66
55	25.07	25.74	26.41	27.09	27.77	28.44	29.13	29.81	30.50	31.18	31.87	32.56	33.26	33.95	34.65	35.35
56	25.55	26.23	26.92	27.61	28.30	28.99	29.69	30.39	31.09	31.79	32.49	33.20	33.91	34.62	35.33	36.04
57	26.03	26.73	27.43	28.13	28.84	29.54	30.25	30.97	31.68	32.39	33.11	33.83	34.56	35.28	36.01	36.74
58	26.51	27.23	27.94	28.66	29.37	30.10	30.82	31.55	32.27	33.00	33.74	34.47	35.21	35.95	36.69	37.43
59	27.00	27.72	28.45	29.18	29.91	30.65	31.39	32.13	32.87	33.61	34.36	35.11	35.86	36.62	37.37	38.13
60	27.48	28.22	28.96	29.71	30.45	31.20	31.96	32.71	33.47	34.23	44.99	35.75	36.52	37.29	38.06	38.83

Table 12-1　Interest per $100 of Amount Financed (continued)

Number of Monthly Payments	APR (Annual Percentage Rate)															
	14.00%	14.25%	14.50%	14.75%	15.00%	15.25%	15.50%	15.75%	16.00%	16.25%	16.50%	16.75%	17.00%	17.25%	17.50%	17.75%
1	1.17	1.19	1.21	1.23	1.25	1.27	1.29	1.31	1.33	1.35	1.37	1.40	1.42	1.44	1.46	1.48
2	1.75	1.78	1.82	1.85	1.88	1.91	1.94	1.97	2.00	2.04	2.07	2.10	2.13	2.16	2.17	2.22
3	2.34	2.38	2.43	2.47	2.51	2.55	2.59	2.64	2.68	2.72	2.76	2.80	2.85	2.89	2.93	2.97
4	2.93	2.99	3.04	3.09	3.14	3.20	3.25	3.30	3.36	3.41	3.46	3.51	3.57	3.62	3.67	3.73
5	3.53	3.59	3.65	3.72	3.78	3.84	3.91	3.97	4.04	4.10	4.16	4.23	4.29	4.35	4.42	4.48
6	4.12	4.20	4.27	4.35	4.42	4.49	4.57	4.64	4.72	4.79	4.87	4.94	5.02	5.01	5.17	5.24
7	4.72	4.81	4.89	4.98	5.06	5.15	5.23	5.32	5.40	5.49	5.58	5.66	5.75	5.83	5.92	6.00
8	5.32	5.42	5.51	5.61	5.71	5.80	5.90	6.00	6.09	6.19	6.29	6.38	6.48	6.58	6.67	6.77
9	5.92	6.03	6.14	6.25	6.35	6.46	6.57	6.68	6.78	6.89	7.00	7.11	7.22	7.32	7.43	7.54
10	6.53	6.65	6.77	6.88	7.00	7.12	7.24	7.36	7.48	7.60	7.72	7.84	7.96	8.08	8.19	8.31
11	7.14	7.27	7.40	7.53	7.66	7.79	7.92	8.05	8.18	8.31	8.44	8.57	8.70	8.83	8.96	9.09
12	7.74	7.89	8.03	8.17	8.31	8.45	8.59	8.74	8.88	9.02	9.16	9.30	9.45	9.59	9.73	9.87
13	8.36	8.51	8.66	8.81	8.97	9.12	9.27	9.43	9.58	9.73	9.89	10.04	10.20	10.35	10.50	10.66
14	8.97	9.13	9.30	9.46	9.63	9.79	9.96	10.12	10.29	10.45	10.67	10.78	10.95	11.11	11.28	11.45
15	9.59	9.76	9.94	10.11	10.29	10.47	10.64	10.82	11.00	11.17	11.35	11.53	11.71	11.88	12.06	12.24
16	10.20	10.39	10.58	10.77	10.95	11.14	11.33	11.52	11.71	11.90	12.09	12.28	12.46	12.65	12.84	13.03
17	10.82	11.02	11.22	11.42	11.62	11.82	12.02	12.22	12.42	12.62	12.83	13.03	13.23	13.43	13.63	13.83
18	11.45	11.66	11.87	12.08	12.29	12.50	12.72	12.93	13.14	13.35	13.57	13.78	13.99	14.21	14.42	14.64
19	12.07	12.30	12.52	12.74	12.97	13.19	13.41	13.64	13.86	14.09	14.31	14.54	14.76	14.99	15.22	15.44
20	12.70	12.93	13.17	13.41	13.64	13.88	14.11	14.35	14.59	14.82	15.06	15.30	15.54	15.77	16.01	16.25
21	13.33	13.58	13.82	14.07	14.32	14.57	14.82	15.06	15.31	15.56	15.81	16.06	16.31	16.56	16.81	17.07
22	13.96	14.22	14.48	14.74	15.00	15.26	15.52	15.78	16.04	16.30	16.57	16.83	17.09	17.36	17.62	17.88
23	14.59	14.87	15.14	15.41	15.68	15.96	16.23	16.50	16.78	17.05	17.32	17.60	17.88	18.15	18.43	18.70
24	15.23	15.51	15.80	16.08	16.37	16.65	16.94	17.22	17.51	17.80	18.09	18.37	18.66	18.95	19.24	19.53
25	15.87	16.17	16.46	16.76	17.06	17.35	17.65	17.95	18.25	18.55	18.85	19.15	19.45	19.75	20.05	20.36
26	16.51	16.82	17.13	17.44	17.75	18.06	18.37	18.68	18.99	19.30	19.62	19.93	20.24	20.56	20.87	21.19
27	17.15	17.47	17.80	18.12	18.44	18.76	19.09	19.41	19.74	20.06	20.39	20.71	21.04	21.37	21.69	22.02
28	17.80	18.13	18.47	18.80	19.14	19.47	19.81	20.15	20.48	20.82	21.16	21.50	21.84	22.18	22.52	22.86
29	18.45	18.79	19.14	19.49	19.83	20.18	20.53	20.88	21.23	21.58	21.94	22.29	22.64	22.99	23.35	23.70
30	19.10	19.45	19.81	20.17	20.54	20.90	21.26	21.62	21.99	22.35	22.72	23.08	23.45	23.81	24.18	24.55
31	19.75	20.12	20.49	20.87	21.24	21.61	21.99	22.37	22.74	23.12	23.50	23.88	24.26	24.64	25.02	25.40
32	20.40	20.79	21.17	21.56	21.95	22.33	22.72	23.11	23.50	23.89	24.28	24.68	25.07	25.46	25.86	26.25
33	21.06	21.46	21.85	22.25	22.65	23.06	23.46	23.86	24.26	24.67	25.07	25.48	25.88	26.29	26.70	27.11
34	21.72	22.13	22.54	22.95	23.37	23.78	24.19	24.61	25.03	25.44	25.86	26.28	26.70	27.12	27.54	27.97
35	22.38	22.80	23.23	23.65	24.08	24.51	24.94	25.36	25.79	26.23	26.66	27.09	27.52	27.96	28.39	28.83
36	23.04	23.48	23.92	24.35	24.80	25.24	25.68	26.12	26.57	27.01	27.46	27.90	28.35	28.80	29.25	29.70
37	23.70	24.16	24.69	25.06	25.51	25.97	26.42	26.88	27.34	27.80	28.26	28.72	29.18	29.64	30.10	30.57
38	24.37	24.84	25.30	25.77	26.24	26.70	27.17	27.64	28.11	28.59	29.06	29.53	30.01	30.49	30.96	31.44
39	25.04	25.52	26.00	26.48	26.96	27.44	27.92	28.41	28.89	29.38	29.87	30.36	30.85	31.34	31.83	32.32
40	25.71	26.20	26.70	27.19	27.69	28.18	28.68	29.18	29.68	30.18	30.68	31.18	31.68	32.19	32.69	33.20
41	26.39	26.89	27.40	27.91	28.41	28.92	29.44	29.95	30.46	30.97	31.49	32.01	32.52	33.04	33.56	34.08
42	27.06	27.58	28.10	28.62	29.15	29.67	30.19	30.72	31.25	31.78	32.31	32.84	33.37	33.90	34.44	34.97
43	27.74	28.27	28.81	29.34	29.88	30.42	30.96	31.50	32.04	32.58	33.13	33.67	34.22	34.76	35.31	35.86
44	28.42	28.97	29.52	30.07	30.62	31.17	31.72	32.28	32.83	33.39	33.95	34.51	35.07	35.63	36.19	36.78
45	29.11	29.67	30.23	30.79	31.36	31.92	32.49	33.06	33.63	34.20	34.77	35.35	35.92	36.50	37.08	37.66
46	29.79	30.36	30.94	31.52	32.10	32.68	33.26	33.84	34.43	35.01	35.60	36.19	36.78	37.37	37.96	38.56
47	30.48	31.07	31.66	32.25	32.84	33.44	34.03	34.63	35.23	35.83	36.43	37.04	37.64	38.25	38.86	39.46
48	31.17	31.77	32.37	32.98	33.59	34.20	34.81	35.42	36.03	36.65	37.27	37.88	38.50	39.13	39.75	40.37
49	31.86	32.48	33.09	33.71	34.34	34.96	35.59	36.21	36.84	37.47	38.10	38.74	39.37	40.01	40.65	41.29
50	32.55	33.18	33.82	34.45	35.09	35.73	36.37	37.01	37.65	38.30	38.94	39.59	40.24	40.89	41.55	42.20
51	33.25	33.89	34.54	35.19	35.84	36.49	37.15	37.81	38.46	39.17	39.79	40.45	41.11	41.78	42.45	43.12
52	33.95	34.61	35.27	35.93	36.60	37.27	37.94	38.61	39.28	39.96	40.63	41.31	41.99	42.67	43.36	44.04
53	34.65	35.32	36.00	36.68	37.36	38.04	38.72	39.41	40.10	40.79	41.48	42.17	42.87	43.57	44.27	44.97
54	35.35	36.04	36.73	37.42	38.12	38.82	39.52	40.22	40.92	41.63	42.33	43.04	43.75	44.47	45.18	45.90
55	36.05	36.76	37.46	38.17	38.88	39.60	40.31	41.03	41.74	42.47	43.19	43.91	44.64	45.37	46.10	46.83
56	36.76	37.48	38.20	38.92	39.65	40.38	41.11	41.84	42.57	43.31	44.05	44.79	45.53	46.27	47.02	47.77
57	37.47	38.20	38.94	39.68	40.42	41.16	41.91	42.65	43.40	44.15	44.91	45.66	46.42	47.18	47.94	47.71
58	38.18	38.93	39.68	40.43	41.19	41.95	42.71	43.47	44.23	45.00	45.77	46.54	47.32	48.09	48.87	49.65
59	38.89	39.66	40.42	41.19	41.96	42.74	43.51	44.29	45.07	45.85	46.64	47.42	48.21	49.01	49.80	50.60
60	39.61	40.39	41.17	41.95	42.74	43.53	44.32	45.11	45.91	46.71	47.51	48.31	49.12	49.92	50.73	51.55

Table 12-1 Interest per $100 of Amount Financed (continued)

Number of Monthly Payments	APR (Annual Percentage Rate)															
	18.00%	18.25%	18.50%	18.75%	19.00%	19.25%	19.50%	19.75%	20.00%	20.25%	20.50%	20.75%	21.00%	21.25%	21.50%	21.75%
1	1.50	1.52	1.54	1.56	1.58	1.60	1.62	1.65	1.67	1.69	1.71	1.73	1.75	1.77	1.79	1.81
2	2.26	2.29	2.32	2.35	2.38	2.41	2.44	2.48	2.51	2.54	2.57	2.60	2.63	2.66	2.70	2.73
3	3.01	3.06	3.10	3.14	3.18	3.23	3.27	3.31	3.35	3.39	3.44	3.48	3.52	3.56	3.60	3.65
4	3.78	3.83	3.88	3.94	3.99	4.04	4.10	4.15	4.20	4.25	4.31	4.36	4.41	4.47	4.52	4.57
5	4.54	4.61	4.67	4.74	4.80	4.86	4.93	4.99	5.06	5.12	5.18	5.25	5.31	5.37	5.44	5.50
6	5.32	5.39	5.46	5.54	5.61	5.69	5.76	5.84	5.91	5.99	6.06	6.14	6.21	6.29	6.36	6.44
7	6.09	6.18	6.26	6.35	6.43	6.52	6.60	6.69	6.78	6.86	6.95	7.04	7.12	7.21	7.29	7.38
8	6.87	6.96	7.06	7.16	7.26	7.35	7.45	7.55	7.64	7.74	7.84	7.94	8.03	8.13	8.23	8.33
9	7.65	7.76	7.87	7.97	8.08	8.19	8.30	8.41	8.52	8.63	8.73	8.84	8.95	9.06	9.17	9.28
10	8.43	8.55	8.67	8.79	8.91	9.03	9.15	9.27	9.39	9.51	9.63	9.75	9.88	10.00	10.12	10.24
11	9.22	9.35	9.49	9.62	9.75	9.88	10.01	10.14	10.28	10.41	10.54	10.67	10.80	10.94	11.07	11.20
12	10.02	10.16	10.30	10.44	10.59	10.73	10.87	11.02	11.16	11.31	11.45	11.59	11.74	11.88	12.02	12.17
13	10.81	10.97	11.12	11.28	11.43	11.59	11.74	11.90	12.05	12.21	12.36	12.52	12.67	12.83	12.99	13.14
14	11.61	11.78	11.95	12.11	12.28	12.45	12.61	12.78	12.95	13.11	13.28	13.45	13.62	13.79	13.95	14.12
15	12.42	12.59	12.77	12.95	13.13	13.31	13.49	13.67	13.85	14.03	14.21	14.39	14.57	14.75	14.93	15.11
16	13.22	13.41	13.60	13.80	13.99	14.18	14.37	14.56	14.75	14.94	15.13	15.33	15.52	15.71	15.90	16.10
17	14.04	14.24	14.44	14.64	14.85	15.05	15.25	15.46	15.66	15.86	16.07	16.27	16.48	16.68	16.89	17.09
18	14.85	15.07	15.28	15.49	15.71	15.93	16.14	16.36	16.57	16.79	17.01	17.22	17.44	17.66	17.88	18.09
19	15.67	15.90	16.12	16.35	16.58	16.81	17.03	17.26	17.49	17.72	17.95	18.18	18.41	18.64	18.87	19.10
20	16.49	16.73	16.97	17.21	17.45	17.69	17.93	18.17	18.41	18.66	18.90	19.14	19.38	19.63	19.87	20.11
21	17.32	17.57	17.82	18.07	18.33	18.58	18.83	19.09	19.34	19.60	19.85	20.11	20.36	20.62	20.87	21.13
22	18.15	18.41	18.68	18.94	19.21	19.47	19.74	20.01	20.27	20.54	20.81	21.08	21.34	21.61	21.88	22.15
23	18.98	19.26	19.54	19.81	20.09	20.37	20.65	20.93	21.21	21.49	21.77	22.05	22.33	22.61	22.90	23.18
24	19.82	20.11	20.40	20.69	20.98	21.27	21.56	21.86	22.15	22.44	22.74	23.03	23.33	23.62	23.92	24.21
25	20.66	20.96	21.27	21.57	21.87	22.18	22.48	22.79	23.10	23.40	23.71	24.02	24.32	24.63	24.94	25.25
26	21.50	21.82	22.14	22.45	22.77	23.09	23.41	23.73	24.04	24.36	24.68	25.01	25.33	25.65	25.97	26.29
27	22.35	22.68	23.01	23.44	23.67	24.00	24.33	24.67	25.00	25.33	25.67	26.00	26.34	26.67	27.01	27.34
28	23.20	23.55	23.89	24.23	24.58	24.92	25.27	25.61	25.96	26.30	26.65	27.00	27.35	27.70	28.05	28.40
29	24.06	24.41	24.27	25.13	25.49	25.84	26.20	26.56	26.92	27.28	27.64	28.00	28.37	28.73	29.09	29.46
30	24.92	25.29	25.66	26.03	26.40	26.77	27.14	27.52	27.89	28.26	28.64	29.01	29.39	29.77	30.14	30.52
31	25.78	26.16	26.55	26.93	27.32	27.70	28.09	28.47	28.86	29.25	29.64	30.03	30.42	30.81	31.20	31.59
32	26.65	27.04	27.44	27.84	28.24	28.64	29.04	29.44	29.84	30.24	30.64	31.05	31.45	31.85	32.26	32.67
33	27.52	27.93	28.34	28.75	29.16	29.57	29.99	30.40	30.82	31.23	31.65	32.07	32.49	32.91	33.33	33.75
34	28.39	28.81	29.24	29.66	30.09	30.52	30.95	31.37	31.80	32.23	32.67	33.10	33.53	33.96	34.40	34.83
35	29.27	29.71	30.14	30.58	31.02	31.47	31.91	32.35	32.79	33.24	33.68	34.13	34.58	35.03	35.47	35.92
36	30.15	30.60	31.05	31.51	31.96	32.42	32.87	33.33	33.79	34.25	34.71	35.17	35.63	36.09	36.56	37.02
37	31.03	31.50	31.97	32.43	32.90	33.37	33.84	34.32	34.79	35.26	35.74	36.21	36.69	37.16	37.64	38.12
38	31.92	32.40	32.88	33.37	33.85	34.33	34.82	35.30	35.79	36.28	36.77	37.26	37.75	38.24	38.73	39.23
39	32.81	33.31	33.80	34.30	34.80	35.30	35.80	36.30	36.80	37.30	37.81	38.31	38.82	39.32	39.83	40.34
40	33.71	34.22	34.73	35.24	35.75	36.26	36.78	37.29	37.81	38.33	38.85	39.37	39.89	40.41	40.93	41.46
41	34.61	35.13	35.66	36.18	36.71	37.24	37.77	38.30	38.83	39.36	39.89	40.43	40.96	41.50	42.04	42.58
42	35.51	36.05	36.59	37.13	37.67	38.21	38.76	39.30	39.85	40.40	40.95	41.50	42.05	42.60	43.15	43.71
43	36.42	36.97	37.52	38.08	38.63	39.19	39.75	40.31	40.87	41.44	42.00	42.57	43.13	43.70	44.27	44.84
44	37.33	37.89	38.46	39.03	39.60	40.18	40.75	41.33	41.90	42.48	43.06	43.64	44.22	44.81	45.39	45.98
45	38.24	38.82	39.41	39.99	40.58	41.17	41.75	42.35	42.94	43.53	44.13	44.72	45.32	45.92	46.52	47.12
46	39.16	39.75	40.35	40.95	41.55	42.16	42.76	43.37	43.98	44.58	45.20	45.81	46.42	47.03	47.65	48.27
47	40.08	40.69	41.30	41.92	42.54	43.15	43.77	44.40	45.02	45.64	46.27	46.90	47.53	48.16	48.79	49.42
48	41.00	41.63	42.26	42.89	43.52	44.15	44.79	45.43	46.07	46.71	47.35	47.99	48.64	49.28	49.93	50.58
49	41.93	42.57	43.22	43.86	44.51	45.16	45.81	46.46	47.12	47.77	48.43	49.09	49.75	50.41	51.08	51.74
50	42.86	43.52	44.18	44.84	45.50	46.17	46.83	47.50	48.17	48.84	49.52	50.19	50.87	51.55	52.23	52.91
51	43.79	44.47	45.14	45.82	46.50	47.18	47.86	48.55	49.23	49.92	50.61	51.30	51.99	52.69	53.38	54.08
52	44.73	45.42	46.11	46.80	47.50	48.20	48.89	49.59	50.30	51.00	51.71	52.41	53.12	53.83	54.55	55.26
53	45.67	46.38	47.08	47.79	48.50	49.22	49.93	50.65	51.37	52.09	52.81	53.53	54.26	54.98	55.71	56.44
54	46.62	47.34	48.06	48.79	49.51	50.24	50.97	51.70	52.44	53.17	53.91	54.65	55.39	56.14	56.88	57.63
55	47.57	48.30	49.04	49.78	50.52	51.27	52.02	52.76	53.52	54.27	55.02	55.78	56.54	57.30	58.08	58.82
56	48.52	49.27	50.03	50.78	51.54	52.30	53.06	53.83	54.60	55.37	56.14	56.91	57.68	58.46	59.24	60.02
57	49.47	50.24	51.01	51.79	52.56	53.34	54.12	54.90	55.68	56.47	57.25	58.04	58.84	59.63	60.43	61.22
58	50.43	51.22	52.00	52.79	53.58	54.38	55.17	55.97	56.77	57.57	58.38	59.18	59.99	60.80	61.62	62.43
59	51.39	52.20	53.00	53.80	54.61	55.42	56.23	57.05	57.87	58.68	59.51	60.33	61.15	61.98	62.81	63.64
60	52.36	53.18	54.00	54.82	55.64	56.47	57.30	58.13	58.96	59.80	60.64	61.48	62.32	63.17	64.01	64.86

To help in finding the closest table value, you can use the procedure described in the How-To box.

HOW TO Find the Closest Table Value in the APR Table

1. Find the two table values that the given value is between.
2. Subtract the lower table value from the given value.
3. Subtract the given value from the higher table value.
4. Compare the results of steps 2 and 3 and select the column with the smaller difference.
5. If the results of steps 2 and 3 are the same, the given amount is *exactly halfway* between the two table values and the annual percentage rate is halfway between the two percentage rates at the top of the table.

TIP! **How Formulas Evolve**

Formulas often represent the result of several manipulations, so that fewer steps are required when using the final version of the formula.

Since Table 12-1 uses the finance charge per $100 of the amount financed, the amount financed is divided by $100, then the finance charge is divided by the result. Examine the manipulations.

Interest per $100 = finance charge ÷ (amount financed ÷ 100)

Interest per $100 = finance charge ÷ (amount financed × $\frac{1}{100}$)   **Convert division to equivalent multiplication.**

Interest per $100 = finance charge ÷ $\frac{\text{amount financed}}{100}$ **Multiply.**

Interest per $100 = finance charge × $\frac{100}{\text{amount financed}}$ **Convert division to equivalent multiplication.**

Interest per $100 = $\frac{\text{finance charge} \times 100}{\text{amount financed}}$ **Multiply.**

The final version of the formula gives the same results as the original version. The original version gives a logical sequence of steps, while the final version simplifies the calculations to be made.

SELF-CHECK 12.4

1. Use the constant ratio formula to estimate the annual percentage rate on a loan of $1,500 borrowed for two years with interest of $265. The loan is repaid in monthly payments. Round to the nearest tenth of a percent.

2. What is the estimated annual percentage rate on a loan of $3,800 borrowed for three years with interest of $518 if the loan is repaid in monthly payments? Round to the nearest tenth of a percent.

3. A loan of $2,750 is borrowed for 18 months and repaid in monthly payments. If the interest on the loan is $412, find the approximate annual percentage rate. Round to the nearest tenth of a percent.

4. Leon Griffin made a loan of $5,800 for 30 months and is repaying it in monthly payments. He is paying $1,215 interest on the loan. What is the approximate annual percentage rate for the loan? Round to the nearest tenth of a percent.

5. Alvin Ailey borrowed $3,715 for two years and is repaying it in monthly payments. If the loan company is charging $698 interest, estimate the annual percentage rate.

6. A fishing boat is purchased for $5,600 and financed for 36 months. If the total finance charge is $1,025, find the annual percentage rate using Table 12-1.

7. An air compressor costs $780 and is financed with monthly payments for 12 months. The total finance charge is $90. Find the annual percentage rate using Table 12-1.

8. Use Table 12-1 to find the APR for the loan in exercise 3. Compare the rate from the table with the rate calculated using the constant ratio formula.

9. Use Table 12-1 to find the APR for the loan in exercise 4. Compare the rate from the table with the rate calculated using the constant ratio formula.

10. Use Table 12-1 to find the APR for the loan in exercise 5. Compare the rate from the table with the rate calculated using the constant ratio formula.

11. Summarize and generalize the comparisons made in exercises 8–10.

12. Jim Meriweather purchased an engraving machine for $28,000 and financed it for 36 months. The total finance charge was $5,036. Use Table 12-1 to find the annual percentage rate.

12.5 Home Mortgages

 Find the monthly mortgage payment and total interest.

 Complete a monthly amortization schedule.

The purchase of a home is one of the most costly purchases individuals or families make in a lifetime. Most individuals must borrow money to pay for the home. Home loans are generally referred to as **mortgages** because the lending agency requires that the home be held as **collateral.** If the payments are not made as scheduled, the lending agency can take possession of the home and sell it to pay against the loan.

As a home buyer makes payments on a mortgage, the home buyer builds equity in the home. The home buyer's **equity** is the difference of the expected selling price of a home or **market value** and the balance owed on the home. A home may increase in value as a result of rising prices and average prices of other homes in the neighborhood. This increase in value also increases the owner's equity in the home.

A home buyer may select from several types of first mortgages. A **first mortgage** is the primary mortgage on a home and is ordinarily made at the time of purchase of the home. The agency holding the first mortgage has the first right to the proceeds up to the amount of the mortgage and settlement fees from the sale of the home if the homeowner fails to make required payments.

One type of first mortgage is the **conventional mortgage.** Money for a conventional mortgage is usually obtained through a savings and loan institution or a bank. These loans are not insured by a government program. Two types of conventional mortgages are the **fixed-rate mortgage** (FRM) and the **adjustable-rate mortgage** (ARM). The rate of interest on the loan for a fixed-rate mortgage remains the same for the entire time of the loan. Fixed-rate mortgages have several payment options. The number of years of the loan may vary, but 15- and 30-year loans are the most common. The home buyer makes the same payment (principal plus interest) each month of the loan. Another option is the **biweekly mortgage.** The home buyer makes 26 equal payments each year rather than 12. This method builds equity more quickly than the monthly payment method.

Another option for fixed-rate loans is the **graduated payments mortgage.** The home buyer makes small payments at the beginning of the loan and larger payments at the end. Home buyers who expect their income to rise may choose this option.

The rate of interest on a loan for an adjustable-rate mortgage may escalate (increase) or de-escalate (decrease) during the time of the loan. The rate of adjustable-rate mortgages depends on the prime lending rate of most banks.

Several government agencies insure that first mortgage loans will be repaid. Loans with this insurance include those made under the Federal Housing Administration (FHA) and the Veterans Administration (VA). These loans may be obtained through a savings and loan institution, a bank, or a mortgage lending company and are insured by a government program.

Interest paid on home loans is an allowable deduction on personal federal income tax under certain conditions. For this reason, many homeowners choose to borrow money for home improvements, college education, and the like, by making a home equity loan. These types of loans are a **second mortgage** or an **equity line of credit** and are made against the equity in the home. In the case of a loan default, the second mortgage lender has rights to the proceeds of the sale of the home *after* the first mortgage has been paid.

1 Find the monthly mortgage payment and total interest.

The repayment of the loan in equal installments that are applied to principal and interest over a specific period of time is called the **amortization** of a loan. To calculate the **monthly mortgage payment,** it is customary to use an amortization table, a business or financial calculator that has this chart programmed into the calculator, or computer software. The monthly payment table gives the factor that is multiplied by the dollar amount of the loan in thousands to give the total monthly payment including principal and interest. A portion of a monthly payment table is shown in Table 12-2.

The interest rate for first mortgages has fluctuated between 7% and 10% for the past few years. Second mortgage rates are generally higher than first mortgage rates.

 HOW TO Find the Monthly Mortgage Payment Using a per-$1,000 Monthly Payment Table

1. Find the amount financed: subtract the down payment from the purchase price.

2. Find the $1,000 units of amount financed: divide the amount financed (from step 1) by $1,000.

3. Locate the table value for the number of years financed and the annual interest rate.

4. Multiply the table value from step 3 by the $1,000 units from step 2.

$$\text{Monthly mortgage payment} = \frac{\text{amount financed}}{\$1,000} \times \text{table value}$$

Table 12–2 Monthly Payment of Principal and Interest per $1,000 of Amount Financed

Years Financed	Annual Interest Rate									
	7%	7½%	8%	8½%	9%	9½%	10%	10½%	11%	11½%
10	11.61	11.87	12.14	12.40	12.67	12.94	13.22	13.50	13.78	14.06
12	10.28	10.55	10.83	11.11	11.39	11.67	11.96	12.25	12.54	12.84
15	8.99	9.27	9.56	9.85	10.15	10.45	10.75	11.06	11.37	11.69
17	8.40	8.69	8.99	9.29	9.59	9.90	10.22	10.54	10.86	11.19
20	7.75	8.06	8.37	8.68	9.00	9.33	9.66	9.99	10.33	10.67
22	7.43	7.75	8.07	8.39	8.72	9.05	9.39	9.73	10.08	10.43
25	7.07	7.39	7.72	8.06	8.40	8.74	9.09	9.45	9.81	10.17
30	6.65	6.99	7.34	7.69	8.05	8.41	8.78	9.15	9.53	9.91
35	6.39	6.74	7.11	7.47	7.84	8.22	8.60	8.99	9.37	9.77

Years Financed	Annual Interest Rate								
	12%	12½%	13%	13½%	14%	14½%	15%	15½%	16%
10	14.35	14.64	14.94	15.23	15.53	15.83	16.14	16.45	16.76
12	13.14	13.44	13.75	14.06	14.38	14.69	15.01	15.34	15.66
15	12.01	12.33	12.66	12.99	13.32	13.66	14.00	14.34	14.69
17	11.52	11.85	12.19	12.53	12.88	13.23	13.58	13.94	14.30
20	11.02	11.37	11.72	12.08	12.44	12.80	13.17	13.54	13.92
22	10.78	11.14	11.51	11.87	12.24	12.62	12.99	13.37	13.75
25	10.54	10.91	11.28	11.66	12.04	12.43	12.81	13.20	13.59
30	10.29	10.68	11.07	11.46	11.85	12.25	12.65	13.05	13.45
35	10.16	10.56	10.96	11.36	11.76	12.17	12.57	12.98	13.39

Table values show the monthly payment of a $1,000 mortgage for the given number of years at the given annual interest rate if the interest is compounded monthly. Table values can be generated using

the formula: $M = P \times \dfrac{J}{1 - (1 + J)^{-N}}$, where M = monthly payment, P = principal or initial amount of the loan, J = the monthly interest rate expressed in fraction or decimal form (annual rate in decimal form ÷ 12), and N = total number of months of the loan (number of years × 12).

EXAMPLE Lunelle Miller is purchasing a home for $87,000. Home Federal Savings and Loan has approved her loan application for a 30-year fixed-rate loan at 10% annual interest. If Lunelle agrees to pay 20% of the purchase price as a down payment, calculate the monthly payment.

The down payment is

$$\$87{,}000 \times 0.20 = \$17{,}400$$

Calculate the amount to be financed.

$$\$87{,}000 - \$17{,}400 = \$69{,}600$$

Determine how many thousands of dollars will be financed.

$$\$69{,}600 \div \$1{,}000 = 69.6$$

Use Table 12-2 to find the factor for financing a loan for 30 years with a 10% interest rate. This factor is 8.78 .

Multiply the number of thousands times the factor.

$$69.6 \times \$8.78 = \$611.09$$

The monthly payment of $611.09 includes the principal and interest.

Often, a person wants to know the total amount of interest that will be paid during the entire loan.

> ### ? HOW TO Find the Total Interest
>
> 1. Find the total of the payments: multiply the number of payments by the amount of the payment.
> 2. Subtract the amount financed from the total of the payments.
>
> **Total interest = number of payments × amount of payment − amount financed**

EXAMPLE Calculate the total interest paid on the loan in the previous example.

Total interest = number of payments × amount of payment − amount financed

$$= \boxed{30 \times 12 \times \$611.09} - \boxed{\$69,600}$$

$$= \boxed{\$219,992.40} - \boxed{\$69,600}$$

$$= \$150,392.40$$

The total interest is $150,392.40.

The two examples show how to calculate the monthly payment and the total interest for a mortgage loan. There are other costs associated with purchasing a home. Lending companies require the borrower to pay **points** at the time the loan is made or closed. Payment of points is a one-time payment of a percent of the loan that is an additional cost of making the mortgage. One point is 1%, two points is 2%, and so on.

Other costs related to buying a home may include attorney fees, sales commissions, taxes, and insurance. Since the lending agency must be assured that the property taxes and insurance are paid on the property, the annual costs of these items may be prorated each year and added to the monthly payment for that year. These funds are held in escrow until the taxes or insurance payment is due, at which time the lending agency makes the payment for the home owner. These additional costs make the monthly payment more than just the principal and interest payment we found in the preceding examples.

EXAMPLE If the annual insurance premium for Lunelle's home is $923 and the annual tax on the property is $950, find the adjusted monthly payment that includes principal, interest, tax, and insurance.

$923 + \$950 = \boxed{\$1,873}$	**Annual taxes and insurance needed in escrow**
$\boxed{\$1,873} \div 12 = \$156.08$	**Monthly payment for taxes and insurance**
$\$611.09 + \boxed{\$156.08} = \$767.17$	**Adjusted monthly payment**

The adjusted monthly payment is $767.17.

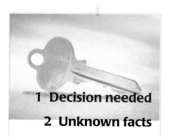

1 Decision needed

2 Unknown facts

EXAMPLE Qua Wau is trying to determine whether to accept a 25-year 9% mortgage or a 20-year 9% mortgage on the house he is planning to buy. He needs to finance $125,700 and has planned to budget $1,250 monthly for his payment of principal and interest. Which mortgage should Qua choose?

Which mortgage should Qua choose?

Monthly payment and total cost for 25-year mortgage, and monthly payment and total cost for 20-year mortgage.

3 Known facts	Amount financed: $125,700
	Annual interest rate: 9%
	Monthly budget allowance: $1,250

4 Relationships	Total cost = monthly payment × 12 × years financed
	Number of $1,000 units of amount financed = amount financed ÷ $1,000
	Monthly payment = number of $1,000 units of amount financed × table value

5 Estimation Since the 20-year mortgage is for less time, but the same interest rate as the 25-year loan, the total cost of the 20-year mortgage is less than the total cost of the 25-year mortgage. The monthly payment for the 20-year mortgage should be more than the payment for the 25-year mortgage and may exceed the budget allowance.

6 Calculation

Number of $1,000 units financed = $125,700 ÷ $1,000

= 125.7

25-Year Mortgage
The Table 12-2 value for 25 years and 9% is 8.40 .

Monthly payment = number of $1,000 units financed × table value

= 125.7 × 8.40

= $1,055.88

Total cost = monthly payment × 12 × years financed

= $1,055.88 × 12 × 25

= $316,764

20-Year Mortgage
The Table 12-2 value for 20 years and 9% is 9.00 .

Monthly payment = number of $1,000 units financed × table value

= 125.7 × 9.00

= $1,131.30

Total cost = monthly payment × 12 × years financed

= $1,131.30 × 12 × 20

= $271,512

7 Interpretation The monthly payment for the 25-year mortgage is $1,055.88 for a total cost of $316,764. The monthly payment for the 20-year mortgage is $1,131.50 for a total cost of $271,512.

8 Decision made **Qua's budget of $1,250 monthly can cover either monthly payment. He would save $45,252 over the 20-year period if he chooses the 20-year plan. That is the plan he should choose.** Other considerations that could impact his decision would be the return on an investment of the difference in the monthly payments if an annuity was started with the difference.

2 Complete a monthly amortization schedule.

Homeowners are often given an **amortization schedule** that shows the amount of principal and interest for each payment of the loan. With some loan arrangements, extra amounts paid with the monthly payment are credited against the principal, allowing for the mortgage to be paid sooner.

1. For the first month:
   (a) Find the interest portion of the first monthly payment: multiply the original principal by the monthly interest rate.

   Interest portion of the first monthly payment = original principal × monthly interest rate

   (b) Find the principal portion of the monthly payment: subtract the interest portion of the first monthly payment (from step 1a) from the monthly payment (not including taxes or insurance).

   Principal portion of the first monthly payment = monthly payment − interest portion of the first monthly payment

   (c) Find the first end-of-month principal: subtract the principal portion of the first monthly payment (from step 1b) from the original principal.

   First end-of-month principal = original principal − principal portion of the first monthly payment

2. For each remaining month in turn:
   (a) Find the interest portion of the monthly payment: multiply the previous end-of-month principal by the monthly interest rate.

   Interest portion of the monthly payment = previous end-of-month principal × monthly interest rate

   (b) Find the principal portion of the monthly payment: subtract the interest portion of the monthly payment (from step 2a) from the monthly payment (not including taxes or insurance).

   Principal portion of the monthly payment = monthly payment − interest portion of the monthly payment

   (c) Find the end-of-month principal: subtract the principal portion of the monthly payment (from step 2b) from the previous end-of-month principal.

   End-of-month principal = previous end-of-month principal − principal portion of the monthly payment

EXAMPLE   Complete the first two rows of the amortization schedule for Lunelle's mortgage (from the example on page 503).

First month

$$\text{Interest} = \text{original principal} \times \text{monthly rate}$$

$$= \$69{,}600 \times \frac{0.1}{12} \qquad \boxed{10\% = 0.1}$$

$$= \$580.00$$

Principal portion of monthly payment = monthly payment (without insurance and taxes) − interest portion of monthly payment

$$= \$611.09 - \$580.00$$

$$= \$31.09$$

End-of-month principal = previous end-of-month principal − principal portion of monthly payment

$$= \$69{,}600 - \$31.09$$

$$= \$69{,}568.91$$

Second month

$$\text{Interest portion} = \$69{,}568.91 \times \frac{0.1}{12}$$

$$= \$579.74$$

$$\text{Principal portion of monthly payment} = \$611.09 - \$579.74$$

$$= \$31.35$$

$$\text{End-of-month principal} = \$69{,}568.91 - \$31.35$$

$$= \$69{,}537.56$$

The first two rows of an amortization schedule for this loan are shown in the following chart.

	Portion of Payment Applied to:		
Month	**Interest** [Previous End-of-Month Principal × Monthly Rate]	**Principal** [Monthly Payment − Interest Portion]	**End-of-Month Principal** [Previous End-of-Month Principal − Principal Portion]
1	$580.00	$31.09	$69,568.91
2	$579.74	$31.35	$69,537.56

Computers are normally used to generate an amortization schedule that shows the interest and principal breakdown for each payment of the loan.

SELF-CHECK 12.5

1. Find the down payment and amount financed for a home that sells for $67,000. The down payment must be 15% of the selling price.

2. Find the monthly payment for the mortgage in exercise 1 if it is financed for 25 years at $8\frac{1}{2}\%$.

3. Find the total interest for the mortgage in exercise 1.

4. Stephen Black has just purchased a home for $155,000. Northridge Mortgage Company has approved his loan application for a 25-year fixed-rate loan at $9\frac{1}{2}\%$. Stephen has agreed to pay 18% of the purchase price as a down payment. Calculate the down payment, amount of mortgage, and monthly payment.

5. Find the total interest Stephen will pay if he pays the loan on schedule.

6. If Stephen Black could budget an additional $100 for housing, could he reduce the number of years required to repay the loan to 20 years?

7. If Stephen made the loan for 20 years, how much interest would he save?

8. Make an amortization schedule for the first three months of Stephen's 25-year loan.

9. Calculate the interest paid and principal paid for the first two months of Stephen's loan if the loan is a 20-year loan, and find the principal owed at the end of the second month.

10. Justin Wimmer is financing $69,700 for a home at 8.5% interest with a 20-year fixed-rate loan. Calculate the interest paid and principal paid for the first two months of the loan and find the principal owed at the end of the second month.

11. Heike Drechsler is financing $84,700 for a home in the mountains. The 17-year fixed-rate loan has an interest rate of 9%. Calculate the interest paid and principal paid for the first two months and the principal owed at the end of the second month.

12. Conchita Martinez has made a $210,300 loan for a home near Albany, New York. Her 20-year fixed-rate loan has an interest rate of $8\frac{1}{2}\%$. Calculate the principal paid and interest paid for the first two months of the loan and find the principal owed at the end of the second month.

Debt Snowball

Credit card usage has become widespread in the United States, with the latest surge in users coming from the group least able to pay the high interest rates—college students. Research indicates that at least two-thirds of college students and 74% of American households have at least one major credit card, and the typical cardholder carries seven cards! The average balance per card has increased significantly in the last three years. Many credit card holders first obtained credit cards through special introductory offers of rates as low as 2% APR for the first six months. Often the cardholder does not realize that the rate esclates to a higher than normal rate after the introductory period and that higher rate applies to the current unpaid balance.

Many college students who work part-time find themselves charging everyday necessities such as food and gasoline on credit cards charging an average of 18% interest. In addition to their student loan(s), many students graduate from college having several credit cards with balances in the thousands! It is no wonder that credit counselors are deluged with college students seeking help with debt reduction.

Many financial counselors teach the "debt snowball" method of getting out of debt. First destroy or put away *all* credit cards. Then list the debts.
Suppose a student owes:

Item	Balance	Payment	Interest Rate
Visa	$1,800	$150	18%
Car	8,250	275	5
MasterCard	790	80	18
Student Loan	9,000	150	9
Dentist	350	50	15

Now arrange the debts in order with the smallest balance first, regardless of interest rate or payment. (This is to ensure success early on so the student will stick with the program!)

Item	Balance	Payment	Interest Rate
Dentist	$350	$50	15%
MasterCard	790	80	18
Visa	1,800	150	18
Car	8,250	275	5
Student Loan	9,000	150	9

The debts will be paid off in this order. Suppose the student sells her or his used textbooks back to the bookstore and pays off the dentist in the first month. Instead of then pocketing the $50 dental payment each month, she or he should add it to the next payment on the list. The student is then paying MasterCard $130 per month until paid off in the seventh month. The student then adds the $130 to the $150 Visa payment. Because the student has already been paying on Visa for seven months, it will be paid off in just a few more months. He or she will continue in this fashion until all balances are paid.

Exercises

Use the above information to answer the following:

1. Complete the following chart to verify that MasterCard will be paid off in the seventh month. Assume that the previous month's payment has been received before the monthly interest is calculated on the unpaid balance. Find the total of the payments needed to pay off this $790 account in seven months. How much interest accrued during this six-month period?

Month	Beg. Bal.	−	Payment	=	Unpaid Bal.	+	Interest	=	New Bal.
1	$790.00	−	80	=	710.00	+	10.65	=	$720.65
2	720.65	−	130	=	590.65	+	8.86	=	599.51

2. Complete a similar chart to find the month in which Visa will be paid off.

Month	Beg. Bal.	−	Payment	=	Unpaid Bal.	+	Interest	=	New Bal.
1	$790.00	−	80	=	710.00	+	10.65	=	$720.65

3. In what month will the car be paid off? This loan includes principal and interest. The full amount is paid and then an interest refund for early payoff will be received at a later time. In how many months was the car loan scheduled to be paid off, and how many months early will it be paid off with the debt snowball method?

4. How long will it take to pay off the student loan and be debt-free using the debt-snowball method? This loan also includes principal and interest with an interest refund for early payoff to be received later.

5. How long would it have taken this student to get out of debt by making the regularly scheduled payments? How many months early did the debt snowball method get this student out of debt?

6. Use the rule of 78 to find the amount of finance charge refund when the car installment loan is paid off early by the debt snowball method. The original loan of $10,000 was for 48 months with an 8% simple interest finance charge assessed for the entire 48 months, or a total finance charge of $3,200.

7. The student loan is an installment loan on tuition of $7,200 financed with 5% simple interest assessed for the payback period of 60 months (which starts shortly after graduation). Use the rule of 78 to find the interest refunded if this loan is paid off early by the debt snowball method.

8. Although most people who want to be debt-free expect to have a home mortgage payment, it too is a debt. Give three reasons many financial counselors recommend against paying off a home mortgage early.

Answers

1. The completed chart:

Month	Beg. Bal.	−	Payment	=	Unpaid Bal.	+	Interest	=	New Bal.
1	$790.00	−	80	=	710.00	+	10.65	=	$720.65
2	720.65	−	130	=	590.65	+	8.86	=	599.51
3	599.51	−	130	=	469.51	+	7.04	=	476.55
4	476.55	−	130	=	346.55	+	5.20	=	351.75
5	351.75	−	130	=	221.75	+	3.33	=	225.08
6	225.08	−	130	=	95.08	+	1.43	=	96.51
7	96.51	−	96.51	=	.00				

The payments total is $826.51; subtracting $790 leaves accrued interest of $36.51 over this six-month period.

2. Visa should be paid off in the 11th month:

Month	Beg. Bal.	−	Payment	=	Unpaid Bal.	+	Interest	=	New Bal.
1	$1800.00	−	150.00	=	1650.00	+	24.75	=	1674.75
2	1674.75	−	150.00	=	1524.75	+	22.87	=	1547.62
3	1547.62	−	150.00	=	1397.62	+	20.96	=	1418.58
4	1418.58	−	150.00	=	1268.58	+	19.03	=	1287.61
5	1287.61	−	150.00	=	1137.61	+	17.06	=	1154.67
6	1154.67	−	150.00	=	1004.67	+	15.07	=	1019.74
7	1019.74	−	150.00	=	869.74	+	13.05	=	882.79
8	882.79	−	280.00	=	602.79	+	9.04	=	611.83
9	611.83	−	280.00	=	331.83	+	4.98	=	336.81
10	336.81	−	280.00	=	56.81	+	0.85	=	57.66
11	57.66	−	57.66	=	.00				

3. When Visa is paid off in the 11th month $3,025 has already been paid on the car loan during the previous 11 months, leaving a balance of $5,225. Dividing $5,225 by the accelerated payment of $555 ($280 + $275) gives about 9.4 or 10 additional months to pay off the balance. It will be paid off in the 21st month. It was scheduled to be paid off in 30 months, so it was paid off nine months early.

4. When the car loan is paid off in the 21st month, the student loan has already been paid $3,150 ($150 × 21) leaving a balance of $5,850. Dividing $5,850 by the accelerated payment of $705 ($555 + $150) gives about 8.3 or 9 months to pay off the balance, so it should be paid off in the 30th month. By using the debt snowball method, the student should be debt-free in 30 months!

5. If the student makes the regularly scheduled payments, it will take him or her 60 months to pay off the student loan and be debt-free. So the debt snowball method cut the time in half, and saved the student 30 months!

6. The denominator of the refund fraction is the sum of 1, 2, . . . 48 = 1176. The numerator of the refund fraction is the sum of 1, 2, . . . 9 = 45. Multiplying $\frac{45}{1176}$ by the finance charge of $3,200 gives a refund of $122.45 for paying off the loan nine months early.

7. Subtracting the $7,200 tuition payment from the $9,000 installment price leaves a finance charge of $1,800. The numerator of the refund fraction is the sum of 1, 2, . . . 30 = 465. The denominator is the sum of 1, 2, . . . 60 = 1,830. Multiplying $\frac{465}{1830}$ by the finance charge of $1,800 gives a refund of $457.38 for paying off the loan 30 months early.

8. Many financial counselors advise against paying off home mortgage loans because (a) home mortgage rates are usually several points lower than what your money would typically earn in the stock market or a mutual funds account, so your money would earn more if you invested it elsewhere; (b) most people pay their mortgage religiously every month, but if the mortgage were paid off, it might be tempting to skip savings payments into another fund; and (c) money invested in stocks or mutual funds is very "liquid," meaning you can get cash quickly in case of an emergency, but getting money out that has been invested in real estate can be very time consuming and can create other expenses such as moving expenses and the expense of finding other housing.

Section 12.1

Find the
installment
price given
the
installment
payment.
(page 482)

1. Find the total of the installment payments: multiply the number of installment payments by the installment payment.

Total of installment payments = number of installment payments
$\times$ installment payment

2. Add the down payment to the total of the installment payments.

Installment price = total of installment payments + down payment

> **Find the installment price of a computer that is paid for in 24 monthly payments of \$113 if a down payment of \$50 is made.**
>
> $$(24 \times \$113) + \$50 = \$2,712 + \$50 = \$2,762$$

2

Find the
installment
payment given
the
installment
price.
(page 483)

1. Find the total of the installment payments: subtract the down payment from the installment price.

Total of installment payments = installment price $-$ down payment

2. Divide the total of installment payments by the number of installment payments.

$$\text{Installment payments} = \frac{\text{total of installment payments}}{\text{number of payments}}$$

> **Find the monthly payment on a computer if the cash price is \$3,285. A 14% interest rate is charged on the cash price, and there are 12 monthly payments.**
>
> $$\$3,285 \times 0.14 \times 1 = \$459.90$$
>
> $$\textbf{Installment price} = \$3,285 + \$459.90 = \$3,744.90$$
>
> $$\textbf{Monthly payment} = \frac{\$3,744.90}{12} = \$312.08$$

> **A computer has an installment price of \$2,187.25 when financed over 18 months. If a \$100 down payment is made, find the monthly payment.**
>
> $$\$2,187.25 - \$100 = \$2,087.25$$
>
> $$\frac{\$2,087.25}{18} = \$115.96$$

Section 12.2

1

Find the
interest
refund using
the rule of 78.
(page 485)

Find the interest refund using the rule of 78.
1. Find the period sequence numbers: number the periods of the loan, so that the last period is 1, the next to the last is 2, and so on.
2. Find the denominator of the refund fraction: add the sequence numbers of all the periods.
3. Find the numerator of the refund fraction: add the sequence numbers of the periods for which an interest refund is due.
4. Multiply the total interest by the refund fraction.

Interest refund = total interest $\times$ refund fraction

Find the interest refund on a loan that has a total finance charge of $892 and was made for 24 months. The loan is paid in full with 10 months (payments) remaining.

$$\text{Refund fraction} = \frac{\text{sum of sequence numbers of periods remaining}}{\text{sum of all period sequence numbers}}$$

$$= \frac{\text{sum of 1 to 10}}{\text{sum of 1 to 24}}$$

$$= \frac{55}{300} = \frac{11}{60}$$

$$\text{Refund} = \$892 \times \frac{11}{60} = \$163.53$$

Find the sum of consecutive numbers beginning with 1. Multiply the largest number by 1 more than the largest number and divide the product by 2.

$$\text{Sum of consecutive numbers beginning with 1} = \frac{\text{largest number} \times (\text{largest number} + 1)}{2}$$

Find the interest refund on a loan with 10 payments remaining out of 24 payments if the total interest was $892.

$$\text{Refund} = \text{total interest} \times \frac{\text{sum of 1 to 10}}{\text{sum of 1 to 24}}$$

$$\text{Sum of 1 to 10} = \frac{10(11)}{2} = 55$$

$$\text{Sum of 1 to 24} = \frac{24(25)}{2} = 300$$

$$\text{Refund} = \$892 \times \frac{11}{60}$$

$$= \$163.53$$

Section 12.3

Find the unpaid balance using the unpaid balance method. (page 490)

1. Find the interest for the previous monthly period: multiply the unpaid balance as of the first day of the previous monthly period by the monthly interest rate.

    Interest = unpaid balance × monthly interest rate

2. Find the total purchases and cash advances during the previous monthly period: add all purchases or cash advances charged to the account during the previous monthly period.

3. Find the total payments for the previous monthly period: add all payments credited to the account during the previous monthly period.

4. To the unpaid balance at the beginning of the previous monthly period, add the interest for the previous monthly period from step 1 and add the total purchases and cash advances from step 2. Then, subtract the total payments from step 3.

Unpaid balance at the beginning of the monthly period
= unpaid balance at the beginning of previous monthly period
+ interest for previous monthly period
+ total purchases and cash advances during previous monthly period
− total payments during previous monthly period

A charge account has an unpaid balance of $1,384.37 and the monthly interest rate is 1.75%. Find the interest.

$$\$1{,}384.37 \times 0.0175 = \$24.23$$

To this account these transactions were made during the month: purchases of $23.85, $41.18, and $123.74; cash advance of $100.00; payment of $200.00. Find the unpaid balance.

$$\text{Total purchases: } \$23.85 + \$41.18 + \$123.74 = \$188.77$$

$$\$1{,}384.37 + \$24.23 + \$188.77 + \$100.00 - \$200.00 = \$1{,}497.37$$

2   Find the unpaid balance using the average daily balance method.
(page 491)

1. Find the daily unpaid balance for each day in the monthly period.
   (a) Find the total purchases and cash advances for the day: add all the purchases and cash advances charged to the account during the day.
   (b) Find the total credits for the day: add all the payments and adjustments credited to the account during the day.
   (c) To the previous daily unpaid balance, add the total purchases and cash advances for the day (from step 1a). Then, subtract the total payments for the day (from step 1b).

Daily unpaid balance = previous daily unpaid balance
   + total purchases and cash advances for the day − total credits for the day

2. Add the unpaid balances from step 1 for each day and divide the sum by the number of days in the monthly period.

$$\text{Average daily balance} = \frac{\text{sum of daily unpaid balances}}{\text{number of days in monthly period}}$$

A credit card has a balance of $398.42 on September 14, the first day of the billing cycle. A charge of $182.37 is posted to the account on September 16. Another charge of $82.21 is posted to the account on September 25. The amount of a returned item ($19.98) is posted to the account on October 10 and a payment of $500 is made on October 12. The billing period ends on October 13. Find the average daily balance and finance charge if a monthly rate of 1.3% is assessed.

Date	Daily Unpaid Balance	Number of Days	Partial Sum
September 14–15	$398.42	2 days	$ 796.84
September 16–24	580.79	9 days	5,227.11
September 25–October 9	663.00	15 days	9,945.00
October 10–11	643.02	2 days	1,286.04
October 12–13	143.03	2 days	286.06
Total		30 days	$17,541.05

Average daily balance = $17,541.05 ÷ 30 = $584.70
Finance charge = $584.70 × 0.013 = $7.60

Section 12.4

1   Estimate the annual percentage rate using the constant ratio formula.
(page 495)

1. Substitute known values into the formula.

Approximate annual percentage rate
$$= \frac{2 \times \text{number of payments per year} \times \text{total interest}}{\text{amount financed} \times (\text{number of payments} + 1)}$$

2. Solve the formula for the unknown.

> Estimate the annual percentage rate for a loan of $13,850 that is repaid in 42 monthly installments. The interest for the loan is $2,382.20.
>
> $$\text{Approximate APR} = \frac{2(12)(\$2,382.20)}{\$13,850(43)}$$
>
> $$= 0.096 = 9.6\%$$

2 Find the annual percentage rate using a table. (page 496)

1. Find the interest per $100 of amount financed: multiply the total finance charge by $100 and divide by the amount financed.

$$\text{Interest per } \$100 = \frac{\text{total finance charge} \times \$100}{\text{amount financed}}$$

2. Find the row corresponding to the number of monthly payments. Move across the row to find the number closest to the value from step 1. Read up the column to find the annual percentage rate for that column.

> Find the annual percentage rate on a loan of $500 that is repaid in 36 monthly installments. The interest for the loan is $95.
>
> $$\text{Interest per } \$100 = \frac{\$95 \times \$100}{\$500} = \$19$$
>
> In the row for 36 months, move across to 19.14 (nearest to 19). APR is at the top of the column, 11.75%.

Section 12.5

1 Find the monthly mortgage payment and total interest. (page 502)

Find the monthly mortgage payment using a per-$1,000 monthly payment table.
1. Find the amount financed: subtract the down payment from the purchase price.
2. Find the $1,000 units of amount financed: divide the amount financed (from step 1) by $1,000.
3. Locate the table value for the number of years financed and the annual interest rate.
4. Multiply the table value from step 3 by the $1,000 units from step 2.

$$\text{Monthly mortgage payment} = \frac{\text{amount financed}}{\$1,000} \times \text{table value}$$

Find the total interest.
1. Find the total of the payments: multiply the number of payments by the payment.
2. Subtract the amount financed from the total of the payments.

$$\text{Total interest} = \text{number of payments} \times \text{payment} - \text{amount financed}$$

> Find the monthly payment and the total interest for a home selling for $90,000 if a 10% down payment is made, payments are made for 30 years, and the annual interest rate is $10\frac{1}{2}\%$.
>
> $$\$90,000 \times 0.1 = \$9,000 \text{ down payment}$$
>
> $$\$90,000 - \$9,000 = \$81,000 \text{ mortgage amount}$$
>
> $$\$81,000 \div \$1,000 = 81 \text{ } \$1,000 \text{ units}$$

The table value for 30 years and $10\frac{1}{2}\%$ is 9.15.

$$\text{Payment} = 81 \times \$9.15 = \$741.15$$

$$\text{Total interest} = \$741.15 \times 30 \times 12 - 81,000 = \$266,814 - \$81,000$$

$$= \$185,814$$

2 Complete a monthly amortization schedule. (page 505)

1. For the first month:
   (a) Find the interest portion of the first monthly payment: multiply the original principal by the monthly interest rate.

   Interest portion of the first monthly payment = original principal
   $$\times \text{ monthly interest rate}$$

   (b) Find the principal portion of the monthly payment: subtract the interest portion of the first monthly payment (from step 1a) from the monthly payment (not including taxes or insurance).

   Principal portion of the first monthly payment = monthly payment
   $$- \text{ interest portion of first monthly payment}$$

   (c) Find the first end-of-month principal: subtract the principal portion of the first monthly payment (from step 1b) from the original principal.

   First end-of-month principal = original principal
   $$- \text{ principal portion of the first monthly payment}$$

2. For each remaining month in turn:
   (a) Find the interest portion of the monthly payment: multiply the previous end-of-month principal by the monthly interest rate.

   Interest portion of the monthly payment = previous end-of-month principal
   $$\times \text{ monthly interest rate}$$

   (b) Find the principal portion of the monthly payment: subtract the interest portion of the monthly payment (from step 2a) from the monthly payment (not including taxes or insurance).

   Principal portion of the monthly payment = monthly payment
   $$- \text{ interest portion of the monthly payment}$$

   (c) Find the end-of-month principal: subtract the principal portion of the monthly payment (from step 2b) from the previous end-of-month principal.

   End-of-month principal = previous end-of-month principal
   $$- \text{ principal portion of the monthly payment}$$

Complete an amortization schedule for three months of payments on a $90,000 mortgage at 8% for 30 years.

$$\text{Monthly payment} = \frac{\$90,000}{\$1,000} \times \text{table value}$$

$$= 90 \times 7.34$$

$$= \$660.60$$

Month 1

$$\text{Interest portion} = \$90,000 \times \frac{0.08}{12}$$

$$= \$600$$

$$\text{Principal portion} = \$660.60 - 600$$

$$= \$60.60$$

$$\text{End-of-month principal} = \$90,000 - \$60.60$$

$$= \$89,939.40$$

Month 2

$$\text{Interest portion} = \$89,939.40 \times \frac{0.08}{12}$$

$$= \$599.60$$

$$\text{Principal portion} = \$660.60 - \$599.60$$

$$= \$61.00$$

$$\text{End-of-month principal} = \$89,939.40 - \$61.00$$

$$= \$89,878.40$$

Month 3

$$\text{Interest portion} = \$89,878.40 \times \frac{.08}{12}$$

$$= \$599.19$$

$$\text{Principal portion} = \$660.60 - \$599.19$$

$$= \$61.41$$

$$\text{End-of-month principal} = \$89,878.40 - \$61.41$$

$$= \$89,816.99$$

| Month | Portion of Payment Applied to: | | End-of-Month Principal |
	Interest	Principal	
1	$600	$60.60	$89,939.40
2	599.60	61.00	89,878.40
3	599.19	61.41	89,816.99

WORDS TO KNOW

consumer credit (p. 482)
installment loans (p. 482)
basic installment loans (p. 482)
open-end loans (p. 482)
finance charges (p. 482)
carrying charges (p. 482)
cash price (p. 482)

down payment (p. 482)
amount financed (p. 482)
installment payment (p. 482)
installment price (p. 482)
rule of 78 (p. 485)
refund fraction (p. 486)
line-of-credit accounts (p. 489)

unpaid balance method (p. 490)
average daily balance method (p. 491)
annual percentage rate (APR) (p. 494)
constant ratio formula (p. 495)
mortgages (p. 501)

collateral (p. 501)
equity (p. 501)
market value (p. 501)
first mortgage (p. 501)
conventional mortgage (p. 501)
fixed-rate mortgage (p. 502)

adjustable-rate mortgage (p. 502)
biweekly mortgage (p. 502)
graduated payments mortgage
  (p. 502)
second mortgage (p. 502)
equity line of credit (p. 502)

amortization (p. 502)
monthly mortgage payment
  (p. 502)
points (p. 504)
amortization schedule (p. 505)

CHAPTER 12 CONCEPTS ANALYSIS

1. Use the two formulas given in the How-To box: Find the Installment Price (p. 482) to write a single formula to find the installment price of an item.

2. Use the two formulas given in the How-To box: Find the Installment Payment Given the Installment Price (p. 483) to write a single formula to find the installment payment of an item.

3. Explain the mistake in the solution of the problem and correct the solution.
   Dawn Mayhall financed a car and the loan of 42 months required $3,827 interest. She paid the loan off after making 20 payments. How much interest should be refunded if the rule of 78 is used?
   Solution

   $$\frac{20(21)}{42(43)} \times \$3{,}827 = \frac{420}{1{,}806} \times \$3{,}827 = \$890$$

   Thus, $890 should be refunded.

4. Explain the mistake in the solution and correct the solution.
   Ava Landry agreed to pay $2,847 interest for a 36-month loan to redecorate her greeting card shop. However, business was better than expected and she repaid the loan with 16 months remaining. If the rule of 78 was used, how much interest should she get back?
   Solution:

   $$\frac{15(16)}{35(36)} \times \$2{,}847 = \frac{240}{1{,}260} \times \$2{,}847 = \$542.29$$

   Thus, $542.29 should be refunded.

5. Find the sum of consecutive numbers from 1 to 10 by arranging them in ascending order, then in descending order, so that 1 and 10, 2 and 9, 3 and 8, etc., align.

6. Explain why the formula for finding the sum of consecutive numbers requires that the product be divided by 2.

7. Explain why the formula for finding the sum of consecutive numbers requires the product of the largest number and one *more* than the largest number rather than one *less* than the largest number.

8. Give three examples of finding the sum of consecutive odd numbers beginning with 1.

9. Write a formula to find the sum of consecutive odd numbers beginning with 1 if n is the largest number.

10. Can the formula developed in exercise 9 be used to find the sum of consecutive even numbers beginning with 2? Give an example and explain it.

CHAPTER 12 ASSIGNMENT EXERCISES

Section 12.1

1. Find the installment price of a notebook computer system bought on the installment plan with $250 down and 12 payments of $111.33.

2. A television set has been purchased on the installment plan with a down payment of $120 and six monthly payments of $98.50. Find the installment price of the television set.

3. Find the monthly payment on a water bed if the installment price is $1,050, the down payment is $200, and there are 10 monthly payments.

4. A dishwasher sold for a $983 installment price with a down payment of $150 and 12 monthly payments. How much is each payment?

5. If the cash price of a refrigerator is $879 and a down payment of $150 is made, how much is to be financed?

6. What is the cash price of a chair if the installment price is $679, the finance charge is $102, and there was no down payment?

Section 12.2

Use the rule of 78 to find the finance charge refund in each of the following.

	Finance Charge	Number of Monthly Payments	Remaining Payments	Interest Refund
7.	$238	12	4	
8.	$1,076	18	6	
9.	$2,175	24	10	
10.	$476	12	5	
11.	$896	18	4	
12.	$683	15	11	

Use the rule of 78 to solve the following problems.

13. The finance charge on a computer was $1,778. The loan for the computer was to be paid in 18 monthly payments. Find the finance charge refund if it is paid off in eight months.

14. Find the refund fraction on a 48-month loan if it is paid off after 20 months.

15. Becky Whitehead has a loan with $1,115 in finance charges, which she paid in full after 8 of the 18 monthly payments. What is her finance charge refund?

16. Lanny Jacobs made a loan to purchase a computer. Find the refund due on this loan with interest charges of $657 if it is paid off after paying 7 of the 12 monthly payments.

17. Alice Dubois was charged $455 in finance charges on a loan for 15 months. Find the finance charge refund if she pays off the loan in full after 10 payments.

18. Suppose you have borrowed money that is being repaid at $45 a month for 12 months. What is the finance charge refund after making eight payments if the finance charge is $105?

19. Find the finance charge refund on a 15-month loan with monthly payments of $103.50 if you decide to pay off the loan at the end of the 10th month. The finance charge is $215.55.

20. You have purchased a new stereo on the installment plan. The plan calls for 12 monthly payments of $45 and a $115 finance charge. After nine months you decide to pay off the loan. How much is the refund?

21. If you purchase a fishing boat for 18 monthly payments of $106 and an interest charge of $238, how much is the refund after 10 payments?

22. The interest for an automobile loan is $2,843. The automobile is financed for 36 monthly payments, and interest refunds are made using the rule of 78. How much interest should be refunded if the loan is paid in full with 22 months still remaining?

23. Find the interest on an unpaid balance of $265 with an interest rate of $1\frac{1}{2}\%$.

24. Find the finance charge on $371 if the interest charged is 1.4% of the unpaid balance.

25. Find the finance charge on a credit card with an unpaid balance of $465 if the rate charged is 1.25%.

26. Find the new unpaid balance on an account with a previous balance of $263.50, purchases of $38.75, a payment of $35, and a finance charge of 1.5% of the unpaid balance.

27. Use the unpaid balance to find the new unpaid balance on an account with a previous balance of $155, purchases of $47.38, a payment of $20, and an interest charge of 1.8%.

28. A new desk for an office has a cash price of $1,500 and can be purchased on the installment plan with a 12.5% finance charge. The desk will be paid for in 12 monthly payments. Find the amount of the finance charge, the total price, and the amount of each monthly payment, if there was no down payment.

29. On June 1 the unpaid balance on a credit card was $174. During the month, purchases of $32, $14.50, and $28.75 are made. Using the unpaid balance method, find the unpaid balance on July 1 if the finance charge is 1.4% of the unpaid balance and a payment of $50 is made on June 15.

30. On August 1 the unpaid balance on a credit card was $206. During the month, purchases of $98.65 and a payment of $60 were made. Using the unpaid balance method and a finance charge of 1.5%, find the unpaid balance on September 1.

31. Use the following activity chart to find the unpaid balance on November 1. The billing cycle ended on October 31, and the finance charge is 1.5% of the average daily balance.

Date Posted	Activity	Amount
October 1	Billing date	Previous balance $426.40
October 7	Purchase	41.60
October 10	Payment	70
October 15	Purchase	31.25
October 20	Purchase	26.80

32. On January 1 the previous balance for Lynn's charge account was $569.80. On the following days, purchases were posted:
January 13 $38.50 jewelry
January 21 $44.56 clothing
On January 16 a $50 payment was posted. Using the average daily balance method, find the finance charge and unpaid balance on February 1 if the bank charges interest of 1.5% per month.

Section 12.4

Use the constant ratio formula to estimate the annual percentage rate for the following exercises. Round results to the nearest tenth of a percent.

33. Find the annual percentage rate on a loan of $1,500 for 18 months if the loan requires $190 interest and is repaid monthly.

34. Find the annual percentage rate on a loan that is repaid weekly for 25 weeks if the amount of the loan is $300. The loan requires $20 interest.

35. Find the annual percentage rate on a loan of $3,820 if the monthly payment is $120 for 36 months.

36. Find the annual percentage rate on a loan of $700 with 12 monthly payments. The loan requires $101 interest.

37. A vacuum cleaner was purchased on the installment plan with 10 monthly payments of $10.50 each. If the cash price was $95 and there was no down payment, find the annual percentage rate.

Use Table 12-1 to find the annual percentage rate for the following.

38. A queen-size brass bed costs $1,155 and is financed with monthly payments for three years. The total finance charge is $415.80. Find the annual percentage rate.

39. A merchant charged $420 in cash for a dining room set that could be bought for $50 down and $40.75 per month for 10 months. What is the annual percentage rate?

40. John Edmonds borrowed $500. He repaid the loan in 22 monthly payments of $26.30 each. Find the annual percentage rate.

41. An electric mixer was purchased on the installment plan for a down payment of $60 and 11 monthly payments of $11.05 each. The cash price was $170. Find the annual percentage rate.

42. A loan of $3,380 was paid back in 30 monthly payments with an interest charge of $620. Find the annual percentage rate to the nearest tenth of a percent.

43. A word processor was purchased by paying $50 down and 24 monthly payments of $65 each. The cash price was $1,400. Find the annual percentage rate to the nearest tenth of a percent.

44. A 6 × 6 color enlarger costs $1,295 and is financed with monthly payments for two years. The total finance charge is $310.80. Find the annual percentage rate.

Section 12.5

Hullett Houpt is purchasing a home for $97,000. He will finance the mortgage for 15 years and pay 11% interest on the loan. He makes a down payment that is 20% of the purchase price. Use Table 12-2 as needed.

45. Find the down payment.

46. Find the amount of the mortgage.

47. If Hullett is required to pay two points for making the loan, how much will the points cost?

48. Find the monthly payment that includes principal and interest.

49. Find the total interest Hullett will pay over the 15-year period.

50. Calculate the monthly payment and the total interest Hullett would have to pay if he decided to make the loan for 30 years instead of 15 years.

51. How much interest can be saved by paying for the home in 15 years rather than 30 years?

52. Find the interest portion and principal portion for the first payment of Hullett's 15-year loan.

53. Make an amortization schedule for the first three payments of the 15-year loan in exercise 49.

54. Make an amortization schedule for the first three payments of the 30-year loan in exercise 50.

Month	Portion of Payment Applied to: Interest	Principal	End-of-Month Principal
1			
2			
3			

Month	Portion of Payment Applied to: Interest	Principal	End-of-Month Principal
1			
2			
3			

55. Write formulas for generating the first 12 months of an amortization schedule for a loan of $69,600 at 10% annual interest for 30 years. The remainder of the amortization schedule can be generated by using the Copy and Paste functions of the spreadsheet program if desired.

(a) Write a formula to generate the Payments Remaining

(b) Write formulas to compute the monthly interest and principal.

(c) Write formulas to compute the Principal Owed, Accumulated Interest, and Accumulated Principal paid for the remainder of the spreadsheet. Hint: Formulas from the cells in Row 4 can be copied and pasted to remaining cells in a column.

56. Complete the spreadsheet using the formulas.

```
Microsoft Excel - chapter 12 worksheet.xls                                                _ □ ×
 D ☞ ⊟ 🖨 🖨 Q ᵂ  ✕ 🖻 🖻 ᗄ  �🄰 ▾ ⎙ ▾  ⬡ Σ ⨍ ⍖ Ⓩ 🔟 ⅍ 100% ▾ ❓ .
 File  Edit  View  Insert  Format  Tools  Data  Window  Help                              _ ⬚ ×
 Times New Roman    ▾ 14 ▾  B I U ≡ ≡ ≡ ⊞ $ % , ⁺⁰ ⁰⁰ ⌁ ⌁ ▦ ▾ ♢ ▾ A ▾ .
     J18        ▾       =
```

	A	B	C	D	E	F	G	H
1	Partial Amortization Schedule for home loan of $69,600.00 for 30 years at 10%							
2	Payments Remaining	Rate	Principal Owed	Mo. Payment	Interest	Principal	Accumulated Interest	Accum. Principal Paid
3	360	0.10	$69,600.00	$610.79				
4								
5								
6								
7								
8								
9								
10								
11								
12								
13								
14								
15								

```
I◄ ◄ ► ►I \ Sheet1 ⧵ Sheet2 ⧵ Sheet3 /                              I◄I                ►I
```

Challenge Problem

57. Bob and Julie Malena need to finance $80,000 on their new home. After checking with several mortgage companies, they have narrowed their choices to two options.

Option 1: 20 years at 11%

Option 2: 25 years at 10%

If the Malenas can budget for either monthly payment, which option do you recommend? Why?

CHAPTER 12 PRACTICE TEST

1. Find the finance charge on an item with a cash price of $469 if the installment price is $503 and no down payment was made.

2. An item with a cash price of $578 can be purchased on the installment plan in 15 monthly payments of $46. Find the installment price if no down payment was made. Find the finance charge.

3. A copier that originally cost $300 was sold on the installment plan at $28 per month for 12 months. Find the installment price if no down payment was made. Find the finance charge.

4. Use Table 12-1 to find the annual percentage rate for the loan in exercise 3.

5. Use the constant ratio formula to estimate the annual percentage rate, to the nearest tenth of a percent, for the copier in exercise 3.

6. Use the constant ratio formula to estimate the annual percentage rate, to the nearest tenth of a percent, on a loan of $3,000 at 9% for three years if the loan had interest of $810 and was repaid monthly.

7. Find the interest on an unpaid balance of $165 if the monthly interest rate is $1\frac{3}{4}\%$.

8. Find the yearly rate of interest on a loan if the monthly rate is 2%.

9. Find the interest refunded on a 15-month loan with total interest of $72 if the loan is paid in full with six months remaining.

10. Find the annual interest rate on a loan of $1,600 for 24 months if $200 interest is charged and the loan is repaid in monthly payments.

11. Find the annual interest rate on a loan that is repaid weekly for 26 weeks if the amount of the loan is $1,075. The interest charged is $60.

12. Office equipment was purchased on the installment plan with 12 monthly payments of $11.20 each. If the cash price was $120 and there was no down payment, find the annual percentage rate.

13. Use the unpaid balance method to find the new unpaid balance on an account with a previous balance of $205.60, purchases of $67.38, a payment of $40, and a finance charge of 1.75%.

14. A canoe has been purchased on the installment plan with a down payment of $75 and 10 monthly payments of $80 each. Find the installment price of the canoe.

15. Find the monthly payment when the installment price is $2,300, a down payment of $400 is made, and there are 12 monthly payments.

16. How much is to be financed on a cash price of $729 if a down payment of $75 is made?

17. Find the refund fraction on a four-year loan if it is paid off in 25 months.

18. The unpaid balance on a credit card at the beginning of the month is $288.93. During the month, purchases totaling $75.60 and one payment of $50 were made. Using the unpaid balance method and a finance rate of 1.9% per month, find the unpaid balance at the beginning of the next month.

19. Use the following activity chart to find the average daily balance and finance charge for July. The monthly interest rate is 1.75%. The billing cycle has 31 days.

20. Ginger Canoy has purchased a home for $122,000. She plans to finance $100,000 for 15 years at $9\frac{1}{2}\%$ interest. Calculate the monthly payment and the total interest. Use Table 12-2.

Date Posted	Activity	Amount
July 1	Billing date	Previous balance $441.05
July 5	Payment	$75.00
July 16	Purchase	23.50
July 26	Purchase	31.40

21. Make Ginger an amortization schedule for the first two months of the mortgage.

	Portion of Payment Applied to:		
Month	Interest	Principal	End-of-Month Principal
1			
2			

Self-Check 12.1

1. $6 \times \$108.20 + 100 = \$749.20$
2. $\$579 - \$125 = \$454$
3. $12 \times \$106.32 + \$100 = \$1,375.84$
4. $18 \times \$97.42 + \$80 = \$1,833.56$
5. $8 \times \$82.56 + \$100 = \$760.48$
6. $\$503 \times 24 = \$12,072$
7. Finance charge $= \$2,987 \times 0.19 \times 1.5 = \$851.30$
   Installment price $= \$2,987 + \$851.30 = \$3838.30$
   Monthly payment $= \$3,838.30 \div 18 = \$213.24$
8. $\$2590 \times 24\% \times 1 = \$621.60$
   $$\frac{\$621.60 + \$2,590}{12} = \$267.63$$
9. $\dfrac{\$929 - \$100}{12} = \$69.08$
10. $\dfrac{\$625 - \$75}{18} = \$30.56$
11. $\dfrac{\$2,357 - \$250}{24} = \$87.79$
12. Finance charge $= \$3,780 \times 0.13 \times 3 = \$1,474.20$
    Installment price $= \$3,780 + \$1,474.20 = \$5,254.20$
    Monthly payment $= \dfrac{\$5,254.20}{36} = \$145.95$

Self-Check 12.2

1. $\dfrac{\overset{4}{\cancel{8}}(\overset{1}{\cancel{9}})}{\underset{\underset{1}{\cancel{2}}}{18}(19)} = \dfrac{4}{19}$

2. $18 - 12 = 6$ months remaining
   $$\dfrac{6(\overset{1}{\cancel{7}})}{18(19)} = \dfrac{7}{57}$$
   $$\dfrac{7}{57} \times \$205 = \$25.18$$

3. $48 - 28 = 20$ months remaining
   $$\dfrac{20(\overset{1}{\cancel{21}})}{\underset{\underset{4}{\cancel{12}}}{\cancel{48}}(49)} = \dfrac{5}{28}$$

4. 28 months remaining
   $$\dfrac{\overset{1}{\cancel{28}}(29)}{48(49)} = \dfrac{29}{84}$$
   $$\dfrac{29}{84} \times \$1,645 = \$567.92$$

5. 15 months remaining
   $$\dfrac{15(16)}{42(43)} = \dfrac{40}{301}$$
   $$\dfrac{40}{301} \times \$2,397 = \$318.54$$

6. 10 payments remaining
   $$\dfrac{10(11)}{36(37)} = \dfrac{55}{666}$$
   $$\dfrac{55}{666} \times \$3,227 = \$266.49$$

Self-Check 12.3

1. $\$275.69 \times 0.023 = \$6.34$
2. $\$176.95 \times 0.016 = \$2.83$
   $\$176.95 + \$2.83 - \$45$
   $= \$134.78$
3. $\$3,805 \times 0.012 = \$45.66$

4. $\$3,805 + \$45.66 + \$4,983 - \$7,000 = \$1,833.66$
5. $\$1,833.66 \times 0.012 = \$22.00$
   $\$1,833.66 + \$22.00 + \$75.00 - \$500.00 =$
   $\$1,430.66$

6. $\$897.52 \times 0.01 = \$8.98$ (rounded)

7. Average daily balance $= \dfrac{(15 \times \$2,534.95) + (7 \times \$1,534.95) + (7 \times \$1,892.57)}{29}$

   $= \dfrac{38,024.25 + 10,744.65 + 13,247.99}{29}$

   $= \dfrac{62,016.89}{29}$

   $= \$2,138.51$ Interest $= \$2,138.51 \times 0.008333333 = \$17.82$

8.
$$\text{March 1–5: } 5 \times \$128.50 = \$642.50$$
$$\$128.50 - \$20 = \$108.50$$
$$\text{March 6–19: } 14 \times \$108.50 = \$1,519.00$$
$$\$108.50 + \$25.60 = \$134.10$$

$$\text{March 20–31: } 12 \times \$134.10 = \$1,609.20$$
$$\$642.50 + \$1,519.00 + \$1,609.20 = \$3,770.70$$
$$\$3,770.70 \div 31 = \$121.64$$

9. $\$121.64 \times 0.018 = \$2.19$

10.

Date	Unpaid Balance	Number of Days	Total
May 4–May 6	$283.57	3	$850.71
May 7–May 11	303.30	5	1,516.50
May 12–May 17	357.12	6	2,142.72
May 18–May 28	157.12	11	1,728.32
May 29–June 3	272.30	6	1,633.80
31 days in cycle		31	$7,872.05

$$\text{Average daily balance} = \frac{\$7,872.05}{31} = \$253.94$$

11. Finance charge $= \$253.94 \times 0.0142 = \$3.61$

12. $\$272.30 + \$3.61 = \$275.91$

Self-Check 12.4

1. $\text{APR} = \dfrac{2 \times 12 \times \$265}{\$1,500 \times (24 + 1)} = 0.170 \text{ or } 17.0\%$

2. $\text{APR} = \dfrac{2 \times 12 \times \$518}{\$3,800 \times (36 + 1)} = 0.088 \text{ or } 8.8\%$

3. $\text{APR} = \dfrac{2 \times 12 \times \$412}{\$2,750 \times (18 + 1)} = 0.189 \text{ or } 18.9\%$

4. $\text{APR} = \dfrac{2 \times 12 \times \$1,215}{\$5,800 \times (30 + 1)} = 0.162 \text{ or } 16.2\%$

5. $\text{APR} = \dfrac{2 \times 12 \times \$698}{\$3,715 \times (24 + 1)} = 0.180 \text{ or } 18.0\%$

6. $\dfrac{\$1,025 \times \$100}{\$5,600} = \$18.30$

In the row for 36 months, move across to 18.29 (nearest to $18.30). The APR at the top of this column is 11.25%.

7. $\dfrac{\$90 \times \$100}{\$780} = \$11.54$

In the row for 12 months, move across to 11.59 (nearest to 11.54). The APR at the top of this column is 20.75%.

8. $\dfrac{\$412 \times \$100}{\$2,750} = \$14.98$

In the row for 18 months, move across to 15.07 (nearest to 14.98). The APR at the top of this column is 18.25%. Compare with 18.9% using the formula.

9. $\dfrac{\$1,215 \times \$100}{\$5,800} = \$20.95$

In the row for 30 months, move across to 20.90 (nearest to 20.95). The APR at the top of this column is 15.25%. Compare with 16.2% using the formula.

10. $\dfrac{\$698 \times \$100}{\$3,715} = \$18.79$

In the row for 24 months, move across to 18.66 (nearest to 18.79). The APR at the top of this column is 17.00%. Compare with 18.0% using the formula.

11. The APR using the table value seems to be consistently lower than the APR found by using the formula.

12. $\dfrac{\$5,036 \times \$100}{\$28,000} = \$17.99$

In the row for 36 months, move across to 17.86 (nearest to 17.99). The APR at the top of this column is 11.00%.

Self-Check 12.5

1. Down payment $= \$67,000 \times 0.15 = \$10,050$
Amount financed $= \$67,000 - \$10,050 = \$56,950$

2. $\$56,950 \div \$1,000 = \$56.95$
The Table 12–2 value for 25 years and $8\frac{1}{2}\%$ is 8.06.
Monthly payment $= \$56.95 \times \$8.06 = \$459.02$

3. Amount paid = \$459.02 × 12 × 25 = \$137,706
Total interest = \$137,706 − \$56,950 = \$80,756

4. Down payment = \$155,000 × 0.18 = \$27,900
Amount of mortgage = \$155,000 − \$27,900 = \$127,100
The Table 12–2 value for 25 years and $9\frac{1}{2}\%$ is 8.74.
\$127,100 ÷ \$1,000 = 127.1
Monthly payment = 127.1 × \$8.74 = \$1,110.85

5. Total paid = \$1,110.85 × 12 × 25 = \$333,255.00
Interest paid = \$333,255.00 − \$127,100 = \$206,155

6. The Table 12–2 value for 20 years and $9\frac{1}{2}\%$ is 9.33.
\$127,100 ÷ 1,000 = 127.1
Monthly payment = 127.1 × \$9.33 = \$1,185.84
This monthly payment is only \$74.99 more than the monthly payment for the 25-year loan. So, he could reduce the number of years required to repay the loan to 20 years.

7. Total paid = \$1,185.84 × 12 × 20 = \$284,601.60
Interest paid = \$284,601.60 − \$127,100 = \$157,501.60
Interest savings = \$206,155.00 − \$157,501.60 = \$48,653.40

8. *Month 1*

Interest portion of payment = $\$127,100 \times \dfrac{0.095}{12}$

$$= \$1,006.21$$

Principal portion of payment = \$1,110.85 − \$1,006.21 = \$104.64
End-of-month principal \$127,100 − \$104.64 = \$126,995.36

Month 2

Interest portion of payment = $\$126,995.36 \times \dfrac{0.095}{12}$

$$= \$1,005.38$$

Principal portion of payment = \$1,110.85 − \$1,005.38 = \$105.47
End-of-month principal = \$126,995.36 − \$105.47 = \$126,889.89

Month 3

Interest portion of payment = $\$126,889.89 \times \dfrac{0.095}{12}$

$$= \$1,004.54$$

Principal portion of payment = \$1,110.85 − \$1,004.54 = \$106.31
End-of-month principal = \$126,889.89 − \$106.31 = \$126,783.58

| Month | Portion of Payment Applied to: | | End-of-Month Principal |
	Interest	Principal	
1	1,006.21	104.64	126,995.36
2	1,005.38	105.47	126,889.89
3	1,004.54	106.31	126,783.58

9. *Month*

Interest portion of payment = $\$127,100 \times \dfrac{0.095}{12}$

$$= \$1,006.21$$

Principal portion of payment = \$1,185.84 − \$1,006.21 = \$179.63
End-of-month principal = \$127,100 − \$179.63 = \$126,920.37

Month 2

Interest portion of payment = $\$126,920.37 \times \dfrac{0.095}{12}$

$$= \$1,004.79$$

Principal portion of payment = \$1,185.84 − \$1,004.79 = \$181.05
End-of-month principal = \$126,920.37 − \$181.05 = \$126,739.32

10. Find the monthly payment.

20 years at $8\frac{1}{2}$% gives a Table 12-2 value of 8.68.

$69,700 ÷ $1000 = 69.7

Monthly payment = 69.7 × $8.68 = $605.00

Month 1

Interest portion of payment = $69,700 × $\dfrac{0.085}{12}$

$$= \$493.71$$

Principal portion of payment = $605.00 − $493.71 = $111.29

End-of-month principal = $69,700 − $111.29 = $69,588.71

Month 2

Interest portion of payment = $69,588.71 × $\dfrac{0.085}{12}$

$$= \$492.92$$

Principal portion of payment = $605.00 − $492.92 = $112.08

End-of-month principal = $69,588.71 − $112.08 = $69,476.63

11. Find the monthly payment.

17 years at 9% gives a Table 12-2 value of 9.59.

$84,700 ÷ $1,000 = 84.7

Monthly payment = 84.7 × $9.59 = $812.27

Month 1

Interest portion of payment = $84,700 × $\dfrac{0.09}{12}$

$$= \$635.25$$

Principal portion of payment = $812.27 − $635.25 = $177.02

End-of-month principal = $84,700 − $177.02 = $84,522.98

Month 2

Interest portion of payment = $84,522.98 × $\dfrac{0.09}{12}$

$$= \$633.92$$

Principal portion of payment = $812.27 − $633.92 = $178.35

End-of-month principal = $84,522.98 − $178.35 = $84,344.63

12. Find the monthly payment.

20 years at $8\frac{1}{2}$% gives a Table 12-2 value of 8.68.

$210,300 ÷ $1,000 = 210.3

Monthly payment = 210.3 × 8.68 = $1,825.40

Month 1

Interest portion of payment = $210,300 × $\dfrac{0.085}{12}$

$$= \$1,489.63$$

Principal portion of payment = $1,825.40 − $1,489.63 = $335.77

End-of-month principal = $210,300 − $335.77 = $209,964.23

Month 2

Interest portion of payment = $209,964.23 × $\dfrac{0.085}{12}$

$$= \$1,487.25$$

Principal portion of payment = $1,825.40 − $1,487.25 = $338.15

End-of-month principal = $209,964.23 − $338.15 = $209,626.08

CHAPTER

13

Depreciation

13.1 Straight-Line Method of Depreciation

1 Depreciate an asset and prepare a depreciation schedule using the straight-line method.

13.2 Units-of-Production Method of Depreciation

1 Depreciate an asset and prepare a depreciation schedule using the units-of-production method.

13.3 Sum-of-the-Years'-Digits Method of Depreciation

1 Depreciate an asset and prepare a depreciation schedule using the sum-of-the-years'-digits method.

13.4 Declining-Balance Method of Depreciation

1 Depreciate an asset and prepare a depreciation schedule using the declining-balance method.

13.5 Cost-Recovery Depreciation Systems

1 Depreciate an asset and prepare a depreciation schedule using the modified accelerated cost-recovery system (MACRS).

13.6 Section 179 Deductions

1 Depreciate an asset after taking a section 179 deduction.

Good Decisions through Teamwork

As a team, identify 10 different assets that may be depreciated, for example, farming equipment, a car, or a high-speed color copier. Make your list as varied as possible and include the cost of the asset, the useful life or recovery period for the asset, and the salvage value.

Individually, interview a tax accountant about the various ways each asset can be depreciated, the recommended method for each asset, and the rationale for each recommendation. Be sure to discuss section 179 deductions as an option.

Report back to your team with the results of your interview. Are the results consistent with other team members' results? If not, investigate further.

When the team is satisfied that the best options for depreciation have been chosen, prepare a summary of the team's findings and decisions. Be prepared to answer questions orally from your classmates.

Buildings, machinery, equipment, furniture, and other items bought for the operation of a business are included among the **assets** of that business. The dollar value of each asset is used in figuring the value and profitability of the business and in figuring the taxable income for the business. The expense of running a business, including the purchase of assets, can be deducted from the company's taxable income before taxes are calculated, so it is important to have a way of keeping track of the value of assets.

Some assets have a useful life of one year or less, and their costs can be deducted from the business's income in the year they are purchased. The cost of items that are expected to last more than a year can be prorated and deducted over a period of years, called the **estimated life,** or **useful life,** of the item. During this time period, the asset *depreciates,* or decreases in value. At the end of an asset's estimated life, it may still have a dollar value, called the **salvage value,** or **scrap value.** The amount an asset decreases in value from its original cost is called its **depreciation.**

This chapter is concerned with determining the amount an asset has depreciated. This involves the question of how the estimated life of a piece of equipment is to be defined. In years? In miles driven, if it is a car? In items produced, if it is a machine? It also involves a question of what percentage of the original cost can be deducted each year. Some types of equipment may be used more extensively some years than others; some machines depreciate rapidly at first and slowly later; some machines may not wear out but may become outdated because a better model has been invented. All these factors must be considered in choosing the method of depreciation for a particular asset.

This chapter examines five widely used depreciation methods: straight-line, units-of-production, sum-of-the-years'-digits, declining-balance, and the modified accelerated cost-recovery system (MACRS). The Internal Revenue Service (IRS) regulates the methods of depreciation that are allowed for income tax purposes. In general, the same depreciation method must be used throughout the useful life of any particular asset. The IRS requires the use of the modified accelerated cost-recovery system of depreciation unless special circumstances are approved by the IRS. The IRS limits the use of many methods of depreciation, so you should consult IRS publications or an accountant before choosing a depreciation method.

13.1 Straight-Line Method of Depreciation

 Depreciate an asset and prepare a depreciation schedule using the straight-line method.

A commonly used method of depreciation for internal business purposes is the **straight-line depreciation** method. It is easy to use because the depreciation is the same for each full year the equipment is used.

If you know the original cost of an asset, its estimated useful life, and its salvage value, you can find the yearly depreciation amount. In calculating depreciation, by whatever method, the cost of an asset means the **total cost,** including shipping and installation charges if the asset is a piece of equipment. The **depreciable value** is the cost minus the salvage value.

HOW TO Find the Yearly Depreciation Using the Straight-Line Method

1. Find the *total cost* of the asset: add shipping and installation charges to the cost.

$$\text{Total cost} = \text{cost} + \text{shipping} + \text{installation}$$

2. Find the *depreciable value:* subtract the salvage value from the total cost.

$$\text{Depreciable value} = \text{total cost} - \text{salvage value}$$

3. Find the *yearly depreciation:* divide the depreciable value by the years of expected life.

$$\text{Yearly depreciation} = \frac{\text{depreciable value}}{\text{years of expected life}}$$

EXAMPLE Use the straight-line method to find the yearly depreciation for a plating machine that has an expected useful life of five years. The plating machine cost $27,300, its shipping costs totaled $250, installation charges came to $450, and its salvage value is $1,000.

$$\text{Total cost} = \text{cost of asset} + \text{shipping} + \text{installation}$$
$$= \$27,300 + \$250 + \$450 = \boxed{\$28,000}$$
$$\text{Depreciable value} = \text{total cost} - \text{salvage value}$$
$$= \boxed{\$28,000} - \$1,000$$
$$= \boxed{\$27,000}$$
$$\text{Yearly depreciation} = \frac{\text{depreciable value}}{\text{years of expected life}}$$
$$= \frac{\boxed{\$27,000}}{5} = \$5,400$$

The depreciation is $5,400 per year.

Options for a Series of Calculations

The depreciable value in the preceding example can be calculated continuously:

$$\frac{\$27,300 + \$250 + \$450 - \$1,000}{5}$$

When using a basic calculator, use the "equals" key to complete the calculations in the numerator before dividing by the denominator.

$$\boxed{AC} \; 27300 \; \boxed{+} \; 250 \; \boxed{+} \; 450 \; \boxed{-} \; 1000 \; \boxed{=} \; \boxed{\div} \; 5 \; \boxed{=} \Rightarrow 5400$$

When using a scientific, business, or graphing calculator, parentheses may be used.

$$\boxed{AC} \; \boxed{(} \; 27300 \; \boxed{+} \; 250 \; \boxed{+} \; 450 \; \boxed{-} \; 1000 \; \boxed{)} \; \boxed{\div} \; 5 \; \boxed{=} \Rightarrow 5400$$

TIP! Total Cost versus Depreciable Value

A common mistake in figuring yearly depreciation using the straight-line method is to divide the total cost rather than the depreciable value by the expected life. See what happens when this is done with the preceding example:

$$\text{Yearly depreciation} = \frac{\text{depreciable value}}{\text{years of expected life}}$$

$$= \frac{\text{total cost of equipment} - \text{salvage value}}{\text{years of expected life}}$$

$$= \frac{\$28,000 - \$1,000}{5} = \frac{\$27,000}{5} = \$5,400$$

CORRECT

$$\text{Yearly depreciation} = \frac{\text{total cost of equipment}}{\text{years of expected life}} = \frac{\$28,000}{5} = \$5,600$$

INCORRECT

A **depreciation schedule** is often the best way to record the depreciation of an asset over time. No matter which method of depreciation is used, the depreciation schedule shows consistent information. For each year of depreciation, the following values are recorded: the year's depreciation, the *accumulated depreciation,* and the year's *end-of-year book value.* **Accumulated depreciation** is the year's depreciation plus the sum of all previous years' depreciation. The first year's **end-of-year book value** is the total cost minus the year's depreciation. For all other years, the year's end-of-year book value is the previous end-of-year book value minus the year's depreciation.

HOW TO Prepare a Depreciation Schedule

1. For the first year of expected life:
   (a) Find the year's depreciation.
   (b) Find the *first end-of-year book value:* subtract the first year's depreciation from the total cost.

   First end-of-year book value = total cost − first year's depreciation

2. For each remaining year of expected life:
   (a) Find the year's depreciation.
   (b) Find the *year's accumulated depreciation:* add the year's depreciation to the sum of all the previous years' depreciation.

   Year's accumulated depreciation = year's depreciation + sum of all the previous years' depreciation

   (c) Find the *year's end-of-year book value:* subtract the year's depreciation from the previous end-of-year book value.

   Year's end-of-year book value = previous end-of-year book value − year's depreciation

3. Make a table with the following column headings and fill in the data: year, depreciation, accumulated depreciation, end-of-year book value.

Following is the depreciation schedule for the plating machine of the preceding example.

Table 13-1 Straight-Line Depreciation Schedule for Plating Machine

Total Cost: $28,000	Year	Depreciation	Accumulated Depreciation	End-of-Year Book Value
	1	$5,400	$5,400	$22,600
	2	5,400	10,800	17,200
	3	5,400	16,200	11,800
	4	5,400	21,600	6,400
	5	5,400	27,000	1,000

Notice that for straight-line depreciation the end-of-year book value cannot be less than the salvage value. The final accumulated depreciation plus the salvage value must equal the total cost.

SELF-CHECK 13.1

1. Find the depreciable value of an asset that costs $5,323 and has a scrap value of $500.

2. Use the straight-line method to find the yearly depreciation for a van that costs $18,000, has an expected life of three years, and has a salvage value of $3,000.

3. Find the yearly depreciation for a computer network system that costs $21,500, has an expected life of four years, and has a salvage value of $4,000. Use straight-line depreciation.

4. Find the straight-line depreciation for a security system that costs $5,800, has an expected life of three years, and has a salvage value of $1,500.

5. A tractor costs $25,000, has an expected life of 12 years, and has a salvage value of $2,500. Use straight-line depreciation to find the yearly depreciation. Make a depreciation schedule for the first three years' depreciation.

6. Prepare a straight-line depreciation schedule for the first four years of depreciation of a forklift that costs $9,450, is expected to be used for 12 years, and is projected to be scrapped for $500.

7. Find the yearly straight-line depreciation of a notebook computer system including the computer and monitor, networking equipment, and a postscript printer that costs $6,300 and has a scrap value of $600 after an expected life of five years in a college engineering lab.

8. Make a straight-line depreciation schedule for an asset that costs $7,500 and has a scrap value of $1,200. The useful life of the asset is eight years.

9. Write a paragraph that describes the process for making a straight-line depreciation schedule.

13.2 Units-of-Production Method of Depreciation

 Depreciate an asset and prepare a depreciation schedule using the units-of-production method.

Machines and other types of equipment that are used heavily for a period of time and then left to sit idle for another period of time, sometimes months, are often depreciated using the **units-of-production depreciation** method. For example, earth-moving equipment and farm equipment are often idle during the winter months. Instead of basing depreciation on the expected lifetime of a piece of equipment in years, this method takes into account how the equipment is used, for example, how many items it has produced, how many miles it has been driven, how many hours it has operated, or how many times it has performed some particular operation.

The units-of-production method of depreciation is used for internal accounting purposes. Special written permission from the IRS is required for this method to be used on tax returns. Companies that use this method internally often adjust to a method acceptable by the IRS for tax-reporting purposes.

To use the units-of-production method, you must find the **unit depreciation**— how much the asset depreciates with each unit produced or each mile driven.

? **HOW TO** **Find the Depreciation for Units Produced Using the Units-of-Production Method**

1. Find the *unit depreciation:* divide the depreciable value by the units produced during the expected life. Keep the full calculator value of the quotient.

$$\text{Unit depreciation} = \frac{\text{depreciable value}}{\text{units produced during expected life}}$$

2. Multiply the unit depreciation by the units produced.

Depreciation for units produced = unit depreciation × units produced

---

 A label-making machine that costs $28,000 after shipping and installation is expected to print 50,000,000 labels during its useful life. If the salvage value of the machine is $1,000, find the unit depreciation and depreciation for printing 2,125,000 labels.

$$\text{Unit depreciation} = \frac{\text{depreciable value}}{\text{units produced during expected life}}$$

$$= \frac{\$28,000 - \$1,000}{50,000,000}$$

$$= \boxed{\$0.00054}$$

Do not round the unit depreciation.

$$\text{Depreciation} = \text{unit depreciation} \times \text{units produced}$$

$$= \boxed{\$0.00054} \times 2,125,000 = \$1,147.50$$

The depreciation is $1,147.50.

Combine Two Formulas Using Continuous Calculations

The calculations in both formulas can be performed continuously.

$$\text{Depreciation} = \frac{\text{total cost} - \text{salvage value}}{\text{units produced during expected life}} \times \text{units produced}$$

$\boxed{\text{AC}}\ 28000\ \boxed{-}\ 1000\ \boxed{=}\ \boxed{\div}\ 50000000\ \boxed{\times}\ 2125000\ \boxed{=} \Rightarrow 1147.5$

The depreciation of the label maker for its entire useful life is recorded in the depreciation schedule shown in Table 13-2. Note that the table shows the number of labels made each year and that the number differs from year to year. This pattern of use is typical of equipment that is depreciated by the units-of-production method.

Table 13-2   Units-of-Production Depreciation Schedule for the Label Maker

Total Cost $28,000	Year	Labels Printed	Depreciation	Accumulated Depreciation	End-of-Year Book Value
	1	2,125,000	$ 1,147.50	$ 1,147.50	$26,852.50
	2	11,830,000	6,388.20	7,535.70	20,464.30
	3	12,765,000	6,893.10	14,428.80	13,571.20
	4	12,210,000	6,593.40	21,022.20	6,977.80
	5	11,070,000	5,977.80	27,000.00	1,000.00
Totals		50,000,000	$27,000.00		

 TIP!   **Check Your Schedule Calculation**

One way to check your schedule calculation is to find the totals of the labels printed and the yearly depreciations. The total labels printed should equal the useful life. The total of the yearly depreciations should equal the depreciable value and the last entry in the accumulated depreciation column.

SELF-CHECK 13.2

 1   *Round unit depreciation to the nearest hundredth of a cent when necessary.*

1. A van that costs $18,000 is expected to be driven 75,000 miles during its useful life. If the salvage value of the van is $3,000, find the unit depreciation and the depreciation for 56,000 miles.

2. A company car is purchased for $23,580 and is expected to be driven 95,000 miles before being sold. The expected salvage value for the car is $2,300. Find the unit depreciation for the car.

3. An engraving machine that costs $28,700 is being set up on a unit depreciation schedule. The scrap value of the machine is anticipated to be $2,500. If the machine will engrave 300,000 objects during its useful life, find the unit depreciation. What is the first year's depreciation if 28,452 objects are engraved?

4. Chou's Meat Processing Company purchased a meat cutting machine for $7,500. Its expected life is 60,000 hours, and it will have a salvage value of $600. Use units-of-production depreciation to find the year's depreciation on the machine if it is used 8,500 hours during the first year.

5. A printing machine is expected to be operational for 90,000 hours. If the machine costs $84,500 and has a projected salvage value of $2,900, find the unit depreciation. The machine is used for 3,853 hours the first year. What is the first year's depreciation?

6. Describe the process of finding the unit depreciation using the units-of-production depreciation method. Also describe how each year's depreciation is calculated.

13.3 Sum-of-the-Years'-Digits Method of Depreciation

 Depreciate an asset and prepare a depreciation schedule using the sum-of-the-years'-digits method.

The straight-line depreciation method of depreciating an asset is the simplest way to depreciate it, but it is not always the most realistic method of depreciation to use. Most equipment depreciates more during its first year of operation than during any other subsequent year. Many businesses prefer to use a method that shows the largest depreciation during the first year or two. One such method is the **sum-of-the-years'-digits depreciation** method.

To find a year's depreciation, we find the year's **depreciation rate** and multiply it by the depreciable value. The numerator of the year's depreciation rate is the number of years of expected life *remaining*. The denominator of the year's depreciation rate is the sum of the numbers from 1 to the years of expected life. Remember from section 12.2 the formula for finding such a sum. If, for example, the expected life is five years, then the sum from 1 to 5 is

$$\frac{5(5 + 1)}{2} = \frac{5(6)}{2} = \frac{30}{2} = 15$$

If the expected life is five years, the denominator of each year's depreciation rate is 15.

Year	Years Remaining Sum of 1 to 5
1	$\dfrac{5}{15}$
2	$\dfrac{4}{15}$
3	$\dfrac{3}{15}$
4	$\dfrac{2}{15}$
5	$\dfrac{1}{15}$

HOW TO Find the Year's Depreciation Using the Sum-of-the-Years'-Digits Method

1. Find the *year's depreciation rate:*

    (a) Find the sum from 1 to the number of years of expected life.

        Sum from 1 to the years of expected life

$$= \frac{\text{(years of expected life)(1 + years of expected life)}}{2}$$

    (b) Divide the years remaining of expected life by the sum from step 1a.

        Year's sum-of-the-years' depreciation rate

$$= \frac{\text{years remaining of expected life}}{\text{sum from 1 to the years of expected life}}$$

2. Multiply the depreciable value by the year's depreciation rate.

    Year's depreciation = depreciable value × year's depreciation rate

---

The end-of-year book value for the first year is the difference between the total cost and the first year's depreciation. In the years that follow, the end-of-year book value is the difference between the previous year's end-of-year book value and the year's depreciation. The depreciation and end-of-year book value for each year of the useful life can be organized in a depreciation schedule.

EXAMPLE Find the depreciation for each of the five years of expected life of a bottle-capping machine that costs $27,300 and has a shipping cost of $250, an installation cost of $450, and a salvage value of $1,000. Make a depreciation schedule.

$$\text{Denominator of depreciation rate} = \frac{5(6)}{2} = \boxed{15} \qquad \textbf{Sum of 1 to 5}$$

Write the depreciation rate for each year.

$$\frac{5}{15}, \frac{4}{15}, \frac{3}{15}, \frac{2}{15}, \frac{1}{15} \qquad \textbf{Years remaining}$$

$$\uparrow \quad \uparrow \quad \uparrow \quad \uparrow \quad \uparrow$$

$$\text{Year} \quad 1 \quad 2 \quad 3 \quad 4 \quad 5$$

$$\text{Depreciable value} = \text{total cost} - \text{salvage value}$$

$$(\$27,300 + \$250 + \$450) - \$1,000 = \boxed{\$27,000}$$

$$\text{Year's depreciation} = \text{Depreciable value} \times \text{depreciation rate}$$

$$= \frac{\overset{9,000}{\boxed{\$27,000}}}{1} \times \frac{\overset{1}{5}}{\underset{\underset{1}{3}}{15}}$$

$$= \boxed{\$9,000} \text{ (year 1)}$$

$$\text{Year 1 end-of-year book value} = \text{total cost} - \text{depreciation}$$

$$= \$28,000 - \boxed{\$9,000}$$

$$= \$19,000$$

The results of the calculations for the remaining years can be organized in a depreciation schedule (Table 13-3).

Table 13-3 Sum-of-the-Years'-Digits Depreciation
Schedule for Bottle-Capping Machine

Total Cost $28,000	Year	Depreciation Rate	Depreciation	Accumulated Depreciation	End-of-Year Book Value
	1	$\frac{5}{15}$	$9,000	$ 9,000	$19,000
	2	$\frac{4}{15}$	7,200	16,200	11,800
	3	$\frac{3}{15}$	5,400	21,600	6,400
	4	$\frac{2}{15}$	3,600	25,200	2,800
	5	$\frac{1}{15}$	1,800	27,000	1,000
		$\frac{15}{15} = 1$	27,000		

TIP! Built-in Checks

One way to check your calculations in the depreciation schedule in Table 13-3 is to add the columns for the depreciation rate and depreciation.

- The sum of the depreciation rates should equal 1.
- The sum of the depreciation amounts should equal the depreciable value.
- The last entry in the accumulated depreciation column is the depreciable value.
- The last entry in the end-of-year book value column is the salvage value.

Use the Memory Function for Entering Repeated Values

Since the depreciable value is used in the depreciation calculation for each year, the memory function on a calculator can be used. The calculator sequence for the first year's depreciation is

$\boxed{AC}$ $\boxed{MC}$ 27000 $\boxed{M+}$ $\boxed{AC}$ 5 $\boxed{\div}$ 15 $\boxed{=}$ $\boxed{\times}$ $\boxed{MR}$ $\boxed{=}$ $\Rightarrow$ 9000

If a basic calculator is used, the answer should be rounded to 9,000. If a scientific calculator is used, the display will show 9,000.

The calculator sequence for subsequent calculations will be

$\boxed{AC}$ (year's depreciation rate fraction) $\boxed{\times}$ $\boxed{MR}$ $\boxed{=}$ $\Rightarrow$ year's depreciation

TIP! Fractions versus Decimal Equivalents

Rates can be written as fractions or decimal equivalents. For example, $\frac{5}{15} = 0.33\overline{3}$, $\frac{4}{15} = 0.26\overline{6}$, $\frac{3}{15} = 0.2$, $\frac{2}{15} = 0.13\overline{3}$, and $\frac{1}{15} = 0.06\overline{6}$.
When decimals are repeating decimals, using the fraction form gives the most accurate result.

5 $\boxed{\div}$ 15 $\boxed{=}$ $\boxed{\times}$ 27000 $\boxed{=}$ $\Rightarrow$ 9,000

0.333333333 $\boxed{\times}$ 27000 $\boxed{=}$ 27000 $\Rightarrow$ 8999.999991

TIP! **Which Fraction Goes First?**

A common mistake is to list the smallest fraction rather than the largest fraction for the first year's depreciation fraction. In the preceding example, the smallest fraction is $\frac{1}{15}$ and the largest is $\frac{5}{15}$. The confusion often occurs because the smallest fraction goes with the largest year; that is, year 5 uses $\frac{1}{15}$, and year 1 uses $\frac{5}{15}$.

Let's look at how to figure the depreciation for year 1 from the example again, showing both the correct and incorrect ways to do it.

Year 1	Year 1
$\frac{5}{15} \times \$27,000 = \$9,000$	$\frac{1}{15} \times \$27,000 = \$1,800$
CORRECT	**INCORRECT**

An easy way to check yourself on this is to remember that, when using the sum-of-the-years'-digits method, the *first* year's depreciation should be the *largest*. This shows you that $9,000 is correct and $1,800 is wrong for the first year's depreciation.

SELF-CHECK 13.3

1. Find the denominator of the depreciation rate if the expected life is (a) 8 years and (b) 12 years.

2. Use the sum-of-the-years'-digits method to find the depreciation for each of the three years of the expected life of a van that has a total cost of $18,000 and a salvage value of $3,000.

3. Use the sum-of-the-years'-digits method to make a depreciation schedule for an asset that has a total cost of $9,000 and a scrap value of $1,500 after four years.

4. Brown Shipping Company is making a depreciation schedule for one of its new tractor/trailer rigs by using the sum-of-the-years'-digits method of depreciation. The rig has a total cost of $45,000 and is expected to be in service for 10 years. The scrap value is approximated to be $3,500. Find the depreciation rate for each of the 10 years.

5. Make a sum-of-the-years'-digits depreciation schedule for the first four years' depreciation of the rig in exercise 4.

6. Describe the process for finding the depreciation rate for each year's depreciation using the sum-of-the-years'-digits depreciation method.

7. How do you use the depreciation rate to find the year's depreciation when you are using the sum-of-the-years'-digits depreciation method?

13.4 Declining-Balance Method of Depreciation

 Depreciate an asset and prepare a depreciation schedule using the declining-balance method.

Another way to calculate depreciation so that the depreciation is large in the early years of the asset's life and becomes smaller in the later years is by using the **declining-balance method.**

The **straight-line rate** of depreciation is a fraction with a numerator of 1 and a denominator equal to the number of useful years of an asset. The **double-declining rate** is twice the straight-line rate. The double-declining-balance method is also referred to as the **200%-declining-balance method.** Other declining-balance rates are possible, too, and each rate is some factor times the straight-line rate.

? HOW TO Find the Year's Depreciation Using the Declining-Balance Method

1. Find the yearly depreciation rate:

   (a) Using *straight-line declining balance:* divide 1 by the years of expected life.

   $$\text{Yearly straight-line depreciation rate} = \frac{1}{\text{years of expected life}}$$

   (b) Using other declining-balance depreciation rates, such as *double-declining-balance* or *150%-declining-balance:* multiply the yearly straight-line depreciation rate by the appropriate factor.

   Yearly double-declining depreciation rate
   = yearly straight-line depreciation rate × 2

   Yearly 150%-declining depreciation rate
   = yearly straight-line depreciation rate × 1.5

2. For the first year, multiply the total cost by the yearly depreciation rate.

   First year's depreciation = total cost × yearly depreciation rate

3. For all other years, multiply the previous end-of-year book value by the yearly depreciation rate.

   Year's depreciation = previous end-of-year book value
   × yearly depreciation rate

EXAMPLE An ice cream freezer has a useful life of six years. Find the yearly (a) straight-line rate expressed as a decimal and percent, (b) double-declining rate expressed as a decimal and percent, and (c) 150%-declining rate expressed as a decimal and percent.

(a) Yearly straight-line rate $= \dfrac{1}{\text{years of expected life}} = \dfrac{1}{6}$

$$\frac{1}{6} = 0.16666 \text{ (decimal equivalent)}$$

$$= 16.67\% \text{ (percent equivalent)}$$

The yearly straight-line rate is 0.1667 or 16.67%.

(b) Yearly double-declining rate = straight-line rate $\times$ 2 = $\dfrac{1}{6} \times 2 = \dfrac{2}{6} = \dfrac{1}{3}$

$$\frac{1}{3} = 0.33333 \text{ (decimal equivalent)}$$

$$= 33.33\% \text{ (percent equivalent)}$$

The yearly double-declining rate is 0.3333 or 33.33%.

(c) 150%-declining rate = straight-line rate $\times$ 1.5

$$= \frac{1}{6} \times 1.5 = 0.16666 \times 1.5$$

$$= 0.25 \text{ (decimal equivalent)}$$

$$= 25\% \text{ (percent equivalent)}$$

The yearly 150%-declining rate is 0.25 or 25%.

   In declining-balance depreciation, the depreciation for the first year is based on the total cost of the asset. Do *not* subtract the salvage value from the total cost to find the depreciation for the first year. At the end of the year, subtract the year's depreciation from the total cost of the asset, not the depreciable value, to get the end-of-year book value. The end-of-year book value for any year *cannot* drop below the salvage value of the asset. In such cases when calculations would cause the end-of-year book value to be less than the salvage value, the year's ending value will be the salvage value, and the year's depreciation is adjusted. There will then be no further depreciation in future years.

EXAMPLE   A packaging machine costing $28,000 with an expected life of five years and a resale value of $1,000 is depreciated by the declining-balance method at twice the straight-line rate. Prepare a depreciation schedule.

$$\text{Double-declining rate} = \text{straight-line rate} \times 2$$

$$= \frac{1}{\text{years of expected life}} \times 2$$

$$= \frac{1}{5} \times 2 = \frac{2}{5} = 0.4 = 40\%$$

$$\text{Year 1 depreciation} = \text{total cost} \times \text{double-declining rate}$$

$$= \$28,000 \times 0.4$$

$$= \$11,200$$

$$\text{End-of-year 1 book value} = \text{total cost} - \text{depreciation}$$

$$= \$28,000 - \$11,200$$

$$= \$16,800$$

$$\text{Year 2 depreciation} = \text{previous end-of-year book value} \times \text{double-declining rate}$$

$$= \$16,800 \times 0.4$$

$$= \$6,720$$

$$\text{End-of-year 2 book value} = \text{previous end-of-year book value} - \text{depreciation}$$
$$= \$16,800 - \boxed{\$6,720}$$
$$= \boxed{\$10,080}$$
$$\text{Year 3 depreciation} = \boxed{\$10,080} \times 0.4$$
$$= \boxed{\$4,032}$$
$$\text{End-of-year 3 book value} = \$10,080 - \boxed{\$4,032}$$
$$= \boxed{\$6,048}$$
$$\text{Year 4 depreciation} = \boxed{\$6,048} \times 0.4$$
$$= \boxed{\$2,419.20}$$
$$\text{End-of-year 4 book value} = \$6,048 - \boxed{\$2,419.20}$$
$$= \boxed{\$3,628.80}$$
$$\text{Year 5 depreciation} = \boxed{\$3,628.80} \times 0.4$$
$$= \boxed{\$1,451.52}$$
$$\text{End-of-year 5 book value} = \$3,628.80 - \boxed{\$1,451.52}$$
$$= \boxed{\$2,177.28}$$

Table 13–4 Double-Declining Balance Depreciation Schedule for Packaging Machine

Total Cost: $28,000	Year	Depreciation	Accumulated Depreciation	End-of-Year Book Value
	1	$11,200.00	$11,200.00	$16,800.00
	2	6,720.00	17,920.00	10,080.00
	3	4,032.00	21,952.00	6,048.00
	4	2,419.20	24,371.20	3,628.80
	5	1,451.52	25,822.72	2,177.28

TIP! Which Amount Do I Start With?

Be sure to *start with the total cost of the asset* when using the declining-balance method. A common error is to use total cost − salvage value, rather than total cost. That is, in the previous example,

$$\text{Depreciation for year 1} = \text{total cost} \times \text{declining balance rate}$$

$$\$28,000 \times 0.4 = \$11,200$$

CORRECT

$$\text{Total cost} - \text{salvage value} = \$28,000 - \$1,000 = \$27,000$$
$$\text{Depreciation for year 1} = \$27,000 \times 0.4 = \$10,800$$

INCORRECT

1. An acid disposal tank has a useful life of three years. Find (a) the straight-line rate of depreciation expressed as a decimal and percent and (b) the double-declining rate expressed as a decimal and percent.

2. A van costing $18,000 with an expected life of four years and a salvage value of $1,000 is depreciated by the declining-balance method at twice the straight-line rate. Determine the depreciation and the year-end book value for each of the four years.

3. Use the double-declining-balance method to make a depreciation schedule for equipment that cost $4,500 and has a salvage value of $300. The equipment is expected to last five years.

4. A robot designed to paint cars costs $25,000 and is expected to last eight years. It will have a scrap value of $2,500. Use the 200%-declining-balance method to make a depreciation schedule for the robot.

5. Use 150%-declining-balance depreciation to find the first year's depreciation for a trailer specially designed for landscaping work. The trailer costs $3,000, is expected to last four years, and is expected to have a salvage value of $300.

13.5 Cost-Recovery Depreciation Systems

1 Depreciate an asset and prepare a depreciation schedule using the modified accelerated cost-recovery system (MACRS).

In 1981 the Internal Revenue Service enacted the **accelerated cost-recovery system (ACRS)** for the depreciation of property placed in service after 1980. This method of depreciation, which is used in figuring depreciation for federal income tax purposes, allows businesses to write off the cost of assets more quickly than in the past. The other methods of depreciation are used for accounting purposes. The faster depreciation was meant to encourage businesses to invest in more assets despite an economic slowdown at the time.

Under ACRS, property was depreciated over a 3-, 5-, 10-, 15-, or 19-year recovery period, depending on the type of property. The **recovery period** is used in this system instead of estimated useful life. In most cases the recovery period allowed by ACRS was much shorter than the estimated useful life would have been. The IRS listed examples of types of property in each of the time categories to guide taxpayers. The following is taken from an IRS publication for items placed into service and depreciated using ACRS.

3-year property: Automobiles, tractor units for use over the road, light-duty trucks, and certain special manufacturing tools

5-year property: Most equipment, office furniture, and fixtures

10-year property: Certain real property such as public utility property, theme park structures, and mobile homes

15-year or 19-year real property: All real property placed in service before March 15, 1984, such as buildings not designated as 10-year property

Even though ACRS is no longer used when placing property in service, 19-year property that was placed in service before 1987 is still being depreciated using ACRS *cost-recovery* (or depreciation) rates set by the IRS.

Companies that placed properties in service using ACRS prepared a depreciation schedule when an item was placed in service. This enabled the company to determine each year's depreciation from the schedule rather than making the calculation each year.

The Tax Reform Act of 1986 introduced some changes in the depreciation rates for property put in use after 1986 (but not affecting property in use before 1986). These changes comprise the **modified accelerated cost-recovery system** or **MACRS.** The following is a list of property classes with examples, taken from IRS Publication 53, that can be depreciated under the MACRS.

3-year property: This class includes tractor units for use over the road, any race horse over two years old when placed in service, and any other horse over 12 years old when placed in service.

5-year property: This class includes automobiles, taxis, buses, trucks, computers and peripheral equipment, office machinery (typewriters, calculators, copiers, etc.), and any property used in research and experimentation.

7-year property: This class includes office furniture and fixtures (desks, file cabinets, etc.), and any property that does not have a class life and that has not been designated by law as being in any other class.

10-year property: This class includes vessels, barges, tugs, similar water transportation equipment, any single-purpose agricultural or horticultural structure, and any tree or vine bearing fruits or nuts.

15-year property: This class includes shrubbery, fences, roads, bridges, and service station buildings.

20-year property: This class includes farm buildings other than agricultural or horticultural structures.

IRS Publication 534 outlines all the options that may be used in figuring depreciation with MACRS. Some of the options involve placing properties in service at various times during the year. Several tables of rates are provided in IRS publications. MACRS rates when property is placed in service midyear are shown in Table 13-5.

Table 13-5 MACRS Cost-Recovery Rates, Half-Year Convention, in Percents

	Recovery Period					
Year	3-Year	5-Year	7-Year	10-Year	15-Year	20-Year
1	33.33	20.00	14.29	10.00	5.00	3.750
2	44.45	32.00	24.49	18.00	9.50	7.219
3	14.81	19.20	17.49	14.40	8.55	6.677
4	7.41	11.52	12.49	11.52	7.70	6.177
5		11.52	8.93	9.22	6.93	5.713
6		5.76	8.92	7.37	6.23	5.285
7			8.93	6.55	5.90	4.888
8			4.46	6.55	5.90	4.522
9				6.56	5.91	4.462
10				6.55	5.90	4.461
11				3.28	5.91	4.462
12					5.90	4.461
13					5.91	4.462
14					5.90	4.461
15					5.91	4.462
16					2.95	4.461
17						4.462
18						4.461
19						4.462
20						4.461
21						2.231

Source: IRS Publication 534, MARCS Table A-1

Notice in Table 13-5 that each recovery period has a depreciation rate for one year more than the recovery period indicates. The first and last years in the recovery period are partial years. Thus, the largest amount of depreciation is realized in the second year, which is the first full year.

 HOW TO Find the Year's Depreciation Using the MACRS Method

1. According to IRS publications, determine the asset's recovery period (expected life).
2. Find the year's MACRS rate: using Table 13-5, locate the MACRS rate for the year and recovery period.
3. Multiply the year's MACRS rate by the total cost of the asset.

Year's depreciation = year's MACRS rate × total cost

 TIP! **What Makes MACRS Easier?**

Two major differences in the MACRS method of depreciation are:

1. You do not have to find a depreciable value.
2. You do not have to determine a salvage value.

EXAMPLE Find the depreciation for each year for a boiler that was purchased for $28,000 and placed in service at midyear under the MACRS method of depreciation as a five-year property.

$$\text{Year 1 depreciation} = \text{MACRS rate} \times \text{total cost}$$
$$= 20\% \times \boxed{\$28,000}$$
$$= 0.20 \times \boxed{\$28,000}$$
$$= \$5,600$$

Year 2 depreciation = $0.32 \times \boxed{\$28,000} = \$8,960$

Year 3 depreciation = $0.192 \times \boxed{\$28,000} = \$5,376$

Year 4 depreciation = $0.1152 \times \boxed{\$28,000} = \$3,225.60$

Year 5 depreciation = $0.1152 \times \boxed{\$28,000} = \$3,225.60$

Year 6 depreciation = $0.0576 \times \boxed{\$28,000} = \$1,612.80$

The sum of the yearly depreciations should equal the total cost.

$\$5,600 + \$8,960 + \$5,376 + \$3,225.60 + \$3,225.60 + \$1,612.80 = \boxed{\$28,000}$

These calculations are most useful if they are organized into a depreciation schedule like the one shown in Table 13-6.

Table 13–6 MACRS Depreciation Schedule for Boiler

Total Cost: $28,000	Year	MACRS Rate	Depreciation	Accumulated Depreciation	End-of-Year Book Value
	1	20.00	$5,600.00	$5,600.00	$22,400.00
	2	32.00	8,960.00	14,560.00	13,440.00
	3	19.20	5,376.00	19,936.00	8,064.00
	4	11.52	3,225.60	23,161.60	4,838.40
	5	11.52	3,225.60	26,387.20	1,612.80
	6	5.76	1,612.80	28,000.00	0

 TIP! What Happens to the Salvage Value?

MACRS allows for 100% of the total cost of a property to be depreciated. Add the percents in any recovery period column of Table 13-5. The sum is 100% for every recovery period. Other methods of depreciation do not allow an asset to be depreciated below its salvage value. When MACRS is used to depreciate an asset, the salvage value is treated as income when the asset is sold.

SELF-CHECK 13.5

 1

1. Find the depreciation for the ninth year for a mobile home that was purchased for $58,000 and placed in service under the MACRS method of depreciation as a 10-year property.

2. Use the MACRS table to find the eighth year's depreciation for a property that cost $45,000 and is depreciated over a 10-year period.

3. Find the depreciation for the 14th year of a rental house that cost $83,500 and is placed in service as a 15-year property under the MACRS method of depreciation.

4. Complete a depreciation schedule for the mobile home in exercise 1.

5. Find the depreciation for each year for a tractor that was purchased for $18,000 and placed in service midyear under the MACRS method of depreciation as a three-year property.

6. Use the MACRS method to make a depreciation schedule for a property that cost $4,800 and was placed in service midyear with a three-year recovery period.

7. Use the MACRS method to find the depreciation for the 17th year of a municipal sewer that is placed in service at midyear as a 20-year property with a cost of $385,400.

8. A barn that cost $45,000 to construct is placed in service midyear as a 20-year property. What is the MACRS depreciation for year 7?

9. A computer network that costs $18,500 is placed in service midyear as a five-year property using MACRS. Make a depreciation schedule for the computer system.

10. Kentucky Thoroughbred Farms has a racehorse that is just over two years old. The racehorse, a three-year property, is being placed in service midyear with a total cost of $83,500. Use the modified accelerated cost-recovery system to find the depreciation that can be taken for the horse for the years of its service.

13.6 Section 179 Deductions

 Depreciate an asset after taking a section 179 deduction.

The purchase of certain qualifying property can be treated for tax purposes as a one-time expense rather than as a capital expenditure that is depreciated over several years. During the first year that a qualifying property is purchased and placed in service, a deduction under **section 179** of the IRS tax code of up to $22,000 for the 2001–2002 tax years can be taken. The amount that is claimed under section 179 is subtracted from the original price of the property, and the balance can be depreciated using any of the approved methods of depreciation. The $22,000 deduction can be claimed on one property or spread to more than one property. However, this deduction is only available the first year that a property or properties are purchased and placed in service, except under special circumstances. As with other IRS regulations, the maximum amount of the deduction, the circumstances under which the deduction is allowed, and the circumstances under which the deduction can be carried over to a future year are subject to change annually. It is necessary to consult IRS publications regularly for current requirements. These can be viewed on the web at www.irs.gov.

Certain conditions must be met before you can elect to take a section 179 deduction. One is that the property is placed in service *for business purposes* in the first year it is purchased. For instance, if a car is purchased for personal use and in a future year placed in service for business use, the section 179 deduction is not allowed. In general, eligible property is tangible, depreciable personal property that is used for the production of income. Finally, a section 179 deduction can only be used to reduce taxable income and not to create a net loss. Under certain conditions, a section 179 deduction can be carried over to future years when the taxable income for a given year has already been reduced to zero by other deductions. Estates and trusts cannot elect the section 179 deduction.

> **? HOW TO** Depreciate an Asset After Taking a Section 179 Deduction
>
> **1.** Decide how much of the maximum section 179 deduction allowance, currently $22,000, to apply to the asset.
>
> **2.** Subtract the elected section 179 deduction from the total cost of the asset.
>
> **3.** Apply an approved depreciation method to the value from step 2, instead of to the actual total cost.

EXAMPLE Find the first-year depreciation using MACRS on a computer network system (five-year eligible property) that is purchased and placed in service at midyear. The price of the property is $47,250 and the maximum $22,000 section 179 deduction is elected.

$$\text{Depreciation} = (\text{total cost} - \text{section 179 deduction}) \times \text{MACRS rate}$$
$$= (\$47,250 - \$22,000) \times 20\%$$
$$= \$25,250 \times 0.2$$
$$= \$5,050$$

The first-year depreciation is $5,050.

SELF-CHECK 13.6

1. Find the third-year depreciation using MACRS for a taxi (five-year property) that is purchased and placed in service at midyear. The price of the taxi is $23,971 and the maximum $22,000 section 179 deduction was elected when the taxi was placed in service.

2. Find the third-year depreciation for a tractor/trailer rig that costs $82,980 and is purchased and placed in service at midyear. The maximum $22,000 section 179 deduction is elected for this three-year property.

3. A barge costing $76,840 is purchased and placed in service at midyear. The maximum $22,000 section 179 deduction is elected for this 10-year property. Find the eighth-year depreciation amount for the barge.

4. The Circle B Farm placed a rice storage facility into service using the MACRS cost-recovery, half-year convention rates. What is the amount of depreciation for year 2 if the cost was $25,300 and a section 179 deduction of $22,000 was elected?

5. The Genesceo Citrus Farm placed 2,000 tangerine trees into service at a cost of $25 per tree. What is the first year's depreciation if MACRS cost-recovery, half-year convention rates are used with a section 179 deduction of $10,000?

Small Businesses Benefit from Section 179 Deduction—But It Has Its Limits!

Provisions of IRS Code 179 allow a sole proprietor, partnership, or corporation to fully expense eligible tangible property in the year it is purchased. Property not eligible for this deduction includes buildings and their structural components, income-producing property such as investment or rental property, property held by an estate or trust, property acquired by gift or inheritance, property used in a passive activity, property purchased from related parties, and property used outside the United States.

The Section 179 deduction is not automatic. The business owner must elect to take this deduction. What are the advantages of the Section 179 deduction? The most obvious advantage is to immediately expense appropriate business expenses rather than depreciatng them over multiple years. Another advantage is to lower the adjusted gross income (AGI) that impacts deductions that are limited by the AGI. Also, a full Section 179 deduction can be taken even when the eligible property is placed in service on the last day of the year.

Why not use the Section 179 deduction for all eligible property? It does have its limits. One limit is a maximum deduction allowed in a year. For 2002 that limit is $24,000 and in 2003 the limit is $25,000. Another limit applies if the total investment of property that is eligible for the Section 179 deduction in a given year exceeds $200,000. The deduction limit of $24,000 (for 2002) will be decreased by the amount in excess of $200,000. This means that if a business owner does not spread large purchases over multiple years, the allowable Section 179 deduction will be decreased or nonexistent.

A third limit is that a Section 179 deduction cannot be used to generate a taxable loss. In other words, the deduction may be taken only when the adjusted gross income is a positive amount. Income from employee and spouse's wages, sole proprietorships, partnerships and S-corporations can form the basis of this adjusted gross income.

Exercises

1. A taxpayer places a laser engraver costing $52,000 in service in December 2002. What is the maximum Section 179 deduction that can be elected? What portion of the cost of the engraver will have to be depreciated?

2. On June 15, 2003, Park Avenue Deli installs new kitchen equipment that costs $210,000. What is the maximum Section 179 deduction that can be taken?

3. A taxpayer has a gross taxable income of $45,000 earned from his employer; his spouse did not have an employer but established a small home-based business. She purchased a computer in 2002 that cost $2,100 but her business had no income. How much Section 179 deduction can this family take on 2002 income tax return?

4. A taxpayer and spouse have a gross taxable income of $18,000. The small business they placed in service on April 18, 2002, purchased landscaping equipment totaling $28,000. What is the maximum Section 179 deduction they may take?

Answers

1. The maximum Section 179 deduction for 2002 is $24,000. Therefore, the limit that can be deducted is $24,000. $28,000 will have to be depreciated.

2. $210,000 - $200,000 = $10,000$ (excess of $200,000 by which the Section 179 limit of $25,000 is decreased)

$25,000 - $10,000 = $15,000$ (maximum allowable Section 179 deduction)

3. Since the goss taxable income for the family (assuming they file a joint tax return) is $45,000, the entire cost of the computer ($2,100) can be deducted because it is less than the Section 179 limit for 2002.

4. Since the couple's gross taxable income was $18,000, that is the maximum Section 179 deduction they may take in 2002 because a deduction that would cause a loss is not allowable.

CHAPTER 13	OVERVIEW	
	Section Outcome	**Important Points with Examples**

Section 13.1

 Depreciate an asset and prepare a depreciation schedule using the straight-line method. (page 532)

Find the yearly depreciation using the straight-line method.

1. Find the *total cost* of the asset: add shipping and installation charges to the cost.

$$\text{Total cost} = \text{cost} + \text{shipping} + \text{installation}$$

2. Find the *depreciable value:* subtract the salvage value from the total cost.

$$\text{Depreciable value} = \text{total cost} - \text{salvage value}$$

3. Divide the depreciable value by the years of expected life.

$$\text{Yearly depreciation} = \frac{\text{depreciable value}}{\text{years of expected life}}$$

Prepare a depreciation schedule.

1. For the first year of expected life:
   (a) Find the year's depreciation.
   (b) Find the *first end-of-year book value:* subtract the first year's depreciation from the total cost.

   $$\text{First end-of-year book value} = \text{total cost} - \text{first year's depreciation}$$

2. For each remaining year of expected life:
   (a) Find the year's depreciation.
   (b) Find the *year's accumulated depreciation:* add the year's depreciation to the sum of all the previous years' depreciation.

$$\text{Year's accumulated depreciation} = \text{year's depreciation} + \text{sum of all the previous years' depreciation}$$

   (c) Find the *year's end-of-year book value:* Subtract the year's depreciation from the previous end-of-year book value.

$$\text{Year's end-of-year book value} = \text{previous end-of-year book value} - \text{year's depreciation}$$

3. Make a table with the following column headings and fill in the data: year, depreciation, accumulated depreciation, end-of-year book value.

Make a straight-line depreciation schedule for a property that costs $3,700 and has a salvage value of $400 at the end of three years.

$$\text{Depreciable value} = \$3,700 - \$400$$
$$= \$3,300$$
$$\text{Yearly depreciation} = \frac{\$3,300}{3}$$
$$= \$1,100$$

Total Cost: $3,700	Year	Depreciation	Accumulated Depreciation	End-of-Year Book Value
	1	$1,100	$1,100	$2,600
	2	1,100	2,200	1,500
	3	1,100	3,300	400

Section 13.2

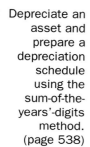

Depreciate an asset and prepare a depreciation schedule using the units-of-production method. (page 536)

Find the depreciation for units produced using the units-of-production method.

1. Find the *unit depreciation:* divide the depreciable value by the units produced during the expected life.

$$\text{Unit depreciation} = \frac{\text{depreciable value}}{\text{units produced during expected life}}$$

2. Multiply the unit depreciation by the units produced.

$$\text{Depreciation for units produced} = \text{unit depreciation} \times \text{units produced}$$

Make a units-of-production depreciation schedule for a vehicle that costs $18,900 and has a resale value of $3,000 after 150,000 miles. The vehicle is driven 39,270 miles the first year, 37,960 miles the second year, 38,520 miles the third year, and 34,250 miles the fourth year.

$$\text{Unit depreciation} = \frac{\$18,900 - \$3,000}{150,000} = 0.106$$

Total Cost: $18,900	Year	Miles Driven	Depreciation	Accumulated Depreciation	End-of-Year Book Value
	1	39,270	$4,162.62	$ 4,162.62	$14,737.38
	2	37,960	4,023.76	8,186.38	10,713.62
	3	38,520	4,083.12	12,269.50	6,630.50
	4	34,250	3,630.50	15,900.00	3,000.00

Section 13.3

Depreciate an asset and prepare a depreciation schedule using the sum-of-the-years'-digits method. (page 538)

Find the year's depreciation using the sum-of-the-years'-digits method.

1. Find the *year's depreciation rate:*

(a) Find the sum from 1 to the number of years of expected life.

Sum from 1 to the number of years of expected life
$$= \frac{(\text{years of expected life})(1 + \text{years of expected life})}{2}$$

(b) Divide the years remaining of expected life by the sum from step 1a.

$$\text{Year's sum-of-the-years' depreciation rate} = \frac{\text{years remaining of expected life}}{\text{sum from 1 to the years of expected life}}$$

2. Multiply the year's depreciable value by the year's depreciation rate.

Year's depreciation = depreciable value × year's depreciation rate

Make a sum-of-the-years'-digits schedule for a property that costs $3,700 and has a salvage value of $400 at the end of three years.

Depreciable value = cost − salvage value

$$= \$3,700 - \$400 \qquad \text{Sum of the years' digits} = \frac{N(N+1)}{2}$$

$$= \$3,300 \qquad\qquad\qquad\qquad = \frac{3(3+1)}{2}$$

$$= 6$$

$$\text{Depreciation rate} = \frac{\text{years remaining}}{\text{sum of the years of expected life}}$$

$$= \frac{\text{years remaining}}{6}$$

Total Cost: $3,700	Year	Depreciation Rate	Depreciation	Accumulated Depreciation	End-of-Year Book Value
	1	$\frac{3}{6}$	$1,650	$1,650	$2,050
	2	$\frac{2}{6}$	1,100	2,750	950
	3	$\frac{1}{6}$	550	3,300	400

Section 13.4

 Depreciate an asset and prepare a depreciation schedule using the declining-balance method. (page 542)

Find the year's depreciation using the declining-balance method.

1. Find the yearly depreciation rate:
   (a) Using *straight-line declining balance:* divide 1 by the number of years of expected life.

   $$\text{Yearly straight-line depreciation rate} = \frac{1}{\text{years of expected life}}$$

   (b) Using other declining-balance depreciation rates, such as *double-declining-balance* or *150%-declining-balance:* Multiply the yearly straight-line depreciation rate by the appropriate factor.

Yearly double-declining depreciation rate = yearly straight-line depreciation rate × 2

Yearly 150%-declining depreciation rate = yearly straight-line depreciation rate × 1.5

2. For the first year, multiply the total cost by the yearly depreciation rate.

   First year's depreciation = total cost × yearly depreciation rate

3. For all other years, multiply the previous end-of-year book value by the yearly depreciation rate.

   Year's depreciation = previous end-of-year book value × yearly depreciation rate

Make a double-declining-balance schedule of depreciation for a property that costs $3,700 and has a salvage value of $400 after three years' use.

Yearly double-declining rate

$$= \frac{1}{3} \times 2 = \frac{2}{3} = 0.666667$$

Total Cost: $3,700	Year	Depreciation	Accumulated Depreciation	End-of-Year Book Value
	1	$2,466.67	$2,466.67	$1,233.33
	2	822.22	3,288.89	411.11
	3	11.11	3,300.00	400.00

*Remember, an asset *cannot* be depreciated below its salvage value. So the depreciation for year 3 is $411.11 − $400 = $11.11.

Section 13.5

 Depreciate an asset and prepare a depreciation schedule using the modified accelerated cost-recovery system (MACRS). (page 545)

Find the year's depreciation using the MACRS method.
1. According to IRS publications, determine the asset's recovery period (expected life).
2. Find the year's MACRS rate: Using Table 13-5, locate the MACRS rate for the year and recovery period.
3. Multiply the year's MACRS rate by the total cost of the asset. (Note: 100% of the asset's value is depreciated.)

$$\text{Year's depreciation} = \text{year's MACRS rate} \times \text{total cost}$$

Make a MACRS depreciation schedule for a property that costs $3,700, is put into service at midyear, and is to be depreciated over a three-year recovery period. The salvage value is $200.

Total Cost: $3,700	Year	MACRS Rate	Depreciation	Accumulated Depreciation	End-of-Year Book Value
	1	33.33	$1,233.21	$1,233.21	$2,466.79
	2	44.45	1,644.65	2,877.86	822.14
	3	14.81	547.97	3,425.83	274.17
	4	7.41	274.17	3,700.00	0

Section 13.6

1 Depreciate an asset after taking a section 179 deduction. (page 549)

1. Decide how much of the maximum section 179 deduction allowance, currently $22,000, to apply to the asset.
2. Subtract the elected section 179 deduction from the total cost of the asset.
3. Apply an approved depreciation method to the value from step 2, instead of to the actual total cost.

Trip's Nursery constructs a greenhouse for $36,000 and places it in service at midyear as a 10-year property under the MACRS. If the maximum section 179 deduction of $22,000 is taken the first year, what is the first-year depreciation?

$$\text{Depreciable amount} = \$36,000 - \$14,000$$

$$= \$14,000$$

$$\text{Year 1 depreciation} = 0.1 \times \$14,000$$

$$= \$2,200$$

assets (p. 532)
estimated life (p. 532)
useful life (p. 532)
salvage value (p. 532)
scrap value (p. 532)
depreciation (p. 532)
straight-line depreciation (p. 532)
total cost (p. 532)
depreciable value (p. 532)
depreciation schedule (p. 534)
accumulated depreciation (p. 534)
end-of-year book value (p. 534)
units-of-production depreciation (p. 536)

unit depreciation (p. 536)
sum-of-the-years'-digits depreciation (p. 538)
depreciation rate (p. 538)
declining-balance method (p. 542)
straight-line rate (p. 542)
double-declining rate (p. 542)
200%-declining-balance method (p. 542)
accelerated cost-recovery system (ACRS) (p. 545)
recovery period (p. 545)
modified accelerated cost-recovery system
    (MACRS) (p. 546)
section 179 deductions (p. 549)

CHAPTER 13 CONCEPTS ANALYSIS

1. Use the three formulas in the How-To box: Find the Yearly Depreciation Using the Straight-Line Method (pp. 532–535) to write one formula to find the yearly depreciation.

2. Combine the two formulas in the How-To box: Find the Depreciation for Units Produced Using the Units-of-Production Method (p. 536) to write one formula to find the depreciation for units produced.

3. Observing patterns in business formulas and calculations enables the businessperson to better estimate or predict results and trends.

   Examine Table 13-3 and explain the pattern found in the Depreciation column. Explain how each subsequent year's depreciation can be found without using the depreciation rate fraction.

4. In Table 13-3, examine each year's amounts for Accumulated Depreciation and End-of-Year Book Value and describe the correlation between these two amounts.

5. In Table 13-3, compare the pattern identified in the Accumulated Depreciation column with the pattern formed by the data in the End-of-Year Book Value column.

6. Examine Table 13-5 and explain why the second year's depreciation percent is larger than any of the other years' percents.

7. Make a chart that shows the depreciation method and the value that is used as the basis for depreciation for the five depreciation methods described in this chapter.

8. Both declining-balance depreciation and MACRS depreciation use the total cost of an asset as the basis for depreciation. Explain the difference in the way the ending book value is handled in the two methods.

9. Explain how you could use only the data in Table 13-5 to verify that any asset that is depreciated using the MACRS method can be depreciated for its entire cost.

10. Give at least two circumstances in which a section 179 deduction is not permitted on a company's asset.

CHAPTER 13 ASSIGNMENT EXERCISES

Section 13.1

1. A company automobile has a total cost of $14,500 and a trade-in (salvage) value of $2,500 after five years. Find its depreciable value.

2. A computer system was purchased for $7,500. Shipping charges were $75 and installation charges were $50. What was the total cost of the computer system?

Use straight-line depreciation to fill in the yearly depreciation column. Round answers to the nearest cent.

	Total Cost	Salvage Value	Expected Life	Yearly Depreciation
3.	$ 7,200	$ 300	3 years	
4.	6,000	50	11 years	
5.	12,000	2,500	5 years	
6.	50,000	5,000	10 years	
7.	100,000	10,000	20 years	
8.	82,500	12,000	12 years	

9. A machine was purchased by the Wabash Company for $5,900. Its normal life expectancy is four years. If it can be traded in for $900 at the end of this time, determine the yearly depreciation by the straight-line method.

10. A stamping machine was purchased by Deskin Glass Company for $8,595. Freight and installation costs were $405. If it will be worth $2,000 after seven years, find the annual depreciation using the straight-line method.

11. Station WMAT spent $5,000 for a new television camera. This camera will be replaced in five years. If the scrap value will be $500, determine the annual depreciation by the straight-line method.

12. A dress factory paid $14,000 for an assembly-line system. If the used equipment will be worth $2,000 at the end of 15 years, find the annual depreciation by the straight-line method.

13. The Acme Management Corporation purchased a computer for $5,400. Its life expectancy is projected to be four years, and the salvage value will be $800. Make a straight-line depreciation schedule like Table 13-1.

Total Cost: $5,400	Year	Depreciation	Accumulated Depreciation	End-of-Year Book Value

14. Make a depreciation schedule for exercise 12 showing the first four years.

Total Cost: $14,000	Year	Depreciation	Accumulated Depreciation	End-of-Year Book Value

Section 13.2

15. A machine costs $2,500 and has an expected life of 25,000 hours. Find the unit depreciation for the machine if its salvage value is $400.

16. A cutting machine costs $32,500 and has an expected life of 100,000 hours. Find the unit depreciation for the machine if its salvage value is $2,000.

Fill in the unit depreciation and year's depreciation columns.

	Cost	Scrap Value	Expected Life	Hours Operated This Year	Unit Depreciation	Year's Depreciation
17.	$42,000	$2,000	80,000 (hours)	6,700		
18.	$25,000	$2,500	90,000	7,000		
19.	$4,340	$340	16,000	2,580		
20.	$19,000	$1,000	45,000	8,000		
21.	$2,370	$420	7,800	1,520		

22. SERV-U Computer Service Company bought a laser printer for $15,000. The machine is expected to operate for 28,000 hours, after which its trade-in value will be $1,000. Find the unit depreciation for the printer. The first year the machine was operated 4,160 hours. Find the depreciation for the year.

23. A bottle-making machine costs $12,000 and has a scrap value of $1,500. It is expected to make 1.5 million bottles during its useful life. Find the depreciation when 1 million bottles have been produced.

24. BEST Delivery Service purchased a delivery truck for $18,500 and expected to resell it for $2,000 after driving it 150,000 miles. Find the unit depreciation for the truck.

25. Make a depreciation schedule like Table 13-2 for the truck in exercise 24. The truck is driven 28,580 miles the first year, 32,140 miles the second year, 29,760 miles the third year, 31,810 miles the fourth year, and 27,710 miles the fifth year.

Total Cost: $18,500	Year	Miles Driven	Depreciation	Accumulated Depreciation	End-of-Year Book Value

26. Make a depreciation schedule for the printer in exercise 22 to show the depreciation for three years if it was operated 3,140 hours the second year and 6,820 hours the third year.

Total Cost: $15,000	Year	Hours Used	Depreciation	Accumulated Depreciation	End-of-Year Book Value

27. Find the unit depreciation for an air conditioning–heating unit that costs $7,800 and has a scrap value of $600 if it is expected to operate 40,000 hours.

28. If the unit in exercise 27 operates 2,190 hours the first year, what is the depreciation for the year?

29. If the unit in exercise 27 operates 4,599 hours the second year, what is the depreciation for the year?

30. Wee-Kare Child Care Center purchased a van for $21,500 and expects it to be driven 75,000 miles. If the resale value of the van is projected to be $6,500, find the unit depreciation for the van.

31. In exercise 30 employees of Wee-Kare Child Care Center drove the van 19,740 miles the first year. Find the depreciation for the year.

32. In exercise 30 employees of Wee-Kare Child Care Center drove the van 2,584 miles the second year. Find the depreciation.

Section 13.3

Using the sum-of-the-years'-digits method, find the denominator of the depreciation rates for assets with the given expected life.

33. 7 years

34. 12 years

35. 8 years

36. 2 years

37. 15 years

38. 20 years

39. 25 years

40. 40 years

41. Using the sum-of-the-years'-digits method, make a depreciation schedule for a machine that costs $4,200 and will be worth $750 at the end of five years.

Total Cost: $4,200	Year	Depreciation Rate	Depreciation	Accumulated Depreciation	End-of-Year Book Value

42. Make a sum-of-the-years'-digits depreciation schedule for an asset that costs $21,500 and will be worth $5,000 at the end of eight years.

Total Cost: $16,500	Year	Depreciation Rate	Depreciation	Accumulated Depreciation	End-of-Year Book Value

Section 13.4

Find the decimal equivalent expressed to six decimal places for (a) the straight-line declining rate and (b) the double-declining rate for the given expected life.

43. 4 years   **44.** 11 years   **45.** 16 years   **46.** 15 years

47. Carneal Enterprises purchased a tractor at a cost of $8,500. If the estimated life of the tractor is eight years and the estimated scrap value is $1,500, prepare a declining-balance depreciation schedule using a straight-line rate.

Total Cost: $8,500	Year	Depreciation	Accumulated Depreciation	End-of-Year Book Value

48. Concon Corp. bought office equipment for $6,000. At the end of three years, its scrap value is $750. Use a double-declining rate to make a depreciation schedule. Note that an asset *cannot* be depreciated below its scrap value.

Total Cost: $6,000	Year	Depreciation	Accumulated Depreciation	End-of-Year Book Value

49. Make a depreciation schedule using the double-declining rate for three years for a computer costing $21,000 with an estimated life of three years and a resale value of $1,000.

Total Cost: $21,000	Year	Depreciation	Accumulated Depreciation	End-of-Year Book Value

50. Make a depreciation schedule using a 150%-declining-balance for three years for furniture that costs $15,000 and has a salvage value of $500.

Total Cost: $15,000	Year	Depreciation	Accumulated Depreciation	End-of-Year Book Value

Section 13.5

Round answers to the nearest cent.

51. Find the depreciation for the 10th year for a theme park structure that was purchased for $14,489 and placed in service under the MACRS as a 10-year property.

52. Find the depreciation for each of the final three years for property purchased for $113,984 and placed in service under the MACRS as a 15-year property.

53. Find the depreciation for the ninth year for a property that was purchased for $302,588 and placed in service under the MACRS as a 10-year property.

54. Find the depreciation for the 15th year of a 15-year rental property purchased for $182,500 and placed in service before March 15, 1994, under the MACRS.

55. Find the depreciation for each year for a laser printer that costs $5,800 and was placed in service midyear under the MACRS as a five-year property.

56. Find the depreciation for each year for a forklift that costs $27,400 and was placed in service midyear under the MACRS as a 10-year property.

57. Make a depreciation schedule like Table 13-6 for an asset that costs $3,270 and was placed in service midyear under the MACRS as a three-year property.

Total Cost: $3,270	Year	MACRS Rate	Depreciation	Accumulated Depreciation	End-of-Year Book Value

*adjusted

58. Make a depreciation schedule like Table 13-6 for an asset that costs $16,250 and was placed in service midyear under the MACRS as a five-year property.

Total Cost: $16,250	Year	MACRS Rate	Depreciation	Accumulated Depreciation	End-of-Year Book Value

Section 13.6

59. Find the MACRS depreciation for year 4 for office furniture that costs $24,900 and is placed in service at midyear as a seven-year property. The maximum $22,000 section 179 deduction is elected for this property.

60. A hothouse that costs $23,500 is placed in service at midyear as a ten-year property under the MACRS. The owner chooses to take the maximum $22,000 section 179 deduction for this property. What is the depreciation for the fifth year?

61. Write formulas for generating a depreciation schedule for a rental property that costs $83,400 and is placed in service at midyear as a 15-year property under the MACRS method of depreciation.

(a) Copy the Cost to all cells in its column so these cells can be used to calculate the depreciation.

(b) Write formulas to calculate the Depreciation for each of the 16 years.

(c) Write formulas to calculate the Accumulated Depreciation and Ending Book Value for each year.

Accumulated Depreciation   Ending Book Value

62. Complete the spreadsheet using the formulas.

	A	B	C	D	E	F	G	H	I	J	K
1	\multicolumn{6}{MACRS Depreciation Schedules for Rental House for 15 Years}					
2	Year	Rate	Cost	Depreciation	Accum. Depreciation	End Book Value					
3	1	5.00%	$83,500.00								
4	2	9.50%									
5	3	8.55%									
6	4	7.70%									
7	5	6.93%									
8	6	6.23%									
9	7	5.90%									
10	8	5.90%									
11	9	5.91%									
12	10	5.90%									
13	11	5.91%									
14	12	5.90%									
15	13	5.91%									
16	14	5.90%									
17	15	5.91%									
18	16	2.95%									

Challenge Problem

63. A new minivan was purchased for $24,400 and currently has an end-of-year book value of $20,080 after one year of operation. Find the year's rate of depreciation. What will be the end-of-year book value of this minivan after two years if the rate of depreciation remains the same?

CHAPTER 13 PRACTICE TEST

1. Using the sum-of-the-years'-digits method, find the denominator of the depreciation rates for assets with an expected life of seven years.

2. Find the depreciable value of an asset that costs $38,490 and has a scrap value of $4,800 if the straight-line method of depreciation is used.

3. The purchase price of a van was $33,500. It cost $3,350 to customize the van for special use and $50 for delivery. What is the total cost of the van for depreciation purposes?

4. Make a depreciation schedule to show the annual straight-line depreciation, accumulated depreciation, and end-of-year book value for furniture that costs $4,500 and has a scrap value of $700. The useful life of the furniture is five years.

Total Cost: $4,500	Year	Depreciation	Accumulated Depreciation	End-of-Year Book Value

5. A pizza delivery car was purchased for $19,580. The car is expected to be driven 125,000 miles before being sold for $500. What is the unit depreciation on the car (depreciation per mile)?

6. A machine that costs $58,000 and will sell for $8,000 is expected to be useful for 100,000 hours. Find the depreciation per hour for the machine. If the machine is used 6,500 hours the first year, find the depreciation for the year.

7. Using the sum-of-the-years'-digits method, find the denominator of the depreciation rates for an asset with an expected life of (a) 24 years and (b) 27 years.

8. Use the sum-of-the-years'-digits method to make a depreciation schedule for an asset that costs $7,500 and has a salvage value of $1,500. The asset is to be used for three years.

Total Cost: $7,500	Year	Depreciation Rate	Depreciation	Accumulated Depreciation	End-of-Year Book Value

9. An asset has a useful life of 12 years. Find (a) the straight-line declining rate and (b) the double-declining rate of depreciation. Write the rates as decimals with six places and percents rounded to the nearest hundredth percent.

10. Use the double-declining-balance method to make a depreciation schedule for a piece of equipment that costs $2,780 and has a salvage value of $300. The equipment is expected to be used for four years.

Total Cost: $2,780	Year	Depreciation	Accumulated Depreciation	End-of-Year Book Value

11. Use the MACRS to find the first year's depreciation on an asset that costs $8,580 if the asset is placed in service at midyear to be depreciated over a three-year period.

12. Use the MACRS to make a depreciation schedule for a vehicle that was placed in service at midyear and cost $13,580. The vehicle is to be depreciated over a three-year period.

Total Cost: $13,580	Year	MACRS Rate	Depreciation	Accumulated Depreciation	End-of-Year Book Value

13. Use the MACRS to find the depreciation for the fourth year for office furniture that costs $17,872. A recovery period of seven years is used for tax purposes.

14. Capital equipment for a marine biological research lab costing $49,800 is placed in service at midyear as a five-year property under the MACRS. The maximum section 179 deduction of $22,000 is taken the first year. What is the first-year depreciation?

15. For the lab in exercise 14, what was the total deduction for the lab claimed by the research company on its federal income tax form the first year the equipment was purchased?

SELF-CHECK 13.1

1. Depreciable value $= \$5,323 - \$500 = \$4,823$

2. Yearly depreciation $= \dfrac{\text{cost of equipment} - \text{salvage value}}{\text{years of expected life}}$

$$= \dfrac{\$18,000 - \$3,000}{3} = \dfrac{\$15,000}{3}$$

$$= \$5,000$$

3. Yearly depreciation $= \dfrac{\text{cost} - \text{salvage value}}{\text{years of expected life}}$

$$= \dfrac{\$21,500 - \$4,000}{4} = \dfrac{\$17,500}{4} = \$4,375$$

4. Yearly depreciation $= \dfrac{\text{cost} - \text{salvage value}}{\text{years of expected life}}$

$$= \dfrac{\$5,800 - \$1,500}{3}$$

$$= \dfrac{\$4,300}{3} = \$1,433.33$$

5.

Total Cost: $25,000	Year	Depreciation	Accumulated Depreciation	End-of-Year Book Value
	1	$1,875	$1,875	$23,125
	2	1,875	3,750	21,250
	3	1,875	5,625	19,375

6.

Total Cost: $9,450	Year	Depreciation	Accumulated Depreciation	End-of-Year Book Value
	1	$745.83	$745.83	$8,704.17
	2	745.83	1,491.66	7,958.34
	3	745.83	2,237.49	7,212.51
	4	745.83	2,983.32	6,466.68

7. Yearly depreciation $= \dfrac{\$6,300 - \$600}{5} = \$1,140$

8. Yearly depreciation $= \dfrac{\$7,500 - \$1,200}{8} = \$787.50$

Total Cost: $7,500	Year	Depreciation	Accumulated Depreciation	End-of-Year Book Value
	1	$787.50	$ 787.50	$6,712.50
	2	787.50	1,575.00	5,925.00
	3	787.50	2,362.50	5,137.50
	4	787.50	3,150.00	4,350.00
	5	787.50	3,937.50	3,562.50
	6	787.50	4,725.00	2,775.00
	7	787.50	5,512.50	1,987.50
	8	787.50	6,300.00	1,200.00

9. Find the yearly depreciation by subtracting the salvage value from the cost and dividing the result by the number of years the object is in service. Subtract this amount to find the end-of-year book value and repeat the process for each year the object is depreciated.

SELF-CHECK 13.2

1. Unit depreciation $= \dfrac{\$18,000 - \$3,000}{\$75,000} = \$0.20$ per mile

Depreciation after 56,000 miles $= \$0.20 \times 56,000 = \$11,200$

2. Unit depreciation $= \dfrac{\$23,580 - \$2,300}{95,000} = \$0.224$ per mile

3. Unit depreciation $= \dfrac{\$28,700 - \$2,500}{300,000} = \$0.087\overline{3}$

Depreciation for 28,452 objects $= \$0.0873 \times 28,452 = \$2,483.86$

4. Unit depreciation $= \dfrac{\$7,500 - \$600}{60,000} = \dfrac{\$6,900}{60,000} = \$0.115$ per hour

Year's depreciation $= \$0.115 \times 8,500 = \$977.50$

5. Unit depreciation $= \dfrac{\$84,500 - \$2,900}{90,000} = \$0.9067$ per hour

First year's depreciation $= \$0.9067 \times 3,853 = \$3,493.52$

6. Unit depreciation is found by subtracting the scrap value from the cost and dividing by the number of units of service the asset is expected to provide. To find the depreciation for a year, multiply the unit depreciation by the number of units (miles, hours, etc.) of service provided by the asset in the given year.

SELF-CHECK 13.3

1. (a) $\dfrac{8(8+1)}{2} = \dfrac{8(9)}{2} = 36$

(b) $\dfrac{12(12+1)}{2} = \dfrac{12(13)}{2} = 78$

2. Denominator of depreciation rate $= 3 + 2 + 1 = 6$

Depreciation rate for each year: $\dfrac{3}{6}, \dfrac{2}{6}, \dfrac{1}{6}$

Original cost $-$ salvage value $= \$18,000 - \$3,000 = \$15,000$

Year 1 depreciation $= \$15,000 \times \dfrac{3}{6} = \$7,500$

Year 2 depreciation $= \$15,000 \times \dfrac{2}{6} = \$5,000$

Year 3 depreciation $= \$15,000 \times \dfrac{1}{6} = \$2,500$

3.

Total Cost: $9,000	Year	Depreciation Rate	Depreciation	Accumulated Depreciation	End-of-Year Book Value
	1	$\dfrac{4}{10}$	$3,000	$3,000	$6,000
	2	$\dfrac{3}{10}$	2,250	5,250	3,750
	3	$\dfrac{2}{10}$	1,500	6,750	2,250
	4	$\dfrac{1}{10}$	750	7,500	1,500

4. Sum of the years' digits $= \dfrac{10(10+1)}{2} = \dfrac{10(11)}{2} = 55$

Year	1	2	3	4	5	6	7	8	9	10
Rate	$\dfrac{10}{55}$,	$\dfrac{9}{55}$,	$\dfrac{8}{55}$,	$\dfrac{7}{55}$,	$\dfrac{6}{55}$,	$\dfrac{5}{55}$,	$\dfrac{4}{55}$,	$\dfrac{3}{55}$,	$\dfrac{2}{55}$,	$\dfrac{1}{55}$

5.

Total Cost: $45,000	Year	Depreciation Rate	Depreciation	Accumulated Depreciation	End-of-Year Book Value
	1	$\dfrac{10}{55}$	$7,545.45	$7,545.45	$37,454.55
	2	$\dfrac{9}{55}$	6,790.91	14,336.36	30,663.64
	3	$\dfrac{8}{55}$	6,036.36	20,372.72	24,627.28
	4	$\dfrac{7}{55}$	5,281.82	25,654.54	19,345.46

6. To find the denominator of each year's rate fraction, find the sum of the numbers from 1 through the number of the years of the object's expected life. The numerator of the depreciation rate for the first year is the number of years of expected life, while the numerator of the depreciation rate for the last year is 1.

7. Multiply the year's depreciation rate by the depreciable value to get the depreciation for the year.

SELF-CHECK 13.4

1. (a) $\frac{1}{3} = 0.33333 = 33.33\%$

(b) $\frac{1}{3} \times 2 = \frac{2}{3} = 0.66666 = 66.67\%$

2. Double-declining rate $= \frac{1}{4} \times 2 = \frac{2}{4} = \frac{1}{2} = 0.5 = 50\%$

Year 1 depreciation $= \$18,000 \times 0.5 = \$9,000$
End-of-year-1 book value $= \$18,000 - \$9,000 = \$9,000$
Year 2 depreciation $= \$9,000 \times 0.5 = \$4,500$
End-of-year-2 book value $= \$9,000 - \$4,500 = \$4,500$
Year 3 depreciation $= \$4,500 \times 0.5 = \$2,250$
End-of-year-3 book value $= \$4,500 - \$2,250 = \$2,250$
Year 4 depreciation $= \$2,250 \times 0.5 = \$1,125$
End-of-year-4 book value $= \$2,250 - \$1,125 = \$1,125$

3. Double-declining rate $= \frac{1}{5} \times 2 = \frac{2}{5} = 0.4 = 40\%$

Total Cost: $4,500	Year	Depreciation	Accumulated Depreciation	End-of-Year Book Value
	1	$1,800.00	$1,800.00	$2,700.00
	2	1,080.00	2,880.00	1,620.00
	3	648.00	3,528.00	972.00
	4	388.80	3,916.80	583.20
	5	233.28	4,150.08	349.92

4. 200%-declining rate $= \frac{1}{8} \times 2 = \frac{2}{8} = \frac{1}{4} = 0.25 = 25\%$

Total Cost: $25,000	Year	Depreciation	Accumulated Depreciation	End-of-Year Book Value
	1	$6,250.00	$ 6,250.00	$18,750.00
	2	4,687.50	10,937.50	14,062.50
	3	3,515.63	14,453.13	10,546.87
	4	2,636.72	17,089.85	7,910.15
	5	1,977.54	19,067.39	5,932.61
	6	1,483.15	20,550.54	4,449.46
	7	1,112.37	21,662.91	3,337.09
	8	834.27	22,497.18	2,502.82

5. 150%-declining rate $= \frac{1}{4} \times 1.5 = 0.375 = 37.5\%$

First year's depreciation $= \$3,000 \times 0.375 = \$1,125$

1. Year 9 depreciation = 6.56% × total cost = 0.0656 × $58,000 = $3,804.80
2. Year 8 depreciation = 6.55% × total cost = 0.0655 × $45,000 = $2,947.50
3. Year 14 depreciation = 5.90% × total cost = 0.059 × $83,500 = $4,926.50

4.

Total Cost: $58,000	Year	MACRS Rate	Depreciation	Accumulated Depreciation	End-of-Year Book Value
	1	10.00	$ 5,800	$5,800	$52,200
	2	18.00	10,440	16,240	41,760
	3	14.40	8,352	24,592	33,408
	4	11.52	6,681.60	31,273.60	26,726.40
	5	9.22	5,347.60	36,621.20	21,378.80
	6	7.37	4,274.60	40,895.80	17,104.20
	7	6.55	3,799	44,694.80	13,305.20
	8	6.55	3,799	48,493.80	9,506.20
	9	6.56	3,804.80	52,298.60	5,701.40
	10	6.55	3,799	56,097.60	1,902.40
	11	3.28	1,902.40	58,000	0

5. Year 1 depreciation = 33.33% × cost
   = 0.3333 × $18,000 = $5,999.40
   Year 2 depreciation = 44.45% × cost
   = 0.4445 × $18,000 = $8,001
   Year 3 depreciation = 14.81% × cost
   = 0.1481 × $18,000 = $2,665.80
   Year 4 depreciation = 7.41% × cost
   = 0.0741 × $18,000 = $1,333.80

6.

Total Cost: $4,800	Year	MACRS Rate	Depreciation	Accumulated Depreciation	End-of-Year Book Value
	1	33.33	$1,599.84	$1,599.84	$3,200.16
	2	44.45	2,133.60	3,733.44	1,066.56
	3	14.81	710.88	4,444.32	355.68
	4	7.41	355.68	4,800.00	0

7. Year 17 depreciation = 4.462% × $385,400 = 0.04462 × $385,400 = $17,196.55
8. Year 7 depreciation = 4.888% × $45,000 = 0.04888 × $45,000 = $2,199.60

9.

Total Cost: $18,500	Year	MACRS Rate	Depreciation	Accumulated Depreciation	End-of-Year Book Value
	1	20.00	$3,700.00	$3,700.00	$14,800.00
	2	32.00	5,920.00	9,620.00	8,880.00
	3	19.20	3,552.00	13,172.00	5,328.00
	4	11.52	2,131.20	15,303.20	3,196.80
	5	11.52	2,131.20	17,434.40	1,065.60
	6	5.76	1,065.60	18,500.00	0

10. Year 1 depreciation = 0.3333 × $83,500 = $27,830.55
Year 2 depreciation = 0.4445 × $83,500 = $37,115.75
Year 3 depreciation = 0.1481 × $83,500 = $12,366.35
Year 4 depreciation = 0.0741 × $83,500 = $6,187.35

SELF-CHECK 13.6

1. Year 3 depreciation = (total cost − section 179 deduction) × MACRS rate
= ($23,971 − $22,000) × 19.2%
= $1,971 × 0.192
= $378.43
2. Year 3 depreciation = ($82,980 − $22,000) × 14.81%
= $60,980 × 0.1481
= $9,031.14
3. Year 8 depreciation = ($76,840 − $22,000) × 6.55%
= $54,840 × 0.0655
= $3,592.02
4. Year 2 depreciation = ($25,300 − $22,000) × 7.219%
(20-year property) = $3,300 × 0.07219
= $238.23
5. 2,000 × $25 = $50,000.00 (total cost)
Year 1 depreciation = ($50,000 − $10,000) × 10.00%
(10-year property) = $40,000 × 0.10
= $4,000

14

Inventory, Turnover, and Overhead

14.1 Inventory

1 Use the specific identification inventory method to find the cost of goods sold.

2 Use the weighted-average inventory method to find the cost of goods sold.

3 Use the first-in, first-out (FIFO) inventory method to find the cost of goods sold.

4 Use the last-in, first-out (LIFO) inventory method to find the cost of goods sold.

5 Use the retail inventory method to find the cost of goods sold.

6 Compare methods for determining inventory.

14.2 Turnover and Overhead

1 Find the inventory turnover rate.

2 Find the department overhead based on sales.

3 Find the department overhead based on floor space.

Good Decisions through Teamwork

Working in teams, choose a local, small retail store and develop a plan to investigate how this business takes inventory. The investigation should include, but not be limited to, these questions: Does this business have a perpetual inventory system? How frequently is a physical count taken? Which method does the business use to assign inventory value? Why does the business use its particular method? Report your findings to the class and discuss how and why the inventory methods of the teams' businesses differ. Prepare a written report of your results and discussions.

As an extension of this inventory activity, the team may choose a larger store that has several departments and investigate how the store calculates turnover and what turnover rate is standard for this type of business. Methods used by the business to allocate overhead to departments may also be investigated.

Any business needs to know the value of goods on hand that are available for sale or for use in manufacturing items for sale. Any business also needs to know how often all merchandise is sold or used and replaced with new merchandise. The expenses incurred in operating the business are also other critical pieces of information needed to run a successful business. A knowledge of these concepts—inventory, turnover, and overhead—is important for making wise business decisions and for preparing required tax documents.

14.1 Inventory

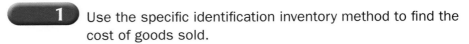 Use the specific identification inventory method to find the cost of goods sold.

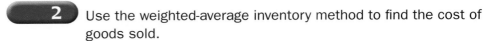 Use the weighted-average inventory method to find the cost of goods sold.

Use the first-in, first-out (FIFO) inventory method to find the cost of goods sold.

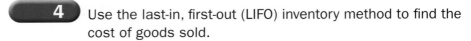 Use the last-in, first-out (LIFO) inventory method to find the cost of goods sold.

Use the retail inventory method to find the cost of goods sold.

Compare methods for determining inventory.

Merchandise available for sale on a certain date is called **inventory.** The value of inventory is important for a number of reasons. Two of the financial statements covered in Chapter 15 require inventory values, as do various tax documents. Inventory may be checked weekly, monthly, quarterly, semiannually, annually, or at any other specific interval of time. At the end of the specified time, a physical count is made of the merchandise on hand. This type of inventory is called a **periodic inventory,** or physical inventory.

Many stores have computerized the inventory process so that the inventory is adjusted with each sale. That is, a count of merchandise on hand is available at any time. This continual inventory method is called **perpetual inventory.** Even with a perpetual inventory system, a physical count is made periodically to verify and adjust the inventory records. A discrepancy between the perpetual inventory and the actual inventory is sometimes a result of theft or loss due to damage.

Once a count of merchandise has been made, the merchandise is given a value according to various accounting methods. What makes this process time consuming is that the cost of the goods purchased during a specific period may vary. For example, at one point in a month coffee may be purchased at $2.79 a pound. The next time coffee is ordered, the cost may be $2.93 a pound. This section discusses five methods commonly used by accountants to assign a value to an inventory: specific identification; weighted-average; first-in, first-out (FIFO); last-in, first-out (LIFO); and retail.

For the purpose of examining the various methods of assigning the value to inventory, we use an overly simplified set of circumstances. In actual practice the process involves many different items. For our example we use the inventory records for 12-inch battery clocks. Table 14-1 gives these records.

Throughout this discussion, the same formula is used. It shows how to find the **cost of goods sold (COGS):**

Cost of goods sold = cost of goods available for sale − cost of ending inventory

Table 14-1 Inventory Report for Battery Wall Clocks

Date of Purchase	Units Purchased	Cost per Unit
Beginning inventory	29	$8
January 15	18	7
February 4	9	10
March 3	14	8

The data in Table 14-1 are used to find the cost of goods available for sale. These amounts remain the same throughout the discussion. The cost of the ending inventory and the cost of goods sold vary with each method.

 Use the specific identification inventory method to find the cost of goods sold.

Many companies code their incoming merchandise with the purchase price or cost. Their inventory values are based on the actual cost of each item available for sale. This system of evaluating inventory is the **specific identification inventory method.** This method is best for low-volume, high-cost items, such as automobiles or fine jewelry, since a company must be able to identify the actual cost of the specific individual items bought. The name of this method is derived from the fact that in each case, when calculating the cost of goods available for sale and the cost of ending inventory, an *exact price per unit* is available.

 HOW TO Find the Cost of Goods Sold (COGS) Using the Specific Identification Inventory Method

1. Find the cost of goods available for sale: multiply the number of units purchased by the cost per unit.

Cost of goods available for sale =
number of units purchased × cost per unit

2. Find the cost of ending inventory: multiply the number of units in ending inventory by the cost per unit.

Cost of ending inventory =
number of units in ending inventory × cost per unit

3. Find the cost of goods sold (COGS): subtract the cost of ending inventory from the cost of goods available for sale.

Cost of goods sold = cost of goods available for sale
− cost of ending inventory

EXAMPLE Use the ending inventory information in Table 14-2 to calculate the cost of goods available for sale using the specific identification method. Then determine the cost of goods sold.

Find the cost of goods available for sale:

$$29 \times \$8 = \$232 \qquad 18 \times \$7 = \$126$$
$$9 \times \$10 = \quad 90 \qquad 14 \times \$8 = \$112$$
$$\$232 + \$126 + \$90 + \$112 = \boxed{\$560}$$

Table 14-2 Cost of Goods Available for Sale and the Ending Inventory for 12-inch Battery Clocks

Date of Purchase	Units Purchased	Cost per Unit	Total Cost	Ending Inventory
Beginning inventory	29	$8	$232	14
January 15	18	7	126	5
February 4	9	10	90	3
March 3	+14	8	112	___
Goods available for sale	70		$560	22

Find the cost of ending inventory:

$$14 \times \$8 = \$112 \qquad 5 \times \$7 = \$35 \qquad 3 \times \$10 = \$30$$
$$\$112 + \$35 + \$30 = \boxed{\$177}$$

Cost of goods sold = cost of goods available for sale − cost of ending inventory

$$= \boxed{\$560} - \boxed{\$177}$$
$$= \$383$$

The cost of goods sold is $383.

 Use the weighted-average inventory method to find the cost of goods sold.

Another way to place a value on the ending inventory is the **weighted-average inventory method.** The cost of goods available for sale is divided by the number of units available for sale to get the average unit cost. This method takes less time than finding exact prices for each unit. It often is used with goods that are similar in cost and have a relatively stable cost.

? HOW TO Find the Cost of Goods Sold (COGS) Using the Weighted-Average Inventory Method

1. Find the cost of goods available for sale.

   Cost of goods available for sale =
   number of units purchased × cost per unit

2. Find the average unit cost: divide the cost of goods available for sale by the number of units available for sale.

   $$\text{Average unit cost} = \frac{\text{cost of goods available for sale}}{\text{number of units available for sale}}$$

3. Find the cost of ending inventory: multiply the number of units in ending inventory by the average unit cost.

   Cost of ending inventory = number of units in ending inventory
   × average unit cost

4. Find the cost of goods sold (COGS).

   COGS = cost of goods available for sale − cost of ending inventory

---

EXAMPLE   Calculate the cost of ending inventory and the COGS using the weighted-average method and the data in Table 14-2.

$$\text{Average unit cost} = \frac{\text{cost of goods available for sale}}{\text{units of goods available for sale}} = \frac{\$560}{70} = \$8$$

$$\text{Cost of ending inventory} = \text{units of ending inventory} \times \text{average unit cost}$$

$$= 22 \times \$8$$

$$= \$176$$

$$\text{Cost of goods sold} = \text{cost of goods available for sale} - \text{cost of ending inventory}$$

$$= \$560 - \$176$$

$$= \$384$$

The cost of goods sold is $384.

3   Use the first-in, first-out (FIFO) inventory method to find the cost of goods sold.

Many companies, especially those who want the cost of inventory to match replacement costs as closely as possible, use the **FIFO (first-in, first-out) inventory method.** In the FIFO method, the earliest units purchased (the first in) are assumed to be the first units sold (the first out). In this method, the ending inventory is assumed to consist of the latest units purchased. Thus, the cost of the goods available for sale is relatively close to the current cost for purchasing additional items.

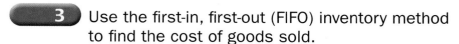

HOW TO Find the Cost of Goods Sold (COGS) Using the First-In, First-Out (FIFO) Inventory Method

1. Find the cost of goods available for sale.

   Cost of goods available for sale = number of units purchased × cost per unit

2. Find the assigned cost per unit: assign a cost per unit in the ending inventory by assuming these units were the latest units purchased.

3. Find the cost of ending inventory: multiply the number of units in ending inventory by the assigned cost per unit.

   Cost of ending inventory = number of units in ending inventory
   × assigned cost per unit

4. Find the cost of goods sold (COGS).

   Cost of goods sold = cost of goods available for sale
   − cost of ending inventory

EXAMPLE   Use the information from Table 14-2 to find the cost of goods sold using the FIFO method.

Assign a cost per unit in the ending inventory by assuming that these units were the latest units purchased.

There are 22 units in the ending inventory, and by this method they must be the latest units purchased. Count back in the table from the most recently purchased units until you have 22 units.

Mar. 3   14 units at $8 per unit
22 − 14 = 8 units left to be assigned

Multiply the cost per unit by the number of units. Add to get the cost of ending inventory.

Mar. 3   14 units × $8 = $112
Feb. 4   8 units × $10 = $80
                22 units $192

Cost of goods sold = cost of goods available for sale − cost of ending inventory

= $560 − $192

= $368

The cost of goods sold is $368.

 Use the last-in, first-out (LIFO) inventory method to find the cost of goods sold.

A fourth method for determining the cost of the ending inventory and the cost of goods sold is the **LIFO (last-in, first-out) inventory method.** In this method, the latest units purchased (the last in) are assumed to be the first units sold (the first out). The ending inventory is assumed to consist of the earliest units purchased. The cost of the ending inventory is figured on the cost of the oldest stock. Thus, the difference between the cost of the goods available for sale and the replacement costs for new goods could be significant. Also, the short-term profit on goods sold would be less since the newer, higher-priced goods were sold first. At some later point, when the low-priced goods are sold, the profits will be high.

Even though this method does not follow natural business practices of rotating stock to maintain freshness or quality, there are some economic advantages to using this method under certain conditions.

 HOW TO Find the Cost of Goods Sold (COGS) Using the Last-In, First-Out (LIFO) Inventory Method

1. Find the cost of goods available for sale.

Cost of goods available for sale = number of units purchased × cost per unit

2. Find the assigned cost per unit: assign a cost per unit in the ending inventory by assuming these units were the earliest units purchased.

3. Find the cost of ending inventory: multiply the number of units in ending inventory by the assigned cost per unit.

Cost of ending inventory = number of units in ending inventory × assigned cost per unit

4. Find the cost of goods sold (COGS).

Cost of goods sold = cost of goods available for sale − cost of ending inventory

EXAMPLE   Use the information from Table 14–2 to find the cost of goods sold using the LIFO method.

Assign a cost for each unit in the ending inventory by assuming these units were the earliest units purchased.

There are 22 items in the ending inventory, and by this method they must be the earliest units purchased. Count from the top of the table until you have 22 items. These items are all from beginning inventory.

$$\text{Beginning inventory: 22 items at \$8 per unit}$$

Multiply the cost per unit by the number of units.

$$\text{Beginning inventory: \$8} \times \text{22 items} = \boxed{\$176}$$

$$\text{Cost of goods sold} = \text{cost of goods available for sale} - \text{cost of ending inventory}$$

$$= \$560 - \boxed{\$176}$$

$$= \$384$$

The cost of goods sold is \$384.

5 Use the retail inventory method to find the cost of goods sold.

Sometimes businesses do not make monthly or periodic inventories. Instead, they *estimate* the cost of inventory rather than count goods individually. One method used to estimate inventory is called the **retail method.**

The retail method uses a ratio that compares the cost of goods available for sale to the retail value of those goods. That is, it compares what it costs to buy the goods with what the goods sell for. To use this method to find the cost of goods sold, you also need to know the dollar value of sales. Take note that we refer to the cost of ending inventory as the **ending inventory at cost,** and we refer to the retail value of ending inventory as the **ending inventory at retail.**

 **HOW TO** Find the Cost of Goods Sold (COGS) Using the Retail Inventory Method

1. Find the cost of goods available for sale:

Cost of goods available for sale = number or units purchased × cost per unit

2. Find the retail value of goods available for sale.

3. Find the cost ratio: divide the cost of goods available for sale by the retail value of goods available for sale.

$$\text{Cost ratio} = \frac{\text{cost of goods available for sale}}{\text{retail value of goods available for sale}}$$

4. Find the ending inventory at retail: subtract the dollar value of sales from the retail value of goods available for sale.

Ending inventory at retail = retail value of goods available for sale − sales

5. Find the ending inventory at cost: multiply the ending inventory at retail by the cost ratio.

Ending inventory at cost = ending inventory at retail × cost ratio

6. Find the cost of goods sold.

Cost of goods sold = cost of goods available for sale − ending inventory at cost

OR   **Cost of goods sold = dollar value of sales × cost ratio**

Chapter 14 Inventory, Turnover, and Overhead   **579**

EXAMPLE Use the information from Table 14-2, and the retail value information below to find the cost of the ending inventory and the cost of goods sold using the retail method.

Date of Purchase	Retail Value
Beginning inventory	$331
January 15	180
February 4	129
March 3	160
Goods available for sale	$800
Sales	$487

According to Table 14-2, the cost of goods available for sale is $560. Their retail price is $800.

$$\text{Cost ratio} = \frac{\text{cost of goods available for sale}}{\text{retail value of goods available for sale}} = \frac{\$560}{\$800} = 0.7$$

Ending inventory at retail = retail value of goods available for sale − retail value of sales

$$= \$800 - \$487 = \$313$$

Ending inventory at cost = ending inventory at retail × cost ratio

$$= \$313 \times 0.7 = \$219.10$$

Cost of goods sold = dollar value of sales × cost ratio

$$= \$487 \times 0.7 = \$340.90$$

or

= cost of goods available for sale − ending inventory at cost

$$= \$560.00 - \$219.10$$

$$= \$340.90$$

The ending inventory at cost is $219.10 and the cost of goods sold is $340.90.

Finding Several Results by Chaining Calculations

The business or desktop calculator can be used to:

1. Find the retail value of goods available for sale, and save it in memory.

$$\boxed{\text{AC}}\ 331\ \boxed{+}\ 180\ \boxed{+}\ 129\ \boxed{+}\ 160\ \boxed{=}\ \boxed{\text{M}^+} \Rightarrow 800$$

2. Find the cost of goods available for sale, and leave in display.

$$\boxed{\text{CE/C}}\ 232\ \boxed{+}\ 126\ \boxed{+}\ 90\ \boxed{+}\ 112\ \boxed{=} \Rightarrow 560\ (\text{Do not clear.})$$

3. Find the cost ratio. Display still shows 560.

$$\boxed{\div}\ \boxed{\text{MRC}}\ \boxed{\text{MRC}}\ \boxed{=}\ \boxed{\text{M}^+} \Rightarrow 0.7$$

The first $\boxed{\text{MRC}}$ recalls 800 from memory; the second $\boxed{\text{MRC}}$ clears 800 from memory so that a new number can be stored there. Now the cost ratio is in memory.

4. Find the retail value of ending inventory.
   Clear display but do not clear memory.

$$\boxed{\text{CE/C}}\ 800 - 487\ \boxed{=} \Rightarrow 313 \ (\text{Do not clear.})$$

5. Find the cost of ending inventory. Display still shows 313.

$$\boxed{\times}\ \boxed{\text{MRC}}\ \boxed{=} \Rightarrow 219.10$$

Find the cost of goods sold.

$$\boxed{\text{CE/C}}\ 487\ \boxed{\times}\ \boxed{\text{MRC}}\ \boxed{=} \Rightarrow 340.90$$

These strategies will be modified slightly when using a scientific or graphing calculator.

6 Compare methods for determining inventory.

Each of the different methods of figuring the value of inventory has advantages and disadvantages, depending on current economic conditions, tax regulations, and so on. However, it is important to know that once a business has selected a method, it must get approval from the Internal Revenue Service to change methods.

This section shows the result of calculating the value of the same inventory by each of the five different methods. Table 14-3 compares the five methods and their results.

Table 14–3 Summary of Inventory Methods Based on Table 14-2 Data

Method	Cost of Ending Inventory	Cost of Goods Sold	Comment
Specific identification	$177	$383	The most accurate method, but also the most time consuming.
Weighted-average	176	384	Perhaps the easiest to use, but appropriate only when the economy is relatively stable. Radical changes in prices may result in a distorted inventory value.
First-in, first-out (FIFO)	192	368	The value of ending inventory is closely related to the current market price of the goods. During high inflation, this method produces the highest income.
Last-in, first-out (LIFO)	176	384	The value of ending inventory may vary significantly from the current market price of the goods. During high inflation, this method produces lower income, which results in a lower income tax for the company.
Retail	219.10	340.90	Cost of ending inventory is based on the retail values and the net sales. Since the information needed for using this method is easily accessible, this is one of the most efficient methods.

EXAMPLE Mark Deskin operates Contemporary Home Accessories in the local shopping mall. He is responsible for both purchasing and inventory, as well as sales. His inventory data are in Table 14-2. Which method of inventory is best for his business?

1 Decision needed	Which method of inventory is best for Mark's business?
2 Unknown facts	Costs of goods sold for the various inventory methods.
3 Known facts	Beginning inventory, purchases, and ending inventory as reflected in Table 14-2.
4 Relationships	Refer to Table 14-3.
5 Estimation	Not appropriate for this problem.
6 Calculation	Refer to the previous four examples where calculations for each type of inventory method have been made.
7 Interpretation	The Snack and Go Cart is a small business with no employees. All responsibilities of the business are assumed by the owner, Mark Deskin.
8 Decision made	**Since the retail method for estimating inventory is a method approved by the IRS for determining inventory, and it is the most efficient of the methods, Mark chooses to use this method.**

> **TIP! Let the Title Be Your Guide**
>
> The title of each method for finding the cost of goods sold contains key words to help you remember the procedures.
>
> | *Method* | *Clue* |
> |---|---|
> | • Specific Identification | *Specific* cost to be determined. |
> | • Weighted-average | Varying costs to be *averaged*. |
> | • FIFO | Cost of *most recently purchased* merchandise is used. |
> | • LIFO | Cost of *oldest* merchandise is used. |
> | • Retail | COGS is calculated from *retail value,* and the ratio of retail value to cost is shown. |

SELF-CHECK 14.1

 Use the specific identification inventory method for exercises 1–6.

1. Complete Inventory Table A for total cost of purchases, goods available for sale, cost of goods available for sale, and ending inventory. Total retail value is calculated in exercise 21.

Inventory Table A

Date of Purchase	Units Purchased	Cost per Unit	Total Cost	Retail Price per Unit	Total Retail Value
Beginning inventory	42	$850	_____	$975	_____
February 5	21	1,760	_____	2,115	_____
February 19	17	965	_____	1,206	_____
March 3	28	480	_____	600	_____
Goods available for sale			_____		_____
Units sold	74				
Ending inventory	___				

2. Cost Table A shows a breakdown of the ending inventory from Inventory Table A according to various costs per unit. Complete Cost Table A.

Cost Table A

Cost per Unit	Number of Units on Hand	Total Cost
$850	9	_____
1,760	11	_____
965	8	_____
480	6	_____
Ending inventory	___	_____

3. Use Inventory Table A and Cost Table A to calculate the cost of goods sold.

4. Complete Inventory Table B for total cost of purchases, goods available for sale, cost of goods available for sale, and ending inventory. Total retail value is calculated in exercise 24.

Inventory Table B

Date of Purchase	Units Purchased	Cost per Unit	Total Cost	Retail Price per Unit	Total Retail Value
Beginning inventory	96	$12	_____	$18	_____
April 12	23	9	_____	13	_____
May 8	15	11	_____	17	_____
June 2	37	15	_____	21	_____
Goods available for sale	___		_____		_____
Units sold	89		_____		_____
Ending inventory	___				

5. Cost Table B breaks down the ending inventory from Inventory Table B. Complete Cost Table B.

6. Use Inventory Table B and Cost Table B to calculate the cost of goods sold.

Cost Table B

Cost per Unit	Number of Units on Hand	Total Cost
$12	43	_____
9	11	_____
11	7	_____
15	21	_____
Ending inventory	___	_____

2 *Use the weighted-average inventory method for exercises 7–12.*

7. Calculate the average unit cost for Inventory Table A.

8. Calculate the cost of ending inventory for Inventory Table A.

9. Calculate the cost of goods sold for Inventory Table A.

10. Calculate the average unit cost for Inventory Table B.

11. Calculate the cost of ending inventory for Inventory Table B.

12. Calculate the cost of goods sold for Inventory Table B.

 3 *Use the first-in, first-out inventory method for exercises 13–16.*

13. Determine the unit costs for units in ending inventory for Inventory Table A.

14. Find the cost of goods sold for Inventory Table A.

16. Find the cost of goods sold for Inventory Table B.

15. Determine the unit costs for units in ending inventory for Inventory Table B.

4 *Use the last-in, first-out inventory method for exercises 17–20.*

17. Determine the unit costs for units in ending inventory for Inventory Table A.

18. Find the cost of goods sold for Inventory Table A.

19. Determine the unit costs for units in ending inventory for Inventory Table B.

20. Find the cost of goods sold for Inventory Table B.

5 *Use the retail method for exercises 21–26.*

21. Complete Inventory Table A for total retail price of purchases and retail price of goods available for sale.

22. Find the cost ratio for Inventory Table A.

23. Find the cost of goods sold if sales total $78,982 for Table A.

24. Complete Inventory Table B for total retail price and retail value of goods available for sale.

25. Find the cost ratio for Inventory Table B.

26. Find the cost of goods sold if sales total $1,691 for Table B.

6

27. The Rutledge Equipment Company is examining inventory methods and would like to choose the one that is the most efficient and least costly. Which method would be a good choice and why?

28. Thweatt Trailer Sales is computerizing its inventory and would like to use the computer to track inventory in order to keep the most accurate records. Which inventory method is it likely to select?

14.2 Turnover and Overhead

1 Find the inventory turnover rate.

2 Find the department overhead based on sales.

3 Find the department overhead based on floor space.

Most businesses must keep careful records of their **inventory turnover,** which is how often the inventory of merchandise is sold and replaced. The rate of inventory turnover varies greatly according to the type of business. A restaurant, for example, should have a high turnover rate but probably carries a small inventory of goods. A furniture company, on the other hand, normally keeps a larger inventory but has a relatively low turnover.

 **TIP!** **Inventory Sell Through**

Retailers also use the term *sell through* to discuss the rate inventory is turned over.

Knowing the turnover of a business can be useful in making future decisions and in analyzing business practices. For example, a low turnover rate may indicate some or all of the following:

1. Too much capital (company's money) is tied up in inventory.
2. Customers are dissatisfied with merchandise choice, quality, or price.
3. Merchandise is not properly marketed.

On the other hand, a high turnover rate may indicate some or all of the following:

1. Inventory is too small for the demand, resulting in a loss in sales because merchandise is "out of stock."
2. Merchandise is highly desirable.
3. Merchandise prices may be significantly lower than the competition's prices.

Lending institutions use the turnover rate as one of the factors considered in making business loans. There are two ways to calculate turnover rate: *at cost* or *at retail*. Cost means the price at which the company buys the merchandise. Retail means the price at which the company sells the merchandise.

 1 Find the inventory turnover rate.

To calculate the turnover rate *at cost,* divide the cost of goods sold by the average inventory at cost.

$$\text{Inventory turnover rate at } \boxed{\text{cost}} = \frac{\text{cost of goods sold}}{\text{average inventory at } \boxed{\text{cost}}}$$

To calculate the turnover rate at *retail*, divide the net sales by the average inventory at retail.

$$\text{Inventory turnover rate at } \boxed{\text{retail}} = \frac{\text{net sales}}{\text{average inventory at } \boxed{\text{retail}}}$$

Turnover rate can cover any period of time, but is usually calculated monthly, semiannually (twice a year), or yearly.

 HOW TO Find the Turnover Rate at Cost

1. Find the average inventory at cost.

   Average inventory at cost
   $$= \frac{\text{beginning inventory at cost} + \text{ending inventory at cost}}{2}$$

2. Divide the cost of goods sold by the average inventory at cost.

   $$\text{Turnover rate at cost} = \frac{\text{cost of goods sold}}{\text{average inventory at cost}}$$

The formula for finding inventory turnover is often referred to as the **inventory turnover ratio.** The ratio shows the number of times a business's inventory has been sold during a specified period. For example, an inventory turnover of 3 to 1 for one year means that a store sold three times the value of the average inventory during the year. Its "sell through" rate is 3 to 1. Another way of saying this is that the merchandise has been sold and replaced three times during the year.

EXAMPLE   Ann's Dress Shop had net sales of $52,500 at cost for the month of September. The cost of inventory at the beginning of September was $15,980 and at the end of September was $18,000. Find the average inventory at cost and the turnover rate at cost for September.

$$\text{Average inventory at cost} = \frac{\$15,980 + \$18,000}{2}$$

$$= \frac{\$33,980}{2}$$

$$= \$16,990$$

$$\text{Turnover rate at cost} = \frac{\$52,500}{\$16,990}$$

$$\text{Turnover rate at cost} = 3 \text{ (rounded)}$$

The average inventory at cost is $16,990 and the turnover rate at cost is three times.

? HOW TO Find the Turnover Rate at Retail

1. Find the average inventory at retail.

Average inventory at retail

$$= \frac{\textbf{beginning inventory at retail} + \textbf{ending inventory at retail}}{2}$$

2. Divide the sales by the average inventory at retail.

$$\textbf{Turnover rate at retail} = \frac{\textbf{sales}}{\textbf{average inventory at retail}}$$

EXAMPLE   A local Hungarian restaurant had net sales of $32,000 for the month of June. The retail price of inventory at the beginning of June was $7,000, and at the end of June was $9,000. Find the average inventory at retail and the turnover rate at retail for June.

First, find the average inventory at retail.

$$\text{Average inventory} = \frac{\text{beginning inventory at retail} + \text{ending inventory at retail}}{2}$$

$$= \frac{\$7,000 + \$9,000}{2} = \frac{\$16,000}{2} = \$8,000$$

Then, find the turnover rate at retail.

$$\text{Turnover rate at retail} = \frac{\text{net sales}}{\text{average inventory at retail}}$$

$$= \frac{\$32,000}{\$8,000}$$

$$= 4$$

The turnover rate at retail is four times in the month of June. Note that the rate is *not* written in percent form.

Lending institutions examine the turnover rate when determining the risk of a business repaying a loan. An acceptable turnover rate varies based on the type of merchandise and whether the business is expanding. A high turnover rate indicates a good cash flow and is desirable unless sales are lost due to out-of-stock merchandise.

In general a rate of less than two to three times per year is a reason for concern unless the company is undergoing extensive expansion that involves expanding its inventory. Three to four times per year is usually judged to be a good turnover rate for nonperishable or nonseasonal inventory goods unless the average turnover for the particular industry is higher.

 TIP! What Makes a Turnover Rate Good or Bad?

Suppose a business has a turnover rate of 3 or 3 to 1. Is that good? A turnover rate alone doesn't give much information. Comparing a turnover rate to previous rates, to rates of similar businesses, and to rates required by lending institutions makes this information more meaningful. Businesses make calculations that help in making good business decisions.

2 Find the department overhead based on sales.

A business encounters many expenses other than buying stock (merchandise to sell) and equipment. It must pay salaries, rent or mortgages, utilities, taxes, and insurance fees. It must buy office supplies and keep up equipment. These expenses, along with depreciation, are called **overhead.** The ratio between overhead and sales can say much about a firm's efficiency or inefficiency. Overhead is another factor that lending institutions use in making decisions about business loans.

In addition, companies sometimes need to know not only how much total overhead expenses are, but also the overhead expense of each department so that excessive overhead expenses of certain departments can be reduced to increase profits. There are many methods of calculating overhead by department. Two of the most widely used methods are according to sales and according to floor space. Other ways of calculating overhead are similar to these two and apply a similar problem-solving approach.

Using the sales method, the company determines what fraction of the total sales was made by each department. This department sales fraction is multiplied by the total sales to find the overhead for each department.

 HOW TO Find the Department Overhead Based on Sales

1. Find the total sales: add the sales of individual departments.
2. Find the department sales rate: divide the department sales by the total sales.

$$\text{Department sales rate} = \frac{\text{department sales}}{\text{total sales}}$$

3. Find the overhead assigned to the department by sales: multiply the department sales rate by the total overhead.

Department overhead = department sales rate × total overhead

EXAMPLE   Just For Fun's overhead totaled $8,000 during one month. Find the overhead for each department, based on total sales, if the store had the following monthly sales by department: cameras, $5,000; jewelry, $8,200; sporting goods, $6,700; silver, $9,200; and toys, $12,000.

Setting up and completing a table like the one that follows helps organize the information and calculations. List the sales of each department in the second column, then find the total sales. In the third column, divide the department sales by the total sales to find the sales rate for each department. In the fourth column, multiply the sales rate by the total overhead to find each department's overhead.

Department	Sales	Sales Rate	Overhead*
Cameras	$5,000	$\frac{\$5,000}{\$41,100}$ or 0.121655	0.121655 × $8,000 or $973.24
Jewelry	8,200	$\frac{8,200}{41,100}$ or 0.199513	0.199513 × 8,000 or 1,596.11
Sporting goods	6,700	$\frac{6,700}{41,100}$ or 0.163017	0.163017 × 8,000 or 1,304.14
Silver	9,200	$\frac{9,200}{41,100}$ or 0.223844	0.223844 × 8,000 or 1,790.75
Toys	$12,000	$\frac{12,000}{41,100}$ or 0.291971	0.291971 × 8,000 or 2,335.77
Total	**$41,100**	$\frac{41,100}{41,100}$ or 1.000000	$8,000.01

*Full calculator values are used for all calculations.

TIP! **Using Conversion Factors**

In both methods for allocating overhead by department, a value by department is divided by a total value. A conversion factor can be found for making all these calculations. We apply the property that dividing by a value is the same as multiplying by its reciprocal.

In the previous example every sales amount per department is divided by the total sales of $41,000. The reciprocal of $41,100 is $\frac{1}{\$41,100}$ or 1 ÷ $41,100. 1 ÷ $41,100 = 0.002433090024.

The sales rate is multiplied by the total overhead, which is $8,000 for the example. To complete the conversion factor, multiply the reciprocal of $41,100 by the overhead $8,000.

$$0.002433090024 \times \$8,000 = 0.1946472019$$

Now, use this conversion factor and the calculator memory function to recalculate the overhead by department in the example.

A computer spreadsheet can also be used to generate the table.

Department	Sales	Conversion Factor	Overhead
Cameras	$5,000	0.1946472019	$973.24
Jewelry	8,200	0.1946472019	1,596.11
Sporting goods	6,700	0.1946472019	1,304.14
Silver	9,200	0.1946472019	1,790.75
Toys	12,000	0.1946472019	2,335.77
Total	$41,100	0.1946472019	$8,000.01

3 Find the department overhead based on floor space.

Another way of distributing overhead is according to how much floor space each department occupies. This method is similar to the sales method. A rate for each department is calculated, this time by dividing the department's floor space by the total floor space. To find the overhead for the department, multiply the department floor-space rate by the total overhead.

 HOW TO Find Department Overhead Based on Floor Space

1. Find the total floor space: add the square feet of floor space in each department.

2. Find the department floor space rate.

$$\text{Department floor space rate} = \frac{\text{floor space in department}}{\text{total floor space}}$$

3. Find the overhead assigned to the department by floor space: multiply the department floor space rate by the total overhead.

Department overhead by floor space = department floor space rate × total overhead.

 TIP! Making Periodic Checks of Calculations

When an example requires several calculations, it is helpful to periodically check your work rather than only check the final result.

Interim Check: In the next example, the total of the sales rates should be 1 or very close to 1.

Final Check: The sum of the amounts of overhead for each department should be the total overhead or very close to the total overhead.

EXAMPLE The Super Store assigns overhead to its various departments according to the floor space used by each department. The store's total overhead is $25,000. Find the overhead for each department if each department uses the following square feet: junior department, 3,000; women's wear, 4,000; men's wear, 3,500; children's wear, 3,000; china and silver, 2,500; housewares, 2,500; linens, 2,000; toys, 1,500; carpets, 3,500; and cosmetics, 500. Round the *final* answers to the nearest cent if necessary.

As in the previous example, the following table organizes all the information and results. This table could also be generated using a spreadsheet.

Department	Floor Space in Square Feet	Floor Space Rate	Overhead*
Junior department	3,000	$\frac{3,000}{26,000}$ or 0.115385	0.115385 × $25,000 or $2,884.62
Women's wear	4,000	$\frac{4,000}{26,000}$ or 0.153846	0.153846 × 25,000 or 3,846.15
Men's wear	3,500	$\frac{3,500}{26,000}$ or 0.134615	0.134615 × 25,000 or 3,365.38
Children's wear	3,000	$\frac{3,000}{26,000}$ or 0.115385	0.115385 × 25,000 or 2,884.62
China and silver	2,500	$\frac{2,500}{26,000}$ or 0.096154	0.096154 × 25,000 or 2,403.85
Housewares	2,500	$\frac{2,500}{26,000}$ or 0.096154	0.096154 × 25,000 or 2,403.85
Linens	2,000	$\frac{2,000}{26,000}$ or 0.076923	0.076923 × 25,000 or 1,923.08
Toys	1,500	$\frac{1,500}{26,000}$ or 0.057692	0.057692 × 25,000 or 1,442.31
Carpets	3,500	$\frac{3,500}{26,000}$ or 0.134615	0.134615 × 25,000 or 3,365.38
Cosmetics	500	$\frac{500}{26,000}$ or 0.019231	0.019231 × 25,000 or 480.77
Total	26,000	$\frac{26,000}{26,000}$ or 1.000000	$25,000.01

*Full calculator values are used for all calculations.

SELF-CHECK 14.2

1. Rutledge Equipment Company had net sales of $335,000. The beginning inventory at retail was $122,000 and the ending inventory at retail was $155,000. Find the turnover rate at retail.

2. The 7th Inning Baseball Card Shop had a beginning inventory cost of $59,800. The ending inventory cost was $48,500. If the cost of the goods sold during the period was $117,500, find the turnover rate at cost.

3. University Trailer Sales had a beginning inventory cost of $38,440. The ending inventory cost was $52,833. The cost of merchandise sold during the period was $184,302. Find the turnover rate based on cost.

4. Jeremiah Williams, owner of The Lamb Shop, needed to calculate the turnover rate based on retail prices. Net sales of $225,294 were recorded for a recent year. The retail price of inventory at the beginning of the year was $89,023 and was $68,392 at the end of the year. Find the turnover rate at retail for the year.

5. Overhead for one month at the Allimore Department Store totaled $6,000. Find the overhead for each department, based on sales, if the store had the following monthly sales by department: toys, $4,000; appliances, $6,600; children's clothing, $6,800; books, $4,600; and furniture, $8,400.

6. Carlisle's Stock Trailer Sales had overhead expenses that totaled $4,932 during one month. The business had the following departmental sales for the month: cattle trailers, $8,523; utility trailers, $6,201; boat trailers, $2,932; parts, $1,392. Find the overhead for each department, based on sales.

7. Dale Crosby's Gift Shop had overhead expenses totaling $2,732 during the month of August. The business recorded departmental sales for the month of August as follows: china, $3,923; silver, $8,923; crystal, $2,932; linens, $1,923; new gifts, $6,291; antiques, $8,923. Use this information to find the overhead for each department based on sales.

8. Savemore Discount Clothing Store assigns overhead to its various departments according to the floor space used by each department. The store's total monthly overhead is $15,800. Find the overhead for each department using the following square feet for each department: women's clothing, 2,000; men's clothing, 1,200; children's clothing, 2,500. Round *final* answers to the nearest cent if necessary.

9. Hughes' Trailer Manufacturer assigns overhead to its departments according to the floor space used by each department. The company's total monthly overhead for the month of April is $7,832. Find the overhead for each department using the following square feet for each department: welding bay, 2,100; paint shop, 1,950; axles and steel storage, 780; flooring lumber, 380; office space, 500.

10. Make a conversion factor for the data in the last example in this section (p. 589) and use the conversion factor to calculate the overhead for each department.

Around The Business World

OPEC Oil Inventory

Recently, the Organization of Petroleum Exporting Countries (OPEC) decided to increase its oil supply by 10% to 27.5 million barrels a day. Oil traders and analysts predicted that oil prices would fall because of the larger supply. Indeed oil prices dropped 25% when non-OPEC oil producers, who account for about 40% of global oil supplies, increased their oil inventory. Leaders of OPEC's 11 country members made this unusual move to prevent a big drop in oil prices.

The usual economic model states that as supply (inventory) increases, price decreases, and when supply decreases, price increases. Using this model, one would expect OPEC to cut oil production in order to protect their $26 per barrel price. However, with world oil consumption at a record high and rising, OPEC leaders bet that although oil prices would drop by $1 a barrel for a couple of weeks (fueling even higher oil consumption), prices would recover quickly and perhaps even rise slightly to $28 a barrel, due to increased oil demand. Hence, they predict that increasing their oil supply will not result in large oil inventories because consumers will buy more oil as fast as OPEC can produce it. By increasing its oil supply, OPEC is preparing to meet the rising global demand for oil at a competitive price that will both keep its market share of customers and afford healthy profits for OPEC nations.

The biggest oil exporter, Saudi Arabia, saw its recommended quota increase to 8.8 million barrels a day. Analysts estimate that Saudi Arabia had been producing about 8.17 million barrels a day before the quota increase. OPEC quota recommendations are not followed by all member nations; some pump all the oil they can!

Exercises

Use the above information to answer the following:

1. What was OPEC's oil quota for Saudi Arabia before the 10% increase?

2. Find the difference between Saudi Arabia's OPEC quota and its actual production before the 10% increase. At $18 a barrel, how much additional gross income per year did this amount to?

3. If Saudi Arabia pumps the recommended 8.8 million barrels a day, what percent increase is this over its former actual production? Round to the nearest tenth of a percent.

4. If Saudi Arabia increases its actual production by 10%, how many barrels a day will it pump? Round to the nearest hundredth of a barrel.

5. Use your answer from exercise 4 to predict Saudi Arabia's gross yearly oil income if it increases its actual production by 10% and sells at $18 a barrel. What is the oil income if oil sells for $19.15 a barrel?

6. How much money would Saudi Arabia lose if oil prices drop by $1 a barrel for two weeks following the quota increase, if they produce OPEC's quota limit?

Answers

1. Saudi Arabia's quota before the increase was 8 million barrels a day.

2. Saudi Arabia produced 0.17 million barrels above its quota. The additional 0.17 million barrels a day amounts to additional income of $1,116,900,000 per year.

3. The 0.63 million barrel a day increase amounts to a 7.7% increase.

4. 110% of 8.17 million barrels is 8.99 million barrels a day.

5. 8.99 million barrels a day $\times$ 365 days $\times$ \$18 a barrel = \$5.90643 $\times$ 10^{10} or $59,064,300,000 per year. At \$19.15 a barrel, Saudi Arabia's gross oil income would be \$62,837,852,500 per year.

6. 8.8 million barrels a day $\times$ 14 days $\times$ \$1 a barrel = $123,200,000 lost during this 2-week period.

CHAPTER	OVERVIEW
14	**Section**
	Outcome

Important Points with Examples

Section 14.1

 1

Use the specific identification inventory method to find the cost of goods sold. (page 575)

1. Find the cost of goods available for sale: multiply the number of units purchased by the cost per unit.

    Cost of goods available for sale = number of units purchased $\times$ cost per unit

2. Find the cost of ending inventory: multiply the number of units in ending inventory by the cost per unit.

    Cost of ending inventory = number of units in ending inventory $\times$ cost per unit

3. Find the cost of goods sold (COGS): subtract the cost of ending inventory from the cost of goods available for sale.

    Cost of goods sold = cost of goods available for sale $-$ cost of ending inventory

---

Use the specific identification method to find the cost of goods available for sale, the cost of the ending inventory, and the cost of goods sold.

Date of Purchase	Units Purchased	Cost per Unit	Total Cost
Beginning inventory	17	$10	$170
January 8	25	8	200
February 3	22	12	264
March 5	20	8	160
Goods available for sale			$794

Cost per Unit	Units	Total Cost
$10	12	$120
8	19	152
12	11	132
8	16	128
Ending inventory		$532

Cost of goods sold = cost of goods available for sale
$-$ cost of ending inventory = \$794 $-$ \$532 = \$262

Use the weighted-average inventory method to find the cost of goods sold. (page 576)

1. Find the cost of goods available for sale.

   Cost of goods available for sale = number of units purchased × cost per unit

2. Find the average unit cost: divide the cost of goods available for sale by the number of units available for sale.

$$\text{Average unit cost} = \frac{\text{cost of goods available for sale}}{\text{number of units available for sale}}$$

3. Find the cost of ending inventory: multiply the number of units in ending inventory by the average unit cost.

   Cost of ending inventory = number of units in ending inventory × average unit cost

4. Find the cost of goods sold.

   Cost of goods sold = cost of goods available for sale − cost of ending inventory

Find the average unit cost using the following table.

Date of Purchase	Units Purchased	Cost per Unit	Total Cost
Beginning inventory	18	$18	$324
April 6	25	19	475
May 4	26	12	312
June 9	22	8	176
Goods available for sale	91		$1,287

$$\text{Average unit cost} = \frac{\$1,287}{91} = \$14.14$$

Now find the cost of ending inventory and the cost of goods sold, if ending inventory is 50 units.

$$\text{Cost of ending inventory} = 50 \times \$14.14 = \$707.14$$

$$\text{Cost of goods sold} = \$1,287.00 - \$707.14 = \$579.86$$

Use the first-in, first-out (FIFO) inventory method to find the cost of goods sold. (page 577)

1. Find the cost of goods available for sale.

   Cost of goods available for sale = number of units purchased × cost per unit

2. Find the assigned cost per unit: assign a cost per unit in the ending inventory by assuming these units were the latest units purchased.

3. Find the cost of ending inventory: multiply the number of units in ending inventory by the assigned cost per unit.

   Cost of ending inventory = number of units in ending inventory
   × assigned cost per unit

4. Find the cost of goods sold.

   Cost of goods sold = cost of goods available for sale − cost of ending inventory

Find the cost of goods sold and the cost of the ending inventory if 465 units are in ending inventory.

Date of Purchase	Units Purchased	Cost per Unit	Total Cost
Beginning inventory	222	$10	$2,220
January 15	142	12	1,704
February 5	134	15	2,010
March 2	141	24	3,384
Goods available for sale	639		$9,318

Units sold = 639 − 465 = 174

Date of Purchase	Number of Units in Ending Inventory	Cost per Unit	Total Cost
Beginning inventory	48 (222 − 174)	$10	$480
January 15	142	12	1,704
February 5	134	15	2,010
March 2	141	24	3,384
Ending inventory	465		$7,578

Cost of goods sold = $9,318 − $7,578 = $1,740

4 Use the last-in, first-out (LIFO) inventory method to find the cost of goods sold. (page 578)

1. Find the cost of goods available for sale.

   Cost of goods available for sale = number of units purchased × cost per unit

2. Find the assigned cost per unit: assign a cost per unit in the ending inventory by assuming these units were the earliest units purchased.

3. Find the cost of ending inventory: Multiply the number of units in ending inventory by the assigned cost per unit.

   Cost of ending inventory = number of units in ending inventory
   × assigned cost per unit

4. Find the cost of goods sold.

   Cost of goods sold = cost of goods available for sale − cost of ending inventory

Find the cost of goods sold and the cost of the ending inventory if 282 units are in ending inventory.

Date of Purchase	Units Purchased	Cost per Unit	Total Cost
Beginning inventory	111	$10	$1,110
April 12	343	12	4,116
May 8	191	9	1,719
June 10	106	24	2,544
Goods available for sale	751		$9,489

$$\text{Units sold} = 751 - 282 = 469$$

$$\text{Units purchased: May } 8 + \text{June } 10 = 191 + 106 = 297 \text{ units}$$
$$469 - 297 = 172 \text{ units from April 12}$$

Date of Purchase	Units in Ending Inventory	Cost per Unit	Total Cost
Beginning inventory	111	$10	$1,110
April 12	171 (343 − 172)	12	2,052
Ending inventory	282		$3,162

$$\text{Cost of goods sold} = \$9,489 - \$3,162 = \$6,327$$

5 Use the retail inventory method to find the cost of goods sold. (page 579)

1. Find the cost of goods available for sale.

   Cost of goods available for sale = number of units purchased × cost per unit

2. Find the retail value of goods available for sale.
3. Find the cost ratio: divide the cost of goods available for sale by the retail value of goods available for sale.

$$\text{Cost ratio} = \frac{\text{cost of goods available for sale}}{\text{retail value of goods available for sale}}$$

4. Find the ending inventory at retail: subtract the dollar value of sales from the retail value of goods available for sale.

   Ending inventory at retail = retail value of goods available for sale − sales

5. Find the ending inventory at cost: multiply the ending inventory at retail by the cost ratio.

   Ending inventory at cost = ending inventory at retail × cost ratio

6. Find the cost of goods sold.

   Cost of goods sold = cost of goods available for sale − ending inventory at cost

   OR

   Cost of goods sold = sales × cost ratio

Find the cost of goods sold and the cost of the ending inventory.

	Cost	Retail
Beginning inventory	$4,824	$6,030
Purchases	872	1,090
Goods available for sale	$5,696	$7,120
Sales		$2,464
Ending inventory		$4,656

$$\text{Cost ratio} = \frac{\$5,696}{\$7,120} = 0.8$$

$$\text{Ending inventory at cost} = \$4,656 \times 0.8 = \$3,724.80$$

$$\text{Cost of goods sold} = \$5,696 - \$3,724.80 = \$1,971.20$$

6 Compare methods for determining inventory. (page 581)

- Specific identification
- Weighted-average
- First-in, first-out (FIFO)
- Last-in, first-out (LIFO)
- Retail

Most accurate, most time consuming
Easiest to use, appropriate when economy stable
If inflation high, income highest
If inflation high, income lowest
Most efficient

> **Which inventory method are you most likely to choose if:**
>
> **(a) you have a small business and want an efficient and low-cost method?**
>
> **(b) your inventory is computerized and sales are scanned and inventory records are automatically updated?**
>
> **(a) retail (b) specific identification**

Section 14.2

1 Find the inventory turnover rate. (page 585)

Find the turnover rate at cost.

1. Find the average inventory at cost.

$$\text{Average inventory at cost} = \frac{\text{beginning inventory at cost} + \text{ending inventory at cost}}{2}$$

2. Divide the cost of goods sold by the average inventory at cost.

$$\text{Turnover rate at cost} = \frac{\text{cost of goods sold}}{\text{average inventory at cost}}$$

Find the turnover rate at retail.

1. Find the average inventory at retail.

$$\text{Average inventory at retail} = \frac{\text{beginning inventory at retail} + \text{ending inventory at retail}}{2}$$

2. Divide the sales by the average inventory at retail.

$$\text{Turnover rate at retail} = \frac{\text{sales}}{\text{average inventory at retail}}$$

> **A store had net sales of $10,000 ($5,000 cost) with a beginning inventory of $5,000 retail ($2,500 cost) and an ending inventory of $6,000 retail ($3,000 cost). Find the turnover rate at retail and at cost.**
>
> $$\text{Average inventory at retail} = \frac{\$5,000 + \$6,000}{2} = \$5,500$$
>
> $$\text{Turnover at retail} = \frac{\$10,000}{\$5,500} = 1.818182$$
>
> $$\text{Average inventory at cost} = \frac{\$2,500 + \$3,000}{2} = \$2,750$$
>
> $$\text{Turnover rate at cost} = \frac{\$5,000}{\$2,750} = 1.818182$$

2
Find the
department
overhead
based on
sales.
(page 587)

1. Find the total sales: add the sales of individual departments.
2. Find the department sales rate: divide the department sales by the total sales.

$$\text{Department sales rate} = \frac{\text{department sales}}{\text{total sales}}$$

3. Find the overhead assigned to the department by sales: multiply the department sales rate by the total overhead.

$$\text{Department overhead} = \text{department sales rate} \times \text{total overhead}$$

Make a table to show the overhead by departments if overhead is assigned based on total sales and the store had the following monthly sales by department: paint, $5,000; lumber, $6,200; wall coverings, $3,200; plumbing, $3,200; and electrical, $1,500. Overhead expenses during the month are $1,780.

Multiply each department's sales rate by the total overhead to find the overhead for each department.

Department	Sales	Sales Rate	Overhead
Paint	$5,000	$\frac{5,000}{19,100}$ or 0.261780	0.261780 $\times$ $1,780 or $465.97
Lumber	6,200	$\frac{6,200}{19,100}$ or 0.324607	0.324607 $\times$ 1,780 or 577.80
Wall coverings	3,200	$\frac{3,200}{19,100}$ or 0.167539	0.167539 $\times$ 1,780 or 298.22
Plumbing	3,200	$\frac{3,200}{19,100}$ or 0.167539	0.167539 $\times$ 1,780 or 298.22
Electrical	1,500	$\frac{1,500}{19,100}$ or 0.078534	0.078534 $\times$ 1,780 or 139.79
Total	**$19,100**	$\frac{19,100}{19,100}$ or 0.999999*	$1,780.00

*Sum of rounded decimal equivalents.

3
Find the
department
overhead
based on floor
space.
(page 589)

1. Find the total floor space: add the square feet of floor space in each department.
2. Find the department floor space rate.

$$\text{Department floor space rate} = \frac{\text{floor space in department}}{\text{total floor space}}$$

3. Find the overhead assigned to the department by floor space: multiply the department floor space rate by the total overhead.

$$\text{Department overhead} = \text{department floor space rate} \times \text{total overhead}$$

Make a table to show the overhead for a store that had $25,000 in overhead, if overhead is calculated based on number of square feet a department uses: department 1: 5,100; department 2: 4,120; department 3: 1,200; department 4: 2,500

Department	Floor Space in Square Feet	Floor Space Rate	Overhead
1	5,100	$\frac{5,100}{12,920}$ or 0.394737	0.394737 × $25,000 or $9,868.42
2	4,120	$\frac{4,120}{12,920}$ or 0.318885	0.318885 × 25,000 or 7,972.14
3	1,200	$\frac{1,200}{12,920}$ or 0.092879	0.092879 × 25,000 or 2,321.98
4	2,500	$\frac{2,500}{12,920}$ or 0.193498	0.193498 × 25,000 or 4,837.46
Total	12,920	$\frac{12,920}{12,920}$ or 0.999999*	$25,000.01

*Sum of rounded decimal equivalents.

WORDS TO KNOW

inventory (p. 574)
periodic inventory (p. 574)
perpetual inventory (p. 574)
cost of goods sold (COGS) (p. 574)
specific identification inventory
  method (p. 575)

weighted-average inventory
  method (p. 576)
FIFO (first-in, first-out) inventory
  method (p. 577)
LIFO (last-in, first-out) inventory
  method (p. 578)

retail method (p. 579)
ending inventory at cost (p. 579)
ending inventory at retail (p. 579)
inventory turnover (p. 584)
inventory turnover ratio (p. 585)
overhead (p. 587)

CHAPTER 14 CONCEPTS ANALYSIS

1. Combine the formulas in steps 1 and 2 of the How-To box: Find the Cost of Goods Sold Using the Specific Identification Inventory Method (p. 575) to rewrite the formula in step 3 to find the cost of goods sold.

2. Combine the formulas in steps 1 and 2 of the How-To box: Find the Cost of Goods Sold Using the Weighted-Average Inventory Method (p. 576) to rewrite the formula in step 3 to find the cost of ending inventory.

3. Combine the formulas in steps 1, 3, and 4 of the How-To box: Find the Cost of Goods Sold Using the First-In, First-Out Inventory Method (p. 578) to find the cost of goods sold.

4. Explain the difference between a turnover rate at retail and a turnover rate at cost.

5. Discuss the difference in finding the cost of goods sold using the specific inventory method and using the retail method.

6. Explain the difference in the assumptions made in using the FIFO inventory method versus the LIFO inventory method.

7. Combine the formulas in steps 1 and 3 of the How-To box: Find the Cost of Goods Sold Using Retail Inventory Method (p. 579) to find the cost ratio.

8. Combine and simplify the formulas in steps 1 and 2 in the How-To box: Find the Turnover Rate at Cost (p. 585) to solve for turnover rate at cost.

9. Combine and simplify the formulas in steps 1 and 2 in the How-To box: Find the Turnover Rate at Retail (p. 586).

10. Combine the formulas in steps 2 and 3 in the How-To box: Find the Department Overhead Based on Sales (p. 589) into one formula that can be used to find department overhead.

ASSIGNMENT EXERCISES

Section 14.1

1. Find the cost of goods available for sale using the following table.

Exercise 1

Date of Purchase	Units Purchased	Cost per Unit	Total Cost
Beginning inventory	182	$21	
August 20	78	27	
September 12	39	28	
October 2	52	21	_____
Cost of goods available for sale			

2. Find the cost of goods available for sale using the following table.

Exercise 2

Date of Purchase	Units Purchased	Cost per Unit
Beginning inventory	25	$18
June 8	10	19
July 7	18	20
August 3	22	17

Use the specific identification method for exercises 3–6.

3. Find the cost of ending inventory using the following table showing a breakdown of unit costs for ending inventory.

Exercise 3

Cost per Unit	Units	Total Cost
$21	13	
27	64	
28	29	
21	48	

4. Find the cost of ending inventory using the following table showing a breakdown of unit costs for ending inventory.

Exercise 4

Cost per Unit	Units
$18	17
19	12
20	7
17	14

5. Find the cost of goods sold using the tables in exercises 1 and 3.

6. Find the cost of goods sold using the tables in exercises 2 and 4.

Use the weighted-average method for exercises 7–10.

7. Find the average unit cost using the table in exercise 1.

8. Find the average unit cost using the following table.

Exercise 8

Date of Purchase	Units Purchased	Cost per Unit
Beginning inventory	21	$12
May 12	10	10
June 9	16	11
July 5	20	13
Units sold	46	

9. Find the cost of ending inventory and the cost of goods sold using the tables in exercises 1 and 3.

10. Find the cost of the ending inventory and the cost of goods sold using the table in exercise 8.

Use the first-in, first-out method for exercises 11–12.

11. Find the cost of goods sold and the cost of the ending inventory using the table from exercise 1 and the fact that the ending inventory is 96 units.

12. Find the cost of goods sold and the cost of the ending inventory using the following table and the fact that the ending inventory is 500 units.

Exercise 12

Date of Purchase	Number of Units Purchased	Cost per Unit
Beginning inventory	221	$16
April 15	328	15
May 12	167	12
June 5	201	9

Use the last-in, first-out method for exercises 13–14.

13. Find the cost of goods sold and the cost of the ending inventory using the table from exercise 1 and the fact that the ending inventory is 200 units.

14. Find the cost of goods sold and the cost of the ending inventory using the following table and the table in exercise 12.

Exercise 14

Date of Purchase	Number of Units in Ending Inventory	Cost per Unit
Beginning inventory	221	$16
April 15	4	15
May 12	0	12
June 5	0	9
Cost of ending inventory	225	

Use the retail method for exercise 15.

15. Find the cost of goods sold and the cost of the ending inventory using the table in exercise 1, the following table, and the fact that sales are $5,000.

Exercise 15

Date of Purchase	Retail Price per Unit
Beginning inventory	$26
August 20	$32
September 12	$35
October 2	$26

16. Use the following inventory costs to find the average inventory cost: $2,596; $3,872.

Complete the tables for exercises 17–20. Round to the nearest tenth.

	Beginning Inventory at Retail	Ending Inventory at Retail	Sales	Turnover Rate at Retail
17.	$8,920	$7,460	$19,270	___
18.	$51,266	$42,780	$25,000	___

	Beginning Inventory at Retail	Ending Inventory at Retail	Cost of Goods Sold	Turnover Rate at Cost
19.	$8,000	$10,000	$36,000	___
20.	$26,108	$5,892	$73,600	___

21. Find the turnover rate at retail for a business with sales of $75,000 and an average inventory at retail of $15,000.

22. At Best Buy Hardware, the nuts and bolts department had $1,500 in sales for the month, the electrical department had $4,000, and the paint department had $2,300. The total overhead was $3,800. Find each department's overhead based on sales.

23. Department 1 had $5,200 in sales for the month, department 2 had $4,700, department 3 had $6,520, department 4 had $4,870, and department 5 had $2,010. The total overhead was $10,000. Find each department's overhead based on sales.

24. A corner grocery store has a monthly overhead of $1,500. Find each department's monthly overhead based on sales if department sales were as follows: meats, $1,200; groceries, $2,400; dairy, $600; and housewares, $800.

25. Tyson's Fixit Store has a monthly overhead of $9,200. Find each department's monthly overhead based on floor space using the following square feet for each department: hardware, 800; plumbing, 600; tools, 400; supplies, 600.

26. Department A uses 5,000 square feet of floor space, department B uses 2,500, department C uses 4,300, and department D uses 2,700. The total overhead is $8,200. Find each department's overhead based on floor space.

27. The office photocopy machine is on the blink again. You are responsible for replacing the photocopier with a more powerful model and equitably charging each department its share of the cost of the new copier. The new copier costs $7,580 and is expected to produce 500,000 copies in its lifetime. You decide that each department's share should be based on the number of copies the department makes. The following record of use was recorded at the end of the first year. How much do you charge the four departments for the first year?

Exercise 27

Department	Copies Made
Purchasing	8,711
Personnel	30,872
Payroll	32,521
Secretarial pool	52,896

Spreadsheet Exercises

28. Write formulas for generating department overhead based on floor space for 7th Inning Memorabilia Shop for the month of February if the month's expenses are: Telephone, $256.25; Utilities, $315.75; Rent, $2,845.78; Maintenance, $192.40.

Names for constants can be created in Excel™ by clicking on the Insert menu, pointing to Name, then clicking Define. Enter the name of the constant in the Names in Workbook box. Type an = (equal sign) and the constant value in the Refers box, then click ok. Create a name for each of the monthly expenses in the worksheet.

(a) Write a formula to find the total of the department fractions to use as a check figure. Find the sum of the floor space for all departments and put the total in B8. Write a formula to calculate the fraction of total floor space for each department and put the total in C8.

(b) Total the expenses for Telephone, Utilities, Rent, and Maintenance. Write the formula for the total in B14.

(c) Write formulas to calculate the Departmental Expenses for each of the five departments.

(d) Write a formula to sum the departmental expenses to ensure the total is the same as the total found in column B14.

29. Complete the spreadsheet using the formulas.

	A	B	C	D	E	F	G	H
1	7th Inning Memorabilia Shop and Restaurant Monthly Overhead by Department Floor Space							
2	Department	Floor Space	Fraction	Dept Expenses				
3	Gallery	4,250						
4	Engraving	2,675						
5	Framing	3,500						
6	Restaurant	4,500						
7	Cards	5,200						
8	Totals							
9								
10	Telephone	$256.25						
11	Utilitites	$315.75						
12	Rent	$2,845.78						
13	Maintenance	$192.40						
14	Total expenses							

Challenge Problems

30. If the copy machine in exercise 27 continues to be used at the same rate in future years, how many years of useful life should be expected? What percent of the cost of the machine was charged to each department during the first year?

31. Verify that approximately the entire cost of the machine in exercise 27 will be charged out by the end of the time period that was projected in exercise 28 by calculating each year's charges for each department. (Assume that each department has the same number of copies each year.)

32. Explain how analysis such as that in exercises 28 and 29 can be used to verify calculations and increase understanding of a problem.

CHAPTER 14 PRACTICE TEST

1. Find the cost of goods available for sale using the following table.

Date of Purchase	Units Purchased	Cost per Unit
Beginning inventory	26	$10
March 12	32	13
April 3	29	9
May 5	25	12

2. Find the cost of the ending inventory using the specific identification method and the following table showing a breakdown of units costs for ending inventory.

Cost per Unit	Units
$10	17
13	12
9	15
12	25

3. Find the cost of goods sold using the specific identification method and the tables in exercises 1 and 2.

4. Find the average unit cost using the table in exercise 1.

5. Find the cost of ending inventory and the cost of goods sold using the weighted-average method and the tables in exercises 1 and 2.

6. Find the cost of goods sold and the cost of the ending inventory using the FIFO method, the table in exercise 1, and the fact that the ending inventory is 32 units.

7. Find the cost of goods sold and the cost of the ending inventory using the LIFO method, the table in exercise 1, and the fact that the ending inventory is 82 units.

8. AMX Department Store's overhead totaled $12,000 during one month. The sales by department for the month were as follows: cameras, $12,000; toys, $14,000; hardware, $13,500; garden supplies, $8,400; sporting goods, $9,500; and clothing, $28,600. Find the monthly overhead for all departments.

9. Office Supply World assigns overhead to a department based on the square feet of office space it occupies. The overhead for a month totaled $9,000 and each department occupies the following number of square feet: furniture, 2,000; computer supplies, 1,600; consumable office supplies, 2,500; leather goods, 1,200; and administrative services, 800. Find each department's overhead.

10. A restaurant had a beginning inventory at retail of $13,900 and an ending inventory at retail of $10,000. If the sales were $47,800, find the turnover rate at retail.

11. A retail parts business had an average inventory at retail of $258,968 and sales of $756,893. Find the rate of turnover at retail to the nearest hundredth.

12. A plant had an average inventory at cost of $13,000 and sales of $26,000. Find the rate of turnover at cost.

SELF-CHECK SOLUTIONS

SELF-CHECK 14.1

1. $42 \times \$850 = \$35,700$
$21 \times \$1,760 = \$36,960$
$17 \times \$965 = \$16,405$
$28 \times \$480 = \$13,440$
Goods available for sale $= 42 + 21 + 17 + 28 = 108$
Cost of goods available for sale $= \$35,700 + \$36,960 + \$16,405 + \$13,440 = \$102,505$
Ending inventory $= 108 - 74 = 34$

2. $9 \times \$850 = \$7,650$
$11 \times \$1,760 = \$19,360$
$8 \times \$965 = \$7,720$
$6 \times \$480 = \$2,880$
Total number of units on hand $= 9 + 11 + 8 + 6 = 34$
Cost of ending inventory $= \$7,650 + \$19,360 + \$7,720 + \$2,880 = \$37,610$

3. Cost of goods sold = $102,505 − $37,610 = $64,895

4. 96 × $12 = $1,152
23 × $9 = $207
15 × $11 = $165
37 × $15 = $555
Goods available for sale = 96 + 23 + 15 + 37 = 171
Cost of goods available for sale = $1,152 + $207 + $165 + $555 = $2,079
Ending inventory = 171 − 89 = 82

5. 43 × $12 = $516
11 × $9 = $99
7 × $11 = $77
21 × $15 = $315
Total number of units on hand = 43 + 11 + 7 + 21 = 82
Cost of ending inventory = $516 + $99 + $77 + $315 = $1,007

6. Cost of goods sold = $2,079 − $1,007 = $1,072

7. Average unit cost = $\dfrac{\$102,505}{108} = \$949.12$

8. Cost of ending inventory = 34 × $949.12 = $32,270.08

9. Cost of goods sold = $102,505 − $32,270.08 = $70,234.92

10. Average unit cost = $\dfrac{\$2,079}{171} = \$12.16$

11. Cost of ending inventory = 82 × $12.16 = $997.12

12. Cost of goods sold = $2,079 − $997.12 = $1,081.88

13. 34 items are in the ending inventory.
March 3:   28 units @ $480 per unit
February 19:   6 units @ $965 per unit
Total   34

14. Cost of ending inventory = 28 × $480 + 6 × $965 = $13,440 + $5,790 = $19,230
Cost of goods sold = $102,505 − $19,230 = $83,275

15. 82 items are in the ending inventory.
June 2:   37 units @ $15 per unit
May 8:   15 units @ $11 per unit
April 12:   23 units @ $9 per unit
Beginning: 7 units @ $12 per unit
Total   82

16. Cost of ending inventory = 37 × $15 + 15 × $11 + 23 × $9 + 7 × $12 = $555 + $165 + $207 + $84 = $1,011
Cost of goods sold = $2,079 − $1,011 = $1,068

17. 34 items are in the ending inventory.
Beginning: 34 units @ $850 per unit

18. Cost of ending inventory = 34 × $850 = $28,900
Cost of goods sold = $102,505 − $28,900 = $73,605

19. 82 items are in the ending inventory.
Beginning: 82 units @ $12 per unit

20. Cost of ending inventory = 82 × $12 = $984
Cost of goods sold = $2,079 − $984 = $1,095

21. 42 × $975 = $40,950
21 × $2,115 = $44,415
17 × $1,206 = $20,502
28 × $600 = $16,800
Total = $122,667

22. Cost ratio = $\dfrac{\$102,505}{\$122,667} = 0.836$

23. Cost of goods sold = $78,982 × 0.836 = $66,028.95

24. 96 × $18 = $1,728
23 × $13 = $299
15 × $17 = $255
37 × $21 = $777
Total = $3,059

25. Cost ratio = $\dfrac{\$2,079}{\$3,059} = 0.680$

26. Cost of goods sold = $1,691 × 0.68 = $1,149.88

27. Retail because it is the most efficient

28. Specific identification; they will use a computerized inventory tracker.

1. Average inventory at retail $= \dfrac{\$122,000 + \$155,000}{2}$ $\$138,500$

Turnover rate at retail $= \dfrac{\$335,000}{\$138,500} = 2.42$ times

2. Average inventory at cost $= \dfrac{\$59,800 + \$48,500}{2} = \$54,150$

Turnover rate at cost $= \dfrac{\$117,500}{\$54,150} = 2.17$ times

3. Average inventory at cost $= \dfrac{\$38,440 + \$52,833}{2} = \$45,636.50$

Turnover rate at cost $= \dfrac{\$184,302}{\$45,636.50} = 4.04$ times

4. Average inventory at retail $= \dfrac{\$89,023 + \$68,392}{2} = \$78,707.50$

Turnover rate $= \dfrac{\$225,294}{\$78,707.50} = 2.86$ times

5.

Department	Sales	Sales Rate	Overhead
Toys	$4,000	$\dfrac{\$4,000}{\$30,400}$ or 0.131579	0.131579 × $6,000 or $789.47
Appliances	6,600	$\dfrac{6,600}{30,400}$ or 0.217105	0.217105 × 6,000 or 1,302.63
Children's clothing	6,800	$\dfrac{6,800}{30,400}$ or 0.223684	0.223684 × 6,000 or 1,342.10
Books	4,600	$\dfrac{4,600}{30,400}$ or 0.151316	0.151316 × 6,000 or 907.90
Furniture	8,400	$\dfrac{8,400}{30,400}$ or 0.276316	0.276316 × 6,000 or 1,657.90
Total	$30,400	$\dfrac{\$30,400}{\$30,400}$ or 1.000000	$6,000.00

6.

Department	Sales	Sales Rate	Overhead
Cattle trailers	$8,523	$\dfrac{\$8,523}{\$19,048}$ or 0.447449	0.447449 × $4,932 or $2,206.82
Utility trailers	6,201	$\dfrac{6,201}{19,048}$ or 0.325546	0.325546 × 4,932 or 1,605.59
Boat trailers	2,932	$\dfrac{2,932}{19,048}$ or 0.153927	0.153927 × 4,932 or 759.17
Parts	1,392	$\dfrac{1,392}{19,048}$ or 0.073079	0.073079 × 4,932 or 360.42
Total	$19,048	$\dfrac{\$19,048}{\$19,048}$ or 1.000001	$4,932.00

7.

Department	Sales	Sales Rate	Overhead
China	$3,923	$\dfrac{\$3,923}{\$32,915}$ or 0.119186	0.119186 × $2,732 or $325.62
Silver	8,923	$\dfrac{8,923}{32,915}$ or 0.271092	0.271092 × 2,732 or 740.62
Crystal	2,932	$\dfrac{2,932}{32,915}$ or 0.089078	0.089078 × 2,732 or 243.36
Linens	1,923	$\dfrac{1,923}{32,915}$ or 0.058423	0.058423 × 2,732 or 159.61
New gifts	6,291	$\dfrac{6,291}{32,915}$ or 0.191129	0.191129 × 2,732 or 522.17
Antiques	8,923	$\dfrac{8,923}{32,915}$ or 0.271092	0.271092 × 2,732 or 740.62
Total	$32,915	$\dfrac{\$32,915}{\$32,915}$ or 1.000000	$2,732.00

8.

Department	Floor Space in Square Feet	Floor Space Rate	Overhead
Women's clothing	2,000	$\dfrac{2,000}{5,700}$ or 0.350877	0.350877 × $15,800 or $5,543.86
Men's clothing	1,200	$\dfrac{1,200}{5,700}$ or 0.210526	0.210526 × 15,800 or 3,326.31
Children's clothing	2,500	$\dfrac{2,500}{5,700}$ or 0.438596	0.438596 × 15,800 or 6,929.82
Total	5,700	$\dfrac{5,700}{5,700}$ or 0.999999*	$15,799.99

*Sum of rounded decimal equivalents.

9.

Department	Floor Space in Square Feet	Floor Space Rate	Overhead
Welding bay	2,100	$\dfrac{2,100}{5,710}$ or 0.367776	0.367776 × $7,832 or $2,880.42
Paint shop	1,950	$\dfrac{1,950}{5,710}$ or 0.341506	0.341506 × 7,832 or 2,674.68
Axles and steel storage	780	$\dfrac{780}{5,710}$ or 0.136602	0.136602 × 7,832 or 1,069.87
Flooring lumber	380	$\dfrac{380}{5,710}$ or 0.066550	0.066550 × 7,832 or 521.22
Office space	500	$\dfrac{500}{5,710}$ or 0.087566	0.087566 × 7,832 or 685.81
Total	5,710	$\dfrac{5,710}{5,710}$ or 1.000000	$7,832.00

10. $25,000 ÷ 26,000 = 0.96153846
Overhead for Junior department = 0.9615384 × 3,000 = $2,884.62.
Other departments' overhead is calculated in the same manner and should be the same as that given in the example.

15

Financial Statements

15.1 The Balance Sheet

1 Prepare a balance sheet.

2 Prepare a vertical analysis of a balance sheet.

3 Prepare a horizontal analysis of a balance sheet.

15.2 Income Statements

1 Prepare an income statement.

2 Prepare a vertical analysis of an income statement.

3 Prepare a horizontal analysis of an income statement.

15.3 Financial Statement Ratios

1 Find and use financial ratios.

Good Decisions through Teamwork

Pair up with another student whose employment goals are similar to yours. Using newspapers, business journals, and other resources, select three companies that may be desirable employers. Obtain copies of the chosen companies' financial reports. If you select local companies, you may wish to visit those companies to obtain the reports. For national or international companies, find company addresses at your local library or on the Internet and request financial reports in writing.

With your partner, examine the companies' financial reports and take notes on the information included. Select a few key financial ratios to compare for all three companies and discuss their relative financial conditions. Prepare a summary statement on each company's outlook. Individually, select a company that most nearly matches your employment goals; be prepared to share the reasons for your selection with the class.

The financial condition of a business must be monitored all the time. The owner of a business, investors, and creditors need to know the financial condition of the business before they can make decisions and plans. Lending institutions consider the overall financial health of a business before lending money. The stockholders of incorporated businesses expect to receive periodic reports on the financial condition of the corporation. Many companies or organizations hire an auditor once a year to determine this condition. Two financial statements, the *balance sheet* and the *income statement,* are normally prepared as part of this analysis. The balance sheet describes the condition of a business at some exact point in time, whereas the income statement shows what the business did over a period of time.

15.1 The Balance Sheet

1 Prepare a balance sheet.

2 Prepare a vertical analysis of a balance sheet.

3 Prepare a horizontal analysis of a balance sheet.

1 Prepare a balance sheet.

The **balance sheet** is a type of financial statement that indicates the worth or financial condition of a business *as of a certain date.* It does not give any historical background about the company or make future projections, but rather shows the status of the company on a given date. On that date, it answers the questions:

How much does the business own? What are its *assets?*
How much does the business owe? What are its *liabilities?*
How much is the business worth? What is its *equity?*

Assets are properties owned by the business. They include anything of monetary value and things that could be exchanged for cash or other property. **Current assets** are assets that are normally turned into cash within a year. **Plant and equipment** are assets that are used in transacting business and are more long term in nature. These types of assets can be further subdivided as follows:

Current assets

Cash	Money in the bank as well as cash on hand
Accounts receivable	Money that customers owe the business for merchandise or services they have received but have not yet paid for
Notes receivable	Promissory notes owed to the business
Merchandise inventory	Value of merchandise on hand
Office supplies	Value of supplies such as stationery, pens, file folders, and diskettes

Plant and equipment

Business equipment	Value of equipment (tools, display cases, machinery, and so on) that the business owns
Office furniture and equipment	Value of office furniture (desks, chairs, filing cabinets, and so on) and equipment (computers, printers, copiers, calculators, postage meters, fax machines, and the like)
Buildings	Value of the buildings the business owns
Land	Value of the property and grounds on which the buildings stand, and other land the business owns

Liabilities are amounts that the business owes. **Current liabilities** are those that must be paid shortly. **Long-term liabilities** are those that will be paid over a long period of time—a year or more. These types of liabilities can be further subdivided as follows:

Current liabilities	**Accounts payable**	Money owed for merchandise or services that the business has received but has not yet paid for
	Notes payable	Promissory notes that the business owes
	Wages payable	Salaries that a business owes its employees
Long-term liabilities	**Mortgage payable**	The debt owed on buildings and land that the business owns

In addition to its debts to creditors, a firm is considered to owe its investors. This "debt" is expressed as **owner's equity,** also called stockholder's equity, the amount of clear ownership or the owner's rights to the properties. It is the difference between assets and liabilities. For instance, if a business has assets of $175,000 and liabilities of $100,000, the owner's equity is $175,000 − $100,000, or $75,000. Other words used to mean the same thing as owner's equity are **capital, proprietorship,** and **net worth.**

A balance sheet (see Figure 15-1) lists the assets, liabilities, and owner's equity of a business on a specific date, using the basic accounting equation of business:

Basic Accounting Equation:

$$\text{Assets} = \text{liabilities} + \text{owner's equity}:$$

$$A = L + OE$$

Sander's Woodworks
Balance Sheet
December 31, 2001

Assets

Current assets
Cash
Accounts receivable
Merchandise inventory
Total current assets

Plant and equipment
Equipment
Total plant and equipment
Total assets

Liabilities

Current liabilities
Accounts payable
Wages payable
Total current liabilities

Long-term liabilities
Mortgage note payable
Total long-term liabilities
Total liabilities

Owner's Equity
J. Sander's capital
Total liabilities and owner's equity

Figure 15-1 Sander's Woodworks Balance Sheet Template

HOW TO   Prepare a Balance Sheet

1. Find and record the *total assets*, working by asset category.
   (a) List the *current assets* and draw a single line underneath the last entry.
   (b) Add the entries and record the *total current assets*, drawing a single line underneath the total.
   (c) Repeat step 1a for *plant and equipment assets* and step 1b for *total plant and equipment assets.*
   (d) Add the category totals and draw a double line underneath the grand total.

   Total assets = total current assets + total plant and equipment

2. Find and record the *total liabilities*, working by liability category.
   (a) Repeat step 1a for *current liabilities* and step 1b for *total current liabilities.*
   (b) Repeat step 1a for *long-term liabilities* and step 1b for *total long-term liabilities.*
   (c) Add the category totals and draw a single line underneath the total.

   Total liabilities = total current liabilities + total long-term liabilities

3. Find and record the *total owner's equity.*
   (a) List the equity entries and draw a single line underneath the last entry.
   (b) Add the entries and draw a single line underneath the total.

4. Find and record the *total liabilities and owner's equity:* add the total liabilities to the total owner's equity and draw a double line underneath the grand total.

   Total liabilities and owner's equity = total liabilities + total owner's equity

5. Confirm that the double line grand totals from step 1 and step 4 are the same.

   Total assets = total liabilities + owner's equity

TIP!   Single Underline versus Double Underline

One way of distinguishing totals and subtotals on financial statements is by the type of underline used. A single underline may indicate the result of the addition or subtraction that is a subtotal. The double underline indicates the result of addition or subtraction that is a grand total.

EXAMPLE   Prepare a balance sheet, using Figure 15-1 as a guide, for Sander's Woodworks for December 31, 2001. The company assets are: cash, $1,973; accounts receivable, $2,118; merchandise inventory, $18,476; equipment, $18,591. The liabilities are: accounts payable, $2,317; wages payable, $684; mortgage note payable, $15,286. The owner's capital is $22,871.

The completed balance sheet is shown in Figure 15-2.

Sander's Woodworks
Balance Sheet
December 31, 2001

Assets

Current assets
Cash	$1,973
Accounts receivable	2,118
Merchandise inventory	18,476
Total current assets	22,567

Plant and equipment
Equipment	18,591
Total plant and equipment	18,591
Total assets	$41,158

Liabilities

Current liabilities
Accounts payable	2,317
Wages payable	684
Total current liabilities	3,001

Long-term liabilities
Mortgage note payable	15,286
Total long-term liabilities	15,286
Total liabilities	18,287

Owner's Equity
J. Sander's capital	22,871
Total liabilities and owner's equity	$41,158

Figure 15-2   Completed Balance Sheet

 TIP!   When Are Dollar Signs Appropriate?

Writing a dollar sign for every monetary amount makes the balance sheet more difficult to read. Ordinarily, dollar signs are included for the first amount in a list of values and for the totals. Even subtotals generally do not include the dollar sign. Another advantage of this convention is that it makes totals easier to locate.

 TIP!   Computerized Financial Statements

Financial statements are often prepared using a computer spreadsheet program. Key information is entered in specific locations, and calculations are made using formulas.

In the balance sheet in Figure 15-3, key information is entered in cells B7, B8, B9, B12, B17, B18, B21, and B25. Formulas are used to make the calculations for cells B10, B13, B14, B19, B22, B23, and B26.

B10 = B7 + B8 + B9	B13 = B12	B14 = B10 + B13
B19 = B17 + B18	B22 = B21	B23 = B19 + B22
B26 = B23 + B25		

![Microsoft Excel - CLE_SE_03.xls spreadsheet window]

	A	B	C	D	E	F	G	H	I	J
1	Sander's Woodworks									
2	Balance Sheet									
3	December 31, 2001									
4										
5	**Assets**									
6	*Current assets*									
7	Cash	$1,973								
8	Accounts receivable	2,118								
9	Merchandise inventory	18,476								
10	Total current assets									
11	*Plant and equipment*									
12	Equipment	18,591								
13	Total plant and equipment									
14	Total assets									
15	**Liabilities**									
16	*Current liabilities*									
17	Accounts payable	2,317								
18	Wages Payable	684								
19	Total current liabilities									
20	*Long-term liabilities*									
21	Mortgage note payable	15,286								
22	Total long-term liabilities									
23	Total liabilities									
24	**Owner's Equity**									
25	J. Sander's capital	22,871								
26	Total liabilities and owner's equity									

Figure 15-3   Balance Sheet Using a Computerized Spreadsheet Template

Key information is entered in highlighted cells. Other cells are the results of calculations determined by formulas.

2   Prepare a vertical analysis of a balance sheet.

A **vertical analysis** of a balance sheet shows the ratio of each item on the balance sheet to the *total assets*. To find these ratios, we use the percentage formula $R = \frac{P}{B}$. Each item on the balance sheet is a percentage P, and the total assets are the base B. Their ratio R is expressed as a percent.

For instance, if total assets are $50,000, a liability of $5,000 is 10% of total assets.

$$R = \frac{P}{B} = \frac{\text{liability}}{\text{total assets}} = \frac{\$5,000}{\$50,000} = 0.1 = 10\%$$

? HOW TO Prepare a Vertical Analysis of a Balance Sheet

1. Prepare a balance sheet of assets, liabilities, and owner's equity.
2. Create an additional column labeled *percent:* for each item, divide the amount of the item by the total assets and record the result as a percent.

$$\text{Percent of total assets} = \frac{\text{amount of item}}{\text{total assets}} \times 100\%$$

EXAMPLE Prepare a vertical analysis of the balance sheet for Sander's Woodworks shown in Figure 15-2.

For each item, divide the amount of the item by the total assets.

Cash: $\dfrac{\$1,973}{\$41,158} = 0.0479372 \times 100\% =$ 4.8% (nearest tenth of a percent)

Accounts receivable: $\dfrac{\$2,118}{\$41,158} = 0.0514602 =$ 5.1%

Inventory: $\dfrac{\$18,476}{\$41,158} = 0.4489042 =$ 44.9%

Equipment: $\dfrac{\$18,591}{\$41,158} = 0.4516983 =$ 45.2%

Total assets: $\dfrac{\$41,158}{\$41,158} = 1 =$ 100%

Accounts payable: $\dfrac{\$2,317}{\$41,158} = 0.0562953 =$ 5.6%

Wages payable: $\dfrac{\$684}{\$41,158} = 0.0166189 =$ 1.7%

Mortgage note payable: $\dfrac{\$15,286}{\$41,158} = 0.3713980 =$ 37.1%

Total liabilities: $\dfrac{\$18,287}{\$41,158} = 0.4443122 =$ 44.4%

Capital: $\dfrac{\$22,871}{\$41,158} = 0.5556878 =$ 55.6%

Total liabilities and owner's equity: $\dfrac{\$41,158}{\$41,158} = 1 =$ 100%

Note that the percent both for total assets and for total liabilities and owner's equity is 100%.

The completed balance sheet is shown in Figure 15-4.

Learning Strategy Long Problems Don't Have to Be Difficult

Sometimes we let ourselves become overwhelmed by the mere length of a problem. Look at the previous example. Each step of the solution involves skills that we have previously used many times. Here are some tips to help you manage longer problems:

- Get a global or overall understanding of the problem you are solving.
- Make a prediction or estimate of the solution.
- Get a global or overall understanding of the process you are using to solve the problem.
- List in your own words (as briefly as possible) the steps of the process.
- Focus on one step at a time.
- Examine the solution to see if it matches your prediction or estimate.

Figure 15-4 Vertical Analysis of Sander's Woodworks Balance Sheet

Sander's Woodworks
Balance Sheet
December 31, 2001

	Amount	Percent
Assets		
Current assets		
Cash	$1,973	4.8
Accounts receivable	2,118	5.1
Merchandise inventory	18,476	44.9
Total current assets	22,567	54.8
Plant and equipment		
Equipment	18,591	45.2
Total plant and equipment	18,591	45.2
Total assets	$41,158	100.0
Liabilities		
Current liabilities		
Accounts payable	2,317	5.6
Wages payable	684	1.7
Total current liabilities	3,001	7.3
Long-term liabilities		
Mortgage note payable	15,286	37.1
Total long-term liabilities	15,286	37.1
Total liabilities	18,287	44.4
Owner's Equity		
J. Sander's capital	22,871	55.6
Total liabilities and owner's equity	$41,158	100.0

 TIP! Checking Calculations

The percent values for all the assets should add up to 100%. The percent values for all the liabilities plus the percent value for the owner's equity should add up to 100%. Minor discrepancies may occur due to rounding.

 **Use Memory Function to Enter a Value Used in Several Calculations**

Since each item on the balance sheet is divided by the total assets, the memory of a calculator can be used to facilitate the calculation.

$\boxed{\text{AC}}$ 41158 $\boxed{\text{M}^+}$ Enter total assets into memory.
Clear display. Do not clear memory.

Enter the first amount:

$\boxed{\text{CE/C}}$ 1973 $\boxed{\div}$ $\boxed{\text{MRC}}$ $\boxed{\%}$ $\Rightarrow$ 4.79372

Enter second amount:

$\boxed{\text{CE/C}}$ 2118 $\boxed{\div}$ $\boxed{\text{MRC}}$ $\boxed{\%}$ $\Rightarrow$ 5.14602

Continue with each amount.

TIP! Watch the Base!

Be careful to use the total assets as the base when figuring each percent. Look what happens to the percent for *Wages payable* in Figure 15-4 if the total liabilities is used for the base instead of total assets:

$$R = \frac{P}{B} = \frac{\text{wages payable}}{\text{total assets}} \qquad\qquad R = \frac{P}{B} = \frac{\text{wages payable}}{\text{total liabilities}}$$

$$= \frac{\$684}{\$41,158} = 0.0166189, \text{ or } 1.7\% \qquad = \frac{\$684}{\$18,287} = 0.0374036, \text{ or } 3.7\%$$

CORRECT   **INCORRECT**

Comparing balance sheets from two years may reveal important trends in a business's operations. Such a **comparative balance sheet** can be seen in Figure 15-5. Note that data for the most recent year are entered in the first columns.

Figure 15-5 Vertical Analysis of Sander's Woodworks Comparative Balance Sheet

Sander's Woodworks
Comparative Balance Sheet
December 31, 2001 and 2002

	2002		2001	
	Amount	**Percent**	**Amount**	**Percent**
Assets				
Current assets				
Cash	$2,184	5.7	$1,973	4.8
Accounts receivable	4,308	11.3	2,118	5.1
Merchandise inventory	17,317	45.6	18,476	44.9
Total current assets	23,809	62.6	22,567	54.8
Plant and equipment				
Equipment	14,203	37.4	18,591	45.2
Total plant and equipment	14,203	37.4	18,591	45.2
Total assets	$38,012	100.0	$41,158	100.0
Liabilities				
Current liabilities				
Accounts payable	1,647	4.3	2,317	5.6
Wages payable	894	2.4	684	1.7
Total current liabilities	2,541	6.7	3,001	7.3
Long-term liabilities				
Mortgage note payable	12,715	33.4	15,286	37.1
Total long-term liabilities	12,715	33.4	15,286	37.1
Total liabilities	15,256	40.1	18,287	44.4
Owner's Equity				
J. Sander's capital	22,756	59.9	22,871	55.6
Total liabilities and owner's equity	$38,012	100.0	$41,158	100.0

3 **Prepare a horizontal analysis of a balance sheet.**

Another way to analyze information on a comparative balance sheet is to compare item by item in a **horizontal analysis.** While a vertical analysis compares each item to total assets, a horizontal analysis compares the same item for two different years, recording both the amount of increase (or decrease), and the increase (or decrease) as a percent of the earlier year's amount.

HOW TO Prepare a Horizontal Analysis of a Comparative Balance Sheet

1. Prepare a balance sheet for two or more years: record each year's amounts in separate columns.
2. Create an additional column labeled *amount of increase (decrease):* for each yearly item,
   (a) Subtract the smaller amount from the larger amount and record the difference.
   (b) If the earlier year's amount is larger than the more recent year's amount, record the difference from step 2a as a decrease by using parentheses or a negative (minus) sign.
3. Create an additional column labeled *percent increase (decrease):* for each yearly item, divide the amount of increase (decrease) by the earlier year's amount and record the difference as a percent.

$$\text{Percent increase (decrease)} = \frac{\text{amount of increase (decrease)}}{\text{earlier year's amount}} \times 100\%$$

EXAMPLE   Prepare a horizontal analysis for Sander's Woodworks using the yearly amounts in Figure 15-5.

Cash: $2,184 − $1,973 = $211 (increase)

$211 ÷ $1,973 = 0.106944 × 100% = 10.7% (increase)

Accounts receivable: $4,308 − $2,118 = $2,190 (increase)

$2,190 ÷ $2,118 = 1.033994 = 103.4% (increase)

Inventory: $18,476 − $17,317 = $1,159 (decrease)

$1,159 ÷ $18,476 = 0.062730 = 6.3% (decrease)

Equipment: $18,591 − $14,203 = $4,388 (decrease)

$4,388 ÷ $18,591 = 0.236028 = 23.6% (decrease)

Total assets: $41,158 − $38,012 = $3,146 (decrease)

$3,146 ÷ $41,158 = 0.076437 = 7.6% (decrease)

Accounts payable: $2,317 − $1,647 = $670 (decrease)

$670 ÷ $2,317 = 0.289167 = 28.9% (decrease)

Salaries payable: $894 − $684 = $210 (increase)

$210 ÷ $684 = 0.307018 = 30.7% (increase)

Mortgage note payable: $15,286 − $12,715 = $2,571 (decrease)

$2,571 ÷ $15,286 = 0.168193 = 16.8% (decrease)

Total liabilities: $18,287 − $15,256 = $3,031 (decrease)

$3,031 ÷ $18,287 = 0.165746 = 16.6% (decrease)

J. Sander's Capital: $22,871 − $22,756 = $115 (decrease)

$115 ÷ $22,871 = 0.0050282 = 0.5% (decrease)

Total liabilities and owner's equity:

$$\boxed{\$41{,}158} - \$38{,}012 = \boxed{\$3{,}146} \text{ (decrease)}$$
$$\$3{,}146 \div \boxed{\$41{,}158} = 0.0764371 = \boxed{7.6\%} \text{ (decrease)}$$

If the horizontal analysis has been made properly, the amount of change for any *total* should equal the sum of the increases minus all decreases in the category. Also, the total liabilities and owner's equity amount of change should equal the total assets amount of change. The percent of change for the total is *not* the sum of the percents of increases and the difference of percents of decreases. This is because the base is different for each entry.

Figure 15-6 Horizontal Analysis of Sander's Woodworks Comparative Balance Sheet

			Sander's Woodworks Comparative Balance Sheet December 31, 2001, and 2002	
			Increase (Decrease)*	
	2002	**2001**	**Amount**	**Percent**
Assets				
Cash	$2,184	$1,973	$ 211	10.7
Accounts receivable	4,308	2,118	2,190	103.4
Inventory	17,317	18,476	(1,159)	(6.3)
Equipment	14,203	18,591	(4,388)	(23.6)
Total assets	$38,012	$41,158	($3,146)	(7.6)
Liabilities				
Accounts payable	1,647	2,317	(670)	(28.9)
Wages payable	894	684	210	30.7
Mortgage note payable	12,715	15,286	(2,571)	(16.8)
Total liabilities	15,256	18,287	(3,031)	(16.6)
Owner's Equity				
J. Sander's capital	22,756	22,871	(115)	(0.5)
Total liabilities and owner's equity	$38,012	$41,158	($3,146)	(7.6)

*Parentheses indicate decrease.

 TIP! **Which Year Is the Base in the Percent of Increase?**

In a horizontal analysis, the *earlier* year is always the base year in calculating percent increase or decrease. It is possible to have a 0% change if there is no dollar change in the amounts.

 Working with Decreases and Negative Values

If the most recent year is *always* entered first, a decrease is indicated in the calculator display with a minus sign.

$$17317 \boxed{-} 18476 \boxed{=} \Rightarrow -1159$$

To find percent decrease, do not clear the calculator. The percent decrease will also be a negative value.

$$\boxed{\div} 18476 \boxed{=} \boxed{\times} 100 \boxed{=} \Rightarrow -6.2730 \text{ or } -6.3\%$$

1. Prepare a balance sheet for Miss Muffins' Bakery for December 31, 2002. The company assets are: cash, $1,985; accounts receivable, $4,219; merchandise inventory, $2,512. The liabilities are: accounts payable, $3,483; wages payable, $1,696. The owner's capital is $3,537.

2. Expand the balance sheet for exercise 1 to include figures for 2001. The company assets are: cash, $1,762; accounts receivable, $3,785; merchandise inventory, $2,036. The liabilities are: accounts payable, $3,631; wages payable, $1,421. The owner's capital is $2,531.

3. Prepare the balance sheet for O'Dell's Nursery for December 31, 2002. The company assets are: cash $8,917; accounts receivable, $7,521; merchandise inventory, $17,826. The liabilities are: accounts payable, $10,215; wages payable, $3,716. The owner's capital is $20,333.

4. Expand the balance sheet for exercise 3 for 2001. The company assets are: cash $12,842; accounts receivable, $5,836; merchandise inventory, $18,917. The liabilities are: accounts payable, $8,968; wages payable, $2,582. The owner's capital is $26,045.

5. Complete the vertical analyses on the comparative balance sheet for Miss Muffins' Bakery for 2002. (Use parentheses to indicate decreases.)

6. Complete the vertical analyses on the comparative balance sheet for Miss Muffins' Bakery for 2002.

7. Complete the vertical analyses on the comparative balance sheet for O'Dell's Nursery for 2002.

8. Complete the vertical analyses on the comparative balance sheet for O'Dell's Nursery for 2002.

3

9. Complete the horizontal analyses showing differences in dollar amounts on the comparative balance sheet for Miss Muffins' Bakery.

10. Complete the horizontal analyses showing percent increases (decreases) on the comparative balance sheet for Miss Muffins' Bakery.

11. Complete the horizontal analyses showing differences in dollar amounts on the comparative balance sheet for O'Dell's Nursery.

12. Complete the horizontal analyses showing percent increases (decreases) on the comparative balance sheet for O'Dell's Nursery.

15.2 Income Statements

1 Prepare an income statement.

2 Prepare a vertical analysis of an income statement.

3 Prepare a horizontal analysis of an income statement.

Another important financial statement, the **income statement,** shows the net income of a business *over a period of time.* (Remember, the balance sheet shows the financial condition of a business at a specific time.)

Among the many terms on an income statement are the following:

Total Sales	Earnings from the sale of goods or the performance of services
Sales returns or allowances	Refunds or adjustments for unsatisfactory merchandise or services

Net sales	The difference between the total sales and the sales returns or allowances
Cost of goods sold	Cost to the business for merchandise or goods sold
Gross profit or **Gross margin**	The difference between the net sales and the cost of goods sold
Operating expenses	The overhead or cost incurred in operating the business. Examples of operating expenses are utilities, rent, insurance, permits, taxes, and employees' salaries.
Net income or **net profit**	The difference between the gross profit (gross margin) and the operating expenses

1 Prepare an income statement.

Calculating the cost of goods sold is an important part of preparing an income statement. Reviewing some of the concepts in Chapter 14, the cost of goods sold is the difference of the cost of goods available for sale and the cost of ending inventory. The cost of goods available for sale is the cost of the beginning inventory plus the cost of purchases. There are various ways to find the cost of ending inventory.

Important relationships pertaining to the income statement are summarized below.

> Net sales = total sales − sales returns and allowances
>
> Cost of goods sold = cost of beginning inventory + cost of purchases
> − cost of ending inventory
>
> Gross profit = net sales − cost of goods sold
>
> Net income = gross profit − operating expenses

HOW TO Prepare an Income Statement

1. Find and record *net sales*.
   - **(a)** Record *gross sales*.
   - **(b)** Record *sales returns and allowances*.
   - **(c)** Subtract sales returns and allowances from gross sales.

     Net sales = gross sales − sales returns and allowances

2. Find and record *cost of goods sold*.
   - **(a)** Record cost of beginning inventory.
   - **(b)** Record cost of purchases.
   - **(c)** Record cost of ending inventory.
   - **(d)** Add cost of beginning inventory and cost of purchases and subtract cost of ending inventory.

     Cost of goods sold = cost of beginning inventory
     + cost of purchases − cost of ending inventory

3. Find and record *gross profit from sales:* subtract cost of goods sold from net sales.

     Gross profit from sales = net sales − cost of goods sold

4. Find and record *total operating expenses:* list the operating expenses and add the entries.

5. Find and record *net income:* subtract the operating expenses from the gross profit.

     Net income = gross profit from sales − operating expenses

EXAMPLE Complete the portion of the income statement shown for the Corner Grocery using the given information.

Gross sales: $25,283; returns and allowances: $492; cost of beginning inventory: $5,384; cost of purchases: $18,923; cost of ending inventory: $5,557; total operating expenses: $3,750

Net sales = gross sales − returns and allowances
$$= \$25,283 - \$492$$
$$= \$24,791$$

Cost of goods sold = cost of beginning inventory + cost of purchases
− cost of ending inventory
$$= \$5,384 + \$18,923 - \$5,557$$
$$= \$18,750$$

Gross profit = net sales − cost of goods sold
$$= \$24,791 - \$18,750$$
$$= \$6,041$$

Net income = gross profit − operating expenses
$$= \$6,041 - \$3,750$$
$$= \$2,291$$

The completed income statement is shown in Figure 15-7.

Corner Grocery Income Statement for the Month Ending June 30, 2002	
Net sales	$24,791
Cost of goods sold	18,750
Gross profit	6,041
Operating expenses	3,750
Net income	$2,291

Figure 15-7 Income Statement for Corner Grocery

 **2** Prepare a vertical analysis of an income statement.

Just as you do with a vertical analysis of a balance sheet, to make a **vertical analysis of an income statement** you use the percentage formula $R = \frac{P}{B}$, in which each entry on the income statement is a percentage P, net sales is the base B, and their ratio R is expressed as a percent.

> **TIP!** **What Is the Base on a Vertical Analysis of an Income Statement?**
>
> Income statements, like balance sheets, can be examined using a vertical analysis format. As with balance sheets, each item on the income statement is expressed as a percent of a base figure. For income statements, *net sales is the base.*

1. Prepare an income statement.
2. Create an additional column labeled *percent of net sales:* for each item, divide the amount of the item by the net sales and record the result as a percent.

$$\text{Percent of net sales} = \frac{\text{amount of item}}{\text{net sales}} \times 100\%$$

EXAMPLE   Figure 15-8 is an income statement for Pearson's Gift Shop. Complete a vertical analysis of the statement.

Pearson's Gift Shop
Income Statement
for the Year Ending December 31, 2002

Gross sales	$246,891
Sales returns and allowances	7,835
Net sales	239,056
Cost of beginning inventory, January 1, 2002	8,247
Cost of purchases	148,542
Less: cost of ending inventory, December 31, 2002	9,583
Cost of goods sold	147,206
Gross profit from sales	91,850
Salary	18,500
Insurance	5,700
Utilities	1,900
Maintenance	280
Rent	6,000
Depreciation	1,500
Total operating expenses	33,880
Net income	$57,970

Figure 15-8   Pearson's Income Statement

For each item, divide the amount by the net sales and record the result as a percent. For instance,

Gross sales: $\dfrac{\text{gross sales}}{\text{net sales}} \times 100\% = \dfrac{\$246{,}891}{\$239{,}056} \times 100\% = 1.03277 \times 100\% = 103.3\%$

The completed vertical analysis is shown in Figure 15-9.

Pearson's Gift Shop
Income Statement
for the Year Ending December 31, 2002

	Amount	Percent of Net Sales
Revenue		
Gross sales	$246,891	103.3
Sales returns and allowances	7,835	3.3
Net sales	239,056	100.0
Cost of goods sold		
Beginning inventory, January 1, 2002	8,247	3.4
Purchases	148,542	62.1
Less: ending inventory, December 31, 2002	9,583	4.0
Cost of goods sold	147,206	61.6
Gross profit from sales	91,850	38.4
Operating expenses		
Salary	18,500	7.7
Insurance	5,700	2.4
Utilities	1,900	0.8
Maintenance	280	0.1
Rent	6,000	2.5
Depreciation	1,500	0.6
Total operating expenses	33,880	14.2
Net income	$57,970	24.2

Figure 15-9 Vertical Analysis of Pearson's Gift Shop's Income Statement

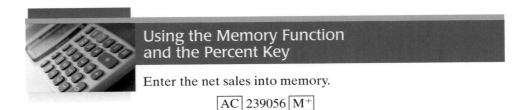

Using the Memory Function and the Percent Key

Enter the net sales into memory.

$$\boxed{AC}\ 239056\ \boxed{M^+}$$

Divide each entry by net sales and use the percent key.

$$\boxed{CE/C}\ 246891\ \boxed{\div}\ \boxed{MRC}\ \boxed{\%} \Rightarrow 103.27747$$

$$\boxed{CE/C}\ 7835\ \boxed{\div}\ \boxed{MRC}\ \boxed{\%} \Rightarrow 3.27747$$

Continue by dividing each item by the net sales, which is stored in memory.

An income statement can also contain information for more than one year. Figure 15-10 shows a vertical analysis of a comparative income statement.

Davis Company
Comparative Income Statement
for the Years Ending June 30, 2002 and 2003

	2003		2002	
	Amount	**Percent of Net Sales**	**Amount**	**Percent of Net Sales**
Net sales	$242,897	100.0	$239,528	100.0
Cost of goods sold	116,582	48.0	115,351	48.2
Gross profit	126,315	52.0	124,177	51.8
Operating expenses	38,725	15.9	37,982	15.9
Net income	$87,590	36.1	$86,195	36.0

Figure 15-10   Vertical Analysis of the Davis Company's Comparative Income Statement

3 Prepare a horizontal analysis of an income statement.

The horizontal analysis of an income statement is similar to the horizontal analysis of a balance sheet. Items on the statement are compared for more than one period. A **comparative income statement** is used for displaying more than one income period. The **horizontal analysis of an income statement** examines the increase or decrease of an item from one period to another.

HOW TO Prepare a Horizontal Analysis of a Comparative Income Statement

1. Prepare an income statement for two or more years: record each year's amounts in separate columns.

2. Create an additional column labeled *amount of increase (decrease):* for each yearly item:

   (a) Subtract the smaller amount from the larger amount and record the difference.

   (b) If the earlier year's amount is larger than the later year's amount, record the difference from step 2a as a decrease by using parentheses.

3. Create an additional column labeled *percent increase (decrease):* for each yearly item, divide the amount of increase (decrease) by the earlier year's amount and record the difference as a percent.

$$\text{Percent increase (decrease)} = \frac{\text{amount of increase (decrease)}}{\text{earlier year's amount}} \times 100\%$$

EXAMPLE   Prepare a horizontal analysis for the Davis Company using the yearly amounts in Figure 15-10.

For each item, find the amount of increase or decrease by subtracting the earlier year's amount from the later year's amount. For the Davis Company, the later year's amounts are all larger than the earlier year's amounts, so the difference of each amount is recorded as an increase in every case.

Next, find the percent increase by dividing the amount of increase by the earlier year's amount. For instance,

$$\text{Percent increase in net sales} = \frac{\text{amount of increase}}{2002\ \text{amount}}$$

$$= \frac{\$242,897 - \$239,528}{\$239,528}$$

$$= \frac{\$3,369}{\$239,528}$$

$$= 1.4\%$$

The completed analysis is shown in Figure 15-11.

Davis Company
Comparative Income Statement
for the Years Ending June 30, 2002 and 2003

			Increase (Decrease)	
	2003	2002	Amount	Percent of net sales
Net sales	$242,897	$239,528	$3,369	1.4
Cost of goods sold	116,582	115,351	1,231	1.1
Gross profit	126,315	124,177	2,138	1.7
Operating expenses	38,725	37,982	743	2.0
Net income	$87,590	$86,195	$1,395	1.6

Figure 15-11   Horizontal Analysis of the Davis Company's Comparative Income Statement

SELF-CHECK 15.2

1. Complete the income statement for Sitha Ros' Oriental Groceries for the years 2001 and 2002.

Sitha Ros' Oriental Groceries
Income Statement
for the Years Ending June 30, 2001 and 2002

			Increase (Decrease)	
	2002	2001	Amount	Percent of Net Sales
Net sales	$97,384	$92,196		
Cost of goods sold	82,157	72,894		
Gross profit				
Operating expenses	4,783	3,951		
Net income				

2. Complete the portion for July 31, 2001 of the income statement shown for Miss Muffins' Bakery using the given information: gross sales, $32,596; returns and allowances, $296; cost of beginning inventory, $16,872; cost of purchases, $33,596; cost of ending inventory, $21,843; total operating expenses, $1,894.

Miss Muffins' Bakery
Comparative Income Statement
for the Months Ending
July 31, 2001 and July 31, 2002

	2002	2001	Increase (Decrease)	
			Amount	Percent
Net sales				
Cost of goods sold				
Gross profit				
Operating expenses				
Net income				

3. Miss Muffins' Bakery recorded financial information for the month ending July 31, 2002. Use the information to extend the income statement for exercise 2: gross sales, $35,403; returns and allowances, $342; cost of beginning inventory, $17,403; cost of purchases, $27,983; cost of ending inventory, $22,583; total operating expenses, $3,053.

4. Extend the income statement for Sitha Ros' Oriental Groceries to include a vertical analysis for 2001 and for 2002.

5. Extend the income statement for Miss Muffins' Bakery to include a vertical analysis for 2001 and 2002.

6. Extend the income statements for Sitha Ros' Oriental Groceries to include the amounts of increase or decrease and the percents of increase or decrease for a horizontal analysis.

7. Extend the income statement for Miss Muffins' Bakery to include the amounts of increase or decrease and the percents of increase or decrease for a horizontal analysis.

15.3 Financial Statement Ratios

 Find and use financial ratios.

Financial statements organize and summarize information about the financial condition of a business. Using information from financial statements, **financial ratios** give businesses a way to evaluate their business compared to their past performance and to other businesses. Financial ratios are used by lending institutions and stockholders to determine the financial well-being of a business.

 Find and use financial ratios.

Current Ratio It is important to know whether a business has enough assets to cover its liabilities. The **working capital** of a business is the current assets minus current liabilities. But that amount alone does not tell much about the relative financial condition of the business: Look at the following information about Aaron's Air Conditioning and Zelda's Zeppelins:

	Aaron's Air Conditioning	Zelda's Zeppelins
Current assets	$11,000	$615,000
Current liabilities	− 5,000	− 609,000
Working capital	$6,000	$6,000

$$\text{Working capital} = \text{current assets} - \text{current liabilities}$$

Both companies have the same working capital, but Zelda's *owes* almost as much as it *owns*. To compare these companies, we need to use ratios. A commonly used ratio in business is the **current ratio** (also called the **working capital ratio**), which is the ratio of current assets to current liabilities.

$$\text{Current ratio} = \frac{\text{current assets}}{\text{current liabilities}}$$

The current ratio for Aaron's Air Conditioning, for example, is the ratio of $11,000 to $5,000.

$$\text{Aaron's' current ratio} = \frac{\text{Aaron's' current assets}}{\text{Aaron's' current liabilities}} = \frac{\$11,000}{\$5,000}$$

This ratio expresses the fact that Aaron's has $11,000 in current assets for $5,000 of current liabilities. If we write this ratio in decimal form, we have an equivalent ratio whose denominator is 1:

$$\frac{\$11,000}{\$5,000} = 2.2 = \frac{2.2}{1}$$

Thus Aaron's' current ratio is 2.2 to 1, telling us that Aaron's has $2.20 in current assets for every $1 in current liabilities.

The current ratio for Zelda's Zeppelins is the ratio of $615,000 to $609,000. Writing Zelda's' current ratio in decimal form, we are able to see the usefulness of current ratio as a way of comparing businesses.

$$\text{Zelda's' current ratio} = \frac{\text{Zelda's' current assets}}{\text{Zelda's' current liabilities}} = \frac{\$615,000}{\$609,000} = 1.01 = \frac{1.01}{1}$$

This ratio tells us that Zelda's has $1.01 in current assets for every $1 in current liabilities. Since Aaron's' ratio is 2.2 to 1, we see that for every $1 of current liability, Aaron's has more than twice as much in current assets as does Zelda's. There are many financial ratios we might calculate, but the basic process is the same for all.

? HOW TO Find a Financial Ratio

1. Write one amount as the numerator of a fraction and a second amount as the denominator.

2. Write the fraction in decimal form (or, for some ratios, in percent form).

EXAMPLE   Find the current ratio of a business whose current assets are $18,000 and whose current liabilities are $12,000.

Write the ratio of current assets to current liabilities in decimal form.

$$\text{Current ratio} = \frac{\text{current assets}}{\text{current liabilities}} = \frac{\$18,000}{\$12,000} = 1.5$$

The current ratio is 1.5, or 1.5 to 1.

Many lending companies consider a current ratio of 2 to 1 (2:1) to be the minimum acceptable current ratio for approving a loan to a business. The business in the preceding example, for instance, may find it difficult to get a loan because its current ratio is 1.5.

Acid-Test Ratio.   Another ratio used to evaluate the financial condition of a business is the **acid-test ratio,** sometimes called the **quick ratio.** Instead of using all of the current assets of a business, the acid-test ratio uses only the **quick current assets,** those assets that can be readily exchanged for cash: marketable securities, accounts receivable, and notes receivable. Merchandise inventory is a current asset but it is not included because a loss would probably occur if a business were to make a quick sale of all merchandise.

$$\text{Acid-test ratio (quick ratio)} = \frac{\text{quick current assets}}{\text{current liabilities}}$$

EXAMPLE   Find the acid-test ratio if the balance sheet shows the following amounts:

Cash = $17,342

Marketable securities = $0

Receivables = $10,345

Current liabilities = $26,345

$$\text{Acid-test ratio} = \frac{\$17,342 + \$10,345}{\$26,345} = \frac{\$27,687}{\$26,345} = 1.05 \text{ (nearest hundredth)}$$

The acid-test ratio is 1.05 to 1.

If the acid-test ratio is 1:1, the business is in a satisfactory financial condition and has the ability to meet its obligations. If the ratio is significantly *less* than 1:1 (such as 0.85:1), the business is in poor financial condition; and if the ratio is significantly *more* than 1:1 (such as 1.15:1), the business is in good financial condition.

Ratios to Net Sales.   Other useful ratios can be determined from an income statement. Two of the most important are the *operating ratio* and the *gross profit margin ratio.* These two are also called **ratios to net sales.** These ratios make comparisons possible between the major elements of the statement and net sales. These ratios are usually expressed in percent form, rather than decimal form, and they usually (but do not necessarily) cover one year.

Remember, the first amount in a ratio appears in the numerator and the second amount appears in the denominator. In both of the ratios to net sales, the denominator is the net sales.

The **operating ratio** indicates the amount of sales dollars that are used to pay for the cost of goods and administrative expenses. A ratio of less than 1:1 is desirable. The lower the operating ratio, the more income there is to meet financial obligations.

$$\text{Operating ratio} = \frac{\text{cost of goods sold} + \text{operating expenses}}{\text{net sales}}$$

The **gross profit margin ratio** shows the average spread between cost of goods sold and the selling price. The desirable gross profit margin ratio varies with the type of business. For example, a jewelry store might expect to have a ratio of 0.6 to 1 because there is a high rate of markup in jewelry. An auto parts store may, however, have a ratio of 0.25 to 1.

$$\text{Gross profit margin ratio} = \frac{\text{gross profit from sales}}{\text{net sales}}$$

$$= \frac{\text{net sales} - \text{cost of goods sold}}{\text{net sales}}$$

EXAMPLE Based on the income statement in Figure 15-12, find the operating ratio and the gross profit margin ratio for Vincent's Gift Shop. Express results in percent form, rounded to the nearest tenth of a percent.

Vincent's Gift Shop Income Statement for the Year Ending December 31, 2002	
Net sales	$173,157
Cost of beginning inventory	37,376
Cost of purchases	123,574
Cost of goods available for sale	160,950
Cost of ending inventory	34,579
Cost of goods sold	126,371
Gross profit	46,786
Operating expenses	17,643
Net income	$29,143

Figure 15-12   Income Statement for Vincent's Gift Shop

$$\text{Operating ratio} = \frac{\text{cost of goods sold} + \text{operating expenses}}{\text{net sales}}$$

$$= \frac{\$126,371 + \$17,643}{\$173,157}$$

$$= 0.831696 \text{ or } 83.2\%$$

The operating ratio is 0.832 to 1 or 83.2%.

$$\text{Gross profit margin ratio} = \frac{\text{net sales} - \text{cost of goods sold}}{\text{net sales}}$$

$$= \frac{\$173,157 - \$126,371}{\$173,157}$$

$$= 0.270194 \text{ or } 27.0\%.$$

The gross profit margin ratio is 0.270 to 1 or 27.0%.

Other Financial Ratios.   Many other comparisons of data are found on the balance sheet, income statement, or other financial documents that are useful in analyzing various aspects of the business. For instance, the **asset turnover ratio** compares the net sales to the average total assets. This comparison shows the average return in sales for each $1 invested in assets. The **total debt to total assets ratio** compares the total liabilities to the total assets. This comparison shows total indebtedness of the company for each $1 in assets.

The calculations for determining these ratios are the same as for determining any ratio. The amount in the numerator is divided by the amount in the denominator to give a decimal equivalent. This decimal equivalent can be interpreted as a comparison of the decimal equivalent to 1 or it can be interpreted as a percent by multiplying the decimal equivalent by 100%.

$$\text{Asset turnover ratio} = \frac{\text{net sales}}{\text{average total assets}}$$

$$\text{Debt ratio} = \frac{\text{total liabilities}}{\text{total assets}}$$

Interpreting Financial Ratios. A business needs to track its own progress over several periods of time to compare its results to industry standards. A business uses financial ratios for internal decision making or to distribute to stockholders, banks, and prospective investors or buyers to show the financial status of the business. In Table 15-1 you will see some possible interpretations of financial ratios. Keep in mind, just as one statistic does not give a total picture, one ratio does not give a complete profile of a business's financial status.

EXAMPLE Arsella would like to apply for a loan to expand Vincent's Gift Shop. The business's current assets are $58,482 and total liabilities are $32,289. Other information about the business can be found in the preceding example. Analyze the financial condition of the business using information given in Table 15-1. Should Arsella plan to expand the business at this time?

1 Decision needed Should Arsella expand the business at this time?

2 Known facts Total assets: $58,482
Total liabilities: $32,289
Ending inventory: $34,579
Net sales: $173,157
Operating expenses: $17,643
Cost of goods sold: $126,371

3 Unknown facts Current ratio
Acid-test ratio
Operating ratio
Gross profit margin ratio
Asset turnover ratio
Total debt to total assets ratio

4 Relationships See Table 15-1.

5 Estimation Not appropriate for this problem.

6 Calculation $$\text{Current ratio} = \frac{\text{current assets}}{\text{current liabilities}} = \frac{\$58,482}{\$32,289} = 1.81$$

$$\text{Acid-test ratio} = \frac{\text{quick current assets}}{\text{current liabilities}} = \frac{\$58,482 - \$34,579}{\$32,289} = 0.74$$

$$\text{Operating ratio} = \frac{\text{COGS} + \text{operating expenses}}{\text{net sales}} = \frac{\$126,371 + \$17,743}{\$173,157} = 0.83$$

$$\text{Gross profit margin ratio} = \frac{\text{gross profit from sales}}{\text{net sales}} = \frac{\text{net sales} - \text{COGS}}{\text{net sales}}$$

$$= \frac{\$173,157 - \$126,371}{\$173,157} = 0.27$$

$$\text{Asset turnover ratio} = \frac{\text{net sales}}{\text{total assets}} = \frac{\$173,157}{\$58,482} = 2.96$$

$$\text{Total debt to total assets ratio} = \frac{\text{total debts}}{\text{total assets}} = \frac{\$32,289}{\$58,482} = 0.55$$

7 Interpretation

The current ratio, operating ratio, gross profit margin ratio, and total debt to total assets ratio demonstrate a business with a healthy financial status. The acid-test ratio may indicate a potential cash flow problem, but the extremely high asset turnover ratio shows that inventory can be quickly turned into cash.

8 Decision made

This is an acceptable time to expand the business.

Table 15-1 Financial Ratio Analysis

Ratio	Value less than 1	Value = 1	Value more than 1
Current ratio = $\dfrac{\text{current assets}}{\text{current liabilities}}$	Debts greater than assets; potentially major problems	Debts and assets are equal	Assets greater than debts; current ratio of 2 is desirable.
Acid-test ratio = $\dfrac{\text{quick current assets}}{\text{current liabilities}}$	Cash flow could be a problem	Business is in satisfactory condition	Business is in good financial condition
Operating ratio = $\dfrac{\text{COGS + oper. expenses}}{\text{net sales}}$	Desirable	Marginal	Undesirable
Gross profit margin ratio = $\dfrac{\text{gross profit from sales}}{\text{net sales}}$	0.25 to 0.40 is industry average	Uncommon except for businesses with low turnover and high investment	Undesirable
Asset turnover ratio = $\dfrac{\text{net sales}}{\text{average total assets}}$	0.04 to 1.0 is industry average	Uncommon	Uncommon
Debt ratio = $\dfrac{\text{total liabilities}}{\text{total assets}}$	0.05 to 0.75 is industry average	Debt ratio is too high	Debt ratio is dangerously high

SELF-CHECK 15.3

1. Find the current ratio for George's business and the current ratio for José's business, given the following information:

	George	José
Current assets	$28,000	$840,000
Current liabilities	−$ 7,000	−$819,000
Working capital	$21,000	$ 21,000

2. Find the acid-test ratio if the balance sheet shows the following amounts: cash, $32,981; receivables, $12,045; marketable securities, $0; current liabilities, $22,178.

3. Find the operating ratio for Sol's Dry Goods if the income statement for the month shows net sales, $15,500; cost of goods sold, $7,500; gross profit, $8,000; operating expenses, $3,500; net income, $4,500. Express results to the nearest tenth of a percent.

4. Find the gross profit margin ratio for Sol's Dry Goods in exercise 3 to the nearest tenth of a percent.

New Homes Inventory Turnover Ratio

The inventory turnover ratio, the ratio of inventory to sales, is important to an individual business and to its entire industry because it can be used to predict supply and demand, growth and decline, price increases and decreases, as well as other related markers.

The U.S. Commerce Department recently discovered an anomaly in the turnover ratio of new homes. The new home turnover ratio was about 6:1, meaning that for every new home sold, there were six completed unsold new homes. Now, this ratio has dropped to about 4:1, a level not seen since the recession of the early 1970s. Since new homes had sold very well during this two-year period, it appeared that the number of new single-family housing starts had decreased significantly (to account for the lowered ratio). The Commerce Department wondered if fewer housing starts (reduced supply) would lead to escalating housing prices, which in turn would cause explosive growth (increased demand) in the new home construction industry. The related mortgage banking industry would also be affected by higher mortgage interest rates as buyers compete for loan funds.

Economists' investigations have indicated that this would not occur due to several factors. First, changes in financing and sales practices have increased the number of new homes that are sold before they are built or completed. Less than 30% of new homes sold in a recent time period were ready to be occupied. Buying a house before it is completed gives the buyer the opportunity to select many, if not all, features such as floor plan, carpet, wallpaper, lighting fixtures, appliances, paint, and so forth. The vast majority of new home buyers today prefer to have as much input as possible into the design and decoration of their house; this is a new home's main selling point. Prior to 1995, most new home buyers did not get their mortgage loan approved until the house was completed and inspected. Builders were reluctant to customize houses prior to closing, so most new homes were completed before they were sold. Today buyers and builders are easily prequalified for mortgage loans, allowing most new homes to be sold before completion.

A second factor in the lower turnover ratio was discovered as the Commerce Department reviewed and revised its data-collection methods. They learned that they had been overestimating new home inventories and underestimating new home sales for years! This suggests that the current low ratios are probably not out of line with historical norms. In other words, today's apparently low new home inventories do not reflect a radical imbalance between supply and demand that could cause prices to explode and touch off a large building surge. The National Association of Home Builders believes that today's housing industry can operate very well with leaner stocks of unsold new homes, and expects only moderate increases in housing starts and prices in the near future.

Exercises

Use the above information to answer the following:

1. What percent of new home buyers purchase their home before completion?
2. Give at least two reasons builders are reluctant to customize new homes before closing.
3. Would an individual builder like a higher or lower new home inventory turnover ratio, and why?
4. What would a sudden significantly lower new homes turnover ratio mean to an individual builder who knows that prior ratios were calculated correctly? Give two scenarios and the builder's recourse that could return the ratio to its previous level.

5. What would a sudden significantly higher new homes turnover ratio mean to an individual builder who knows that prior ratios were calculated correctly?

6. What would a sudden significantly higher new homes turnover ratio mean to the home construction and mortgage banking industries?

Answers

1. About 70% (100% − 30%) purchase their new home before completion.

2. Builders may find it hard to sell a customized house to another customer (if the deal falls through) due to either unorthodox custom treatment selections or to very expensive customization, which raises the house price significantly higher than those in its neighborhood. (Answers may vary.)

3. Since builders make money selling their houses at a profit, they typically want the lowest inventory turnover ratio possible. If this ratio is too high, the builder loses money paying construction loans on the unsold completed houses.

4. Either the builder has recently decreased new housing starts while new home sales remained stable, or new home sales increased while new housing starts remained stable. The builder could raise the ratio in both scenarios by increasing new housing starts, which would give buyers more of a selection. The builder would not want to raise the ratio by decreasing new home sales!

5. Either the builder has recently increased new housing starts while new home sales remained stable, or new home sales decreased while new housing starts remained stable. The builder could raise the ratio in both scenarios by halting new housing starts or by increasing new home sales (by new marketing techniques, lowering prices, etc.).

6. A higher inventory turnover could be caused either by an increase in housing starts or a decrease in new home sales. Regardless of the reasons, this lowered ratio could mean a halt to housing starts, which could raise housing prices of new and previously owned homes as buyers compete for fewer houses. A lowered ratio could cause mortgage interest rates to fall, in an effort to boost both the home construction and mortgage banking industries.

Section 15.1

Prepare a
balance
sheet.
(page 612)

1. Find and record the *total assets.* Balance sheets may be prepared by asset category.
   (a) List the *current assets* and draw a single line underneath the last entry.
   (b) Add the entries and record the *total current assets,* drawing a single line underneath the total.
   (c) Repeat step 1a for *plant and equipment assets* and step 1b for *total plant and equipment assets.*
   (d) Add the category totals and draw a double line underneath the grand total.

Total assets = total current assets + total plant and equipment

2. Find and record the *total liabilities.* Balance sheets may be prepared by liability category.
   (a) Repeat step 1a for *current liabilities* and step 1b for *total current liabilities.*
   (b) Repeat step 1a for *long-term liabilities* and step 1b for *total long-term liabilities.*
   (c) Add the category totals and draw a single line underneath the total.

Total liabilities = total current liabilities + total long-term liabilities

3. Find and record the *total owner's equity.*
   (a) List the equity entries and draw a single line underneath the last entry.
   (b) Add the entries and draw a single line underneath the total.
4. Find and record the *total liabilities and owner's equity:* Add the total liabilities to the total owner's equity and draw a double line underneath the grand total.

Total liabilities and owner's equity = total liabilities + total owner's equity

5. Confirm that the double line grand total from step 1 and step 4 are the same.

Total assets = total liabilities + owner's equity

Roy Russell's Security Service Balance Sheet	
	2002
Assets	
Cash	$ 8,000
Accounts receivable	4,860
Inventory	19,823
Equipment	8,925
Total assets	$41,608
Liabilities	
Accounts payable	11,281
Wages payable	11,185
Total liabilities	22,466
Owner's equity	19,142
Total liabilities and owner's equity	$41,608

2

Prepare a
vertical
analysis of a
balance
sheet.
(page 616)

1. Prepare a balance sheet of assets, liabilities, and owner's equity.
2. Create an additional column labeled *percent:* for each item, divide the amount of the item by the total assets and record the result as a percent.

$$\text{Percent of total assets} = \frac{\text{amount of item}}{\text{total assets}} \times 100\%$$

Following is a vertical analysis of the balance sheet on page 637. Each entry in the percent column is a percent of total assets. For example, for the item *cash*, the percent is

$$\frac{\text{cash}}{\text{total assets}} = \frac{\$8,000}{\$41,608} \times 100\% = 0.192271 \times 100\% = 19.2\%$$

Roy Russell's Security Service Balance Sheet		
	2002	**Percent of Total Assets**
Assets		
Cash	$8,000	19.2
Accounts receivable	4,860	11.7
Inventory	19,823	47.6
Equipment	8,925	21.5
Total assets	$41,608	100.0
Liabilities		
Accounts payable	11,281	27.1
Wages payable	11,185	26.9
Total liabilities	22,466	54.0
Owner's equity	19,142	46.0
Total liabilities and owner's equity	$41,608	100.0

3

Prepare a horizontal analysis of a balance sheet. (page 619)

1. Prepare a balance sheet for two years: record each year's amounts in separate columns.
2. Create an additional column labeled *amount of increase (decrease):* for each yearly item,
   (a) Subtract the smaller amount from the larger amount and record the difference.
   (b) If the earlier year's amount is larger than the later year's amount, record the difference from step 2a as a decrease by using parentheses.
3. Create an additional column labeled *percent increase (decrease):* for each yearly item, divide the amount of increase (decrease) by the earlier year's amount and record the difference as a percent.

$$\text{Percent increase (decrease)} = \frac{\text{amount of increase (decrease)}}{\text{earlier year's amount}} \times 100\%$$

Following is a horizontal analysis of the corporation balance sheet that extends the balance sheet used earlier. Notice that an additional year's data are given, and two *increase (decrease)* columns, one for *amount* and one for *percent,* are given as well. Notice that parentheses indicate that an item decreased from the earlier year to the later year.

			Increase	Percent Increase
Roy Russell's Security Service				
Balance Sheet				
	2003	**2002**	**(Decrease)**	**(Decrease)**
Assets				
Cash	$8,983	$8,000	$983	12.3
Accounts receivable	3,952	4,860	(908)	(18.7)
Inventory	22,507	19,823	2,684	13.5
Equipment	12,784	8,925	3,859	43.2
Total assets	$48,226	$41,608	6,618	15.9
Liabilities				
Accounts payable	12,197	11,281	916	8.1
Wages payable	5,872	11,185	(5,313)	(47.5)
Total liabilities	18,069	22,466	(4,397)	(19.6)
Owner's equity	30,157	19,142	11,015	57.5
Total liabilities and owner's equity	$48,226	$41,608	$6,618	$15.9

Section 15.2

Prepare an income statement. (page 623)

1. Find and record *net sales.*
   (a) Record *gross sales.*
   (b) Record *sales returns and allowances.*
   (c) Subtract sales returns and allowances from gross sales.

   Net sales = gross sales − sales returns and allowances

2. Find and record *cost of goods sold.*
   (a) Record cost of beginning inventory.
   (b) Record cost of purchases.
   (c) Record cost of ending inventory.
   (d) Add cost of beginning inventory and cost of purchases and subtract cost of ending inventory.

   Cost of goods sold = cost of beginning inventory + cost of purchases
   − cost of ending inventory

3. Find and record *gross profit from sales:* subtract cost of goods sold from net sales.

   Gross profit from sales = net sales − cost of goods sold

4. Find and record *total operating expenses:* list the operating expenses and add the entries.

5. Find and record *net income:* subtract the operating expenses from the gross profit.

   Net income = gross profit from sales − operating expenses

The Triple X corporation records the following data for the year 2002: gross sales, $187,700; sales returns and allowances, $8,200; cost of beginning inventory, $83,540; cost of purchases, $127,386; cost of ending inventory, $64,126; operating expenses, $18,500. Using this data, prepare an income statement.

Net sales = gross sales − sales returns and allowances

= $187,700 − $8,200

= $179,500

$$\text{Cost of goods sold} = \text{cost of beginning inventory} + \text{cost of purchases} - \text{cost of ending inventory}$$

$$= \$83,540 + \$127,386 - \$64,126$$

$$= \$146,800$$

$$\text{Gross profit from sales} = \text{net sales} - \text{cost of goods sold}$$

$$= \$179,500 - \$146,800$$

$$= \$32,700$$

$$\text{Net income} = \text{gross profit from sales} - \text{operating expenses}$$

$$= \$32,700 - \$18,500$$

$$= \$14,200$$

Triple X Corporation
Income Statement for 2002

Net sales	$179,500
Cost of goods sold	
Beginning inventory	83,540
Purchases	127,386
Goods available for sale	210,926
Less: ending inventory	64,126
Cost of goods sold	146,800
Gross profit	32,700
Operating expenses	18,500
Net income	$14,200

2   Prepare a vertical analysis of an income statement. (page 624)

1. Prepare an income statement.
2. Create an additional column labeled *percent of net sales:* for each item, divide the amount of the item by the net sales and record the result as a percent.

$$\text{Percent of net sales} = \frac{\text{amount of item}}{\text{net sales}} \times 100\%$$

Following is a vertical analysis of the income statement for Triple X Corporation. Each entry in the percent column is a percent of net sales. For example, for the item *net income,* the percent is

$$\frac{\text{net income}}{\text{net sales}} = \frac{\$14,200}{\$179,500} \times 100\% = 0.079109 \times 100\% = 7.9\%$$

```
                Triple X Corporation
                  Income Statement

                                                    Percent
                                    2002          of Net Sales

   Net sales                       $179,500           100.0
   Cost of goods sold
   Beginning inventory               83,540            46.5
   Purchases                        127,386            71.0
   Goods available for sale         210,926           117.5
   Less: ending inventory            64,126            35.7
   Cost of goods sold               146,800            81.8
   Gross profit                      32,700            18.2
   Operating expenses                18,500            10.3
   Net income                      $ 14,200             7.9
```

3

Prepare a
horizontal
analysis of an
income
statement.
(page 627)

1. Prepare an income statement for two or more years: record each year's amounts in separate columns.
2. Create an additional column labeled *amount of increase (decrease):* for each yearly item:
   (a) Subtract the smaller amount from the larger amount and record the difference.
   (b) If the earlier year's amount is larger than the later year's amount record the difference from step 2a as a decrease by using parentheses.
3. Create an additional column labeled *percent increase (decrease):* for each yearly item, divide the amount of increase (decrease) by the earlier year's amount and record the difference as a percent.

$$\text{Percent increase (decrease)} = \frac{\text{amount of increase (decrease)}}{\text{earlier year's amount}} \times 100\%$$

Following is a horizontal analysis of the Triple X corporation income statement that extends the income statement in the previous section. Notice that an additional year's data are given, and two *increase (decrease)* columns, one for *amount* and one for *percent,* are given as well. Notice that parentheses indicate that an item decreased from the earlier year to the later year.

```
                        Triple X Corporation
                    Comparative Income Statement

                                                  Increase      Percent of
                          2003        2002       (Decrease)     Net Sales

  Net sales             $215,832    $179,500      $36,332          20.2
  Cost of goods sold
  Beginning inventory     95,843      83,540       12,303          14.7
  Purchases              107,395     127,386      (19,991)        (15.7)
  Goods available for sale 203,238    210,926       (7,688)         (3.6)
  Less: ending inventory  79,583      64,126       15,457          24.1
  Cost of goods sold     123,655     146,800      (23,145)        (15.8)
  Gross profit            92,177      32,700       59,477         181.9
  Operating expenses      25,713      18,500        7,213          39.0
  Net income            $ 66,464    $ 14,200      $52,264         368.1
```

1 Find and use financial ratios. (page 629)

1. Write one amount as the numerator of a fraction and a second amount as the denominator.
2. Write the fraction in decimal form (or, for some ratios, in percent form).

$$\text{Current ratio} = \frac{\text{current assets}}{\text{current liabilities}}$$

$$\text{Acid-test ratio} = \frac{\text{quick current assets}}{\text{current liabilities}}$$

$$\text{Operating ratio} = \frac{\text{cost of goods sold} + \text{operating expenses}}{\text{net sales}}$$

$$\text{Gross profit margin ratio} = \frac{\text{gross profit from sales}}{\text{net sales}}$$

$$\text{Asset turnover ratio} = \frac{\text{net sales}}{\text{total assets}}$$

$$\text{Total debt to total assets ratio} = \frac{\text{total liabilities}}{\text{total assets}}$$

Use the income statements amounts for 2002 for the Triple X Corporation (p. 641) to find the financial ratios. Additional information needed from the balance sheet is total assets, $108,000; current assets, $40,000; quick current assets: cash, $15,892; marketable securities, $10,000; and receivables, $7,486; total liabilities, $57,000; current liabilities, $28,000.

$$\text{Current ratio} = \frac{\text{current assets}}{\text{current liabilities}} = \frac{\$40,000}{\$28,000} = 1.43 \text{ to } 1$$

$$\text{Acid-test ratio} = \frac{\text{quick current assets}}{\text{current liabilities}} = \frac{\$15,892 + \$10,000 + \$7,486}{\$28,000}$$
$$= 1.19 \text{ to } 1$$

$$\text{Operating ratio} = \frac{\text{cost of goods sold} + \text{operating expenses}}{\text{net sales}}$$
$$= \frac{\$146,800 + \$18,500}{\$179,500} = 0.921 \text{ or } 92.1\%$$

$$\text{Gross profit margin ratio} = \frac{\text{gross profit from sales}}{\text{net sales}} = \frac{\$179,500 - \$146,800}{\$179,500}$$
$$= 0.182 \text{ or } 18.2\%$$

$$\text{Asset turnover ratio} = \frac{\text{net sales}}{\text{total assets}} = \frac{\$179,500}{\$108,000} = 1.66 \text{ to } 1$$

$$\text{Total debt to total ratio} = \frac{\text{total liabilities}}{\text{total assets}} = \frac{\$57,000}{\$108,000} = 0.528 \text{ to } 1$$

WORDS TO KNOW

balance sheet (p. 612)
assets (p. 612)
current assets (p. 612)
plant and equipment (p. 612)

cash (p. 612)
accounts receivable (p. 612)
notes receivable (p. 612)
merchandise inventory (p. 612)

office supplies (p. 612)
business equipment (p. 612)
office furniture and equip-
    ment (p. 612)

CHAPTER 15 CONCEPTS ANALYSIS

1. Use the formulas in the How-To box: Prepare a Balance Sheet (p. 614) to explain the formula: Total current assets + total plant and equipment = total liabilities + total owner's equity.

2. Explain how the formula, Gross profit = net sales − cost of goods sold, can be rearranged to find net sales.

3. If you have the formula, Net profit = gross profit − operating expenses, and the net profit is $25,982 and operating expenses are $150,986, write an equation to find gross profit.

4. Explain how the formula
$$\text{Percent of net sales} = \frac{\text{amount of item}}{\text{net sales}}$$
can be rearranged to find the amount of the item.

5. Compare the formula in step 3 of the How-To box: Prepare a Horizontal Analysis of a Comparative Income Statement (p. 627) with the formula you would use to find the percent of sales tax if you know the amount of tax and the amount (price) of the item.

6. How do the two formulas in exercise 5 compare to the basic percentage formula $P = RB$?

7. Explain why the same formula $P = RB$ can be used to calculate an increase or a decrease.

8. If a current ratio for a company equals 1, what is the relationship of the current assets to the current liabilities?

9. If the current ratio is less than 1, what is the relationship of the current assets to the current liabilities?

10. If a company has an acid-test ratio that is greater than 1, what is the relationship of the quick current assets to current liabilities?

Section 15.1

1. Complete the following balance sheet for Fawcett's Plumbing Supplies.

Fawcett's Plumbing Supplies
Balance Sheet
March 31, 2003

Assets	
Current assets	
Cash	$1,724.00
Office supplies	173.00
Accounts receivable	9,374.00
Total current assets	
Plant and equipment	
Equipment	12,187.00
Total plant and equipment	12,187.00
Total assets	
Liabilities	
Current liabilities	
Accounts payable	2,174.00
Wages payable	674.00
Property and taxes payable	250.00
Total current liabilities	
Total liabilities	
Owner's Equity	
D. W. Fawcett's, capital	20,360.00
Total liabilities and owner's equity	

2. Complete the following balance sheet for Rooter Company.

Rooter Company
Balance Sheet
June 30, 2004

Assets	
Current assets	
Cash	$2,350.00
Supplies	175.00
Accounts receivable	8,956.00
Total current assets	
Plant and equipment	
Equipment	11,375.00
Total plant and equipment	11,375.00
Total Assets	
Liabilities	
Current liabilities	
Accounts payable	1,940.00
Wages payable	855.00
Rent payable	775.00
Total current liabilities	
Total liabilities	
Owner's Equity	
Wilson Rooter's, capital	19,286.00
Total liabilities and owner's equity	

3. Complete the vertical analysis and horizontal analysis of the comparative balance sheet for Seymour's Videos, Inc. Express percents to the nearest tenth of a percent.

			Increase (Decrease)		Percent of Total Assets	
Seymour's Videos, Inc. Comparative Balance Sheet December 31, 2003 and 2004	2004	2003	Amount	Percent	2004	2003
Assets						
Current assets						
Cash	$2,374	$2,184				
Accounts receivable	5,374	4,286				
Merchandise inventory	15,589	16,107				
Total assets						
Liabilities						
Current liabilities						
Accounts payable	7,384	6,118				
Wages payable	1,024	964				
Total liabilities						
Owner's Equity						
James Seymour's, capital	14,929	15,495				
Total liabilities and owner's equity						

4. Complete the vertical analysis and the horizontal analysis of the comparative balance sheet for Miller's Model Ships. Express percents to the nearest tenth of a percent.

			Increase (Decrease)		Percent of Total Assets	
Miller's Model Ships Comparative Balance Sheet December 31, 2002 and 2003	2003	2002	Amount	Percent	2003	2002
Assets						
Current assets						
Cash	$2,176	$1,948				
Accounts receivable	2,789	1,742				
Merchandise inventory	4,985	5,450				
Total assets						
Liabilities						
Current liabilities						
Accounts payable	901	872				
Wages payable	1,342	1,224				
Insurance payable	690	680				
Total liabilities						
Owner's Equity						
Kathy Miller's, capital	7,017	6,364				
Total liabilities and owner's equity						

5. Complete the following income statement and vertical analysis.

Marten's Family Store Income Statement For year ending December 31, 2001		Percent of Net Sales
Revenue		
Gross sales	$238,923	
Sales returns and allowances	13,815	
Net sales		
Cost of goods sold		
Beginning inventory, January 1, 2001	25,814	
Purchases	109,838	
Ending inventory, December 31, 2001	23,423	
Cost of goods sold		
Gross profit from sales		
Operating expenses		
Salary	42,523	
Rent	8,640	
Utilities	1,484	
Insurance	2,842	
Fees	860	
Depreciation	1,920	
Miscellaneous	3,420	
Total operating expenses	61,689	
Net income		

6. Complete the following income statement and vertical analysis. Express percents to the nearest tenth of a percent.

Serpa's Gifts Income Statement For year ending December 31, 2002		Percent of Net Sales
Revenue		
Gross sales	$148,645	
Sales returns and allowances	8,892	
Net sales		
Cost of goods sold		
Beginning inventory, January 1, 2002	12,100	
Purchases	47,800	
Ending inventory, December 31, 2002	11,950	
Cost of goods sold		
Gross profit from sales		

continued

Operating expenses		
Salary	25,500	
Rent	4,500	
Utilities	1,445	
Insurance	2,100	
Fees	225	
Depreciation	1,240	
Miscellaneous	750	
Total operating expenses		
Net income		

7. Complete the following horizontal analysis of a comparative income statement.

Alonzo's Auto Parts
Comparative Income Statement
For years ending June 30, 2001 and 2002

	2002	2001	Increase (Decrease) Amount	Percent
Revenue				
Gross sales	$291,707	$275,873		
Sales returns and allowances	5,895	6,821		
Net sales				
Cost of goods sold				
Beginning inventory, July 1	35,892	32,587		
Purchases	157,213	146,999		
Ending inventory, June 30	32,516	30,013		
Cost of goods sold				
Gross profit from sales				
Operating expenses				
Salary	42,000	40,000		
Insurance	3,800	3,800		
Utilities	1,986	2,097		
Rent	3,600	3,300		
Depreciation	4,000	4,500		
Total operating expenses		53,697		
Net income				

8. Complete the following horizontal analysis of a comparative income statement. Express percents to the nearest tenth of a percent.

Designer Crafts Comparative Income Statement For years ending December 31, 2002 and 2003			Increase (Decrease)	
	2003	**2002**	**Amount**	**Percent**
Revenue				
Gross sales	$239,873	$236,941		
Sales returns and allowances	12,815	13,895		
Net sales				
Cost of goods sold				
Beginning inventory, January 1	27,814	25,887		
Purchases	123,213	112,604		
Ending inventory, December 31	24,482	23,838		
Cost of goods sold	126,545	114,653		
Gross profit from sales				
Operating expenses				
Salary	44,772	42,640		
Insurance	3,006	2,863		
Utilities	1,597	1,521		
Rent	3,600	3,600		
Depreciation	4,100	3,400		
Total operating expenses				
Net income				

Section 15.3

Find the current ratio for each of the following businesses. Round answers to the nearest hundredth.

Current Assets	Current Liabilities
9. $1,231,704	$784,184
10. $32,194	$38,714
11. $174,316	$125,342
12. $724,987	$334,169

Find the acid-test ratio for each of these businesses. Express the answer to the nearest hundredth.

13. Stevens Gift Shop: cash, $2,345; accounts receivable, $5,450; government securities, $4,500; accounts payable, $6,748; notes payable, $7,457.

14. Central Office Supply: cash, $5,745; accounts receivable, $12,496; accounts payable, $10,475.

15. Find the acid-test ratio for Edna Nunez and Company if the balance sheet shows cash, $23,500; marketable securities, $0; receivables, $12,300; current liabilities, $27,800.

16. Find the acid-test ratio for Jefferson's Photo if the balance sheet shows cash, $6,700; marketable securities, $0; receivables, $12,756; current liabilities, $18,345.

17. Find the operating ratio and gross profit margin ratio for the following income statement:

Corner Grocery
Income Statement
for the Month Ending June 30, 2002

Net sales	$25,000
Cost of goods sold	$18,750
Gross profit	$6,250
Operating expenses	$3,750
Net income	$2,500

18. Find the operating ratio for M. Ng's Grocery if the income statement for the month shows net sales, $23,500; cost of goods sold, $16,435; gross profit, $7,065; operating expenses, $3,100; net income, $3,965. Express answer to the nearest tenth of a percent.

19. Find the operating ratio for A to Z Sales if the income statement for the month shows net sales, $173,200; cost of goods sold, $138,400; gross profit, $34,800; operating expenses, $16,300; net income, $18,500. Express answer to the nearest tenth of a percent.

20. Find the gross profit margin ratio for the business in exercise 18 to the nearest tenth of a percent.

21. Find the gross profit margin ratio for the business in exercise 19 to the nearest tenth of a percent.

Spreadsheet Exercises

22. Write formulas completing the comparative balance sheet for Molene Internet Store.

(a) Find the Total Assets for 2001 and 2002.

(b) Find the Total Liabilities for 2001 and 2002.

(c) Find the Total Liabilities and Owner's Equity for 2001 and 2002.

(d) Find the amount of increase (decrease) for 2002 over 2001 for each category.

(e) Find the percent of increase (decrease) for 2002 over 2001 for each category.

(g) Find the percent of total assets for each category in 2001 and 2002.

23. Complete the spreadsheet using the formulas.

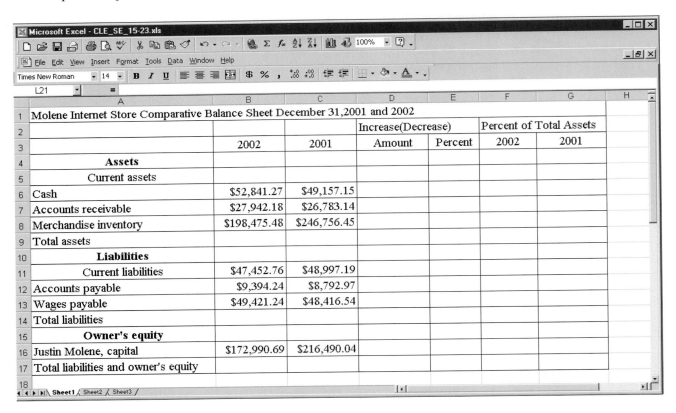

Molene Internet Store Comparative Balance Sheet December 31,2001 and 2002			Increase(Decrease)		Percent of Total Assets	
	2002	2001	Amount	Percent	2002	2001
Assets						
Current assets						
Cash	$52,841.27	$49,157.15				
Accounts receivable	$27,942.18	$26,783.14				
Merchandise inventory	$198,475.48	$246,756.45				
Total assets						
Liabilities						
Current liabilities	$47,452.76	$48,997.19				
Accounts payable	$9,394.24	$8,792.97				
Wages payable	$49,421.24	$48,416.54				
Total liabilities						
Owner's equity						
Justin Molene, capital	$172,990.69	$216,490.04				
Total liabilities and owner's equity						

Challenge Problem

24. Is There a Profit in the Cards? Cedar-Crest Greeting Card Company ended the year 2001 with assets that totaled $120,000. The assets for 2002 increased to $580,000. What was the rate of growth for Cedar-Crest?

1. Complete the horizontal analysis of the following comparative balance sheet. Express percents to the nearest tenth of a percent.

O'Toole's Hardware Store
Comparative Balance Sheet
December 31, 2000 and 2001

	2001	2000	Increase (Decrease) Amount	Increase (Decrease) Percent
Assets				
Current assets				
Cash	$7,318	$5,283		
Accounts receivable	3,147	3,008		
Merchandise inventory	63,594	60,187		
Total current assets				
Plant and equipment				
Building	36,561	37,531		
Equipment	8,256	4,386		
Total plant and equipment				
Total assets				
Liabilities				
Current liabilities				
Accounts payable	5,174	4,563		
Wages payable	780	624		
Total current liabilities				
Long-term liabilities				
Mortgage note payable	34,917	36,510		
Total long-term liabilities				
Total liabilities				
Owner's Equity				
James O'Toole, capital	78,005	68,698		
Total liabilities and owner's equity				

2. Find the current ratio to the nearest hundredth for 2001 for O'Toole's Hardware Store.

3. Find the acid-test ratio to the nearest hundredth for 2001 for O'Toole's Hardware Store.

4. Find the current ratio to the nearest hundredth for 2000 for O'Toole's Hardware Store.

5. Find the acid-test ratio to the nearest hundredth for 2000 for O'Toole's Hardware Store.

6. Complete the horizontal analysis of the following comparative income statement.

Mile Wide Woolens, Inc.
Comparative Income Statement
for Years Ending December 31, 2002 and 2003

	2003	2002	Increase (Decrease) Amount	Increase (Decrease) Percent
Revenue				
Gross sales	$219,827	$205,852		
Sales returns and allowances	8,512	7,983		
Net sales				
Cost of goods sold				
Beginning inventory, January 1	42,816	40,512		
Purchases	97,523	94,812		
Ending inventory, December 31	43,182	42,521		
Cost of goods sold				
Gross profit from sales				
Operating expenses				
Salary	28,940	27,000		
Insurance	800	750		
Utilities	1,700	1,580		
Rent	3,600	3,000		
Depreciation	2,000	2,400		
Total operating expenses				
Net income				

7. Find the operating ratio for Mile Wide for 2002 and 2003.

8. Find the gross profit margin ratio for Mile Wide for 2002 and 2003.

SELF-CHECK 15.1
Solutions for exercises 1, 2, 5, 6, 9,10

Miss Muffins' Bakery Comparative Balance Sheet December 31, 2001 and 2002			Increase (Decrease)		Percent of Total Assets	
	2002	**2001**	**Amount**	**Percent**	**2002**	**2001**
Assets						
Current assets						
Cash	$1,985	$1,762	$ 223	12.7	22.8	23.2
Accounts receivable	4,219	3,785	434	11.5	48.4	49.9
Merchandise inventory	2,512	2,036	476	23.4	28.8	26.8
Total assets	$8,716	$7,583	$1,133	14.9	100.0	100.0
Liabilities						
Current liabilities						
Accounts payable	3,483	3,631	(148)	(4.1)	40.0	47.9
Wages payable	1,696	1,421	275	19.4	19.5	18.7
Total liabilities	5,179	5,052	127	2.5	59.4	66.6
Owner's Equity						
Mildred Galloway, capital	3,537	2,531	1,006	39.7	40.6	33.4
Total liabilities and owner's equity	$8,716	$7,583	$1,133	14.9	100.0	100.0

Solutions for exercises 3, 4, 7, 8, 11, 12

O'Dell's Nursery Comparative Balance Sheet December 31, 2001 and 2002			Increase (Decrease)		Percent of Total Assets	
	2002	**2001**	**Amount**	**Percent**	**2002**	**2001**
Assets						
Current assets						
Cash	$8,917	$12,842	($3,925)	(30.1)	26.0	34.2
Accounts receivable	7,521	5,836	1,685	28.9	22.0	15.5
Merchandise inventory	17,826	18,917	(1,091)	(5.8)	52.0	50.3
Total assets	$34,264	$37,595	($3,331)	(8.9)	100.0	100.0
Liabilities						
Current liabilities						
Accounts payable	10,215	8,968	1,247	13.9	29.8	23.9
Wages payable	3,716	2,582	1,134	43.9	10.8	6.9
Total liabilities	13,931	11,550	2,381	20.6	40.7	30.7
Owner's Equity						
Janelle O'Dell, capital	20,333	26,045	(5,712)	(21.9)	59.3	69.3
Total liabilities and owner's equity	$34,264	$37,595	($ 3,331)	(8.9)	100.0	100.0

Solutions for exercises 1, 4, 6

	2002		2001		Increase (Decrease)	
	Amount	**Percent**	**Amount**	**Percent**	**Amount**	**Percent**

Sitha Ros' Oriental Groceries
Income Statement for the Years Ending June 30, 2001 and 2002

	2002 Amount	2002 Percent	2001 Amount	2001 Percent	Incr (Decr) Amount	Incr (Decr) Percent
Net sales	$97,384	100.0	$92,196	100.0	$ 5,188	5.6
Cost of goods sold	82,157	84.4	72,894	79.1	9,263	12.7
Gross profits	15,227	15.6	19,302	20.9	(4,075)	(21.1)
Operating expenses	4,783	4.9	3,951	4.3	832	21.1
Net income	$10,444	10.7	$15,351	16.7	($ 4,907)	(32.0)

Solutions for exercises 2, 3, 5, 7

2001

Net Sales $= \$32,596 - \$296 = \$32,300$
Cost of goods sold $= \$16,872 + \$33,596 - \$21,843 = \$28,625$
Gross profit $= \$32,300 - \$28,625 = \$3,675$
Net profit $= \$3,675 - \$1,894 = \$1,781$

2002

$\$35,403 - \$342 = \$35,061$
$\$17,403 + \$27,983 - \$22,583 = \$22,803$
$\$35,061 - \$22,803 = \$12,258$
$\$12,258 - \$3,053 = \$9,205$

Miss Muffins' Bakery
Income Statement for the Months Ending July 31, 2001 and July 31, 2002

	2002 Amount	2002 Percent	2001 Amount	2001 Percent	Incr (Decr) Amount	Incr (Decr) Percent
Net sales	$35,061	100.0	$32,300	100.0	$2,761	8.5
Cost of goods sold	22,803	65.0	28,625	88.6	(5,822)	(20.3)
Gross profit	12,258	35.0	3,675	11.4	8,583	233.6
Operating expenses	3,053	8.7	1,894	5.9	1,159	61.2
Net income	$9,205	26.3	$1,781	5.5	$7,424	416.8

1. George's $= \dfrac{\text{current assets}}{\text{current liabilities}} = \dfrac{\$28,000}{\$7,000} = 4 \text{ or } 4{:}1.$

José's $= \dfrac{\$840,000}{\$819,000} = 1.03 \text{ or } 1.03{:}1$

2. Acid-test ratio $= \dfrac{\text{quick current assets}}{\text{current liabilities}} = \dfrac{\$32,981 + \$12,045}{\$22,178} = \dfrac{\$45,026}{\$22,178}$

$= 2.03 \text{ or } 2.03 \text{ to } 1$

3. Operating ratio $= \dfrac{\text{cost of goods sold} + \text{operating expenses}}{\text{net sales}}$

$= \dfrac{\$7,500 + \$3,500}{\$15,500} = \dfrac{\$11,000}{\$15,500} = 0.709677 \text{ or } 71.0\%$

4. Gross profit margin $= \dfrac{\text{net sales} - \text{cost of goods sold}}{\text{net sales}}$

$= \dfrac{\$15,500 - \$7,500}{\$15,500} = \dfrac{\$8,000}{\$15,500}$

$= 0.516129 \text{ or } 51.6\%$

16

Insurance

16.1 Fire Insurance

1 Find fire insurance premiums using a rate table.

2 Find the compensation with a coinsurance clause.

16.2 Motor Vehicle Insurance

1 Find automobile insurance premiums using a rate table.

16.3 Life Insurance

1 Find life insurance premiums using a rate table.

Good Decisions through Teamwork

You are purchasing a new $115,000 home and making a down payment of $11,500. The mortgage company requires that the property be insured for at least the amount of the loan. However, you may want to protect your equity in the property and the contents of your home. The property assessor has valued the lot at $24,000 and the structure at $91,000. The property is located in a flood zone. It is also located in an earthquake region. Thus, you may want to include both flood and earthquake insurance in your policy. Your budget will allow $1,000 at most per year for homeowner's insurance.

With your team, determine what insurance options you will consider. Include the amount of coverage for structures and contents and any additional coverage you will purchase. Contact at least three insurance agents, discuss your insurance needs, and get a price quote. As a team, review the quotes for your property and decide which insurance offer you will accept. Report to the class your choice and the reasons for making that choice.

Insurance is a form of protection against unexpected financial loss. Businesses and individuals need insurance to help bear the burden of accidents and acts of God that result in large financial losses. Insurance helps distribute the burden of financial loss among those who share the same type of risk. Many types of insurance are available, such as fire, life, homeowner's, health, accident, automobile, and others. Many insurance companies offer a **comprehensive policy** that protects the insured against several risks. It is common, for example, to purchase fire, flood, and earthquake insurance in one comprehensive policy. The combined rate for a comprehensive policy is usually lower than if each type of protection is purchased separately.

Before we can discuss specific types of insurance, we need to understand some important terms used in the insurance field.

Insured (policyholder)	The individual, organization, or business that carries the insurance or financial protection against loss
Insurer (underwriter)	The insurance company that assures payment for a specific loss according to contract provisions
Policy	The contract between the insurer and the insured
Premium	The amount paid by the insured for the protection provided by the policy
Face value	The maximum amount of insurance provided by the policy
Beneficiary	The individual, organization, or business to whom the proceeds of the policy are payable

16.1   Fire Insurance

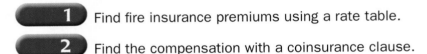 Find fire insurance premiums using a rate table.

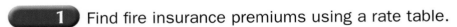 Find the compensation with a coinsurance clause.

Fire insurance provides protection against fire losses or losses that may result directly from attempts to extinguish a fire, such as damage caused by water and chemical extinguishers and damage to property by firefighters.

1 Find fire insurance premiums using a rate table.

Rates for fire insurance vary according to several factors, such as type of structure, location, proximity to the fire department, rating of the fire department, water supply, and fire hazards. Most states have developed a system for classifying rates according to these factors. For example, a class A building might be made of brick instead of wood. Or the contents of the building might be classed as resistant to fire damage, such as bags of cement, rather than fabric, which would be much more flammable (easily burned). Table 16-1 shows a sample classification system. The area rankings in the left column are based on how close the buildings are to a fire station and how easy access is to the building and its contents.

Table 16-1   Annual Fire Insurance Rates per $100 of Face Value

	Building Classification					
	Class A		Class B		Class C	
Area Rank	Building	Contents	Building	Contents	Building	Contents
1	$0.59	$0.64	$0.75	$0.89	$0.94	$1.11
2	0.60	0.65	0.76	0.91	0.96	1.13
3	0.62	0.67	0.78	0.93	0.98	1.16

As you can see from Table 16-1, insurance rates are expressed as an annual amount per $100 of coverage. To find the annual premium, divide the amount of coverage by $100 and multiply by the rate in the table. Do this for both building and contents.

> **? HOW TO** Find an Annual Fire Insurance Premium Amount Using a Table
>
> 1. Locate the annual rate for the building (or contents) being insured according to the building's area rank and its class.
> 2. Divide the building (or contents) policy's face value by $100 and multiply the quotient by the rate from step 1.
>
> $$\text{Annual premium} = \frac{\text{face value}}{\$100} \times \text{rate}$$

EXAMPLE The building owned and occupied by O'Toole's Hardware is insured for $85,000. Its contents are insured for $50,000. If it is a class B building located in area 2, find the annual premium for the building and contents.

Annual premium for building

$$= \frac{\text{face value}}{\$100} \times \text{rate}$$

$$= \frac{\$85,000}{\$100} \times \$0.76 = \mathbf{\$646}$$

> **Look up the annual rate for a building classified as class B in area 2. The rate is $0.76. Multiply $85,000 divided by $100 times the rate.**

Annual premium for contents

$$= \frac{\text{face value}}{\$100} \times \text{rate}$$

$$= \frac{\$50,000}{\$100} \times \$0.91 = \mathbf{\$455}$$

> **Look up the annual rate for contents classified as class B in area 2. The rate is $0.91. Multiply $0.91 times $50,000 divided by $100.**

The annual premium for the building is $646 and the premium for its contents is $455.

2 Find the compensation with a coinsurance clause.

Because a fire rarely destroys a whole building or all of its contents, many businesses take out policies that cover only a portion of the value of the building or its contents. Thus, they save money on premiums by covering only 40% of their property's value, for example. To encourage businesses to take out full insurance, insurance companies offer plans that include a **coinsurance clause.** Such a clause means that the insured gets full protection or compensation up to the value of the policy from the insurance company only if the property is insured for 80% of its replacement value. If the policy covers only 40% of the value, then the insurance company pays only a portion of the loss.

The following How-To box shows how to calculate the amount the insurance company pays if your policy has a coinsurance clause and you do *not* have full coverage.

HOW TO Find the Compensation with a Coinsurance Clause

1. Find the face value required by the 80% coinsurance clause for full compensation: multiply 0.8 by the replacement value of the property.
2. Divide the face value of the policy by the value from step 1 and multiply this quotient by the amount of loss (up to the face value of the policy).

Compensation (up to amount of loss)

$$= \text{amount of loss (up to the face value)} \times \frac{\text{face value of policy}}{80\% \text{ of replacement value of property}}$$

EXAMPLE Budget Construction owns a building with a replacement value of $200,000. It has a fire insurance policy with an 80% coinsurance clause, and a face value of $130,000. There is a fire, and the building damage is figured to be $50,000. What will the insurance company pay as compensation?

To find out if Budget carries as much insurance as its coinsurance clause requires for full protection, multiply $0.8 \times \$200,000 = \$160,000$. Budget has a policy worth only $130,000, so it does not get full compensation for the loss.

Use the formula to find the compensation:

$$\text{Compensation} = \text{loss} \times \frac{\text{face value of policy}}{80\% \text{ of replacement value}}$$

$$\text{Compensation} = \$50,000 \times \frac{\$130,000}{\$160,000} = \$40,625$$

Budget receives $40,625 compensation for its loss of $50,000.

If Budget had carried a policy for 80% of the replacement value of its property, it would have gotten $50,000 \times \dfrac{\$160,000}{\$160,000} = \$50,000$ compensation for the loss.

TIP! Maximum Compensation for a Loss

When calculating the compensation an insurance company will pay, if the policy has a coinsurance clause, the compensation for the amount of loss can be *no more than the face value of the policy,* regardless of the actual dollar value of the loss.

McLean's Machine Shop is insured for 80% of the replacement value. The replacement value of the shop is $105,000. A fire causes $90,000 worth of damage to the property. How much compensation will McLean's receive from the insurance company?

$$0.8 \times \$105,000 = \$84,000 \text{ face value of policy}$$

$$\$84,000 \times \frac{\$84,000}{\$84,000} = \$84,000 \qquad \$90,000 \times \frac{\$84,000}{\$84,000} = \$90,000$$

CORRECT   **INCORRECT**

Compensation cannot exceed the face value of the policy.

Find Premiums for Special Purpose Insurance.   Many businesses are operated from a home and additional insurance is needed. This additional insurance is often purchased in the form of a rider on a homeowner's or business policy. A **rider** is insurance coverage for a special purpose, and an additional premium is added to the basic premium.

Table 16-2 describes some common special purpose coverage. It compares costs for these various types of insurance for a home office.

Table 16-2   Common Special Purpose Coverage

Product	What It Does	Average Annual Cost	Considerations
Computer Coverage	Protects equipment from fire, theft, and sometimes spills, power surges, and accidents.	$100 to $150 for $10,000 coverage	A rider to a homeowner's policy or a specialized policy. (Check to see if data is covered)
Business Pursuits Liability	Protects business property from theft, fire, and other hazards included in your homeowner's policy. Also protects you from liability suits stemming from business activities at home or away.	$50 to $100	A rider to a homeowner's policy; you can't always get this if you're a bonafide business.
Commercial Liability	Protects the same as a business pursuits rider, but more comprehensive, usually higher limits.	$140 to $350 minimum	May include business extras, like business interruption coverage, business property all rolled into one.
Professional Liability	Protects you from suits stemming from mistakes you make or bad advice you give in a professional context.	$1,000 minimum more typically $2,500 to $5,000 and up	Best bought as an industry-specific policy; also called errors-and-omissions or malpractice insurance.
Business Interruption	Makes up the money you lose when fire, theft, or similar disasters destroy your office and business records.	Minimum of $100 per $10,000 of coverage	Can come as a rider to a computer policy or a commercial liability policy.
Disability Insurance	Pays if you cannot work.	$1,000 and up, for a 40-year-old male, seeking $3,000 monthly benefits	Hard to get if you're home-based, hard to collect on, too. Costs vary according to occupation.
Auto Insurance	Covers you for accidents that occur while you're on business-related trips.	Maybe nothing extra but check with your insurer	Let your company know what kind of business mileage you put on your car; if it's low, coverage may not cost you extra or it could even lower premiums.
Workers' Compensation	Compensates employees for costs (including lost income) of work-related injuries.	Varies by state, occupation, and salary	Required, in specific format, if you have employees

Reprinted by permission from *Home Office Computing* magazine.

1. Find the annual fire insurance premium on a class A building located in area 3 if the building is insured for $120,000 and its contents are insured for $75,000.

A class C building and its contents are located in area 1 and are insured for $150,000 and $68,000, respectively.

2. Find the total annual insurance premium.

3. If a 2% charge is added to the annual premium when payments are made semiannually, how much would semiannual payments be?

4. Chandler Burford owns a class B office building located in area 2. What is the annual fire insurance premium if the building is insured for $350,000 and the contents are insured for $100,000.

5. Alice Murillo owns a class A building located in area 1. The building is insured for $200,000 and the contents are insured for $85,000. A 2% charge is added to the annual premium because she pays the insurance quarterly. How much is her quarterly payment?

 The market value of a building is $255,000. It has been insured for $204,000 in a fire insurance policy with an 80% coinsurance clause.

6. What part of a loss due to fire will the insurance company pay?

7. If a fire causes damages valued at $75,000, what is the amount of compensation?

8. A building valued at $295,000 is insured in a policy that contains an 80% coinsurance clause. The face value of the policy is $100,000. If the building is a total loss, what is the amount of compensation?

9. Mays Jewelry Store owns a property that has a replacement value of $395,000. How much insurance is required on the property if a coinsurance clause exists?

10. Mays Jewelry Store had a fire that resulted in a loss valued at $83,000. How much compensation is the insurance company obligated to pay if the property is insured for $220,000?

11. What does the phrase "$100 to $150 for $10,000 coverage" mean in the Average Annual Cost for Computer Coverage? Give a numerical example.

12. Assume you own a business in your home. Discuss which types of insurance you would consider necessary and which types you would consider optional. Include the insurance types discussed in this textbook as well as in the table.

13. Assume you own a $40,000 business in your home. Use the data in the table to compute the minimum yearly payment for the following special coverage: computer, $10,000; business pursuits liability, minimum; business interruption, $10,000.

16.2 Motor Vehicle Insurance

 Find automobile insurance premiums using a rate table.

Motor vehicle insurance is a major expense item for individuals and businesses because of the high risk of personal injury or death and damage to property. Insurance for motor vehicles may be purchased to protect the individual or business from several risks. These include liability for personal injury and property damage; damage or loss to the insured vehicle and its occupants caused by a collision; and damage or loss to the insured vehicle caused by theft, fire, flood, storms, and other incidents that may not be related to a collision. These types of insurance generally fall into three types: liability, comprehensive, and collision.

Liability insurance protects the insured from losses incurred in a vehicle accident resulting in personal injury or property damage if the accident is the fault of the insured or a designated driver.

Comprehensive insurance protects the insured's vehicle from damage caused by fire, theft, vandalism, and other risks, such as falling debris, storm damage, or road hazards such as rocks.

Collision insurance protects the insured's vehicle from damage (both personal and property) caused by an automobile accident in which the driver of the insured vehicle is *also* at fault. This type of insurance is also used when the driver of the vehicle who is at fault does not have insurance coverage.

Some states have **no-fault insurance** programs. In these states, all parties involved in an accident submit a claim for personal and property damages to their own insurance company if the amount is under a certain stated maximum. However, a person can still pursue legal action for additional compensation if the damage is above the stated maximum.

1 Find automobile insurance premiums using a rate table.

Factors that affect the cost of automobile insurance include the location of the vehicle (large city, small town, rural area); the total distance traveled per year and the distance traveled to work each day; the types of use (such as pleasure, traveling to and from work, strictly business); the driving record and training of the insured driver(s); the academic grades of drivers who are still in school; the age, sex, and marital status of the insured driver(s); the type and age of the vehicle; and the amount of coverage desired. Accident statistics and probabilities involving these factors are used in determining appropriate insurance rates.

Table 16-3 shows a hypothetical annual rate schedule for liability insurance. Notice that there are several columns of information. The **territory** refers to the type of area in which the car is kept and driven. The **driver class** refers to such personal information about the driver as age, sex, or marital status. The 25/50 under the **bodily injury** heading means the insurance company will pay up to $25,000 for bodily injury of one individual in an accident and no more than a total of $50,000 per accident for bodily injury, regardless of the number of individuals injured in the accident. The 10, 25, 50 under the **property damage** heading indicates the premium for coverage of $10,000, $25,000, or $50,000, for damage to the property of others, including other vehicles or property such as fences, buildings, utility poles, and so on, that are involved in the accident.

Table 16-3   Annual Automobile Liability Insurance Premiums

Territory	Driver Class	Bodily Injury Coverage			Property Damage Coverage		
		25/50	50/100	100/300	10	25	50
1	A	$287	$330	$378	$155	$178	$204
	B	417	480	551	225	258	297
	C	732	841	965	394	453	519
2	A	194	218	248	104	118	134
	B	281	318	363	151	172	195
	C	491	556	633	265	300	341

HOW TO Find an Annual Automobile Liability Insurance Premium Using a Table

1. Locate the bodily injury premium according to territory, driver class, and per person/per accident bodily injury coverage.
2. Locate the property damage premium according to territory, driver class, and property damage coverage.
3. Add the premiums from step 1 and step 2.

Liability premium = bodily injury premium + property damage premium

EXAMPLE   Use Table 16-3 to find the annual premium for an automobile liability insurance policy in which the insured lives in territory 1, is class A, and wishes to have 50/100/10 coverage.

The cost of 50/100 bodily injury coverage for territory 1 and class A is $330. The cost of $10,000 property damage insurance for territory 1 and class A is $155. Therefore, **the total cost of the insurance package is $330 + $155 = $485.**

Insurance tables for collision insurance are set up much the same way as Table 16-3. However, these policies usually include a *deductible clause,* which means the insured must pay a specified amount (the **deductible amount**) before the insurance company will begin to pay.

TIP! What If Damages Exceed the Book Value of the Vehicle?

As vehicles age, they generally decrease in value. The value of a particular year, make, and model of a vehicle is published for car dealers and insurance companies. This value is referred to as the **book value** of a vehicle. If the damages resulting from an accident exceed the book value, the insurance company will only pay for the book value. When this situation occurs, the vehicle is commonly said to be **totaled.**

SELF-CHECK 16.2

1. Find the annual premium for an automobile liability insurance policy if the insured lives in territory 2 and is classified as a class C driver. The policy contains 25/50/10 coverage.

2. Compare the annual premium on a 50/100/10 policy for a class C driver in territory 1 to a policy with the same coverage for a class C driver in territory 2.

3. What are the monthly payments on an automobile liability insurance policy for a class B driver in territory 1 with 50/100/25 coverage? Assume no additional fee is required for the monthly payment option.

4. How much will an automobile liability insurance policy pay an injured person with medical expenses of $8,362 if the insured has a policy with 25/50/10 coverage? How much must the insured pay the injured party?

16.3 Life Insurance

 Find life insurance premiums using a rate table.

Life insurance provides financial assistance to the surviving dependents of the insured person in the event of the insured person's death. Although anyone may purchase life insurance, companies often insure the lives of their employees as a fringe benefit of employment. In partnerships the beneficiary is often the surviving partner. Several types of life insurance policies are available, some of which even function as savings programs. In this section, we look at two types of life insurance policies in common use: *term* and *straight-life.*

Term insurance is purchased for a certain period of time, such as 5, 10, or 20 years. For example, those insured under a 10-year term policy pay premiums for 10 years or until they die, whichever occurs first. If the insured dies during the 10-year period, the beneficiary of the policy receives the face value of the policy. If the insured is still living at the end of the 10-year period, the insurance ends and the policy has no cash value. The insured can then renew the policy, but at a higher rate than paid before. Term insurance is the least expensive type of life insurance.

People who take out **straight-life (ordinary life) insurance** policies agree to pay premiums for their entire lives. At the time of the insured's death, a beneficiary receives the face value of the policy. This type of policy also builds up a cash value. Policyholders who cancel their policy are entitled to a certain sum of money back, depending on the amount that was paid in. Thus, another difference between term and straight-life insurance is that a straight-life policy has a cash value, whereas a term policy does not.

 Find life insurance premiums using a rate table.

Table 16-4 shows typical rates for the two types of policies that have been discussed. Using this information and the formula for annual premium will allow you to find many types of premiums.

Table 16-4 Annual Life Insurance Premium
Rates per $1,000 of Face Value

| Age | Five-Year Term | | Straight-Life | |
	Male	Female	Male	Female
20	5.26	4.96	12.03	11.06
30	5.50	5.16	15.25	13.70
40	7.86	6.46	21.41	17.97
50	15.46	10.70	32.99	26.37
60	31.40	17.74	54.67	42.30

? HOW TO Find an Annual Life Insurance Premium Using a Table

1. Locate the annual rate in Table 16-4 according to type of policy, age, and sex.
2. Divide the policy face value by $1,000 and multiply the quotient by the rate from step 1.

$$\text{Annual premium} = \frac{\text{face value}}{\$1,000} \times \text{rate}$$

EXAMPLE   Find the annual premium of an insurance policy with a face value of $25,000 for a 30-year-old male for (a) a five-year term policy; (b) a straight-life policy.

$$\text{Annual premium} = \frac{\text{face value}}{\$1,000} \times \text{rate}$$ The face value is $25,000.

$$= \frac{\$25,000}{\$1,000} \times \text{rate}$$

$$= 25 \times \text{rate}$$

Look at Table 16-4 to find the rate for each type of policy.

(a) five-year term policy: $25 \times \$5.50 = \$137.50$

(b) straight-life policy: $25 \times \$15.25 = \$381.25$

The annual premium for a five-year term policy is $137.50 and for a straight-life policy is $381.25.

Don't Forget the Memory Functions!

The calculator sequence is a multiplication application. The memory function can be used to store the number 25 so that it does not have to be reentered each time.

| AC | 25 | M⁺ | × | 5.5 | = | ⇒ 137.5
| CE/C | MRC | × | 15.25 | = | ⇒ 381.25

Since it is often inconvenient to make large annual payments, most companies allow payments to be made semiannually (twice a year), quarterly (every three months), or monthly for slightly higher rates than would apply on an annual basis. Table 16-5 shows some typical rates for periods of less than one year.

EXAMPLE   Use Tables 16-4 and 16-5 to find the (a) semiannual, (b) quarterly, and (c) monthly premiums for a $30,000 straight-life policy on a 40-year-old female.

$$\text{Annual premium} = \frac{\text{amount of coverage}}{\$1,000} \times \text{rate}$$

Table 16-5 Premium Rates for Periods Less than One Year

$$= \frac{\$30,000}{\$1,000} \times \$17.97$$ The face value is $30,000. The rate, according to Table 16-4, is $17.97.

$$= 30 \times \$17.97 = \$539.10$$

Find the period rates in Table 16-5.

Period	Percent of Annual Premium
Semiannually	51.00
Quarterly	26.00
Monthly	8.75

(a) Semiannual premium:
$539.10 × 51%
= $539.10 × 0.51 = $274.94

Annual premium × semiannual rate = semiannual premium

(b) Quarterly premium:
$539.10 × 26%
= $539.10 × 0.26 = $140.17

Annual premium × quarterly rate = quarterly premium

(c) Monthly premium

$539.10 × 8.75%

= $539.10 × 0.0875 = $47.17

| Annual premium × monthly rate = monthly premium |

The semiannual premium is $274.94, quarterly is $140.17, and monthly is $47.17.

Don't Forget to Use Decimal Equivalents of Percent Rates!

Again, the calculator sequence is a multiplication (after converting the percent to a decimal). The memory function can be used to store $539.10.

AC MC 539.1 M⁺ × .51 = ⇒ 274.94
CE/C MRC × .26 = ⇒ 140.17
CE/C MRC × .0875 = ⇒ 47.17

SELF-CHECK 16.3

1 *Use Tables 16-4 and 16-5 to solve each of the following.*

1. Find the annual premium for an insurance policy with a face value of $45,000 for a 20-year-old female for a five-year term policy.

2. Find the annual premium for a straight-life insurance policy with a face value of $45,000 for a 20-year-old female.

3. What are the quarterly payments on a $100,000 straight-life insurance policy for a 30-year-old male?

4. What are the monthly payments on a $50,000 straight-life insurance policy for a 50-year-old male?

5. Compare a five-year term policy for $75,000 for a 40-year-old male to the same policy for a 40-year-old female.

6. Compare a five-year term policy for $75,000 for a 60-year-old male to the same policy for a 60-year-old female.

7. Why are the rates for a female in exercises 5 and 6 lower than those for a male?

8. Why are the premiums higher if paid in more than one payment per year?

Around The Business World

Sport-Utility Vehicle Insurance

Sport-utility vehicles (SUVs) accounted for a third of all new car sales, and many in the insurance industry say they can no longer ignore the financial risks these vehicles represent. The reason is simple: SUVs do more damage in a wreck than average cars, due to the physical mismatch when a 5,500-pound SUV collides with a 3,000-pound midsize sedan or a 2,000-pound compact car. Newton's second law of motion (F = ma) says that the heavier vehicle strikes with much greater force than the lighter one, resulting in more vehicle damage and medical injuries for the lighter car and its occupants. In addition, an SUV typically hits the smaller car above its bumpers, compounding the damage and injuries.

In the past, insurance companies have disregarded the make and model of a vehicle when setting rates for liability coverage and used only the age, gender, marital status, location, vehicle use, and driving record of the insured to set liability rates. But now some insurance companies are increasing liability rates by as much as 20% on these SUV behemoths. By rating SUVs separately, these companies are then able to reduce liability rates for ordinary cars by as much as 10% for some types of coverage.

On the flip side, an SUV better protects the occupants and vehicle in a crash, so insurance companies pay less in SUV repairs and medical treatment. So SUV customers can expect to pay lower insurance premiums for collision and medical payments coverage. The verdict is still out on any differences in comprehensive insurance claims.

Example: The annual liability insurance premium for a 30-year-old married male with a good driving record is $400 with the following limits: bodily injury $100,000 each person; $300,000 each occurrence; property damage $100,000 each occurrence. His uninsured motorist coverage with the same limits costs $120 per year. His collision coverage on a late model sedan costs $240 per year for actual cash value replacement, less a $200 deductible. The annual medical payments premium is $30 for $10,000 of coverage. Towing and labor coverage costs him an additional $6 per year.

His insurance company has just announced plans to rate SUVs separately, charging SUV drivers 20% more for liability and uninsured motorist coverage, while reducing these premiums by 10% for ordinary car drivers. They also plan to reduce collision, medical payments, and towing premiums for SUV drivers by 10%, while increasing these premiums by 20% for drivers of ordinary cars.

Exercises

Use the given information to answer the following:

1. If the 30-year-old married male elects to pay his auto insurance by automatic bank draft from his checking account, find the amount to be deducted each month. Assume that his insurance company doesn't add a finance charge.

2. What will his annual premium be once the announced changes in ratings take place? By how much did his monthly bank draft change? Rounded to the nearest tenth, what percent increase or decrease does this amount to?

3. If he trades his sedan for a similarly aged and priced SUV, find his annual premium after the announced changes in ratings take place. By how much did his monthly bank draft change from the original amount? Rounded to the nearest tenth, what percent increase or decrease of the original premium does this amount to?

4. For each pair of drivers similar to this man, one SUV driver and one ordinary car driver, what is the net change in insurance premiums collected by this company once the announced changes take effect? What is the average annual net change per driver? Rounded to the nearest tenth, what percent increase or decrease does this amount to per driver?

5. Assume that this insurance company covers about 1,200,000 drivers and that about one-third of them drive SUVs, while the rest drive ordinary cars. Find the net change in premiums collected by this company once the changes take effect. What percent increase does this amount to?

6. Why is the percent increase per driver found in exercise 5 different from the percent increase per driver found in exercise 4?

Answers

1. The total annual premium of $796 amounts to $66.33 per month.

2. Under the announced changes, the total annual premium of $799.20 amounts to $66.60 per month or 27¢ more per month. This is a 0.4% *increase* in rates for sedan owners.

3. Under the announced changes, the SUV total annual premium of $872.40 amounts to $72.70 per month or $6.37 more per month. This is a 9.6% increase in rates for SUV owners.

4. Previously, each driver would have paid $796 for coverage in these five areas, or a total of $1,592 per year for both drivers. Under the announced changes, they pay $872.40 and $799.20, or a total of $1,671.60 per year for both drivers. This results in an annual net increase in premiums of $79.60 for these two drivers, or an average of $39.80 per driver. This amounts to an average increase of 5% per driver.

5. Before the changes, 1,200,000 drivers paying an average of $796 per year yielded $955,200,000 per year in annual insurance premiums. After the changes, 400,000 SUV drivers will pay $872.40 per year, and 800,000 sedan drivers will pay $799.20 per year, yielding a total of $988,320,000 per year in annual insurance premiums. This results in a net increase of $33,120,000 or 3.5%.

6. In exercise 4 there were equal numbers of SUV and ordinary car drivers (one each), but in exercise 5 ordinary car drivers outnumbered SUV drivers by 2 to 1. So the weighted average in exercise 5 was different from the unweighted average in exercise 4.

Section Outcome

Important Points with Examples

Section 16.1

Find fire insurance premiums using a rate table. (page 658)

1. Locate the annual rate for the building (or contents) being insured, according to the building's area rank and its class.

2. Divide the building (or contents) policy's face value by $100 and multiply the quotient by the rate from step 1.

$$\text{Annual premium} = \frac{\text{face value}}{\$100} \times \text{rate}$$

Use Table 16-1 to find the annual premium for building and contents if a building is insured for $120,000 and its contents are insured for $350,000. The building is a class C building in area 3.

Annual premium for building:

$$\frac{\$120,000}{\$100} \times \$0.98 = \$1,176$$

Annual premium for contents:

$$\frac{\$350,000}{\$100} \times \$1.16 = \$4,060$$

Total premium:

$$\$1,176 + \$4,060 = \$5,236$$

2

Find the compensation with a coinsurance clause.
(page 659)

1. Find the face value required by the 80% coinsurance clause for full compensation: multiply 0.8 by the replacement value of the property.
2. Divide the face value of the policy by the value from step 1 and multiply this quotient by the amount of loss (up to the face value of the policy).

Compensation (up to amount of loss)

$$= \text{amount of loss (up to face value)} \times \frac{\text{face value of policy}}{80\% \text{ of replacement value of property}}$$

A property valued at $325,000 is insured in a policy that contains an 80% coinsurance clause. The face value of the policy is $200,000. What is the amount of compensation if a fire results in a total loss of the property?

$$\text{Compensation} = \$200,000 \times \frac{\$200,000}{0.8 \times \$325,000}$$

$$\text{Compensation} = \$200,000 \times 0.769230769$$

$$\text{Compensation} = \$153,846.15$$

Even though the fire caused damages valued at $325,000, the insured receives only $153,846.15 in compensation.

Section 16.2

Find automobile insurance premiums using a rate table.
(page 663)

1. Locate the bodily injury premium according to territory, driver class, and per person/per accident bodily injury coverage.
2. Locate the property damage premium according to territory, driver class, and property damage coverage.
3. Add the premiums from step 1 and step 2.

Liability premium = bodily injury premium + property damage premium

Liability insurance: covers the insured if responsible for an accident resulting in injury to another person or damage to another person's property.

Comprehensive insurance: covers the insured's vehicle for damage or loss that was not caused in an accident involving another vehicle.

Collision insurance: covers the insured for personal injury and property damage caused by an automobile accident in which other insurance does not apply.

Use Table 16-3 to find the annual premium for an automobile liability insurance policy in which the insured lives in territory 2, is in class C, and wishes to have 25/50/10 coverage.

The cost of 25/50 bodily injury coverage for territory 2 and class C is $491. The cost of $10,000 property damage is $265. The total premium is

$$\$491 + \$265 = \$756$$

Section 16.3

Find life insurance premiums using a rate table. (page 665)

1. Locate the annual rate in Table 16-4 according to type of policy, age, and sex.
2. Divide the policy face value by $1,000 and multiply this quotient by the rate from step 1.

$$\text{Annual premium} = \frac{\text{face value}}{\$1,000} \times \text{rate}$$

Use Table 16-4 to find the annual premium for a 40-year-old male for a $50,000 (a) five-year term policy and (b) straight-life policy.

(a) five-year policy: $\dfrac{\$50,000}{\$1,000} \times \$7.86 = \$393$

(b) straight-life policy: $\dfrac{\$50,000}{\$1,000} \times \$21.41 = \$1,070.50$

Type of Life Insurance	Year's Premium Is Paid and Coverage Lasts	Cash Value
Five-year term	Five years	No
Straight-life	Life of insured	Yes

Use Tables 16-4 and 16-5 to find the quarterly premium for a $50,000 straight-life policy on a 30-year-old female.

$$\begin{pmatrix} \text{Monthly, quarterly,} \\ \text{or semiannual} \\ \text{premium} \end{pmatrix} = \begin{pmatrix} \text{annual} \\ \text{premium} \end{pmatrix} \times \begin{pmatrix} \text{rate from} \\ \text{Table 16-5} \end{pmatrix}$$

Annual premium =

$$\frac{\$50,000}{\$1,000} \times \$13.70 = \$685$$

Quarterly premium =

$$\$685 \times 0.26 = \$178.10$$

WORDS TO KNOW

insurance (p. 658)
comprehensive policy (p. 658)
insured (p. 658)
policyholder (p. 658)
insurer (p. 658)
underwriter (p. 658)
policy (p. 658)
premium (p. 658)
face value (p. 658)
beneficiary (p. 658)

fire insurance (p. 658)
coinsurance clause (p. 659)
rider (p. 661)
motor vehicle insurance (p. 662)
liability insurance (p. 663)
comprehensive insurance (p. 663)
collision insurance (p. 663)
no-fault insurance (p. 663)
territory (p. 663)
driver class (p. 663)

bodily injury (p. 663)
property damage (p. 663)
deductible amount (p. 664)
book value (p. 664)
totaled (p. 664)
life insurance (p. 665)
term insurance (p. 665)
straight-life insurance (p. 665)
ordinary life insurance (p. 665)

CHAPTER 16   CONCEPTS ANALYSIS

1. The formula for finding an annual fire insurance premium amount using a table with rates per $100 of face value (Table 16-1) is given on page 658. Another source may have a table giving rates per $1,000 of face value. How will the formula change for using this table?

2. If the new rates for the table described in exercise 1 are equivalent to the rates in Table 16-1, what would the new rates be? Revise Table 16-1 to show the equivalent rates per $1,000.

3. If a business had fire insurance to cover 60% of the property's value, and fire damages were 40% of the total value, what percent will the insurance company with an 80% coinsurance clause pay for the loss?

4. If a business had fire insurance to cover 80% of the property's value, and fire damages were 90% of the total value, what percent will the insurance company with an 80% coinsurance clause pay for the loss?

5. If a car rental agency charges $8.50 per day for insurance coverage, this would be equivalent to what annual premium? Why do you suppose no difference is made for territory or driver class?

6. Why is straight-life insurance more expensive than term-life insurance?

7. Justify why the life insurance premiums are higher for males than females who are in the same age category.

8. The formula given for using Table 16-4 is
$$\text{Annual premium} = \frac{\text{face value}}{\$1,000} \times \text{rate}.$$
Is the formula:
$$\text{Annual premium} = \text{face value} \times \frac{\text{rate}}{\$1,000}$$
equivalent? Why or why not?

9. Examine the two formulas given in exercise 8. Which formula do you think is more practical to use? Why?

10. Convert the rates in Table 16-4 to rates per $10,000 of face value.

Section 16.1

Using Table 16-1, find the annual fire insurance premium for each of the following.

| | Area Rank | Class | Face Value of Policy | | Annual Premium | | |
			Building	Contents	Building	Contents	Total
1.	3	A	$72,000	$26,000			
2.	1	C	$38,000	$21,000			
3.	2	B	$116,000	$41,700			
4.	2	A	$78,500	$32,300			
5.	3	C	$105,000	$63,500			
6.	1	B	$258,000	$79,000			

The following policies include an 80% coinsurance clause. A fire has caused the given amount of damage. Determine the compensation paid by the insurance company.

	Value of Building	Face Value of Policy	Will the Owner Receive Full Compensation?	Amount of Damage	Compensation
7.	$105,600	$ 84,480		$17,000	
8.	$ 95,800	$ 72,300		$22,000	
9.	$131,300	$105,040		$65,000	
10.	$261,500	$115,500		$85,000	

Use Table 16-1 when necessary to solve the following problems.

11. A sign company owns a class A building in area 2 valued at $95,000. The building is insured for $60,000 and the policy has an 80% coinsurance clause. How much will the owner of the sign company receive from his policy if a fire causes $38,000 in damages?

12. What part of the damages will Hampton Insurance Company pay on a building damaged by fire if the market value is $86,000 and it is insured for $68,800? The policy contains an 80% coinsurance clause.

13. Robyn Presley insures her class B building located in area 3 for $60,000 and the contents for $35,000. Find the total annual insurance premium.

14. In area 1, a class C building is insured for $105,000 and its contents for $55,000. If no extra charge is added for semiannual payments, find the premium paid every six months.

15. Find the total annual premium for full coverage of a class A building in area 1 if it is worth $85,000 and its contents are worth $23,200.

16. (a) The Greenwood Rental building is worth $86,900. The building is a class A building in area 3. What is the annual fire insurance premium on the building and its contents if the contents are valued at $32,000?

    (b) If the premium can be paid semiannually with a 2% annual charge added, what is the amount to be paid every six months?

17. The Country Store is valued at $73,500. To satisfy the 80% coinsurance clause of the policy, for how much should the owner insure the building?

18. (a) John Long owns a building with a market value of $121,300. He has insured the building for $85,800. A fire has caused $52,370 in damages. How much will the insurance company pay as compensation if his policy contains an 80% coinsurance clause?

    (b) If he had insured the building for 80% of its value, how much compensation would he receive?

19. How much must the insured pay on a building worth $65,700 if it receives fire damages totaling $17,000? The building is insured for $50,000 and the fire insurance policy contains an 80% coinsurance clause.

20. Harry's Plumbing Company is in a building worth $75,000. Harry has insured the building for $50,000 with a policy containing an 80% coinsurance clause. Fire loss is found to be $37,500.
    (a) How much will the insurance company pay for the loss?

    (b) How much of the loss must Harry pay?

Section 16.2

Use Table 16-3 to find the total annual premium for each of the following automobile liability insurance policies.

	Territory	Driver Class	Total Coverage	Annual Premium
21.	1	B	25/50/10	
22.	2	A	50/100/10	
23.	1	C	100/300/25	
24.	2	B	50/100/25	
25.	2	C	50/100/10	
26.	1	A	100/300/50	

Use Table 16-3 to solve the following problems.

27. (a) Explain what an insurance policy with 50/100/25 coverage means.

    (b) If you live in territory 1 and are classified as a class A driver, what would be the total cost of the annual premium for this policy?

28. If Louisa Gonzales is a class C driver and lives in territory 1, what is her annual automobile liability insurance premium if she chooses $100,000 for bodily injury for each individual with $300,000 total bodily injury and $50,000 for property damage?

29. The company car for the Greenwood Rental Agency in territory 2 for a class C driver is insured with 50/100/25 coverage. What is the annual insurance premium?

30. Aggawal Montoya is a class B driver who lives in territory 1. He is carrying automobile insurance with 100/300/50 coverage and pays the premium annually. How much does he pay each year?

31. If you have an accident that damages a fence, up to what amount would your automobile liability insurance policy pay if you have 25/50/10 coverage?

32. Larry Tremont has a collision insurance policy with a $200 deductible clause. If he hits a tree and causes $876 in damages to his car, how much must he pay and how much will the insurance company pay for his damages?

33. Sally Greenspan would like to buy a no-fault insurance policy for $20,000 and an uninsured motorist policy worth $25,000. The cost is $8.17 per $1,000 for the no-fault insurance and $7.93 per $1,000 for the uninsured motorist coverage. What is the cost of Sally's total annual premium?

34. Fred Case has an auto liability insurance policy with 25/50/10 coverage. He is responsible for an accident in which Sara Love, riding in another car, is injured. Her medical expenses totaled $36,243 and damages to her car totaled $4,756. What is the total amount Fred's insurance will pay?

35. As a class A driver in territory 1, Laura Jansky is buying an auto liability insurance policy with 100/300/25 coverage. She would like to pay the premium quarterly. Her insurance agent has explained that a $3.50 charge is added to each quarterly payment.
   (a) How much will her quarterly payments be?

   (b) How much will she have paid at the end of the year?

36. John Malinowsky has auto liability insurance with 25/50/10 coverage. In an accident for which John is responsible, a couple is injured. The husband has medical expenses of $23,268, and his wife's expenses are $21,764. Damage to their car totaled $2,769. How much will John's insurance company pay? How much should John pay?

37. Cheuk NamLam is a class A driver living in territory 1. He has auto liability insurance with 50/100/25 coverage. He is in an accident in which a woman is injured and has medical expenses of $55,452. Her car has $5,678 in damages. What is Cheuk's annual premium?

38. How much should Cheuk's insurance company pay the woman for her medical expenses and the damages to her car if he is responsible for the accident (see exercise 37)?

Section 16.3

Use Table 16-4 to find the annual premium of each of the following life insurance policies.

	Sex	Age	Policy Type	Face Value	Annual Premium
39.	Male	20	Five-year term	$30,000	
40.	Male	30	Five-year term	$90,000	
41.	Female	20	Straight-life	$60,000	
42.	Male	50	Straight-life	$100,000	

Use Tables 16-4 and 16-5 to find the following premiums.

	Sex	Age	Policy Type	Face Value	Premium Annual	Monthly	Quarterly
43.	Female	60	Straight-life	$50,000			
44.	Male	20	Straight-life	$40,000			
45.	Female	30	Straight-life	$80,000			
46.	Male	40	Five-year term	$100,000			

47. Explain the differences between term and straight-life insurance policies.

48. If Sam Molla has a five-year term insurance policy with a value of $40,000 purchased at age 35, how much will his beneficiary receive if he dies at age 39? How much will the beneficiary receive if he dies at 41?

49. (a) Find the annual premium paid by Sara Cushion, age 30, on a straight-life insurance policy for $25,000?

(b) Find the quarterly premium Sara would pay on the straight-life policy.

50. Find the annual premium paid on a straight-life insurance policy for $60,000 taken out at age 30 by a male. How much has he paid by age 45?

51. A straight-life policy purchased at age 60 by a male costs how much more per $1,000 than the same policy for a female age 60?

52. How much more would $50,000 in straight-life insurance cost in total annual premiums than $50,000 in five-year term life insurance if both policies were purchased by a 20-year-old male?

53. How much more would be paid in monthly premiums than in annual premiums on a $50,000 straight-life term policy taken out at age 30 by a male?

54. Find the difference in monthly payments paid by a 40-year-old female on a five-year term policy and a straight-life policy for $60,000.

55. How much are the total quarterly payments paid by Erich Shultz, age 40, and his wife Demetria, age 30, if each has a straight-life insurance policy for $70,000?

56. Write formulas for Jacobs Insurance Broker policyholder premiums.

(a) Find the Building Premium.   (b) Find the Contents Premium.   (c) Find the Total Annual Premium.

57. Complete the spreadsheet using the formulas.

Microsoft Excel - CLE_SE_16-57.xls

File Edit View Insert Format Tools Data Window Help

Times New Roman   14   B I U

N18   =

	A	B	C	D	E	F	G	H	I	J
1			Jacobs Insurance Broker - Annual Policyholder Premiums							
2	Name	Area	Face Value		Building	Rate		Premium		Annual
3		Rank	Building	Contents	Class	Building	Contents	Building	Contents	Pemium
4	Aaron, Bonnie	1	$195,380.00	$85,267.00	A	$0.59	$0.64			
5	Buhler, Noreen	1	$194,400.00	$97,400.00	B	$0.75	$0.89			
6	Ganong, Roger	3	$89,840.00	$46,000.00	A	$0.62	$0.67			
7	Hampton, Robert	1	$163,200.00	$79,500.00	C	$0.94	$1.11			
8	Jackson, William	2	$295,600.00	$146,400.00	B	$0.76	$0.91			
9	McDonald, Mark	2	$326,550.00	$164,500.00	A	$0.60	$0.65			
10	Nu, Jung Pao	3	$62,800.00	$28,500.00	C	$0.98	$1.16			
11	Riviera, Jose	2	$217,300.00	$105,300.00	B	$0.65	$0.76			
12	Roux, Jeffrey	2	$195,300.00	$95,600.00	B	$0.96	$1.13			
13	Sanders, Donna	3	$85,000.00	$46,300.00	B	$0.78	$0.93			

Sheet1 / Sheet2 / Sheet3 /

Challenge Problems

58. Manny Bober has a fire insurance policy with a value of $120,000. His annual premium is $0.95 per $100 of coverage. If Manny cancels the policy after 300 days, what is his refund if the refund is prorated based on a 360-day year?

59. A universal life insurance policy is a relatively new type of life insurance in which the company invests the cash value of your policy and gives you a certain percent of the returns on their investments. An annual report, similar to the portion shown in Figure 16-1, shows the amount of cash value, the face value of the policy, and the interest earned. Examine the annual statement and find:

(a) The death benefits of this policy

(b) The monthly premiums

(c) The total cash value of the policy

(d) The total interest credited

(e) The guaranteed interest rate for the cash value accumulation

60. In Figure 16-1, examine the cash value at the end of each month. Determine a formula for finding the cash value.

C and M Insurance Company
Annual Report
Universal Life Insurance Policy

Kevin Presley—Policyholder		Soc. Sec. Number: 080–05–3182
Death benefit beg. of year:	60,000.00	Cash value
Death benefit end of year:	60,000.00	End of prior year: 650.92
Current specified amount	60,000.00	Impaired by loans: 0.00

Summary of Activity for Policy Year Ending 03/04/02

Month Begin	Gross Premium	Loading	Cost of Insurance	Expense Charges	Interest(4) Credited	Partial Withdrawal	Loan(5) Activity	Cash Value
03/04	35.00	2.80	8.08	0.00	4.89	0.00	0.00	679.93
04/04	35.00	2.80	8.07	0.00	5.10	0.00	0.00	709.16
05/04	35.00	2.80	8.07	0.00	5.30	0.00	0.00	738.59
06/04	35.00	2.80	8.07	0.00	5.52	0.00	0.00	768.24
07/04	35.00	2.80	8.06	0.00	5.72	0.00	0.00	798.10
08/04	35.00	2.80	8.06	0.00	5.92	0.00	0.00	828.16
09/04	35.00	2.80	8.05	0.00	6.13	0.00	0.00	858.44
10/04	35.00	2.80	8.05	0.00	6.34	0.00	0.00	888.93
11/04	35.00	2.80	8.05	0.00	6.58	0.00	0.00	919.66
12/04	35.00	2.80	8.04	0.00	6.70	0.00	0.00	950.52
01/04	35.00	2.80	8.04	0.00	7.02	0.00	0.00	981.70
02/04	35.00	2.80	8.03	0.00	7.29	0.00	0.00	1013.16
			(3)		(1)	(2)		
Total	420.00	33.60	96.67	0.00	72.51	0.00		

Negative values indicate that premium was not paid prior to the contract's issue date or monthly anniversary date. Subsequent premium payments increase these values.

Policy values as of 03/04/02:
Cash value:	1,013.16	(1)Interest credited	
Unpaid loans:	0.00	Guaranteed portion:	34.32
Policy surrender charges:	0.00	Excess portion:	38.19
Policy surrender value:	1,013.16	(2)Partial withdrawal charges	
(3)Rider charges included:	0.00	Included in above:	0.00

(4)Current annual interest rate schedule applicable to cash value accumulation:
Type cash value accumulated	RATE
Primary, unimpaired by loans	9.000
Impaired by policy loans	4.500

(5)The current loan interest rate is 8.000% payable in arrears.
The death benefit is reduced by any outstanding loan balance.

The guaranteed interest rate for the life of the policy is 4.500%.
Your planned periodic premium is $35.00 paid monthly.

Figure 16-1 Universal Life Insurance Policy Report

1. Find the annual premium on a $95,000 straight-life insurance policy for a 40-year-old male.

2. Find the annual premium on a 25/50/25 automobile liability insurance policy for a class C driver in territory 2.

3. Find the face value of a fire-protection policy on a building worth $87,500 if it is insured for 75% of its market value.

4. How much will a 50/100/10 automobile liability insurance policy pay for medical expenses of a couple injured in an accident if their total expenses were $53,768, but the expenses of each were less than $50,000?

5. Find the monthly payments on a five-year term insurance policy for $75,000 for a 30-year-old male.

6. How much are the quarterly premiums on a 50/100/25 automobile liability insurance policy for a class B driver in territory 1 if a 2% charge is added to annual premiums that are paid quarterly?

7. How much more are the annual premiums for a class A driver in territory 2 than for a class A driver in territory 1 if both have 25/50/10 coverage?

8. A building and its contents are insured for $78,000 and $12,760, respectively. Find the total annual premium if the building is a class C building in area 3.

9. Find the quarterly payments on a five-year term life insurance policy for $95,000 on a 40-year-old female.

10. If you have 25/50/10 automobile liability insurance and have an accident that is your fault and injures the driver of the other car, how much must you pay for the $4,562 in damages to his car and $25,760 in medical expenses?

11. Explain the difference between term and straight-life insurance policies.

12. How much insurance do you need on a $68,500 building if you wish to satisfy the 80% coinsurance clause?

13. How much more would be paid by a 30-year-old female in monthly premiums than in annual premiums for a $60,000 straight-life insurance policy?

14. Compare the cost per year of a straight-life insurance policy for $70,000 to a five-year term policy for a 60-year-old male.

15. If you have a collision insurance policy with a $250 deductible clause, how much of the $675 damage to your car will the policy cover?

16. How much will a five-year term policy pay to the beneficiary upon the death of a 26-year-old female if she purchased the $30,000 policy at age 20?

17. The market value of a building is $72,500. It has been insured for $50,000 with an 80% coinsurance clause. If a fire causes $62,000 in damages, how much of the damages will the policy cover?

18. A $67,200 building is insured for $40,000 by a fire insurance policy containing an 80% coinsurance clause. A fire causes $12,365 in damages. How much of the loss does the insured have to pay?

19. Find the semiannual premium for a 50/100/25 automobile liability insurance policy for a class A driver in territory 2 if there is no additional charge for semiannual payment.

20. Fire causes $18,700 in damages to a $98,000 building insured for $70,000. An 80% coinsurance clause is included. How much of the damages will the insurer pay?

1. Building: $\dfrac{\$120,000}{\$100} \times \$0.62 = \$744$

   Contents: $\dfrac{\$75,000}{\$100} \times \$0.67 = \$502.50$

   Total annual premium: $\$744 + \$502.50 = \$1,246.50$

2. Building: $\dfrac{\$150,000}{\$100} \times \$0.94 = \$1,410$

   Contents: $\dfrac{\$68,000}{\$100} \times \$1.11 = \$754.80$

   Total annual premium: $\$1,410 + \$754.80 = \$2,164.80$

3. Charge: $\$2,164.80 \times 0.02 = \$43.30$

   Semiannual premium: $(\$2,164.80 + \$43.30) \div 2 = \$2,208.10 \div 2 = \$1,104.05$

4. $\dfrac{\$350,000}{\$100} \times \$0.76 = \$2,660$

   $\dfrac{\$100,000}{\$100} \times \$0.91 = \$910$

   $\$2,660 + \$910 = \$3,570$

5. $\dfrac{\$200,000}{\$100} \times \$0.59 = \$1,180$

   $\dfrac{\$85,000}{\$100} \times \$0.64 = \$544$

   $\$1,180 + \$544 = \$1,724$

   $\$1,724 \times 0.02 = \$34.48$

   $\$1,724 + \$34.48 = \$1,758.48$

   $\$1,758.48 \div 4 = \$439.62$

6. $0.80 \times \$255,000 = \$204,000$; since this is 80%, the insurance company will pay all losses up to the face value of the policy, which is $204,000.

7. $75,000

8. Face value required for full compensation: $0.8 \times \$295,000$
   $= \$236,000$

   Actual compensation:

   $\$100,000 \times \dfrac{\$100,000}{\$236,000}$

   $= \$42,372.88$

9. $\$395,000 \times 0.8 = \$316,000$

10. $\$83,000 \times \dfrac{\$220,000}{\$316,000} = \$57,784.81$

11. The expected cost is a range of values. For $20,000 coverage the cost would be twice the cost for $10,000. $\$100 \times 2 = \$200$; $\$150 \times 2 = \$300$. The range would be $200 to $300.

12. Answers will vary.

13.

Type of coverage	Amount	Premium
Computer	$10,000	$100 to $150
Business Pursuits Liability	minimum	50 to 100
Business Interruptions	10,000	100 to 100
Totals		$250 to $350

The range is from $250 to $350.

1. $\$491 + \$265 = \$756$

2. Class C driver in territory 1:   Class C driver in territory 2:

   $\$841 + \$394 = \$1,235$ $\$556 + \$265 = \$821$

   Cost for driver in territory 1 is $414 more.

3. Annual premium: $\$480 + \$258 = \$738$

   Monthly premium: $\$738 \div 12 = \$61.50$

4. $8,362 for injuries; $0 paid by insured

1. $\dfrac{\$45{,}000}{\$1{,}000} \times \$4.96 = \$223.20$

2. $\dfrac{\$45{,}000}{\$1{,}000} \times \$11.06 = \$497.70$

3. $\dfrac{\$100{,}000}{\$1{,}000} \times \$15.25 \times 0.26$
   $= \$396.50$

4. $\dfrac{\$50{,}000}{\$1{,}000} \times \$32.99 \times \$0.0875 = \$144.33$

5. Male: $\dfrac{\$75{,}000}{\$1{,}000} \times \$7.86 = \$589.50$

   Female: $\dfrac{\$75{,}000}{\$1{,}000} \times \$6.46 = \$484.50$

   The male pays a higher premium.

6. Male: $\dfrac{\$75{,}000}{\$1{,}000} \times \$31.40 = \$2{,}355$

   Female: $\dfrac{\$75{,}000}{\$1{,}000} \times \$17.74 = \$1{,}330.50$

   The male pays a higher premium.

7. Females have a longer life expectancy than males; thus, the insurance rates are lower.

8. It requires more time and more record-keeping for the insurance company to process the additional payments.

17

Taxes

17.1 Sales Tax

1 Use tables to find the sales tax.

2 Use the percent method to find the sales tax.

3 Find the marked price and the sales tax from the total price.

17.2 Property Tax

1 Find the assessed value.

2 Calculate property tax.

3 Determine the property tax rate.

17.3 Income Taxes

1 Find taxable income.

2 Use the tax tables to calculate income tax.

3 Use the tax rate schedules to calculate income tax.

Good Decisions through Teamwork

With members of your team, contact your local city and county tax assessor to find the current assessment rates for various types of property. Select a property from the list below and determine the rate at which the property is assessed, the tax rate for both city and county taxes if applicable, and the total annual tax that must be paid on the property. Properties include:

- 160 acres of farmland with an estimated market value of $192,000
- A townhome with an estimated market value of $275,000
- A duplex rental property with an estimated market value of $218,000
- A railroad yard with an estimated market value of $3,587,000
- A natural gas property with an estimated market value of $489,500

Prepare a report and make a presentation of your team's findings to the class.

Taxes affect everyone in one way or another. A **tax** is money collected by a government for its own support and for providing services to the populace. Governments use tax money to pay the salaries of government officials and employees. Tax monies run and staff public schools, parks, and playgrounds; build and maintain roads and highways; and provide police and fire protection, health services, unemployment compensation, and numerous other benefits.

To meet these many needs, governments have a variety of tax types from which to choose. Among the most common are sales taxes, property taxes, and income taxes.

17.1 Sales Tax

1 Use tables to find the sales tax.

2 Use the percent method to find the sales tax.

3 Find the marked price and the sales tax from the total price.

The sales tax is probably the first type of tax that most people encounter since most states have sales taxes. Sales taxes are determined by state and local governments. At the time of a purchase, a store collects an extra amount, called a **sales tax,** and later pays it to the state. In some states, county or city governments charge a local sales tax in addition to the state sales tax. Many states charge no sales tax on food or medicine, and some states make other exceptions. New Jersey, for example, does not charge tax on clothing.

In some areas a sales tax is charged only on purchases made and delivered within the tax area. For instance, if an item is purchased in one state and delivered to another, the sales tax is not always charged. This also applies to many catalog and Internet purchases. State laws vary and change often, and it is the responsibility of the seller to determine if tax is exempt on a sale. However, the state to which large purchases are delivered may impose its sales tax. For instance, if an automobile is purchased in one state and delivered to another, the state into which it is delivered may require that sales tax be paid before the automobile can be registered.

Several ways of figuring the amount of sales tax are in common use. Most businesses use computerized cash registers that allow the current tax rate to be programmed into the cash register. Then the register automatically figures sales tax. In most states the sales tax is a specified percent of the selling price.

1 Use tables to find the sales tax.

For convenience, many state and local governments distribute **sales tax tables** to businesses that request them. These tables allow employees to determine the proper sales tax quickly. Table 17-1 shows a small portion of a sales tax table. Note that the *state* sales tax rate in Table 17-1 is 5.5%. There is also a local sales tax of 2.25%. The result is a combined tax rate of 7.75%.

Table 17-1   Total Sales Tax (7.75%) Combining Local Tax (2.25%) and State Tax (5.5%)

Purchase Price			Purchase Price		
From	To	Tax	From	To	Tax
0.01	0.10	0.00	4.97	5.09	0.39
0.11	0.19	0.01	5.10	5.22	0.40
0.20	0.32	0.02	5.23	5.35	0.41
0.33	0.45	0.03	5.36	5.48	0.42
0.46	0.58	0.04	5.49	5.61	0.43
0.59	0.70	0.05	5.62	5.74	0.44
0.71	0.83	0.06	5.75	5.87	0.45
0.84	0.96	0.07	5.88	5.99	0.46
0.97	1.09	0.08	6.00	6.12	0.47
1.10	1.22	0.09	6.13	6.25	0.48
1.23	1.35	0.10	6.26	6.38	0.49
1.36	1.48	0.11	6.39	6.51	0.50
1.49	1.61	0.12	6.52	6.64	0.51
1.62	1.74	0.13	6.65	6.77	0.52
1.75	1.87	0.14	6.78	6.90	0.53
1.88	1.99	0.15	6.91	7.03	0.54
2.00	2.12	0.16	7.04	7.16	0.55
2.13	2.25	0.17	7.17	7.29	0.56
2.26	2.38	0.18	7.30	7.41	0.57
2.39	2.51	0.19	7.42	7.54	0.58
2.52	2.64	0.20	7.55	7.67	0.59
2.65	2.77	0.21	7.68	7.80	0.60
2.78	2.90	0.22	7.81	7.93	0.61
2.91	3.03	0.23	7.94	8.06	0.62
3.04	3.16	0.24	8.07	8.19	0.63
3.17	3.29	0.25	8.20	8.32	0.64
3.30	3.41	0.26	8.33	8.45	0.65
3.42	3.54	0.27	8.46	8.58	0.66
3.55	3.67	0.28	8.59	8.70	0.67
3.68	3.80	0.29	8.71	8.83	0.68
3.81	3.93	0.30	8.84	8.96	0.69
3.94	4.06	0.31	8.97	9.09	0.70
4.07	4.19	0.32	9.10	9.22	0.71
4.20	4.32	0.33	9.23	9.35	0.72
4.33	4.45	0.34	9.36	9.48	0.73
4.46	4.58	0.35	9.49	9.61	0.74
4.59	4.70	0.36	9.62	9.74	0.75
4.71	4.83	0.37	9.75	9.87	0.76
4.84	4.96	0.38	9.88	9.99	0.77

HOW TO   Use a Table to Find the Sales Tax

1. Read the table's title and any explanatory notes about sales tax requirements.
2. If the price is within the scope of the table,
   (a) Locate the interval row that includes the price.
   (b) In the tax column, locate the tax corresponding to the price interval.
3. If the price is beyond the scope of the table,
   (a) Choose two or more smaller prices within the scope of the table and whose sum is the original price.
   (b) Calculate the sales tax on each smaller price, according to step 2.
   (c) Add the taxes from step 3b.

EXAMPLE Find the sales tax on a purchase of $4.30 using the sales tax rate given in Table 17-1.

$4.30 falls within the interval $4.20–$4.32. The sales tax from the table is $0.33.

The sales tax for $4.30 is $0.33.

Table 17-1 shows the tax on purchases only up to $9.99. To find the tax on a purchase of more than $9.99, you could use Table 17-1 by adding the taxes charged on two or more smaller prices whose sum is the original price.

EXAMPLE Use Table 17-1 to find the sales tax for a purchase of $16.43.

In Table 17-1, find two amounts that add together to equal $16.43.

$9.99 + $6.44 = $16.43	**$9.99 and $6.44 are both in Table 17-1.**
$0.77	
+ $0.50	**From Table 17-1, the tax on $9.99 is $0.77, and the tax on $6.44 is $0.50. Add the two amounts of tax to find the total tax due.**
$1.27	

The tax on a purchase of $16.43 is $1.27.

The table method for finding the sales tax is generally used by only very small businesses. Some examples of circumstances in which a tax table may be used are sales at a flea market or craft show, by a street vendor, or at a garage sale. By far the most common method for finding sales tax is the percent method.

2 Use the percent method to find the sales tax.

You can find sales tax without tables by taking the appropriate percent of the purchase price and rounding to the nearest cent. From Table 17–1, the sales tax on $0.58 is $0.04 and the sales tax on $0.59 is $0.05. To compare, find 7.75% of each of the amounts. Use the decimal equivalent of 7.7590.

$$\$0.58 \times 0.0775 = \$0.04495 \qquad \$0.59 \times 0.0775 = \$0.045725$$
$$= \$0.04 \qquad\qquad\qquad = \$0.05$$
(rounded to the nearest cent) (rounded to the nearest cent)

The calculated tax is the same as the amount in the table. We can find the tax on any amount by multiplying the amount by 7.75%. With large amounts, multiplying by a percent is usually quicker than using the table, especially when a calculator or electronic cash register is available. Remember to round the tax to the nearest cent.

 HOW TO Use the Percent Method to Find the Sales Tax

1. Express the sales tax rate as tax per $1.00 of the purchase price or as a percent: write the given percent as a decimal.
2. Multiply the purchase price or marked price by the sales tax rate from step 1.

Sales tax = purchase price × sales tax rate

where sales tax rate = tax per $1.00 of the purchase price or a percent of the purchase price.

EXAMPLE Find the sales tax on $128.72 at six cents per $1.00 or 6%.

$128.72 × 6% = $128.72 × 0.06

= $7.72 (rounded)

> **Multiply the purchase price by 6%.**
> **Change the percent to a decimal (0.06).**
> **Round the answer to the nearest cent.**

The sales tax is $7.72.

Since sales tax tables are not always readily available and since technology is so readily available, it is convenient and practical to use percents to figure sales tax. In most states sales tax is figured by multiplying the purchase price by a percent of the purchase price. The popularity of straight percent sales tax rates has coincided with the growing availability of computerized cash registers that automatically figure such taxes and inexpensive handheld calculators.

 Find the marked price and the sales tax from the total price.

Some circumstances make it more convenient to include the sales tax in the quoted price. These circumstances may include sporting events, amusement parks, flea markets, or other places where making change can be difficult and time consuming. In these instances the sales tax eventually must be calculated so that the proper tax is turned over to the tax agency. When the sales tax is not itemized, you may want to know how much the sales tax was or what the *marked price* of the item was. The **marked price** is the purchase price or the price before sales tax is added. The **total price** is the marked price plus the sales tax.

> **? HOW TO** Find the Marked Price and the Sales Tax from the Total Price
>
> **1.** Find the marked price:
>   **(a)** Express the sales tax rate as tax per $1.00 or percent of the purchase (marked) price: write the given percent as a decimal.
>   **(b)** Add 1 to the sales tax rate from step 1a.
>   **(c)** Divide the total price by the sum from step 1b.
>
> $$\text{Marked price} = \frac{\text{total price}}{1 + \text{sales tax rate}}$$
>
>   Where sales tax rate = tax per $1.00 or percent of the purchase (marked) price.
> **2.** Find the sales tax: subtract the marked price from the total price.
>
> $$\text{Sales tax} = \text{total price} - \text{marked price}$$

TIP! **Why Add 1 to the Sales Tax Rate?**

In the formula for finding the marked price from the total price, the denominator is 1 + sales tax rate.

In calculating sales tax directly from the marked price, the marked price is the base

$$\text{Sales tax} = \text{Sales tax rate} \times \text{marked price}$$

$$\text{Percentage} = \text{rate} \times \text{base}$$

The total price is the marked price plus the sales tax.

$$\text{Total price} = \text{marked price} + \text{sales tax}$$

The corresponding rates are:

$$\text{Total price rate} = \text{marked price rate} + \text{sales tax rate}$$

Since the marked price is the base, the marked price rate is 100%. Then,

$$\text{Total price rate} = 100\% + \text{sales tax rate}$$

OR

$$\text{Total price rate} = 1 + \text{sales tax rate}$$

To find the marked price, we are using the variation of the percentage formula

$$B = \frac{P}{R} \qquad \text{OR} \qquad \text{marked price} = \frac{\text{total price}}{\text{total price rate}}$$

Thus,

$$\text{Marked price} = \frac{\text{total price}}{1 + \text{sales tax rate}}$$

EXAMPLE At an amusement park concession, the items are priced to include tax. Find the marked price and the sales tax. The sales tax rate is 7%.

Popcorn: $1.50
Soft drink: $2.00
Hot dog: $2.50

$$\text{Marked price} = \frac{\text{total price}}{1 + \text{sales tax rate (as a decimal)}}$$

$$\text{Popcorn marked price} = \frac{\$1.50}{1 + 0.07} = \frac{\$1.50}{1.07} = \$1.40$$

$$\text{Soft drink marked price} = \frac{\$2.00}{1 + 0.07} = \frac{\$2.00}{1.07} = \$1.87$$

$$\text{Hot dog marked price} = \frac{\$2.50}{1 + 0.07} = \frac{\$2.50}{1.07} = \$2.34$$

$$\text{Sales tax} = \text{total price} - \text{marked price}$$

$$\text{Popcorn sales tax} = \$1.50 - \$1.40 = \$0.10$$

$$\text{Soft drink sales tax} = \$2.00 - \$1.87 = \$0.13$$

$$\text{Hot dog sales tax} = \$2.50 - \$2.34 = \$0.16$$

The marked prices for the popcorn, soft drink, and hot dog are $1.40, $1.87, and $2.34. The sales taxes for the popcorn, soft drink, and hot dog are $0.10, $0.13, and $0.16.

TIP! Why Not Just Multiply the Sales Tax Rate Times the Total Price and Subtract?

A common mistake when determining the marked price from the total price is to apply the sales tax rate to the total price and then subtract. Let's try that with the $1.50 popcorn.

$$\text{Popcorn} = \frac{\$1.50}{1 + 0.07}$$

$$= \frac{\$1.50}{1.07}$$

$$= \$1.40 \text{ (marked price)}$$

CORRECT

Popcorn = $1.50 × 0.07

= 0.105

= $0.11 to the nearest cent

$1.50 − $0.11 = $1.39 (marked price)

INCORRECT

What happened? Sales tax is applied to the marked or purchase price. That is, the marked price is the base. To find a percent of the total price, use the total price as the base.

As the marked price increases, the difference would be more dramatic. Look at a painting sold at a flea market for $200 with a sales tax rate of 7%.

$$\text{Marked price} = \frac{\$200}{1 + 0.07}$$

$$= \frac{\$2.00}{1.07}$$

$$= \$186.92 \text{ (rounded)}$$

$$\text{Sales tax} = \$200 - \$186.92$$

$$= \$13.08$$

CORRECT

Sales tax = $200 × 0.07

= $14

Marked price = $200 − $14

= $186

INCORRECT

Here the correct sales tax is $0.92 less than the incorrect calculations.

SELF-CHECK 17.1

1. Use Table 17-1 to find the sales tax for a purchase of $5.86.

2. Find the sales tax on a purchase of $12.36 using the sales tax rate given in Table 17-1.

3. Charles Baker purchased a paperback book for $8.95. Use Table 17-1 to find the sales tax on the purchase.

4. Dwight Campbell purchased a shirt for $17.85. Use Table 17-1 to find the sales tax on the purchase.

5. Find the sales tax on an appliance costing $288.63 if the tax rate is 5.5%.

6. Figure the sales tax on a ring that costs $2,860 in a state with a 6.5% sales tax rate.

7. Barbara Budynas purchased 100 azaleas at a cost of $283. Find the sales tax on the purchase if the rate is 7.25%.

8. Larry Butts paid $195.95 for a new television. He paid sales tax at a rate of $6\frac{3}{4}\%$. How much tax did he pay?

3

9. What is the marked price if a total bill is $182.38 and the sales tax rate is 6%?

10. Clifford Shropshire has a flea market booth and marks all his items so that the price includes state sales tax at a rate of 6.5%. He sold a set of china for $285. How much sales tax should he send to the state?

11. You have agreed to pay $850 for a used utility trailer. The price includes sales tax at a rate of 7.75%. What was the marked price of the trailer and how much tax was paid?

12. You have a receipt for a purchase that shows the total amount of the purchase to be $318.97. The sales tax rate is 8.25%. How much of the $318.97 is the cost of the item and how much is sales tax?

17.2 Property Tax

1 Find the assessed value.

2 Calculate property tax.

3 Determine the property tax rate.

Most states allow cities and counties to collect money by charging a **property tax** on land, houses, buildings, and improvements and on such personal property as automobiles, jewelry, and furniture.

1 Find the assessed value.

Property tax is usually calculated using the assessed value of the property rather than using the **market value** (the expected selling price of the property). The **assessed value** is a specified percent of the estimated market value of the property. This percent, which may vary according to the type of property, is set by the city or county that charges the tax. For example, your city or county may assess farm property and single-family dwellings at 25% of the market value, businesses and multi-family dwellings (duplexes, apartments) at 40% of the market value, and utilities (power companies, telephone companies) at 50% of the market value.

? HOW TO Find the Assessed Value

1. Express the assessment rate as assessed value per $1.00 of market value: write the given percent as a decimal.
2. Multiply the market value of the property by the assessment rate from step 1.

Assessed value = market value × assessment rate

where assessment rate = assessed value per $1.00 of market value.

EXAMPLE Find the assessed value of a farm with a market value of $175,000 if the assessed valuation is 25% of the market value.

$175,000 × 0.25 = $43,750   Find 25% of $175,000.

The assessed value is $43,750.

2 Calculate property tax.

The city or county government, which imposes a property tax, might express the **property tax rate,** the rate of tax that must be paid on a piece of property, in one of several ways. The rate could be stated as a percent of the assessed value, as an amount of tax per $1.00 of assessed value, as an amount of tax per $100 of assessed value, as an amount of tax per $1,000 of assessed value, or in mills. A **mill** is one thousandth ($\frac{1}{1000}$, or 0.001) of a dollar. The next example shows how to calculate the property tax when the same tax is expressed in each of four ways.

? HOW TO Calculate the Property Tax

1. Express the given property tax rate as tax per $1.00 of assessed value:
   (a) If the given rate is a percent of assessed value, write the percent in decimal form.

$$\text{Tax per } \$1.00 = \text{decimal form of percent of assessed value}$$

   (b) If the given rate is tax per $100 of assessed value, divide the tax on $100 by 100.

$$\text{Tax per } \$1.00 = \frac{\text{tax on } \$100}{100}$$

   (c) If the given rate is tax per $1,000 of assessed value, divide the tax on $1,000 by 1,000.

$$\text{Tax per } \$1.00 = \frac{\text{tax on } \$1,000}{1,000}$$

   (d) If the given rate is a number of mills per $1.00 of assessed value, divide the number of mills by 1,000.

$$\text{Tax per } \$1.00 = \frac{\text{mills per } \$1.00}{1,000}$$

2. Multiply the assessed value by the property tax rate (tax per $1.00) from step 1.

Property tax = assessed value × property tax rate

where property tax rate = tax per $1.00 of assessed value.

EXAMPLE   Find the property tax on a home with an assessed value of $90,000 if the property tax rate is (a) 11.08% of the assessed value, (b) $11.08 per $100 of the assessed value, (c) $110.80 per $1,000 of the assessed value, (d) 110.8 mills per $1.00 of assessed value.

(a) Property tax = assessed value × tax rate

$$= \boxed{\$90,000} \times \boxed{0.1108} = \boxed{\$9,972}$$

The property tax is $9,972.

> Write the percent in decimal form as a tax per $1.00 of assessed value.

(b) Property tax = assessed value × $\dfrac{\text{tax on } \$100}{\$100}$

> Write the tax rate as an equivalent amount per $1.00 of assessed value.

$$= \$90,000 \times \frac{\$11.08}{\$100}$$

$$= \boxed{\$90,000} \times \boxed{0.1108} = \boxed{\$9,972}$$

The property tax is $9,972.

> Multiply the assessed value by the property tax rate per $1.00.

(c) Property tax = assessed value $\times \dfrac{\text{tax on }\$1,000}{\$1,000}$

Write the tax rate as an equivalent amount per $1.00 of assessed value.

$$= \$90,000 \times \dfrac{\$110.80}{\$1,000}$$

$$= \$90,000 \times 0.1108 = \$9,972$$

Multiply the assessed value by the property tax rate per $1.00.

The property tax is $9,972.

(d) Property tax = assessed value $\times \dfrac{\text{mills per }\$1.00}{\$1,000}$

Write the tax rate as an equivalent amount per $1.00 of assessed value.

$$= \$90,000 \times \dfrac{110.8 \text{ mills}}{\$1,000}$$

$$= \$90,000 \times 0.1108 = \$9,972$$

Multiply the assessed value by the property tax rate per $1.00.

The property tax is $9,972.

! TIP! Assessed Value versus Market Value

Be sure to use the *assessed value* in calculating the property tax. Look at what happens if you use the market value instead of the assessed value to calculate property tax.

Sue Billing's law office has a market value of $110,000 and an assessed value of $44,280. Her town has a tax rate of $173.60 per $1,000 of assessed value. Find the tax owed.

Tax on assessed value:

$$\$44,280 \times \dfrac{\$173.60}{\$1,000} = \$7,687.01$$

CORRECT

Tax on market value:

$$\$110,000 \times \dfrac{\cancel{\$173.60}}{\$1,000} = \$19,096$$

INCORRECT

---

3 Determine the property tax rate.

How does the city or county decide what the tax rate should be? The local government uses its estimated budget to determine how much money it will need in the year ahead. That amount is then divided by the **total assessed value** of *all* the property in its area. This calculation tells how much tax must be collected for each dollar of assessed property value. The tax rate can be written as a tax per $100 or $1,000 of assessed value by multiplying the tax on $1.00 by 100 or 1,000. Whenever you calculate the tax rate, if the division does not come out even, *round the decimal up* to the next ten-thousandth.

! TIP! Why Is the Tax Rate Always Rounded Up?

Find the tax rate per $1.00 if the total estimated budget is $18,000,000 and the total assessed property value is $118,400,000. Round using ordinary methods.

$$\text{Tax per }\$1.00 = \dfrac{\$18,000,000}{\$118,400,000} = \$0.15$$

Now, calculate the amount of tax that will be collected.

Total tax = assessed value $\times$ tax rate per $1.00 =

$$\$118,400,000 \times \$0.15 = \$17,760,000$$

The amount of money needed for the estimated budget will be short by $240,000. ($18,000,000 − $17,760,000 = $240,000)

HOW TO Determine a Property Tax Rate

1. Select the appropriate formula according to the desired tax rate type.

$$\left(\begin{array}{c}\text{Tax per \$1.00}\\\text{of assessed value}\end{array}\right) = \frac{\text{total estimated budget}}{\text{total assessed property value}}$$

$$\left(\begin{array}{c}\text{Tax per \$100}\\\text{of assessed value}\end{array}\right) = \frac{\text{total estimated budget}}{\text{total assessed property value}} \times 100$$

$$\left(\begin{array}{c}\text{Tax per \$1,000}\\\text{of assessed value}\end{array}\right) = \frac{\text{total estimated budget}}{\text{total assessed property value}} \times 1,000$$

$$\left(\begin{array}{c}\text{Tax, in mills, per \$1.00}\\\text{of assessed value}\end{array}\right) = \frac{\text{total estimated budget}}{\text{total assessed property value}} \times 1,000$$

2. Make calculations using the selected formula.

EXAMPLE   Find the tax rate expressed as tax per $100 of assessed value for Harbortown that anticipates expenses of $95,590,000 and has property assessed at $3,858,758,500.

$$\left(\begin{array}{c}\text{Tax per \$100}\\\text{of assessed value}\end{array}\right) = \frac{\$95,590,000}{\$3,858,758,500} \times \$100$$

$$= \$0.0247722162 \times \$100$$

$$= \$2.48 \text{ (rounded up)}$$

The tax rate is $2.48 per $100 of assessed value.

EXAMPLE   Harbortown (see the previous example) expects an increase in expenses of $5,000,000. To cover these expenses, the choices are to increase the tax rate or to reassess property values. The city assessor's office predicts that the reassessment would cost $100,000 and increase the city's assessment value of property to $4,300,000,000. The city leaders prefer the reassessment choice, but do not want to reassess property value and increase the tax rate in the same year. Which choice should the city leaders make?

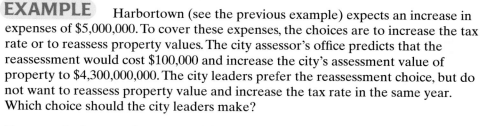

1 Decision needed   To cover the increase in expenses, should property be reassessed or should the tax rate be increased?

2 Known facts   Current expenses: $95,590,000
Expected increase in expenses: $5,000,000
Current assessed property: $3,858,758,500
Current tax rate: $2.48 per $100 of assessed value
Expected reassessment values: $4,300,000,000
Cost of reassessment: $100,000

3 Unknown facts   Total property taxes if property reassessed

4 Relationships   Total property taxes from reassessed property values =

$$\text{Expected reassessed values} \times \frac{\$2.48}{\$100}$$

Expected total expenses if property reassessed =
current expenses + expected increase + cost of reassessment

5 Estimation	Expected revenue between $4,000,000,000 \times \dfrac{\$2}{\$100}$
	and $4,000,000,000 \times \dfrac{\$3}{\$100}$ ($80,000,000 and $120,000,000)
6 Calculation	Total property taxes from reassessment $= \$4,300,000,000 \times \dfrac{\$2.48}{\$100}$
	$= \$106,640,000$
	Expected total expenses $= \$95,590,000 + \$5,000,000 + \$100,000$
	$= \$100,690,000$
7 Interpretation	Property taxes from reassessment ($106,640,000) are more than expected total expenses ($100,690,000).
8 Decision made	Since a reassessment will cover the increase in expenses without a tax increase, **property will be reassessed.**

SELF-CHECK 17.2

1. Find the assessed value of a store with a market value of $150,000 if the rate for assessed value is 35% of market value.

2. Donna McAnally owns an apartment building that has a market value of $583,000. If apartments are assessed at 40% of market value, find the assessed value of Donna's apartment building.

3. Tim Warner's farm has a market value of $385,000. Find the assessed value of the farm if farms are assessed at 25% of the market value.

4. Rebecca Drewrey owns a small telephone company that has a market value of $1,895,000. If the phone company is assessed at 50% of market value, what is the assessed value of the property?

5. What is the tax on a property with an assessed value of $88,500 if the tax rate is 4.5% of the assessed value?

6. Find the property tax on a vacant lot with an assessed value of $32,350 and a tax rate of $4.37 per $100 of assessed value.

7. Find the property tax on a home with an assessed value of $75,000 in a community with a tax rate of $12.75 per $1,000 of assessed value.

8. Calculate the property tax on a store with an assessed value of $150,250 if the tax rate is 58 mills per $1.00 of assessed value.

3

9. Find the tax rate expressed as tax per $1.00 of assessed value in a municipality that has budgeted expenses of $5,985,500 and has property assessed at $230,211,500.

10. Find the tax rate expressed as tax per $100 of assessed value for a town that anticipates expenses of $55,800 and has property assessed at $9,830,000.

11. What is the tax rate expressed as tax per $1,000 of assessed property value in a county that has property assessed at $185,910,000 and has budgeted expenses of $5,810,000?

12. What is the tax rate expressed in mills per $1.00 of assessed value if an incorporated town has a budget of $497,000 and has property assessed at $11,045,000?

17.3 Income Taxes

1 Find taxable income.

2 Use the tax tables to calculate income tax.

3 Use the tax rate schedules to calculate income tax.

Many state governments and the federal government collect much of their revenue through individual and business **income taxes.** Federal income tax regulations are enacted by the Congress of the United States, and the tax laws frequently change.

While the laws and forms change from year to year, the *procedures* for computing income tax remain basically the same. Each year an instruction booklet accompanies the current income tax forms. This booklet explains any recent changes in the tax laws, provides instructions for computing tax and filling out the forms, and contains various tax tables needed for filing an income tax return.

To calculate income tax owed, begin with a business's or individual's **gross income,** which is the money, goods, and property received during the year. From this subtract any adjustments allowed, such as credit for employee expenses that are not reimbursed by the employer; this gives you the **adjusted gross income.** Next, arrive at the **taxable income,** which is the adjusted gross income minus exemptions and deductions. The taxable income is the amount that is used to calculate the taxes owed.

Exemptions provide one of the ways of reducing taxable income. One personal **exemption** or allowance is allowed for the taxpayer, and additional exemptions are allowed for the taxpayer's spouse and other dependents if the gross adjusted income is below a certain level. Other exemptions are allowed if the taxpayer or the spouse is over 65 or blind. The Tax Reform Act of 1986 increased the amount of money that can be subtracted for each personal exemption. The deduction for personal exemptions was generally $2,800 in a recent year.

A taxpayer is allowed to take **deductions,** or to deduct certain expenses such as charitable contributions, interest paid on certain loans, certain taxes, certain losses, excessive medical expenses, and certain miscellaneous expenses, to name a few. Rather than listing these expenses (called **itemized deductions**), the taxpayer may choose to take the **standard deduction.** The standard deduction changes from year to year, but in a recent year it was $7,350 for married taxpayers filing jointly (if both were under 65) or a qualifying widow (widower) with a dependent child; $3,675 for married taxpayers filing separately; $4,400 for single taxpayers; and $6,450 for taxpayers who were the head of a household.

The tax due on taxable personal income depends also on the **filing status** of the taxpayer. Filing status is the marital status of the taxpayer. The individual taxpayer must select the filing status from four categories. The *single* category is for a person who has never married, is legally separated, or is divorced. A husband and wife filing a return together, even if only one had income, are classified as *married filing jointly.* This filing status sometimes results in married persons paying a different tax than single persons with a comparable income. When a husband and wife each file a separate return, they are classified as *married filing separately,* and this status may result in a higher tax liability than the married filing jointly status. The filing status *head of household* should be selected by individuals who provide a home for certain other persons.

1 Find taxable income.

Whether you choose to itemize deductions or use the standard deduction, you must determine your *taxable income* before you can compute the tax. An employer is required to issue each employee a W-2 form, which shows the income earned, income tax withheld, Social Security tax withheld, and Medicare tax withheld for the employee for the calendar year. If a person works for more than one employer in a year, he or she will receive a W-2 form from each employer. Under some circumstances a form 1099 is used to report income to an individual.

TIP! When Do You Expect Your W-2 Form?

The IRS requires employers to deliver or have postmarked W-2 forms by midnight on January 31 following the year the income was earned. Employees who do not receive a W-2 from an employer because of address changes or other changes should contact the employer soon after January 31.

HOW TO Find the Taxable Income

1. Find the adjusted gross income.

Adjusted gross income = gross income − credits

2. Total the deductions and total the exemptions.

3. Subtract both the total deductions and the total exemptions from the adjusted gross income.

Taxable income = adjusted gross income − deductions − exemptions

EXAMPLE Find the taxable income for a family of four (husband, wife, two children) if their adjusted gross income is $37,754 and itemized deductions are $7,345. Use $2,800 as the amount of each personal exemption.

$$\text{Taxable income} = \text{adjusted gross income} - \text{deductions} - \text{exemptions}$$
$$= \$37,754 - \$7,345 - (\$2,800 \times 4)$$
$$= \$37,754 - \$7,345 - \$11,200 = \$19,209$$

The taxable income is $19,809.

 Use the tax tables to calculate income tax.

Once you know your taxable income and filing status, you can figure the taxes owed. **Income tax tables** like those in Table 17-2 are used to find the tax liability for taxable incomes of *less than* $100,000.

HOW TO Use the Tax Tables to Calculate Income Tax

1. Locate the taxable income under the column headed, "If line 38 (taxable income) is—."

2. Move across to the column headed, "And you are—," which has the four categories of filing status listed under it. The tax owed appears under the appropriate category.

EXAMPLE Find the tax owed by a married taxpayer (a) filing separately on a taxable income of $19,478; (b) filing jointly on a taxable income of $19,478.

First, locate the income range in which $19,478 falls. Because $19,478 is *at least* $19,450 *but less than* $19,500, it falls within the range of $19,450–$19,500.

(a) Next, locate the tax for this taxable income range to the right in the column headed *married filing separately*. The tax is $2,921.

(b) For the taxable income range $19,450–$19,500, the tax for a taxpayer *married filing jointly* is also $2,921.

From the previous example and from an inspection of Table 17–2, notice that a taxpayer's filing status (single, married filing jointly, married filing separately, head of household) yields the same tax for taxable incomes that are less than $20,600. As the taxable income increases, the variation among the categories is significant.

 TIP! Settling Up on Income Tax

Most taxpayers have taxes withheld from their paychecks throughout the year. By April 15 of the following year taxpayers are required to file a report that will determine if additional taxes are owed or if a refund is due.

The taxpayer refers to his or her W-2 form to determine the income tax that has been withheld during the year. This tax withheld is subtracted from the tax owed to determine the remaining tax that must be paid. Or, if more tax has been withheld than the taxpayer owes, subtraction will show the tax refund due the employee.

3 Use the tax rate schedules to calculate income tax.

The **tax rate schedules** are used to compute tax on taxable incomes of $100,000 *or more*. There are separate tax rate schedules for single taxpayers, heads of households, and married taxpayers (and certain qualifying widows and widowers).

The **Tax Reform Act of 1986** changed the tax rate structure that had existed in the years before that. An individual's income is taxed at different rates depending on how much of his or her income falls into each of various income brackets. Table 17-3 shows the tax rates for 2000.

 TIP! How Long Should Tax Records Be Kept?

The Internal Revenue Service recommends that a copy of your tax return, worksheets you used, and records of all items be kept in your files. The statute of limitations runs out in 3 years.

? HOW TO Use the Tax Rate Schedules to Figure Income Tax

1. Locate the correct schedule according to filing status.
2. Locate the range in which the taxable income falls.
3. Subtract the low end of the range from the taxable income.
4. Multiply the difference from step 3 by the given percent for the range.
5. Add the tax from step 4 to the given tax for the range.

EXAMPLE Find the tax on a taxable income of (a) $112,418 for a married taxpayer filing jointly using Table 17-3; (b) $128,382 for a married taxpayer filing separately using Table 17-3.

Table 17-2 Portion of Tax Table

If line 39 (taxable income) is—		And you are—			
At least	But less than	Single	Married filing jointly *	Married filing separately	Head of a household
		Your tax is—			

14,000

At least	But less than	Single	Married filing jointly *	Married filing separately	Head of a household
14,000	14,050	2,104	2,104	2,104	2,104
14,050	14,100	2,111	2,111	2,111	2,111
14,100	14,150	2,119	2,119	2,119	2,119
14,150	14,200	2,126	2,126	2,126	2,126
14,200	14,250	2,134	2,134	2,134	2,134
14,250	14,300	2,141	2,141	2,141	2,141
14,300	14,350	2,149	2,149	2,149	2,149
14,350	14,400	2,156	2,156	2,156	2,156
14,400	14,450	2,164	2,164	2,164	2,164
14,450	14,500	2,171	2,171	2,171	2,171
14,500	14,550	2,179	2,179	2,179	2,179
14,550	14,600	2,186	2,186	2,186	2,186
14,600	14,650	2,194	2,194	2,194	2,194
14,650	14,700	2,201	2,201	2,201	2,201
14,700	14,750	2,209	2,209	2,209	2,209
14,750	14,800	2,216	2,216	2,216	2,216
14,800	14,850	2,224	2,224	2,224	2,224
14,850	14,900	2,231	2,231	2,231	2,231
14,900	14,950	2,239	2,239	2,239	2,239
14,950	15,000	2,246	2,246	2,246	2,246

15,000

At least	But less than	Single	Married filing jointly *	Married filing separately	Head of a household
15,000	15,050	2,254	2,254	2,254	2,254
15,050	15,100	2,261	2,261	2,261	2,261
15,100	15,150	2,269	2,269	2,269	2,269
15,150	15,200	2,276	2,276	2,276	2,276
15,200	15,250	2,284	2,284	2,284	2,284
15,250	15,300	2,291	2,291	2,291	2,291
15,300	15,350	2,299	2,299	2,299	2,299
15,350	15,400	2,306	2,306	2,306	2,306
15,400	15,450	2,314	2,314	2,314	2,314
15,450	15,500	2,321	2,321	2,321	2,321
15,500	15,550	2,329	2,329	2,329	2,329
15,550	15,600	2,336	2,336	2,336	2,336
15,600	15,650	2,344	2,344	2,344	2,344
15,650	15,700	2,351	2,351	2,351	2,351
15,700	15,750	2,359	2,359	2,359	2,359
15,750	15,800	2,366	2,366	2,366	2,366
15,800	15,850	2,374	2,374	2,374	2,374
15,850	15,900	2,381	2,381	2,381	2,381
15,900	15,950	2,389	2,389	2,389	2,389
15,950	16,000	2,396	2,396	2,396	2,396

16,000

At least	But less than	Single	Married filing jointly *	Married filing separately	Head of a household
16,000	16,050	2,404	2,404	2,404	2,404
16,050	16,100	2,411	2,411	2,411	2,411
16,100	16,150	2,419	2,419	2,419	2,419
16,150	16,200	2,426	2,426	2,426	2,426
16,200	16,250	2,434	2,434	2,434	2,434
16,250	16,300	2,441	2,441	2,441	2,441
16,300	16,350	2,449	2,449	2,449	2,449
16,350	16,400	2,456	2,456	2,456	2,456
16,400	16,450	2,464	2,464	2,464	2,464
16,450	16,500	2,471	2,471	2,471	2,471
16,500	16,550	2,479	2,479	2,479	2,479
16,550	16,600	2,486	2,486	2,486	2,486
16,600	16,650	2,494	2,494	2,494	2,494
16,650	16,700	2,501	2,501	2,501	2,501
16,700	16,750	2,509	2,509	2,509	2,509
16,750	16,800	2,516	2,516	2,516	2,516
16,800	16,850	2,524	2,524	2,524	2,524
16,850	16,900	2,531	2,531	2,531	2,531
16,900	16,950	2,539	2,539	2,539	2,539
16,950	17,000	2,546	2,546	2,546	2,546

17,000

At least	But less than	Single	Married filing jointly *	Married filing separately	Head of a household
17,000	17,050	2,554	2,554	2,554	2,554
17,050	17,100	2,561	2,561	2,561	2,561
17,100	17,150	2,569	2,569	2,569	2,569
17,150	17,200	2,576	2,576	2,576	2,576
17,200	17,250	2,584	2,584	2,584	2,584
17,250	17,300	2,591	2,591	2,591	2,591
17,300	17,350	2,599	2,599	2,599	2,599
17,350	17,400	2,606	2,606	2,606	2,606
17,400	17,450	2,614	2,614	2,614	2,614
17,450	17,500	2,621	2,621	2,621	2,621
17,500	17,550	2,629	2,629	2,629	2,629
17,550	17,600	2,636	2,636	2,636	2,636
17,600	17,650	2,644	2,644	2,644	2,644
17,650	17,700	2,651	2,651	2,651	2,651
17,700	17,750	2,659	2,659	2,659	2,659
17,750	17,800	2,666	2,666	2,666	2,666
17,800	17,850	2,674	2,674	2,674	2,674
17,850	17,900	2,681	2,681	2,681	2,681
17,900	17,950	2,689	2,689	2,689	2,689
17,950	18,000	2,696	2,696	2,696	2,696

18,000

At least	But less than	Single	Married filing jointly *	Married filing separately	Head of a household
18,000	18,050	2,704	2,704	2,704	2,704
18,050	18,100	2,711	2,711	2,711	2,711
18,100	18,150	2,719	2,719	2,719	2,719
18,150	18,200	2,726	2,726	2,726	2,726
18,200	18,250	2,734	2,734	2,734	2,734
18,250	18,300	2,741	2,741	2,741	2,741
18,300	18,350	2,749	2,749	2,749	2,749
18,350	18,400	2,756	2,756	2,756	2,756
18,400	18,450	2,764	2,764	2,764	2,764
18,450	18,500	2,771	2,771	2,771	2,771
18,500	18,550	2,779	2,779	2,779	2,779
18,550	18,600	2,786	2,786	2,786	2,786
18,600	18,650	2,794	2,794	2,794	2,794
18,650	18,700	2,801	2,801	2,801	2,801
18,700	18,750	2,809	2,809	2,809	2,809
18,750	18,800	2,816	2,816	2,816	2,816
18,800	18,850	2,824	2,824	2,824	2,824
18,850	18,900	2,831	2,831	2,831	2,831
18,900	18,950	2,839	2,839	2,839	2,839
18,950	19,000	2,846	2,846	2,846	2,846

19,000

At least	But less than	Single	Married filing jointly *	Married filing separately	Head of a household
19,000	19,050	2,854	2,854	2,854	2,854
19,050	19,100	2,861	2,861	2,861	2,861
19,100	19,150	2,869	2,869	2,869	2,869
19,150	19,200	2,876	2,876	2,876	2,876
19,200	19,250	2,884	2,884	2,884	2,884
19,250	19,300	2,891	2,891	2,891	2,891
19,300	19,350	2,899	2,899	2,899	2,899
19,350	19,400	2,906	2,906	2,906	2,906
19,400	19,450	2,914	2,914	2,914	2,914
19,450	19,500	2,921	2,921	2,921	2,921
19,500	19,550	2,929	2,929	2,929	2,929
19,550	19,600	2,936	2,936	2,936	2,936
19,600	19,650	2,944	2,944	2,944	2,944
19,650	19,700	2,951	2,951	2,951	2,951
19,700	19,750	2,959	2,959	2,959	2,959
19,750	19,800	2,966	2,966	2,966	2,966
19,800	19,850	2,974	2,974	2,974	2,974
19,850	19,900	2,981	2,981	2,981	2,981
19,900	19,950	2,989	2,989	2,989	2,989
19,950	20,000	2,996	2,996	2,996	2,996

20,000

At least	But less than	Single	Married filing jointly *	Married filing separately	Head of a household
20,000	20,050	3,004	3,004	3,004	3,004
20,050	20,100	3,011	3,011	3,011	3,011
20,100	20,150	3,019	3,019	3,019	3,019
20,150	20,200	3,026	3,026	3,026	3,026
20,200	20,250	3,034	3,034	3,034	3,034
20,250	20,300	3,041	3,041	3,041	3,041
20,300	20,350	3,049	3,049	3,049	3,049
20,350	20,400	3,056	3,056	3,056	3,056
20,400	20,450	3,064	3,064	3,064	3,064
20,450	20,500	3,071	3,071	3,071	3,071
20,500	20,550	3,079	3,079	3,079	3,079
20,550	20,600	3,086	3,086	3,086	3,086
20,600	20,650	3,094	3,094	3,094	3,094
20,650	20,700	3,101	3,101	3,101	3,101
20,700	20,750	3,109	3,109	3,109	3,109
20,750	20,800	3,116	3,116	3,116	3,116
20,800	20,850	3,124	3,124	3,124	3,124
20,850	20,900	3,131	3,131	3,131	3,131
20,900	20,950	3,139	3,139	3,139	3,139
20,950	21,000	3,146	3,146	3,146	3,146

21,000

At least	But less than	Single	Married filing jointly *	Married filing separately	Head of a household
21,000	21,050	3,154	3,154	3,154	3,154
21,050	21,100	3,161	3,161	3,161	3,161
21,100	21,150	3,169	3,169	3,169	3,169
21,150	21,200	3,176	3,176	3,176	3,176
21,200	21,250	3,184	3,184	3,184	3,184
21,250	21,300	3,191	3,191	3,191	3,191
21,300	21,350	3,199	3,199	3,199	3,199
21,350	21,400	3,206	3,206	3,206	3,206
21,400	21,450	3,214	3,214	3,214	3,214
21,450	21,500	3,221	3,221	3,221	3,221
21,500	21,550	3,229	3,229	3,229	3,229
21,550	21,600	3,236	3,236	3,236	3,236
21,600	21,650	3,244	3,244	3,244	3,244
21,650	21,700	3,251	3,251	3,251	3,251
21,700	21,750	3,259	3,259	3,259	3,259
21,750	21,800	3,266	3,266	3,266	3,266
21,800	21,850	3,274	3,274	3,274	3,274
21,850	21,900	3,281	3,281	3,281	3,281
21,900	21,950	3,289	3,289	3,289	3,289
21,950	22,000	3,296	3,296	3,303	3,296

22,000

At least	But less than	Single	Married filing jointly *	Married filing separately	Head of a household
22,000	22,050	3,304	3,304	3,317	3,304
22,050	22,100	3,311	3,311	3,331	3,311
22,100	22,150	3,319	3,319	3,345	3,319
22,150	22,200	3,326	3,326	3,359	3,326
22,200	22,250	3,334	3,334	3,373	3,334
22,250	22,300	3,341	3,341	3,387	3,341
22,300	22,350	3,349	3,349	3,401	3,349
22,350	22,400	3,356	3,356	3,415	3,356
22,400	22,450	3,364	3,364	3,429	3,364
22,450	22,500	3,371	3,371	3,443	3,371
22,500	22,550	3,379	3,379	3,457	3,379
22,550	22,600	3,386	3,386	3,471	3,386
22,600	22,650	3,394	3,394	3,485	3,394
22,650	22,700	3,401	3,401	3,499	3,401
22,700	22,750	3,409	3,409	3,513	3,409
22,750	22,800	3,416	3,416	3,527	3,416
22,800	22,850	3,424	3,424	3,541	3,424
22,850	22,900	3,431	3,431	3,555	3,431
22,900	22,950	3,439	3,439	3,569	3,439
22,950	23,000	3,446	3,446	3,583	3,446

* This column must also be used by a qualifying widow(er).

(Continued on page 62)

Source: IRS Publication 2001 1040 Instructions

Table 17-2 (continued)

2000 Tax Table—*Continued*

If line 39 (taxable income) is—		And you are—			
At least	But less than	Single	Married filing jointly *	Married filing separately	Head of a house-hold
		Your tax is—			

23,000

At least	But less than	Single	Married filing jointly	Married filing separately	Head of household
23,000	23,050	3,454	3,454	3,597	3,454
23,050	23,100	3,461	3,461	3,611	3,461
23,100	23,150	3,469	3,469	3,625	3,469
23,150	23,200	3,476	3,476	3,639	3,476
23,200	23,250	3,484	3,484	3,653	3,484
23,250	23,300	3,491	3,491	3,667	3,491
23,300	23,350	3,499	3,499	3,681	3,499
23,350	23,400	3,506	3,506	3,695	3,506
23,400	23,450	3,514	3,514	3,709	3,514
23,450	23,500	3,521	3,521	3,723	3,521
23,500	23,550	3,529	3,529	3,737	3,529
23,550	23,600	3,536	3,536	3,751	3,536
23,600	23,650	3,544	3,544	3,765	3,544
23,650	23,700	3,551	3,551	3,779	3,551
23,700	23,750	3,559	3,559	3,793	3,559
23,750	23,800	3,566	3,566	3,807	3,566
23,800	23,850	3,574	3,574	3,821	3,574
23,850	23,900	3,581	3,581	3,835	3,581
23,900	23,950	3,589	3,589	3,849	3,589
23,950	24,000	3,596	3,596	3,863	3,596

24,000

At least	But less than	Single	Married filing jointly	Married filing separately	Head of household
24,000	24,050	3,604	3,604	3,877	3,604
24,050	24,100	3,611	3,611	3,891	3,611
24,100	24,150	3,619	3,619	3,905	3,619
24,150	24,200	3,626	3,626	3,919	3,626
24,200	24,250	3,634	3,634	3,933	3,634
24,250	24,300	3,641	3,641	3,947	3,641
24,300	24,350	3,649	3,649	3,961	3,649
24,350	24,400	3,656	3,656	3,975	3,656
24,400	24,450	3,664	3,664	3,989	3,664
24,450	24,500	3,671	3,671	4,003	3,671
24,500	24,550	3,679	3,679	4,017	3,679
24,550	24,600	3,686	3,686	4,031	3,686
24,600	24,650	3,694	3,694	4,045	3,694
24,650	24,700	3,701	3,701	4,059	3,701
24,700	24,750	3,709	3,709	4,073	3,709
24,750	24,800	3,716	3,716	4,087	3,716
24,800	24,850	3,724	3,724	4,101	3,724
24,850	24,900	3,731	3,731	4,115	3,731
24,900	24,950	3,739	3,739	4,129	3,739
24,950	25,000	3,746	3,746	4,143	3,746

25,000

At least	But less than	Single	Married filing jointly	Married filing separately	Head of household
25,000	25,050	3,754	3,754	4,157	3,754
25,050	25,100	3,761	3,761	4,171	3,761
25,100	25,150	3,769	3,769	4,185	3,769
25,150	25,200	3,776	3,776	4,199	3,776
25,200	25,250	3,784	3,784	4,213	3,784
25,250	25,300	3,791	3,791	4,227	3,791
25,300	25,350	3,799	3,799	4,241	3,799
25,350	25,400	3,806	3,806	4,255	3,806
25,400	25,450	3,814	3,814	4,269	3,814
25,450	25,500	3,821	3,821	4,283	3,821
25,500	25,550	3,829	3,829	4,297	3,829
25,550	25,600	3,836	3,836	4,311	3,836
25,600	25,650	3,844	3,844	4,325	3,844
25,650	25,700	3,851	3,851	4,339	3,851
25,700	25,750	3,859	3,859	4,353	3,859
25,750	25,800	3,866	3,866	4,367	3,866
25,800	25,850	3,874	3,874	4,381	3,874
25,850	25,900	3,881	3,881	4,395	3,881
25,900	25,950	3,889	3,889	4,409	3,889
25,950	26,000	3,896	3,896	4,423	3,896

26,000

At least	But less than	Single	Married filing jointly	Married filing separately	Head of household
26,000	26,050	3,904	3,904	4,437	3,904
26,050	26,100	3,911	3,911	4,451	3,911
26,100	26,150	3,919	3,919	4,465	3,919
26,150	26,200	3,926	3,926	4,479	3,926
26,200	26,250	3,934	3,934	4,493	3,934
26,250	26,300	3,945	3,941	4,507	3,941
26,300	26,350	3,959	3,949	4,521	3,949
26,350	26,400	3,973	3,956	4,535	3,956
26,400	26,450	3,987	3,964	4,549	3,964
26,450	26,500	4,001	3,971	4,563	3,971
26,500	26,550	4,015	3,979	4,577	3,979
26,550	26,600	4,029	3,986	4,591	3,986
26,600	26,650	4,043	3,994	4,605	3,994
26,650	26,700	4,057	4,001	4,619	4,001
26,700	26,750	4,071	4,009	4,633	4,009
26,750	26,800	4,085	4,016	4,647	4,016
26,800	26,850	4,099	4,024	4,661	4,024
26,850	26,900	4,113	4,031	4,675	4,031
26,900	26,950	4,127	4,039	4,689	4,039
26,950	27,000	4,141	4,046	4,703	4,046

27,000

At least	But less than	Single	Married filing jointly	Married filing separately	Head of household
27,000	27,050	4,155	4,054	4,717	4,054
27,050	27,100	4,169	4,061	4,731	4,061
27,100	27,150	4,183	4,069	4,745	4,069
27,150	27,200	4,197	4,076	4,759	4,076
27,200	27,250	4,211	4,084	4,773	4,084
27,250	27,300	4,225	4,091	4,787	4,091
27,300	27,350	4,239	4,099	4,801	4,099
27,350	27,400	4,253	4,106	4,815	4,106
27,400	27,450	4,267	4,114	4,829	4,114
27,450	27,500	4,281	4,121	4,843	4,121
27,500	27,550	4,295	4,129	4,857	4,129
27,550	27,600	4,309	4,136	4,871	4,136
27,600	27,650	4,323	4,144	4,885	4,144
27,650	27,700	4,337	4,151	4,899	4,151
27,700	27,750	4,351	4,159	4,913	4,159
27,750	27,800	4,365	4,166	4,927	4,166
27,800	27,850	4,379	4,174	4,941	4,174
27,850	27,900	4,393	4,181	4,955	4,181
27,900	27,950	4,407	4,189	4,969	4,189
27,950	28,000	4,421	4,196	4,983	4,196

28,000

At least	But less than	Single	Married filing jointly	Married filing separately	Head of household
28,000	28,050	4,435	4,204	4,997	4,204
28,050	28,100	4,449	4,211	5,011	4,211
28,100	28,150	4,463	4,219	5,025	4,219
28,150	28,200	4,477	4,226	5,039	4,226
28,200	28,250	4,491	4,234	5,053	4,234
28,250	28,300	4,505	4,241	5,067	4,241
28,300	28,350	4,519	4,249	5,081	4,249
28,350	28,400	4,533	4,256	5,095	4,256
28,400	28,450	4,547	4,264	5,109	4,264
28,450	28,500	4,561	4,271	5,123	4,271
28,500	28,550	4,575	4,279	5,137	4,279
28,550	28,600	4,589	4,286	5,151	4,286
28,600	28,650	4,603	4,294	5,165	4,294
28,650	28,700	4,617	4,301	5,179	4,301
28,700	28,750	4,631	4,309	5,193	4,309
28,750	28,800	4,645	4,316	5,207	4,316
28,800	28,850	4,659	4,324	5,221	4,324
28,850	28,900	4,673	4,331	5,235	4,331
28,900	28,950	4,687	4,339	5,249	4,339
28,950	29,000	4,701	4,346	5,263	4,346

29,000

At least	But less than	Single	Married filing jointly	Married filing separately	Head of household
29,000	29,050	4,715	4,354	5,277	4,354
29,050	29,100	4,729	4,361	5,291	4,361
29,100	29,150	4,743	4,369	5,305	4,369
29,150	29,200	4,757	4,376	5,319	4,376
29,200	29,250	4,771	4,384	5,333	4,384
29,250	29,300	4,785	4,391	5,347	4,391
29,300	29,350	4,799	4,399	5,361	4,399
29,350	29,400	4,813	4,406	5,375	4,406
29,400	29,450	4,827	4,414	5,389	4,414
29,450	29,500	4,841	4,421	5,403	4,421
29,500	29,550	4,855	4,429	5,417	4,429
29,550	29,600	4,869	4,436	5,431	4,436
29,600	29,650	4,883	4,444	5,445	4,444
29,650	29,700	4,897	4,451	5,459	4,451
29,700	29,750	4,911	4,459	5,473	4,459
29,750	29,800	4,925	4,466	5,487	4,466
29,800	29,850	4,939	4,474	5,501	4,474
29,850	29,900	4,953	4,481	5,515	4,481
29,900	29,950	4,967	4,489	5,529	4,489
29,950	30,000	4,981	4,496	5,543	4,496

30,000

At least	But less than	Single	Married filing jointly	Married filing separately	Head of household
30,000	30,050	4,995	4,504	5,557	4,504
30,050	30,100	5,009	4,511	5,571	4,511
30,100	30,150	5,023	4,519	5,585	4,519
30,150	30,200	5,037	4,526	5,599	4,526
30,200	30,250	5,051	4,534	5,613	4,534
30,250	30,300	5,065	4,541	5,627	4,541
30,300	30,350	5,079	4,549	5,641	4,549
30,350	30,400	5,093	4,556	5,655	4,556
30,400	30,450	5,107	4,564	5,669	4,564
30,450	30,500	5,121	4,571	5,683	4,571
30,500	30,550	5,135	4,579	5,697	4,579
30,550	30,600	5,149	4,586	5,711	4,586
30,600	30,650	5,163	4,594	5,725	4,594
30,650	30,700	5,177	4,601	5,739	4,601
30,700	30,750	5,191	4,609	5,753	4,609
30,750	30,800	5,205	4,616	5,767	4,616
30,800	30,850	5,219	4,624	5,781	4,624
30,850	30,900	5,233	4,631	5,795	4,631
30,900	30,950	5,247	4,639	5,809	4,639
30,950	31,000	5,261	4,646	5,823	4,646

31,000

At least	But less than	Single	Married filing jointly	Married filing separately	Head of household
31,000	31,050	5,275	4,654	5,837	4,654
31,050	31,100	5,289	4,661	5,851	4,661
31,100	31,150	5,303	4,669	5,865	4,669
31,150	31,200	5,317	4,676	5,879	4,676
31,200	31,250	5,331	4,684	5,893	4,684
31,250	31,300	5,345	4,691	5,907	4,691
31,300	31,350	5,359	4,699	5,921	4,699
31,350	31,400	5,373	4,706	5,935	4,706
31,400	31,450	5,387	4,714	5,949	4,714
31,450	31,500	5,401	4,721	5,963	4,721
31,500	31,550	5,415	4,729	5,977	4,729
31,550	31,600	5,429	4,736	5,991	4,736
31,600	31,650	5,443	4,744	6,005	4,744
31,650	31,700	5,457	4,751	6,019	4,751
31,700	31,750	5,471	4,759	6,033	4,759
31,750	31,800	5,485	4,766	6,047	4,766
31,800	31,850	5,499	4,774	6,061	4,774
31,850	31,900	5,513	4,781	6,075	4,781
31,900	31,950	5,527	4,789	6,089	4,789
31,950	32,000	5,541	4,796	6,103	4,796

* This column must also be used by a qualifying widow(er).

(Continued on page 63)

Source: IRS Publication 2001 1040 Instructions

Table 17-3 2000 Tax Rate Schedules

2000 Tax Rate Schedules

Use **only** if your taxable income (Form 1040, line 39) is $100,000 or more. If less, use the **Tax Table.** Even though you cannot use the Tax Rate Schedules below if your taxable income is less than $100,000, all levels of taxable income are shown so taxpayers can see the tax rate that applies to each level.

Schedule X—Use if your filing status is **Single**

If the amount on Form 1040, line 39, is: Over-	But not over-	Enter on Form 1040, line 40	of the amount over-
$0	$26,250	--------- 15%	$0
26,250	63,550	$3,937.50 + 28%	26,250
63,550	132,600	14,381.50 + 31%	63,550
132,600	288,350	35,787.00 + 36%	132,600
288,350	---------	91,857.00 + 39.6%	288,350

Schedule Y-1—Use if your filing status is **Married filing jointly** or **Qualifying widow(er)**

If the amount on Form 1040, line 39, is: Over-	But not over-	Enter on Form 1040, line 40	of the amount over-
$0	$43,850	--------- 15%	$0
43,850	105,950	$6,577.50 + 28%	43,850
105,950	161,450	23,965.50 + 31%	105,950
161,450	288,350	41,170.50 + 36%	161,450
288,350	---------	86,854.50 + 39.6%	288,350

Schedule Y-2—Use if your filing status is **Married filing separately**

If the amount on Form 1040, line 39, is: Over-	But not over-	Enter on Form 1040, line 40	of the amount over-
$0	$21,925	--------- 15%	$0
21,925	52,975	$3,288.75 + 28%	21,925
52,975	80,725	11,982.75 + 31%	52,975
80,725	144,175	20,585.25 + 36%	80,725
144,175	---------	43,427.25 + 39.6%	144,175

Schedule Z—Use if your filing status is **Head of household**

If the amount on Form 1040, line 39, is: Over-	But not over-	Enter on Form 1040, line 40	of the amount over-
$0	$35,150	--------- 15%	$0
35,150	90,800	$5,272.50 + 28%	35,150
90,800	147,050	20,854.50 + 31%	90,800
147,050	288,350	38,292.00 + 36%	147,050
288,350	---------	89,160.00 + 39.6%	288,350

Source: IRS Publication 2001 1040 Instructions

(a) The taxpayer would use Schedule Y-1. Schedule Y-1 shows that the taxable income falls in the range $105,950–$161,450.

$$\$112{,}418 - \$105{,}950 = \boxed{\$6{,}468}$$

$$\boxed{\$6{,}468} \times 0.31 = \boxed{\$2{,}005.08}$$

$$\boxed{\$2{,}005.08} + \$23{,}965.50 = \$25{,}970.58$$

The tax is $25,970.58

(b) The taxpayer is married filing separately, so use Schedule Y-2.
The taxable income, $128,382, falls in the range over $80,725 but not over $144,175.

$$\$128{,}382 - \$80{,}725 = \boxed{\$47{,}657}$$

$$\boxed{\$47{,}657} \times 0.36 = \boxed{\$17{,}156.52}$$

$$\boxed{\$17{,}156.52} + \$20{,}585.25 = \$37{,}741.77$$

The tax is $37,741.77.

SELF-CHECK 17.3

1. Find the taxable income for a family of six (husband, wife, four children) whose adjusted gross income is $43,873 and itemized deductions are $9,582. (One exemption = $2,800.)

2. Find the taxable income for a single person whose adjusted gross income is $28,932 and itemized deductions are $4,915. (One exemption = $2,800.)

3. Canty O'Neal has an adjusted gross income of $68,917 and itemized deductions that total $18,473. Canty can claim three exemptions. What is her taxable income? (One exemption = $2,800.)

4. Noel Womack is single and calculates his taxable income to be $30,175. How much tax does he owe? Use Table 17-2.

5. Tommy and Michelle Fernandez have a combined taxable income of $23,300. How much tax should they pay if they file jointly? Use Table 17-2.

6. Vladimir Bozin is a head of a household and has a taxable income of $26,873. Use Table 17-2 to find his tax.

7. Donna Shroyer is single and has a taxable income of $29,897. If her W-2 form shows that she has already paid $5,647 in income taxes for the year, use Table 17-2 to determine if she is due a refund or if she must pay more taxes. How much is the refund or how much must she pay?

3

8. Paul Smith is married and filing his tax jointly with his wife Anna. Their combined taxable income is $167,983. Use the tax rate schedules (Table 17-3) to calculate the tax they must pay.

9. Dr. Steven Katz is single and has a taxable income of $160,842. Use the tax rate schedules (Table 17-3) to calculate his income tax liability.

10. Jack Falcinelli is filing his tax as a head of household. His taxable income is $133,896 and his W-2 form shows he has already paid $34,197.00. Calculate his tax refund or payment.

The Business World

Social Security Benefits

As the baby boom generation, those born from 1946 to 1970, moves into its retirement years in the early part of this century, the Social Security system will continue to provide retirement benefits because of recent changes and continuous monitoring of the system.

Workers currently pay 6.2% of their gross income in Social Security taxes, and their employers match that amount. Social Security taxes currently exceed the retirement benefits paid. The surpluses are put into a trust fund for later use. Congress is committed to safe guarding the financial future of the Social Seccurity trust fund. As currently structured the fund will collect more money than it pays out until 2015. With no change in structure, the fund will be exhausted by 2037 and Social Security taxes collected will pay only 72 percent of benefits owed. Therefore, Congress has time to make appropriate changes to ensure that Social Security will be there when you need it.

Workers who have earned enough credits can start receiving Social Security benefits as early as age 62, but the benefit amount will be less than the full retirement benefit. The table below shows the age at which retirees can start receiving full Social Security benefits.

Age to Receive Full Social Security Benefits	
Year of Birth	**Full Retirement Age**
1937 or earlier	65
1938	65 and 2 months
1939	65 and 4 months
1940	65 and 6 months
1941	65 and 8 months
1942	65 and 10 months
1943–1954	66
1955	66 and 2 months
1956	66 and 4 months
1957	66 and 6 months
1958	66 and 8 months
1959	66 and 10 months
1960 and later	67

Source: Social Security Administration publication 10035

For retirees born after 1960, the full retirement age is 67 and the reduction for starting benefits at 62 is about 30 percent of the full retirement benefits. The reduction at age 63 is about 25 percent; at age 64, about 20 percent; at age 65, about $13\frac{1}{2}$ percent; and at age 66, about $6\frac{2}{3}$ percent.

The intent is that the accumulated benefits from early retirement will be about the same over your lifetime as the total Social Security benefits earned after full retirement age. The benefits from early retirement are smaller in order to take into account the longer period they are received.

We are now living longer, healthier lives and can expect to spend more time in retirement than earlier generations. Achieving the dream of a secure, comfortable retirement can be accomplished when you plan your finances.

Our Social Security benefits can be the foundation of a secure retirement plan. These benefits will need to be supplemented with continued earnings beyond the full retirement age, a pension, savings, or investments.

Financial advisors generally estimate that it will take about 70 percent of preretirement earnings to comfortably maintain our preretirement standard of living. If we have average earnings, our Social Security retirement benefits will replace only about 40 percent of our preretirement earnings.

Exercises

1. If your Social Security annual statement projects that your full retirement benefits at age 67 will be $25,000 annually, calculate early retirement benefits at ages 62, 63, 64, 65, and 66.

2. Based on a full retirement annual benefit of $25,000 and an average life expectancy of 80 years, compare the accumulated lifetime Social Security benefits for a person retiring at ages 62, 63, 64, 65, 66, and 67.

3. Mikki Smith has a preretirement annual income of $62,000. Approximately how much income will she need after retirement to maintain her preretirement standard of living?

4. Estimate the amount of Mikki's retirement income that she can expect from Social Security benefits if she retires at age 67 (full retirement)?

5. Estimate the amount of additional income Mikki will need to maintain her preretirement standard of living.

Answers

1. At 62: $17,500; at 63: $18,750; at 64: $20,000; at 65: $21,667; at 66: $23,333.

2. Age 62 — $315,000
   Age 63 — $318,750
   Age 64 — $320,000
   Age 65 — $325,005
   Age 66 — $326,662
   Age 67 — $325,000

3. $43,400

4. $24,800

5. $18,600

	Section Outcome	Important Points with Examples

Section 17.1

1 Use tables to find the sales tax. (page 684)

1. Read the table's title and any explanatory notes about sales tax requirements.
2. If the price is within the scope of the table,
   (a) Locate the interval row that includes the price.
   (b) In the tax column, locate the tax corresponding to the price interval.
3. If the price is beyond the scope of the table,
   (a) Choose two or more smaller prices within the scope of the table and whose sum is the original price.
   (b) Calculate the sales tax on each smaller price, according to step 2.
   (c) Add the taxes from step 3b.

Use the tax table (Table 17-1) to find the tax on a tool that has a marked price of $8.47.

The interval $8.46 − $8.58 includes $8.47, and the tax is $0.66.

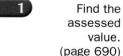

Use the percent method to find the sales tax. (page 686)

1. Express the sales tax rate as tax per $1.00 of the purchase price: write the given percent as a decimal.
2. Multiply the purchase price by the sales tax rate from step 1.

$$\text{Sales tax} = \text{purchase price} \times \text{sales tax rate}$$

where sales tax rate = tax per $1.00 of purchase price.

Use the percent method to find the sales tax on a $685 fax machine taxed at 6.6%.

Tax per $1.00 of purchase price = 6.6% of purchase price

= $0.066 per $1.00 of purchase price

Tax = $685 × $0.066

= $45.21

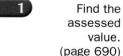

Find the marked price and the sales tax from the total price. (page 687)

1. Find the marked price:
   (a) Express the sales tax rate as tax per $1.00 or percent of the purchase (marked) price: write the given percent as a decimal.
   (b) Add 1 to the sales tax rate from step 1a.
   (c) Divide the total price by the sum from step 1b.

$$\text{Marked price} = \frac{\text{total price}}{1 + \text{sales tax rate}}$$

where sales tax rate = tax per $1.00 of purchase (marked) price.

2. Find the sales tax: subtract the marked price from the total price.

$$\text{Sales tax} = \text{total price} - \text{marked price}$$

Homer Ray sells handcrafted furniture at prices that include the state sales tax. One inlaid table sold for $3,950. Calculate the marked price and the sales tax Homer must send to the state if the tax rate is 8%.

$$\text{Marked price} = \frac{\text{total price}}{1 + \text{sales tax rate}}$$

$$= \frac{\$3,950}{1 + 0.08}$$

$$= \frac{\$3,950}{1.08}$$

$$= \$3,657.41$$

Sales tax = total price − marked price

= $3,950 − $3,657.41

= $292.59

or

$3,657.41 × 0.08

= $292.59

Section 17.2

Find the assessed value. (page 690)

1. Express the assessment rate as assessed value per $1.00 of market value: write the given percent as a decimal.
2. Multiply the market value of the property by the assessment rate from step 1.

$$\text{Assessed value} = \text{market value} \times \text{assessment rate}$$

where assessment rate = assessed value per $1.00 of market value.

Find the assessed value of a home with a market value of $106,000 if the assessed value is 30% of the market value.

$$\$106,000 \times 30\% = \$106,000 \times 0.3 = \$31,800$$

2 Calculate the property tax. (page 691)

1. Determine the appropriate method for calculating property tax.
   Percent of assessed value:
   (a) Property tax = assessed value × tax rate
   (b) Tax per $100 of assessed value:

   $$\text{Property tax} = \frac{\text{assessed value}}{100} \times \text{rate per \$100}$$

   (c) Tax per $1,000 of assessed value:

   $$\text{Property tax} = \frac{\text{assessed value}}{1,000} \times \text{rate per \$1,000}$$

   (d) Mills rate: $\text{Property tax} = \dfrac{\text{assessed value}}{1,000} \times \text{mills}$

2. Make calculations using the appropriate formula.

Find the property tax on a farm with an assessed value of $430,000 for each given tax rate.

The tax rate is 8.05% of the assessed value:

$$\$430,000 \times 8.05\% = \$430,000 \times 0.0805$$
$$= \$34,615$$

The tax rate is $8.05 per $100 of assessed value:

$$\frac{\$430,000}{\$100} \times \$8.05 = \$34,615$$

The tax rate is $80.50 per $1,000 of assessed value:

$$\frac{\$430,000}{\$1,000} \times \$80.50 = \$34,615$$

The tax rate is $80\frac{1}{2}$ mills per $1.00 of assessed value:

$$80\tfrac{1}{2} \text{ mills} = \$0.0805$$
$$\$430,000 \times 0.0805 = \$34,615$$

3 Determine the property tax rate. (page 692)

1. Select the appropriate formula according to the desired tax rate type. Always round up.

   $$\text{Tax per \$1.00 of assessed value} = \frac{\text{total estimated budget}}{\text{total assessed property value}}$$

   $$\text{Tax per \$100 of assessed value} = \frac{\text{total estimated budget}}{\text{total assessed property value}} \times 100$$

   $$\text{Tax per \$1,000 of assessed value} = \frac{\text{total estimated budget}}{\text{total assessed property value}} \times 1,000$$

   $$\text{Tax, in mills, per \$1.00 of assessed value} = \frac{\text{total estimated budget}}{\text{total assessed property value}} \times 1,000$$

2. Make calculations using the selected formula.

Find the tax expressed as tax per $1,000 of assessed value for Piperton if $15,872,000 is anticipated for expenses and the town has property assessed at $651,375,000.

$$\text{Tax per \$1,000 of assessed value} = \frac{\$15,872,000}{\$651,375,000} \times \$1,000$$
$$= \$24.36691614 = \$24.37$$

1 Find taxable income. (page 695)

1. Total the deductions and total the exemptions.
2. Subtract both the total deductions and the total exemptions from the adjusted gross income.

Taxable income = adjusted gross income − deductions − exemptions

> **Toni Wilson and her spouse earned $43,200 gross income and had itemized deductions of $8,700. They have a seven-year-old daughter. Find the taxable income, using $2,800 for each exemption.**
>
> Taxable income = $43,200 − (3 × $2,800) − $8,700
>
> = $43,200 − $8,400 − $8,700 = $26,100

2 Use the tax tables to calculate income tax. (page 696)

1. Locate the taxable income under the column headed, "If line 37 (taxable income) is—."
2. Move across to the column headed, "And you are—," which has the four categories of filing status listed under it. The tax owed appears under the appropriate category.

> **Use Table 17–2 to find Toni's tax if she and her husband file jointly.**
>
> **Find the range of $26,500–$26,550. Move across to the tax in the column "Married filing jointly," which is $3,979.**

3 Use the tax rate schedules to calculate income tax. (page 697)

1. Locate the correct schedule according to filing status.
2. Locate the range in which the taxable income falls.
3. Subtract the low end of the range from the taxable income.
4. Multiply the difference from step 3 by the given percent for the range.
5. Add the tax from step 4 to the given tax for the range.

> **Sue Wilson has a taxable income of $153,897. Her filing status is single. Find the income tax she owes, using Schedule X in Table 17-3. $153,897 falls in the range "over $132,600 but not over $288,350."**
>
> $153,897 − $132,600 = $21,297
>
> $21,297 × 0.36 = $7,666.92
>
> Income tax = $35,787.00 + $7,666.92
>
> = $43,453.92

WORDS TO KNOW

tax (p. 684)
sales tax (p. 684)
sales tax tables (p. 684)
marked price (p. 687)
total price (p. 687)
property tax (p. 690)
market value (p. 690)
assessed value (p. 690)

property tax rate (p. 691)
mill (p. 691)
total assessed value (p. 692)
income taxes (p. 695)
gross income (p. 695)
adjusted gross income (p. 695)
taxable income (p. 695)
exemption (p. 695)

deductions (p. 695)
itemized deductions (p. 695)
standard deduction (p. 695)
filing status (p. 695)
income tax tables (p. 696)
tax rate schedules (p. 697)
Tax Reform Act of 1986 (p. 697)

1. Use Table 17-1 to verify that $0.44 is the sales tax on a purchase price of $5.62 to $5.74 if the rate is 7.75%.

2. Explain why a range of values for purchase price will require the same amount of sales tax.

3. Show that the formulas are equivalent.

$$\text{Marked price} = \frac{\text{total price}}{1 + \text{sales tax}}$$

Sales tax = total price − marked price

4. Explain why the following formulas are equivalent.

$$\text{Tax per } \$1.00 = \frac{\text{tax on } \$100}{\$100}$$

$$\text{Tax per } \$1.00 = \frac{\text{tax on } \$1,000}{\$1,000}$$

5. Examine Table 17-2 to find the income range at which a single person pays more income taxes per person than married persons filing jointly.

6. Examine Table 17-2 to identify the highest income range in which single persons, married persons filing jointly, married persons filing separately, and heads of household all pay the same amount of income taxes.

7. Compare Schedules X, Y-1, and Y-2, and Z in Table 17-3 to determine which type of taxpayer that earns $112,000 would pay the most income tax. Which pays the least?

8. Use Schedule X to find the income tax on an income of $50,000. Compare this tax to the amount of tax required for a single person earning $50,000 in the tax table (Table 17-2).

9. Examine Schedule X in Table 17-3. Explain how a single person with a taxable income of $80,000 pays more tax than a single person with an income of $60,000, even though both incomes are in the same range.

10. Schedule X in Table 17-3 indicates that the maximum percent of income tax is 39.6% of the taxable income. Calculate the income tax for a single person whose taxable income is $300,000. Calculate the tax rate across the entire $300,000. Explain why the overall rate is *less than* 39.6%.

Section 17.1

Use Table 17-1 to find the sales tax on the following purchases.

1. $2.37
2. $3.72
3. $8.10
4. $2.93
5. $4.74

6. $11.04
7. $9.98
8. $29.95
9. $6.52
10. $5.47

Without using the table, calculate the sales tax on the given purchase using the given sales tax rate. (Round to the nearest cent.)

11. $237.42; 6%
12. $523.85; 5%
13. $1,294.26; 4.5%

14. $482.12; 6%
15. $675.93; 5%
16. $2,998.97; 4.5%

Find the marked price if the given total bill includes sales tax at the given rate. (Round to the nearest cent.)

17. $27.45; 5%
18. $139.53; 6%
19. $347.28; 4.5%

20. $53.92; 5%
21. $87.26; 3.5%
22. $3,580.53; $7\frac{1}{4}$%

Section 17.2

Find the assessed value of each property using the following rates:
Farm property or single-family dwellings: 25% of market value
Commercial property or multi-unit family dwellings: 40% of market value
Utilities: 50% of market value

23. Single-family dwelling with market value of $55,000

24. Apartment with market value of $235,000

25. Grocery store with market value of $115,000

26. Farmland with market value of $150,000

27. Power company with market value of $5,175,000

28. Thomas Richardson owns a home on two acres of land. The property has a market value of $215,000. What is the assessed value?

Find the tax on the given assessed value using the given rate.

29. $37,000; $1\frac{1}{2}\%$ of assessed value

30. $45,000; $1\frac{3}{4}\%$ of assessed value

31. $12,500; 2% of assessed value

32. $575,000; 1.8% of assessed value

33. If the county tax rate is $3.74 per $100 of assessed value, find the tax on a property that is assessed at $35,000.

34. If the county tax rate is increased to $4.25 from $3.74 per $100 of assessed value, how much tax would have to be paid on the same (see exercise 33) $35,000? What is the amount of increase?

35. The tax rate for a city is $3.25 per $100 of assessed value. Find the tax on a property that is assessed at $125,000.

36. Vicki Froehlich lives in a city where the tax rate is $21.50 per $1,000 of assessed value. Vicki's home has an assessed value of $31,820. How much city tax must Vicki pay?

37. A home has a market value of $50,000 (assessed value = 25% of market value). Find the amount of county taxes to be paid on the home if the county tax rate is $4.00 per $100 of assessed value.

38. What is the city property tax on the house in exercise 37 if the city tax rate is $3.06 per $100 of assessed valuation?

39. Find the combined city and county tax for the property in exercises 37 and 38.

40. Find the combined city and county property tax on a business whose market value is $200,000 (assessed value is 40% of market value). The business is within the city and county whose tax rates are given in exercises 37 and 38.

Find the tax on the given assessed value using the given rate.

41. $37,000; $14.25 per $1,000 of assessed value

42. $150,000; $15.50 per $1,000 of assessed value

43. $172,500; $16.23 per $1,000 of assessed value

44. $32,250; $13.78 per $1,000 of assessed value

45. $87,500; $12.67 per $1,000 of assessed value

Express the mills as dollars.

46. 34 mills

47. 63 mills

48. 51 mills

49. 72 mills

Find the tax on each property at the given assessed valuation using the given tax rate.

50. $12,500; 65 mills per $1.00 of assessed value

51. $23,275; 55 mills per $1.00 of assessed value

52. $52,575; 71 mills per $1.00 of assessed value

53. $28,750; 64 mills per $1.00 of assessed value

Complete the following table. (Express the tax on $1.00 of assessed valuation to the nearest cent. Round up any remainder.)

	Total Assessed Value	Total Expenses	Tax on $1.00	Tax on $100	Tax on $1,000
54.	$ 11,370,000	$ 386,450			
55.	$ 87,460,00	$ 4,348,800			
56.	$ 5,718,000	$ 374,740			
57.	$528,739,000	$17,205,160			

Section 17.3

Use $2,800 for each allowed personal exemption in exercises 58 to 63.

58. Find the taxable income for Sam and Delois Johns, a husband and wife without children, whose adjusted gross income is $18,378 and itemized deductions are $4,023.

59. Find the taxable income for the Zuckmans, a family of four (husband, wife, two children), if the adjusted gross income is $34,728, and the itemized deductions are $7,246.

60. Find the taxable income for the Shotwells, a family of three (husband, wife, one child), if their adjusted gross income is $72,376 and itemized deductions are $24,375.

61. Find the taxable income for Mario Gravez, a single person whose adjusted gross income is $37,486 and itemized deductions are $3,412.

62. Find the taxable income for the Thungs, a family of three (husband, wife, one child), if their adjusted gross income is $66,833 and itemized deductions are $12,583.

63. Find the taxable income for Lorenda and James Atlas, a husband and wife who have an adjusted gross income of $56,000 and are filing jointly. Their total itemized deductions are $3,589.

Use Table 17-2 (pp. 698–699) to find the tax owed by taxpayers with the following taxable incomes:

64. $19,730 (single)

65. $19,312 (single)

66. $14,069 (single)

67. $26,500 (single)

68. $26,980 (married, filing jointly)

69. $31,500 (married, filing jointly)

70. $28,450 (head of, household)

71. $31,059 (married, filing separately)

Use Table 17-3 to find the tax on the following taxable incomes.

72. $154,456 (married, filing jointly)

73. $172,478 (married, filing separately)

74. $151,200 (head of household)

75. $188,342 (single)

Spreadsheet Exercises

76. Write formulas to complete the worksheet on page 711 to find the federal income tax for the taxpayers whose taxable income and filing status is given. Use the Tax Rate Schedules on page 700 since all the incomes are more than $100,000. Use the key for filing status: S = Single; MJ = Married filing jointly; MS = Married filing separately; HH = Head of household.

(a) From the Tax Rate Schedule, enter the minimum amount for the taxable income range (Range Minimum Taxable Income), the amount of tax for the range minimum (Range Minimum Tax), and the percent of tax for the portion of taxable income above the minimum (Percent Above Minimum) in columns D, E and F, respectively.

(b) Write formulas to find the amount of taxable income above the range minimum (Amount Above Minimum).

(c) Write formulas to find the amount of tax over the tax schedule minimum (Tax Above Minimum).

(d) Write formulas to find the Total Tax amount.

77. Complete the spreadsheet using the formulas.

	A	B	C	D	E	F	G	H	I
1				Federal Income Taxes Based on the Tax Rate Schedules					
2	Name	File Status	Taxable Income	Range Minimum Taxable Income	Range Minimum Tax	Percent Above Minimum	Amount Above Minimum	Tax Above Minimum	Total Tax
3	J. Crowe	S	$123,456.35						
4	M. & I. Lewis	S	$175,356.00						
5	J. Davis	MS	$123,456.35						
6	S. Quant	MS	$175,356.00						
7	P. Allen	HH	$123,456.35						
8	Z. Warren	HH	$175,356.00						
9	R. Ellis	MJ	$123,456.35						
10	M. Dozier	MJ	$175,356.00						

Challenge Problems

78. Many people have discussed the so-called "marriage penalty" when it comes to paying income tax. Examine Schedule X and Schedule Y and explain why there appears to be a penalty for filing using Schedule Y.

79. Before purchasing investment property, an interested buyer can go to the tax assessor's office to find the taxes to be paid on the property. Using a computer provided for this purpose, the assessor can find the assessed value of the property, the tax rate, and the tax. If the property is purchased before the end of the year, the seller will pay the taxes only for the number of days the seller owns the land. This amount is called the seller's *pro rata* share of the annual taxes and can be found by dividing the annual taxes by 365 days to get the taxes due per day and then multiplying by the number of days the land is owned during that year by the seller. The buyer also pays a *pro rata* share.

Dan is interested in buying a piece of investment property. The market value is $30,500 and the assessment rate is 18% of the market value. Dan found the city tax rate to be 92.7 mills per $1.00 of assessed value and the county rate to be 138.4 mills per $1.00 of assessed value. Dan buys the land on April 13. What is Dan's *pro rata* share of the property taxes?

$$\$30,500 \times 0.18 = \$5,490 \text{ assessed value}$$

$$\$5,490 \times 0.0927 = \$508.92 \text{ annual city taxes}$$

$$\$5,490 \times 0.1384 = \$759.82 \text{ annual county taxes}$$

$$\$508.92 + \$759.82 = \$1,268.74 \text{ annual total taxes}$$

The seller owns the land for 102 days from January 1 through April 12.

$$\$1,268.74 \div 365 \times 102 = \$354.55$$
seller's *pro rata* share of the taxes

$$\$1,268.74 - \$354.55 = \$914.19$$
Dan's *pro rata* share of the taxes

Find the seller's *pro rata* share of the city and county taxes on property with a market value of $55,600. The property is assessed at 35% of the market value, city taxes are 107.6 mills per $1.00 of assessed value, and county taxes are 95.8 mills per $1.00 of assessed value. The closing date is June 23, the 174th day of the year.

Find the sales tax on the given marked price using the given sales tax rate.

1. $15.17; 5%   **2.** $18.26; $6\frac{1}{4}$%   **3.** $287.52; $7\frac{3}{4}$%   **4.** $2.98; 6.5%

What is the total price if the given sales tax rate is applied to the given marked price?

5. $187.21; 6%   **6.** $4.25; 5.25%

Find the marked price if the given total price includes sales tax at the given rate.

7. $18.84; 7%   **8.** $7.87; 6.5%   **9.** $52.63; 5.25%

10. A telephone bill of $84.15 is assessed state sales tax at a rate of 6%. Find the tax on the telephone bill.

11. Find the total telephone bill in exercise 10.

12. Find the assessed value of an apartment building (assessed at 40% of the market value) if the market value is $485,298.

13. Find the tax on a utility property if the assessed value of the property is $385,842 and the tax rate is 10.23% of the assessed value.

14. Find the tax on a business property if the assessed value of the property is $176,297 and the tax rate is $7.56 per $100 of assessed value.

15. Find the tax on a home if the assessed value is $24,375 and the tax rate is $43.97 per $1,000.

16. Convert 36 mills to dollars.

17. Find the tax on a property with an assessed value of $46,820 if the property tax rate is 87 mills per $1.00 of assessed value.

18. A property has an assessed value of $72,000. The city tax rate for this property is $4.12 per $100 of assessed valuation. Find the city tax on the property.

19. The property in exercise 18 is located in a county that has set a property tax rate of $2.57 per $100 of assessed value. What is the county tax on the property?

20. Find the tax rate per $100 of assessed value that a county should set if the total assessed property value in the county is $31,800,000 and the total expenses are $957,300.

21. Use Table 17-3 (p. 700) to calculate the amount of tax owed by Erma Thornton Braddy if her taxable income is $152,817 and her filing status is single.

22. Charles Wossum and his wife Ruby are filing their income tax jointly. Their combined taxable income is $29,872. How much tax must they pay? Use Table 17-2 (pp. 698–699).

23. Juanita and Robert Gray have a gross income of $68,521, all of which is subject to income tax. They have two children and plan to file a joint income tax return. If each exemption is $2,800 and they have itemized deductions of $14,521, what is their taxable income?

SELF-CHECK SOLUTIONS

SELF-CHECK 17.1

1. $5.86 is in the range of 5.75 to 5.87. The tax is $0.45.

2. $12.36 − $9.99 = $2.37; tax on $9.99 is $0.77; tax on $2.37 is $0.18; tax on $12.36 is $0.77 + $0.18, or $0.95.

3. $8.95 is in the range of $8.84 to $8.96; the tax is $0.69.

4. $17.85 − $9.99 = $7.86
Tax on $7.86 = $0.61
Tax on $9.99 = $0.77
Tax on $17.85 = $0.77 + $0.61 = $1.38

5. $288.63 × 0.055 = $15.87465 = $15.87 (rounded)

6. $2,860 × 0.065 = $185.90

7. $283 × 0.0725 = $20.5175
= $20.52

8. $195.95 × 0.0675
= $13.226625 = $13.23

9. $\dfrac{\$182.38}{1 + 0.06} = \$172.0566038$
= $172.06

10. $\dfrac{285}{1.065} = \$267.61$
$267.61 × 0.065
= $17.3943662 = $17.39

11. Marked price = $\dfrac{\$850}{1.0775}$
= $788.863109 = $788.86
Sales tax = $788.86 × 0.0775
= $61.13665 = $61.14

12. Marked price = $\dfrac{\$318.97}{1.0825}$
= $294.6605081 = $294.66
Sales tax = $294.66 × 0.0825
= $24.30945 = $24.31

Self-Check 17.2

1. $150,000 × 0.35 = $52,500

2. $583,000 × 0.40 = $233,200

3. $385,000 × 0.25 = $96,250

4. $1,895,000 × 0.5 = $947,500

5. $88,500 × 0.045 = $3,982.50

6. $32,350 ÷ $100 × $4.37 = $1,413.695 = $1,413.70 (rounded)

7. $75,000 ÷ $1,000 × $12.75 = $956.25

8. $150,250 × 0.058 = $8,714.50

9. $\dfrac{\$5,985,500}{\$230,211,500} = \$0.0260000043 = 2.6¢$ per $1.00 assessed value

10. $55,800 ÷ $9,830,000 × $100 = $0.5676500509
= $0.57 (rounded)

11. $\dfrac{\$5,810,000}{\$185,910,000} × \$1,000 = \$31.25168092 = \$31.26$

12. $\dfrac{\$497,000}{\$11,045,000} × \$1,000 = 44.99773653$ mills
= 45 mills

Self-Check 17.3

1. Exemptions = $2,800 × 6 = $16,800
Taxable income = $43,873 − $9,582 − $16,800 = $17,491

2. Exemption = $2,800 × 1 = $2,800
Taxable income = $28,932 − $4,915 − $2,800 = $21,217

3. Exemptions = $2,800 × 3 = $8,400
Taxable income = $68,917 − $18,473 − (3 × $2,800) = $42,044

4. Locate the range that includes $30,175. $30,175 is in the range $30,150–$30,200. Look under the "Single" column. The tax owed is $5,037.

5. Locate the range $23,300–$23,350. Look under the column "Married filing jointly." The tax owed is $3,499.

6. Locate the range $26,850–$26,900. Look under the column "Head of a household." The tax owed is $4,031.

7. Locate the range $29,850–$29,900. Look under the column "Single." The tax owed is $5,161. Tax owed is *less* than tax paid so a refund is due.
Amount of refund = $5,647 − $5,161 = $694

8. Use Schedule Y-1 since Paul is filing jointly with his wife. The taxable income is in the range $161,450–$288,350.
$167,983 − $161,450 = $6,533
$6,533 × 0.36 = $2,351.88
$41,170.50 + $2,351.88 = $43,522.38 (tax owed)

9. Use Schedule X, since Dr. Katz's filing status is "Single."
Taxable income is in the range $132,600–$288,350
$160,842 − $132,600 = $28,242
$28,242 × 0.36 = $10,167.12
$35,787.00 + $10,167.12 = $45,954.12

10. Use Schedule Z, since Jack's filing status is "Head of household."
Taxable income is in the range of $90,800–$147,050.
$133,896 − $90,800 = $43,096
$43,096 × 0.31 = $13,359.76
Tax owed = $20,854.50 + $13,359.76 = $34,214.26
Tax paid is less than tax owed so additional payment is due.
Additional payment = $34,214.26 − $34,197.00 = $17.26

Stocks and Bonds

18.1 Stocks

1 Read stock listings.

2 Calculate and distribute dividends.

3 Calculate current stock yield.

4 Compare price to earnings.

5 Find the cost of buying and the proceeds from selling stocks.

6 Calculate the return on investment.

18.2 Bonds

1 Read bond listings.

2 Calculate the price of bonds.

3 Find the cost of buying and the proceeds from selling bonds.

Good Decisions through Teamwork

Suppose that three months ago each of your team members bought $2,000 worth of stock in one company. From the newspaper's list of stock-exchange companies, choose the company in which each team member invested his or her $2,000.

Individually, research your company's three-month history of weekly closing prices. (Your library is a good source of old newspapers.) Display your closing-price data in a line graph. Investigate several stockbrokers' fees for buying and selling stock.

As a team, determine which team member made the most profitable investment. Choose one team member's stock to sell, decide which broker should handle the sale, and determine the proceeds from the sale. Prepare a summary report, including the line graphs, of your team's investments.

"Dow Plunges 300 Points," "Big Day on Wall Street," "Tech Stocks fall sharply." These and other headlines in your daily paper underscore the important role of stocks and bonds.

But just what are stocks and bonds? How are stocks different from bonds? Both stocks and bonds are sold by companies to raise money and are bought by investors in the hopes of realizing a profit. But these financial instruments work in quite different ways, which we explore in this chapter.

18.1 Stocks

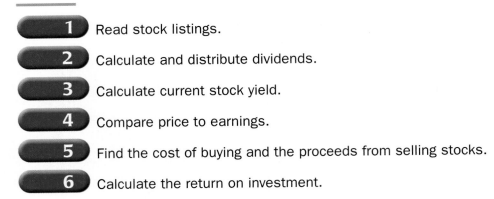

1. Read stock listings.

2. Calculate and distribute dividends.

3. Calculate current stock yield.

4. Compare price to earnings.

5. Find the cost of buying and the proceeds from selling stocks.

6. Calculate the return on investment.

Any incorporated business can issue **stock.** Each **share** of stock represents partial ownership of the corporation. Thus, if a company issues 2 million shares of stock and you own 1 million of them, you own one half of the company.

At the time the company issues (first sells) the stock, each share has a specific value, called the **face value (par value).** A person buying shares of stock receives a certificate of ownership, called a **stock certificate.** If the business is good, stockholders may receive a portion of the company profits in the form of a **dividend** for each share they hold. Some stockholders also have voting rights in corporate affairs.

There are two basic types of stock: **preferred stock** and **common stock.** Holders of preferred stock receive certain preferential financial benefits over common stockholders. But common stockholders have voting rights in the company—one vote per share—that preferred stockholders do not have.

After the stock is issued, people buy and sell their shares in the **stock market** for prices that vary from day to day and within a day. The price of a given company's shares is affected by supply and demand: When more people want to buy than want to sell, the price tends to rise; when more people want to sell than want to buy, the price tends to fall. Keep in mind that for each sale (called a **trade**) there is both a buyer and seller at a given price, but supply and demand exert a pressure on the price to go up or down. Factors that affect demand include good news about a company's product, bad news of higher-than-expected business expenses, international events, or what people think the trend of the national economy or of the business is.

The actual buying and selling of shares is done by a person called a **stockbroker,** who specializes in work in the stock market. Usually a person who wishes to buy or sell stock contacts a broker in person, by phone or fax, or on the Internet. The broker's representative at the actual trading location (such as at the New York Stock Exchange on Wall Street in New York or at the American Stock Exchange in Chicago) performs the transaction. The broker receives a *commission* for the services of both buying and selling stocks.

1 Read stock listings.

The daily prices of stocks, along with other information about the companies, are reported in newspapers and on the Internet. In Figure 18-1, we look at listings from the *New York Times* to see how to read **stock listings.** Stock prices are listed in dollars and cents. Positive and negative signs show the direction of change. Thus +0.13 is read "up thirteen cents" and means the price of each share has gone up by thirteen cents over the previous day's price. Similarly, −1.75 means the price of one share of stock has gone down by $1.75.

① 52-Week High	② Low	③ Stock	④ Div	⑤ Yld %	⑥ P/E	⑦ Sales 100s	⑧ High	⑨ Low	⑩ Last	⑪ Chg
28.50	9.75	AAR	.34	3.0	11	661	11.50	11.06	11.44	+0.38
31.00	19.25	ABM	.62	2.0	17	445	30.63	30.19	30.63	−0.06
26.50	19.38	ABN Amro	.80 e	3.7	. . .	2394	21.81	21.44	21.63	−0.31
26.56	20.25	ACE Cap n	2.22	8.8	. . .	69	25.31	25.25	25.31	+0.06
43.75	14.06	ACE Ltd	.52	1.4	14	32.367	39.00	36.31	38.06	−0.94
8.06	6.31	ACMIn	.78	10.4	q	814	7.50	7.44	7.50	. . .
8.00	6.25	ACM Op	.72 a	10.1	q	38	7.13	7.13	7.13	−0.06
7.69	6.19	ACM Sc	.78	10.6	q	2131	7.38	7.25	7.38	+0.06
6.25	5.13	ACMSp	.60	10.0	q	578	6.00	5.94	6.00	+0.06
9.44	6.19	ACMMD	1.02	15.4	q	1206	6.69	6.50	6.63	+0.13
6.69	4.44	ACM MI	.63	13.6	q	360	4.75	4.63	4.63	+0.06
12.75	10.13	ACMMu	.87	6.9	q	83	12.63	12.44	12.56	+0.06
26.88	16.31	ACNiels	. . .	. . .	25	1372	25.25	24.38	24.63	−0.44
72.81	30.38	AES Cp s	. . .	. . .	47	33763	50.25	46.81	49.94	+0.50
74.94	33.56	AFLAC	.34	0.5	31	10491	70.63	69.19	70.13	+0.75
14.50	9.44	AGCO	.04	0.4	dd	2268	9.94	9.81	9.94	+0.06
23.00	15.50	AGL Res	1.08	5.0	20	1621	22.13	21.50	21.81	−0.25
20.13	7.88	AK Steel	.50	5.7	9	7536	9.19	8.56	8.81	−0.44
25.13	18.00	AMB Pr	1.48	5.9	16	1654	25.13	24.88	25.13	+0.13
25.31	19.44	AMLI Rs	1.88	8.2	6	464	22.88	22.31	22.88	+0.69
39.44	20.75	AMR s	. . .	. . .	5	10393	36.31	35.13	35.81	+0.50
24.25	19.56	AMR Cp 39	1.97	8.2	. . .	87	24.25	23.94	24.06	. . .
9.25	3.13	APT Sat	.41 e	12.9	. . .	78	3.19	3.13	3.19	−0.06
49.88	**34.00**	**APW Ltd n**	**. . .**	**. . .**	**dd**	**1649**	**40.13**	**38.25**	**38.69**	**−1.94**
20.88	14.06	ASA Ltd	.60	4.1	q	979	14.63	14.44	14.56	−0.19
61.00	**18.25**	**AT&T**	**.88**	**4.2**	**12**	**172185**	**21.75**	**21.00**	**21.00**	**−1.00**
36.00	**17.13**	**ATT Wris n**	**. . .**	**. . .**	**. . .**	**30419**	**22.63**	**21.63**	**21.81**	**−1.19**
25.25	21.69	ATT N28	2.06	8.2	. . .	135	25.25	25.06	25.25	+0.06
25.88	21.56	ATT D28	2.03	8.1	. . .	649	25.13	24.94	25.13	+0.13
50.00	17.75	vAVX Cp s	.14	0.8	8	8446	18.00	17.13	17.44	−0.44
81.50	58.25	AXA	2.10 e	3.3	. . .	3688	64.75	63.75	64.06	+1.00
56.44	25.94	AXA Fn	.10	0.2	22	14429	54.63	54.25	54.63	+0.31
22.94	9.00	AZZ	.16 f	0.9	12	134	18.25	18.00	18.13	−0.25
6.00	0.44	Aames s	. . .	. . .	. . .	94	1.00	0.88	0.94	. . .
18.25	**11.47**	**AaronRnt**	**.04**	**0.2**	**13**	**582**	**18.00**	**16.44**	**17.63**	**+1.19**

Figure 18-1 Portion of New York Stock Exchange Listing (Source: *New York Times*)

? HOW TO   Read Stock Listings

1. Columns 1 (High) and 2 (Low) tell the highest and lowest prices at which the stock has sold in the last year (52 weeks), not including this day.

2. Column 3 (Stock) tells the name of the company (in abbreviated form).

3. Column 4 (Div) tells the dividend paid per share of stock the previous year.

4. Column 5 (Yld %) tells the previous year's dividend as a percent of the current price per share. If no dividend was paid the previous year, the entry is ". . .".

5. Column 6 (PE Ratio) tells the stock's price earnings ratio (see page 721).

6. Column 7 (Sales 100s) tells the volume (number) of hundreds of shares traded this day.

7. Columns 8 (High), 9 (Low), and 10 (Last) tell the high price, low price, and last price per share at which the stock sold this day.

8. Column 11 (Chg) tells how much this day's closing price per share differs from the previous day's closing price per share for that stock.

Read the stock listing in Figure 18-1 for ABN Amro.
High is $26.50. Low is $19.38.

Stock name is ABN Amro.

Dividend is $0.80e.

Yield percent is 3.7%.

PE Ratio is . . .

Sales in hundreds is 2394 hundreds or 239,400.

High is $21.81; Low is $21.44; Last is $21.63.

Change is −$0.31.

! TIP!   Explanation of Additional Symbols

Additional symbols in the stock listings are defined or explained in most stock listings. For example, in the *New York Times,* **bold type** marks stocks that rose or fell at least 4 percent, but only if the change was at least 75 cents per share. An underscore means the stock traded more than 1 percent of its total shares outstanding. An *n* following the name of a stock indicates a new issue. An *s* following the name of a stock indicates stock has split by at least 20% within the last year. An *e* following the dividend payment indicates the sum of dividends paid during the last year.

EXAMPLE   Refer to Figure 18-1.

(a) How many shares of AFLAC were traded this day?

(b) What is the difference between the high price and low price of the day?

(c) What was the closing price the previous day?

(a) From column 7, we see that the day's traded shares are 10,491 hundred or 1,049,100 shares.

(b) From columns 8 and 9, we see the difference in high and low is

High 70.63

− Low 69.17

$0.46 difference per share

(c) From column 11, we see the change in price is +$0.75. Since the change is up:

Previous day's closing price = this day's closing price − change

$$\$70.13 - 0.75 = \$69.38$$

Thus, 1,049,100 shares were traded, with a difference between the high and low of $0.46 and a closing price the previous day of $69.38.

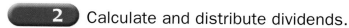 **2** Calculate and distribute dividends.

Now let's take a closer look at some of the more complex information in each stock listing, starting with column 4, "Dividends."

A corporation's board of directors can vote to reinvest any profits into the business or can declare a dividend with some or all of the profits. The dividend can be expressed either as a percentage of the par value of the shares, or as a dollar amount per share. It is usually declared quarterly (every three months), but if a business is in poor financial condition or if the directors so decide, there may be no dividends at all.

Sometimes dividends vary according to whether the stock is preferred stock or common stock. Holders of preferred stock (which has the letters "prf" after its name in stock listing) are entitled to first claim on the corporation's profits and assets. Thus, if a company has limited profits, it must pay all its preferred shareholders dividends before it can pay any of its common stock shareholders. Similarly, in case of bankruptcy, preferred stockholders must be paid before common stockholders. However, only holders of common stock are entitled to a vote in corporate affairs (one vote per share).

Dividends on various kinds of preferred stock are usually fixed, though owners of **participating preferred stock** can receive additional dividends if the company does well. **Convertible preferred stock** allows the stock to be exchanged for a certain number of shares of common stock later. And with **cumulative preferred stock,** dividends are earned every year. If no dividends are paid one year, the amounts not paid are recorded. These **dividends in arrears** must be paid when money becomes available before other preferred or common stock dividends are paid.

HOW TO Calculate and Distribute Dividends from an Available Amount of Money

1. First pay dividends in arrears:
  (a) Multiply the number of shares held by preferred stockholders by the given rate, expressed as dollars per share.
  (b) Subtract these dividends in arrears from the available amount of money.

2. Pay the present year's preferred stock dividends:
  (a) Multiply the number of preferred shares held by stockholders by the given rate.
  (b) Subtract these preferred stock dividends from the difference from step 1b.

3. Pay the common stock dividend: divide the difference from step 2b by the number of common shares held by stockholders. This is the dividend per share paid to common stockholders.

 EXAMPLE Your company has issued 20,000 shares of cumulative preferred stock that will earn dividends at $0.60 per share, and 100,000 shares of common stock. Last year you paid no dividends. This year $250,000 is available for dividends. How are the dividends to be distributed?

Preferred stockholders received no dividends last year, so this year's dividends in arrears must be paid:

$$20{,}000 \times \$0.60 = \boxed{\$12{,}000}$$

The remaining money ($250,000 − $12,000 = $238,000) is distributed to the preferred and common stockholders for this year as follows:

$$\text{To preferred stockholders: } 20{,}000 \times \$0.60 = \boxed{\$12{,}000}$$

Amount left for common stockholders ($238,000 − $12,000 = $226,000) is divided among all the common stockholders.

$$\text{To common stockholders: } \frac{\$226{,}000}{100{,}000} = \$2.26 \text{ per share}$$

Preferred stockholders receive $24,000 and common stockholders receive $226,000.

Notice that the $0.60 dividend per share for the preferred stock is a guaranteed but fixed rate, whereas the dividend per share of common stock has the *potential* to be higher (or lower) than that, but with no guarantee. Last year's common stock owners received no dividends, but this year they received more than did the preferred stockholders in two years. Since dividends are income to the stockholder, they are one measure of the desirability of owning a particular stock.

3 Calculate current stock yield.

The fifth column in Figure 18-1, "Yld %," is sometimes called the current **yield** for the stock. It is a comparative measure of the dividend. It tells (as a percent) how large the dividend is compared to today's closing price for the stock.

? HOW TO Calculate Current Stock Yield

1. Divide the annual dividend per share by the day's closing price.

$$\text{Current stock yield} = \frac{\text{annual dividend per share (column 4)}}{\text{day's closing price (column 10)}}$$

2. Write the quotient as a percent, rounded to the nearest tenth.

EXAMPLE According to Figure 18-1, AMB Pr has a $1.48 per share dividend. The day's closing price is $25.13. Verify the current stock yield quoted in the listing.

$$\text{Current stock yield} = \frac{1.48}{25.13} = 0.0588937525$$
$$= 5.9\%$$

This matches the entry for AMB Pr in the "Yld %" column.

Notice that because the numerator of the fraction is the dividend per share, if no dividend has been declared, there can be no yield. This situation is indicated by three dots in the yield column.

It might seem as if a large yield would always be more desirable than a small one, but if a company is putting its profits into redevelopment instead of dividends, there may be a small yield now. However, if the company becomes a stronger business, the stock price itself might rise. If an investor sold the stock at that later time, the return on the investment then could be high, even though the yield figure now is low.

4 Compare price to earnings.

The sixth column in Figure 18-1, "PE ratio," gives the **price–earnings (PE) ratio.** It is a measure of the price of a share of stock compared with its per-share earnings. The PE ratio, then, is the ratio of the current price per share (at the close of the business day) and the annual net income per share for the last four quarters. The last figure is reported by the company and is found by dividing the company's total earnings by the number of shares owned by stockholders.

? HOW TO Calculate the PE Ratio

1. Divide the closing price per share by the annual earnings per share

$$\text{PE ratio} = \frac{\text{closing price per share (column 10)}}{\text{annual earnings per share}}$$

2. Round to the nearest whole number.

EXAMPLE AMB Pr (Figure 18-1) has a closing price of $25.13 and the annual report shows an annual net income per share of $1.57. What is the PE ratio?

$$\text{PE ratio} = \frac{25.13}{1.57}$$
$$= 16.00636943$$
$$= 16$$

This matches the entry for AMB Pr in the "PE ratio" column.

The PE ratio usually varies between 3 and 50. A high value indicates a high price relative to a stock's earnings. This situation occurs if the price is too high (the stock is overpriced) or if earnings have been low, either as a result of poor business or if the company is not yet earning to its potential. A low PE ratio shows a lower price compared to earnings usually because the price is too low (the stock is undervalued) or people feel the business's potential is poor. If a PE ratio is not given in the stock listings, the company probably has lost money during the past year.

Stocks cannot be judged on any one aspect. One stock may have a high dividend, a high yield, and yet a high PE ratio. A cautious investor "follows the stock market" and seeks advice from knowledgeable persons, such as stockbrokers, in order to tell whether a particular company meets his or her investment needs.

5 Find the cost of buying and the proceeds from selling stocks.

For each purchase or sale of stock, the commission, an added cost of trading stock, must be considered in addition to the purchase or sale price. Broker's commissions can vary; for example, **discount brokers** usually charge less because they do not give advice or provide background research about stocks but only handle buy–sell transactions. Also, the number of shares traded affects the cost of the sale. A group of 100 shares or a multiple of 100 shares is called a **round lot;** a group of less than 100 is called an **odd lot,** and there is an extra charge for trading odd lots.

 **HOW TO** Find the Cost of Buying Stocks

1. Find the cost of the shares: multiply the number of shares by the price per share.
2. Find the commission on the round lot: multiply the round-lot commission rate, expressed as a percent of cost, by the number of shares in the round lot by the price per share.
3. Find the commission on the odd lot: multiply the odd-lot commission rate by the number of shares in the odd lot by the price per share.
4. Add the cost of the shares and the commissions.

EXAMPLE   Your broker charges 2% of the stock price for trading round lots and an additional 1%, on the odd-lot portion. You buy 250 shares of AT&T (Figure 18-1) at $21 per share. What is your total cost for the purchase?

Cost for 250 shares:	$250 \times \$21 =$ $5,250.00
Commission on round lot:	$0.02 \times 200 \times \$21 =$ $ 84.00
Commission on odd lot:	$0.03 \times 50 \times \$21 =$ $ 31.50
Total cost of purchase of stock:	$5,250.00 + $84.00 + $31.50 = $5,365.50

The total cost is $5,365.50.

 HOW TO Find the Proceeds from Selling Stocks

1. Find the selling price of the shares: multiply the number of shares by the price per share.
2. Find the commissions: multiply the commission rate by the number of shares by the price per share, for each type of lot.
3. Subtract the commissions from the selling price of the shares.

EXAMPLE   After a year you sell the 250 shares of AT&T for $54 per share. Your broker charges the same commission rate for selling the stock as he charged for buying. What are your total proceeds from the sale?

Selling price of 250 shares:	$250 \times \$54 =$ $13,500.00
Commission on round lot:	$0.02 \times 200 \times \$54 =$ $ 216.00
Commission on odd lot:	$0.03 \times 50 \times \$54 =$ $ 81.00
Proceeds from sale of stock:	$13,500.00 − $216.00 − $81.00 = $13,203.00

The proceeds are $13,203.00.

 TIP! **Effect on Commissions**

Commission increases the cost of a purchase and decreases the proceeds from a sale. Add the commission when figuring cost; subtract the commission when figuring proceeds.

Some brokerage firms have a flat rate brokerage fee for stock purchases of less than some specified amount, for example, a transaction fee of $42 for purchases less than $12,000.

6 Calculate the return on investment.

Knowing the commissions paid and the dividends earned allows you to get a truer picture of the stock's contribution to your finances. This contribution, called **return on investment (ROI)**, is expressed as a percent, to the nearest hundredth, of the cost of purchasing the stocks.

? HOW TO Calculate Return on Investment (ROI)

1. Find the total gain: from the proceeds, subtract the cost of purchase and add the dividends earned:

$$\text{Total Gain} = \text{proceeds} - \text{cost} + \text{dividend}$$

2. Divide the total gain by the cost of purchase, and express the quotient as a percent:

$$\text{ROI} = \frac{\text{total gain}}{\text{cost of purchase}} \times 100\%$$

EXAMPLE What is the return on your investment in AT&T stock? (See the previous two examples.) Assume your dividends during the past year were $1.00 per share.

$$\text{Dividends} = 250 \text{ shares} \times \$1.00 \text{ per share} = \$250$$

$$\text{Total gain} = \text{proceeds} - \text{cost} + \text{dividends}$$

$$= \$13,203 - \boxed{\$5,365.00} + \$250$$

$$= \boxed{\$8,087.50}$$

$$\text{ROI} = \frac{\text{total gain}}{\text{cost of purchase}} \times 100\%$$

$$= \frac{\$8,087.50}{\$5,365.00} \times 100\%$$

$$= 1.507455732 \times 100\% \text{ or } 151\%$$

Your return on investment is 151%.

SELF-CHECK 18.1

Use information about the common stock for AK Steel (Figure 18-1).

1. What was the closing price in dollars and cents?

2. During the previous year, what was its high price? Its low price?

3. What is the difference between this day's high price and low price?

4. What was the previous day's closing price?

Your company has $200,000 to distribute in dividends. There are 20,000 shares of preferred stock, which earn dividends at $0.50 per share, and 80,000 shares of common stock.

5. How much money goes to preferred stockholders?

6. How much goes to common stockholders?

7. How much per share does a common stockholder receive in dividends to the nearest tenth?

8. What is the current stock yield for AGL Res? Use Figure 18-1.

9. Use information from Figure 18-1 to verify the current stock yield for ACMMu.

10. Use information from Figure 18-1 to find the current stock yield for ACNiels.

11. The stock of a new company is selling for $24.50 and the company has annual earnings of $1.75 per share. What is its PE ratio?

12. AXA Fn has a closing price of $54.63 and from the company's annual report, an annual net income per share of $2.48. Verify the PE ratio given in Figure 18-1.

13. AZZ has a closing price of $18.13. From the company's annual report annual net income per share is $1.51. Verify the PE ratio given in Figure 18-1.

14. Use the PE ratio and closing stock price of ACE Ltd in Figure 18-1 to estimate the annual net income per share.

5

You buy 250 shares of Intrepidation stock at $4 per share. Your broker charges 2% of the stock price for round lots and an additional 1% for odd lots.

15. What was the commission on the round lots? On the odd lots?

16. What was your total cost for purchasing the stock?

17. If you sell these shares through the same broker for $5 per share, what will be the commission on the round lot? On the odd lot?

18. What are your proceeds from the sale?

19. Do you have a gain or loss? How much?

20. Find the total cost of buying 485 shares of AGCO stock if the broker charges 2% for round lots and an additional $\frac{1}{2}$% on odd lots. The purchase price is $9.94 per share.

21. After three years the AGCO stock is sold at $11.12. The broker fee is 2% for round lots and 2.5% for odd lots. Find the total receipt from the stock sale.

22. You purchased 100 shares of stock at $5 per share and sold them for $7 per share. During that time you received $0.50 per share in dividends. What is your net gain if no commissions were paid?

6

23. What is the return on investment to the nearest hundredth of a percent for the Intrepidation stock in exercises 15–19? Assume no dividends were earned during the period the stock was held.

24. What is the return on investment to the nearest hundredth of a percent for the AGCO stock in exercises 20–21 if the dividends for the three-year period totaled $2 per share?

18.2 Bonds

1 Read bond listings.

2 Calculate the price of bonds.

3 Find the cost of buying and the proceeds from selling bonds.

After time passes, a corporation may need to raise more money than its initial offering of stock produced. It can then issue more stock, thereby creating more shares or ownership. However, the company management may be reluctant to do so because additional shares lessen the ownership power (dilute the rights) of the existing stockholders. To raise the needed money, the company may decide to borrow it for a short term from a bank, or for a longer term (five years or more) from the public, by selling bonds. In exchange for money from the sale, the company issues a **bond,** a promise to repay the money at a specific later date and in the meantime to pay interest annually.

A bond has a **face value (par value),** usually $1,000, a date of repayment **(maturity date),** and a fixed *rate of interest* per year. Since a bond obligates the company to future repayment, the public's judgment of the company's future will affect sales of a bond. Investors also look closely at the interest to be paid.

Since bonds are a legal debt of the corporation, if the company goes bankrupt, the bondholder's claims have priority over those of the stockholders. Bonds of businesses that are bankrupt or in financial difficulty, called **junk bonds,** can thus yield a high return—or be next to worthless—making them a risky and speculative investment.

In addition to these **corporate bonds** issued by businesses, state and local governments sell **municipal bonds** and the federal government sells **treasury bonds.** Government bonds are often attractive to investors because the interest payments on them may be exempt from federal income tax. In this text, however, we deal only with corporate bonds.

Corporate bonds come in various types. **Coupon bonds** require the investor to send in a coupon at a specified time to receive interest. **Registered bonds** allow the investor to receive interest automatically by being listed with the corporation. **Convertible bonds** have a provision that allows them to be converted to stock. **Recallable bonds** allow the corporation to repurchase the bonds before the maturity date.

Once bonds are issued, they are bought and sold at varying prices in the **bond market.** Here, as in the stock market, "market conditions" prevail: A bond with high interest payments may be attractive to investors, so its price may rise, causing the bond to *sell at a premium* (a **premium bond**). Or, if interest payments are low, a bond price may tend to drop in order to attract investors, causing the bond to *sell at a discount* (a **discount bond**).

> **! TIP!** **How Much Do I Get at Maturity of a Bond**
>
> Keep in mind that, no matter what the market price of a bond, the corporation pays interest on the face value of $1,000 per bond and repays the face or par value of the bond at maturity.

---

1 Read bond listings.

Figure 18-2 shows how bonds are listed in the *New York Times.*

Because there is less activity in the bond market than in the stock market, prices are given weekly. A quick look at the closing price (Cls) column in Figure 18-2 reveals only two bonds selling at exactly par value (100%). The discount bonds have a listing less than 100%; the premium bonds have a listing greater than 100%. Aames is selling at a discount, whereas the AutDt bond is selling at a premium. Some of the symbols used in the listing are explained in Figure 18-3.

Figure 18-2 Portion of NYSE Bonds Listing (*Source: New York Times*)

①	②	③	④	⑤	⑥	⑦	⑧	⑨
12-Mo.			**Cur**			**Weekly**		
Hi	**Lo**	**Name**	**Yld**	**Vol**	**Hi**	**Lo**	**Cls**	**Chg.**
96	88	AES Cp 8s8	8.6	29	93	91¼	92⅞	+2¾
108⅝	99⅜	AMR 9s16	8.8	218	103	102	102	−1⅛
99¹³⁄₃₂	97	ATT 5⅛01	5.2	21	99⁹⁄₃₂	99⁹⁄₃₂	99⁹⁄₃₂	− ³⁄₃₂
101⅜	98⅛	ATT 7⅛02	7.1	96	101⅛	99¾	100	− ¼
100	97¼	ATT 6½02	6.5	34	99¾	99½	99¾	+ ⅜
100⅛	95¼	ATT 6¾04	6.8	170	99	98⅜	99	+ ½
96⅛	92⅝	ATT 5⅝04	5.9	164	95¾	95	95½	+ ⅛
101⅛	95⅛	ATT 7s05	7.1	100	99⅞	99	99⅛	+ ⅛
102¾	97½	ATT 7½06	7.4	213	101	100⅛	101	+ ¾
103½	98⅞	ATT 7¾07	7.5	23	102⅞	100⅜	102⅞	+1
92¾	85½	ATT 6s09	6.6	93	91⅜	89⅛	91⅜	+1¼
102⅛	91⅝	ATT 8⅛22	8.2	1125	99¼	98⅜	99¼	+ ½
101¾	92¼	ATT 8⅛24	8.2	1212	99¼	98¼	99	+ ⅛
105⅜	95	ATT 8.35s25	8.4	1696	99⅜	98½	99⅜	+ ⅝
90	78	ATT 6½29	7.8	701	82⅞	81⅜	82⅞	+ ⅞
105	95⅝	ATT 8⅝31	8.6	1573	100¾	99⅞	100	− ⅛
90	68	Aames 10½02	13.4	12	79	77	78½	−3⅝
117	45½	Alza zr14	. . .	21	97⅛	92½	92½	−18
72	60	ARetire 5¾02	cv	135	65	64¾	65	. . .
104½	101⅛	Apache 9¼02	9.0	45	103¼	102¾	103¼	+ ⅜
108¼	16½	vjArmW 9¾08f	. . .	390	25¾	22⅛	24	+1
100	97⅜	AscCp dc6s01	6.0	5	99⁷⁄₃₂	99⁷⁄₃₂	99⁷⁄₃₂	+ ⅝
99⅞	98⅛	AscCp 8.15s09	8.2	5	99⅞	99⅞	99⅞	+1¾
121½	113	ARch 10⅞05	9.3	65	117	117	117	. . .
261	110⅛	AutDt zr12	. . .	25	162	162	162	+2

BOND TABLES EXPLAINED

Bonds are interest-bearing debt certificates. Their value is usually quoted as a percentage, with 100 equaling par, or face value. This table shows the issuing company, then the original coupon rate (interest rate) and the last two digits of the maturity year.

Current yield represents the annual percentage return to the purchaser at the current price. The **Cls** column refers to the bond's closing price, and **Chg** is the difference between the week's closing price and the previous week's closing price. A majority of bonds, and all municipal or tax-exempt bonds, are not listed on exchanges; rather they are traded over the counter.

Other footnotes:

cv	Convertible into stock under specified conditions	**rp**	Reduced principal
cld	Called	**st**	Stamped
dc	Selling at a discounted price	**t**	Floating rate
f	Dealt in flat—traded without accrued interest	**x**	Ex interest
k	Treasury bond, non resident aliens exempt from witholding tax	**vj**	In bankruptcy or receivership or being reorganized under the Bankruptcy Act, or securities assumed by such companies
m	Matured bonds		
na	No accrual of interest	**wd**	When distributed
p	Treasury note, non-resident aliens exempt from witholding tax	**wi**	When issued
r	Registered	**zr**	Zero coupon issue

Figure 18-3 Bond Tables Explained (Source: *New York Times*)

HOW TO Read Bond Listings

1. Columns 1 and 2 give the high and low values over the past 12 months.

2. Column 3 (Name) tells the name of the issuing company, the annual interest rate (expressed as a percent of face value), and the last two digits of the year of maturity.

3. Column 4 (Cur Yld) tells the current yield, which is the ratio of the annual interest earned per bond and the current price per bond.

4. Column 5 (Vol) tells the volume (number) of bonds traded; note that, unlike stock listings, this figure does not represent hundreds of bonds traded, so if the entry is 10, it means that 10, not 1,000, bonds have been traded this week.

5. Columns 6 and 7 give the weekly high and low values.

6. Column 8 (Cls) tells the closing price per bond as a percent of the face value per bond; an entry of $97\frac{3}{4}$ means the bond sold for $97\frac{3}{4}$% of $1,000 per bond, or 0.9775 times $1,000 per bond, or $977.50 per bond.

7. Column 9 (Chg) tells how much this week's closing price per bond differs from the previous week's closing price per bond, as a percent of the face value per bond.

EXAMPLE   Refer to Figure 18-2.

(a) What are the interest rate and the year of maturity for Apache?

(b) How many bonds were sold on this week?

(c) What was the net change for the week?

(a) From column 3, we see the interest rate is $9\frac{1}{4}$%, and the year of maturity is 2002.

(b) From column 5, we see the number of bonds sold this day is 45.

(c) From column 9, we see the change is $+\frac{3}{8}$, or up $\frac{3}{8}$% of $1,000, or up $3.38.

TIP! Stock Symbols

What does s mean in between the rate and maturity date?
For an interest rate that is a whole percent, the letter s (for *space*) is inserted to separate the rate and the maturity date. A listing of 8s08 means 8% maturing in 2008.

2 Calculate the price of bonds.

Even though a bond has a face value of $1,000, bonds on the bond market are bought and sold for more or less than $1,000. Column 4 in Figure 18–2 gives the closing price per bond as a percent of $1,000.

HOW TO Calculate the Price of a Bond

1. Locate the percent of $1,000 that the bond was selling for at the close of the week (column 8).

2. Multiply the decimal equivalent of the percent by $1,000.

3. Round the product to the nearest cent.

EXAMPLE Calculate the closing price of an Apache bond.

From column 8, the closing price as a percent of face value was $103\frac{1}{4}\% = 103.25\% = \boxed{1.0325}.$

$$\text{Closing bond price} = \boxed{\$1,000} \times \text{percent in column 8}$$

$$= \boxed{1,000} \times \boxed{1.0325}$$

$$= \$1,032.50$$

The closing bond price is $1,032.50.

EXAMPLE Calculate the previous week's closing price per bond for AMR (Figure 18-2).

The bond closed at 102% of its face value, down $1\frac{1}{8}\%$ of its face value from the previous week's closing price. The previous week's closing price was this week's closing price plus $1\frac{1}{8}\%$ of the face value.

$$\text{Previous week's closing listing} = 102\% + 1\frac{1}{8}\% = 103\frac{1}{8}\%$$

$$103\frac{1}{8}\% = 103.125\% = \boxed{1.03125}$$

$$\text{Previous week's bond price} = \$1,000 \times \boxed{1.03125} = \$1,031.25.$$

The previous week's bond price is $1,031.25.

3 Find the cost of buying and the proceeds from selling bonds.

Broker's fees or commissions for trading bonds vary, but for purposes of our discussion, let us consider the commission to be $5 for each bond traded. As with stocks, commissions increase the cost of buying bonds and reduce the proceeds from selling bonds.

HOW TO Calculate the Cost of Buying and the Proceeds from Selling

1. Find the cost or proceeds of the bonds: multiply the number of bonds by the price per bond.

Cost or Proceeds = number of bonds × price per bond

2. Find the commission: multiply the commission per bond by the number of bonds.

Commission = commission per bond × number of bonds

3. Find the total cost: add the commission to the cost of the bonds.

Total cost = cost of bonds + commission

4. Find the net proceeds: subtract the commission from the proceeds.

Net proceeds = proceeds − commission

EXAMPLE Three Apache bonds are sold at the week's closing price (see Figure 18-2). What will be the net proceeds from the sale of the bonds (after deducting broker's fees)?

The price of one bond, as listed, is $103\frac{1}{4}\%$ of face value.

$$103\frac{1}{4}\% = 103.25\% = 1.0325$$

$$\$1,000 \times 1.0325 = \$1,032.50 \text{ price of one bond}$$

For three bonds, the receipts will be $3 \times \$1,032.50 = \$3,097.50$, before commission.

For three bonds, the commission is $3 \times \$5 = \$15$.

Subtract $15 commission for the three bonds, $\$3,097.50 - \$15 = \$3,082.50$, the net receipts from the sale.

The net proceeds are $3,082.50.

Investors in bonds, like investors in stocks, want to know the **yield** of their investments. In Figure 18-2 the "Cur Yld" (current yield) column gives a measure of how profitable the investment is. **Current bond yield,** sometimes called **average annual yield,** compares annual earnings (interest) with the closing price of a bond. It is expressed as a percent of face value.

 HOW TO Calculate Current Bond Yield

1. Divide the annual interest per bond in dollars by the current price per bond in dollars. Interest is calculated on the $1,000 face value of the bond.

$$\text{Current bond yield} = \frac{\text{annual interest per bond}}{\text{current price per bond}}$$

2. Express the answer as a percent.

EXAMPLE Verify the current bond yield for the ATT bond that matures in 2005 (Figure 18-2).

According to column 3, the interest rate is 7%. The interest, then, is $0.07 \times \$1,000$ per bond, or $\$70.00$ per bond. From column 8, the closing price is $99\frac{1}{8}\%$ of face value, which is $0.99125 \times \$1,000$ per bond, or $\$991.25$ per bond. The current bond yield is

$$\frac{\$70.00}{\$991.25} = 0.0706 = 7.1\%$$

This matches the figure listed under "Cur Yld." **The current bond yield does not include commissions and is 7.1%.**

Interest is paid on the $1,000 face value of the bond. Although the stated interest rate for the ATT bond is 7%, the current bond yield is higher, at 7.1%.

 TIP! Discounted Bonds versus Premium Bonds

A discounted bond always has a higher yield than its stated interest rate, while a premium bond always has a lower yield than its stated interest rate.

EXAMPLE It is 2002 and Dottie Todd wants to invest approximately $10,000 in bonds. After significant research she has narrowed her choices to ATT 7s05 and ARch $10\frac{7}{8}$05. She will have to pay $5 per bond in commissions. If she plans to keep the bonds until maturity, which ones should she buy?

1 Decision needed

Should Dottie buy the ATT 7s05 or ARch $10\frac{7}{8}$05 bonds?

2 Unknown facts

ATT 7s05 will earn 7% interest per year for three years and costs $991.25.
ARch $10\frac{7}{8}$05 will earn $10\frac{7}{8}$% interest per year for three years and costs $1,170.

3 Known facts

ROI for ATT 7s05
ROI for ARch $10\frac{7}{8}$05

4 Relationships

Cost of purchase = number of bonds × cost per bond + commission
Total gain = number of bonds × $1,000 + earned interest − cost of purchase
$$\text{ROI} = \frac{\text{total gain}}{\text{cost of purchase}}$$

5 Estimation

ATT will earn less interest, but cost less.
ARch will earn more interest, but cost more.

6 Calculation

ATT 7s05:

Cost of bonds = 10 × $991.25 = $9,912.50
Commission = 10 × $5 = $50
Cost of purchase = $9,912.50 + $50 = $9,962.50
Interest earned = $10,000 × 0.07 × 3 = $2,100.00
Total gain = $10,000 + $2,100.00 − $9,962.50
= $2,137.50
$$\text{ROI} = \frac{\$2,137.50}{\$9,962.50} = 21.46\%$$

ARch $10\frac{7}{8}$05:

Cost of bonds = 10 × $1,170 = $11,700
Commission = 10 × $5 = $50
Cost of purchase = $11,700 + $50 = $11,750
Interest earned = $10,000 × 0.10875 × 3 = $3,262.50
Total gain = $10,000 + $3,262.50 − $11,750
= $1,512.50
$$\text{ROI} = \frac{\$1,512.50}{\$11,750} = 12.87\%$$

7 Interpretation

ROI for ATT 7s05 is 21.46% and for ARch $10\frac{7}{8}$05 is 12.87%.

8 Decision made

Dottie should buy the ATT 7s05 bonds because the return on investment is greater.

1. Refer to Figure 18-2 to determine the interest rate and maturity of a bond issued by AMR.

2. What is the current yield for the bond issue of ATT, which has an interest rate of $7\frac{3}{4}\%$ and matures in 2007?

3. How many bonds for the ARetire issue maturing in 2002 were traded in the week shown in the bond listing in Figure 18-2?

4. A bond pays 8% annual interest and is selling for 102% of face value. What is its current yield?

5. Which of the first two ATT bonds (Figure 18-2) is producing the greater current yield?

2

6. Use Figure 18-2 to find the selling price at the close of the selling week of the bond issue for ATT that matures in 2031.

7. Calculate the closing price of an ATT bond that matures in 2029.

8. What is the price of a bond listed as $98\frac{1}{2}\%$?

9. From Figure 18-2, what was the previous week's closing bond price for an ATT bond that matures in 2009.

3

10. What are the net proceeds from the sale of four Alza bonds at the week's closing price (p. 726)? Broker's fees for this sale are $20 per bond.

11. Find the total cost of purchasing five ATT bonds with a maturity date of 2029 if they are purchased at the week's closing price and the broker's commission is $15 per bond.

12. Verify the current bond yield for the ATT bond issue that matures in 2022.

The Stock Market over the Long Term

Most people look to the stock market for long term financial growth and to provide security for retirement. During a term of investment over 20 or more years, most funds experience periods of growth and periods of decline. However, most investors look at the average growth over the long term.

In recent years the stock market has had some uncharacteristic growth periods, and many new investors expected the market to continue indefinitely at this growth rate. There was much speculation before the millennium that the stock market might crash or take a severe downturn. In January 2000, the market remained stable. However, later in the year and into the early part of 2001 the market had a significant decline. Many stock market historians call such periods *market corrections*.

Even though investors should expect fluctuations in the market, investors continue to have confidence in the stock market. At the beginning of the 1990s, the market equity fund assets were 240 billion dollars. This grew to 4.04 trillion dollars by the end of 1999.

So, what can realistically be expected of the stock market over the long term?

Historically, one out of every four years the stock market will experience a market correction. These market corrections are unavoidable, but they have never been permanent or long lasting. In fact, the three out of four years when the market is growing more than compensates for the one down year.

Experienced investors maintain cash reserves so they are not forced to liquidate their stock (sell their stock) during periods of market corrections. Also, successful investors take advantage of the market correction periods to buy stock. The key to successful investing in the stock market is to think long-term and spend a significant amount of time researching prospective stocks and monitoring the stocks currently owned (portfolio). Investors often pay a professional for advice on investing. These data regarding the history of the stock market will increase your awareness of market trends over the long term.

	Are Your Expectations of the Stock Market Realistic?	
Time Period (Years)	**Start Date Through 12/31/00**	**Dow Jones Industrial Average Annual Return**
70	12/31/30	10.88%
50	12/31/50	12.36
25	12/31/75	15.03
10	12/31/90	17.88
5	12/31/95	18.21
1	12/31/99	−4.66

Source: ©2001 TowersData, Inc.

Ten 20% market corrections occurred between 1946 and 2000. On the average, one 20% correction occurs every five years. The only 20% correction in the Dow in the 1990s took place in the third quarter of 1990. There were no other 20% corrections in the 1990s. A market correction occurred in 2001; however, those who analyze the market have not yet declared this to be a 20% correction.

Exercises

1. By what percent did market equity fund assets grow during the decade of the 1990s?
2. If you made a $1,000 investment December 31, 1999, what would it have been worth on December 31, 2000?
3. If you made a $1,000 investment December 31, 1995, what would it have been worth on December 31, 2000? (Use the formula $A = p(1 + r)^t$ where A is the accumulated amount, p is the beginning investment, r is the annual rate of return, and t is the number of years.)
4. If you made a $1,000 investment December 31, 1990, what would it have been worth on December 31, 2000? (Use the formula $A = p(1 + r)^t$ where A is the accumulated amount, p is the beginning investment, r is the annual rate of return, and t is the number of years.)
5. If you made a $1,000 investment December 31, 1975, what would it have been worth on December 31, 2000? (Use the formula $A = p(1 + r)^t$ where A is the accumulated amount, p is the beginning investment, r is the annual rate of return, and t is the number of years.)
6. If you made a $1,000 investment December 31, 1950, what would it have been worth on December 31, 2000? (Use the formula $A = p(1 + r)^t$ where A is the accumulated amount, p is the beginning investment, r is the annual rate of return, and t is the number of years.)

Answers

1. 1,583% increase.
2. $953.40.
3. $2,308.19
4. $5,180.85
5. $33,134.31
6. $339,302.08

CHAPTER OVERVIEW
18

| Section Outcome | Important Points with Examples |

Section 18.1

Read stock listings. (page 717)

1. Columns 1 (High) and 2 (Low) tell the highest and lowest prices at which the stock has sold in the last year (52 weeks), not including this day.
2. Column 3 (Stock) tells the name of the company (in abbreviated form).
3. Column 4 (Div) tells the dividend paid per share of stock the previous year.
4. Column 5 (Yld %) tells the previous year's dividend as a percent of the current price per share. If no dividend was paid in the previous year, the entry is ". . .".
5. Column 6 (PE Ratio) tells the stock's price earnings ratio (see outcome 4).
6. Column 7 (Sales 100s) tells the volume (number) of hundreds of shares traded this day. An entry of 84 means 8,400 shares were traded.
7. Columns 8 (High), 9 (Low), and 10 (Last) tell the high price, low price, and last price per share at which the stock sold this day.
8. Column 11 (Chg) tells how much this day's closing price per share differs from the previous day's closing price per share for that stock.

Refer to Figure 18-1:

How many shares of ABN Amro were traded this day?

From column 7, 2,394 × 100 = 239,400 shares traded this day

What is the difference between the highest and lowest prices of ABN Amro stock for the year?

From columns 1 and 2, $21.81 − $21.44 = $0.37

2 Calculate and distribute dividends. (page 719)

1. First pay dividends in arrears:
    (a) Multiply the number of shares held by preferred stockholders by the given rate, expressed as dollars per share.
    (b) Subtract the dividends in arrears from the available amount of money.
2. Pay the present year's preferred stock dividends:
    (a) Multiply the number of preferred shares held by stockholders by the given rate.
    (b) Subtract these preferred stock dividends from the difference from step 1b.
3. Pay the common stock dividend: divide the difference from step 2b by the number of common shares held by stockholders. This is the dividend per share for common stockholders.

$500,000 is available for dividends, including $20,000 for dividends in arrears and $20,000 for current preferred stock dividends. How much will be given for common stock dividends?

$500,000 − $40,000 = $460,000

$460,000 is available for common stock dividends. There are 300,000 shares of common stock. What is the dividend per share?

$$\frac{\$460,000}{300,000} = \$1.53 \text{ per share}$$

3 Calculate current stock yield. (page 720)

1. Divide the annual dividend per share by the day's closing price.

$$\text{Current stock yield} = \frac{\text{annual dividend per share (column 4)}}{\text{day's closing price (column 10)}}$$

2. Write the quotient as a percent, rounded to the nearest tenth.

ACMin has a $0.78 dividend per share and a closing price of $7.50. What is its current yield?

$$\frac{0.78}{7.50} = 10.4\%$$

4 Compare price to earnings. (page 721)

1. Divide the closing price per share by the annual earnings per share.

$$\text{PE ratio} = \frac{\text{closing price per share (column 10)}}{\text{annual earnings per share}}$$

2. Round to the nearest whole number.

AAR has a closing price of $11.44 and an annual net income per share of $1.04. What is the PE ratio?

$$\text{PE ratio} = \frac{\$11.44}{\$1.04} = 11$$

PE ratio is 11. Price is "eleven times" earnings.

5 Find the cost of buying and the proceeds from selling stocks. (page 721)

Find the cost of buying stocks.
1. Find the cost of the shares: multiply the number of shares by the price per share.
2. Find the commission on the round lot: multiply the round-lot commission rate, expressed as a percent of cost, by the number of shares in the round lot by the price per share.
3. Find the commission on the odd lot: multiply the odd-lot commission rate by the number of shares in the odd lot by the price per share.
4. Add the cost of the shares and the commissions.

> Taking stock commission to be 2% of the stock price for the round lot and an additional 1% for the odd lot, what is the commission on the purchase of 350 shares of stock selling at $13 per share?
>
> Commission on round lot: 0.02 × 300 × $13 = $78
>
> Commission on odd lot: 0.03 × 50 × $13 = $19.50
>
> Total commission: $97.50
>
> You purchase 350 shares of stock at $13 per share. Commission is $97.50. What is your total cost for the purchase?
>
> Cost of stock: 350 × $13 = $4,550
>
> Cost of purchase: $4,550 + $97.50 = $4,647.50

Find the proceeds from selling stocks.
1. Find the selling price of the shares: multiply the number of shares by the price per share.
2. Find the commissions: multiply the commission rate by the number of shares by the price per share, for each type of lot.
3. Subtract the commissions from the selling price of the shares.

> You sell 350 shares of stock at $15 per share with 2% and 3% commission rates for round and odd lots. What are your proceeds from the sale?
>
> From stock: 350 × $15 = $5,250
>
> Commission: 0.02 × 300 × 15 = 90
>
> 0.03 × 50 × 15 = 22.50
>
> $90 + $22.50 = $112.50
>
> Proceeds from sale: $5,250 − $112.50 = $5,137.50

6 Calculate the return on investment. (page 723)

1. Find the total gain: from the proceeds subtract the cost of the purchase and add the annual dividends earned.

$$\text{Total gain} = \text{proceeds} - \text{cost} + \text{dividends}.$$

2. Divide the total gain by the cost of the purchase and express the quotient as a percent.

$$\text{ROI} = \frac{\text{total gain}}{\text{cost of purchase}}$$

Find the return on investment for a stock sale if the proceeds are $5,137.50, the cost is $4,647.50, and the dividends are $290.

Total gain is $5,137.50 − $4,647.50 + $290 = $780

$$\text{ROI} = \frac{\$780}{\$4,647.50} = 0.167832 = 17\%$$

Section 18.2

 Read bond listings. (page 725)

1. Column 1 and 2 give the high and low values over the past 12 months.
2. Column 3 (Name) tells the name of the issuing company, the annual interest rate (expressed as a percent of the face value), and the last two digits of the year of maturity.
3. Column 4 (Cur Yld) tells the current yield, which is the ratio of the annual interest earned per bond and the current price per bond.
4. Column 5 (Vol) tells the volume (number) of bonds traded; note that, unlike stock listings, this figure does not represent hundreds of bonds traded. So if the entry is 10, it means that 10, not 1,000, bonds have been traded this day.
5. Column 6 and 7 give the weekly high and low values.
6. Column 8 (Cls) tells the closing price per bond as a percent of the face value per bond; an entry of $97\frac{3}{4}$ means the bond sold for $97\frac{3}{4}$% of $1,000 per bond, or 0.9775 times $1,000 per bond, or $977.50 per bond.
7. Column 9 (Chg) tells how much this week's closing price differs from the previous week's closing price per bond, as a percent of the face value per bond.

A bond is listed as having a closing price of $80\frac{3}{8}$, up $\frac{1}{8}$ from last week's close. What is the price today? What was it last week?

$80\frac{3}{8}$% of face value is 0.80375 × $1,000 or $803.75 per bond today.

$80\frac{3}{8}$% − $\frac{1}{8}$% = $80\frac{1}{4}$% or $802.50 per bond last week.

Bond A has 15 listed in the "volume" column. How many bonds were traded today?

15 in the "volume" column means 15 bonds were traded.

A bond is listed at $6\frac{5}{8}$05. How much interest is paid annually?

The interest rate is $6\frac{5}{8}$%.

$6\frac{5}{8}$% of $1,000 is $66.25.

What is the maturity date of the bond?

The bond matures in 2005 as indicated by 05 after the interest rate of $6\frac{5}{8}$.

 Calculate the price of bonds. (page 727)

1. Locate the percent of $1,000 that the bond was selling for at the close of the week (column 4).
2. Multiply the decimal equivalent of the percent by $1,000.
3. Round the product to the nearest cent.

You purchase five bonds listed at $98\frac{1}{2}$. What is the cost of the bonds?

For one bond: $98\frac{1}{2}\%$ of $\$1,000 = 0.985 \times \$1,000 = \$985$
For five bonds: $5 \times \$985 = \$4,925$

Cost of bonds: $\$4,925$

3 Calculate the cost of buying and the proceeds from selling bonds. (page 728)

1. Find the cost or proceeds of the bonds: multiply the number of bonds by the price per bond.

    Cost or Proceeds = number of bonds × price per bond.

2. Find the commission: multiply the commission per bond by the number of bonds.

    Commission = number of bonds × commission per bond.

3. Find the total cost: add the commission to the cost of the bonds.

    Total cost = cost of bonds + commission.

4. Find the net proceeds: subtract the commission from the proceeds.

    Net proceeds = proceeds − commission.

Find the total cost of purchasing three ATT $8\frac{1}{8}22$ bonds at the week's closing price (see Figure 18-2) if the commission is $10 per bond.

Cost = $3 \times \$992.50 = \$2,977.50$

Commission = $3 \times \$10 = \$30$

Total cost = $\$2,977.50 + \$30 = \$3,007.50$

WORDS TO KNOW

stock (p. 716)
share (p. 716)
face value (pp. 716, 725)
par value (pp. 716, 725)
stock certificate (p. 716)
dividend (pp. 716, 719)
preferred stock (p. 716)
common stock (p. 716)
stock market (p. 716)
trade (p. 716)
stockbroker (p. 716)
stock listings (p. 717)
participating preferred stock
    (p. 719)

convertible preferred stock
    (p. 719)
cumulative preferred stock
    (p. 719)
dividends in arrears (p. 719)
yield (pp. 720, 729)
price–earnings (PE) ratio (p. 721)
discount brokers (p. 721)
round lot (p. 721)
odd lot (p. 721)
return on investment (ROI)
    (p. 723)
bond (p. 725)
maturity date (p. 725)

junk bonds (p. 725)
corporate bonds (p. 725)
municipal bonds (p. 725)
treasury bonds (p. 725)
coupon bonds (p. 725)
registered bonds (p. 725)
convertible bonds (p. 725)
recallable bonds (p. 725)
bond market (p. 725)
premium bond (p. 725)
discount bond (p. 725)
current bond yield (p. 729)
average annual yield (p. 729)

1. In the columns for listing stock information, some columns give necessary information for finding additional information and other columns give convenience information that could have been generated by information in other columns. Give an example of a column giving convenience information.

2. To find the previous day's price of a stock, you use the current day's price and the amount of change. When do you add and when do you subtract? Give a strategy for predicting the result that will help you to avoid carelessly performing the wrong operation.

3. Using the formula

$$\text{PE ratio} = \frac{\text{closing price per share}}{\text{annual earnings per share}},$$

write a formula and explain your rationale for finding the annual earnings per share for the stock listing information.

4. How are bonds different from stocks?

5. How are bonds different from certificates of deposits or savings accounts?

6. Does column 2 in Figure 18-2 give convenience information or new information that could not be calculated from other table information? Explain your answer.

7. In Figure 18-2 which bonds are discounted bonds and which are premium bonds? How can you tell the difference?

8. When are premium bonds a wise investment? When are discounted bonds a wise investment?

Section 18.1

For exercises 1–4 and 10–14, refer to Figure 18-4.

1. (a) How many shares of Pepsico were traded?

   (b) What is the difference between the high and low prices of the last 52 weeks?

   (c) What was the difference between the day's high and low trading prices for one share of Pepsico stock?

   (d) What was the previous day's closing price?

2. (a) What was the last dividend paid for one share of Pepsico stock?

   (b) What is this day's closing price?

   (c) Using the information from (a) and (b), determine the current yield on Pepsico stock. Round to the nearest hundredth percent.

3. (a) How much money was paid in dividends for one share of Pan Pacifi stock? For 50 shares? For 100 shares?

   (b) What is this day's closing price for one share of PerkinElm stock?

   (c) What is the calculated current yield on PennVA stock? Round to the nearest hundredth percent.

4. (a) Calculate the current yield for PPLCorp. Does your answer match the "Yld %" figure?

   (b) Which of the two companies, PenRe or Parkwy, has the greater dividend per share?

   (c) Which of the two companies, PenRe or Parkwy, has the greater yield?

① 52-Week High	② Low	③ Stock	④ Div	⑤ Yld %	⑥ P/E	⑦ Sales 100s	⑧ High	⑨ Low	⑩ Last	⑪ Chg
18.00	13.75	P&OPrin n	...	...	18	93	15.88	15.69	15.75	−0.50
31.81	**19.69**	**PG&E Cp**	**1.20**	**5.0**	**60**	**29211**	**24.13**	**23.44**	**24.06**	**+1.19**
74.94	33.50	PMI Grp	.16	0.3	10	3761	58.94	56.50	58.00	+0.31
69.31	36.00	PNC	1.92 f	2.9	16	13135	67.81	66.44	66.56	−0.75
65.06	36.00	PPG	1.60	3.9	11	9566	42.56	41.31	41.44	−0.75
44.81	18.38	PPL Corp	1.06	2.6	11	5107	42.19	40.88	41.25	−0.31
17.56	10.00	PXRE Grp	.24	1.6	dd	483	15.00	14.75	14.88	...
13.31	11.63	PacAS	1.06 a	8.2	q	75	13.00	12.94	12.94	−0.06
20.00	5.75	PacCCyb n	...	...	...	2731	7.00	6.75	6.75	−0.38
23.19	**11.06**	**PacCent**	**.72**	**5.1**	**9**	**5637**	**15.13**	**14.00**	**14.00**	**−1.06**
27.94	19.25	PacGulf	22.00 c	...	16	1611	27.69	27.25	27.50	+0.13
16.38	9.25	PackAmer	...	...	...	2030	14.38	12.75	14.38	+0.31
12.75	**7.50**	**Pactiv**	...	...	...	**13448**	**12.13**	**11.13**	**12.13**	**+0.75**
3.44	1.94	Pakisinv	.06 e	2.7	q	141	2.31	2.25	2.25	...
25.00	17.13	PallCp	.66	3.5	16	5394	19.38	18.81	18.81	−0.50
13.00	0.38 ▼	Pameco s	...	...	...	335	0.38	0.31	0.38	−0.06
22.00	15.13	PanPacif	1.68 a	8.0	13	622	21.19	20.94	21.06	−0.06
23.50	13.13	PanamBev	.24	1.8	dd	1281	13.63	13.38	13.50	−0.13
11.75	4.13	Panavis	...	...	dd	5	4.31	4.31	4.31	...
6.38	2.00	ParTch	...	...	dd	153	2.06	2.00	2.06	...
48.33	12.08	ParkEl s	.24	0.7	23	1506	36.56	35.00	35.50	−1.06
15.38	9.88	ParkPlc	...	...	23	17762	12.88	12.25	12.44	−0.44
7.44	3.00	ParkDrl	...	...	dd	3001	4.56	4.38	4.56	+0.06
54.00	31.00	ParkHan	.68	1.8	10	8409	40.06	38.56	38.56	−0.25
33.13	26.31	Parkwy	2.00	6.9	10	205	28.81	28.31	28.81	+0.44
57.63	28.38	PartnerRe	1.04	1.9	29	914	54.69	53.38	53.63	−0.13
22.94	**7.56**	**Patina**	**.16 f**	**0.8**	**13**	**886**	**20.63**	**19.63**	**20.63**	**+0.81**
11.13	0.50	Patina wt	...	...	...	124	8.13	7.88	8.00	...
13.06	6.50	Paxar	...	...	5	1534	8.50	8.19	8.31	−0.06
69.00	**38.75**	**PaylSh**	...	...	**12**	**2138**	**66.88**	**63.88**	**64.00**	**−3.06**
30.56	22.38	Pearson n	...	...	...	150	26.00	25.38	25.63	+0.06
41.25	16.38	Pechny	.38 e	1.8	...	7	21.00	20.88	21.00	+0.13
22.38	6.44	Pediatrx	...	...	29	903	22.31	22.00	22.00	−0.31
9.75	6.63	PennAm	.21	2.7	dd	11	7.69	7.56	7.69	+0.13
34.31	20.00	PennEMA	.56	1.9	12	5	29.81	29.81	29.81	−0.06
39.25	21.63	PennEm	.56	1.7	12	150	34.50	33.50	33.50	−1.19
21.56	12.25	PennTrty	...	...	6	134	16.75	16.38	16.44	−0.19
29.13	15.56	PennVa	.90	3.1	10	137	28.94	28.38	28.94	+0.56
22.50	8.69	Penney	.50 m	5.4	dd	15372	9.44	9.00	9.31	+0.25
19.75	14.00	PenRE	2.04 f	10.5	8	541	19.44	19.25	19.38	...
13.25	8.38	PenzlQS	.75	6.5	dd	4320	12.56	11.63	11.63	−0.38
5.69	0.63	Pentacn	...	...	dd	123	0.88	0.75	0.75	−0.13
44.63	**23.25**	**Pentair**	**.64**	**2.6**	**10**	**2233**	**25.81**	**24.81**	**24.81**	**−1.13**
36.38	19.50	Penton	.12	0.5	9	673	24.50	24.00	24.50	+0.25
45.88	26.19	PeopEn	2.00	4.7	17	2214	43.69	42.50	42.50	−1.19
9.38	3.81 ▼	PepBoy	.27	7.0	dd	4198	4.00	3.75	3.88	−0.06
41.56	15.88 ▲	PepsiBot	.08	0.2	27	7582	42.50	40.56	42.25	+1.00
6.63	4.00	PepsiGem	...	...	...	15	4.75	4.56	4.56	−0.13
49.94	29.69	PepsiCo	.56	1.1	35	93298	49.69	48.50	48.81	−0.94
121.00	**37.81**	**PerkinElm**	**.56**	**0.5**	**37**	**7686**	**103.94**	**93.13**	**102.25**	**+4.69**

Figure 18-4   New York stock Exchange Table excerpt (Source: *New York Times*)

5. Stock A pays $1 dividend and sells for $5 a share. Stock B pays $1 dividend and sells for $50 a share. Which stock will have the greater yield? Why?

6. You own 100 shares of cumulative preferred stock that pays dividends at $0.85 per share in a company that did not pay any dividends for the past two years. This year you expect to receive dividends in arrears.
(a) How much will you receive for dividends in arrears?

(b) How much will you receive for this year's dividends?

(c) If you had owned 100 shares of common stock that will pay $1.80 per share this year, how much would you have received in dividends from that investment for three years?

7. Your company has 120,000 shares of preferred stock that pays dividends at $0.25 per share and 200,000 shares of common stock. This year $500,000 is to be distributed. The preferred stockholders are also due to receive dividends in arrears for one year.
(a) What is the amount of the dividends in arrears?

(b) How much will go to the preferred stockholders for this year?

(c) How much money will be distributed in all to common stockholders?

(d) What is the dividend per share for the common stockholders?

8. A new company's stock is selling for $18.50 and has annual earnings of $1.20 per share. What is its PE ratio?

9. Penny Stock Corp. stock is selling for $1.25 per share and has annual earnings of $0.10 per share. What is its PE ratio?

For Exercises 10–15, take the rate of commission to be 2% on the round lot and an additional 1% on the odd lot.

10. You wish to purchase 150 shares of PPG at $41.25.
(a) What is the broker's commission on the round lot? On the odd lot?

(b) What is the cost of purchasing the stock, including commission?

11. You wish to purchase 120 shares of PNC at $66.56.
(a) What is the broker's commission on the entire purchase?

(b) Including commission, what is your cost of purchasing the stock?

12. Later you sell the 120 shares of PNC stock (see exercise 11) for $73 per share.
(a) What is the broker's commission on the entire sale?

(b) What are your proceeds from the sale of the stock?

13. (a) Compare your answer in exercise 11(b) with that in exercise 12(b). Do you have a net gain or a net loss? How much?

(b) Assume that you received $0.40 per share in dividends last year. Use that information and your answer to part (a) to calculate the return on your investment in PNC. Round to the nearest hundredth percent.

14. Over a year ago, 125 shares of Pepsico were purchased at $32.75.
   (a) Calculate the commission on the purchase.

   (b) What was the total cost of the purchase?

15. Antonio Lewis sold 240 shares of Pechny at $21.00.
   (a) Calculate the commission on the sale.

   (b) What are his proceeds from the sale of the stock?

16. You purchased 100 shares of PepsiCo stock for $32.10 per share. You received one annual dividend of $0.36 per share. If you sell these shares for $48.81 per share, calculate your ROI.

17. Pechny stock has annual earnings of $0.38 per share and a closing price of $21.00.
   (a) What is the PE ratio of the stock?

   (b) What would the PE ratio be if the closing price were $28.00?

   (c) What would be the PE ratio on the Pechny stock closing at $21.00 if the annual earnings were $1.75 per share?

18. Calculate the return on investment (ROI) of a stock if the total proceeds is $3,455; the total cost, $2,755; and the dividends, $225.

Section 18.2

For Exercises 19–22 and 24, refer to Figure 18-2.

19. (a) How many ATT $6\frac{3}{4}04$ bonds were traded this week?

   (b) What is the annual interest for this bond?

   (c) What is the date of maturity of this bond?

20. (a) What is the dollar price of an ATT bond that is listed at $102\frac{7}{8}\%$?

   (b) What is the dollar price of an ATT bond listed at $99\frac{3}{4}\%$?

   (c) Which of these bonds (AutDt and Alza) is selling at a discount? At a premium?

21. (a) Calculate the previous week's closing price for an VjArmW bond.

   (b) Calculate the previous week's closing price for an Aames bond.

22. True or false? If false, explain why: In the *New York Times* listings, bond prices are given in points (dollars) and stock prices are given as a percent of face value.

For Exercises 23–26, take the commission to be $5 per bond.

23. What is the cost of buying three bonds at the closing price of $83\frac{3}{8}\%$, including commission?

24. How much will it cost to purchase five ATT 8.35s25 bonds at the closing price listed in Figure 18-2? Include commission.

25. After paying commission, what will you receive from the sale of ten Apache $9\frac{1}{4}02$ bonds at 103%?

26. What will be your proceeds from the sale of two ATT 6s09 bonds? Assume that you sell at 101% and commission is deducted.

27. Six bonds are sold at $78\frac{1}{2}$%.
    (a) What is the commission on the sale if commission is $5 per bond?

    (b) What are the proceeds from the sale?

28. Three bonds are purchased at $88\frac{3}{8}$%.
    (a) What is the commission on the sale?

    (b) What is the total cost for the purchase?

29. IntShip bonds earned 9% annual interest and closed at 98%, while LibPrp bonds earned 8% annual interest and closed at 125%. Which bonds have the greater current yield?

30. What is the difference between a premium bond and a discount bond? What is a corporate bond?

31. If a bond has a current price of 150% and annual interest of $15, what is the current yield?

32. Bluegrn, has an $8\frac{1}{4}$% bond.
    (a) How much annual interest does one bond pay?

    (b) If a purchaser holds two bonds for four years, how much interest will the purchaser receive?

    (c) If the purchaser holds the two bonds for 4 years and 21 days, how much interest will the purchaser receive?

33. Webb has a 9% bond.
    (a) How much annual interest does one bond pay?

    (b) If you own two bonds for three years, how much interest will you receive?

34. For a bond with annual interest of $12 and current price of $1,120, what is the current yield?

35. Which has the greater current yield according to Figure 18-2, an Aames $10\frac{1}{2}02$ bond or an AMR 9s16 bond?

36. You have invested $1,000 in bond A with yearly interest of 10% and $1,000 in bond B with yearly interest of 8%. Today's closing price for bond A shows that it is selling at a premium, 120% of face value, whereas bond B is selling at a discount, 80% of face value.
    (a) What is the current yield on bond A?

    (b) What is the current yield on bond B?

    (c) Which is the better investment for a prospective buyer?

37. You own bond C, which has a current price of 80% of face value and annual interest of 6%, and bond D, which has a current price of 120% of face value and annual interest of 10%. Which bond is the better investment for a prospective buyer? Why?

38. Write formulas to complete the worksheet in exercise 39 to find the Stock Value, Weekly Increase (Decrease), and Total Portfolio Value and Net Increase (Decrease).

(a) Write formulas to find the value of each stock at the Close Price.

(b) Write formulas to find the weekly amount of increase or decrease for each stock.

(c) Write a formula to find the total stock value.

(d) Write a formula to find the net amount of increase or decrease of the portfolio.

39. Complete the spreadsheet using the formulas.

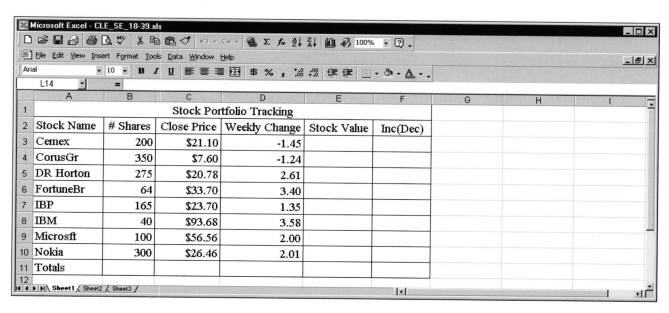

Challenge Problem

40. Linda Wright owns some 8.75% bonds from TollCp, that will mature in six years. She is considering selling these and buying some ConPort 10.5% bonds due in 12 years. If she can sell her TollCp at $90\frac{1}{2}$ and buy ConPort at $104\frac{1}{4}$, which bonds have a better rate of current yield?

For exercises 1–15, consider the commission on stocks to be 2% on the round lots and an additional 1% on the odd lot; consider the face value of the bonds to be $1,000 and the commission on bonds to be $5 per bond.

Use the following stock listing for exercises 1–5.

52 Weeks		Stock	Sym	Div	Yield %	PE	Vol 100s	Hi	Lo	Close	Net Chg
Hi	Lo										
43.63	26.38	McDonaldsCorp.	MCD	.20		21	45,905	32.25	31.44	31.50	−0.06

1. (a) What is the difference between this day's high and low?

   (b) What is this day's closing price, in dollars?

   (c) What was the previous day's closing price, in dollars?

   (d) How many shares were traded this day?

2. Compute the current yield (not listed).

3. Last year you bought 120 shares of PaylSh at $50.50.
   (a) Calculate the commission on that purchase.

   (b) What was your total cost for the purchase?

4. This day you wish to sell your 120 shares of PaylSh at 63.88.
   (a) Calculate the commission on the sale.

   (b) What are your proceeds from the sale of the stock?

5. Use your answers to exercises 3 and 4 and the dividend listed to calculate your return on this investment.

6. Your company has $200,000 to distribute in dividends to three groups:
   A: One year's dividends in arrears for 5,000 shares of cumulative preferred stock ($0.40 per share)
   B: The current year's dividends for those 5,000 shares of preferred stock
   C: Dividends on 75,000 shares of common stock
   (a) How much is distributed to group A?

   (b) How much is distributed to group B?

   (c) How much is distributed to group C?

   (d) What is the dividend per share of common stock?

7. Calculate the current stock yield of PennAm and PennEMA.

| 52 Weeks | | | | Yield | | Vol | | | | |
Hi	Lo	Stock	Div	%	PE	100s	Hi	Lo	Close	Chg
$9.75	$6.63	PennAM	.21	2.7	dd	11	7.69	7.56	7.69	+0.13
$34.31	$20.00	PennEMA	.56	1.9	12	5	29.81	21.81	29.81	−0.06

8. PG&ECp has annual earnings of $0.40 per share and a closing price of $24.06.
   (a) What is the PE ratio of PG&ECp?

   (b) If earnings go up next year, but the price stays the same, will the PE ratio increase or decrease?

   (c) If earnings stay the same next year, but the price goes up, will the PE ratio increase or decrease?

Use the following bond listing for exercises 9–12.

| 12-Mo | | | | | | | | | |
Hi	Lo	Bond	Cur Yield	Vol (S/s in $1,000)	Hi	Lo	Close (LAST)	Net Chg
$106\frac{7}{8}$	60	Polaroid $11\frac{1}{2}$06	18.0	2211	$73\frac{7}{8}$	60	64	$-8\frac{3}{8}$

9. (a) What is the date of maturity of the bond?

   (b) What is the closing price of the bond, in dollars?

   (c) What was the previous week's closing price, in dollars?

10. (a) How much interest was received the previous year on one Polaroid bond?

   (b) Is the bond selling at a discount or at a premium?

11. Assume that three years ago you purchased five Polaroid bonds at 85% of face value and the commission per bond was $5.
   (a) What was the commission on the purchase?

   (b) What was your total cost of purchase?

12. Assume that you sell the five Polaroid bonds this day at $89\frac{7}{8}$%.
   (a) What is the commission on the sale?

   (b) What are your proceeds from the sale?

   (c) Disregard any interest. How much gain or loss do you have on these five bonds?

13. Compare the following two stocks.
   Common stock of Enron Cp (2.48 dividend; $41\frac{1}{2}$ closing price)
   Preferred stock of Enron Cp (10.50 dividend; $145\frac{1}{2}$ closing price)
   Which stock of Enron Cp has the greater current yield, the common stock or the preferred stock?

14. Compare the following two bonds.
   Mobil $7\frac{5}{8}$01 (closing price $94\frac{7}{8}$)
   Mobil $8\frac{5}{8}$04 (closing price $95\frac{1}{8}$)
   Which bond has the greater current yield?

15. As a stockbroker, you must advise your client on a purchase. Stock A is selling for $20 now. Next year an owner can reasonably expect to sell it for $22. Dividends have been steady at $1.00 per year. Stock B is selling for $50 now. Next year an owner can reasonably expect to sell it for $55. Dividends have been steady at $1.00 per year. Without taking commissions into account, which stock, A or B, gives the higher return on investment?

SELF-CHECK 18.1

1. From column 10: $8.81

2. From columns 1 and 2: $20.13; $7.88

3. $9.19 − $8.56 = $0.63

4. $8.81 + 0.44 = $9.25

5. $20,000 × $0.50 = $10,000

6. $200,000 − $10,000 = $190,000

7. $\dfrac{\$190,000}{80,000} =$ $2.38 ($2.375) per share

8. Move down column 3 to AGL Res, then across to column 5. Yield is 5.0%.

9. Read 5.3% from table. Verify: Current stock yield = $\dfrac{0.87}{12.56} = 6.9\%$

10. The "Yld %" column reads ". . .", so no dividend was paid for the last year and there is no yield.

11. PE ratio = $\dfrac{\$24.50}{\$1.75} = 14$

12. $\dfrac{\$54.63}{\$2.48} = 22.02822581$, which rounds to 22

13. $\dfrac{\$18.13}{\$1.51} = 12.00662252$, which rounds to 12

14. Annual net income per share
$$= \dfrac{\text{closing stock price (column 10)}}{\text{PE ratio (column 6)}}$$
$$= \dfrac{38.06}{14} = \$2.72$$

15. $0.02 × 200 × $4 = $16;
$0.03 × 50 × $4 = $6

16. Cost of stock: 250 × $4 = $1,000
Commission: $16 + $6 = $22
Total cost: $1,000 + $22 = $1,022

17. $0.02 × 200 × $5 = $20;
$0.03 × 50 × $5 = $7.50

18. Received for stock: 250 × $5 = $1,250
Commission: $20 + $7.50 = $27.50.
Total proceeds: $1,250 − $27.50 = $1,222.50

19. Gain: $1,222.50 − $1,022 = $200.50

20. 485 × $9.94 = $4,820.90 cost of 485 shares of stock
0.02 × 400 × $9.94 = $79.52 round-lot commission
0.025 × 85 × $9.94 = $21.12 odd-lot commission
Total cost of stock purchase =
$4,820.90 + $79.52 + $21.12 = $4,921.54

21. 485 × $11.12 = $5,393.20 selling price of 485 shares of stock
0.02 × 400 × $11.12 = $88.96 round-lot commission
0.025 × 85 × $11.12 = $23.63 odd-lot commission
Total proceeds from sale of stock =
$5,393.20 − $88.96 − $23.63 = $5,280.61

22. Receipt from sale: 100 × $7 = $700
Dividends: 100 × $0.50 = $ 50
Total gain: $750
Cost of purchase: 100 × $5 = $500
Net gain: $750 − $500 = $250

23. ROI = $\dfrac{\$200.50}{\$1,022} = 19.62\%$

24. Net gain = $5,280.61 − $4,921.54 = $359.07
Dividend = $2 × 485 = $970
Total gain = $359.07 + $970 = $1,329.07
ROI = $\dfrac{\$1,329.07}{\$4,921.54} = 27.01\%$

SELF-CHECK 18.2

1. From Figure 18-2, from column 3, interest rate is 9% and the maturity date is 2016.

2. From the eighth ATT entry, the current yield in column 4 is 7.5.

3. From column 5 of the ARetire entry, the bond volume is 135 bonds.

4. $0.08 \times \$1,000 = \$80$; $1.02 \times \$1,000 = \$1,020$

Current yield $= \dfrac{\$80}{\$1,020} = 0.0784$, or 7.8%

5. From column 3 we see that ATT $5\frac{1}{8}01$ has a current yield of 5.2 and ATT $7\frac{1}{8}02$ has a current yield of 7.1. ATT $7\frac{1}{8}$ 02 has the greater current yield.

6. $1.000 \times \$1,000 = \$1,000$

7. $0.82875 \times \$1,000 = \$828.75$

8. $98\frac{1}{2}\%$ of $\$1,000 = 0.985 \times \$1,000 = \$985$

9. This week's closing price is $91\frac{3}{8}$, up $1\frac{1}{4}$ from last week's closing price. So the previous price was $91\frac{3}{8} - \frac{1}{4}$, or $90\frac{1}{8}$. This is $90\frac{1}{8}\%$ of face value, or \$901.25).

10. $0.925 \times \$1,000 = \$925$
$\$925 \times 4 = \$3,700$; $\$20 \times 4 = 80$
Net proceeds $= \$3,700 - \$80 = \$3,620$

11. $0.82875 \times \$1,000 = \$828.75$
$\$828.75 \times 5 = \$4,143.75$
$\$15 \times 5 = \$75$; $\$4,143.75 + \$75 = \$4,218.75$

12. Annual interest per bond $= 8.12\%$ of face value $= 0.0812 \times \$1,000 = \$81.25$

Current price per bond $= 0.9925 \times \$1,000 = \$992.50$

Current yield $= \dfrac{\$81.25}{\$992.50} = 0.081863 = 8.2\%$

Answers to Odd-Numbered Problems

Chapter 1

Section 1.1

1. four thousand, two hundred nine

3. three hundred one million, nine

5. $7,000,000,000

7. 20,000

9. 400

11. 9,000

13. 830

15. 30,000

17. 28,000,000,000

19. $4,000

21. 300,000; 6,300,000

23. 4,000,000

25. 5,000

27. 10,000,000

29. 400

31. 700,000

33. 20

35. 35

37. 28

39. 30,787

41. 1,832

43. 5,773

45. 44,014

47. 310,000; 318,936

49. 22,000; 21,335

51. 2,600; 2,612

53. 230 items

55. 469 dolls

57. 671 points

59. 9,756

61. 1,865,741

63. 4,715,606

65. 5,322,571

67. 4,000; 4,072

69. 50,000,000; 56,539,090

71. 55,000; 55,632

73. 88 packages

75. 244 fan belts

77. $18,055

79. 4,952,385

81. 782,878

83. 41,772

85. 6,938,694

87. 861,900

89. 16,500

91. 48,000

93. 30,000

95. 47,220,000

97. 162,000

99. 210,000; 254,626

101. 1,550,000; 1,495,184

103. 120 cartridges

105. 140 pieces

107. 336 radios per thousand

109. 45

111. 24

113. 77

115. 54 R 5

117. 7,000; 8805 R6

119. 249 packages

121. $12 average hourly wage

123. 75 cards

125. 20 pairs

127. $256

129. $8 per hour

131. 48 ounces

Section 1.2

133. five tenths

135. one hundred eight thousandths

137. two hundred seventy-five hundred-thousandths

139. seventeen and eight tenths

141. one hundred twenty-eight and twenty-three hundredths

143. five hundred and seven ten-thousandths

145. 0.135

147. 380

149. 1,700

151. $175

153. 1.246

155. 165.8312

157. $20.93

159. 376.74

161. 57.4525

163. 135.6

165. 419.103

167. 325.74

169. 2.3068

171. 0.001474

173. $88.96

175. $92.61

177. 193.41

179. 50.076

181. 21.2352
187. 27,300
193. $12,850.00
199. 8.57
205. 60.713.24
211. 0.0018
217. $0.989 in thousandths   **219.** 20

183. 275.8
189. 17,454
195. 0.15
201. 33.77
207. 8.572
213. 37.49298

185. 198.74
191. 370,000
197. 2.19
203. 1,559.79
209. 0.019874
215. 0.0178

221.

INCOME		
	Gross income	$34,356
	Interest income	282
	Dividend income	455
Total		$35,093
EXPENSES	Living	$16,898
	Home maintenance	495
	Auto maintenance & repair	117
	Insurance premiums (medical, auto, home, life)	1,778
	Taxes (sales, income, FICA real property, personal property)	11,130
	Medical (not covered by insurance)	450
	Planning investment	2,500
	Unspent income	1,725
Total		$35,093

CHAPTER 1   CHAPTER 1   PRACTICE TEST,   p. 49

1. five hundred three
3. 84,300
5. 80,000
7. 2,200; 2,117
9. 45,000; 41,032
11. 1,153 items
13. 30
15. 24.092
17. 224.857
19. 447.12
21. 89.82
23. 2,379.019
25. 179.24
27. $19.20
29. 16

Chapter 2

CHAPTER 2   CHAPTER 2   ASSIGNMENT EXERCISES,   p. 103

Section 2.1

1. Answers will vary. $\frac{3}{5}, \frac{7}{9}, \frac{5}{8}, \frac{100}{301}, \frac{41}{53}$; proper fractions
3. $20\frac{2}{3}$
5. 7
7. $8\frac{1}{2}$
9. $12\frac{2}{5}$
11. $14\frac{22}{25}$
13. $\frac{35}{6}$
15. $\frac{13}{3}$
17. $\frac{100}{3}$
19. $\frac{5}{6}$
21. $\frac{7}{8}$
23. $\frac{3}{8}$
25. $\frac{3}{4}$
27. $\frac{2}{5}$
29. $\frac{7}{9}$
31. $\frac{5}{6}$
33. $\frac{3}{5}$
35. $\frac{2}{3}$
37. $\frac{13}{24}$
39. $\frac{54}{72}$
41. $\frac{10}{12}$
43. $\frac{10}{15}$
45. $\frac{63}{77}$
47. $\frac{117}{143}$
49. $\frac{1}{7}$ of the employees
51. 48
53. 30
55. 168
57. $1\frac{2}{5}$
59. $1\frac{1}{15}$
61. $1\frac{7}{9}$
63. $1\frac{11}{24}$
65. $1\frac{13}{36}$
67. $11\frac{7}{8}$
69. $25\frac{1}{4}$
71. $23\frac{2}{5}$
73. $91\frac{5}{6}$
75. $154\frac{17}{42}$
77. 108
79. 29 yards
81. $\frac{1}{6}$
83. $\frac{1}{6}$
85. $\frac{7}{48}$
87. $3\frac{3}{10}$
89. $1\frac{3}{5}$
91. $1\frac{1}{2}$
93. $3\frac{1}{12}$
95. $2\frac{1}{18}$
97. $42\frac{11}{15}$
99. $1\frac{29}{35}$
101. $12\frac{1}{6}$
103. $2\frac{3}{8}$ feet
105. $\frac{7}{32}$
107. $\frac{5}{18}$
109. $\frac{9}{20}$
111. $3\frac{1}{3}$
113. $2\frac{5}{8}$
115. $\frac{5}{9}$
117. $\frac{7}{18}$
119. $\frac{84}{125}$
121. $\frac{8}{49}$
123. $\frac{3}{41}$
125. $37\frac{1}{10}$
127. $74\frac{47}{48}$
129. $94\frac{2}{7}$
131. $48
133. $4,110
135. $\frac{8}{5}$
137. 4
139. $\frac{4}{13}$
141. $\frac{5}{8}$
143. 3
145. $\frac{10}{21}$
147. $\frac{1}{20}$
149. $3\frac{3}{4}$
151. $\frac{4}{7}$
153. 32 pieces
155. $7\frac{3}{4}\%$ total sales tax rate
157. $1\frac{1}{4}$ inches
159. 12 hours
161. $192 sale price
163. 4 full-length pieces

Section 2.2

165. 23%	**167.** 82%	**169.** 3%	**171.** 34%	**173.** 60.1%	**175.** 100%
177. 300%	**179.** 37%	**181.** 20%	**183.** 400%	**185.** 17%	**187.** 6%
189. 52%	**191.** 10%	**193.** 125%	**195.** 39%	**197.** 33.33%	**199.** 3%
201. 0.98	**203.** 2.56	**205.** 0.917	**207.** 0.005	**209.** 0.06	**211.** 0.36

213. 0.06 **215.** $\frac{1}{10}$ **217.** $\frac{3}{50}$ **219.** $\frac{89}{100}$ **221.** $\frac{9}{20}$ **223.** $2\frac{1}{4}$

225. $\frac{1}{3}, 0.33\frac{1}{3}$ **227.** 12.5%; $\frac{1}{8}$ **229.** 80%, $\frac{4}{5}$ **231.** $P = 81$ **233.** $P = 25$ **235.** $R = 25\%$

237. $R = 33\frac{1}{3}\%$ **239.** $B = 400$ **241.** $P = 15.12$ **243.** $B = \$26,093.75$

245. $P = 1{,}134.24$ **247.** $B = 305.88$ **249.** $R = 250\%$ **251.** $P = 51.44$

253. $P = 24$ **255.** $P = 8.1$ **257.** $B = 30$ **259.** $B = 180$

261. $R = 97\%$ **263.** $R = 2\%$ **265.** $R = 200\%$ **267.** 44.08

269. 0.41 **271.** 232.43 **273.** 6.12% **275.** \$169.26

277. 32 customers **279.** 2,270 people **281.** 74% of the shareholders **283.** 80% of the questions

285. 19.29% (approximately) of the restrooms

287. 26% (rounded) is *not* within the budgeted 25%

289. \$1,212.50

291. $\$1{,}250 \times 25\% = \$1{,}250 \times 0.25 = \$312.50$;

$\frac{\$375}{\$1{,}115} = 0.336 = 34\%$

CHAPTER 2 — CHAPTER 2 PRACTICE TEST, p. 111

1. $\frac{1}{6}$ **3.** $\frac{7}{16}$ **5.** $1\frac{19}{23}$ **7.** $5\frac{5}{6}$

9. $\frac{1}{4}$ has been unloaded; $\frac{1}{2}$ remains to be unloaded.

11. 24% **13.** 60% **15.** 37.5% **17.** $P = \$72$

19. R $= 87\frac{1}{2}\%$ **21.** All 22 rooms **23.** 90 employees **25.** 56,600 automobiles

---

Chapter 3

CHAPTER 3 — CHAPTER 3 ASSIGNMENT EXERCISES, p.152

Section 3.1

1. $P = \$120$ **3.** $P = 142$ feet **5.** $I = \$2{,}025$ **7.** $P = 8s$ **9.** $P = 136$ inches

11. B14 = B5 + B6 + B7 + B8 + B9 + B10 + B11 + B12
C5 = B5/B14*100   C6 = B6/B14*100
C7 = B7/B14*100   C8 = B8/B14*100
C9 = B9/B14*100   C10 = B10/B14*100
C11 = B11/B14*100   C12 = B12/B14*100
C14 = C5 + C6 + C7 + C8 + C9 + C10 + C11 + C12

Section 3.2

13. $N = 7$ **15.** $A = 12$ **17.** $N = 17$

19. $N = 4$ **21.** $A = 24$ **23.** $x = 7$

25. $x = 11$ **27.** $A = 8$ **29.** $X = 7$

31. The number of cards sold is 9. **33.** Five of each card were ordered. **35.** The amount of money spent on supplies was \$96.

37. 416 fan belts should be ordered. **39.** The amount spent on groceries is \$57.50. **41.** Shaquita earns \$8.75 each hour.

43. Molly earns \$272.32 for 37 hours of work. **45.** Wallpaper for the kitchen will cost \$116.73. **47.** The total weight of the shipment is 830 pounds.

49. Each shirt was reduced by $3.02.

51. There were 11 executive desks and 29 secretarial desks.

53. 280 headlights were purchased at a cost of $3,906. 720 taillights were purchased at a total cost of $5,436.

55. $100

CHAPTER 3

CHAPTER 3   PRACTICE TEST,   p. 155

1. $S = \$446$
7. $A = 18$
13. The new salary is $285.

3. $M = S - C$
9. $A = 5$
15. 130 containers are needed.

5. $N = 11$
11. $N = 6$
17. 116 ceramic cups and 284 plastic cups were sold. The value of the ceramic cups was $464. The value of the plastic cups was $994.

19. $27,200

Chapter 4

CHAPTER 4

CHAPTER 4   ASSIGNMENT EXERCISES,   p. 195

Section 4.1

1. Range: 14; Mean: 22; Median: 22; Mode: none
5. Range: $9.27; Mean: $8.42; Median: $5.53; Mode: $13.95
9. 795 students
13. 2,531 students
17. 54.4%
21. Debt retirement
25. (b) Intervals of $10,000 are more appropriate because the data can be shown with fewer intervals than with (a).
29. Answers will vary. Beginning of school, middle of baseball season, too soon for winter sports
33. (b) 5°. The data can be adequately shown on a graph with 5° intervals.
37. 20%
41. $17,000 cost of lot with landscaping; 19.8%
45. 84°
49. Range: 13; Modes: 89, 90

3. Range: $1.02; Mean: $1.44; Median: $1.46; Mode: $1.65
7. Range: $6.75; Mean: $40.34; Median: $40.75; Mode: none
11. 3,997 students
15. Period 5
19. 2002: $65,153; 2003; $68,324
23. Social projects and education costs
27. May, June, July

31. 70°

35. (c) Fluctuating

39. $153
43. 1,198 cars sold
47. Mail to former buyers, phone former buyers

CHAPTER 4

CHAPTER 4   PRACTICE TEST,   p. 201

1. 77
9. $120

17. (c) $5,000, other interval sizes would provide too many or too few intervals

3. 29.5
11. 33.3%

19. Smallest: 250; greatest: 1,117

5. 110

13. Labor: 135°; Materials: 120°; Overhead: 105°
21. 1998, 2000, 2001

7. 165

15. Fresh flowers: $23,712; silk flowers: $17,892
23. 1999, 2002, 2003

Chapter 5

Section 5.1

1.

KRA, INC.
2596 Jason Blvd.
Kansas City, KS 00000

456

June 13 19 XX   87-278/840

PAY TO THE ORDER OF *Ryan Johnson* $ *296.83*

Two hundred ninety-six and 83/100 ——— DOLLARS

Community First Bank
2177 Germantown Rd. South
Germantown, Tennessee 38138

MEMO *washing machine*   *Your Name*

⑆084002781⑆

3.

DEPOSIT TICKET

S & R Consulting Co.
PO Box 921
Flint, MI 00000

DATE *May 8* 19 XX
DEPOSITS MAY NOT BE AVAILABLE FOR IMMEDIATE WITHDRAWAL

SIGN HERE FOR CASH RECEIVED (IF REQUIRED)

Community First Bank
2177 Germantown Road • 7888 Farmington
Germantown, TN 38138 • (901) 754-2400 • Member FDIC

⑆084000026⑆9998

CHECKS AND OTHER ITEMS ARE RECEIVED FOR DEPOSIT SUBJECT TO THE PROVISIONS OF THE UNIFORM COMMERCIAL CODE OR ANY APPLICABLE COLLECTION AGREEMENT.

CASH	CURRENCY	480 00
	COIN	
LIST CHECKS SINGLY		130 00
		278 96
		26-2/840
TOTAL FROM OTHER SIDE		
TOTAL		
LESS CASH RECEIVED		
NET DEPOSIT		894 96

USE OTHER SIDE FOR ADDITIONAL LISTING

BE SURE EACH ITEM IS PROPERLY ENDORSED

5.

786	Date 5/10 19 XX
Amount $ 28.97	
To J. Voss Office Supply	
For Office supplies	

Balance Forward	4307	21
Deposits		
Total	4307	21
Amount This Check	28	97
Balance	4278	24

7.

RECORD ALL TRANSACTIONS THAT AFFECT YOUR ACCOUNT

NUMBER	DATE	DESCRIPTION OF TRANSACTION	DEBIT (–)	√ T	FEE (IF ANY) (–)	CREDIT (+)	BALANCE
							983 47
1213	3/10	Linens, Inc. laundry services	220 00				763 47
1214	3/10	Bugs Away extermination services	65 00				698 47
ATM	3/11	withdrawal	80 00				618 47
Dep	3/12					315 24	933 71

9.

Barter Home Repair
302 Cannon Dr.
Germantown, TN 38138

8212

6/12 19 XX   87-278/840

PAY TO THE ORDER OF *Alpine Industries* $ 85.50

Eighty-five and 50/100 ——— DOLLARS

Community First Bank
2177 Germantown Rd. South
Germantown, Tennessee 38138

MEMO *building supplies*   *Your name*

⑆035008217⑆

11.

RECORD ALL TRANSACTIONS THAT AFFECT YOUR ACCOUNT

NUMBER	DATE	DESCRIPTION OF TRANSACTION	DEBIT (–)	√ T	FEE (IF ANY) (–)	CREDIT (+)	BALANCE
							876 54
234	5/3	Organic materials fertilizer	175 00				701 54
235	5/3	Klean Kuts chain saw	524 82				176 72
	5/5	Deposit				472 39	649 11

13. For Deposit Only
Valley Electric Coop
15-2713140
restricted endorsement

15. The electronic deposit is usually more convenient and safer since the funds are transferred directly from the employer's bank account to the employee's bank account. A disadvantage is that the employee does not actually see the amount deposited and should carefully compare the amount shown on the check stub with the amount deposited. Answers will vary.

Section 5.2

17. 0

19. Four checks

21. $4,675.50

23. 7/7

25. $12.50

27. 3

29. $2,571.37

31. 4/8

33. $5.83

35. 5

37. $3,485.73

39. 6/20

41.

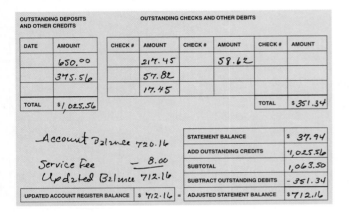

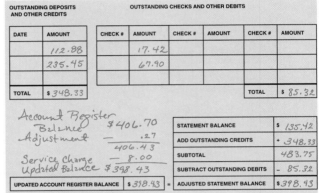

43. Reconciled account
register balance: $712.16

45. Reconciled account
register balance: $398.43

47. F5 = F4 + E5
F6 = F5 + E6
F7 = F6 − D7
F8 = F7 − D8
F9 = F8 − D9
F10 = F9 − D10
F11 = F10 + E11
F12 = F11 − D12
F13 = F12 − D13
F14 = F13 − D14
F15 = F14 − D15
F16 = F15

49. Total assets 2002: $87,637;
Total liabilities 2002: $65,422
Projected assets 2003: $90,830.50;
Projected liabilities 2003; $60,644
2003 net worth: $30,186.50;
Increase in net worth: $7,971.50

CHAPTER 5   CHAPTER 5   PRACTICE TEST,   p. 251

1.

```
0195                Date 5/25  19 XX
Amount  $ 152.50
To  Lon Associates
For  Supplies

Balance Forward    2301  42
Deposits            283  17
Total              2584  59
Amount This Check   152  50
Balance            2432  09
```

3. Five checks

5. $142.38

7. $3,600

9. $1881.49

11. Reconciled account register balance: $1,589.10

OUTSTANDING DEPOSITS AND OTHER CREDITS		OUTSTANDING CHECKS AND OTHER DEBITS					
DATE	AMOUNT	CHECK #	AMOUNT	CHECK #	AMOUNT	CHECK #	AMOUNT
	800.00		243.17		42.12		
	412.13		167.18		16.80		
			13.97				
TOTAL	$1,212.13					TOTAL	$483.24

Account Register balance $1,817.93
Service fee −15.00
      1,802.93
Returned item −213.83
Updated balance 1,589.10

UPDATED ACCOUNT REGISTER BALANCE	$1,589.10	=		
STATEMENT BALANCE			$ 860.21
ADD OUTSTANDING CREDITS			+ 1,212.13
SUBTOTAL			2,072.34
SUBTRACT OUTSTANDING DEBITS			− 483.24
ADJUSTED STATEMENT BALANCE			$1,589.10

Chapter 6

Section 6.1

1. $7,938

3. $53,872

5. $425

7. $255.15

9. $377 (gross earnings)

11. $493 (gross earnings)

13. $483.14

15. $454.02

17. $228.80

19. Regular Hours: 31;
Regular Pay: $248;
$1\frac{1}{2}$ OT Hours: 2;
$1\frac{1}{2}$ OT Pay: $24;
2 OT Hours: 4;
2 OT Pay $64;
Gross Earnings: $336

21. Regular Hours: 40:
Regular Pay: $390;
$1\frac{1}{2}$ OT Hours: 9;
$1\frac{1}{2}$ OT Pay: $131.63;
2 OT Hours: 5;
5 OT Pay: $97.50;
Gross Earnings: $619.13

23. $100 (1 day's pay);
$500 (5 days' pay)

25. $384.80

27. $691.74

29. $910

31. $3,100

33. $800

35. $7,800

37. $1,191.20

39. $334.64

Section 6.2

41. $27

43. $53

45. $31

47. $52.82

49. $447.98

51. $95.92

53. Social Security: $52.50;
Medicare: $12.21

55. Social Security: $1,488;
Medicare: $348

57. Social Security:
$1749.95;
Medicare: $409.26

59. Withholding Tax: $35;
Social Security: $32.55;
Medicare: $7.61;
Total Deductions: $97.10;
Net Earnings: $427.90

61. Withholding Tax: $58;
Social Security: $45.57;
Medicare: $10.66;
Total Deductions: $114.23;
Net Earnings: $620.81

63. Total Deductions:
$122.15; Net income:
$462.85

Section 6.3

65. $552.76

67. $378

69. $1,076.76

71. a. D3 = B3*0.062
D4 = B4*0.062
D5 = B5*0.062
D6 = B6*0.062
D7 = B7*0.062
D8 = B8*0.062
D9 = B9*0.062
D10 = B10*0.062
D11 = B11*0.062

CHAPTER 6   PRACTICE TEST,   p. 293

1. $498
7. $522
13. $1138.90

3. $490
9. Social Security: $47.14; Medicare: $11.04
15. Social Security: $45.57; Medicare: $10.66; Withholding Tax: $92; Net Earnings: $561.65

5. $852
11. $34
17. Social Security: $30.51; Medicare: $7.14; Withholding Tax: $39; Net Earnings: $415.52

19. Social Security: $37.83; Medicare: $8.85; Withholding Tax: $40; Net Earnings: $523.45

21. $378

23. $0

25. Answers will vary; gross earnings is before any deductions are made and net is after deductions.

Chapter 7

CHAPTER 7   ASSIGNMENT EXERCISES,   p. 326

Section 7.1

1. $45
7. $102.50
13. $660 skirts; $1,480 jumpers; $2,140 total list price; $235.40 trade discount
19. $336.03

3. $25.50
9. $19.80
15. $18

5. $7.57
11. $94.50
17. $6.13

25. Trade Discount: $357; Net Price: $1,743
31. Complement: 89%; Net Price: $15.10

21. Trade Discount: $1.25; Net Price: $23.75
27. Complement: 96%; Net Price: $15.33

23. Trade Discount: $0.02; Net Price: $0.87
29. Complement: 94%; Net Price: $130.23

Section 7.2

33. 0.8(0.9); 0.72; $144
39. $3.42 net price
45. 68.35%; 31.65%
51. 16.21%
57. $60 less $9.45 is the better deal.

35. 0.8(0.85)(0.9); 0.612; $918
41. $852.86 total net price
47. 74.34%; 25.66%
53. 14.5%
59. $20 less discount series of 10/10/10 is the better deal.

37. 0.85(0.95); 0.8075; $323
43. 76.5%; 23.5%
49. 28%
55. $400 less 20% is the better deal.

Section 7.3

61. 3% discount
67. $1.40 cash discount; $68.60 net amount

63. Yes
69. a. $7 cash discount; $343 net amount
    b. $3.50 cash discount; $346.50 net amount
    c. $350 (no discount)

65. $5.40 cash discount
71. $13 cash discount; $637 net amount

73. $5,139.06 net amount
75. $824.74 credited to account June 12; $375.26 paid on July 2; $1,175.26 total paid

77. $824.74 credited to account; $325.26 outstanding balance

79. The purchaser

81. Complete the spreadsheet using the formulas.

Microsoft Excel - chapter 7 worksheet.xls

	A	B	C	D	E	F	G	H
1		Invoice 322510 with Trade Discounts						
2	Item #	Item Description	Price	Discount1	Discount2	Discount3	Net Decimal	Net Price
3	588243	Large Easel	$23.50	5%	7%	8%	0.81282	$19.10
4	723468	Beveled Mirror	$45.99	3%	5%	8%	0.84778	$38.99
5	347328	Hor Plate Rack	$12.15	2%	3%	4%	0.912576	$11.09
6	65843	Ver Plate Rack	$12.15	5%	5%	5%	0.857375	$10.42
7	477873	Doll Stand	$3.50	4%	5%	7%	0.84816	$2.97
8	101453	Room Divider	$98.75	1%	3%	4%	0.921888	$91.04
9	454789	Sconce Frosted	$44.28	3%	7%	0%	0.9021	$39.94
10	267811	Sconce Gold	$48.50	3%	3%	3%	0.912673	$44.26
11	115226	Floor Lamp	$46.50	6%	6%	6%	0.830584	$38.62
12	525793	Desk Lamp	$19.98	5%	3%	1%	0.912285	$18.23

83. $711.68; $718.94; $726.20

85. 24.1%

87. 50.5%

INVOICE DATE	TERMS	DATE OF ORDER	ORDERED BY		PHONE NO.	REMIT TO	HARPER General Accounting Office
02/27/XX	2/10, 1/15, n/30	02/27/XX			803-000-4488		

LINE NO.	MANUFACTURER PRODUCT NUMBER	QTY. ORD.	QTY. B.O.	QTY. SHP.	U/M	DESCRIPTION	UNIT PRICE	EXTENDED AMOUNT
001	REMYY370/02253	3	0	3	EA	TONER, F/ROYAL TA210 COP 1	11.90	35.70
002	Sk 1230M402	5	2	3	EA	CORRECTABLE FILM RIBBON	10.95	32.85
003	JRLM01023	10	0	10	EA	COVER-UP CORRECTION TAPE	9.90	99.00
004	rTu123456	9	0	9	EA	PAPER, BOND, WHITE 8 1/2 x 11	58.23	524.07

DATE REC'D.	01460900001	$691.62	5%	$34.58	$0.00	TOTAL INVOICE AMOUNT	$726.20
	OUR ORDER NO.	MDSE. TOTAL	TAX RATE	TAX AMOUNT	FREIGHT AMOUNT		

CHAPTER 7   PRACTICE TEST,   P. 331

CHAPTER 7

1. $110 trade discount

3. $7.31 trade discount; $29.24 net price

5. $250 chair less 20% is the better deal

7. 0.684 net decimal equivalent

9. Receipt of goods

11. $1,080 net price

13. End of month

15. $2 cash discount

17. $392 net amount

19. $489.60 total net price

21. $618.56 amount credited to account; $276.44 outstanding balance

Chapter 8

CHAPTER 8   ASSIGNMENT EXERCISES,   p. 364

CHAPTER 8

Section 8.1

1. $75; 150%

3. 41; $82; 100%, 200%

5. $52.48; $90;48; 58%

7. $45.33; $53.33; 85%; 100%

9. Markup: $6; selling price: $21

11. Cost: $36; Rate of markup: 25%

13. Markup: $39.80; Rate of markup: 25.1%

15. Cost: $24; selling price: $36

17. Cost: $35.70; selling price: $51.00

19. Rate of markup: 31.62%; markup: $18.50

21. Cost: $14; markup: $21

23. $57; 56.14%; 35.96%

25. $0.44; 28.21%; 22%

27. $68.45; $95.83; 28.57%

29. $49.60; $74.40; 60%

31. $16.11; $2.84; 17.63%

33. 13.64%

35. 38.65%

Section 8.2

37. Markdown: $38; Markdown rate: 10.00%

39. Markdown: $24.99; Markdown rate: 27.77%

41. Markdown: $50; Sale price: $199.99

43. Markdown: $19.75; Sale price: $59.25

Section 8.3

45. First reduction: Markdown: $9.90; Sale price: $35.10
Second reduction: Markdown: $10.53; Sale price: $24.57

47. $0.54

49. a. E3 = C3*(100% + D3)
E4 = C4*(100% + D4)
E5 = C5*(100% + D5)
E6 = C6*(100% + D6)
E7 = C7*(100% + D7)
E8 = C8*(100% + D8)
E9 = C9*(100% + D9)
E10 = C10*(100% + D10)
E11 = C11*(100% + D11)
E12 = C12*(100% + D12)

b. G3 = E3 − E3*F3
G4 = E4 − E4*F4
G5 = E5 − E5*F5
G6 = E6 − E6*F6
G7 = E7 − E7*F7
G8 = E8 − E8*F8
G9 = E9 − E9*F9
G10 = E10 − E10*F10
G11 = E11 − E11*F11
G12 = E12 − E12*F12

c. H3 = G3 − C3
H4 = G4 − C4
H5 = G5 − C5
H6 = G6 − C6
H7 = G7 − C7
H8 = G8 − C8
H9 = G9 − C9
H10 = G10 − C10
H11 = G11 − C11
H12 = G12 − C12
H13 = H13 − C13

51. $17.33 per pair

CHAPTER 8 PRACTICE TEST, p. 368

1. $7.16
3. $15.50
5. $22.68
7. $26.07
9. $126.75
11. 25%
13. $160
15. $48.74
17. $1.80
19. Cost: $15.75;
Markup: $29.25

Chapter 9

CHAPTER 9 ASSIGNMENT EXERCISES, p. 406

Section 9.1

1. $120
3. $2,252.25
5. $144
7. Interest: $1,923.75; Maturity value: $6,198.75
9. 15.5%
11. 12.5%
13. 15%
15. 3 years
17. 1.5 years
19. 2 years
21. 6 months
23. $500
25. $1,000
27. $1,500
29. $900
31. $\frac{7}{12}$ year
33. $\frac{4}{3}$ years
35. $\frac{1}{4}$ year
37.
39. $1,050

41. $20
43. $12
45. $16

Section 9.2

47. Ordinary time
49. 117 days
51. 261 days
53. 153 days
55. 167 days
57. 247 days
59. 163 days
61. Ordinary time: August 10; Exact time: August 8
63. Ordinary time: October 12; Exact time: October 11

65. Ordinary time: February 28 of the following year;
Exact time: February 26

67. a. $105; b. $103.56; c. $105

69. a. $51.67; b. $51.29; c. $52

71. First State Bank

73. August 10, 2001

75. $1,910.00

77. $18.63

79. $22.64

81. $10,040.56

83. a.   F3 = YEARFRAC(C3,D3,0)
F4 = YEARFRAC(C4, D4, 1)
F5 = YEARFRAC(C5, D5, 2)
F6 = YEARFRAC(C6,D6,0)
F7 = YEARFRAC(C7,D7,1)
F8 = YEARFRAC(C8,D8,2)
F9 = YEARFRAC(C9,D9,0)
F10 = YEARFRAC(C10,D10,1)
F11 = YEARFRAC(C11,D11,2)
F12 = YEARFRAC(C12,D12,0)
F13 = YEARFRAC(C13,D13,1)
F14 = YEARFRAC(C14,D14,2)

b.   G3 = A3*B3*F3
G4 = A4*B4*F4
G5 = A5*B5*F5
G6 = A6*B6*F6
G7 = A7*B7*F7
G8 = A8*B8*F8
G9 = A9*B9*F9
G10 = A10*B10*F10
G11 = A11*B11*F11
G12 = A12*B12*F12
G13 = A13*B13*F13
G14 = A14*B14*F14

c.   H3 = A3 + G3
H4 = A4 + G4
H5 = A5 + G5
H6 = A6 + G6
H7 = A7 + G7
H8 = A8 + G8
H9 = A9 + G9
H10 = A10 + G10
H11 = A11 + G11
H12 = A12 + G12
H13 = A13 + G13
H14 = A14 + G14

85. Rocky's Market Principal: $840; David's Art Gallery Principal: $2,550; Fortune Hardware Annual Rate: 7.6%; M. Converse & Son Annual Rate: 6.2%; Sun Twins Jai Alai Time: 75 days; Sun Coast Brokerage Time: 200 days
To protect themselves from data loss as described in this question, most financial institutions use a computerized backup system with storage either on disk or magnetic tape.

CHAPTER 9   CHAPTER 9   PRACTICE TEST,   p. 411

1. $210

3. 20% annually

5. 287 days

7. 159 days

9. I = $8,400

11. I = $28.14

13. $665

15. Time: 60 days; Interest: $21.25

17. $\frac{3}{4}$ year or 9 months

19. 20% annually

21. $462.50

23. $64

25. $169.01

27. $44.30

Chapter 10

CHAPTER 10   CHAPTER 10   ASSIGNMENT EXERCISES,   p. 440

Section 10.1

1. $166.40

3. $708.64

5. $524.95

7. $5,372.55

9. $2,189.90

11. $185.46

13. $101.19

15. $13,928.16

17. $1,333.85

19. $1,100 in one year is more than the yield on $900 invested today.

21. 12.55%

23. $0.36

25. $9.23 compound interest: $2,009.23 compound amount

27. The two-year investment yields the greater amount of interest.

Section 10.2

29. $4,633.92

31. $1,126.97

33. $574.37

35. $3,157.64

37. $154.16

39. $1,592.55

41. $2,913.80

43. $11,000 in 18 months is better.

45. $4,781.07

47. Complete the spreadsheet using the formulas.

	A	B	C	D	E	F	G	H	
1		Accumulated Amount and Compound Interest							
2	Exercise	Principal	Periodic Rate	Periods	Accumulated Amount	Interest			
3	4	$2,000.00	8.00%	4.000000	2,720.98	$720.98			
4	5	$8,000.00	3.00%	20.000000	14,448.89	$6,448.89			
5	6	$10,500.00	10.00%	4.000000	15,373.05	$4,873.05			
6	7	$10,500.00	2.00%	16.000000	14,414.25	$3,914.25			
7	8	$8,000.00	2.00%	12.000000	10,145.93	$2,145.93			
8	8	$8,000.00	8.25%	3.000000	10,147.84	$2,147.84			
9	11	$2,000.00	3.00%	3.000000	2,185.45	$185.45			
10	12	$3,500.00	5.00%	8.000000	5,171.09	$1,671.09			
11	13	$800.00	1.50%	8.000000	901.19	$101.19			

49.

Month	Rate	End of Month Balance
Jan.	0.006667	1.006667
Feb.	0.006667	1.013378
Mar.	0.006667	1.020135
Apr.	0.006667	1.026936
May	0.006667	1.033783
June	0.006667	1.040675
July	0.006667	1.047613
Aug.	0.006667	1.054597
Sept.	0.006667	1.061628
Oct.	0.006667	1.068706
Nov.	0.006667	1.075831
Dec.	0.006667	1.083004

CHAPTER 10

CHAPTER 10   PRACTICE TEST,   p. 443

1. $450.09

3. $3,979.30

5. $579.12

7. 12.55%

9. Compounded monthly yields greater interest.

11. $2,669.55

13. $2,951.58

15. $680 in one year is better.

17. Option 2 yields the greater return by $0.68.

19. $1,006.60

Chapter 11

CHAPTER 11

CHAPTER 11   ASSIGNMENT EXERCISES,   p. 471

Section 11.1

1. $37,618

3. $2,730.03

5. $5,359.69

7. $26,362

9. (a) $49,681.11;
(b) $150,478.86

11. $10,188.80

Section 11.2

13. $10,311.07   **15.** $7,870.49   **17.** $7,102.10   **19.** $2,294.19   **21.** $5,591.97

23. $3,407.89   **25.** $19,672.40   **27.** $9,982.50   **29.** $7,586.60

31. a. D3 = FV(C3,B3,A3,0,0)
         D4 = FV(C4,B4,A4,0,0)
         D5 = FV(C5,B5,A5,0,0)
         D6 = FV(C6,B6,A6,0,0)
         D7 = FV(C7,B7,A7,0,0)
         D8 = FV(C8,B8,A8,0,0)

     b. I3 = F3*((1 + H3)^G3 − 1)/H3
         I4 = F4*((1 + H4)^G4 − 1)/H4
         I5 = F5*((1 + H5)^G5 − 1)/H5
         I6 = F6*((1 + H6)^G6 − 1)/H6
         I7 = F7*((1 + H7)^G7 − 1)/H7
         I8 = F8*((1 + H8)^G8 − 1)/H8

33. lump sum today: $22,940
retirement fund balance in 20 years: $73,572
difference in periodic payments total and lump sum
payment: $17,060

CHAPTER 11   CHAPTER 11   PRACTICE TEST,   p. 474

1. $19,350.00 end of second year   **3.** $41,736.31   **5.** $5,727.50   **7.** $60,819.20   **9.** $28,269.88   **11.** $104.74

13. $34,724.80   **15.** $28,240

Chapter 12

CHAPTER 12   CHAPTER 12   ASSIGNMENT EXERCISES,   p. 518

Section 12.1

1. $1,585.96   **3.** $85   **5.** $729

Section 12.2

7. $30.51   **9.** $398.75   **11.** $52.40   **13.** $571.87

15. $358.63   **17.** $56.88   **19.** $26.94   **21.** $50.11

Section 12.3

23. $3.98   **25.** $5.81   **27.** $185.17   **29.** $201.69   **31.** $462.60

Section 12.4

33. 16%   **35.** 8.5%   **37.** 23%   **39.** 21.50%   **41.** 20.50%   **43.** 14.25%

Section 12.5

45. $19,400   **47.** $1,552   **49.** $81,215.80   **51.** $107,415.00

53. Portion of Payment Applied to:

Month	Interest	Principal	End-of-Month Principal
1	$711.33	$170.98	$77,492.02
2	$709.77	$172.54	$77,256.48
3	$708.18	$174.13	$77,082.35

55. a. A4 = A3 − 1
      A5 = A4 − 1
      A6 = A5 − 1
      A7 = A6 − 1
      A8 = A7 − 1
      A9 = A8 − 1
      A10 = A9 − 1
      A11 = A10 − 1
      A12 = A11 − 1
      A13 = A12 − 1
      A14 = A13 − 1

b. E3 = C3*1/12   F3 = D3 − E3
      E4 = C4*1/12   F4 = D3 − E4
      E5 = C5*1/12   F5 = D3 − E5
      E6 = C6*1/12   F6 = D3 − E6
      E7 = C7*1/12   F7 = D3 − E7
      E8 = C8*1/12   F8 = D3 − E8
      E9 = C9*1/12   F9 = D3 − E9
      E10 = C10*1/12   F10 = D3 − E10
      E11 = C11*1/12   F11 = D3 − E11
      E12 = C12*1/12   F12 = D3 − E12
      E13 = C13*1/12   F13 = D3 − E13
      E14 = C14*1/12   F14 = D3 − E14

c. C4 = C3 − F3   G3 = E3   H3 = F3
      C5 = C4 − F4   G4 = G3 + E4   H4 = H3 + F4
      C6 = C5 − F5   G5 = G4 + E5   H5 = H4 + F5
      C7 = C6 − F6   G6 = G5 + E6   H6 = H5 + F6
      C8 = C7 − F7   G7 = G6 + E7   H7 = H6 + F7
      C9 = C8 − F8   G8 = G7 + E8   H8 = H7 + F8
      C10 = C9 − F9   G9 = G8 + E9   H9 = H8 + F9
      C11 = C10 − F10 G10 = G9 + E10 H10 = H9 + F10
      C12 = C11 − F11 G11 = G10 + E11 H11 = H10 + F11
      C13 = C12 − F12 G12 = G11 + E12 H12 = H11 + F12
      C14 = C13 − F13 G13 = G12 + E13 H13 = H12 + F13

57. Option 1 is recommended since it costs $19,824 less in interest.

CHAPTER 12   CHAPTER 12   PRACTICE TEST,   p. 523

1. $34

3. $336 installment price; $36 finance charge

5. 22.2%

7. $2.89

9. $12.60

11. 21.5%

13. $236.58

15. $158.33

17. $\frac{23}{98}$

19. $393.93 average daily balance; $6.89 finance charge

21. Portion of Payment Applied to:

Month	Interest	Principal	End-of-Month Principal
1	$791.67	$253.33	$99,746.67
2	$789.66	$255.34	$99,491.33

Chapter 13

CHAPTER 13   CHAPTER 13   ASSIGNMENT EXERCISES,   p. 556

Section 13.1

1. $12,000   **3.** $2,300   **5.** $1,900   **7.** $4,500   **9.** $1,250   **11.** $900

13. Total Cost: $5,400

Year	Depreciation	Accumulated Depreciation	End-of-Year Book Value
1	$1,150	$1,150	$4,250
2	$1,150	$2,300	$3,100
3	$1,150	$3,450	$1,950
4	$1,150	$4,600	$ 800

Section 13.2

15. $0.084

23. $7,000

17. $0.50; $3,350

25. Total Cost $18.500

Year	Miles Driven	Depreciation	Accumulated Depreciation	End-of-Year Book Value
1	28,580	$3,143.80	$3,143.80	$15,356.20
2	32,140	$3,535.40	$6,679.20	$11,820.80
3	29,760	$3,273.60	$9,952.80	$8,547.20
4	31,810	$3,499.10	$13,451.90	$5,048.10
5	27,710	$3,048.10	$16,500.00	$2,000.00

19. $0.25; $645

21. $0.25; $380

27. $0.18

29. $827.82

31. $3,948

Section 13.3

33. 28

35. 36

37. 120

39. 325

41. Total Cost $4,200

Year	Depreciation Rate	Depreciation	Accumulated Depreciation	End-of-Year Book Value
1	$\frac{5}{15}$	$1,150	$1,150	$3,050
2	$\frac{4}{15}$	$920	$2,070	$2,130
3	$\frac{3}{15}$	$690	$2,760	$1,440
4	$\frac{2}{15}$	$460	$3,220	$980
5	$\frac{1}{15}$	$230	$3,450	$750

Section 13.4

43. a. 0.25 b. 0.5

45. a. 0.0625 b. 0.125

47. Total Cost: $8,500

Year	Depreciation	Accumulated Depreciation	End-of-Year Book Value
1	$1,062.50	$1,062.50	$7,437.50
2	$929.69	$1,992.19	$6,507.81
3	$813.48	$2,805.67	$5,694.33
4	$711.79	$3,517.46	$4,982.54
5	$622.82	$4,140.28	$4,359.72
6	$544.97	$4,685.25	$3,814.75
7	$476.84	$5,162.09	$3,337.91
8	$417.24	$5,579.33	$2,920.67

49. Total Cost: $21,000

Year	Depreciation	Accumulated Depreciation	End-of-Year Book Value
1	$14,000.00	$14,000.00	$7,000.00
2	$4,666.67	$18,666.67	$2,333.33
3	$1,333.33	$20,000.00	$1,000.00

Section 13.5

51. $949.03

53. $19,849.77

55. Year 1: $1,160; Year 2: $1,856; Year 3: $1,113.60; Year 4: $668.16; Year 5: $668.16; Year 6: $334.08

57. Total Cost $3,270

Year	MACRS Rate	Depreciation	Accumulated Depreciation	End-of-Year Book Value
1	33.33%	$1,089.89	$1,089.89	$2,180.11
2	44.45%	$1,453.52	$2,543.41	$726.59
3	14.81%	$484.29	$3,027.70	$242.30
4	7.41%	$242.30*	$3,270.00	$0

*adjusted

Section 13.6

59. $362.21

61. (a) Highlight C3 and press CTRL and *C* to copy. Highlight cells C4 through C18 and press CTRL and *V* to paste.

(b) D3 = B3*C3   (c) Accumulated Depreciation   Ending Book Value

D3 = B3*C3	E3 = D3	F3 = C3 − D3
D4 = B4*C4	E4 = E3 + D4	F4 = C4 − E4
D5 = B5*C5	E5 = E4 + D5	F5 = C5 − E5
D6 = B6*C6	E6 = E5 + D6	F6 = C6 − E6
D7 = B7*C7	E7 = E6 + D7	F7 = C7 − E7
D8 = B8*C8	E8 = E7 + D8	F8 = C8 − E8
D9 = B9*C9	E9 = E8 + D9	F9 = C9 − E9
D10 = B10*C10	E10 = E9 + D10	F10 = C10 − E10
D11 = B11*C11	E11 = E10 + D11	F11 = C11 − E11
D12 = B12*C12	E12 = E11 + D12	F12 = C12 − E12
D13 = B13*C13	E13 = E12 + D13	F13 = C13 − E13
D14 = B14*C14	E14 = E13 + D14	F14 = C14 − E14
D15 = B15*C15	E15 = E14 + D15	F15 = C15 − E15
D16 = B16*C16	E16 = E15 + D16	F16 = C16 − E16
D17 = B17*C17	E17 = E16 + D17	F17 = C17 − E17
D18 = B18*C18	E18 = E16 + D17	F18 = C18 − E18

63. Rate of Depreciation: 17.7%; Depreciation: $3,554.16; End-of-Year Book Value: $16,254.84

CHAPTER 13   PRACTICE TEST,   p. 564

1. 28   **3.** $36,900   **5.** $0.15264   **7.** a. 300 b. 378

9. a. 8.33% b. 16.67%   **11.** $2,859.71   **13.** $2,232.21   **15.** $23,560

CHAPTER 14

CHAPTER 14   ASSIGNMENT EXERCISES,   p. 600

Section 14.1

1. $8,112   **3.** $3,821   **5.** $4,291

7. $23.11

9. Cost of ending inventory: $3,558.94; Cost of goods sold: $4,553.06

11. Cost of goods sold: $5,793; cost of ending inventory: $2,319

13. Cost of goods: $3,804; Cost of ending inventory: $4,308

15. Cost of ending inventory: $4,033.57; Cost of goods sold: $4,078.43

Section 14.2

17. 2.4   **19.** 4   **21.** 5

23. 1: $2,231.76; 2: $2,017.17; 3: $2,798.28; 4: $2,090.13; 5: $862.66

25. Hardware: $3,066.67; Plumbing: $2,300; Tools: $1,533.33; Supplies: $2,300

27. Purchasing: $132.04; Personnel: $468.02; Payroll: $493.02; Secretarial pool: $801.90

29. Complete the spreadsheet using the formulas.

	A	B	C	D	E	F	G	H
1	7th Inning Memorabilia Shop and Restaurant Monthly Overhead by Department Floor Space							
2	Department	Floor Space	Fraction	Dept Expenses				
3	Gallery	4,250	0.211180	$762.40				
4	Engraving	2,675	0.132919	$479.86				
5	Framing	3,500	0.173913	$627.86				
6	Restaurant	4,500	0.223602	$807.25				
7	Cards	5,200	0.258385	$932.82				
8	Totals	20,125	1.000000	$3,610.18				
9								
10	Telephone	$256.25						
11	Utilitites	$315.75						
12	Rent	$2,845.78						
13	Maintenance	$192.40						
14	Total expenses	$3,610.18						

31. Total by department:
$528.24 + $1,872.08 + $1,972.08 + $3,207.60 = $7,580

---

1. $1,237

3. $476

5. Cost of ending inventory: $761.76; Cost of goods sold: $475.24

7. Cost of goods sold: $345; Cost of ending inventory; $892

9. Furniture $2,222.22; Computer supplies: $1,777.78; Consumable office supplies: $2,777.78; Leather goods: $1,333.33; Administrative services: $888.89

11. 2.92

Chapter 15

Section 15.1

1.

Fawcett's Plumbing Supplies
Balance Sheet
March 31, 2003

Assets
Current assets

Cash	$ 1,724.00
Office supplies	173.00
Accounts receivable	9,374.00
Total current assets	
Plant and equipment	
Equipment	12,187.00
Total plant and equipment	12,187.00
Total Assets	

Liabilities
Current liabilities

Accounts payable	2,174.00
Wages payable	674.00
Property and taxes payable	250.00
Total current liabilities	
Total Liabilities	

Owner's Equity

D. W. Fawcett, Capital	20,360.00
Total Liabilities and Owner's Equity	

3.

Seymour's Videos, Inc.
Comparative Balance Sheet
December 31, 2003 and 2004

	2004	2003	Increase (Decrease) Amount	Increase (Decrease) Percent	Percent of Total Assets 2004	Percent of Total Assets 2003
Assets						
Current assets						
Cash	$2,374	$2,184	$190	8.7	10.2	9.7
Accounts receivable	5,374	4,286	1,088	25.4	23.0	19.0
Merchandise inventory	15,589	16,107	(518)	(3.2)	66.8	71.3
Total assets	$23,337	$22,577	$760	3.4	100.0	100.0
Liabilities						
Current liabilities						
Accounts payable	7,384	6,118	1,266	20.7	31.6	27.1
Wages payable	1,024	964	60	6.2	4.4	4.3
Total liabilities	8,408	7,082	$1,326	18.7	36.0	31.4
Owner's Equity						
James Seymour's, capital	14,929	15,495	(566)	(3.7)	64.0	68.6
Total liabilities and owner's equity	$23,337	$22,577	$760	3.4	100.0	100.0

Section 15.2

5.

Marten's Family Store
Income Statement
For year ending December 31, 2001

		Percent of Net Sales
Revenue		
Gross sales	$238,923	106.1
Sales returns and allowances	13,815	6.1
Net sales	225,108	100.0
Cost of goods sold		
Beginning inventory, January 1, 2001	25,814	11.5
Purchases	109,838	48.8
Ending inventory, December 31, 2001	23,423	10.4
Cost of goods sold	112,229	49.9
Gross profit from sales	$112,879	50.1
Operating expenses		
Salary	42,523	18.9
Rent	8,640	3.8
Utilities	1,484	0.7
Insurance	2,842	1.3
Fees	860	0.4
Depreciation	1,920	0.9
Miscellaneous	3,420	1.5
Total operating expenses	61,689	27.4
Net income	$51,190	22.7

7.

Alonzo's Auto Parts
Comparative Income Statement
For years ending June 30, 2001 and 2002

	2002	2001	Increase (Decrease) Amount	Increase (Decrease) Percent
Revenue				
Gross sales	$291,707	$275,873	$15,834	5.7
Sales returns and allowances	5,895	6,821	(926)	(13.6)
Net sales	285,812	269,052	16,760	6.2
Cost of goods sold				
Beginning inventory, July 1	35,892	32,587	3,305	10.1
Purchases	157,213	146,999	10,214	6.9
Ending inventory, June 30	32,516	30,013	2,503	8.3
Cost of goods sold	160,589	149,573	11,016	7.4
Gross profit from sales	$125,223	$119,479	$5,744	4.8
Operating expenses				
Salary	42,000	40,000	2,000	5.0
Insurance	3,800	3,800	0	0
Utilities	1,986	2,097	(111)	(5.3)
Rent	3,600	3,300	300	9.1
Depreciation	4,000	4,500	(500)	(11.1)
Total operating expenses	55,386	53,697	1,689	3.1
Net income	$69,837	$65,782	$4,055	6.2

Section 15.3

9. 1.57 to 1   **11.** 1.39 to 1   **13.** 0.87 to 1   **15.** 1.29 to 1

17. Operating ratio: 0.9 or 90%;   **19.** 0.893187067, or 89.3%   **21.** 0.2009237875, or 20.1%
Gross profit margin: 0.25 or 25%

23.

Microsoft Excel - CLE_SE_15-23.xls							

Molene Internet Store Comparative Balance Sheet December 31, 2001 and 2002

			Increase(Decrease)		Percent of Total Assets	
	2002	2001	Amount	Percent	2002	2001
Assets						
Current assets						
Cash	$52,841.27	$49,157.15	$3,684.12	7.49%	18.92%	15.23%
Accounts receivable	$27,942.18	$26,783.14	$1,159.04	4.33%	10.01%	8.30%
Merchandise inventory	$198,475.48	$246,756.45	-$48,280.97	-19.57%	71.07%	76.47%
Total assets	$279,258.93	$322,696.74	-$43,437.81	-13.46%	100.0%	100.00%
Liabilities						
Current liabilities	$47,452.76	$48,997.19	-$1,544.43	-3.15%	16.99%	15.18%
Accounts payable	$9,394.24	$8,792.97	$601.27	6.84%	3.36%	2.72%
Wages payable	$49,421.24	$48,416.54	$1,004.70	2.08%	17.70%	15.00%
Total liabilities	$106,268.24	$106,206.70	$61.54	0.06%	38.05%	32.91%
Owner's equity						
Justin Molene, capital	$172,990.69	$216,490.04	-$43,499.35	-20.09%	61.95%	67.09%
Total liabilities and owner's equity	$279,258.93	$322,696.74	-$43,437.81	-13.46%	100.0%	100.00%

CHAPTER 15

CHAPTER 15 PRACTICE TEST, p. 651

1.

O'Toole's Hardware Store
Comparative Balance Sheet
December 31, 2000 and 2001

	2001	2000	Increase (Decrease) Amount	Increase (Decrease) Percent
Assets				
Current assets				
Cash	$7,318	$5,283	$2,035	38.5
Accounts receivable	3,147	3,008	139	4.6
Merchandise inventory	63,594	60,187	3,407	5.7
Total current assets	74,059	68,478	$5,581	8.2
Plant and equipment				
Building	36,561	37,531	(970)	(2.6)
Equipment	8,256	4,386	3,870	88.2
Total plant and equipment	44,817	41,917	2,900	6.9
Total assets	$118,876	$110,395	$8,481	7.7
Liabilities				
Current liabilities				
Accounts payable	5,174	4,563	611	13.4
Wages payable	780	624	156	25.0
Total current liabilities	5,954	5,187	767	14.8
Long-term liabilities				
Mortgage note payable	34,917	36,510	(1,593)	(4.4)
Total long-term liabilities	34,917	36,510	(1,593)	(4.4)
Total liabilities	40,871	41,697	($826)	(2.0)
Owner's Equity				
James O'Toole, capital	78,005	68,698	9,307	13.5
Total liabilities and owner's equity	$118,876	$110,395	$8,481	7.7

3. 1.76 to 1

5. 1.60 to 1

7. Operating ratio for 2002: 0.645 or 64.5%; Operating ratio for 2003: 0.540 or 54.0%

Chapter 16

Section 16.1

1. $620.60   **3.** $1,261.07   **5.** $1,765.60   **7.** $17,000   **9.** $65,000
11. $30,000   **13.** $793.50   **15.** $649.98   **17.** $58,800   **19.** $828.01

Section 16.2

21. $642   **23.** $1,418   **25.** $821

27. a. $50,000 individual bodily injury per accident; $100,000 total bodily injury per accident, and $25,000 property damage per accident.
b. $508

29. $856   **31.** $10,000

33. $361.65   **35.** a. $142.50   b. $570   **37.** $708

Section 16.3

39. $157.80   **41.** $663.60   **43.** $2,115; $185.06; $549.90   **45.** $1,096; $95.90; $284.96

47. Term insurance is not as expensive as straight-life. In term insurance, the premium is paid for a fixed period of time, whereas straight-life premiums are paid for the entire life of the insured. Coverage of term policy is for the term of the policy only, and it has no cash value. Coverage of straight-life is for the insured's entire life, and it has some cash value if canceled or cashed in.

49. a. $342.50; b. $89.05   **51.** $12.37 more per $1,000   **53.** $38.14   **55.** $639

59. (a) $60,000
(b) $35
(c) $1,013.16
(d) $72.51
(e) 4.500%

57.

Name	Area Rank	Face Value Building	Face Value Contents	Building Class	Rate Building	Rate Contents	Premium Building	Premium Contents	Annual Pemium
Aaron, Bonnie	1	$195,380.00	$85,267.00	A	$0.59	$0.64	$1,152.74	$545.71	$1,698.45
Buhler, Noreen	1	$194,400.00	$97,400.00	B	$0.75	$0.89	$1,458.00	$866.86	$2,324.86
Ganong, Roger	3	$89,840.00	$46,000.00	A	$0.62	$0.67	$557.01	$308.20	$865.21
Hampton, Robert	1	$163,200.00	$79,500.00	C	$0.94	$1.11	$1,534.08	$882.45	$2,416.53
Jackson, William	2	$295,600.00	$146,400.00	B	$0.76	$0.91	$2,246.56	$1,332.24	$3,578.80
McDonald, Mark	2	$326,550.00	$164,500.00	A	$0.60	$0.65	$1,959.30	$1,069.25	$3,028.55
Nu, Jung Pao	3	$62,800.00	$28,500.00	C	$0.98	$1.16	$615.44	$330.60	$946.04
Riviera, Jose	2	$217,300.00	$105,300.00	B	$0.65	$0.76	$1,412.45	$800.28	$2,212.73
Roux, Jeffrey	2	$195,300.00	$95,600.00	B	$0.96	$1.13	$1,874.88	$1,080.28	$2,955.16
Sanders, Donna	3	$85,000.00	$46,300.00	B	$0.78	$0.93	$663.00	$430.59	$1,093.59

Jacobs Insurance Broker - Annual Policyholder Premiums

1. $2,033.95   **3.** $65,625   **5.** $36.09   **7.** $144
9. $159.56

11. Term insurance is not as expensive as straight-life. In term insurance, the premium is paid for a fixed period of time, whereas straight-life premiums are paid for the entire life of the insured. Coverage of term insurance is for the term of the policy only, and it has no cash value. Coverage of straight-life is for the insured's entire life, and it has some cash value if cancelled or cashed in.

13. $41.16   **15.** $425   **17.** $43,103.45   **19.** $168

Chapter 17

CHAPTER 17   ASSIGNMENT EXERCISES,   p. 707

Section 17.1

1. $0.18	**3.** $0.63	**5.** $0.37	**7.** $0.77	**9.** $0.51	**11.** $14.25
13. $58.24	**15.** $33.80	**17.** $26.14	**19.** $332.33	**21.** $84.31	

Section 17.2

23. $13,750   **25.** $46,000   **27.** $2,587,500   **29.** $555

31. $250   **33.** $1,309   **35.** $4,062.50   **37.** $500 county tax

39. $882.50   **41.** $527.25   **43.** $2,799.68   **45.** $1,108.63 (nearest cent)

47. $0.063   **49.** $0.072   **51.** $1,280.13   **53.** $1,840

55. $0.05; $4.98; $49.73   **57.** $0.04; $3.26; $32.54

Section 17.3

59. $16,082   **61.** $31,274   **63.** $46,811   **65.** $2,899   **67.** $4,015

69. $4,729   **71.** $5,851   **73.** $54,635.24   **75.** $55,854.12

77.   **79.** $1,886.91

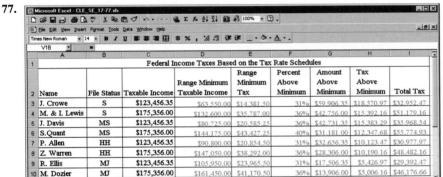

CHAPTER 17   PRACTICE TEST,   p. 712

1. $0.76 (rounded)   **3.** $22.28 (rounded)   **5.** $198.44   **7.** $17.61 (rounded)

9. $50.00 (rounded)   **11.** $89.20   **13.** $39,471.64 (rounded)   **15.** $1,071.77 (rounded)

17. $4,073.34   **19.** $1,850.40   **21.** $43,065.12   **23.** $42,800

Chapter 18

Section 18.1

1. a. 9,329,800 b. $20.25
c. $1.19 d. $49.75

3. a. $1.68; $84.00; $168.00
b. $102.25 c. 3.11%

5. Stock A has the greater yield. Stock A earns the same dividend as Stock B, but with a smaller investment.

7. a. $30,000 b. $30,000
c. $440,000 d. $2.20

9. 12.5, or 13

11. a. $173.06 b. $8,160.26

13. a. $409.94 gain b. 5.61%

15. a. $109.20 b. $5,149.20

17. a. 55 b. 74 c. 12

Section 18.2

19. a. 170 b. $67.50 c. 2004

21. a. $102\frac{1}{4}\%$ of face value; in dollars, $1,022.50
b. $82\frac{1}{8}\%$ of face value; in dollars, $821.25

23. $2,516.25

25. $10,250.00

27. a. $30 b. $4,680

29. IntShip bonds

31. 1%

33. a. $90 b. $540

35. Aames (13.4)

37. Bond D has the greater yield, so bond D is the better investment.

39. Complete the spreadsheet using the formulas.

1. a. $0.81 b. $31.50 per share c. $31.56 per share
d. 4,590,500 shares

3. a. $131.30 b. $6,191.30

5. 21.1%

7. Yield, PennAm: 4.9%; Yield, PennEMA: 4.2%

9. a. 2006 b. $640 per bond c. $723.75

11. a. $25 b. $4,275

13. Preferred stock

15. Stock A

Glossary/Index

Accelerated cost-recovery system (ACRS): a method of depreciation of assets for tax purposes that allows businesses to write off costs of certain assets more quickly than with other methods of depreciation. Items can no longer be placed in service using this method, 545

Account register: a bound set of blank forms supplied by a bank and kept with the checks; it is used to record all checks, deposits, interest, and other transactions and to keep a running account balance, 213

Accounts payable: money owed for merchandise or services that the business has received but has not yet paid for, 613

Accounts receivable: money that customers owe the business for the merchandise or services they have received but have not yet paid for, 612

Accumulated depreciation: the current year's depreciation plus all previous years' depreciation, 534

Acid-test ratio (quick ratio): a ratio used to determine the financial condition of a business; the ratio of quick current assets to current liabilities, 631

Addends: numbers being added, 8

Adjustable rate mortgage (ARM): a loan made so that the interest rate varies, usually with the prime rate of interest, 502

Adjusted bank statement balance: consists of the balance on the bank statement plus any outstanding deposits minus any outstanding checks, 220

Adjusted gross income: gross income minus any allowable credits, 269; 695

Allowances: *See* Sales returns, 622

Amortization of a loan: the repayment of a loan in equal installments that are applied to principal and interest over a specific period of time, 502

Amortization schedule: shows the amount of principal and interest for each payment of the loan, 505

Amount credited: amount by which an invoice is reduced when a partial payment is received and a partial cash discount is allowed, 315

Amount financed: the total paid in regular payments, 482

Amount of an annuity: the sum of the annuity payments plus the interest, 450

Annual percentage rate (APR): the effective interest rate or the equivalent annual simple interest rate, 424, 494
tables, 426, 427
using the constant ratio formula, 495

Annual percentage yield (APY): the effective rate of interest when identifying the rate of earnings on an investment, 424

Annuity: a series of equal periodic payments put into an interest-bearing account for a specific number of periods, 450
annuities due, 450
ordinary annuity future value tables, 452
simple interest basis of annuity future value, 453

Annuity certain: annuity with a specified number of periods, 450

Annuity due: annuity with payment made at beginning of each period, 450

Approximate number: a rounded number, 7

Assessed value: a percentage of the estimated market value of a property. The percent is set by the city or county that charges the tax, 690

Asset turnover ratio: the ratio of net sales to the average total assets, 632

Assets: buildings, machinery, equipment, furniture, and other properties owned by the business, including anything of monetary value and anything that can be exchanged for cash or other property, 532, 612

Associative property of addition: when more than two numbers are added, two are grouped and added first, then the sum is added to another number; the grouping property of addition, 8

Automatic draft: a regular monthly bill paid electronically from a bank account, 211

Automatic teller machine (ATM): a computerized banking service offered by many banks; the account holder can perform many banking functions using a bank card and bank computer, without the help of a bank teller, 219

Average annual yield: *See* Current bond yield, 729

Average daily balance: the sum of the daily balances divided by the number of days in the billing cycle, 491

Average daily balance method: the daily balances of the account are determined, then the sum of these balances is divided by the number of days in the billing cycle. This is then multiplied by the monthly interest rate to find the finance charge for the month, 491

Balance sheet: a type of financial statement that indicates the worth or financial condition of a business as of a certain date, 612
comparative, 619
horizontal analysis of, 619
preparing, 614
vertical analysis of, 616

Bank discount: the interest or fee on a discounted note that is subtracted from the amount borrowed at the time the loan is made, 394

Bank draft: *See* Check, 210

Bank memo: a notice sent to the account holder to advise that corrections have been made to the account, 209

Bank reconciliation: a process in which the bank statement and the account holder's checkbook are brought into agreement, 219

Bank records:
bank statements, 217
checking account forms, 208

Bank statement: monthly statement sent by the bank to an account holder listing all transactions in the account for that month, 217

Banker's rule: the most common method that banks use to calculate the interest on a loan; ordinary interest using exact time, 390

Bar graph: a graph made with horizontal or vertical bars and used to compare several related values, 176

Base: the original or entire amount in a percentage problem, 83

Basic installment loan: A loan in which the amount borrowed plus interest is repaid in a specified number of equal payments, 482

Beneficiary: the individual, organization, or business to whom the proceeds of an insurance policy are payable, 658

Bill of lading: a document included on each shipment of goods that shows important information about the shipment, such as content, distribution, and freight charges, 316

Biweekly: every other week, 26 periods per year, 262

Biweekly mortgage: the homebuyer makes 26 equal payments each year rather than 12; this method builds equity more quickly than the monthly payment method, 502

Bodily injury: personal injury sustained in an accident, 663

Bond: a legal promise to repay an amount of money at a fixed time, with annual interest, given by a corporation, municipality, or the federal government, 725
convertible, 725
corporate, 725
cost of buying, 722
coupon, 725
discount, 725
junk, 725
PE ratio, 721
premium, 725
proceeds from selling, 722
reading listings, 726
recallable, 725
registered, 725
treasury, 725
yield, 725

Bond market: the buying or selling of bonds to the public; the location where such trades are made, 725

Bond price, 727–728

Bond value, 729

Bond yield, 729

Book value: the value of a particular year, make, and model of a vehicle, 664

Buildings: asset that is long term in nature; value of buildings business owns, 612

Business equipment: asset; equipment that the business owns (tools, display cases, machinery, etc., 612

Capital: *See* Owner's equity, 613

Carrying charges: *See* Finance charges, 482

Cash: money in the bank as well as cash on hand, 612

Greatest common divisor (GCD): the greatest or largest number that will divide into a group of two or more numbers, 63

Gross earnings (gross pay): total amount of earnings before any deductions are made, 262

based on commission, 265
based on hourly wage, 263
based on piecework wage, 264
based on salary, 262

Gross income: income from various sources, such as salary, investments, etc., before exemptions and deductions are subtracted, 695

Gross margin: *See* Gross profit, 623

Gross pay, 262

Gross profit: the difference between the net sales and the cost of goods sold, 623; *See also* Markup, 338, 352

Gross profit margin ratio: shows the average spread between cost of goods sold and the selling price, 632

Higher terms: a fraction written in an equivalent value, determined by multiplying the numerator and denominator by the same number; the process is used in the addition and subtraction of fractions, 63

Horizontal analysis of an income statement: an analysis of a comparative financial statement for two or more periods that compares entries on a horizontal line, 627

Horizontal analysis of balance sheet: a comparison of items on a balance sheet for two different years, recording both the amount of increase (or decrease) and the increase (or decrease) as a percent of the earlier year's amount, 619

Hourly rate (hourly wage): rate of pay for each hour worked, 263

Hourly wage: *See* Hourly rate, 263

Improper fraction: a fraction with a numerator equal to or larger than its denominator with a value equal to or greater than one, 59

Income statement: a statement that shows the net income (or loss) of a business over a period of time, 619

horizontal analysis of, 627
preparing, 623
vertical analysis of, 624

Income tax: tax paid on individual and business income to the federal government and some state governments, 695

Income tax tables: used to find the tax liability for taxable incomes of less than $100,000, 696, 698–699

Increase: when the difference in two amounts is from a smaller amount to a larger amount, 182

Installment loan: a loan that is paid back through a specified number of payments, 482

Installment payment: amount of periodic payments, 482

Installment price: total amount paid, including the down payment and all payments, 482

Insurance: a form of protection against unexpected financial loss, 658

fire, 658
life, 665
motor vehicle, 662

Insured: policy holder; the individual, organization, or business that carries the insurance or financial protection against loss, 658

Insurer: underwriter; the insurance company that assures payment for a specific loss according to contract provisions, 658

Interest: the price or fee for using money, 376

Interest period: the length of time during which the interest on a loan or investment is compounded, 418

Interpret financial ratios, 633

Inventory: value of merchandise that is available for sale on a certain date, 574

comparing methods for determining, 581
first-in, first-out (FIFO) method, 577
last-in, first-out (LIFO) method, 578
retail method, 579
specific identification method, 575
turnover and overhead, 584, 585
weighted-average method, 576

Inventory turnover: the frequency with which the inventory is sold and replaced, 584

Inventory turnover ratio: the formula for finding inventory turnover, 585

Itemized deductions: complete listing of all deductions claimed by the taxpayer when filing the regular 1040 form; used instead of the standard deduction, 695

Junk bonds: bonds of businesses that are bankrupt or having financial difficulty, 725

Key words, 137

Known fact: relevant fact that is known or given, 111

Knuckle method, 311

Land: property and grounds on which the building stands and other land business owns, 612

Least common denominator (LCD): the least or smallest number into which each two or more denominators divides evenly, 64

Length: the two long sides of a rectangle, 121

Liabilities: amounts that the business owes, 613

Liability insurance: protects the owner of a vehicle if an accident causes personal injury or property damage and is the fault of the insured or the insured's designated driver, 663

Life insurance: a type of insurance that makes a payment to the surviving beneficiaries of insured persons in the event of their death, 665

LIFO (last-in, first-out) inventory method: a method of determining the cost of the ending inventory in which each sale is assumed to be from the goods most recently purchased; that is, the oldest goods are assumed to be the goods remaining in the ending inventory, 578

Line graph: a graph made with a series of connected line segments used to show data trends visually, 177

Line-of-credit accounts: another name for open-end loans, 482

List price: suggested price at which merchandise is sold to consumers, 300

Long-term liabilities: liabilities that are to be paid over a long period of time, 613

Lowest terms: a fraction is in lowest terms if the numerator and denominator cannot be divided evenly by any number except 1, 62

Maker: the person or company borrowing money, 394

Manufacturer's price list: a list that the manufacturer's representative follows; usually includes freight payment terms, 316

Margin: markup or gross profit, 338

Markdown: the amount the selling price is reduced, 338, 351

Marked price: the price of an item before sales tax is added, 687

Market value: the expected selling price of a piece of property, 501, 690

Marketable securities: current assets such as government bonds, which can be quickly turned into cash without loss, 631

Markup (gross profit or margin): the difference between selling price and cost, 338, 352

comparing markup based on cost with markup based on selling price, 341
finding final selling price for a series of markups, 351
finding the selling price to achieve a desired profit, 354
using cost as a base in markup applications, 339
using selling price as a base in markup applications, 341

Maturity date: the date on which a loan is due to be repaid, 394; the date on which a corporation will repay the face value of a bond, 725

Maturity value: the amount of principal plus the amount of interest, 378, 418

Mean: the sum of a set of values divided by the number of values in the set, 169

Median: the middle value in a set of values that are arranged in order from smallest to largest or largest to smallest, 169

Medicare tax: a federal tax used to provide healthcare benefits to retired and disabled workers, 274

Merchandise inventory: merchandise on hand, 612

Mill: one thousandth of a dollar ($0.001), 691

Minuend: the original amount from which a number is subtracted, 12

Mixed number: a number composed of both a whole number and a fraction, 59

adding and subtracting, 64–69
multiplying and dividing, 64–74

Mixed percents: percents with mixed numbers and mixed decimals, 79

Mode: the value that occurs most frequently in a group of values, 170

Modified accelerated cost-recovery system (MACRS): a method of depreciation of assets for tax purposes that is a modification of the ACRS method; it added two new classes of property, reclassified some types of property, and changed the depreciation rates in each category, 546

Monthly: once a month; there are 12 periods per year, 262

Monthly mortgage payment: the amount paid each month, usually determined by consulting an amortization table, 502

Mortgage: the agreement that gives the lender a claim on the real property until the loan is fully paid, 501
  amortization schedule, 502
  monthly mortgage payment and total interest, 502
  See also individual types

Mortgage payable: the debt owed on buildings and land that the business owns, 613

Motor vehicle insurance: includes liability, comprehensive, and collision insurance for the owners of motor vehicles, 662

Multiplicand: the number that is being multiplied; the first number in a multiplication problem, 14

Multiplier: the number we multiply by, 14

Municipal bonds: bonds issued by state and local governments, 725

Net amount: the amount remaining once a cash discount is deducted from a net price, 312

Net decimal equivalent: the decimal that results from multiplying the complement of each discount rate in a series discount, 305

Net earning (net pay): amount of pay left after deductions are made (*also called* take-home pay), 262

Net income: the difference between the gross profit (gross margin) and the operating expenses, 623

Net pay: *See* Net earnings, 262

Net price (net amount): the amount paid by the retailer for an article; this amount is the difference in the list price and the trade discount of the article, 300
  calculating using end-of-month terms, 313
  calculating using ordinary dating terms, 311
  calculating using receipt-of-goods terms, 314
  freight terms and, 316
  net decimal equivalent and, 305
  single discount equivalent and, 307
  and trade discount series, 304

Net profit: *See* Net income, 623

Net sales: The difference between the total sales and the sales returns or allowances, 623

Net worth: *See* Owner's equity, 613

No-fault insurance: program in a number of states that allows each person involved in an accident to submit a claim for damages to his or her own insurance company if the amount is under a certain stated maximum, 663

Nonsufficient funds (NSF) fee: a fee charged to your account when you write a check and do not have enough money in your account to cover it, 218

Nonterminating (or repeating) decimal: the quotient of a division that does not come out even, no matter how many decimal places it is carried to, 75

Notes payable: Promissory notes that the business owes, 613

Notes receivable: Promissory notes owed to the business, 612

Numerator: the top term of a fraction or the number being divided, 58

Odd lot: a group of less than 100 shares of stock; there is an extra charge for trading odd lots, 721

Office furniture and equipment: office furnishings (desks, filing cabinets, and so on) and equipment (computers, printers, copiers, calculators, postage meters, fax machines, and the like), 612

Office supplies: supplies such as stationery, pens, file folders, and diskettes, 612

Open-end loan: a loan in which there is no fixed number of payments—the borrower keeps making payments until the amount is paid off, and the interest is computed on the unpaid balance at the end of each payment period, 482
  average daily balance method, 491
  unpaid balance method, 490

Operating expenses: the overhead or cost incurred in operating the business, 623

Operating ratio: the amount of sales dollars that are used to pay for the cost of goods and administrative expenses, 631

Order of operations: *See* Standard order of operations, 121

Ordinary annuity: annuity with payment made at end of periods, 450

Ordinary annuity present value table, 462

Ordinary balance: the amount owed after a partial payment and partial cash discount are deducted, 315

Ordinary interest: interest that is calculated using 360 days to find the ratio per day, 388

Ordinary life insurance: *See* Straight-life insurance, 665

Ordinary time: 30 days per month regardless of the month of the year, 385

Outstanding balance: the amount owed after a partial payment and partial cash discount are deducted, 315

Outstanding checks or deposits: checks or deposits that do not reach the bank in time to appear on the monthly statement, 219

Overhead: expenses required for the operation of a business, such as salaries, rent, office supplies, taxes, insurance, and maintenance of equipment, 587
  based on floor space, 589
  based on sales, 587

Overtime pay: earnings based on the overtime rate, 263

Overtime rate: rate of pay for hours worked beyond 40 hours in a week (sometimes given for work on holidays); it must be at least 1.5 times the regular pay rate, 263

Owner's equity: the value of a business once liabilities have been paid off; that is, the difference in total assets and total liabilities. Also referred to as capital, proprietorship, and net worth, 613

Par value: *See* Face value, 716

Partial cash discount: amount of cash discount allowed when partial payment is made, 315

Partial dividend: parts of the dividend when a dividend has more digits than a divisor, 16

Partial payment: payment that is eligible for a cash discount when the invoice is not paid in full, 315

Partial product: the product of one digit of the multiplier and the multiplicand, 14

Partial quotient: the quotient of a partial dividend and the divisor, 16

Participating preferred stock: stock that will earn additional dividends if the company does well, 719

Payee: the person or company to whom a check is made out—the one who gets the money, 394

Payor: the bank holding the account, 210

Payroll:
  employer's payroll taxes, 278–281
  gross pay, 262

Percent: a hundredth of a whole amount; a fraction with a denominator of 100; *percent* means *per hundred,* 78
  mixed, 79
  using the percentage formula, 83–90
  writing as a number, 80–82
  writing numbers as, 79–82

Percentage: a portion of the base in a percentage problem, 83

Percentage formula: Percentage = Rate × Base, or $P = R \times B$, 83

Percentage method income: adjusted gross income after deducting a tax-exempt amount based on the withholding allowances claimed. This income is used in calculating income tax by the percentage method, 269

Percentage method withholding: the amount of an employee's gross income that is exempt from withholding, 272

Percentage proportion: a variation of the percentage formula that is written in the form of a proportion, 90

Perimeter: the distance around the edges of a square, triangle, rectangle, or other geometric shape, 120

Period interest rate: when using compound interest, the rate of interest for compounding period, 418

Periodic inventory: a physical count of the merchandise on hand at the end of a specified time to determine the value of merchandise available for sale, 574

Perpetual inventory: a record of the amount and value of merchandise available for sale at any given time. Inventory records for this type of inventory are kept on computer and are adjusted with the sale of each item, 574

Piecework rate: pay rate based on the amount of acceptable work done, 264

Place-value system: a system in which a digit has a value according to its place, or position, in a number, 5

Plant and equipment: assets used in transacting business; more long term in nature than current assets, 612

Point-of-sale: transactions where money is transferred electronically when a sale is made, 210

Points: a one time payment of a percent of the loan that is an additional cost of making the mortgage, 504

Policy: the contract between the insurer and the insured, 658

Policy holder: *See* Insured, 658

Policy premium, 658

Portion: a part of the original number or entire quantity; represented by a percentage, 83

Preferred stock: a type of stock with preferential rights such as a fixed dividend (compare with common stock), 716

Premium: the amount paid by the insured for the protection provided by the policy, 658

Premium bond: a bond selling for more than its face value, 725

Premium (insurance), 658

Prepay and add: a shipping term that indicates that the seller pays the freight charges and then adds the cost of the invoice, 316

Present value: the amount of money needed at present to yield, or earn, a specified amount at a future date, 430
    based on annual compounding for one year, 430
    based on future value using a $1.00 present value table, 431, 432

Present value of an annuity: the lump sum amount that must be invested now to equal the future value of an annuity, 461

Price-earnings (PE) ratio: closing price per share of stock divided by the annual net income per share, 721

Prime interest rate: the lowest rate at which money is loaned to the most preferred borrowers, 377

Prime number: a whole number larger than 1 that is divisible only by itself and 1, 65

Principal: the amount of money borrowed or invested, 376

Problem solving: decision key for, 11
    using equations, 137
    with decimals, 22
    with fractions, 58
    with percents, 78
    with whole numbers, 4

Proceeds: the amount that the maker of a discounted note receives; proceeds = face value − discount, 394

Product: the answer, or result, in multiplication, 14

Promissory note: a legal document or instrument by which the borrower promises to repay a loan, 393
    simple discount notes, 394
    third-party discount notes, 395

Proper fraction: a fraction with a numerator smaller than its denominator; a fraction with a value less than 1, 85

Property damage: damage to the property of others, including vehicles, 663

Property tax: a tax collected by cities and counties on land, houses, buildings, and improvements, 690

Property tax rate: the rate of tax that must be paid on a piece of property; set by the city or county collecting the tax, 691

Proportion: an equation in which both sides are fractions or ratios, 31

Proprietorship: *See* Owner's equity, 613

Protractor: a measuring device to measure angles, 179

Quick current assets: cash assets or assets that can be readily exchanged for cash, such as marketable securities and receivables, 631

Quick ratio: *See* Acid-test ratio, 631

Quota: a specific amount of work to be completed; often a commission or bonus is earned if work exceeds quota, 265

Quotient: the answer, or result, of division, 16

Range (or spread): the result when the smallest number is subtracted from the largest number in a group of numbers, 168

Rate: a percent that indicates how the base and percentage are related; the percent or decimal or fractional equivalent of the percent that is charged or earned for the use of money, 83, 376

Rate of change: increase or decrease; find by using the percentage formula $R = P/B$, 182

Ratio: the comparison of two numbers by division that can also be written as a fraction, 31, 182

Ratios to net sales: ratios determined from an income statement that make comparisons possible between the major elements of the statement and net sales; these ratios (usually expressed in percents) usually cover a one-year period, 631

Real property: land or anything permanently attached to the land, such as buildings and fences, 690

Recallable bonds: allows corporation to repurchase bonds before maturity date, 725

Receipt of goods (ROG) discount: sales terms in which the discount is determined from the day the goods are received instead of the invoice date, 314

Reciprocals: two numbers that give a product of 1 when multiplied by each other, 7/8 and 8/7 are reciprocals, 72

Recovery period: the length of time over which an item may be depreciated, 545

Rectangle: a four-sided shape with equal angles and opposite sides equal; the two long sides are called length, the two short sides are called width, 121

Refund fraction: a fraction that shows what portion of the total finance charge has not been used at the time the loan is paid off, 486

Registered bonds: bonds that allow the investor to receive interest automatically by being listed with the corporation, 725

Regular pay: earnings based on the hourly wage, 263

Relationships: equations and solving problems, 138

Remainder: the amount left over if division does not come out even, 16

Repeating decimal: *See* Nonterminating decimal, 75

Restricted endorsement: occurs when the payee signs a check on the back and adds special instructions such as changing the payee or restricting the check for deposit only, 214

Retail method: a method of determining the value of inventory by comparing the cost of goods available for sale at cost and at retail, 579

Return on investment (ROI): total gain on a purchase divided by the total cost of the purchase, 723

Returned check: a check returned to the payee because it was not honored by the maker's bank, 218

Returned check fee: a fee charged to your account when someone writes you a check without the funds to cover it and you deposit it in your account, 218

Revolving charge accounts: open-end loans, in which borrowers keep making payments at a stated rate of interest until the loan is paid off; additional charges can be made at any time as long as they are below the credit limit, 489

Rider: additional insurance coverage for a special purpose; additional premium is added to the basic premium, 661

Round lot: a group of 100 shares of stock or a multiple of 100 shares, 721

Round, rounding, rounded: a procedure to find an estimated or approximate answer, 7

Rule of 78: a method used to calculate the refund due when a loan is paid off early, 485

Salary: a set amount of money paid to an employee for work done during a specific time period, 262

Salary plus commission: a certain basic salary that is earned in addition to a commission on sales, 265

Sales returns: refunds or adjustments for unsatisfactory merchandise of services, 622

Sales tax: an amount of money added to the price of an item, collected by the store when the item is sold and paid to the state or local government, 684

Sales tax tables: tables distributed by many state and local governments that list the proper sales tax on various dollar amounts, 684

Salvage value (scrap value): the estimated dollar value of an asset at the end of the asset's estimated useful life, 532

Scrap value: *See* Salvage value, 532

Second mortgage: a note whose holder has second rights to the proceeds from the sale of a home, 502

Section 179: a deduction of up to $18,000 per year that is treated as an expense for the purchase of property, 549

Self-employment (SE) tax: a self-employed person must pay Social Security tax and Medicare tax, 275

Selling price: the price at which merchandise is sold to consumers, 338

Semiannually: twice a year, 2 periods per year, 419

Semimonthly: twice a month, 24 periods in a year, 262

Service charge: a fee the bank charges for operation of a checking account, 217

Share: one unit of stock, 716

Signature card: a record maintained by the bank which records the signature of persons authorized to make withdrawals from an account, 211

Simple discount note: a loan made by a bank at a simple interest with interest collected at the time the loan is made, 394

Simple discount rate: a discount note for which the simple interest was deducted from the face value of the note, 419

Simple interest: the amount of money paid or earned on a loan or investment of a lump sum for a specified period of time, 376
    finding the principal, rate, or time using the simple interest formula, 381–383
    formula, 376
    fractional parts of a year, 380
    maturity value of a loan, 378
    tables, 392

Single discount equivalent: a percent that is the complement of the percent form of the net decimal equivalent. It gives a net price that is equivalent to a net price resulting from applying a series of trade discounts, 307

Single discount rate: a term used to indicate that only one discount rate is applied to the list price, 300
  complements of, 301
  finding the net price using, 301
  finding the trade discount using, 301

Sinking fund: an annuity established at compound interest over a period of time to accumulate to a desired future value, 450
  payments, 459
  present value of an ordinary annuity, 461

Social Security tax: a federal tax that goes into a fund that pays monthly benefits to retired and disabled workers, 274
  calculating employee's contribution to, 275
  employer's contribution to, 275

Specific identification inventory method: incoming merchandise that is available for sale is coded with the actual cost, so the inventory is based on the actual cost of the item, 575

Spread: See Range, 168

Spreadsheet: a table of rows and columns, 123

Square: a four-sided shape whose sides and corner angles are equal, 120

Standard deduction: a taxpayer may choose to subtract a standard deduction from the adjusted gross income rather than itemize his or her deductions. The amount of a standard deduction varies from year to year, 695

Standard order of operations: the agreed-upon order for evaluating expressions with multiple operations. Parentheses first, all multiplications and divisions from left to right next, then all additions and subtractions from left to right, 121

State unemployment tax (SUTA): a state tax paid by the employer for each employee; used for paying unemployment benefits, 279

Statistics: manageable and meaningful information obtained from sets of data, 168
  mean, 169
  median, 169
  mode, 170
  range, 168
  using, 168

Stock: a part ownership of a corporation; can be bought and sold, 716
  calculating return on investment (ROI), 723
  cost of buying and proceeds from selling, 721
  current yield, 720
  dividends, 719
  price to earnings (PE) ratio, 721
  reading listings, 717–718

Stock certificate: the documents showing information of ownership, 716

Stock listings: daily prices and other information about the companies reported in newspapers and on the Internet, 717

Stock market: the buying or selling of stocks to the public; the location where such trades are made, 716

Stockbroker: a specialist in stock market trading and investments, 716

Straight commission: salary based entirely on a percent of total sales, 265

Straight-life (ordinary life) insurance: a type of life insurance in which those insured agree to pay premiums for their entire lives. At the time of the insured's death, a beneficiary will receive the face value of the policy. Straight-life insurance policy builds up a cash value, 665

Straight-line depreciation: a method of depreciation in which the amount of depreciation of an asset is spread equally over the number of years of useful life of the asset, 532

Straight-line rate: when used with the declining-balance method of depreciation, the straight-line rate is a fraction with a numerator of 1 and a denominator equal to the number of useful years of an asset. This fraction is usually expressed as a decimal equivalent when making calculations and a percent equivalent when identifying the rate of depreciation, 542

Straight piecework: wages based entirely on the quantity of acceptable work done, 264

Subtrahend: the amount being subtracted, 12

Suggested retail price (catalog price or list price): the price at which a product should be sold to the consumer; this price is usually listed in a manufacturer's catalog, 300

Sum, or total: answer or result in addition, 8

Sum-of-the-years'-digits depreciation: a method of depreciating an asset by allowing the greatest depreciation during the first year and a decreasing amount of depreciation each year thereafter, 538

Table: one or more lists of numerical information grouped in some meaningful form, 174

Take-home pay: See Net earnings (net pay), 262

Tax: money collected by the government to pay for its upkeep and to provide services to tax payers, 684
  income, 695
  property tax, 691
  sales tax, 684

Tax rate schedules: used to figure tax on taxable incomes of $50,000 or more, 697

Tax Reform Act of 1986: changed the tax rate; income is taxed at different rates depending on how much income falls into each of various income brackets, 697

Taxable income: gross income minus exemptions and deductions, 695

Term: the length of time for which money is borrowed or invested, 394

Term insurance: a type of life insurance that is purchased for a certain period of time, such as 5 or 10 years, and then must be renewed. It is the least expensive type of life insurance, 665

Terminating decimal: the quotient of a division of a fraction that comes out even, with no remainder, 75

Territory: for insurance purposes-refers to the type of area in which a car is kept and driven, 663

Third party: the bank to which a business may sell a promissory note, 395

Third-party discount note: a note arranged with a third party or bank by the payee of a note so that the proceeds can be received before the maturity date, 395

Time: the number of days, months, or years that money is loaned or invested, 376

Time and a half: another name for overtime rate, 263

Total: See Sum, 8

Total assessed value: the value assigned to a property by a governing body responsible for collecting taxes on that property, 692
Total assets, 614

Total cost: cost of an asset plus shipping and installation charges, 532

Total debt to total assets ratio: a comparison of total liabilities to total assets, 632

Total (or installment) price: the total amount that must be paid when the purchase is paid for over a given period of time, 482

Total price: marked price plus sales tax, 687

Total sales: earnings from the sale of goods or the performance of services, 622

Totaled: damages to a vehicle resulting from an accident exceed the book value, 664

Trade: a purchase or sale of stocks or bonds, 716

Trade discount: the amount deducted by the manufacturer from the list price of an article or the result of multiplying the list price by the single discount rate, 300

Trade discount series: trade discounts that are deducted successively from the list price by the manufacturer to promote a particular item or encourage additional business from a retailer, 304

Treasury bonds: issued by the federal government, 725

Turnover. See Inventory turnover, 584

200%-declining-balance depreciation: See Double-declining-balance method, 542

Underwriter: See Insurer, 658

Undiscounted note: a promissory note for which the interest is not collected when the note is made, 395

Unemployment taxes, 279

Unit depreciation: the amount that the asset depreciates with each unit produced or each mile driven, 536

Units-of-production depreciation: a method of depreciation that is based on the expected number of units produced by an asset, such as miles driven for a vehicle or labels produced for a label machine; each year's depreciation is based on the number of units of work produced by the asset during the year, 536

Unknown fact: the quantity in a problem or an equation that is not given or known; usually represented by a letter in an equation, 138

Unpaid balance: the amount that has not been paid off at the end of the month, 490

Unpaid balance method: interest accrues on the unpaid balance as of the first day of the monthly period regardless of the charges or payments made to the account during the month; interest is calculated by multiplying the unpaid balance on the first day of the monthly period by the monthly rate of interest, 490

GENERAL TIPS FOR USING A CALCULATOR

In the business world a calculator s become a regular part of the daily utine. Most businesses expect an nployee to be able to make calcula- ns in a timely fashion and have no servations about the use of a calcu- or. However, you must realize that ing a calculator does not take the ace of understanding the mathemati- l or business concepts. Rather, it es you to concentrate on the plan d estimation steps in the decision- aking process.

Following are some standard keys nd on most calculators. Other cal- lator keys such as the percent key], memory keys $\boxed{M+}$ $\boxed{M-}$ $\boxed{MR}$, the ction key $\boxed{a\%}$, and others are intro- ced in calculator boxes in the text.

$\boxed{C}$ or $\boxed{C}$ Clears or initializes the cal- culator. Resets the calcula- tor to zero.

$\boxed{E}$ or $\boxed{C}$ Clears the number being en- tered, but does not clear pre- viously entered numbers.

Notice a key labeled $\boxed{c}$ may represent either the "all clear" key or the "clear entry" key. *Since calculator key labels are NOT standardized, it is very important to test your calculator or to refer to the owner's manual to determine how a key functions on any given calculator.*

$\boxed{+}$ The plus key is used in addition.

$\boxed{-}$ The minus key is used in sub- traction.

$\boxed{\times}$ The times key is used in multipli- cation.

$\boxed{\div}$ The divided by key is used in di- vision.

$\boxed{=}$ The equal key instructs the calcu- lator to perform the calculations that have been entered.

$\boxed{T}$ The total key performs addition and subtraction calculations on some calculators.

$\boxed{\cdot}$ Decimal point

Various types of calculators have various conventions for making calcu- lations. The most common types of calculators used in business are the office calculator and the personal cal- culator. The *office calculator* generally is a desk model or a portable model that can give both an electronic display of the number currently being entered or the result of a calculation as well as a list of the numbers and calculations printed on paper. The *personal calcu- lator* is generally smaller, fits easily into a pocket, briefcase, or handbag, and provides only the electronic dis- play.

For our purposes in this text, we will illustrate the process for making calculations on the most common cal- culator currently available. Keep in mind that the exact keystrokes may vary from manufacturer to manufac- turer, or even from model to model.

Examine the following illustrations for making basic calculations.

Example	Office Calculator Keystrokes	Personal Calculator Keystrokes	Display
28 + 93	$\boxed{28}$ $\boxed{+}$ 93 $\boxed{+}$ T	$\boxed{28}$ $\boxed{+}$ 93 $\boxed{=}$	121.
47 − 29	$\boxed{47}$ $\boxed{+}$ 29 $\boxed{-}$ T	$\boxed{47}$ $\boxed{-}$ 29 $\boxed{=}$	18.
41 × 18	$\boxed{41}$ $\boxed{\times}$ 18 $\boxed{=}$	$\boxed{41}$ $\boxed{\times}$ 18 $\boxed{=}$	738.
85 ÷ 4	$\boxed{85}$ $\boxed{\div}$ 4 $\boxed{=}$	$\boxed{85}$ $\boxed{\div}$ 4 $\boxed{=}$	21.25

·y points to remember:
·der:
·The order in which numbers are en- ·ered in addition or multiplication ·roblems does not matter.
·The order in which numbers are en- ·ered in subtraction or division prob- ·ems does matter.
·mber of digits:
·A calculator can be set to round to a ·ertain place value automatically. On ·he office calculator, the decimal set- ·ing F indicates that the decimal ·floats." There may be no digits ·fter the decimal in some calcula- ·ions, there may be two or three dig- ·ts after the decimal, and so on. The ·decimal can be "fixed" so that a cer- ·ain number of digits follows if de- ·sired. The standard choices on an ·ffice calculator are 0, 2,3, or 4 digits ·fter the decimal. In "fixed" mode, ·he specified number of digits will

follow the decimal even if zeros need to be added or if the exact calcula- tion has to be rounded.
Rounding:
• When a division operation does not come out even or continues indefi- nitely, a calculator will either show as many digits as the display will allow, or it will round the final digit in the dis- play based on the next digit that it has calculated in its internal memory. To determine how the calculator handles nonterminating divisions, divide 2 by 3. If the display shows 0.666666666, the calculator has not rounded the division. If the display shows 0.666666667, then the calculator has rounded the last digit in the display based on the next digit in the calcula- tion, which is 6.
Testing your calculator:
• The most important thing to remem- ber about your calculator is that it is

a calculation tool; it does not "think." It does exactly what the operator in- structs it to do. To test the way your calculator handles certain calcula- tions, enter a problem for which you can find the answer mentally. Then check your mental calculation with the calculator result. When you are satisfied that you understand how the calculator is operating, enter cal- culations for which mental calcula- tions cannot be made. However, *al- ways* estimate your expected result as a safeguard against errors in key- stroking.
Get to know your calculator:
• It is helpful to use the same calcula- tor regularly rather than using a vari- ety of calculators. This will help you become familiar with the way your calculator operates.